W9-ATX-482

DIS 5/2 B7
Proof CM

INTERLIBRARY LOAN POLICIES DIRECTORY

INTERLIBRARY LOAN POLICIES

DIRECTORY

LESLIE R. MORRIS
AND
PATSY FOWLER BRAUTIGAM

SECOND
EDITION

AMERICAN LIBRARY ASSOCIATION   CHICAGO 1984

To Sandie and Gerald:

They understand

Printed on 50-pound Glatfelter, a pH-neutral stock,

and bound in 10-point Carolina cover stock

by Braun-Brumfield, Inc.

Library of Congress Cataloging in Publication Data

Morris, Leslie R.
    Interlibrary loan policies directory.

    Rev. ed. of: Interlibrary loan policies directory/
Sarah Katharine Thomson.
    1. Inter-library loans--United States. 2. Libraries--
United States--Directories. I. Brautigam, Patsy Fowler.
II. Thomson, Sarah Katharine, 1928-   . Interlibrary
loan policies directory. III. American Library
Association. IV. Title.
Z713.5.U6M67 1983   025.6'2   83-11897
ISBN 0-8389-0393-2

Copyright ©1984 by the American Library Association.

All rights reserved except those which may be granted
by Sections 107 and 108 of the Copyright Revision Act
of 1976. Printed in the United States of America.

Preface

During 1981, interlibrary loan librarians reported increasing incidences of monetary charges for interlibrary loans of books and a rise in charges for periodical copying. Our libraries, like many other budget-conscious libraries, try to minimize these lending charges by dealing primarily with those institutions that will exchange loans promptly and reciprocally, or at least economically. Due to the variety of our requests, we needed to know the interlibrary loan policies maintained by a large number of libraries. We attempted to gather an extensive listing, but the obtaining of these policies was a difficult, time-consuming, and ofter ineffective procedure. In addition, we found that these problems were shared by other libraries that tried to acquire loan policy information on a broad scale. As an outgrowth of this need, in January of 1982 we sent a prospectus for a compilation of interlibrary loan policies to twelve publishers. This book is the result.

The libraries we surveyed were selected from a wide range of public, academic, and special libraries, and we used several sources and criteria in selecting them. First, we sent questionnaires to the 272 libraries listed in Sarah K. Thomson's Interlibrary Loan Policies Directory. Second, we consulted the Fall 1975 edition of Library Statistics of Colleges and Universities (the most recent edition that had interlibrary loan data) to obtain a listing of those libraries that had lent 500 or more interlibrary loans in one year. Third, we purchased from Bowker a mailing list of academic and public libraries that have book budgets in excess of $100,000.00. There was considerable duplication among these sources. The result was a list of 968 libraries, 832 (86%) of which returned the questionnaires.

The questionnaires themselves were a combination of several questionnaires and interlibrary loan policy statements that various libraries have used. We realize that it is not possible to include every topic that might be relevant to an interlibrary loan transaction. Our intention instead was to select those items that are most frequently needed for interlibrary loan and to elicit these policies from a large number of libraries. Judging from the responses received, we feel that we accomplished this goal.

The physical arrangement of the entries is in alphabetical order by state and then in alphabetical order by library or institution within each state. The computer-generated index at the back of the book is arranged by major term or terms (i.e., University of Texas at Dallas is listed under "Texas" and under "Dallas" but not under "University"), and includes the name of the state under which the entry appears. Each entry includes all topics that were covered in the questionnaire, as they were answered by the responding library. Our original intention was to publish this manual in looseleaf format to facilitate updating, but this procedure was not feasible at this time. Our hope instead is to update this information in three years with a new edition.

We feel that this book will be very helpful, both to libraries that participate in computerized interlibrary loan systems as well as to smaller academic, public, and high school libraries that have no other access to this loan information. We know that errors of omission and commission are inevitable, despite all our efforts to the contrary. We apologize for these ahead of time, and we ask you to direct all corrections, updates, or inquiries to Leslie R. Morris.

Finally we wish to thank Herbert Bloom, Senior Editor at ALA, Evelyn McElwee, the Director's Secretary at Xavier University, and the staff at the Law Library of Louisiana for all of their patience and support.

DIRECTORY QUESTIONNAIRE

NUC CODE:_____

OCLC CODE:_____

ADDRESS: Interlibrary Loan

_____
_____
_____

TELEPHONE:_____

LIST NAMES OF BRANCHES WITH
SEPARATE POLICIES:

_____
_____
_____

BOOKS:
  Will Lend: Yes_____ No_____
  Length of Loan:_____
  Renewable: Yes_____ No_____
  Charges:_____
  Average Turnaround Time:_____
  _____

  If you have indicated that a
  book is not to be lent, will
  you on receipt of a letter
  from the requesting library
  search the index for given
  entries?_____
  _____

PERIODICALS:
                Will   Will Not
                Lend   Lend
  Bound: _____   _____
  Unbound: _____   _____
  Loan Period: _____
  Renewable: Yes_____ No_____
  Will lend if article exceeds
  _____ number of pages

MICROFORMS:
  Will Lend: Yes_____ No_____
  Specific Types of Microforms:
  _____

GOVERNMENT PUBLICATIONS:
  Will Lend: Yes_____ No_____

DISSERTATIONS:
  Will Lend: Yes_____ No_____
  Available from University
    Microfilms since_____

THESES:
  Will Lend: Yes_____ No_____

AUDIO-VISUAL MATERIALS:
  Records: Yes_____ No_____
  Cassettes: Yes_____ No_____
  Other (slides, filmstrips,
    etc.): Yes_____ No_____

COMPUTER SOFTWARE:
  Will Lend: Yes_____ No_____

PHOTODUPLICATION SERVICE:
  No charge up to _____ exposures
  Charge Per Exposure:_____
  Minimum/handling Fee:_____
  Average Turnaround Time:_____
  _____

MICROFILMING SERVICE:
  Service Available:
            Yes_____ No_____
  Charges:_____

DO YOU CHARGE THE BORROWING
  LIBRARY FOR POSTAGE?_____

FOR HOW LONG DO YOU SUSPEND ILL
  SERVICE OVER THE CHRISTMAS
  HOLIDAYS?_____

ARE THERE ANY GROUPS OF LIBRARIES
  FOR WHICH YOU WAIVE FEES? IF
  SO, PLEASE NAME THEM:_____
  _____
  _____

Interlibrary Loan Policies

ALABAMA PUBLIC LIBRARY SERVICE

NUC CODE: None

OCLC CODE: ASL

ADDRESS: Interlibrary Loan
Alabama Public Library
Service
6030 Monticello Dr.
Montgomery, AL   36130

TELEPHONE: (205) 277-7330

LIST NAMES OF BRANCHES WITH
SEPARATE POLICIES: None

BOOKS:
Will Lend: Yes
Length of Loan: 4 weeks
Renewable: Yes, if not
on reserve
Charges: None
Average Turnaround Time:
1 week
If you have indicated that a
book is not to be lent, will
you on receipt of a letter
from the requesting library
search the index for given
entries? (Not answered)

PERIODICALS:
Bound: Will not lend
Unbound: Will not lend
Loan Period: N/A
Renewable: N/A
Will lend if article exceeds
_____ number of pages (Not
answered)

MICROFORMS:
Will Lend: Yes
Specific Types of Microforms:
(Not answered)

GOVERNMENT PUBLICATIONS:
Will Lend: Yes

DISSERTATIONS:
Will Lend: Yes

THESES:
Will Lend: Yes

AUDIO-VISUAL MATERIALS:
Records: Will not lend
Cassettes: Will not lend
Other (slides, filmstrips,
etc.): Will not lend

COMPUTER SOFTWARE:
Will Lend: No

PHOTODUPLICATION SERVICE:
No charge up to a reasonable
number of exposures
Charge Per Exposure: None
Minimum/handling Fee: None
Average Turnaround Time:
1 week

MICROFILMING SERVICE:
Service Available: No
Charges: N/A

DO YOU CHARGE THE BORROWING
LIBRARY FOR POSTAGE? No

FOR HOW LONG DO YOU SUSPEND ILL
SERVICE OVER THE CHRISTMAS
HOLIDAYS? No suspension

ARE THERE ANY GROUPS OF LIBRARIES
FOR WHICH YOU WAIVE FEES? IF
SO, PLEASE NAME THEM: None

AUBURN UNIVERSITY

NUC CODE: AAP

OCLC CODE: AAA

ADDRESS: Interlibrary Loan
Ralph Brown Draughon
Library
Auburn University
Auburn, AL   36849

TELEPHONE: (205) 826-4500

LIST NAMES OF BRANCHES WITH
SEPARATE POLICIES: (Not
answered)

BOOKS:
Will Lend: Yes
Length of Loan: 2 weeks from
receipt
Renewable: (Not answered)
Charges: (Not answered)
Average Turnaround Time:
(Not answered)
If you have indicated that a
book is not to be lent, will
you on receipt of a letter
from the requesting library
search the index for given
entries? (Not answered)

PERIODICALS:
Bound: Will lend
Unbound: Will lend
Loan Period: (Not answered)
Renewable: (Not answered)
Will lend if article exceeds
_____ number of pages (Not
answered)

MICROFORMS:
Will Lend: (Not answered)
Specific Types of Microforms:
N/A

GOVERNMENT PUBLICATIONS:
Will Lend: (Not answered)

DISSERTATIONS:
Will Lend: Yes; 1960 to
present available from
University Microfilms

THESES:
Will Lend: Yes

AUDIO-VISUAL MATERIALS:
Records: (Not answered)
Cassettes: (Not answered)
Other (slides, filmstrips,
etc.): (Not answered)

COMPUTER SOFTWARE:
Will Lend: (Not answered)

PHOTODUPLICATION SERVICE:
No charge up to 0 exposures
Charge Per Exposure: 10¢
Minimum/handling Fee: $2.00
Average Turnaround Time:
(Not answered)

MICROFILMING SERVICE:
Service Available: Yes
Charges: (Not answered)

DO YOU CHARGE THE BORROWING
LIBRARY FOR POSTAGE? No

FOR HOW LONG DO YOU SUSPEND ILL
SERVICE OVER THE CHRISTMAS
HOLIDAYS? Dec.15-Jan.4

ARE THERE ANY GROUPS OF LIBRARIES
FOR WHICH YOU WAIVE FEES? IF
SO, PLEASE NAME THEM: (Not
answered)

BIRMINGHAM PUBLIC LIBRARY

NUC CODE: AB

OCLC CODE: ABJ

ADDRESS: Interlibrary Loan
           Birmingham Public
             Library
           2020 Park Place
           Birmingham, AL   35203

TELEPHONE: (205) 254-2655

LIST NAMES OF BRANCHES WITH
  SEPARATE POLICIES: None

BOOKS:
   Will Lend: Yes
   Length of Loan: 2 weeks use
   Renewable: Yes
   Charges: None
   Average Turnaround Time:
     1-3 days
   If you have indicated that a
     book is not to be lent, will
     you on receipt of a letter
     from the requesting library
     search the index for given
     entries? (Not answered)

PERIODICALS:
   Bound: Will not lend
   Unbound: Will not lend
   Loan Period: N/A
   Renewable: N/A
   Will lend if article exceeds
     _____ number of pages (Not
     answered)

MICROFORMS:
   Will Lend: Yes
   Specific Types of Microforms:
     Microfilm (will not lend
     microfiche)

GOVERNMENT PUBLICATIONS:
   Will Lend: Yes, federal only

DISSERTATIONS:
   Will Lend: No

THESES:
   Will Lend: No

AUDIO-VISUAL MATERIALS:
   Records: Will not lend
   Cassettes: Will not lend
   Other (slides, filmstrips,
     etc.): Will not lend

COMPUTER SOFTWARE:
   Will Lend: Do not own

PHOTODUPLICATION SERVICE:
   No charge up to 0 exposures
   Charge Per Exposure: 10¢
   Minimum/handling Fee: $1.00
   Average Turnaround Time:
     1-3 days

MICROFILMING SERVICE:
   Service Available: No
   Charges: N/A

DO YOU CHARGE THE BORROWING
  LIBRARY FOR POSTAGE? No

FOR HOW LONG DO YOU SUSPEND ILL
  SERVICE OVER THE CHRISTMAS
  HOLIDAYS? No suspension

ARE THERE ANY GROUPS OF LIBRARIES
  FOR WHICH YOU WAIVE FEES? IF
  SO, PLEASE NAME THEM: Waive
  photocopy charges up to 30
  pages for member of ALIN
  (Alabama Library Information Network)

JACKSONVILLE STATE UNIVERSITY

NUC CODE: AJacT

OCLC CODE: AJB

ADDRESS: Interlibrary Loan
           Jacksonville State
             University Library
           Jacksonville, AL   36201

TELEPHONE: (205) 435-9820

LIST NAMES OF BRANCHES WITH
  SEPARATE POLICIES: None

BOOKS:
   Will Lend: Yes
   Length of Loan: 2 weeks use
   Renewable: Yes
   Charges: $1.00 per title
   Average Turnaround Time:
     1 day
   If you have indicated that a
     book is not to be lent, will
     you on receipt of a letter
     from the requesting library
     search the index for given
     entries? (Not answered)

PERIODICALS:
   Bound: Will not lend
   Unbound: Will not lend
   Loan Period: N/A
   Renewable: N/A
   Will lend if article exceeds
     _____ number of pages (Not
     answered)

MICROFORMS:
   Will Lend: Yes
   Specific Types of Microforms:
     Microfilm and microfiche
     (for research only)

GOVERNMENT PUBLICATIONS:
   Will Lend: Yes

DISSERTATIONS:
   Will Lend: Yes, for research
     only

THESES:
   Will Lend: Yes, for research
     only

AUDIO-VISUAL MATERIALS:
   Records: Will not lend
   Cassettes: Will not lend
   Other (slides, filmstrips,
     etc.): Will not lend

COMPUTER SOFTWARE:
   Will Lend: Do not own

PHOTODUPLICATION SERVICE:
   No charge up to 0 exposures
   Charge Per Exposure: 10¢
   Minimum/handling Fee: $1.00
   Average Turnaround Time:
     1 day

MICROFILMING SERVICE:
   Service Available: No
   Charges: N/A

DO YOU CHARGE THE BORROWING
  LIBRARY FOR POSTAGE? Yes

FOR HOW LONG DO YOU SUSPEND ILL
  SERVICE OVER THE CHRISTMAS
  HOLIDAYS? Approximately
  Dec.8-Jan.7

ARE THERE ANY GROUPS OF LIBRARIES
  FOR WHICH YOU WAIVE FEES? IF
  SO, PLEASE NAME THEM: None

MOBILE PUBLIC LIBRARY

NUC CODE: MoB

OCLC CODE: AMP

ADDRESS: Interlibrary Loan
Mobile Public Library
701 Government St.
Mobile, AL 36602

TELEPHONE: (205) 476-0332

LIST NAMES OF BRANCHES WITH
SEPARATE POLICIES: None

BOOKS:
Will Lend: Yes
Length of Loan: 28 days
Renewable: Yes, if no
reserves
Charges: None
Average Turnaround Time:
(Not answered)
If you have indicated that a
book is not to be lent, will
you on receipt of a letter
from the requesting library
search the index for given
entries? Yes

PERIODICALS:
Bound: Will not lend
Unbound: Will not lend
Loan Period: N/A
Renewable: N/A
Will lend if article exceeds
_____ number of pages (Not
answered)

MICROFORMS:
Will Lend: No
Specific Types of Microforms:
N/A

GOVERNMENT PUBLICATIONS:
Will Lend: Yes

DISSERTATIONS:
Will Lend: Do not own

THESES:
Will Lend: Do not own

AUDIO-VISUAL MATERIALS:
Records: Will not lend
Cassettes: Will not lend
Other (slides, filmstrips,
etc.): Will not lend

COMPUTER SOFTWARE:
Will Lend: Do not own

PHOTODUPLICATION SERVICE:
No charge up to 0 exposures
Charge Per Exposure: 10¢
Minimum/handling Fee: None
Average Turnaround Time:
(Not answered)

MICROFILMING SERVICE:
Service Available: No
Charges: N/A

DO YOU CHARGE THE BORROWING
LIBRARY FOR POSTAGE? No

FOR HOW LONG DO YOU SUSPEND ILL
SERVICE OVER THE CHRISTMAS
HOLIDAYS? 2 days

ARE THERE ANY GROUPS OF LIBRARIES
FOR WHICH YOU WAIVE FEES? IF
SO, PLEASE NAME THEM:
Birmingham Public Library,
University of South Alabama,
Springhill College, Mobile
College

PUBLIC LIBRARY OF SELMA AND DALLAS COUNTY

NUC CODE: (Not answered)

OCLC CODE: (Not answered)

ADDRESS: Interlibrary Loan
Public Library of
Selma and Dallas
County
1103 Selma Ave.
Selma, AL 36701

TELEPHONE: (205) 875-3535

LIST NAMES OF BRANCHES WITH
SEPARATE POLICIES: None

BOOKS:
Will Lend: Yes
Length of Loan: 1 month
Renewable: No
Charges: None
Average Turnaround Time:
(Not answered)
If you have indicated that a
book is not to be lent, will
you on receipt of a letter
from the requesting library
search the index for given
entries? (Not answered)

PERIODICALS:
Bound: Will not lend
Unbound: Will not lend
Loan Period: N/A
Renewable: N/A
Will lend if article exceeds
_____ number of pages (Not
answered)

MICROFORMS:
Will Lend: No
Specific Types of Microforms:
N/A

GOVERNMENT PUBLICATIONS:
Will Lend: (Not answered)

DISSERTATIONS:
Will Lend: (Not answered)

THESES:
Will Lend: (Not answered)

AUDIO-VISUAL MATERIALS:
Records: Will lend
Cassettes: Will lend
Other (slides, filmstrips,
etc.): Will lend

COMPUTER SOFTWARE:
Will Lend: (Not answered)

PHOTODUPLICATION SERVICE:
No charge up to 0 exposures
Charge Per Exposure: 20¢
Minimum/handling Fee: None
Average Turnaround Time:
(Not answered)

MICROFILMING SERVICE:
Service Available: No
Charges: N/A

DO YOU CHARGE THE BORROWING
LIBRARY FOR POSTAGE? No

FOR HOW LONG DO YOU SUSPEND ILL
SERVICE OVER THE CHRISTMAS
HOLIDAYS? (Not answered)

ARE THERE ANY GROUPS OF LIBRARIES
FOR WHICH YOU WAIVE FEES? IF
SO, PLEASE NAME THEM: None

TUSKEGEE INSTITUTE

NUC CODE: ATT

OCLC CODE: (Not answered)

ADDRESS: Interlibrary Loan
           Reference Div.
           Hollis Burke Frissell
           Library
           Tuskegee Institute
           Tuskegee Institute, AL
           36088

TELEPHONE: (205) 727-8896

LIST NAMES OF BRANCHES WITH
   SEPARATE POLICIES: None

BOOKS:
   Will Lend: Yes
   Length of Loan: 1-2 weeks
   Renewable: No
   Charges: Postage
   Average Turnaround Time:
      (Not answered)
   If you have indicated that a
      book is not to be lent, will
      you on receipt of a letter
      from the requesting library
      search the index for given
      entries? (Not answered)

PERIODICALS:
   Bound: Will not usually lend
   Unbound: Will not usually
      lend
   Loan Period: (Not answered)
   Renewable: (Not answered)
   Will lend if article exceeds
      10-15 pages

MICROFORMS:
   Will Lend: Yes
   Specific Types of Microforms:
      Depends upon "in library"
      use

GOVERNMENT PUBLICATIONS:
   Will Lend: Yes

DISSERTATIONS:
   Will Lend: Yes

THESES:
   Will Lend: Yes

AUDIO-VISUAL MATERIALS:
   Records: Will not lend
   Cassettes: Will not lend
   Other (slides, filmstrips,
      etc.): Will lend

COMPUTER SOFTWARE:
   Will Lend: Do not own

PHOTODUPLICATION SERVICE:
   No charge up to 0 exposures
   Charge Per Exposure: 10¢
   Minimum/handling Fee: $1.00
   Average Turnaround Time:
      (Not answered)

MICROFILMING SERVICE:
   Service Available: No
   Charges: N/A

DO YOU CHARGE THE BORROWING
   LIBRARY FOR POSTAGE? Yes

FOR HOW LONG DO YOU SUSPEND ILL
   SERVICE OVER THE CHRISTMAS
   HOLIDAYS? 2 weeks

ARE THERE ANY GROUPS OF LIBRARIES
   FOR WHICH YOU WAIVE FEES? IF
   SO, PLEASE NAME THEM: None

UNIVERSITY OF ALABAMA

NUC CODE: AU

OCLC CODE: ALM

ADDRESS: Interlibrary Loan
           Service
           Box S Library
           University of Alabama
           University, AL 35486

TELEPHONE: (205) 348-5298

LIST NAMES OF BRANCHES WITH
   SEPARATE POLICIES:
      Health Sciences Library
      Law School Library

BOOKS:
   Will Lend: Yes
   Length of Loan: 3 weeks use
   Renewable: Rarely
   Charges: None
   Average Turnaround Time:
      1-2 days
   If you have indicated that a
      book is not to be lent, will
      you on receipt of a letter
      from the requesting library
      search the index for given
      entries? Yes

PERIODICALS:
   Bound: Will occasionally lend
   Unbound: Will not lend
   Loan Period: 1-2 weeks
   Renewable: No
   Will lend if article exceeds
      25 Xerox exposures

MICROFORMS:
   Will Lend: Yes, positive
      films only
   Specific Types of Microforms:
      Films

GOVERNMENT PUBLICATIONS:
   Will Lend: Yes, most of them

DISSERTATIONS:
   Will Lend: Yes, film only,
      1958-date; 1952-1957 micro-
      cards for sale for $5.00
      per set from AU; 1958 to
      present available from
      University Microfilms

THESES:
   Will Lend: Yes, if 2nd copy
      available

AUDIO-VISUAL MATERIALS:
   Records: Will not lend
   Cassettes: Will not lend
   Other (slides, filmstrips,
      etc.): (Not answered)

COMPUTER SOFTWARE:
   Will Lend: (Not answered)

PHOTODUPLICATION SERVICE:
   No charge up to 3 exposures
   Charge Per Exposure: (Not
      answered)
   Minimum/handling Fee: $2.00
   Average Turnaround Time:
      1-2 days

MICROFILMING SERVICE:
   Service Available: No
   Charges: N/A

DO YOU CHARGE THE BORROWING
   LIBRARY FOR POSTAGE? No

FOR HOW LONG DO YOU SUSPEND ILL
   SERVICE OVER THE CHRISTMAS
   HOLIDAYS? Dec.12-Jan.4

ARE THERE ANY GROUPS OF LIBRARIES
   FOR WHICH YOU WAIVE FEES? IF
   SO, PLEASE NAME THEM: U.S.
   Government libraries

UNIVERSITY OF ALABAMA AT BIRMINGHAM

NUC CODE: (Not answered)

OCLC CODE: ABC

ADDRESS: Interlibrary Loan
          University College
          Mervyn H. Sterne
            Library
          University of Alabama
            at Birmingham
          University Station
          Birmingham, AL 35294

TELEPHONE: (205) 934-6364

LIST NAMES OF BRANCHES WITH
  SEPARATE POLICIES: None

BOOKS:
  Will Lend: Yes
  Length of Loan: 2 weeks
  Renewable: Yes
  Charges: None
  Average Turnaround Time:
    1 week
  If you have indicated that a
    book is not to be lent, will
    you on receipt of a letter
    from the requesting library
    search the index for given
    entries? (Not answered)

PERIODICALS:
  Bound: Will not lend
  Unbound: Will not lend
  Loan Period: N/A
  Renewable: N/A
  Will lend if article exceeds
    _____ number of pages (Not
    answered)

MICROFORMS:
  Will Lend: No
  Specific Types of Microforms:
    Will lend local newspapers
    on microfilm

GOVERNMENT PUBLICATIONS:
  Will Lend: No, with
    exceptions

DISSERTATIONS:
  Will Lend: Yes. Medical
    School dissertations
    available from University
    Microfilms since 1952;
    available from University
    College since 1971

THESES:
  Will Lend: Yes

AUDIO-VISUAL MATERIALS:
  Records: Will not lend
  Cassettes: Will not lend
  Other (slides, filmstrips,
    etc.): Will not lend

COMPUTER SOFTWARE:
  Will Lend: No

PHOTODUPLICATION SERVICE:
  No charge up to 0 exposures
  Charge Per Exposure: 10¢
  Minimum/handling Fee: $1.00
  Average Turnaround Time:
    1 week

MICROFILMING SERVICE:
  Service Available: No
  Charges: N/A

DO YOU CHARGE THE BORROWING
  LIBRARY FOR POSTAGE? No

FOR HOW LONG DO YOU SUSPEND ILL
  SERVICE OVER THE CHRISTMAS
  HOLIDAYS? No suspension

ARE THERE ANY GROUPS OF LIBRARIES
  FOR WHICH YOU WAIVE FEES? IF
  SO, PLEASE NAME THEM: None

ALASKA STATE LIBRARY

NUC CODE: Ak

OCLC CODE: (Not answered)

ADDRESS: Interlibrary Loan
Alaska State Library
Pouch G
Juneau, AK 99811-0571

TELEPHONE: (907) 465-2988

LIST NAMES OF BRANCHES WITH
SEPARATE POLICIES: None

BOOKS:
Will Lend: Yes
Length of Loan: 2 weeks
from receipt
Renewable: Yes
Charges: (Not answered)
If you have indicated that a
book is not to be lent, will
you on receipt of a letter
from the requesting library
search the index for given
entries? (Not answered)

PERIODICALS:
Bound: Will not lend
Unbound: Will not lend
Loan Period: N/A
Renewable: N/A
Will lend if article exceeds
_____ number of pages (Not
answered)

MICROFORMS:
Will Lend: Yes
Specific Types of Microforms:
(Not answered)

GOVERNMENT PUBLICATIONS:
Will Lend: (Not answered)

DISSERTATIONS:
Will Lend: (Not answered)

THESES:
Will Lend: (Not answered)

AUDIO-VISUAL MATERIALS:
Records: (Not answered)
Cassettes: (Not answered)
Other (slides, filmstrips,
etc.): (Not answered)

COMPUTER SOFTWARE:
Will Lend: (Not answered)

PHOTODUPLICATION SERVICE:
No charge up to a reasonable
number of exposures
Charge Per Exposure: (Not
answered)
Minimum/handling Fee: None
Average Turnaround Time:
(Not answered)

MICROFILMING SERVICE:
Service Available: Yes
Charges: (Not answered)

DO YOU CHARGE THE BORROWING
LIBRARY FOR POSTAGE? No

FOR HOW LONG DO YOU SUSPEND ILL
SERVICE OVER THE CHRISTMAS
HOLIDAYS? No suspension

ARE THERE ANY GROUPS OF LIBRARIES
FOR WHICH YOU WAIVE FEES? IF
SO, PLEASE NAME THEM: None

ANCHORAGE MUNICIPAL LIBRARIES

NUC CODE: (Not answered)

OCLC CODE: (Not answered)

ADDRESS: Interlibrary Loan
Anchorage Municipal
Libraries
524 W. 6th St.
Anchorage, AK 99501

TELEPHONE: (907) 264-4831

LIST NAMES OF BRANCHES WITH
SEPARATE POLICIES: None

BOOKS:
Will Lend: Yes
Length of Loan: 2 weeks from
receipt
Renewable: Yes
Charges: None
Average Turnaround Time:
Varies with mail
If you have indicated that a
book is not to be lent, will
you on receipt of a letter
from the requesting library
search the index for given
entries? (Not answered)

PERIODICALS:
Bound: Will lend
Unbound: Will lend
Loan Period: 2 weeks
Renewable: Yes
Will lend if article exceeds
_____ number of pages

MICROFORMS:
Will Lend: Yes
Specific Types of Microforms:
(Not answered)

GOVERNMENT PUBLICATIONS:
Will Lend: Yes

DISSERTATIONS:
Will Lend: Yes

THESES:
Will Lend: Yes

AUDIO-VISUAL MATERIALS:
Records: Will lend
Cassettes: Will lend
Other (slides, filmstrips,
etc.): Will lend

PHOTODUPLICATION SERVICE:
No charge up to 20 exposures
Charge Per Exposure: (Not
answered)
Minimum/handling Fee: (Not
answered)
Average Turnaround Time:
(Not answered)

MICROFILMING SERVICE:
Service Available: No
Charges: N/A

DO YOU CHARGE THE BORROWING
LIBRARY FOR POSTAGE? No

FOR HOW LONG DO YOU SUSPEND ILL
SERVICE OVER THE CHRISTMAS
HOLIDAYS? No suspension

ARE THERE ANY GROUPS OF LIBRARIES
FOR WHICH YOU WAIVE FEES? IF
SO, PLEASE NAME THEM: None

ARIZONA STATE LIBRARY

NUC CODE: Az

OCLC CODE: AZP

ADDRESS: Interlibrary Loan
Department of Library,
Archives, and Public
Records
3rd Floor - Capitol
Phoeniz, AZ 85007

TELEPHONE: (602) 255-3701

LIST NAMES OF BRANCHES WITH
SEPARATE POLICIES: None

BOOKS:
Will Lend: Yes
Length of Loan: 2 weeks use
Renewable: Yes
Charges: None
Average Turnaround Time:
1 day
If you have indicated that a
book is not to be lent, will
you on receipt of a letter
from the requesting library
search the index for given
entries? (Not answered)

PERIODICALS:
Bound: Will not lend
Unbound: Will not lend
Loan Period: N/A
Renewable: N/A
Will lend if article exceeds
_____ number of pages (Will
not lend, regardless of
length of article)

MICROFORMS:
Will Lend: Yes
Specific Types of Microforms:
Microfiche, microfilm

GOVERNMENT PUBLICATIONS:
Will Lend: Yes

DISSERTATIONS:
Will Lend: Do not own

THESES:
Will Lend: Do not own

AUDIO-VISUAL MATERIALS:
Records: Do not own
Cassettes: Do not own
Other (slides, filmstrips,
etc.): Do not own

COMPUTER SOFTWARE:
Will Lend: Do not own

PHOTODUPLICATION SERVICE:
No charge up to 10 exposures
Charge Per Exposure: 15¢
Minimum/handling Fee: $2.00
Average Turnaround Time:
1 day

MICROFILMING SERVICE:
Service Available: No
Charges: N/A

DO YOU CHARGE THE BORROWING
LIBRARY FOR POSTAGE? Yes

FOR HOW LONG DO YOU SUSPEND ILL
SERVICE OVER THE CHRISTMAS
HOLIDAYS? No suspension

ARE THERE ANY GROUPS OF LIBRARIES
FOR WHICH YOU WAIVE FEES? IF
SO, PLEASE NAME THEM: CHAIN,
AMIGOS

ARIZONA STATE UNIVERSITY

NUC CODE: AzTeS

OCLC CODE: AZS

ADDRESS: Interlibrary Loan
Service
University Library
Arizona State
University
Tempe, AZ 85287

TELEPHONE: (602) 965-3282

LIST NAMES OF BRANCHES WITH
SEPARATE POLICIES: None

BOOKS:
Will Lend: Yes
Length of Loan: 2 weeks
Renewable: Yes
Charges: None
Average Turnaround Time:
2 days
If you have indicated that a
book is not to be lent, will
you on receipt of a letter
from the requesting library
search the index for given
entries? Yes

PERIODICALS:
Bound: Will not usually lend
Unbound: Will not lend
Loan Period: N/A
Renewable: N/A
May lend if article exceeds
50 pages

MICROFORMS:
Will Lend: Yes, except for
HRAF
Specific Types of Microforms:
(Not answered)

GOVERNMENT PUBLICATIONS:
Will Lend: Yes

DISSERTATIONS:
Will Lend: Yes; 1960 to
present available from
University Microfilms

THESES:
Will Lend: Yes

AUDIO-VISUAL MATERIALS:
Records: Will not lend
Cassettes: Will lend
Other (slides, filmstrips,
etc.): Will not lend

COMPUTER SOFTWARE:
Will Lend: No

PHOTODUPLICATION SERVICE:
No charge up to 0 exposures
Charge Per Exposure: 15¢
Minimum/handling Fee: 50¢
Average Turnaround Time:
5 days

MICROFILMING SERVICE:
Service Available: Yes
Charges: $8.00 per reel

DO YOU CHARGE THE BORROWING
LIBRARY FOR POSTAGE? No

FOR HOW LONG DO YOU SUSPEND ILL
SERVICE OVER THE CHRISTMAS
HOLIDAYS? No suspension

ARE THERE ANY GROUPS OF LIBRARIES
FOR WHICH YOU WAIVE FEES? IF
SO, PLEASE NAME THEM: AMIGOS
members who have signed the
ILL code; libraries with
which we have a reciprocal
agreement

FLAGSTAFF CITY-COCONINO COUNTY PUBLIC LIBRARY

NUC CODE: (Not answered)

OCLC CODE: (Not answered)

ADDRESS: Interlibrary Loan
Flagstaff City-
Coconino County
Public Library
324 West Aspen
Flagstaff, AZ 86001

TELEPHONE: (602) 774-1134

LIST NAMES OF BRANCHES WITH
SEPARATE POLICIES: None

BOOKS:
Will Lend: Yes
Length of Loan: 1 month
Renewable: Yes, if no
requests
Charges: (Not answered)
Average Turnaround Time:
(Not answered)
If you have indicated that a
book is not to be lent, will
you on receipt of a letter
from the requesting library
search the index for given
entries? Yes

PERIODICALS:
Bound: Will not lend
Unbound: Will not lend
Loan Period: N/A
Renewable: N/A
Will lend if article exceeds
_____ number of pages (N/A)

MICROFORMS:
Will Lend: Do not own
Specific Types of Microforms:
N/A

GOVERNMENT PUBLICATIONS:
Will Lend: Do not own

DISSERTATIONS:
Will Lend: Do not own

THESES:
Will Lend: Do not own

AUDIO-VISUAL MATERIALS:
Records: Will not lend
Cassettes: Will not lend
Other (slides, filmstrips,
etc.): Will not lend

COMPUTER SOFTWARE:
Will Lend: Do not own

PHOTODUPLICATION SERVICE:
No charge up to 10 exposures
Charge Per Exposure: 10¢
Minimum/handling Fee: $1.00
Average Turnaround Time:
(Not answered)

MICROFILMING SERVICE:
Service Available: No
Charges: N/A

DO YOU CHARGE THE BORROWING LIBRARY
FOR POSTAGE? No

FOR HOW LONG DO YOU SUSPEND ILL
SERVICE OVER THE CHRISTMAS
HOLIDAYS? No suspension

ARE THERE ANY GROUPS OF LIBRARIES
FOR WHICH YOU WAIVE FEES? IF
SO, PLEASE NAME THEM: No groups

MESA PUBLIC LIBRARY

NUC CODE: AzM

OCLC CODE: MSA

ADDRESS: Interlibrary Loan
Mesa Public Library
64 E. 1st St.
Mesa, AZ 85201

TELEPHONE: (602) 834-2732

LIST NAMES OF BRANCHES WITH
SEPARATE POLICIES: None

BOOKS:
Will Lend: Yes
Length of Loan: 2 weeks
Renewable: Yes
Charges: None
Average Turnaround Time:
4 days
If you have indicated that a
book is not to be lent, will
you on receipt of a letter
from the requesting library
search the index for given
entries? (Not answered)

PERIODICALS:
Bound: Will not lend
Unbound: Will not lend
Loan Period: N/A
Renewable: N/A
Will lend if article exceeds
_____ number of pages (N/A)

MICROFORMS:
Will Lend: No
Specific Types of Microforms:
N/A

GOVERNMENT PUBLICATIONS:
Will Lend: Do not own

DISSERTATIONS:
Will Lend: Do not own

THESES:
Will Lend: Do not own

AUDIO-VISUAL MATERIALS:
Records: Will not lend
Cassettes: Do not own
Other (slides, filmstrips,
etc.): Do not own

COMPUTER SOFTWARE:
Will Lend: Do not own

PHOTODUPLICATION SERVICE:
No charge up to 10 exposures
Charge Per Exposure: 10¢
Minimum/handling Fee: N/A
Average Turnaround Time:
4 days

MICROFILMING SERVICE:
Service Available: No
Charges: N/A

DO YOU CHARGE THE BORROWING LIBRARY
FOR POSTAGE? No

FOR HOW LONG DO YOU SUSPEND ILL
SERVICE OVER THE CHRISTMAS
HOLIDAYS? 3 days

ARE THERE ANY GROUPS OF LIBRARIES
FOR WHICH YOU WAIVE FEES? IF
SO, PLEASE NAME THEM: AMIGOS
network libraries

NORTHERN ARIZONA UNIVERSITY

NUC CODE: AzFU

OCLC CODE: AZN

ADDRESS: Interlibrary Loan
Northern Arizona
University Library
Flagstaff, AZ
86011-0051

TELEPHONE: (602) 523-2171

LIST NAMES OF BRANCHES WITH
SEPARATE POLICIES: None

BOOKS:
Will Lend: Yes
Length of Loan: 2 weeks use
Renewable: Yes, usually
Charges: None
Average Turnaround Time:
2 days
If you have indicated that a
book is not to be lent, will
you on receipt of a letter
from the requesting library
search the index for given
entries? (Not answered)

PERIODICALS:
Bound: Will not lend
Unbound: Will not lend
Loan Period: N/A
Renewable: N/A
Will lend if article exceeds
_____ number of pages (Will
not lend, regardless of
length of article)

MICROFORMS:
Will Lend: Yes
Specific Types of Microforms:
(Not answered)

GOVERNMENT PUBLICATIONS:
Will Lend: Yes

DISSERTATIONS:
Will Lend: Yes, stack copy
only; available from
University Microfilms since
1974

THESES:
Will Lend: Yes, stack copy
only

AUDIO-VISUAL MATERIALS:
Records: Will not lend
Cassettes: Will not lend
Other (slides, filmstrips,
etc.): Will not lend

COMPUTER SOFTWARE:
Will Lend: No

PHOTODUPLICATION SERVICE:
No charge up to 0 exposures
Charge Per Exposure: 15¢
Minimum/handling Fee: $3.00
Average Turnaround Time:
2 days

MICROFILMING SERVICE:
Service Available: No
Charges: N/A

DO YOU CHARGE THE BORROWING
LIBRARY FOR POSTAGE? No

FOR HOW LONG DO YOU SUSPEND ILL
SERVICE OVER THE CHRISTMAS
HOLIDAYS? No suspension

ARE THERE ANY GROUPS OF LIBRARIES
FOR WHICH YOU WAIVE FEES? IF
SO, PLEASE NAME THEM: Free
photocopying to non-profit
libraries in Arizona

PHOENIX PUBLIC LIBRARY

NUC CODE: AzPH

OCLC CODE: PNX

ADDRESS: Interlibrary Loan
Phoenix Public Library
12 E. McDowell Rd.
Phoenix, AZ 85021

TELEPHONE: (602) 262-4606

LIST NAMES OF BRANCHES WITH
SEPARATE POLICIES: None

BOOKS:
Will Lend: Yes
Length of Loan: 2 weeks
Renewable: Yes
Charges: None
Average Turnaround Time:
48 hours
If you have indicated that a
book is not to be lent, will
you on receipt of a letter
from the requesting library
search the index for given
entries? (Not answered)

PERIODICALS:
Bound: Will not lend
Unbound: Will not lend
Loan Period: N/A
Renewable: N/A
Will lend if article exceeds
_____ number of pages
(Will not lend)

MICROFORMS:
Will Lend: No
Specific Types of Microforms:
N/A

GOVERNMENT PUBLICATIONS:
Will Lend: Yes

DISSERTATIONS:
Will Lend: No

THESES:
Will Lend: No

AUDIO-VISUAL MATERIALS:
Records: Will not lend
Cassettes: Will not lend
Other (slides, filmstrips,
etc.): Will not lend

COMPUTER SOFTWARE:
Will Lend: No

PHOTODUPLICATION SERVICE:
No charge up to 10 exposures
Charge Per Exposure: 10¢
Minimum/handling Fee: None
Average Turnaround Time:
24 hours

MICROFILMING SERVICE:
Service Available: No
Charges: N/A

DO YOU CHARGE THE BORROWING LIBRARY
FOR POSTAGE? No

FOR HOW LONG DO YOU SUSPEND ILL
SERVICE OVER THE CHRISTMAS
HOLIDAYS? No suspension of
ILL service

ARE THERE ANY GROUPS OF LIBRARIES
FOR WHICH YOU WAIVE FEES? IF
SO, PLEASE NAME THEM: None

TEMPE PUBLIC LIBRARY

NUC CODE: (Not answered)

OCLC CODE: (Not answered)

ADDRESS: Interlibrary Loan
Tempe Public Library
3500 S. Rural
Tempe, AZ 85282

TELEPHONE: (602) 968-8231

LIST NAMES OF BRANCHES WITH
SEPARATE POLICIES: None

BOOKS:
Will Lend: Yes
Length of Loan: 2 weeks
Renewable: Yes
Charges: None
Average Turnaround Time:
(Not answered)
If you have indicated that a
book is not to be lent, will
you on receipt of a letter
from the requesting library
search the index for given
entries? Yes

PERIODICALS:
Bound: Will not lend
Unbound: Will not lend
Loan Period: N/A
Renewable: N/A
Will lend if article exceeds
_____ number of pages (Not
answered)

MICROFORMS:
Will Lend: No
Specific Types of Microforms:
N/A

GOVERNMENT PUBLICATIONS:
Will Lend: No

DISSERTATIONS:
Will Lend: Do not own

THESES:
Will Lend: Do not own

AUDIO-VISUAL MATERIALS:
Records: Will not lend
Cassettes: Will not lend
Other (slides, filmstrips,
etc.): Do not own

COMPUTER SOFTWARE:
Will Lend: No

PHOTODUPLICATION SERVICE:
No charge up to _____
exposures (Not answered)
Charge Per Exposure: 10¢
Minimum/handling Fee: None
Average Turnaround Time:
(Not answered)

MICROFILMING SERVICE:
Service Available: No
Charges: N/A

DO YOU CHARGE THE BORROWING
LIBRARY FOR POSTAGE? No

FOR HOW LONG DO YOU SUSPEND ILL
SERVICE OVER THE CHRISTMAS
HOLIDAYS? No suspension

ARE THERE ANY GROUPS OF LIBRARIES
FOR WHICH YOU WAIVE FEES? IF
SO, PLEASE NAME THEM: None

TUCSON PUBLIC LIBRARY

NUC CODE: AzT

OCLC CODE: AZT

ADDRESS: Interlibrary Loan
Tucson Public Library
P. O. Box 27470
Tucson, AZ 85726

TELEPHONE: (602) 791-4393

LIST NAMES OF BRANCHES WITH
SEPARATE POLICIES: None

BOOKS:
Will Lend: Yes
Length of Loan: 3 weeks use
Renewable: Yes, usually
Charges: None
Average Turnaround Time:
3 days
If you have indicated that a
book is not to be lent, will
you on receipt of a letter
from the requesting library
search the index for given
entries? (Not answered)

PERIODICALS:
Bound: Will not lend
Unbound: Will not lend
Loan Period: N/A
Renewable: N/A
Will lend if article exceeds
_____ number of pages (N/A)

MICROFORMS:
Will Lend: No
Specific Types of Microforms:
N/A

GOVERNMENT PUBLICATIONS:
Will Lend: Yes, usually

DISSERTATIONS:
Will Lend: Do not own

THESES:
Will Lend: Do not own

AUDIO-VISUAL MATERIALS:
Records: Will not lend
Cassettes: Will not lend
Other (slides, filmstrips,
etc.): Will not lend

COMPUTER SOFTWARE:
Will Lend: No

PHOTODUPLICATION SERVICE:
No charge up to _____ exposures
(Not answered)
Charge Per Exposure: 10¢
Minimum/handling Fee: 50¢
minimum
Average Turnaround Time: 3 days

MICROFILMING SERVICE:
Service Available: No
Charges: N/A

DO YOU CHARGE THE BORROWING LIBRARY
FOR POSTAGE? No

FOR HOW LONG DO YOU SUSPEND ILL
SERVICE OVER THE CHRISTMAS
HOLIDAYS? No suspension of
service

ARE THERE ANY GROUPS OF LIBRARIES
FOR WHICH YOU WAIVE FEES? IF
SO, PLEASE NAME THEM: Photocopies up to 50 pages free to
signers of AMIGOS ILL Code and
to CHAIN (Channeled Arizona
Information Network) libraries

UNIVERSITY OF ARIZONA

NUC CODE: AzU

OCLC CODE: AZU

ADDRESS: Interlibrary Loan
University of Arizona
Libraries
Tucson, AZ 85721

TELEPHONE: (602) 626-1942

LIST NAMES OF BRANCHES WITH
SEPARATE POLICIES: None

BOOKS:
Will Lend: Yes
Length of Loan: 3 weeks
Renewable: No
Charges: None
Average Turnaround Time:
1-3 days
If you have indicated that a
book is not to be lent, will
you on receipt of a letter
from the requesting library
search the index for given
entries? (Not answered)

PERIODICALS:
Bound: Will lend in some
circumstances
Unbound: Will not lend
Loan Period: 1 week
Renewable: No
Will lend if article exceeds
_____ number of pages (Not
answered)

MICROFORMS:
Will Lend: Yes
Specific Types of Microforms:
Microfiche, microfilm

GOVERNMENT PUBLICATIONS:
Will Lend: Yes

DISSERTATIONS:
Will Lend: Yes. 1950 to
present available from
University Microfilms

THESES:
Will Lend: Yes. 1982 to
present available from
University Microfilms

AUDIO-VISUAL MATERIALS:
Records: Will not lend
Cassettes: Will not lend
Other (slides, filmstrips,
etc.): Will not lend

COMPUTER SOFTWARE:
Will Lend: No

PHOTODUPLICATION SERVICE:
No charge up to 0 exposures
Charge Per Exposure: 20¢
Minimum/handling Fee: $3.00
Average Turnaround Time:
3-5 days

MICROFILMING SERVICE:
Service Available: No
Charges: N/A

DO YOU CHARGE THE BORROWING
LIBRARY FOR POSTAGE? If
first-class requested

FOR HOW LONG DO YOU SUSPEND ILL
SERVICE OVER THE CHRISTMAS
HOLIDAYS? Dec.10-29

ARE THERE ANY GROUPS OF LIBRARIES
FOR WHICH YOU WAIVE FEES? IF
SO, PLEASE NAME THEM: AMIGOS
libraries signing the AMIGOS
ILL agreement

ARKANSAS STATE LIBRARY

NUC CODE: (Not answered)

OCLC CODE: AST and AKF

ADDRESS: Interlibrary Loan
Arkansas State Library
One Capitol Mall
Little Rock, AR 72201

TELEPHONE: (501) 371-2053

LIST NAMES OF BRANCHES WITH
SEPARATE POLICIES: None

BOOKS:
Will Lend: Yes
Length of Loan: 4 weeks
Renewable: Yes
Charges: (Not answered)
Average Turnaround Time:
(Not answered)
If you have indicated that a
book is not to be lent, will
you on receipt of a letter
from the requesting library
search the index for given
entries? (Not answered)

PERIODICALS:
Bound: Will not lend
Unbound: Will not lend
Loan Period: N/A
Renewable: N/A
Will lend if article exceeds
_____ number of pages (Not
answered)

MICROFORMS:
Will Lend: No
Specific Types of Microforms:
N/A

GOVERNMENT PUBLICATIONS:
Will Lend: Yes

DISSERTATIONS:
Will Lend: (Not answered)

THESES:
Will Lend: (Not answered)

AUDIO-VISUAL MATERIALS:
Records: (Not answered)
Cassettes: (Not answered)
Other (slides, filmstrips,
etc.): (Not answered)

COMPUTER SOFTWARE:
Will Lend: (Not answered)

PHOTODUPLICATION SERVICE:
No charge up to any exposures
Charge Per Exposure: None
Minimum/handling Fee: None
Average Turnaround Time:
(Not answered)

MICROFILMING SERVICE:
Service Available: (Not
answered)
Charges: N/A

DO YOU CHARGE THE BORROWING
LIBRARY FOR POSTAGE? No

FOR HOW LONG DO YOU SUSPEND ILL
SERVICE OVER THE CHRISTMAS
HOLIDAYS? (Not answered)

ARE THERE ANY GROUPS OF LIBRARIES
FOR WHICH YOU WAIVE FEES? IF
SO, PLEASE NAME THEM: (Not
answered)

ARKANSAS STATE UNIVERSITY

NUC CODE: ArStC

OCLC CODE: ASU

ADDRESS: Interlibrary Loan
Dean B. Ellis Library
Arkansas State
University
State University, AR
72467

TELEPHONE: (501) 972-3077, X5
and 12

LIST NAMES OF BRANCHES WITH
SEPARATE POLICIES: None

BOOKS:
Will Lend: Yes
Length of Loan: 3 weeks use
Renewable: Yes
Charges: None
Average Turnaround Time:
12-24 hours
If you have indicated that a
book is not to be lent, will
you on receipt of a letter
from the requesting library
search the index for given
entries? (Not answered)

PERIODICALS:
Bound: Will not lend
Unbound: Will not lend
Loan Period: 1 days use in
exceptional cases
Renewable: No
Will lend if article exceeds
reasonable number of pages,
and, in some other cases,
with one days use

MICROFORMS:
Will Lend: Yes
Specific Types of Microforms:
Film, cards, and fiche

GOVERNMENT PUBLICATIONS:
Will Lend: Yes

DISSERTATIONS:
Will Lend: Yes

THESES:
Will Lend: Yes

AUDIO-VISUAL MATERIALS: Not in
library; must contact AV-
Learning Resources at ASU

COMPUTER SOFTWARE:
Will Lend: (Not answered)

PHOTODUPLICATION SERVICE:
No charge up to 0 exposures
Charge Per Exposure: 10¢
from hardcopy; 15¢ from
microcopy
Minimum/handling Fee: None
Average Turnaround Time:
12-24 hours

MICROFILMING SERVICE:
Service Available: No
Charges: N/A

DO YOU CHARGE THE BORROWING
LIBRARY FOR POSTAGE? No,
unless first-class is
requested

FOR HOW LONG DO YOU SUSPEND ILL
SERVICE OVER THE CHRISTMAS
HOLIDAYS? Dec.18-Jan.4

ARE THERE ANY GROUPS OF LIBRARIES
FOR WHICH YOU WAIVE FEES? IF
SO, PLEASE NAME THEM: Most
Arkansas libraries and
AMIGOS participating
libraries

CENTRAL ARKANSAS LIBRARY SYSTEM

NUC CODE: ArL

OCLC CODE: AKD

ADDRESS: Interlibrary Loan
Central Arkansas
Library System
700 Louisiana St.
Little Rock, AR 72201

TELEPHONE: (501) 370-5951

LIST NAMES OF BRANCHES WITH
SEPARATE POLICIES: None

BOOKS:
Will Lend: Yes
Length of Loan: Approximately
4 weeks
Renewable: Yes, usually
Charges: None
Average Turnaround Time:
48 hours
If you have indicated that a
book is not to be lent, will
you on receipt of a letter
from the requesting library
search the index for given
entries? Yes, but would
depend upon the reason-
ableness of the request
and available staff time

PERIODICALS:
Bound: Will not lend
Unbound: Will not lend
Loan Period: N/A
Renewable: N/A
Will lend if article exceeds
_____ number of pages (Not
answered)

MICROFORMS:
Will Lend: No
Specific Types of Microforms:
N/A

GOVERNMENT PUBLICATIONS:
Will Lend: Yes, except
those in high demand

DISSERTATIONS:
Will Lend: Do not own

THESES:
Will Lend: Do not own

AUDIO-VISUAL MATERIALS:
Records: Do not own
Cassettes: Do not own
Other (slides, filmstrips,
etc.): Do not own

COMPUTER SOFTWARE:
Will Lend: Do not own

PHOTODUPLICATION SERVICE:
No charge up to 0 exposures
Charge Per Exposure: 15¢ for
xerox; 75¢ for microform
copy
Minimum/handling Fee: None
Average Turnaround Time:
48 hours

MICROFILMING SERVICE:
Service Available: No
Charges: N/A

DO YOU CHARGE THE BORROWING
LIBRARY FOR POSTAGE? No

FOR HOW LONG DO YOU SUSPEND ILL
SERVICE OVER THE CHRISTMAS
HOLIDAYS? No suspension

ARE THERE ANY GROUPS OF LIBRARIES
FOR WHICH YOU WAIVE FEES? IF
SO, PLEASE NAME THEM: Those
who have signed the AMIGOS
ILL code

POINSETT COUNTY LIBRARY

NUC CODE: (Not answered)

OCLC CODE: (Not answered)

ADDRESS: Interlibrary Loan
Poinsett County Library
Harrisburg, AR 72432
(501) 578-5666

LOANS ARE MADE THROUGH CROWLEY
RIDGE REGIONAL LIBRARY
315 W. Oak
Jonesboro, AR 72401
(501) 935-5133

LIST NAMES OF BRANCHES WITH
SEPARATE POLICIES: None

BOOKS:
Will Lend: Yes
Length of Loan: 2 weeks
Renewable: Yes
Charges: (Not answered)
Average Turnaround Time:
(Not answered)
If you have indicated that a
book is not to be lent, will
you on receipt of a letter
from the requesting library
search the index for given
entries? (Not answered)

PERIODICALS:
Bound: (Not answered)
Unbound: Will lend
Loan Period: 1 week
Renewable: (Not answered)
Will lend if article exceeds
5 pages

MICROFORMS:
Will Lend: (Not answered)
Specific Types of Microforms:
N/A

GOVERNMENT PUBLICATIONS:
Will Lend: No

DISSERTATIONS:
Will Lend: No

THESES:
Will Lend: No

AUDIO-VISUAL MATERIALS:
Records: Will not lend
Cassettes: Will not lend
Other (slides, filmstrips,
etc.): Will not lend

COMPUTER SOFTWARE:
Will Lend: (Not answered)

PHOTODUPLICATION SERVICE:
No charge up to _____
exposures (Not answered)
Charge Per Exposure: (Not
answered)
Minimum/handling Fee: (Not
answered)
Average Turnaround Time:
(Not answered)

MICROFILMING SERVICE:
Service Available: (Not
answered)
Charges: N/A

DO YOU CHARGE THE BORROWING
LIBRARY FOR POSTAGE? (Not
answered)

FOR HOW LONG DO YOU SUSPEND ILL
SERVICE OVER THE CHRISTMAS
HOLIDAYS? (Not answered)

ARE THERE ANY GROUPS OF LIBRARIES
FOR WHICH YOU WAIVE FEES? IF
SO, PLEASE NAME THEM:
Craighead County-Jonesboro
Public

UNIVERSITY OF ARKANSAS

NUC CODE: ArU

OCLC CODE: AFU

ADDRESS: Interlibrary Loan
University Libraries
University of Arkansas
Fayetteville, AR 72701

TELEPHONE: (501) 575-4101

LIST NAMES OF BRANCHES WITH
SEPARATE POLICIES: None

BOOKS:
Will Lend: Yes
Length of Loan: 2 weeks
Renewable: Yes
Charges: (Not answered)
Average Turnaround Time:
(Not answered)
If you have indicated that a
book is not to be lent, will
you on receipt of a letter
from the requesting library
search the index for given
entries? (Not answered)

PERIODICALS:
Bound: Will not lend
Unbound: Will not lend
Loan Period: N/A
Renewable: N/A
Will lend if article exceeds
_____ number of pages (Not
answered)

MICROFORMS:
Will Lend: Yes
Specific Types of Microforms:
All types

GOVERNMENT PUBLICATIONS:
Will Lend: Yes

DISSERTATIONS:
Will Lend: No. Will photocopy or microfilm pre-1953
dissertations. 1953 to
present available from
University Microfilms

THESES:
Will Lend: Yes

AUDIO-VISUAL MATERIALS:
Records: (Not answered)
Cassettes: (Not answered)
Other (slides, filmstrips,
etc.): (Not answered)

COMPUTER SOFTWARE:
Will Lend: (Not answered)

PHOTODUPLICATION SERVICE:
No charge up to 0 exposures
Charge Per Exposure: $1.50
for up to 15 exposures for
in-state libraries--addi-
tional exposures, 10¢ each.
$3.00 for up to 30 exposures
for out-of-state--additional
exposures, 10¢ each.
Average Turnaround Time:
(Not answered)

MICROFILMING SERVICE:
Service Available: Yes
Charges: Write for prices

DO YOU CHARGE THE BORROWING
LIBRARY FOR POSTAGE? No

FOR HOW LONG DO YOU SUSPEND ILL
SERVICE OVER THE CHRISTMAS
HOLIDAYS? 3 weeks before and
3 weeks after Christmas

ARE THERE ANY GROUPS OF LIBRARIES
FOR WHICH YOU WAIVE FEES? IF
SO, PLEASE NAME THEM: AMIGOS

UNIVERSITY OF ARKANSAS AT LITTLE ROCK

NUC CODE: ArLUA

OCLC CODE: AKU

ADDRESS: Interlibrary Loan
University of Arkansas
at Little Rock
33rd and University
Little Rock, AR 72204

TELEPHONE: (501) 569-3120, X34

LIST NAMES OF BRANCHES WITH
SEPARATE POLICIES: None

BOOKS:
Will Lend: Yes
Length of Loan: 2 weeks
Renewable: Yes
Charges: None
Average Turnaround Time:
48-72 hours
If you have indicated that a
book is not to be lent, will
you on receipt of a letter
from the requesting library
search the index for given
entries? (Not answered)

PERIODICALS:
Bound: Will not lend
Unbound: Will not lend
Loan Period: N/A
Renewable: N/A
Will lend if article exceeds
_____ number of pages (Not
answered)

MICROFORMS:
Will Lend: Yes
Specific Types of Microforms:
Newspapers, microfiche,
microfilm, and ultrafiche

GOVERNMENT PUBLICATIONS:
Will Lend: Yes, sometimes

DISSERTATIONS:
Will Lend: Yes

THESES:
Will Lend: Yes

AUDIO-VISUAL MATERIALS:
Records: Will not lend
Cassettes: Will not lend
Other (slides, filmstrips,
etc.): Will not lend

COMPUTER SOFTWARE:
Will Lend: Do not own

PHOTODUPLICATION SERVICE:
No charge up to 50 exposures
Charge Per Exposure: 10¢
each additional exposure
Minimum/handling Fee: None
Average Turnaround Time:
48-72 hours

MICROFILMING SERVICE:
Service Available: No
Charges: N/A

DO YOU CHARGE THE BORROWING
LIBRARY FOR POSTATE? Only
for oversized materials

FOR HOW LONG DO YOU SUSPEND ILL
SERVICE OVER THE CHRISTMAS
HOLIDAYS? Dec.15-Jan.5

ARE THERE ANY GROUPS OF LIBRARIES
FOR WHICH YOU WAIVE FEES? IF
SO, PLEASE NAME THEM:
Arkansas institutions

UNIVERSITY OF ARKANSAS FOR MEDICAL SCIENCES

NUC CODE: ArU-M

OCLC CODE: AKM

ADDRESS: Interlibrary Loan
Library, slot 586
University of Arkansas
for Medical Sciences
4301 West Markham St.
Little Rock, AR 72205

TELEPHONE: (501) 661-5980

LIST NAMES OF BRANCHES WITH
SEPARATE POLICIES: None

BOOKS:
Will Lend: Yes
Length of Loan: 2 weeks
Renewable: Yes, once
Charges: $4.00 per loaned
item
Average Turnaround Time:
24 hours
If you have indicated that a
book is not to be lent, will
you on receipt of a letter
from the requesting library
search the index for given
entries? (Not answered)

PERIODICALS:
Bound: Will lend
Unbound: Will lend
Loan Period: Bound, 2 weeks;
unbound, 1 week
Renewable: Yes, once
Will lend if article exceeds
50 pages

MICROFORMS:
Will Lend: Yes
Specific Types of Microforms:
Film and fiche

GOVERNMENT PUBLICATIONS:
Will Lend: Yes

DISSERTATIONS:
Will Lend: Yes

THESES:
Will Lend: Yes

AUDIO-VISUAL MATERIALS:
Records: (Not answered)
Cassettes: Will lend
Other (slides, filmstrips,
etc.): Will lend

COMPUTER SOFTWARE:
Will Lend: (Not answered)

PHOTODUPLICATION SERVICE:
No charge up to 0 exposures
Charge Per Exposure: (Not
answered)
Minimum/handling Fee: $4.00
Average Turnaround Time:
24 hours

MICROFILMING SERVICE:
Service Available: No
Charges: N/A

DO YOU CHARGE THE BORROWING
LIBRARY FOR POSTAGE? No

FOR HOW LONG DO YOU SUSPEND ILL
SERVICE OVER THE CHRISTMAS
HOLIDAYS? Will not mail
original material during
December

ARE THERE ANY GROUPS OF LIBRARIES
FOR WHICH YOU WAIVE FEES? IF
SO, PLEASE NAME THEM: None

UNIVERSITY OF CENTRAL ARKANSAS

NUC CODE: (Not answered)

OCLC CODE: (Not answered)

ADDRESS: Interlibrary Loan
Torreyson Library
University of Central
Arkansas
Conway, AR 72032

TELEPHONE: (501) 450-3129, X240

LIST NAMES OF BRANCHES WITH
SEPARATE POLICIES: None

BOOKS:
Will Lend: Yes
Length of Loan: 4 weeks
Renewable: Yes
Charges: Postage
Average Turnaround Time:
2 days
If you have indicated that a
book is not to be lent, will
you on receipt of a letter
from the requesting library
search the index for given
entries? (Not answered)

PERIODICALS:
Bound: Will not lend
Unbound: Will not lend
Loan Period: N/A
Renewable: N/A
Will lend if article exceeds
_____ number of pages (Will
not lend, regardless of
length of article)

MICROFORMS:
Will Lend: Yes
Specific Types of Microforms:
Microfilms and microfiche

GOVERNMENT PUBLICATIONS:
Will Lend: Yes

DISSERTATIONS:
Will Lend: No

AUDIO-VISUAL MATERIALS:
Records: Will not lend
Cassettes: Will not lend
Other (slides, filmstrips,
etc.): Will lend

COMPUTER SOFTWARE:
Will Lend: (Not answered)

PHOTODUPLICATION SERVICE:
No charge up to 0 exposures
Charge Per Exposure: (Not
answered)
Minimum/handling Fee: (Not
answered)
Average Turnaround Time:
(Not answered)

MICROFILMING SERVICE:
Service Available: Yes
Charges: 10¢ per exposure

DO YOU CHARGE THE BORROWING
LIBRARY FOR POSTAGE? Yes

FOR HOW LONG DO YOU SUSPEND ILL
SERVICE OVER THE CHRISTMAS
HOLIDAYS? (Not answered)

ARE THERE ANY GROUPS OF LIBRARIES
FOR WHICH YOU WAIVE FEES? IF
SO, PLEASE NAME THEM: None

ALAMEDA COUNTY LIBRARY

NUC CODE: (Not answered)

OCLC CODE: (Not answered)

ADDRESS: Interlibrary Loan
           Alameda County Library
           Fremont Branch
           39770 Paseo Padre Pkwy.
           Fremont, CA 94538

TELEPHONE: (415) 791-4797

LIST NAMES OF BRANCHES WITH
  SEPARATE POLICIES: None

BOOKS:
  Will Lend: Yes
  Length of Loan: 3 weeks
  Renewable: No
  Charges: None
  Average Turnaround Time:
    (Not answered)
  If you have indicated that a
  book is not to be lent, will
  you on receipt of a letter
  from the requesting library
  search the index for given
  entries? Do not do
    genealogical search. Will
    photocopy if pages
    specified by requestor.

PERIODICALS:
  Bound: Will not lend
  Unbound: Will not lend
  Loan Period: N/A
  Renewable: N/A
  Will lend if article exceeds
    _____ number of pages (Will
    not lend)

MICROFORMS:
  Will Lend: No
  Specific Types of Microforms:
    N/A

GOVERNMENT PUBLICATIONS:
  Will Lend: Yes

DISSERTATIONS:
  Will Lend: No

THESES:
  Will Lend: No

AUDIO-VISUAL MATERIALS:
  Records: Will not lend
  Cassettes: Will not lend
  Other (slides, filmstrips,
    etc.): Will not lend

COMPUTER SOFTWARE:
  Will Lend: No

PHOTODUPLICATION SERVICE:
  No charge up to 10 exposures
  Charge Per Exposure: 10¢
  Minimum/handling Fee: (Not
    answered)
  Average Turnaround Time:
    (Not answered)

MICROFILMING SERVICE:
  Service Available: No
  Charges: N/A

DO YOU CHARGE THE BORROWING
  LIBRARY FOR POSTAGE? No

FOR HOW LONG DO YOU SUSPEND ILL
  SERVICE OVER THE CHRISTMAS
  HOLIDAYS? No suspension

ARE THERE ANY GROUPS OF LIBRARIES
  FOR WHICH YOU WAIVE FEES? IF
  SO, PLEASE NAME THEM: None

ANAHEIM PUBLIC LIBRARY

NUC CODE: (Not answered)

OCLC CODE: (Not answered)

ADDRESS: Interlibrary Loan
           Anaheim Public Library
           500 W. Broadway
           Anaheim, CA 92805

TELEPHONE: (714) 999-1880, X1767

LIST NAMES OF BRANCHES WITH
  SEPARATE POLICIES:
    Interlibrary loans
    available through Central
    library only

BOOKS:
  Will Lend: Yes
  Length of Loan: 35 days
  Renewable: Yes, in some
    cases
  Charges: None
  Average Turnaround Time:
    3-4 days
  If you have indicated that a
  book is not to be lent, will
  you on receipt of a letter
  from the requesting library
  search the index for given
  entries? (Not answered)

PERIODICALS:
  Bound: Will not lend
  Unbound: Will lend
  Loan Period: 35 days
  Renewable: No
  Will lend if article exceeds
    _____ number of pages (Not
    answered)

MICROFORMS:
  Will Lend: No
  Specific Types of Microforms:
    N/A

GOVERNMENT PUBLICATIONS:
  Will Lend: No

DISSERTATIONS:
  Will Lend: No

THESES:
  Will Lend: No

AUDIO-VISUAL MATERIALS:
  Records: Will not lend
  Cassettes: Will not lend
  Other (slides, filmstrips,
    etc.): Will not lend

COMPUTER SOFTWARE:
  Will Lend: No

PHOTODUPLICATION SERVICE:
  No charge up to 20 exposures
  Charge Per Exposure: 10¢ per
    exposure over 20 pages
  Minimum/handling Fee: None
  Average Turnaround Time:
    3-4 days

MICROFILMING SERVICE:
  Service Available: Yes
  Charges: 15¢ per page

DO YOU CHARGE THE BORROWING
  LIBRARY FOR POSTAGE? No

FOR HOW LONG DO YOU SUSPEND ILL
  SERVICE OVER THE CHRISTMAS
  HOLIDAYS? No suspension

ARE THERE ANY GROUPS OF LIBRARIES
  FOR WHICH YOU WAIVE FEES? IF
  SO, PLEASE NAME THEM: None

AZUSA PACIFIC UNIVERSITY

NUC CODE: CAzPC

OCLC CODE: CAP

ADDRESS: Interlibrary Loan
Marshburn Memorial
Library
Azusa Pacific University
Azusa, CA 91702

TELEPHONE: (213) 969-3434, X198

LIST NAMES OF BRANCHES WITH
SEPARATE POLICIES: None

BOOKS:
Will Lend: Yes
Length of Loan: 3 weeks
Renewable: Yes
Charges: $1.00 to out of
state
Average Turnaround Time:
1 day
If you have indicated that a
book is not to be lent, will
you on receipt of a letter
from the requesting library
search the index for given
entries? (Not answered)

PERIODICALS:
Bound: Will not lend
Unbound: Will not lend
Loan Period: N/A
Renewable: N/A
Will lend if article exceeds
_____ number of pages (Not
answered)

MICROFORMS:
Will Lend: No
Specific Types of Microforms:
N/A

GOVERNMENT PUBLICATIONS:
Will Lend: No

DISSERTATIONS:
Will Lend: No

THESES:
Will Lend: No

AUDIO-VISUAL MATERIALS:
Records: Will not lend
Cassettes: Will not lend
Other (slides, filmstrips,
etc.): (Not answered)

COMPUTER SOFTWARE:
Will Lend: No

PHOTODUPLICATION SERVICE:
No charge up to 0 exposures
Charge Per Exposure: 10¢
Minimum/handling Fee: $1.00
Average Turnaround Time:
1 day

MICROFILMING SERVICE:
Service Available: No
Charges: N/A

DO YOU CHARGE THE BORROWING LIBRARY
FOR POSTAGE? $1.00 for out of
state

FOR HOW LONG DO YOU SUSPEND ILL
SERVICE OVER THE CHRISTMAS
HOLIDAYS? Dec.19-Jan.2

ARE THERE ANY GROUPS OF LIBRARIES
FOR WHICH YOU WAIVE FEES? IF
SO, PLEASE NAME THEM: All
California libraries

BERKELEY PUBLIC LIBRARY

NUC CODE: (Not answered)

OCLC CODE: (Not answered)

ADDRESS: Interlibrary Loan
Berkeley Public Library
2090 Kittredge
Berkeley, CA 94704

TELEPHONE: (415) 644-6815

LIST NAMES OF BRANCHES WITH
SEPARATE POLICIES: None

BOOKS:
Will Lend: Yes
Length of Loan: 1 month
Renewable: No
Charges: None
Average Turnaround Time:
(Not answered)
If you have indicated that a
book is not to be lent, will
you on receipt of a letter
from the requesting library
search the index for given
entries? (Not answered)

PERIODICALS:
Bound: Will not lend
Unbound: Will not lend
Loan Period: N/A
Renewable: N/A
Will lend if article exceeds
_____ number of pages (Not
answered)

MICROFORMS:
Will Lend: No
Specific Types of Microforms:
N/A

GOVERNMENT PUBLICATIONS:
Will Lend: No

DISSERTATIONS:
Will Lend: No

THESES:
Will Lend: No

AUDIO-VISUAL MATERIALS:
Records: Will not lend
Cassettes: Will not lend
Other (slides, filmstrips,
etc.): Will not lend

COMPUTER SOFTWARE:
Will Lend: No

PHOTODUPLICATION SERVICE:
No charge up to 30 exposures
Charge Per Exposure: 10¢
Minimum/handling Fee: (Not
answered)
Average Turnaround Time: (Not
answered)

MICROFILMING SERVICE:
Service Available: No
Charges: N/A

DO YOU CHARGE THE BORROWING
LIBRARY FOR POSTAGE? No

FOR HOW LONG DO YOU SUSPEND ILL
SERVICE OVER THE CHRISTMAS
HOLIDAYS? No suspension

ARE THERE ANY GROUPS OF LIBRARIES
FOR WHICH YOU WAIVE FEES? IF
SO, PLEASE NAME THEM: None

BIOLA UNIVERSITY

NUC CODE: CLamB

OCLC CODE: CBC

ADDRESS: Interlibrary Loan
           Biola University Library
           13800 Biola Avenue
           La Mirada, CA 90639

TELEPHONE: (916) 944-0351, X3256

LIST NAMES OF BRANCHES WITH
  SEPARATE POLICIES: None

BOOKS:
  Will Lend: Yes
  Length of Loan: 3 weeks
  Renewable: Yes
  Charges: None
  Average Turnaround Time:
  24 hours
  If you have indicated that a
  book is not to be lent, will
  you on receipt of a letter
  from the requesting library
  search the index for given
  entries? Yes

PERIODICALS:
  Bound: Will not lend
  Unbound: Will not lend
  Loan Period: N/A
  Renewable: N/A
  Will lend if article exceeds
  _____ number of pages (Not
  answered)

MICROFORMS:
  Will Lend: Yes
  Specific Types of Microforms:
  (Not answered)

GOVERNMENT PUBLICATIONS:
  Will Lend: Yes

DISSERTATIONS:
  Will Lend: Yes

THESES:
  Will Lend: Yes

AUDIO-VISUAL MATERIALS:
  Records: Will not lend
  Cassettes: Will not lend
  Other (slides, filmstrips,
    etc.): Will not lend

COMPUTER SOFTWARE:
  Will Lend: No

PHOTODUPLICATION SERVICE:
  No charge up to 10 exposures
  Charge Per Exposure: 10¢
  Minimum/handling Fee: None
  Average Turnaround Time:
  24 hours

MICROFILMING SERVICE:
  Service Available: No
  Charges: N/A

DO YOU CHARGE THE BORROWING
  LIBRARY FOR POSTAGE? No

FOR HOW LONG DO YOU SUSPEND ILL
  SERVICE OVER THE CHRISTMAS
  HOLIDAYS? Only on the holidays
  themselves

ARE THERE ANY GROUPS OF LIBRARIES
  FOR WHICH YOU WAIVE FEES? IF
  SO, PLEASE NAME THEM: None

BURBANK PUBLIC LIBRARY

NUC CODE: None

OCLC CODE: None

ADDRESS: Interlibrary Loan
           Burbank Public Library
           110 No. Glenoaks Blvd.
           Burbank, CA 91503

TELEPHONE: (213) 847-9741

LIST NAMES OF BRANCHES WITH
  SEPARATE POLICIES: None

BOOKS
  Will Lend: Yes
  Length of Loan: 4 weeks
  Renewable: No
  Charges: None
  Average Turnaround Time:
  Same day
  If you have indicated that a
  book is not to be lent, will
  you on receipt of a letter
  from the requesting library
  search the index for given
  entries? Yes

PERIODICALS:
  Bound: Will not lend
  Unbound: Will not lend
  Loan Period: N/A
  Renewable: N/A
  Will lend if article exceeds
  _____ number of pages (Not
  answered)

MICROFORMS:
  Will Lend: No
  Specific Types of Microforms;
  N/A

GOVERNMENT PUBLICATIONS:
  Will Lend: Yes

DISSERTATIONS:
  Will Lend: Yes

THESES:
  Will Lend: Yes

AUDIO-VISUAL MATERIALS:
  Records: Will not lend
  Cassettes: Will not lend
  Other (slides, filmstrips,
    etc.): Will not lend

COMPUTER SOFTWARE:
  Will Lend: No

PHOTODUPLICATION SERVICE:
  No charge up to 10 exposures
  Charge Per Exposure: 10¢
  Minimum/handling Fee: None
  Average Turnaround Time:
  Same day

MICROFILMING SERVICE:
  Service Available: Yes
  Charges: 25¢ per copy

DO YOU CHARGE THE BORROWING
  LIBRARY FOR POSTAGE? No

FOR HOW LONG DO YOU SUSPEND ILL
  SERVICE OVER THE CHRISTMAS
  HOLIDAYS? No suspension

ARE THERE ANY GROUPS OF LIBRARIES
  FOR WHICH YOU WAIVE FEES? IF
  SO, PLEASE NAME THEM: None

CALIFORNIA INSTITUTE OF TECHNOLOGY

NUC CODE: CPT

OCLC CODE: CIT

ADDRESS: Interlibrary Loan
Millikan Memorial
Library, 1-32
California Institute
of Technology
Pasadena, CA 91125

TELEPHONE: (213) 356-6413

LIST NAMES OF BRANCHES WITH
SEPARATE POLICIES: None

BOOKS:
Will Lend: Yes
Length of Loan: 2 weeks use
Renewable: Yes, sometimes
Charges: Postage
Average Turnaround Time:
2 days
If you have indicated that a
book is not to be lent, will
you on receipt of a letter
from the requesting library
search the index for given
entries? Yes

PERIODICALS:
Bound: Will not lend
Unbound: Will not lend
Loan Period: N/A
Renewable: N/A
Will lend if article exceeds
_____ number of pages (Not
answered)

MICROFORMS:
Will Lend: Yes
Specific Types of Microforms:
Special papers

GOVERNMENT PUBLICATIONS:
Will Lend: Yes

DISSERTATIONS:
Will Lend: Yes; 1964 to
present available from
University Microfilms

THESES:
Will Lend: Yes

AUDIO-VISUAL MATERIALS:
Records: Will not lend
Cassettes: Will not lend
Other (slides, filmstrips,
etc.): (Not answered)

COMPUTER SOFTWARE:
Will Lend: No

PHOTODUPLICATION SERVICE:
No charge up to 0 exposures
Charge Per Exposure: 20¢
after first 7
Minimum/handling Fee: $1.70
for 1-7 exposures
Average Turnaround Time:
2 days

MICROFILMING SERVICE:
Service Available: Yes
Charges: Quoted upon request

DO YOU CHARGE THE BORROWING
LIBRARY FOR POSTAGE? Yes

FOR HOW LONG DO YOU SUSPEND ILL
SERVICE OVER THE CHRISTMAS
HOLIDAYS? Dec.10-Jan.1

ARE THERE ANY GROUPS OF LIBRARIES
FOR WHICH YOU WAIVE FEES? IF
SO, PLEASE NAME THEM: None

CALIFORNIA POLYTECHNIC STATE UNIVERSITY

NUC CODE: CS1uSP

OCLC CODE: CPS

ADDRESS: Interlibrary Loan
Robert F. Kennedy
Library
California Polytechnic
State University
San Luis Obispo, CA
93401

TELEPHONE: (805) 546-1222

LIST NAMES OF BRANCHES WITH
SEPARATE POLICIES: None

BOOKS:
Will Lend: Yes
Length of Loan: 2 weeks use
Renewable: Yes
Charges: None
Average Turnaround Time:
2 days
If you have indicated that a
book is not to be lent, will
you on receipt of a letter
from the requesting library
search the index for given
entries? (Not answered)

PERIODICALS:
Bound: Will not lend
Unbound: Will not lend
Loan Period: N/A
Renewable: N/A
Will lend if article exceeds
_____ number of pages (Will
not usually lend)

MICROFORMS:
Will Lend: Yes
Specific Types of Microforms:
Cataloged microfilm (not
periodicals)

GOVERNMENT PUBLICATIONS:
Will Lend: Yes

DISSERTATIONS:
Will Lend: Yes

THESES:
Will Lend: Yes

AUDIO-VISUAL MATERIALS:
Records: Will not lend
Cassettes: Will not lend
Other (slides, filmstrips,
etc.): Will not lend

COMPUTER SOFTWARE:
Will Lend: No

PHOTODUPLICATION SERVICE:
Minimum charge up to 10
exposures
Charge Per Exposure: 10¢ per
page over 10 pages
Minimum/handling Fee: $5.00
Average Turnaround Time:
2 days

MICROFILMING SERVICE:
Service Available: No
Charges: N/A

DO YOU CHARGE THE BORROWING
LIBRARY FOR POSTAGE? No

FOR HOW LONG DO YOU SUSPEND ILL
SERVICE OVER THE CHRISTMAS
HOLIDAYS? Dec.15-Jan.2

ARE THERE ANY GROUPS OF LIBRARIES
FOR WHICH YOU WAIVE FEES? IF
SO, PLEASE NAME THEM: California
State University and University
of California libraries; local
network libraries.

CALIFORNIA STATE COLLEGE AT BAKERSFIELD

NUC CODE: CBaS

OCLC CODE: CBA

ADDRESS: Interlibrary Loan
Library
California State
College at
Bakersfield
9001 Stockdale Hwy.
Bakersfield, CA 93309

TELEPHONE: (805) 833-3172

LIST NAMES OF BRANCHES WITH
SEPARATE POLICIES: None

BOOKS:
Will Lend: Yes
Length of Loan: 3 weeks
Renewable: Yes
Charges: None
Average Turnaround Time:
2-3 days
If you have indicated that a
book is not to be lent, will
you on receipt of a letter
from the requesting library
search the index for given
entries? Yes

PERIODICALS:
Bound: Will lend only within
system
Unbound: Will lend only
within system
Loan Period: 1 week
Renewable: No

MICROFORMS:
Will Lend: No
Specific Types of Microforms:
N/A

GOVERNMENT PUBLICATIONS:
Will Lend: Yes

DISSERTATIONS:
Will Lend: Yes

THESES:
Will Lend: Yes

AUDIO-VISUAL MATERIALS:
Records: Do not own
Cassettes: Do not own
Other (slides, filmstrips,
etc.): Do not own

COMPUTER SOFTWARE:
Will Lend: Do not own

PHOTODUPLICATION SERVICE:
No charge up to 50 exposures
Charge Per Exposure: None
Minimum/handling Fee: None
Average Turnaround Time:
2-3 days

MICROFILMING SERVICE:
Service Available: No
Charges: N/A

DO YOU CHARGE THE BORROWING LIBRARY
FOR POSTAGE? No

FOR HOW LONG DO YOU SUSPEND ILL
SERVICE OVER THE CHRISTMAS
HOLIDAYS? Depends upon
staffing

ARE THERE ANY GROUPS OF LIBRARIES
FOR WHICH YOU WAIVE FEES? IF
SO, PLEASE NAME THEM: None

CALIFORNIA STATE COLLEGE AT SAN BERNARDINO

NUC CODE: (Not answered)

OCLC CODE: (Not answered)

ADDRESS: Interlibrary Loan
Library
California State
College at San
Bernardino
5500 State College Pkwy.
San Bernardino, CA
92407

TELEPHONE: (714) 887-7335

LIST NAMES OF BRANCHES WITH
SEPARATE POLICIES: None

BOOKS:
Will Lend: Yes
Length of Loan: 2 weeks use
Renewable: Yes
Charges: (Not answered)
Average Turnaround Time:
(Not answered)
If you have indicated that a
book is not to be lent, will
you on receipt of a letter
from the requesting library
search the index for given
entries? (Not answered)

PERIODICALS:
Bound: Will not lend
Unbound: Will not lend
Loan Period: N/A
Renewable: N/A
Will lend if article exceeds
_____ number of pages (Not
answered)

MICROFORMS:
Will Lend: Yes
Specific Types of Microforms:
(Not answered)

GOVERNMENT PUBLICATIONS:
Will Lend: (Not answered)

DISSERTATIONS:
Will Lend: Yes

THESES:
Will Lend: Yes

AUDIO-VISUAL MATERIALS:
Records: (Not answered)
Cassettes: (Not answered)
Other (slides, filmstrips,
etc.): (Not answered)

COMPUTER SOFTWARE:
Will Lend: (Not answered)

PHOTODUPLICATION SERVICE:
No charge up to any exposures
Charge Per Exposure: None
Minimum/handling Fee: None
Average Turnaround Time:
(Not answered)

MICROFILMING SERVICE:
Service Available: No
Charges: N/A

DO YOU CHARGE THE BORROWING
LIBRARY FOR POSTAGE? Yes

FOR HOW LONG DO YOU SUSPEND ILL
SERVICE OVER THE CHRISTMAS
HOLIDAYS? (Not answered)

ARE THERE ANY GROUPS OF LIBRARIES
FOR WHICH YOU WAIVE FEES? IF
SO, PLEASE NAME THEM: (Not
answered)

CALIFORNIA STATE LIBRARY

NUC CODE: C

OCLC CODE: (Not answered)

ADDRESS: Interlibrary Loan
State Information and
Reference Center
California State
Library
P. O. Box 2037
Sacramento, CA 95809

TELEPHONE: (916) 322-4570

LIST NAMES OF BRANCHES WITH
SEPARATE POLICIES: None

BOOKS:
Will Lend: Yes
Length of Loan: 5 weeks
Renewable: Yes
Charges: None
Average Turnaround Time:
1 week
If you have indicated that a
book is not to be lent, will
you on receipt of a letter
from the requesting library
search the index for given
entries? (Not answered)

PERIODICALS:
Bound: Will lend
Unbound: Will lend
Loan Period: 3 weeks
Renewable: Yes
Will lend if article exceeds
_____ number of pages (Not
answered)

MICROFORMS:
Will Lend: Yes
Specific Types of Microforms:
N/A

GOVERNMENT PUBLICATIONS:
Will Lend: Yes

DISSERTATIONS:
Will Lend: Yes, but have only
reprints

THESES:
Will Lend: Yes, but have only
reprints

AUDIO-VISUAL MATERIALS:
Have and will lend materials
on library development and
management only.

COMPUTER SOFTWARE:
Will Lend: (Not answered)

PHOTODUPLICATION SERVICE:
No charge up to 20 exposures
Charge Per Exposure: (Not
answered)
Minimum/handling Fee: None
Average Turnaround Time:
(Not answered)

MICROFILMING SERVICE:
Service Available: No
Charges: N/A

DO YOU CHARGE THE BORROWING
LIBRARY FOR POSTAGE? No

FOR HOW LONG DO YOU SUSPEND ILL
SERVICE OVER THE CHRISTMAS
HOLIDAYS? No suspension

ARE THERE ANY GROUPS OF LIBRARIES
FOR WHICH YOU WAIVE FEES? IF
SO, PLEASE NAME THEM: None

CALIFORNIA STATE POLYTECHNIC UNIVERSITY

NUC CODE: CPomCP

OCLC CODE: CPO

ADDRESS: Interlibrary Loan
California State
Polytechnic University
3801 W. Temple Ave.
Pomona, CA 91768

TELEPHONE: (714) 598-4660

LIST NAMES OF BRANCHES WITH
SEPARATE POLICIES: None

BOOKS:
Will Lend: Yes
Length of Loan: 4 weeks
Renewable: No
Charges: None
Average Turnaround Time:
(Not answered)
If you have indicated that a
book is not to be lent, will
you on receipt of a letter
from the requesting library
search the index for given
entries? (Not answered)

PERIODICALS:
Bound: Will not lend
Unbound: Will not lend
Loan Period: N/A
Renewable: N/A
Will lend if article exceeds
_____ number of pages (Not
answered)

MICROFORMS:
Will Lend: No
Specific Types of Microforms:
N/A

GOVERNMENT PUBLICATIONS:
Will Lend: Yes

DISSERTATIONS:
Will Lend: Do not own

THESES:
Will Lend: Yes

AUDIO-VISUAL MATERIALS:
Records: (Not answered)
Cassettes: (Not answered)
Other (slides, filmstrips,
etc.): (Not answered)

COMPUTER SOFTWARE:
Will Lend: (Not answered)

PHOTODUPLICATION SERVICE:
No charge up to any exposures
Charge Per Exposure: None
Minimum/handling Fee: None
Average Turnaround Time:
(Not answered)

MICROFILMING SERVICE:
Service Available: No
Charges: N/A

DO YOU CHARGE THE BORROWING
LIBRARY FOR POSTAGE? No

FOR HOW LONG DO YOU SUSPEND ILL
SERVICE OVER THE CHRISTMAS
HOLIDAYS? No suspension

ARE THERE ANY GROUPS OF LIBRARIES
FOR WHICH YOU WAIVE FEES? IF
SO, PLEASE NAME THEM: (Not
answered)

CALIFORNIA STATE UNIVERSITY AT CHICO

NUC CODE: CCHIS

OCLC CODE: CCH

ADDRESS: Interlibrary Loan
          Meriam Library
          California State
            University, Chico
          Chico, CA 95929

TELEPHONE: (916) 895-6212

LIST NAMES OF BRANCHES WITH
  SEPARATE POLICIES: None

BOOKS:
  Will Lend: Yes
  Length of Loan: 3 weeks
  Renewable: Yes
  Charges: (Not answered)
  Average Turnaround Time:
    2 days
  If you have indicated that a
    book is not to be lent, will
    you on receipt of a letter
    from the requesting library
    search the index for given
    entries? (Not answered)

PERIODICALS:
  Bound: Will lend selectively
  Unbound: Will lend
    selectively
  Loan Period: (Not answered)
  Renewable: (Not answered)
  Will lend if article exceeds
    _____ number of pages (Not
    answered)

MICROFORMS:
  Will Lend: Yes
  Specific Types of Microforms:
    Selective

GOVERNMENT PUBLICATIONS:
  Will Lend: (Not answered)

DISSERTATIONS:
  Will Lend: Yes

THESES:
  Will Lend: Yes

AUDIO-VISUAL MATERIALS:
  Records: Will not lend
  Cassettes: Will not lend
  Other (slides, filmstrips,
    etc.): Will not lend

COMPUTER SOFTWARE:
  Will Lend: (Not answered)

PHOTODUPLICATION SERVICE:
  No charge up to 0 exposures
  Charge Per Exposure: 10¢ over
    first 20
  Minimum/handling Fee: $2.00
    for 20 pages
  Average Turnaround Time: (Not
    answered)

MICROFILMING SERVICE:
  Service Available: Yes
  Charges: N/A

DO YOU CHARGE THE BORROWING
  LIBRARY FOR POSTAGE? No

FOR HOW LONG DO YOU SUSPEND ILL
  SERVICE OVER THE CHRISTMAS
  HOLIDAYS? 3 weeks

ARE THERE ANY GROUPS OF LIBRARIES
  FOR WHICH YOU WAIVE FEES? IF
  SO, PLEASE NAME THEM:
    California State University
    and College System

CALIFORNIA STATE UNIVERSITY AT DOMINGUEZ HILLS

NUC CODE: (Not answered)

OCLC CODE: CDH

ADDRESS: Interlibrary Loan
          California State
            University at
            Dominguez Hills
          Carson, CA 90747

TELEPHONE: (213) 516-3716

LIST NAMES OF BRANCHES WITH
  SEPARATE POLICIES: None

BOOKS:
  Will Lend: Yes
  Length of Loan: 2 weeks
  Renewable: Yes
  Charges: None
  Average Turnaround Time:
    Depends on U.S. mail;
    we send out within 24 hours
  If you have indicated that a
    book is not to be lent, will
    you on receipt of a letter
    from the requesting library
    search the index for given
    entries? (Not answered)

PERIODICALS:
  Bound: Will not lend
  Unbound: Will not lend
  Loan Period: N/A
  Renewable: N/A
  Will lend if article exceeds
    50 pages (inside CSU system
    only)

MICROFORMS:
  Will Lend: No, generally
  Specific Types of Microforms:
    LAC; ERIC; Newsband;
    periodicals on microfilm

GOVERNMENT PUBLICATIONS:
  Will Lend: Yes, generally

DISSERTATIONS:
  Will Lend: No

THESES:
  Will Lend: No

AUDIO-VISUAL MATERIALS:
  Records: Will not lend
  Cassettes: Will not lend
  Other (slides, filmstrips,
    etc.): Will not lend

COMPUTER SOFTWARE:
  Will Lend: No

PHOTODUPLICATION SERVICE:
  No charge up to 0 exposures
  Charge Per Exposure: 25¢
  Minimum/handling Fee: $3.00
  Average Turnaround Time:
    48 hours

MICROFILMING SERVICE:
  Service Available: No
  Charges: N/A

DO YOU CHARGE THE BORROWING
  LIBRARY FOR POSTAGE? Yes

FOR HOW LONG DO YOU SUSPEND ILL
  SERVICE OVER THE CHRISTMAS
  HOLIDAYS? No suspension

ARE THERE ANY GROUPS OF LIBRARIES
  FOR WHICH YOU WAIVE FEES? IF
  SO, PLEASE NAME THEM:
    California State University
    Campus libraries

CALIFORNIA STATE UNIVERSITY AT FULLERTON

NUC CODE: CFIS

OCLC CODE: CFI

ADDRESS: Interlibrary Loan
California State
University Library
P. O. Box 4150
Fullerton, CA 92634

TELEPHONE: (714) 773-2673

LIST NAMES OF BRANCHES WITH
SEPARATE POLICIES: None

BOOKS:
Will Lend: Yes
Length of Loan: 1 month
from September to May;
2 weeks from June to August
Renewable: Yes
Charges: (Not answered)
Average Turnaround Time:
(Not answered)
If you have indicated that a
book is not to be lent, will
you on receipt of a letter
from the requesting library
search the index for given
entries? (Not answered)

PERIODICALS:
Bound: Will not lend
Unbound: Will not lend
Loan Period: N/A
Renewable: N/A
Will lend if article exceeds
_____ number of pages (Not
answered)

MICROFORMS:
Will Lend: Yes
Specific Types of Microforms:
(Not answered)

GOVERNMENT PUBLICATIONS:
Will Lend: (Not answered)

DISSERTATIONS:
Will Lend: Do not own

THESES:
Will Lend: Yes; 1970 to
present available from
University Microfilms

AUDIO-VISUAL MATERIALS:
Records: (Not answered)
Cassettes: (Not answered)
Other (slides, filmstrips,
etc.): (Not answered)

COMPUTER SOFTWARE:
Will Lend: (Not answered)

PHOTODUPLICATION SERVICE:
No charge up to 0 exposures
Charge Per Exposure: 10¢
Handling Fee: 25¢
Average Turnaround Time:
(Not answered)

MICROFILMING SERVICE:
Service Available: (Not
answered)
Charges: N/A

DO YOU CHARGE THE BORROWING
LIBRARY FOR POSTAGE? No

FOR HOW LONG DO YOU SUSPEND ILL
SERVICE OVER THE CHRISTMAS
HOLIDAYS? Dec.15-Jan.7

ARE THERE ANY GROUPS OF LIBRARIES
FOR WHICH YOU WAIVE FEES? IF
SO, PLEASE NAME THEM: (Not
answered)

CALIFORNIA STATE UNIVERSITY AT HAYWARD

NUC CODE: (Not answered)

OCLC CODE: CSH

ADDRESS: Interlibrary Loan
California State
University Library
Hayward, CA 94542

TELEPHONE: (415) 881-3780

LIST NAMES OF BRANCHES WITH
SEPARATE POLICIES: None

BOOKS:
Will Lend: Yes
Length of Loan: 1 month
Renewable: No
Charges: $5.00 for profit
corporations and private
universities
Average Turnaround Time:
(Not answered)
If you have indicated that a
book is not to be lent, will
you on receipt of a letter
from the requesting library
search the index for given
entries? (Not answered)

PERIODICALS:
Bound: Will not lend
Unbound: Will not lend
Loan Period: N/A
Renewable: N/A
Will lend if article exceeds
_____ number of pages (Not
answered)

MICROFORMS:
Will Lend: Yes, sometimes
Specific Types of Microforms:
(Not answered)

GOVERNMENT PUBLICATIONS:
Will Lend: Yes

DISSERTATIONS:
Will Lend: Do not own

THESES:
Will Lend: Yes, for 1 month

AUDIO-VISUAL MATERIALS:
Records: (Not answered)
Cassettes: (Not answered)
Other (slides, filmstrips,
etc.): (Not answered)

COMPUTER SOFTWARE:
Will Lend: (Not answered)

PHOTODUPLICATION SERVICE:
No charge up to 0 exposures
Charge Per Exposure: 10¢
Minimum Fee: $2.00
Average Turnaround Time:
(Not answered)

MICROFILMING SERVICE:
Service Available: No
Charges: N/A

DO YOU CHARGE THE BORROWING
LIBRARY FOR POSTAGE? No

FOR HOW LONG DO YOU SUSPEND ILL
SERVICE OVER THE CHRISTMAS
HOLIDAYS? (Not answered)

ARE THERE ANY GROUPS OF LIBRARIES
FOR WHICH YOU WAIVE FEES? IF
SO, PLEASE NAME THEM: (Not
answered)

CALIFORNIA STATE UNIVERSITY AT LONG BEACH

NUC CODE: CLobS

OCLC CODE: CLO

ADDRESS: Interlibrary Loan
           California State
              University at Long
              Beach
           1250 Bellflower Blvd.
           Long Beach, CA 90840

TELEPHONE: (213) 498-4628

LIST NAMES OF BRANCHES WITH
  SEPARATE POLICIES: None

BOOKS:
  Will Lend: Yes
  Length of Loan: 2 weeks
  Renewable: Yes
  Charges: None for returnable
    materials
  Average Turnaround Time:
    1 week
  If you have indicated that a
    book is not to be lent, will
    you on receipt of a letter
    from the requesting library
    search the index for given
    entries? (Not answered)

PERIODICALS:
  Bound: Will not lend
  Unbound: Will not lend
  Loan Period: N/A
  Renewable: N/A
  Will lend if article exceeds
    an exceptional number of
    pages

MICROFORMS:
  Will Lend: No
  Specific Types of Microforms:
    N/A

GOVERNMENT PUBLICATIONS:
  Will Lend: Yes

DISSERTATIONS:
  Will Lend: No

THESES:
  Will Lend: Yes

AUDIO-VISUAL MATERIALS:
  Records: Will not lend
  Cassettes: Will not lend
  Other (slides, filmstrips,
    etc.): Will lend, depending
    on the request

COMPUTER SOFTWARE:
  Will Lend: No

PHOTODUPLICATION SERVICE:
  No charge up to 0 exposures
  Charge Per Exposure: $1.50
    minimum charge for 15
    exposures or less. 10¢ per
    exposure. We do not charge
    institutions which do not
    charge us.
  Minimum/handling Fee: $1.50
  Average Turnaround Time:
    1 week

MICROFILMING SERVICE:
  Service Available: (Not
    answered)
  Charges: N/A

DO YOU CHARGE THE BORROWING
  LIBRARY FOR POSTAGE? In
    exceptional cases--only
    when postage will be very
    expensive.

FOR HOW LONG DO YOU SUSPEND ILL
  SERVICE OVER THE CHRISTMAS
  HOLIDAYS? No suspension

ARE THERE ANY GROUPS OF LIBRARIES
  FOR WHICH YOU WAIVE FEES? IF
  SO, PLEASE NAME THEM:
    California State University
    sister schools, and librar-
    ies who do not charge us.

CALIFORNIA STATE UNIVERSITY AT LOS ANGELES

NUC CODE: CLS

OCLC CODE: CLA

ADDRESS: Interlibrary Loan
           John F. Kennedy
              Memorial Library
           California State
              University, Los
              Angeles
           5151 State University
              Drive
           Los Angeles, CA 90032

TELEPHONE: (213) 224-2251

LIST NAMES OF BRANCHES WITH
  SEPARATE POLICIES: None

BOOKS:
  Will Lend: Yes
  Length of Loan: 2 weeks
    from date received
  Renewable: Yes
  Charges: None
  Average Turnaround Time:
    2-5 days
  If you have indicated that a
    book is not to be lent, will
    you on receipt of a letter
    from the requesting library
    search the index for given
    entries? No

PERIODICALS:
  Bound: Will lend on special
    occasions
  Unbound: Will not lend
  Loan Period: 1 week from
    date received
  Renewable: No
  Will lend if article exceeds
    40 pages

GOVERNMENT PUBLICATIONS:
  Will Lend: Yes

MICROFORMS:
  Will Lend: Yes
  Specific Types of Microforms:
    Cards, 10 at a time; fiche,
    10 at a time; film, 4 reels
    at a time

DISSERTATIONS:
  Will Lend: No

THESES:
  Will Lend: No

AUDIO-VISUAL MATERIALS:
  Records: Will not lend
  Cassettes: Will not lend
  Other (slides, filmstrips,
    etc.): Will not lend

COMPUTER SOFTWARE:
  Will Lend: No

PHOTODUPLICATION SERVICE:
  Do not charge educational
    institutions
  Average Turnaround Time:
    2-5 days

MICROFILMING SERVICE:
  Service Available: No
  Charges: N/A

DO YOU CHARGE THE BORROWING
  LIBRARY FOR POSTAGE? No

FOR HOW LONG DO YOU SUSPEND ILL
  SERVICE OVER THE CHRISTMAS
  HOLIDAYS? Dec.15-Jan.1

ARE THERE ANY GROUPS OF LIBRARIES
  FOR WHICH YOU WAIVE FEES? IF
  SO, PLEASE NAME THEM: N/A

CALIFORNIA STATE UNIVERSITY AT NORTHRIDGE

NUC CODE: CNoS

OCLC CODE: CNO

ADDRESS: Interlibrary Loan
Oviatt Library
California State
University, Northridge
Northridge, CA 91330

TELEPHONE: (213) 885-2277

LIST NAMES OF BRANCHES WITH
SEPARATE POLICIES: None

BOOKS
Will Lend: Yes
Length of Loan: 2 weeks
Renewable: (Not answered)
Charges: None
Average Turnaround Time:
1 week
If you have indicated that a
book is not to be lent, will
you on receipt of a letter
from the requesting library
search the index for given
entries? (Not answered)

PERIODICALS:
Bound: Usually will not lend,
but negotiable with
librarian's permission
Unbound: Will not lend
Loan Period: 3 days
Renewable: No
Will lend if article exceeds
_____ number of pages
(Negotiable with librarian's
permission)

MICROFORMS:
Will Lend: Yes, but negotiable
with librarian's permission
Specific Types of Microforms;
Will not lend heavily-used
microforms, such as Los
Angeles Times and New York
Times

GOVERNMENT PUBLICATIONS:
Will Lend: Not usually, but
negotiable

DISSERTATIONS:
Will Lend: Yes

THESES:
Will Lend: Yes

AUDIO-VISUAL MATERIALS:
Records: Will not lend
Cassettes: Will not lend
Other (slides, filmstrips,
etc.): Will not lend

COMPUTER SOFTWARE:
Will Lend: No

PHOTODUPLICATION SERVICE:
No charge up to 20 exposures
Charge Per Exposure: (Not
answered)
Minimum/handling Fee: (Not
answered)
Average Turnaround Time:
1 week

MICROFILMING SERVICE:
Service Available: No
Charges: N/A

DO YOU CHARGE THE BORROWING LIBRARY
FOR POSTAGE? (Not answered)

FOR HOW LONG DO YOU SUSPEND ILL
SERVICE OVER THE CHRISTMAS
HOLIDAYS? Only for days
library is not open

ARE THERE ANY GROUPS OF LIBRARIES
FOR WHICH YOU WAIVE FEES? IF
SO, PLEASE NAME THEM: None

CALIFORNIA STATE UNIVERSITY AT SACRAMENTO

NUC CODE: (Not answered)

OCLC CODE: CSA

ADDRESS: Interlibrary Loan
California State
University at
Sacramento Library
2000 Jed Smith Dr.
Sacramento, CA 95819

TELEPHONE: (916) 454-6395

LIST NAMES OF BRANCHES WITH
SEPARATE POLICIES: None

BOOKS:
Will Lend: Yes
Length of Loan: 3-4 weeks
Renewable: Yes
Charges: None
Average Turnaround Time:
2 days
If you have indicated that a
book is not to be lent, will
you on receipt of a letter
from the requesting library
search the index for given
entries? (Not answered)

PERIODICALS:
Bound: Will lend
Unbound: Will lend
Loan Period: 3-7 days
Renewable: No
Will lend if article exceeds
30 pages

MICROFORMS:
Will Lend: Yes
Specific Types of Microforms:
(Not answered)

GOVERNMENT PUBLICATIONS:
Will Lend: Yes

DISSERTATIONS:
Will Lend: No

THESES:
Will Lend: Yes

AUDIO-VISUAL MATERIALS:
Records: Will not lend
Cassettes: Will not lend
Other (slides, filmstrips,
etc.): (Not answered)

COMPUTER SOFTWARE:
Will Lend: No

PHOTODUPLICATION SERVICE:
No charge up to 30 exposures
Charge Per Exposure: None
Minimum/handling Fee: None
Average Turnaround Time:
3-4 days

MICROFILMING SERVICE:
Service Available: Yes
Charges: None

DO YOU CHARGE THE BORROWING
LIBRARY FOR POSTAGE?
Sometimes

FOR HOW LONG DO YOU SUSPEND ILL
SERVICE OVER THE CHRISTMAS
HOLIDAYS? No suspension

ARE THERE ANY GROUPS OF LIBRARIES
FOR WHICH YOU WAIVE FEES? IF
SO, PLEASE NAME THEM: None

CITRUS COLLEGE

NUC CODE: (Not answered)

OCLC CODE: CCI

ADDRESS: Interlibrary Loan
           Citrus College Library
           18824 E. Foothill Blvd.
           P. O. Box R R R
           Azusa, CA 91702-1348

TELEPHONE: (213) 355-0521, X290

LIST NAMES OF BRANCHES WITH
  SEPARATE POLICIES: None

BOOKS:
  Will Lend: Yes
  Length of Loan: 1 month
  Renewable: Yes
  Charges: None
  Average Turnaround Time: (Not
    answered)
  If you have indicated that a
  book is not to be lent, will
  you on receipt of a letter
  from the requesting library
  search the index for given
  entries? (Not answered)

PERIODICALS:
  Bound: Will not lend
  Unbound: Will lend
  Loan Period: 1 month
  Renewable: Yes
  Will lend if article exceeds
    _____ number of pages (Not
  answered)

MICROFORMS:
  Will Lend: Not usually
  Specific Types of Microforms:
  Will lend microfiche

GOVERNMENT PUBLICATIONS:
  Will Lend: Yes

DISSERTATIONS:
  Will Lend: Do not own

THESES:
  Will Lend: Do not own

AUDIO-VISUAL MATERIALS:
  Records: Will not lend
  Cassettes: Will lend
  Other (slides, filmstrips,
    etc.): Will not lend

COMPUTER SOFTWARE:
  Will Lend: No

PHOTODUPLICATION SERVICE:
  No charge up to 15 exposures
  Charge Per Exposure: 10¢
  Minimum/handling Fee: None
  Average Turnaround Time: (Not
    answered)

MICROFILMING SERVICE:
  Service Available: Yes
  Charges: 25¢ per page

DO YOU CHARGE THE BORROWING LIBRARY
FOR POSTAGE? No

FOR HOW LONG DO YOU SUSPEND ILL
SERVICE OVER THE CHRISTMAS
HOLIDAYS? 2 weeks

ARE THERE ANY GROUPS OF LIBRARIES
FOR WHICH YOU WAIVE FEES? IF
SO, PLEASE NAME THEM: None

CLAREMONT COLLEGE

NUC CODE: CCC

OCLC CODE: HDC

ADDRESS: Interlibrary Loan
           Honnold Library
           Claremont Colleges
           Claremont, CA 91711

TELEPHONE: (714) 621-8000, X3721

LIST NAMES OF BRANCHES WITH
  SEPARATE POLICIES:
  Rancho Santa Ana Botanic
    Gardens Library
  School of Theology at
    Claremont Library

BOOKS:
  Will Lend: Yes
  Length of Loan: 2 weeks
  Renewable: Yes
  Charges: Postage
  Average Turnaround Time:
  1 month
  If you have indicated that a
  book is not to be lent, will
  you on receipt of a letter
  from the requesting library
  search the index for given
  entries? Yes, if not too
    busy

PERIODICALS:
  Bound: Will not lend
  Unbound: Will not lend
  Loan Period: N/A
  Renewable: N/A
  Will lend if article exceeds
    _____ number of pages (Will
    not lend, regardless of
    length of article)

MICROFORMS:
  Will Lend: Yes
  Specific Types of Microforms:
  Limited loan policy at
    discretion of circulation
    librarian

GOVERNMENT PUBLICATIONS:
  Will Lend: Yes

DISSERTATIONS:
  Will Lend: Yes, unless very
    recent; all are available
    from University Microfilms

THESES:
  Will Lend: Yes

AUDIO-VISUAL MATERIALS:
  Records: Will not lend
  Cassettes: Will not lend
  Other (slides, filmstrips,
    etc.): Will not lend

COMPUTER SOFTWARE:
  Will Lend: No

PHOTODUPLICATION SERVICE:
  No charge up to 0 exposures
  Charge Per Exposure: 15¢
  Minimum/handling Fee: $2.00
  Average Turnaround Time:
    2 weeks

MICROFILMING SERVICE:
  Service Available: No
  Charges: N/A

DO YOU CHARGE THE BORROWING
LIBRARY FOR POSTAGE? Yes

FOR HOW LONG DO YOU SUSPEND ILL
SERVICE OVER THE CHRISTMAS
HOLIDAYS? No suspension

ARE THERE ANY GROUPS OF LIBRARIES
FOR WHICH YOU WAIVE FEES? IF
SO, PLEASE NAME THEM: None

CONTRA COSTA COUNTY LIBRARY

NUC CODE: (Not answered)

OCLC CODE: None

ADDRESS: Interlibrary Loan
           Contra Costa County
           Library
           1750 Oak Park Blvd.
           Pleasant Hill, CA
           94523

TELEPHONE: (415) 944-3354

LIST NAMES OF BRANCHES WITH
   SEPARATE POLICIES: None

BOOKS:
   Will Lend: Yes
   Length of Loan: 1 month
   Renewable: Yes
   Charges: None
   Average Turnaround Time:
      (Not answered)
   If you have indicated that a
      book is not to be lent, will
      you on receipt of a letter
      from the requesting library
      search the index for given
      entries? (Not answered)

PERIODICALS:
   Bound: Will not lend
   Unbound: Will lend
   Loan Period: 1 month
   Renewable: Yes
   Will lend if article exceeds
      _____ number of pages (Not
      answered)

MICROFORMS:
   Will Lend: No
   Specific Types of Microforms:
      N/A

GOVERNMENT PUBLICATIONS:
   Will Lend: Yes

DISSERTATIONS:
   Will Lend: Do not own

THESES:
   Will Lend: Do not own

AUDIO-VISUAL MATERIALS:
   Records: Do not own
   Cassettes: Do not own
   Other (slides, filmstrips,
      etc.): Do not own

COMPUTER SOFTWARE:
   Will Lend: Do not own

PHOTODUPLICATION SERVICE:
   No charge up to 0 exposures
   Charge Per Exposure: 15¢ per
      page
   Minimum/handling Fee: None
   Average Turnaround Time:
      (Not answered)

MICROFILMING SERVICE:
   Service Available: No
   Charges: N/A

DO YOU CHARGE THE BORROWING
   LIBRARY FOR POSTAGE? No

FOR HOW LONG DO YOU SUSPEND ILL
   SERVICE OVER THE CHRISTMAS
   HOLIDAYS? No suspension

ARE THERE ANY GROUPS OF LIBRARIES
   FOR WHICH YOU WAIVE FEES? IF
   SO, PLEASE NAME THEM: Bay
      Area Library and Information
      System (BALIS)

FRESNO COUNTY FREE LIBRARY

NUC CODE: CF

OCLC CODE: SJL

ADDRESS: Interlibrary Loan
           Fresno County Free
           Library
           2420 Mariposa St.
           Fresno, CA 93721

TELEPHONE: (209) 488-3199

LIST NAMES OF BRANCHES WITH
   SEPARATE POLICIES: None

BOOKS:
   Will Lend: Yes
   Length of Loan: 6 weeks
   Renewable: Yes
   Charges: None
   Average Turnaround Time:
      (Not answered)
   If you have indicated that a
      book is not to be lent, will
      you on receipt of a letter
      from the requesting library
      search the index for given
      entries? Yes

PERIODICALS:
   Bound: Will not lend
   Unbound: Will not lend
   Loan Period: N/A
   Renewable: N/A
   Will lend if article exceeds
      _____ number of pages (Not
      answered)

MICROFORMS:
   Will Lend: No
   Specific Types of Microforms:
      Microfiche; microfilm

GOVERNMENT PUBLICATIONS:
   Will Lend: Yes, some of them

DISSERTATIONS:
   Will Lend: Do not own

THESES:
   Will Lend: Do not own

AUDIO-VISUAL MATERIALS:
   Records: Will not lend
   Cassettes: Will not lend
   Other (slides, filmstrips,
      etc.): Will not lend

COMPUTER SOFTWARE:
   Will Lend: No

PHOTODUPLICATION SERVICE:
   No charge up to 10 exposures
   Charge Per Exposure: 10¢
   Minimum/handling Fee: None
   Average Turnaround Time:
      (Not answered)

MICROFILMING SERVICE:
   Service Available: No
   Charges: N/A

DO YOU CHARGE THE BORROWING LIBRARY
   FOR POSTAGE? No

FOR HOW LONG DO YOU SUSPEND ILL
   SERVICE OVER THE CHRISTMAS
   HOLIDAYS? 2 weeks (Dec.15-
   Jan.2)

ARE THERE ANY GROUPS OF LIBRARIES
   FOR WHICH YOU WAIVE FEES? IF
   SO, PLEASE NAME THEM: None

FULLERTON PUBLIC LIBRARY

NUC CODE: (Not answered)

OCLC CODE: FUP

ADDRESS: Interlibrary Loan
Fullerton Public Library
353 W. Commonwealth Ave.
Fullerton, CA 92632

TELEPHONE: (714) 738-6356

LIST NAMES OF BRANCHES WITH
SEPARATE POLICIES: None

BOOKS:
Will Lend: Yes, except for
reference materials
Length of Loan: 4 weeks
Renewable: No
Charges: Sometimes for
insurance only
Average Turnaround Time:
0-5 months approximately
If you have indicated that a
book is not to be lent, will
you on receipt of a letter
from the requesting library
search the index for given
entries? Contact our
reference department

PERIODICALS:
Bound: Will lend if less than
5 years old
Unbound: Will lend if less
than 5 years old
Loan Period: 4 weeks
Renewable: No
Will lend if article exceeds
_____ number of pages (N/A)

MICROFORMS:
Will Lend: No
Specific Types of Microforms:
Microfilm and microfiche

GOVERNMENT PUBLICATIONS:
Will Lend: Yes

DISSERTATIONS:
Will Lend: Do not own

THESES:
Will Lend: Do not own

AUDIO-VISUAL MATERIALS:
Records: Will not lend
Cassettes: Will lend
Other (slides, filmstrips,
etc.): Will not lend

COMPUTER SOFTWARE:
Will Lend: No

PHOTODUPLICATION SERVICE:
No charge up to 20 exposures
Charge Per Exposure: 10¢
Minimum/handling Fee: None
Average Turnaround Time:
0-5 months approximately

MICROFILMING SERVICE:
Service Available: No
Charges: N/A

DO YOU CHARGE THE BORROWING LIBRARY
FOR POSTAGE? No

FOR HOW LONG DO YOU SUSPEND ILL
SERVICE OVER THE CHRISTMAS
HOLIDAYS? Varies--2-3 days

ARE THERE ANY GROUPS OF LIBRARIES
FOR WHICH YOU WAIVE FEES? IF
SO, PLEASE NAME THEM: Santiago
Library System (SLS)

GLENDALE PUBLIC LIBRARY

NUC CODE: None

OCLC CODE: CGL

ADDRESS: Interlibrary Loan
Glendale Public Library
222 E. Harvard
Glendale, CA 91205

TELEPHONE: (213) 956-2027
(Reference)

LIST NAMES OF BRANCHES WITH
SEPARATE POLICIES: None

BOOKS:
Will Lend: Yes, except
reference books
Length of Loan: Varies
Renewable: (Not answered)
Charges: (Not answered)
Average Turnaround Time:
2 days
If you have indicated that a
book is not to be lent, will
you on receipt of a letter
from the requesting library
search the index for given
entries? (Not answered)

PERIODICALS:
Bound: Will not lend
Unbound: Will not lend
Loan Period: N/A
Renewable: N/A
Will lend if article exceeds
_____ number of pages (Not
answered)

MICROFORMS:
Will Lend: No
Specific Types of Microforms;
N/A

GOVERNMENT PUBLICATIONS:
Will Lend: No

DISSERTATIONS:
Will Lend: No

THESES:
Will Lend: No

AUDIO-VISUAL MATERIALS:
Records: Will not lend
Cassettes: Will not lend
Other (slides, filmstrips,
etc.): Will not lend

COMPUTER SOFTWARE:
Will Lend: No

PHOTODUPLICATION SERVICE:
No charge up to 20 exposures
Charge Per Exposure: 10¢ for
xerox; 25¢ for microprinter
Minimum/handling Fee: (Not
answered)
Average Turnaround Time:
2 days

MICROFILMING SERVICE:
Service Available: No
Charges: N/A

DO YOU CHARGE THE BORROWING LIBRARY
FOR POSTAGE? No, except for
insurance when applicable.

FOR HOW LONG DO YOU SUSPEND ILL
SERVICE OVER THE CHRISTMAS
HOLIDAYS? (Not answered)

ARE THERE ANY GROUPS OF LIBRARIES
FOR WHICH YOU WAIVE FEES? IF
SO, PLEASE NAME THEM: None

GRADUATE THEOLOGICAL UNION LIBRARY

NUC CODE: CBGTU

OCLC CODE: (Not answered)

ADDRESS: Interlibrary Loan
Graduate Theological
Union Library
2400 Ridge Rd.
Berkeley, CA 94709

TELEPHONE: (415) 841-8222

LIST NAMES OF INSTITUTIONS SERVED
BY THIS LIBRARY:
American Baptist Seminary of
the West (formerly
Berkeley Baptist Divinity
School)
Church Divinity School of
the Pacific
Dominican School of
Philosophy and Theology
Franciscan School of
Theology
Jesuit School of Theology
(formerly Alma College,
Los Gatos)
Pacific Lutheran Theological
Seminary
Pacific School of Religion
Saint Albert's College,
Oakland
San Francisco Theological
Seminary, San Anselmo &
Berkeley
Starr King School for the
Ministry

BOOKS:
Will Lend: Yes
Length of Loan: 1 month
Renewable: Yes
Charges: (Not answered)
Average Turnaround Time:
(Not answered)
If you have indicated that a
book is not to be lent, will
you on receipt of a letter
from the requesting library
search the index for given
entries? Yes, for $6.00 per
hour.

MICROFORMS:
Will Lend: Yes
Specific Types of Microforms:
Books on microform

GOVERNMENT PUBLICATIONS:
Will Lend: (Not answered)

DISSERTATIONS:
Will Lend: Yes

THESES:
Will Lend: Yes

AUDIO-VISUAL MATERIALS:
Records: Will lend
Cassettes: Will lend
Other (slides, filmstrips,
etc.): Will lend

COMPUTER SOFTWARE:
Will Lend: (Not answered)

PHOTODUPLICATION SERVICE:
No charge up to 3 exposures
Charge Per Exposure: 10¢
Handling Fee: $1.00 per vol.
Minimum Fee: $2.00
Average Turnaround Time:
(Not answered)

MICROFILMING SERVICE:
Service Available: Yes
Charges: $1.00 per volume
plus $6.00 handling

DO YOU CHARGE THE BORROWING
LIBRARY FOR POSTAGE? Only
for special services, such
as air mail, overseas, etc.

FOR HOW LONG DO YOU SUSPEND ILL
SERVICE OVER THE CHRISTMAS
HOLIDAYS? No suspension

ARE THERE ANY GROUPS OF LIBRARIES
FOR WHICH YOU WAIVE FEES? IF
SO, PLEASE NAME THEM: None

HOOVER INSTITUTION

NUC CODE: CSt-H

OCLC CODE: (Not answered)

ADDRESS: Interlibrary Loan
Hoover Institution
Stanford University
Stanford, CA 94305

TELEPHONE: (415) 497-2058

LIST NAMES OF BRANCHES WITH
SEPARATE POLICIES: None

BOOKS:
Will Lend: Yes
Length of Loan: 2 weeks;
4 weeks, Oriental
languages
Renewable: Yes
Charges: Postage and
insurance
Average Turnaround Time:
3-4 days
If you have indicated that a
book is not to be lent, will
you on receipt of a letter
from the requesting library
search the index for given
entries? Only under
unusual circumstances.

PERIODICALS:
Bound: Will not lend
Unbound: Will not lend
Loan Period: N/A
Renewable: N/A
Will lend if article exceeds
_____ number of pages (Not
answered)

MICROFORMS:
Will Lend: Yes
Specific Types of Microforms:
Will not lend negative
microfilms

GOVERNMENT PUBLICATIONS:
Will Lend: No

DISSERTATIONS:
Will Lend: Yes, if second
copy exists

THESES:
Will Lend: Yes, if second
copy exists

AUDIO-VISUAL MATERIALS:
Records: Do not own
Cassettes: Do not own
Other (slides, filmstrips,
etc.): Do not own

COMPUTER SOFTWARE:
Will Lend: Do not own

PHOTODUPLICATION SERVICE:
No charge up to _____ exposures
(Not answered)
Charge Per Exposure: 30¢
Minimum/handling Fee: $7.00
Average Turnaround Time:
3-4 days

MICROFILMING SERVICE:
Service Available: Yes
Charges: Minimum charge is
$21.50

DO YOU CHARGE THE BORROWING LIBRARY
FOR POSTAGE? Yes

FOR HOW LONG DO YOU SUSPEND ILL
SERVICE OVER THE CHRISTMAS
HOLIDAYS? Approximately from
Dec.12-Jan.2

ARE THERE ANY GROUPS OF LIBRARIES
FOR WHICH YOU WAIVE FEES? IF
SO, PLEASE NAME THEM: RLG
libraries, Consortium of
Western Colleges and
Universities

HUMBOLDT STATE UNIVERSITY

NUC CODE: C

OCLC CODE: CHU

ADDRESS: Interlibrary Loan
          Humboldt State
            University
          Areata, CA 95521

TELEPHONE: (707) 826-4889

LIST NAMES OF BRANCHES WITH
  SEPARATE POLICIES: None

BOOKS:
  Will Lend: Yes
  Length of Loan: 2 weeks use
  Renewable: Yes, usually
  Charges: Postage
  Average Turnaround Time:
    1 week
  If you have indicated that a
  book is not to be lent, will
  you on receipt of a letter
  from the requesting library
  search the index for given
  entries? (Not answered)

PERIODICALS:
  Bound: Will lend
  Unbound: Will not lend
    current periodicals
  Loan Period: 2 weeks
  Renewable: No
  Will lend if article exceeds
    20 pages

MICROFORMS:
  Will Lend: Yes
  Specific Types of Microforms:
    Any, but 5 reels, etc. at
    one time only

GOVERNMENT PUBLICATIONS:
  Will Lend: Yes, usually

DISSERTATIONS:
  Will Lend: No

THESES:
  Will Lend: Yes, if library
    owns second copy

AUDIO-VISUAL MATERIALS:
  Records: Will not lend
  Cassettes: Will not lend
  Other (slides, filmstrips,
    etc.): Will not lend

COMPUTER SOFTWARE:
  Will Lend: No

PHOTODUPLICATION SERVICE:
  No charge up to --- exposures
  Charge Per Exposure: 25¢ from
    paper, 30¢ from film
  Minimum/handling Fee: $1.00
    plus postage
  Average Turnaround Time:
    1 week

MICROFILMING SERVICE:
  Service Available: No
  Charges: N/A

DO YOU CHARGE THE BORROWING
  LIBRARY FOR POSTAGE? Yes

FOR HOW LONG DO YOU SUSPEND ILL
  SERVICE OVER THE CHRISTMAS
  HOLIDAYS? Varies--not long

ARE THERE ANY GROUPS OF LIBRARIES
  FOR WHICH YOU WAIVE FEES? IF
  SO, PLEASE NAME THEM:
    California State Universities

HUNTINGTON LIBRARY

NUC CODE: CSmH

OCLC CODE: (Not answered)

ADDRESS: The Huntington Library
          1151 Oxford Road
          San Marino, CA 91108

TELEPHONE: (213) 792-6141

"UNDER THE TERMS OF OUR DEED OF
TRUST NO MATERIAL IS
PERMITTED TO LEAVE THE
LIBRARY"

LIST NAMES OF BRANCHES WITH
  SEPARATE POLICIES: None

BOOKS:
  Will Lend: No
  Length of Loan: N/A
  Renewable: N/A
  Charges: N/A
  Average Turnaround Time:
    N/A
  If you have indicated that a
  book is not to be lent, will
  you on receipt of a letter
  from the requesting library
  search the index for given
  entries? (Not answered)

PERIODICALS:
  Bound: Will not lend
  Unbound: Will not lend
  Loan Period: N/A
  Renewable: N/A
  Will lend if article exceeds
    _____ number of pages (Will
  not lend)

MICROFORMS:
  Will Lend: No
  Specific Types of Microforms:
    N/A

GOVERNMENT PUBLICATIONS:
  Will Lend: No

DISSERTATIONS:
  Will Lend: No

THESES:
  Will Lend: No

AUDIO-VISUAL MATERIALS:
  Records: Do not own
  Cassettes: Do not own
  Other (slides, filmstrips,
    etc.): Do not own

COMPUTER SOFTWARE:
  Will Lend: Do not own

PHOTODUPLICATION SERVICE:
  (Not answered)

MICROFILMING SERVICE:
  Service Available: Yes
  Charges: (Not answered)

DO YOU CHARGE THE BORROWING LIBRARY
  FOR POSTAGE? N/A

FOR HOW LONG DO YOU SUSPEND ILL
  SERVICE OVER THE CHRISTMAS
  HOLIDAYS? N/A

ARE THERE ANY GROUPS OF LIBRARIES
  FOR WHICH YOU WAIVE FEES? IF
  SO, PLEASE NAME THEM: N/A

INGLEWOOD PUBLIC LIBRARY

NUC CODE: None

OCLC CODE: None

ADDRESS: Interlibrary Loan
Inglewood Public Library
101 W. Manchester Blvd.
Inglewood, CA
90301-1771

TELEPHONE: (213) 649-7614

LIST NAMES OF BRANCHES WITH
SEPARATE POLICIES: None

BOOKS:
Will Lend: Yes
Length of Loan: 1 month
Renewable: No
Charges: None
Average Turnaround Time:
2 days
If you have indicated that a
book is not to be lent, will
you on receipt of a letter
from the requesting library
search the index for given
entries? Yes

PERIODICALS:
Bound: Will not lend
Unbound: Will not lend
Loan Period: N/A
Renewable: N/A
Will lend if article exceeds
_____ number of pages (Will
not lend)

MICROFORMS:
Will Lend: No
Specific Types of Microforms:
N/A

GOVERNMENT PUBLICATIONS:
Will Lend: Yes

DISSERTATIONS:
Will Lend: Do not own

THESES:
Will Lend: Do not own

AUDIO-VISUAL MATERIALS:
Records: Will not lend
Cassettes: Will not lend
Other (slides, filmstrips,
etc.): Will not lend

COMPUTER SOFTWARE:
Will Lend: Do not own

PHOTODUPLICATION SERVICE:
No charge up to 9 exposures
Charge Per Exposure: 10¢
Minimum/handling Fee: None
Average Turnaround Time:
2 days

MICROFILMING SERVICE:
Service Available: No
Charges: N/A

DO YOU CHARGE THE BORROWING LIBRARY
FOR POSTAGE? No

FOR HOW LONG DO YOU SUSPEND ILL
SERVICE OVER THE CHRISTMAS
HOLIDAYS? No suspension

ARE THERE ANY GROUPS OF LIBRARIES
FOR WHICH YOU WAIVE FEES? IF
SO, PLEASE NAME THEM: None

JOHN STEINBECK PUBLIC LIBRARY

NUC CODE: (Not answered)

OCLC CODE: SPU

ADDRESS: Interlibrary Loan
John Steinbeck Public
Library
110 W. San Luis St.
Salinas, CA 93901

TELEPHONE: (408) 758-7311

LIST NAMES OF BRANCHES WITH
SEPARATE POLICIES: None

BOOKS:
Will Lend: Yes
Length of Loan: 4 weeks
Renewable: Yes
Charges: None
Average Turnaround Time:
4 weeks
If you have indicated that a
book is not to be lent, will
you on receipt of a letter
from the requesting library
search the index for given
entries? (Not answered)

PERIODICALS:
Bound: Will not lend
Unbound: Will lend
Loan Period: 4 weeks
Renewable: Yes
Will lend if article exceeds
_____ number of pages (Not
answered)

MICROFORMS:
Will Lend: No
Specific Types of Microforms:
N/A

GOVERNMENT PUBLICATIONS:
Will Lend: No

DISSERTATIONS:
Will Lend: (Not answered)

THESES:
Will Lend: (Not answered)

AUDIO-VISUAL MATERIALS:
Records: Will not lend
Cassettes: Will not lend
Other (slides, filmstrips,
etc.): (Not answered)

COMPUTER SOFTWARE:
Will Lend: No

PHOTODUPLICATION SERVICE:
No charge up to _____ exposures
(Not answered)
Charge Per Exposure: 10¢
Minimum/handling Fee: (Not
answered)
Average Turnaround Time:
4 weeks

MICROFILMING SERVICE:
Service Available: No
Charges: N/A

DO YOU CHARGE THE BORROWING LIBRARY
FOR POSTAGE? Yes

FOR HOW LONG DO YOU SUSPEND ILL
SERVICE OVER THE CHRISTMAS
HOLIDAYS? (Not answered)

ARE THERE ANY GROUPS OF LIBRARIES
FOR WHICH YOU WAIVE FEES? IF
SO, PLEASE NAME THEM: None

KERN COUNTY LIBRARY SYSTEM

NUC CODE: (Not answered)

OCLC CODE: KLC

ADDRESS: Interlibrary Loan
Kern County Library
System
1315 Truxtun Ave.
Bakersfield, CA 93301

TELEPHONE: (805) 861-2137

LIST NAMES OF BRANCHES WITH
SEPARATE POLICIES: These
policies cover all
branches alike.

BOOKS:
Will Lend: Yes, except for
reference, genealogical,
and historical materials
Length of Loan: 30 days
Renewable: Yes
Charges: None
Average Turnaround Time:
1 week
If you have indicated that a
book is not to be lent, will
you on receipt of a letter
from the requesting library
search the index for given
entries? Yes

PERIODICALS:
Bound: Will not lend
Unbound: Yes, if library has
circulating copies
Loan Period: 30 days
Renewable: Yes, for 30 days
Will lend if article exceeds
0 number of pages

MICROFORMS:
Will Lend: No
Specific Types of Microforms:
N/A

GOVERNMENT PUBLICATIONS:
Will Lend: Yes, if library has
circulating copies

DISSERTATIONS:
Will Lend: Do not own

THESES:
Will Lend: Do not own

AUDIO-VISUAL MATERIALS:
Records: Will not lend
Cassettes: Will not lend
Other (slides, filmstrips,
etc.): Will not lend

COMPUTER SOFTWARE:
Will Lend: No

PHOTODUPLICATION SERVICE:
No charge up to 20 exposures
Charge Per Exposure: 10¢ after
first 20
Minimum/handling Fee: None
Average Turnaround Time:
1-2 days

MICROFILMING SERVICE:
Service Available: No
Charges: N/A

DO YOU CHARGE THE BORROWING LIBRARY
FOR POSTAGE? No

FOR HOW LONG DO YOU SUSPEND ILL
SERVICE OVER THE CHRISTMAS
HOLIDAYS? No suspension

ARE THERE ANY GROUPS OF LIBRARIES
FOR WHICH YOU WAIVE FEES? IF
SO, PLEASE NAME THEM: None

LONG BEACH PUBLIC LIBRARY

NUC CODE: CLob

OCLC CODE: CLB

ADDRESS: Interlibrary Loan
Long Beach Public
Library
101 Pacific Ave.
Long Beach, CA 90802

TELEPHONE: (213) 590-6053, ILL
(213) 437-2949, switchboard

LIST NAMES OF BRANCHES WITH
SEPARATE POLICIES: None

BOOKS:
Will Lend: Yes
Length of Loan: 4 weeks
Renewable: Yes
Charges: None
Average Turnaround Time:
3-4 days
If you have indicated that a
book is not to be lent, will
you on receipt of a letter
from the requesting library
search the index for given
entries? Reference
librarians may perform
this service.

PERIODICALS:
Bound: Will not lend
Unbound: Will not lend
Loan Period: N/A
Renewable: N/A
Will lend if article exceeds
_____ number of pages (Not
answered)

MICROFORMS:
Will Lend: No
Specific Types of Microforms:
N/A

GOVERNMENT PUBLICATIONS:
Will Lend: Yes, some of them

DISSERTATIONS:
Will Lend: Do not own

THESES:
Will Lend: Do not own

AUDIO-VISUAL MATERIALS:
Records: Will not lend
Cassettes: Will not lend
Other (slides, filmstrips,
etc.): Will not lend

COMPUTER SOFTWARE:
Will Lend: No

PHOTODUPLICATION SERVICE:
No charge up to 25 exposures
Charge Per Exposure: 15¢
Minimum/handling Fee: $1.00
Average Turnaround Time:
3-4 days

MICROFILMING SERVICE:
Service Available: Yes
Charges: 25¢ per page

DO YOU CHARGE THE BORROWING LIBRARY
FOR POSTAGE? No

FOR HOW LONG DO YOU SUSPEND ILL
SERVICE OVER THE CHRISTMAS
HOLIDAYS? No suspension

ARE THERE ANY GROUPS OF LIBRARIES
FOR WHICH YOU WAIVE FEES? IF
SO, PLEASE NAME THEM: None

LOS ANGELES COUNTY MEDICAL ASSOCIATION

NUC CODE: CLM

OCLC CODE: LAC

ADDRESS: Interlibrary Loan
Los Angeles County
Medical Association
634 South Westlake Ave.
Los Angeles, CA 90057

TELEPHONE: (213) 483-4555

LIST NAMES OF BRANCHES WITH
SEPARATE POLICIES: None

BOOKS:
Will Lend: Yes, except for
reference books
Length of Loan: 2 weeks
Renewable: Yes, for 1 week
Charges: $1.00 plus postage
Average Turnaround Time:
1 week
If you have indicated that a
book is not to be lent, will
you on receipt of a letter
from the requesting library
search the index for given
entries? Yes

PERIODICALS:
Bound: Will lend for 2 weeks
Unbound: Will lend for
2 weeks
Loan Period: 2 weeks
Renewable: Yes, for 1 week
Will lend if article exceeds
_____ number of pages (Not
answered)

MICROFORMS:
Will Lend: Do not own
Specific Types of Microforms:
N/A

GOVERNMENT PUBLICATIONS:
Will Lend: Yes

DISSERTATIONS:
Will Lend: Do not own

THESES:
Will Lend: Do not own

AUDIO-VISUAL MATERIALS:
Records: Do not own
Cassettes: Will lend
Other (slides, filmstrips,
etc.): Will lend

COMPUTER SOFTWARE:
Will Lend: Do not own

PHOTODUPLICATION SERVICE:
No charge up to _____ exposures
(Not answered)
Charge Per Exposure: 10¢ per
exposure plus $1.00 service
Minimum/handling Fee: $1.00
Average Turnaround Time:
1 week

MICROFILMING SERVICE:
Service Available: No
Charges: N/A

DO YOU CHARGE THE BORROWING LIBRARY
FOR POSTAGE? Yes

FOR HOW LONG DO YOU SUSPEND ILL
SERVICE OVER THE CHRISTMAS
HOLIDAYS? No suspension

ARE THERE ANY GROUPS OF LIBRARIES
FOR WHICH YOU WAIVE FEES? IF
SO, PLEASE NAME THEM: None

LOS ANGELES PUBLIC LIBRARY

NUC CODE: CL

OCLC CODE: (Not answered)

ADDRESS: Interlibrary Loan
Los Angeles Public
Library
630 W. 5th St.
Los Angeles, CA 90071

TELEPHONE: (213) 626-7461 or
(213) 626-7555, X249

LIST NAMES OF BRANCHES WITH
SEPARATE POLICIES: None

BOOKS:
Will Lend: Yes
Length of Loan: 4 weeks
Renewable: Yes, upon request
Charges: None
Average Turnaround Time: Not
known
If you have indicated that a
book is not to be lent, will
you on receipt of a letter
from the requesting library
search the index for given
entries? (Not answered)

PERIODICALS:
Bound: Will not lend
Unbound: Will lend circulating
copies
Loan Period: 4 weeks
Renewable: Yes
Will lend if article exceeds
_____ number of pages (Not
answered)

MICROFORMS:
Will Lend: No
Specific Types of Microforms:
N/A

GOVERNMENT PUBLICATIONS:
Will Lend: Yes, if library has
duplicate copies

DISSERTATIONS:
Will Lend: Do not own

THESES:
Will Lend: Do not own

AUDIO-VISUAL MATERIALS:
Records; Will not lend
Cassettes: Will not lend
Other (slides, filmstrips,
etc.): (Not answered)

COMPUTER SOFTWARE:
Will Lend: No

PHOTODUPLICATION SERVICE:
No charge up to _____ exposures
(Not answered)
Charge Per Exposure: 25¢
Minimum/handling Fee: $5.00
handling; $10.00 rush
handling
Newspaper: $1.00 per full page
Average Turnaround Time: Not
known

MICROFILMING SERVICE:
Service Available: No
Charges: N/A

DO YOU CHARGE THE BORROWING LIBRARY
FOR POSTAGE? No; all books are
insured

FOR HOW LONG DO YOU SUSPEND ILL
SERVICE OVER THE CHRISTMAS
HOLIDAYS? No suspension

ARE THERE ANY GROUPS OF LIBRARIES
FOR WHICH YOU WAIVE FEES? IF
SO, PLEASE NAME THEM: No fees
besides charges enumerated.

NO GENEALOGICAL MATERIALS LOANED.
NOT TO BE CONFUSED WITH LOS ANGELES
COUNTY LIBRARY.

MONTEREY COUNTY LIBRARY

NUC CODE: (Not answered)

OCLC CODE: (Not answered)

ADDRESS: Interlibrary Loan
Monterey County Library
26 Central St.
Salinas, CA 93901

TELEPHONE: (408) 424-8611, X395

LIST NAMES OF BRANCHES WITH
SEPARATE POLICIES: None

BOOKS:
Will Lend: Yes, usually
Length of Loan: 1 month
Renewable: Yes
Charges: (Not answered)
Average Turnaround Time:
1 day-3 weeks
If you have indicated that a
book is not to be lent, will
you on receipt of a letter
from the requesting library
search the index for given
entries? (Not answered)

PERIODICALS:
Bound: Will not lend
Unbound: Will lend current
year only
Loan Period: 1 month
Renewable: Yes
Will lend if article exceeds
_____ number of pages (Not
answered)

MICROFORMS:
Will Lend: Yes
Specific Types of Microforms:
Microfilm of census records,
periodicals are for library
use only

GOVERNMENT PUBLICATIONS:
Will Lend: Yes

DISSERTATIONS:
Will Lend: Do not own

THESES:
Will Lend: Do not own

AUDIO-VISUAL MATERIALS:
Records: Will lend
Cassettes: Will lend
Other (slides, filmstrips,
etc.): Do not own

COMPUTER SOFTWARE:
Will Lend: Do not own

PHOTODUPLICATION SERVICE:
No charge up to 10 exposures
Charge Per Exposure: 15¢
Minimum/handling Fee: None
Average Turnaround Time:
1 week

MICROFILMING SERVICE:
Service Available: No
Charges: N/A

DO YOU CHARGE THE BORROWING LIBRARY
FOR POSTAGE? No

FOR HOW LONG DO YOU SUSPEND ILL
SERVICE OVER THE CHRISTMAS
HOLIDAYS? No suspension

ARE THERE ANY GROUPS OF LIBRARIES
FOR WHICH YOU WAIVE FEES? IF
SO, PLEASE NAME THEM: None

NEWPORT BEACH PUBLIC LIBRARY

NUC CODE: None

OCLC CODE: CNB

ADDRESS: Interlibrary Loan
Newport Beach Public
Library
856 San Clemente Dr.
Newport Beach, CA 92660

TELEPHONE: (714) 640-2108

LIST NAMES OF BRANCHES WITH
SEPARATE POLICIES: We have
4 branches, all with same
policies

BOOKS:
Will Lend: Yes
Length of Loan: 4 weeks
Renewable: No
Charges: None
Average Turnaround Time:
1 week
If you have indicated that a
book is not to be lent, will
you on receipt of a letter
from the requesting library
search the index for given
entries? Yes

PERIODICALS:
Bound: Will not lend
Unbound: Will lend
Loan Period: 4 weeks
Renewable: No
Will lend if article exceeds
_____ number of pages (Not
answered)

MICROFORMS:
Will Lend: No
Specific Types of Microforms:
N/A

GOVERNMENT PUBLICATIONS:
Will Lend: No

DISSERTATIONS:
Will Lend: No

THESES:
Will Lend: No

AUDIO-VISUAL MATERIALS:
Records: Will not lend
Cassettes: Will not lend
Other (slides, filmstrips,
etc.): Will not lend

COMPUTER SOFTWARE:
Will Lend: No

PHOTODUPLICATION SERVICE:
No charge up to 10 exposures
Charge Per Exposure: (Not
answered)
Minimum/handling Fee: (Not
answered)
Average Turnaround Time:
1 week

MICROFILMING SERVICE:
Service Available: No
Charges: N/A

DO YOU CHARGE THE BORROWING LIBRARY
FOR POSTAGE? No

FOR HOW LONG DO YOU SUSPEND ILL
SERVICE OVER THE CHRISTMAS
HOLIDAYS? No suspension

ARE THERE ANY GROUPS OF LIBRARIES
FOR WHICH YOU WAIVE FEES? IF
SO, PLEASE NAME THEM: None

NORTHROP UNIVERSITY

NUC CODE: (Not answered)

OCLC CODE: (Not answered)

ADDRESS: Interlibrary Loan
           Pacific Technical
             Information Services
           Northrop University
           Inglewood, CA 90306

TELEPHONE: (213) 776-5466

LIST NAMES OF BRANCHES WITH
   SEPARATE POLICIES: None

BOOKS:
   Will Lend: Yes
   Length of Loan: 2 weeks
      from date of receipt
   Renewable: (Not answered)
   Charges: $6.00 plus postage
   Average Turnaround Time:
      2 weeks
   If you have indicated that a
      book is not to be lent, will
      you on receipt of a letter
      from the requesting library
      search the index for given
      entries? (Not answered)

PERIODICALS:
   Bound: Will not lend
   Unbound: Will not lend
   Loan Period: N/A
   Renewable: N/A
   Will lend if article exceeds
      _____ number of pages (Not
      answered)

MICROFORMS:
   Will Lend: No
   Specific Types of Microforms:
      N/A

GOVERNMENT PUBLICATIONS:
   Will Lend: Yes, sometimes

DISSERTATIONS:
   Will Lend: No

THESES:
   Will Lend: No

AUDIO-VISUAL MATERIALS:
   Records: Will not lend
   Cassettes: Will not lend
   Other (slides, filmstrips,
      etc.): Will not lend

COMPUTER SOFTWARE:
   Will Lend: No

PHOTODUPLICATION SERVICE:
   No charge up to _____ exposures
      (Not answered)
   Charge Per Exposure: 30¢
   Minimum/handling Fee: $6.00
      plus postage
   Average Turnaround Time:
      2 weeks

MICROFILMING SERVICE:
   Service Available: No
   Charges: N/A

DO YOU CHARGE THE BORROWING LIBRARY
   FOR POSTAGE? Yes

FOR HOW LONG DO YOU SUSPEND ILL
   SERVICE OVER THE CHRISTMAS
   HOLIDAYS? No suspension

ARE THERE ANY GROUPS OF LIBRARIES
   FOR WHICH YOU WAIVE FEES? IF
   SO, PLEASE NAME THEM: None

OCCIDENTAL COLLEGE LIBRARY

NUC CODE: CLO

OCLC CODE: CCO

ADDRESS: Interlibrary Loan
           Occidental College
             Library
           1600 Campus Road
           Los Angeles, CA 90041

TELEPHONE: (213) 259-2818

LIST NAMES OF BRANCHES WITH
   SEPARATE POLICIES: None

BOOKS:
   Will Lend: Yes
   Length of Loan: 4 weeks
   Renewable: Yes
   Charges: None
   Average Turnaround Time:
      1 day
   If you have indicated that a
      book is not to be lent, will
      you on receipt of a letter
      from the requesting library
      search the index for given
      entries? (Not answered)

PERIODICALS:
   Bound: Will not lend
   Unbound: Will not lend
   Loan Period: N/A
   Renewable: N/A
   Will lend if article exceeds
      _____ number of pages (N/A)

MICROFORMS:
   Will Lend: No, except for
      duplicate copies of
      Occidental College theses
      if on microform.

GOVERNMENT PUBLICATIONS:
   Will Lend: No

DISSERTATIONS:
   Will lend if library has a
      second copy

THESES:
   Will lend if library has a
      second copy

AUDIO-VISUAL MATERIALS:
   Records: Will not lend
   Cassettes: Will not lend
   Other (slides, filmstrips,
      etc.): Will not lend

COMPUTER SOFTWARE:
   Will Lend: No

PHOTODUPLICATION SERVICE:
   No charge up to _____ exposures
      (Not answered)
   Charge Per Exposure: 10¢
   Minimum/handling Fee: $5.00
   Average Turnaround Time:
      1 day

MICROFILMING SERVICE:
   Service Available: Yes
   Charges: 10¢ per frame and
      $5.00 handling

DO YOU CHARGE THE BORROWING LIBRARY
   FOR POSTAGE? No

FOR HOW LONG DO YOU SUSPEND ILL
   SERVICE OVER THE CHRISTMAS
   HOLIDAYS? Dec.23-Jan.2

ARE THERE ANY GROUPS OF LIBRARIES
   FOR WHICH YOU WAIVE FEES? IF
   SO, PLEASE NAME THEM: None

ORANGE COUNTY PUBLIC LIBRARY

NUC CODE: None

OCLC CODE: None

ADDRESS: Interlibrary Loan
Orange County Public
Library
431 City Drive South
Orange, CA 92668

TELEPHONE: (Not answered)

LIST NAMES OF BRANCHES WITH
SEPARATE POLICIES: None

BOOKS:
Will Lend: Yes
Length of Loan: 1 month
Renewable: Yes
Charges: None
Average Turnaround Time:
Depends on whether in
circulation, reserved
ahead, etc.
If you have indicated that a
book is not to be lent, will
you on receipt of a letter
from the requesting library
search the index for given
entries? Yes

PERIODICALS:
Bound: Will not lend
Unbound: Will not lend
Loan Period: N/A
Renewable: N/A
Will lend if article exceeds
_____ number of pages (Not
answered)

MICROFORMS:
Will Lend: No
Specific Types of Microforms:
N/A

GOVERNMENT PUBLICATIONS:
Will Lend: No

DISSERTATIONS:
Will Lend: Do not own

THESES:
Will Lend: Do not own

AUDIO-VISUAL MATERIALS:
Records: Will not lend
Cassettes: Will not lend
Other (slides, filmstrips,
etc.): (Not answered)

COMPUTER SOFTWARE:
Will Lend: NO

PHOTODUPLICATION SERVICE:
No charge up to 20 exposures
Charge Per Exposure: 10¢ per
page after the first 20
Minimum/handling Fee: (Not
answered)
Average Turnaround Time: 1 week
if book or periodical not in
circulation

MICROFILMING SERVICE:
Service Available: No
Charges: N/A

DO YOU CHARGE THE BORROWING LIBRARY
FOR POSTAGE? No

FOR HOW LONG DO YOU SUSPEND ILL
SERVICE OVER THE CHRISTMAS
HOLIDAYS? No suspension

ARE THERE ANY GROUPS OF LIBRARIES
FOR WHICH YOU WAIVE FEES? IF
SO, PLEASE NAME THEM: Does not
apply

ORANGE PUBLIC LIBRARY

NUC CODE: (Not answered)

OCLC CODE: (Not answered)

ADDRESS: Interlibrary Loan
Orange Public Library
101 N. Center St.
Orange, CA 92666

TELEPHONE: (714) 532-0391

LIST NAMES OF BRANCHES WITH
SEPARATE POLICIES: None

BOOKS:
Will Lend: Yes
Length of Loan: 3 weeks
Renewable: Yes, if there
are no reserves
Charges: None at present
Average Turnaround Time:
10 days
If you have indicated that a
book is not to be lent, will
you on receipt of a letter
from the requesting library
search the index for given
entries? Yes

PERIODICALS:
Bound: Will not lend
Unbound: Will lend
Loan Period: 3 weeks
Renewable: Yes
Will lend if article exceeds
_____ number of pages (Will
not lend. Will xerox
article if necessary.

MICROFORMS:
Will Lend: No
Specific Types of Microforms:
N/A

GOVERNMENT PUBLICATIONS:
Will Lend: Yes, but we have
a very limited number of them

DISSERTATIONS:
Will Lend: No

THESES:
Will Lend: No

AUDIO-VISUAL MATERIALS:
Records: Will lend
Cassettes: Will lend
Other (slides, filmstrips,
etc.): (Not answered)

COMPUTER SOFTWARE:
Will Lend: No

PHOTODUPLICATION SERVICE:
No charge up to 20 exposures
Charge Per Exposure: (Not
answered)
Minimum/handling Fee: None at
present
Average Turnaround Time:
10 days

MICROFILMING SERVICE:
Service Available: No
Charges: N/A

DO YOU CHARGE THE BORROWING LIBRARY
FOR POSTAGE? Not at present

FOR HOW LONG DO YOU SUSPEND ILL
SERVICE OVER THE CHRISTMAS
HOLIDAYS? No suspension
except days closed

ARE THERE ANY GROUPS OF LIBRARIES
FOR WHICH YOU WAIVE FEES? IF
SO, PLEASE NAME THEM: We have
no fees at present; however,
we may have to institute some
in the near future.

PALO ALTO CITY LIBRARY

NUC CODE: (Not answered)

OCLC CODE: (Not answered)

ADDRESS: Interlibrary Loan
           Palo Alto City Library
           1213 Newell Road
           Palo Alto, CA 94303

TELEPHONE: (415) 329-2664

LIST NAMES OF BRANCHES WITH
    SEPARATE POLICIES: None

BOOKS:
    Will Lend: Yes
    Length of Loan: 3-4 weeks
    Renewable: Subject to local
    demand
    Charges: None
    Average Turnaround Time:
    2 weeks
    If you have indicated that a
    book is not to be lent, will
    you on receipt of a letter
    from the requesting library
    search the index for given
    entries? Yes

PERIODICALS:
    Bound: Will not lend
    Unbound: Will not lend
    Loan Period: N/A
    Renewable: N/A
    Will lend if article exceeds
    _____ number of pages (Not
    answered)

MICROFORMS:
    Will Lend: No
    Specific Types of Microforms:
    N/A

GOVERNMENT PUBLICATIONS:
    Will Lend: No

DISSERTATIONS:
    Will Lend: Do not own

THESES:
    Will Lend: Do not own

AUDIO-VISUAL MATERIALS:
    Records: Will not lend
    Cassettes: Will not lend
    Other (slides, filmstrips,
    etc.): Will not lend

COMPUTER SOFTWARE:
    Will Lend: No

PHOTODUPLICATION SERVICE:
    No charge up to 10 exposures
    Charge Per Exposure: 10¢ per
    page
    Minimum/handling Fee: (Not
    answered)
    Average Turnaround Time:
    2 weeks

MICROFILMING SERVICE:
    Service Available: No
    Charges: N/A

DO YOU CHARGE THE BORROWING
    LIBRARY FOR POSTAGE? No

FOR HOW LONG DO YOU SUSPEND ILL
    SERVICE OVER THE CHRISTMAS
    HOLIDAYS? No suspension

ARE THERE ANY GROUPS OF LIBRARIES
    FOR WHICH YOU WAIVE FEES? IF
    SO, PLEASE NAME THEM: None

PALOS VERDES LIBRARY DISTRICT

NUC CODE: (Not answered)

OCLC CODE: (Not answered)

ADDRESS: Interlibrary Loan
           Palos Verdes Library
           District
           650 Deep Valley Drive
           Rolling Hills Estates,
           CA 90274

TELEPHONE: (213) 377-9584

LIST NAMES OF BRANCHES WITH
    SEPARATE POLICIES: None

BOOKS:
    Will Lend: Yes
    Length of Loan: 3 weeks
    from receipt
    Renewable: No
    Charges: None
    Average Turnaround Time:
    (Not answered)
    If you have indicated that a
    book is not to be lent, will
    you on receipt of a letter
    from the requesting library
    search the index for given
    entries? (Not answered)

PERIODICALS:
    Bound: Will not lend
    Unbound: Will not lend
    Loan Period: N/A
    Renewable: N/A
    Will lend if article exceeds
    _____ number of pages (Not
    answered)

MICROFORMS:
    Will Lend: No
    Specific Types of Microforms:
    N/A

GOVERNMENT PUBLICATIONS:
    Will Lend: Yes

DISSERTATIONS:
    Will Lend: Yes

THESES:
    Will Lend: Yes

AUDIO-VISUAL MATERIALS:
    Records: Will lend
    Cassettes: Will lend
    Other (slides, filmstrips,
    etc.): Do not own

COMPUTER SOFTWARE:
    Will Lend: Do not own

PHOTODUPLICATION SERVICE:
    No charge up to 20 exposures
    Charge Per Exposure: (Not
    answered)
    Minimum/handling Fee: (Not
    answered)
    Average Turnaround Time: (Not
    answered)

MICROFILMING SERVICE:
    Service Available: No
    Charges: N/A

DO YOU CHARGE THE BORROWING LIBRARY
    FOR POSTAGE? No

FOR HOW LONG DO YOU SUSPEND ILL
    SERVICE OVER THE CHRISTMAS
    HOLIDAYS? No suspension

ARE THERE ANY GROUPS OF LIBRARIES
    FOR WHICH YOU WAIVE FEES? IF
    SO, PLEASE NAME THEM: None

PASADENA PUBLIC LIBRARY

NUC CODE: (Not answered)

OCLC CODE: (Not answered)

ADDRESS: Interlibrary Loan
Pasadena Public Library
285 E. Walnut St.
Pasadena, CA 91101

TELEPHONE: (213) 577-4064

LIST NAMES OF BRANCHES WITH
SEPARATE POLICIES: None

BOOKS:
Will Lend: Yes
Length of Loan: 1 month
Renewable: Yes
Charges: (Not answered)
Average Turnaround Time:
(Not answered)
If you have indicated that a
book is not to be lent, will
you on receipt of a letter
from the requesting library
search the index for given
entries? (Not answered)

PERIODICALS:
Bound: Will not lend
Unbound: Will not lend
Loan Period: N/A
Renewable: N/A
Will lend if article exceeds
_____ number of pages (Not
answered)

MICROFORMS:
Will Lend: No
Specific Types Of Microforms:
N/A

GOVERNMENT PUBLICATIONS:
Will Lend: Yes

DISSERTATIONS:
Will Lend: (Not answered)

THESES:
Will Lend: (Not answered)

AUDIO-VISUAL MATERIALS:
Records: (Not answered)
Cassettes: (Not answered)
Other (slides, filmstrips,
etc.): (Not answered)

COMPUTER SOFTWARE:
Will Lend: (Not answered)

PHOTODUPLICATION SERVICE:
No charge up to 5 exposures
Charge Per Exposure: 25¢
Handling Fee: $5.00
Average Turnaround Time: (Not
answered)

MICROFILMING SERVICE:
Service Available: (Not
answered)
Charges: N/A

DO YOU CHARGE THE BORROWING LIBRARY
FOR POSTAGE? No

FOR HOW LONG DO YOU SUSPEND ILL
SERVICE OVER THE CHRISTMAS
HOLIDAYS? (Not answered)

ARE THERE ANY GROUPS OF LIBRARIES
FOR WHICH YOU WAIVE FEES? IF
SO, PLEASE NAME THEM:
Metropolitan cooperative
library system

PEPPERDINE UNIVERSITY

NUC CODE: (Not answered)

OCLC CODE: CPE

ADDRESS: Interlibrary Loan
Payson Library
Pepperdine University
Malibu, CA 90265

TELEPHONE: (213) 456-4244

LIST NAMES OF BRANCHES WITH
SEPARATE POLICIES: None

BOOKS:
Will Lend: Yes
Length of Loan: 4 weeks use
Renewable: Yes
Charges: (Not answered)
Average Turnaround Time:
(Not answered)
If you have indicated that a
book is not to be lent, will
you on receipt of a letter
from the requesting library
search the index for given
entries? (Not answered)

PERIODICALS:
Bound: Will not lend
Unbound: Will not lend
Loan Period: N/A
Renewable: N/A
Will lend if article exceeds
_____ number of pages (Not
answered)

MICROFORMS:
Will Lend: No
Specific Types of Microforms:
N/A

GOVERNMENT PUBLICATIONS:
Will Lend: Yes

DISSERTATIONS:
Will Lend: No

THESES:
Will Lend: Yes

AUDIO-VISUAL MATERIALS:
Records: (Not answered)
Cassettes: (Not answered)
Other (slides, filmstrips,
etc.): (Not answered)

COMPUTER SOFTWARE:
Will Lend: (Not answered)

PHOTODUPLICATION SERVICE:
No charge up to _____ exposures
(Not answered)
Charge Per Exposure: 10¢
Handling Fee: $1.00
Average Turnaround Time: (Not
answered)

MICROFILMING SERVICE:
Service Available: (Not
answered)
Charges: N/A

DO YOU CHARGE THE BORROWING LIBRARY
FOR POSTAGE? (Not answered)

FOR HOW LONG DO YOU SUSPEND ILL
SERVICE OVER THE CHRISTMAS
HOLIDAYS? Dec.12-Dec.31

ARE THERE ANY GROUPS OF LIBRARIES
FOR WHICH YOU WAIVE FEES? IF
SO, PLEASE NAME THEM: (Not
answered)

SRI INTERNATIONAL LIBRARY

NUC CODE: (Not answered)

OCLC CODE: (Not answered)

ADDRESS: Interlibrary Loan
SRI International
Menlo Park, CA 94025

TELEPHONE: (415) 859-2637

LIST NAMES OF BRANCHES WITH
SEPARATE POLICIES: None

BOOKS:
Will Lend: Yes
Length of Loan: 2 weeks
Renewable: Yes
Charges: Postage and
insurance reimbursement
Average Turnaround Time:
3-5 days
If you have indicated that a
book is not to be lent, will
you on receipt of a letter
from the requesting library
search the index for given
entries? Non-circulating
material can be searched.

PERIODICALS:
Bound: Will lend, usually
locally
Unbound: Will lend, usually
locally
Loan Period: 1 week
Renewable: Yes
Will lend if article exceeds
20 pages, but usually only
to local libraries

MICROFORMS:
Will Lend: No
Specific Types of Microforms:
N/A

GOVERNMENT PUBLICATIONS:
Will Lend: Yes

DISSERTATIONS:
Will Lend: Yes, if owned

THESES:
Will Lend: Yes, if owned

AUDIO-VISUAL MATERIALS:
Records: (Not answered)
Cassettes: (Not answered)
Other (slides, filmstrips,
etc.): Will lend fiche

PHOTODUPLICATION SERVICE:
No charge up to 0 exposures
Charge Per Exposure: (Not
answered)
Minimum/handling Fee: (Not
answered)
Average Turnaround Time:
3-5 days

MICROFILMING SERVICE:
Service Available: No
Charges: N/A

DO YOU CHARGE THE BORROWING LIBRARY
FOR POSTAGE? Yes, for loans

FOR HOW LONG DO YOU SUSPEND ILL
SERVICE OVER THE CHRISTMAS
HOLIDAYS? Christmas through
New Year's Day

ARE THERE ANY GROUPS OF LIBRARIES
FOR WHICH YOU WAIVE FEES? IF
SO, PLEASE NAME THEM: Those
that send postage-included
labels; those that do not
have the facilities for
reimbursing postage.

SACRAMENTO CITY-COUNTY LIBRARY

NUC CODE: None

OCLC CODE: None

ADDRESS: Interlibrary Loan
Sacramento City-County
Library
Central Library
828 I St.
Sacramento, CA 95814

TELEPHONE: (916) 449-5203

LIST NAMES OF BRANCHES WITH
SEPARATE POLICIES: None

BOOKS:
Will Lend: Yes
Length of Loan: 2-3 weeks
Renewable: Yes
Charges: None
Average Turnaround Time:
1 week
If you have indicated that a
book is not to be lent, will
you on receipt of a letter
from the requesting library
search the index for given
entries? (Not answered)

PERIODICALS:
Bound: Will not lend
Unbound: Will not lend
Loan Period: N/A
Renewable: N/A
Will lend if article exceeds
_____ number of pages (Not
answered)

MICROFORMS:
Will Lend: No
Specific Types of Microforms:
N/A

GOVERNMENT PUBLICATIONS:
Will Lend: Yes

DISSERTATIONS:
Will Lend: No

THESES:
Will Lend: No

AUDIO-VISUAL MATERIALS:
Records: Will not lend
Cassettes: Will not lend
Other (slides, filmstrips,
etc.): Will not lend

COMPUTER SOFTWARE:
Will Lend: No

PHOTODUPLICATION SERVICE:
No charge up to 0 exposures
Charge Per Exposure: 10¢
Minimum/handling Fee: $1.00
Average Turnaround Time:
1 week

MICROFILMING SERVICE:
Service Available: No
Charges: N/A

DO YOU CHARGE THE BORROWING
LIBRARY FOR POSTAGE? No

FOR HOW LONG DO YOU SUSPEND ILL
SERVICE OVER THE CHRISTMAS
HOLIDAYS? No suspension

ARE THERE ANY GROUPS OF LIBRARIES
FOR WHICH YOU WAIVE FEES? IF
SO, PLEASE NAME THEM:
Mountain Valley Library
System

SAN DIEGO COUNTY LIBRARY

NUC CODE: CSdCL

OCLC CODE: None

ADDRESS: Interlibrary Loan
           San Diego County Library
           5555 Overland Ave.
           Building 15
           San Diego, CA 92123

TELEPHONE: (714) 565-3567

LIST NAMES OF BRANCHES WITH
  SEPARATE POLICIES: None

BOOKS
  Will Lend: Yes
  Length of Loan: 28 days
  Renewable: No
  Charges: None
  Average Turnaround Time:
    5 days if book is on the
    shelf
  If you have indicated that a
    book is not to be lent, will
    you on receipt of a letter
    from the requesting library
    search the index for given
    entries? Yes

PERIODICALS:
  Bound: Will not lend
  Unbound: Will not lend
  Loan Period: N/A
  Renewable: N/A
  Will lend if article exceeds
    _____ number of pages (Not
  answered)

MICROFORMS:
  Will Lend: No
  Specific Types Of Microforms:
    N/A

GOVERNMENT PUBLICATIONS:
  Will Lend: Yes

DISSERTATIONS:
  Will Lend: Do not own

THESES:
  Will Lend: Do not own

AUDIO-VISUAL MATERIALS:
  Records: (Not answered)
  Cassettes: Will lend only to
    libraries within Serra
    Regional Library System
  Other (slides, filmstrips,
    etc.): Will not lend

COMPUTER SOFTWARE:
  Will Lend: Do not own

PHOTODUPLICATION SERVICE:
  No charge up to _____ exposures
    (Not answered)
  Charge Per Exposure: 10¢ per
    page
  Minimum/handling Fee: None
  Average Turnaround Time:
    3 days

MICROFILMING SERVICE:
  Service Available: No
  Charges: N/A

DO YOU CHARGE THE BORROWING LIBRARY
  FOR POSTAGE? No

FOR HOW LONG DO YOU SUSPEND ILL
  SERVICE OVER THE CHRISTMAS
  HOLIDAYS? No suspension

ARE THERE ANY GROUPS OF LIBRARIES
  FOR WHICH YOU WAIVE FEES? IF
  SO, PLEASE NAME THEM: None

SAN DIEGO PUBLIC LIBRARY

NUC CODE: CSd

OCLC CODE: None

ADDRESS: Interlibrary Loan
           San Diego Public Library
           820 "E" Street
           San Diego, CA 92101-6478

TELEPHONE: (714) 236-5823

LIST NAMES OF BRANCHES WITH
  SEPARATE POLICIES: None

BOOKS
  Will Lend: Yes
  Length of Loan: 4 weeks
  Renewable: Yes, 3 weeks
    extension if requested
  Charges: None
  Average Turnaround Time:
    48 hours
  If you have indicated that a
    book is not to be lent, will
    you on receipt of a letter
    from the requesting library
    search the index for given
    entries? No

PERIODICALS:
  Bound: Will not lend
  Unbound: Will not lend
  Loan Period: N/A
  Renewable: N/A
  Will lend if article exceeds
    _____ number of pages (Not
  answered)

MICROFORMS:
  Will Lend: No
  Specific Types of Microforms:
    N/A

GOVERNMENT PUBLICATIONS:
  Will Lend: No

DISSERTATIONS:
  Will Lend: No

THESES:
  Will Lend: No

AUDIO-VISUAL MATERIALS:
  Records: Will not lend
  Cassettes: Do not own
  Other (slides, filmstrips,
    etc.): Do not own

COMPUTER SOFTWARE:
  Will Lend: No

PHOTODUPLICATION SERVICE:
  No charge up to _____ exposures
    (Not answered)
  Charge Per Exposure: 30¢ first
    page; 15¢ each additional
    page
  Minimum/handling Fee: 30¢
    postage
  Average Turnaround Time: (Not
    answered)

MICROFILMING SERVICE:
  Service Available: No
  Charges: N/A

DO YOU CHARGE THE BORROWING LIBRARY
  FOR POSTAGE? No

FOR HOW LONG DO YOU SUSPEND ILL
  SERVICE OVER THE CHRISTMAS
  HOLIDAYS? No suspension

ARE THERE ANY GROUPS OF LIBRARIES
  FOR WHICH YOU WAIVE FEES? IF
  SO, PLEASE NAME THEM: None

SAN DIEGO STATE UNIVERSITY

NUC CODE: CSdS

OCLC CODE: (Not answered)

ADDRESS: Interlibrary Loan
University Library
San Diego State
University
San Diego, CA
92182-0511

TELEPHONE: (714) 265-6014

LIST NAMES OF BRANCHES WITH
SEPARATE POLICIES: None

BOOKS:
Will Lend: Yes
Length of Loan: 2 weeks
Renewable: Yes
Charges: (Not answered)
Average Turnaround Time:
(Not answered)
If you have indicated that a
book is not to be lent, will
you on receipt of a letter
from the requesting library
search the index for given
entries? (Not answered)

PERIODICALS:
Bound: Will not lend
Unbound: Will not lend
Loan Period: N/A
Renewable: N/A
Will lend if article exceeds
_____ number of pages (Not
answered)

MICROFORMS:
Will Lend: Yes
Specific Types of Microforms:
Selective

GOVERNMENT PUBLICATIONS:
Will Lend: (Not answered)

DISSERTATIONS:
Will Lend: Yes

THESES:
Will Lend: Yes

AUDIO-VISUAL MATERIALS:
Records: (Not answered)
Cassettes: (Not answered)
Other (slides, filmstrips,
etc.): (Not answered)

COMPUTER SOFTWARE:
Will Lend: (Not answered)

PHOTODUPLICATION SERVICE:
No charge up to 0 exposures
Charge Per Exposure: (Not
answered)
Minimum Fee: $3.00 for 1-15
pages
Average Turnaround Time:
(Not answered)

MICROFILMING SERVICE:
Service Available: No
Charges: N/A

DO YOU CHARGE THE BORROWING
LIBRARY FOR POSTAGE? No

FOR HOW LONG DO YOU SUSPEND ILL
SERVICE OVER THE CHRISTMAS
HOLIDAYS? No suspension

ARE THERE ANY GROUPS OF LIBRARIES
FOR WHICH YOU WAIVE FEES? IF
SO, PLEASE NAME THEM: (Not
answered)

SAN FRANCISCO PUBLIC LIBRARY

NUC CODE: (Not answered)

OCLC CODE: BAS

ADDRESS: Interlibrary Loan
San Francisco Public
Library
Civic Center
San Francisco, CA 94102

TELEPHONE: (415) 558-3191

LIST NAMES OF BRANCHES WITH
SEPARATE POLICIES: None

BOOKS:
Will Lend: Yes
Length of Loan: 1 month
Renewable: No
Charges: No charges to CLSA
member libraries. Out-of-
state and non-CLSA member
libraries will be charged
$2.50 per volume.
Average Turnaround Time:
(Not answered)
If you have indicated that a
book is not to be lent, will
you on receipt of a letter
from the requesting library
search the index for given
entries? (Not answered)

PERIODICALS:
Bound: Will not lend
Unbound: Will not lend
Loan Period: N/A
Renewable: N/A
Will lend if article exceeds
_____ number of pages (Not
answered)

MICROFORMS:
Will Lend: No
Specific Types of Microforms:
N/A

GOVERNMENT PUBLICATIONS:
Will Lend: No

DISSERTATIONS:
Will Lend: No

THESES:
Will Lend: No

AUDIO-VISUAL MATERIALS:
Records: Will not lend
Cassettes: Will not lend
Other (slides, filmstrips,
etc.): Will not lend

COMPUTER SOFTWARE:
Will Lend: No

PHOTODUPLICATION SERVICE:
No charge up to 10 exposures,
but only to CLSA member
libraries
Charge Per Exposure: 25¢
Minimum/handling Fee: $2.50
for out-of-state and non-
CLSA member libraries
Average Turnaround Time: (Not
answered)

MICROFILMING SERVICE:
Service Available: No
Charges: N/A

DO YOU CHARGE THE BORROWING LIBRARY
FOR POSTAGE? No

FOR HOW LONG DO YOU SUSPEND ILL
SERVICE OVER THE CHRISTMAS
HOLIDAYS? No suspension

ARE THERE ANY GROUPS OF LIBRARIES
FOR WHICH YOU WAIVE FEES? IF
SO, PLEASE NAME THEM: CLSA
member libraries

SAN FRANCISCO STATE UNIVERSITY

NUC CODE: CSfSt

OCLC CODE: CSF

ADDRESS: Interlibrary Loan
           San Francisco State
              University Library
           1630 Holloway Ave.
           San Francisco, CA 94132

TELEPHONE: (415) 469-1727

LIST NAMES OF BRANCHES WITH
  SEPARATE POLICIES: None

BOOKS:
  Will Lend: Yes
  Length of Loan: 4 weeks
    portal to portal
  Renewable: Yes
  Charges: None
  Average Turnaround Time:
    5 days
  If you have indicated that a
    book is not to be lent, will
    you on receipt of a letter
    from the requesting library
    search the index for given
    entries? Yes

PERIODICALS:
  Bound: Will not lend
  Unbound: Will not lend
  Loan Period: N/A
  Renewable: N/A
  Will lend if article exceeds
    _____ number of pages (Will
  not lend)

MICROFORMS:
  Will Lend: No
  Specific Types of Microforms:
    N/A

GOVERNMENT PUBLICATIONS:
  Will Lend: Yes

DISSERTATIONS:
  Will Lend: No

THESES:
  Will Lend: Yes

AUDIO-VISUAL MATERIALS:
  Records: Will not lend
  Cassettes: Will not lend
  Other (slides, filmstrips,
    etc.): Will not lend

COMPUTER SOFTWARE:
  Will Lend: No

PHOTODUPLICATION SERVICE:
  No charge up to 10 exposures
  Charge Per Exposure: 10¢
  Minimum/handling Fee: None
  Average Turnaround Time:
    5 days

MICROFILMING SERVICE:
  Service Available: No
  Charges: N/A

DO YOU CHARGE THE BORROWING LIBRARY
  FOR POSTAGE: No

FOR HOW LONG DO YOU SUSPEND ILL
  SERVICE OVER THE CHRISTMAS
  HOLIDAYS? No suspension

ARE THERE ANY GROUPS OF LIBRARIES
  FOR WHICH YOU WAIVE FEES? IF
  SO, PLEASE NAME THEM: California
  state universities, University
  of California at Berkeley.

SAN JOSE PUBLIC LIBRARY

NUC CODE: (Not answered)

OCLC CODE: SJP

ADDRESS: Interlibrary Loan
           San Jose Public Library
           180 W. San Carlos St.
           San Jose, CA 95113

TELEPHONE: (408) 227-4769 or
                 227-5327

LIST NAMES OF BRANCHES WITH
  SEPARATE POLICIES: (Not
  answered)

BOOKS:
  Will Lend: Yes
  Length of Loan: 4 weeks
  Renewable: Yes
  Charges: None for CLSA
    libraries; $5.00 for out-
    of-state and corporate
    libraries
  Average Turnaround Time:
    (Not answered)
  If you have indicated that a
    book is not to be lent, will
    you on receipt of a letter
    from the requesting library
    search the index for given
    entries? (Not answered)

PERIODICALS:
  Bound: Will not lend
  Unbound: Will not lend
  Loan Period: N/A
  Renewable: N/A
  Will lend if article exceeds
    _____ number of pages (Will
    not lend, regardless of
    length of article)

MICROFORMS:
  Will Lend: No
  Specific Types of Microforms:
    N/A

GOVERNMENT PUBLICATIONS:
  Will Lend: Yes

DISSERTATIONS:
  Will Lend: (Not answered)

THESES:
  Will Lend: (Not answered)

AUDIO-VISUAL MATERIALS:
  Records: (Not answered)
  Cassettes: (Not answered)
  Other (slides, filmstrips,
    etc.): (Not answered)

COMPUTER SOFTWARE:
  Will Lend: (Not answered)

PHOTODUPLICATION SERVICE:
  No charge up to 0 exposures
  Charge Per Exposure: 10¢
  Handling Fee: $2.00 for out-
    of-state and corporate
    libraries
  Average Turnaround Time:
    (Not answered)

MICROFILMING SERVICE:
  Service Available: (Not
    answered)
  Charges: N/A

DO YOU CHARGE THE BORROWING
  LIBRARY FOR POSTAGE? No

FOR HOW LONG DO YOU SUSPEND ILL
  SERVICE OVER THE CHRISTMAS
  HOLIDAYS? (Not answered)

ARE THERE ANY GROUPS OF LIBRARIES
  FOR WHICH YOU WAIVE FEES? IF
  SO, PLEASE NAME THEM: CLSA
  libraries

SAN JOSE STATE UNIVERSITY

NUC CODE: CSjC

OCLC CODE: CSJ

ADDRESS: Interlibrary Loan
Clark Library
Washington Square
San Jose State
University
San Jose, CA 95192

TELEPHONE: (408) 277-3361

LIST NAMES OF BRANCHES WITH
SEPARATE POLICIES: None

BOOKS:
Will Lend: Yes
Length of Loan: 2 weeks from
receipt
Renewable: Yes
Charges: $10.00 per request
to industry libraries in
California
Average Turnaround Time:
3-7 days
If you have indicated that a
book is not to be lent, will
you on receipt of a letter
from the requesting library
search the index for given
entries? Yes

PERIODICALS:
Bound: Will not lend
Unbound: Will not lend
Loan Period: N/A
Renewable: N/A
Will lend if article exceeds
_____ number of pages (Will
not lend, regardless of
length of article)

MICROFORMS:
Will Lend: Sometimes
Specific Types of Microforms:
Microcard, microfilm,
microfiche--lent depending
upon material and demand

GOVERNMENT PUBLICATIONS:
Will Lend: Yes

DISSERTATIONS:
Will Lend: Yes, if 2nd copy
available

THESES:
Will Lend: Yes, if 2nd copy
available

AUDIO-VISUAL MATERIALS:
Records: Will lend
Cassettes: Will lend
Other (slides, filmstrips,
etc.): Will lend

COMPUTER SOFTWARE:
Will Lend: No

PHOTODUPLICATION SERVICE:
No charge up to 0 exposures
Charge Per Exposure: 10¢
Minimum/handling Fee: None
Average Turnaround Time:
3-7 days

MICROFILMING SERVICE:
Service Available: No
Charges: N/A

DO YOU CHARGE THE BORROWING
LIBRARY FOR POSTAGE? No

FOR HOW LONG DO YOU SUSPEND ILL
SERVICE OVER THE CHRISTMAS
HOLIDAYS? No suspension

ARE THERE ANY GROUPS OF LIBRARIES
FOR WHICH YOU WAIVE FEES? IF
SO, PLEASE NAME THEM: CSUC
schools; UCLA; UC at
Berkeley; libraries in
systemwide agreement

SAN LUIS OBISPO CITY-COUNTY LIBRARY

NUC CODE: (Not answered)

OCLC CODE: (Not answered)

ADDRESS: Interlibrary Loan
San Luis Obispo City-
County Library
P. O. Box X
San Luis Obispo, CA
93406

TELEPHONE: (805) 549-5781

LIST NAMES OF BRANCHES WITH
SEPARATE POLICIES: None

BOOKS:
Will Lend: Yes
Length of Loan: 4 weeks
Renewable: Yes
Charges: (Not answered)
Average Turnaround Time:
3 weeks
If you have indicated that a
book is not to be lent, will
you on receipt of a letter
from the requesting library
search the index for given
entries? Reference books
will not be loaned. We
would search index for
entries.

PERIODICALS:
Bound: Will not lend
Unbound: Will not lend
Loan Period: N/A
Renewable: N/A
Will lend if article exceeds
_____ number of pages (Not
answered)
Will photocopy articles

MICROFORMS:
Will Lend: Yes
Specific Types of Microforms:
Local history; newspapers

GOVERNMENT PUBLICATIONS:
Will Lend: (Not answered)

DISSERTATIONS:
Will Lend: (Not answered)

THESES:
Will Lend: (Not answered)

AUDIO-VISUAL MATERIALS:
Records: Will lend
Cassettes: Will lend
Other (slides, filmstrips,
etc.): Will not lend

COMPUTER SOFTWARE:
Will Lend: (Not answered)

PHOTODUPLICATION SERVICE:
No charge up to 10 exposures
Charge Per Exposure: 10¢
Minimum/handling Fee: (Not
answered)
Average Turnaround Time:
1 week

MICROFILMING SERVICE:
Service Available: No
Charges: N/A

DO YOU CHARGE THE BORROWING
LIBRARY FOR POSTAGE? No

FOR HOW LONG DO YOU SUSPEND ILL
SERVICE OVER THE CHRISTMAS
HOLIDAYS? No suspension

ARE THERE ANY GROUPS OF LIBRARIES
FOR WHICH YOU WAIVE FEES? IF
SO, PLEASE NAME THEM: None

SAN MATEO PUBLIC LIBRARY

NUC CODE: (Not answered)

OCLC CODE: (Not answered)

ADDRESS: Interlibrary Loan
San Mateo Public
Library
55 W. 3rd Ave.
San Mateo, CA   94402

TELEPHONE: (415) 574-6950

LIST NAMES OF BRANCHES WITH
SEPARATE POLICIES: None

BOOKS:
Will Lend: Yes
Length of Loan: 1 month
Renewable: No
Charges: None
Average Turnaround Time:
(Not answered)
If you have indicated that a
book is not to be lent, will
you on receipt of a letter
from the requesting library
search the index for given
entries? Yes

PERIODICALS:
Bound: Will not lend
Unbound: Will lend 1967 to
date
Loan Period: 2 weeks
Renewable: No
Will lend if article exceeds
_____number of pages (Will
not lend)

MICROFORMS:
Will Lend: No
Specific Types of Microforms:
N/A

GOVERNMENT PUBLICATIONS:
Will Lend: Not generally but
possibly with special
permission

DISSERTATIONS:
Will Lend: Do not own

THESES:
Will Lend: Do not own

AUDIO-VISUAL MATERIALS:
Records: Will not lend
Cassettes: Will not lend
Other (slides, filmstrips,
etc.): (Not answered)

COMPUTER SOFTWARE:
Will Lend: Do not own

PHOTODUPLICATION SERVICE:
No charge up to 10 exposures
Charge Per Exposure: 10¢
Minimum/handling Fee: (Not
answered)
Average Turnaround Time:
(Not answered)

MICROFILMING SERVICE:
Service Available: (Not
answered)
Charges: N/A

DO YOU CHARGE THE BORROWING LIBRARY
FOR POSTAGE? No

FOR HOW LONG DO YOU SUSPEND ILL
SERVICE OVER THE CHRISTMAS
HOLIDAYS? No suspension

ARE THERE ANY GROUPS OF LIBRARIES
FOR WHICH YOU WAIVE FEES? IF
SO, PLEASE NAME THEM: None

SANTA ANA PUBLIC LIBRARY

NUC CODE: (Not answered)

OCLC CODE: (Not answered)

ADDRESS: Interlibrary Loan
Santa Ana Public Library
26 Civic Center Plaza
P. O. Box 1988
Santa Ana, CA 92702

TELEPHONE: (714) 834-4032 or
(714) 834-4049

LIST NAMES OF BRANCHES WITH
SEPARATE POLICIES: None

BOOKS:
Will Lend: Yes
Length of Loan: 30 days
Renewable: No
Charges: None
Average Turnaround Time:
3 days if on shelf
If you have indicated that a
book is not to be lent, will
you on receipt of a letter
from the requesting library
search the index for given
entries? N/A

PERIODICALS:
Bound: Will not lend
Unbound: Will lend 1966 to
present
Loan Period: 30 days
Renewable: No
Will lend if article exceeds
_____ number of pages (Not
answered)

MICROFORMS:
Will Lend: Do not own
Specific Types of Microforms:
N/A

GOVERNMENT PUBLICATIONS:
Will Lend: No

DISSERTATIONS:
Will Lend: Do not own

THESES:
Will Lend: Do not own

AUDIO-VISUAL MATERIALS:
Records: Will not lend
Cassettes: Will not lend
Other (slides, filmstrips,
etc.): Do not own

COMPUTER SOFTWARE:
Will Lend: Do not own

PHOTODUPLICATION SERVICE:
No charge up to 10 exposures
Charge Per Exposure: 10¢ each
after first 10
Minimum/handling Fee: None
Average Turnaround Time:
3 days

MICROFILMING SERVICE:
Service Available: No
Charges: N/A

DO YOU CHARGE THE BORROWING LIBRARY
FOR POSTAGE? No

FOR HOW LONG DO YOU SUSPEND ILL
SERVICE OVER THE CHRISTMAS
HOLIDAYS? Open during
Christmas holidays

ARE THERE ANY GROUPS OF LIBRARIES
FOR WHICH YOU WAIVE FEES? IF
SO, PLEASE NAME THEM: None

SANTA BARBARA PUBLIC LIBRARY

NUC CODE: CSTB

OCLC CODE: BGC

ADDRESS: Interlibrary Loan
Santa Barbara Public
Library
40 E. Anapamu St.
Santa Barbara, CA   93101

TELEPHONE: (805) 962-7653, X38

LIST NAMES OF BRANCHES WITH
SEPARATE POLICIES: None

BOOKS:
Will Lend: Yes
Length of Loan: 4 weeks
Renewable: Yes
Charges: None
Average Turnaround Time:
8 days
If you have indicated that a
book is not to be lent, will
you on receipt of a letter
from the requesting library
search the index for given
entries? (Not answered)

PERIODICALS:
Bound: Will lend
Unbound: Will lend
Loan Period: 2 weeks
Renewable: Yes
Will lend if article exceeds
_____ number of pages (Not
answered)

MICROFORMS:
Will Lend: Yes
Specific Types of Microforms:
Microfilm

GOVERNMENT PUBLICATIONS:
Will Lend: Yes

DISSERTATIONS:
Will Lend: No

THESES:
Will Lend: No

AUDIO-VISUAL MATERIALS:
Records: Will not lend
Cassettes: Will not lend
Other (slides, filmstrips,
etc.): Will not lend

COMPUTER SOFTWARE:
Will Lend: No

PHOTODUPLICATION SERVICE:
No charge up to 10 exposures
Charge Per Exposure: 15¢
Minimum/handling Fee: None
Average Turnaround Time:
8 days

MICROFILMING SERVICE:
Service Available: No
Charges: N/A

DO YOU CHARGE THE BORROWING
LIBRARY FOR POSTAGE? No

FOR HOW LONG DO YOU SUSPEND ILL
SERVICE OVER THE CHRISTMAS
HOLIDAYS? No suspension

ARE THERE ANY GROUPS OF LIBRARIES
FOR WHICH YOU WAIVE FEES? IF
SO, PLEASE NAME THEM: None

SANTA CRUZ PUBLIC LIBRARY

NUC CODE: None

OCLC CODE: None

ADDRESS: Interlibrary Loan
Santa Cruz Public
Library
224 Church St.
Santa Cruz, CA   95060

TELEPHONE: (408) 429-3520

LIST NAMES OF BRANCHES WITH
SEPARATE POLICIES: None

BOOKS:
Will Lend: Yes
Length of Loan: 3 weeks
Renewable: No
Charges: None
Average Turnaround Time:
1 week, if book is on shelf
If you have indicated that a
book is not to be lent, will
you on receipt of a letter
from the requesting library
search the index for given
entries? (Not answered)

PERIODICALS:
Bound: Will not lend
Unbound: Will lend
Loan Period: 1 week
Renewable: No
Will lend if article exceeds
_____ number of pages (Not
answered)

MICROFORMS:
Will Lend: No
Specific Types of Microforms:
N/A

GOVERNMENT PUBLICATIONS:
Will Lend: Yes

DISSERTATIONS:
Will Lend: Yes, some of them

THESES:
Will Lend: Yes, some of them

AUDIO-VISUAL MATERIALS:
Records: Will lend
Cassettes: Will lend
Other (slides, filmstrips,
etc.): Will not lend

COMPUTER SOFTWARE:
Will Lend: No

PHOTODUPLICATION SERVICE:
No charge up to 10 exposures
Charge Per Exposure: 10¢
after first 10
Minimum/handling Fee: None
Average Turnaround Time:
1 week

MICROFILMING SERVICE:
Service Available: Yes
Charges: 10¢ after 10 pages

DO YOU CHARGE THE BORROWING LIBRARY
FOR POSTAGE? No

FOR HOW LONG DO YOU SUSPEND ILL
SERVICE OVER THE CHRISTMAS
HOLIDAYS? 1 week

ARE THERE ANY GROUPS OF LIBRARIES
FOR WHICH YOU WAIVE FEES? IF
SO, PLEASE NAME THEM: None

SONOMA COUNTY LIBRARY

NUC CODE: CStr=Santa Rosa Public
            CStrCL=Sonoma County
(These 2 libraries are now
 merged)

OCLC CODE: NOB (This is the
OCLC code for the North Bay
Cooperative, which handles
all of Sonoma County's ILL
loans)

ADDRESS: Interlibrary Loan
            Sonoma County Library
            3rd and E Streets
            Santa Rosa, CA 95404

TELEPHONE: (707) 545-0801

LIST NAMES OF BRANCHES WITH
SEPARATE POLICIES: None

BOOKS:
    Will Lend: Yes, except for
    rare and heavily-used
    reference books
    Length of Loan: 4 weeks;
    some reference books are
    2 week loans
    Renewable: No
    Charges: None
    Average Turnaround Time:
    2 days
    If you have indicated that a
    book is not to be lent, will
    you on receipt of a letter
    from the requesting library
    search the index for given
    entries? Yes

PERIODICALS:
    Bound: Will lend, but we
    prefer to copy articles
    Unbound: Will lend, but we
    prefer to copy articles
    Loan Period: 2 weeks
    Renewable: No
    Will lend if article exceeds
    an excessive number of pages

MICROFORMS:
    Will Lend: Yes
    Specific Types of Microforms:
    Microfilm and microfiche

GOVERNMENT PUBLICATIONS:
    Will Lend: Yes

DISSERTATIONS:
    Will Lend: Do not own

THESES:
    Will Lend: Do not own

AUDIO-VISUAL MATERIALS:
    Records: Will not lend
    Cassettes: Will not lend
    Other (slides, filmstrips,
    etc.): Do not own

COMPUTER SOFTWARE:
    Will Lend: Do not own

PHOTODUPLICATION SERVICE:
    No charge up to --- exposures
    Charge Per Exposure: (Not
    answered)
    Minimum/handling Fee: (Not
    answered)
    Average Turnaround Time:
    1 week

MICROFILMING SERVICE:
    Service Available: No
    Charges: N/A

DO YOU CHARGE THE BORROWING
LIBRARY FOR POSTAGE? No

FOR HOW LONG DO YOU SUSPEND ILL
SERVICE OVER THE CHRISTMAS
HOLIDAYS? No suspension

ARE THERE ANY GROUPS OF LIBRARIES
FOR WHICH YOU WAIVE FEES? IF
SO, PLEASE NAME THEM: None

SONOMA STATE UNIVERSITY

NUC CODE: CCotS

OCLC CODE: CSO

ADDRESS: Interlibrary Loan
            Ruben Salazar Library
            Sonoma State University
            1801 East Cotati Ave.
            Rohnert Park, CA 94928

TELEPHONE: (707) 664-2866

LIST NAMES OF BRANCHES WITH
SEPARATE POLICIES: None

BOOKS:
    Will Lend: Yes
    Length of Loan: 1 month
    Renewable: Yes, if no
    reserves
    Charges: None
    Average Turnaround Time:
    24 hours
    If you have indicated that a
    book is not to be lent, will
    you on receipt of a letter
    from the requesting library
    search the index for given
    entries? Yes; we will do
    this for non-circulating
    books

PERIODICALS:
    Bound: Will not lend
    Unbound: Will lend
    Loan Period: 2 weeks
    Renewable: Yes
    Will lend if article exceeds
    _____ number of pages (Not
    answered)

MICROFORMS:
    Will Lend: Yes
    Specific Types of Microforms:
    (Not answered)

GOVERNMENT PUBLICATIONS:
    Will Lend: Yes, at Documents
    Librarian's discretion

DISSERTATIONS:
    Will Lend: Do not own

THESES:
    Will Lend: Do not own

AUDIO-VISUAL MATERIALS:
    Records: Will not lend
    Cassettes: Will not lend
    Other (slides, filmstrips,
    etc.): Will not lend

COMPUTER SOFTWARE:
    Will Lend: No

PHOTODUPLICATION SERVICE:
    No charge up to _____
    exposures (Not answered)
    Charge Per Exposure: 10¢
    Minimum/handling Fee: $2.00
    Average Turnaround Time:
    1 week

MICROFILMING SERVICE:
    Service Available: No
    Charges: N/A

DO YOU CHARGE THE BORROWING
LIBRARY FOR POSTAGE? No

FOR HOW LONG DO YOU SUSPEND ILL
SERVICE OVER THE· CHRISTMAS
HOLIDAYS? No suspension

ARE THERE ANY GROUPS OF LIBRARIES
FOR WHICH YOU WAIVE FEES? IF
SO, PLEASE NAME THEM: We do
not charge photoduplication
fees to academic and non-
profit libraries

STANFORD UNIVERSITY

NUC CODE: CSt

OCLC CODE: None

ADDRESS: Interlibrary Loan
Stanford University
Libraries
Stanford, CA 94305

TELEPHONE: (415) 497-9448

LIST NAMES OF BRANCHES WITH
SEPARATE POLICIES:
Law Library
Hoover Institution
Lane Medical Library
Graduate School of Business
(Jackson)

BOOKS:
Will Lend: Yes
Length of Loan: 4 weeks from
receipt
Renewable: No, generally
Charges: None
Average Turnaround Time:
2-3 weeks, door to door
If you have indicated that a
book is not to be lent, will
you on receipt of a letter
from the requesting library
search the index for given
entries? No, but we would
photocopy index.

PERIODICALS:
Bound: Will not lend
Unbound: Will not lend
Loan Period: N/A
Renewable: N/A
Will lend if article exceeds
_____ number of pages (Will
not lend, but will photocopy)

MICROFORMS:
Will Lend: Yes
Specific Types of Microforms:
Microfilm

GOVERNMENT PUBLICATIONS:
Will Lend: Yes

DISSERTATIONS:
Will Lend: No

THESES:
Will Lend: Yes, but pre-1953
only

AUDIO-VISUAL MATERIALS:
Records: Will not lend
Cassettes: Will not lend
Other (slides, filmstrips,
etc.): Will not lend

COMPUTER SOFTWARE:
Will Lend: No

PHOTODUPLICATION SERVICE:
No charge up to 0 exposures
Miscellaneous Charges:
Library searching and
obtaining material, $1.00
per title
Library identifying incomplete
or inaccurate references,
$2.00 per title
Handling and postage, domestic
minimum, $1.00
Handling and postage, foreign
minimum, $2.00
Paper Copy:
1-20 pages, $3.00
21-50 pages, $7.50
51-80 pages, $12.00
81-110 pages, $16.50
111-150 pages, $22.50
151-200 pages, $30.00
over 200 pages, 15¢ per print
Average Turnaround Time:
2 weeks

MICROFILMING SERVICE:
Service Available: Not at
present
Charges: N/A

DO YOU CHARGE THE BORROWING
LIBRARY FOR POSTAGE? No

FOR HOW LONG DO YOU SUSPEND ILL
SERVICE OVER THE CHRISTMAS
HOLIDAYS? Dec.15-Jan.3

ARE THERE ANY GROUPS OF LIBRARIES
FOR WHICH YOU WAIVE FEES? IF
SO, PLEASE NAME THEM: No
photocopying charges for
RLG member libraries

STANISLAUS COUNTY FREE LIBRARY

NUC CODE: (Not answered)

OCLC CODE: (Not answered)

ADDRESS: Interlibrary Loan
Stanislaus County Free
Library
1500 I Street
Modesto, CA 95354

TELEPHONE: (209) 571-6834

LIST NAMES OF BRANCHES WITH
SEPARATE POLICIES: None

BOOKS:
Will Lend: Yes
Length of Loan: 4 weeks
Renewable: Yes, 1 time
Charges: None
Average Turnaround Time:
24 hours
If you have indicated that a
book is not to be lent, will
you on receipt of a letter
from the requesting library
search the index for given
entries? (Not answered)

PERIODICALS:
Bound: Will not lend
Unbound: Will not lend
Loan Period: N/A
Renewable: N/A
Will lend if article exceeds
_____ number of pages (Not
answered)

MICROFORMS:
Will Lend: No
Specific Types of Microforms:
N/A

GOVERNMENT PUBLICATIONS:
Will Lend: No

DISSERTATIONS:
Will Lend: Do not own

THESES:
Will Lend: Do not own

AUDIO-VISUAL MATERIALS:
Records: Will not lend
Cassettes: Will not lend
Other (slides, filmstrips,
etc.): Will not lend

COMPUTER SOFTWARE:
Will Lend: Do not own

PHOTODUPLICATION SERVICE:
No charge up to 0 exposures
Charge Per Exposure: 10¢
Minimum/handling Fee: None
Average Turnaround Time:
24 hours

MICROFILMING SERVICE:
Service Available: No
Charges: N/A

DO YOU CHARGE THE BORROWING
LIBRARY FOR POSTAGE? Yes, for
out-of-state

FOR HOW LONG DO YOU SUSPEND ILL
SERVICE OVER THE CHRISTMAS
HOLIDAYS? No suspension

ARE THERE ANY GROUPS OF LIBRARIES
FOR WHICH YOU WAIVE FEES? IF
SO, PLEASE NAME THEM: 49-99/
CLS/CAL members

STOCKTON-SAN JOAQUIN COUNTY PUBLIC LIBRARY

NUC CODE: CSto

OCLC CODE: CSP

ADDRESS: Interlibrary Loan
           Stockton-San Joaquin
           County Public
           Library
           605 N. El Dorado
           Stockton, CA 95202

TELEPHONE: (209) 944-8461

LIST NAMES OF BRANCHES WITH
  SEPARATE POLICIES: None

BOOKS:
  Will Lend: Yes
  Length of Loan: 3 weeks
  Renewable: Yes
  Charges: (Not answered)
  Average Turnaround Time:
    3 days
  If you have indicated that a
    book is not to be lent, will
    you on receipt of a letter
    from the requesting library
    search the index for given
    entries? We will search
      index for reference
      materials.

PERIODICALS:
  Bound: Will not lend
  Unbound: Will lend
  Loan Period: 1 week
  Renewable: Yes
  Will lend if article exceeds
    20 pages

MICROFORMS:
  Will Lend: Yes
  Specific Types of Microforms:
    Microfiche, 35mm microfilm

GOVERNMENT PUBLICATIONS:
  Will Lend: Yes

DISSERTATIONS:
  Will Lend: Do not own

THESES:
  Will Lend: Do not own

AUDIO-VISUAL MATERIALS:
  Records: Will not lend
  Cassettes: Will not lend
  Other (slides, filmstrips,
    etc.): Will not lend

COMPUTER SOFTWARE:
  Will Lend: No

PHOTODUPLICATION SERVICE:
  No charge up to 10 exposures
  Charge Per Exposure: 15¢ per
    page after first 10 pages;
    25¢ per page from microfiche
  Minimum/handling Fee: None
  Average Turnaround Time:
    24 hours

MICROFILMING SERVICE:
  Service Available: No
  Charges: N/A

DO YOU CHARGE THE BORROWING
  LIBRARY FOR POSTAGE? No

FOR HOW LONG DO YOU SUSPEND ILL
  SERVICE OVER THE CHRISTMAS
  HOLIDAYS? No suspension

ARE THERE ANY GROUPS OF LIBRARIES
  FOR WHICH YOU WAIVE FEES? IF
  SO, PLEASE NAME THEM: None

SUNNYVALE PUBLIC LIBRARY

NUC CODE: CXv

OCLC CODE: SXP

ADDRESS: Interlibrary Loan
           Sunnyvale Public
           Library
           665 West Olive Ave.
           Sunnyvale, CA 94086

TELEPHONE: (408) 738-5565

LIST NAMES OF BRANCHES WITH
  SEPARATE POLICIES:
  Sunnyvale Patent Information
    Clearinghouse
  1500 Partridge Ave.
  Bldg. 7
  Sunnyvale, CA 94087

BOOKS:
  Will Lend: Yes
  Length of Loan: 1 month
  Renewable: No
  Charges: None
  Average Turnaround Time:
    3 days
  If you have indicated that a
    book is not to be lent, will
    you on receipt of a letter
    from the requesting library
    search the index for given
    entries? (Not answered)

PERIODICALS:
  Bound: Will not lend
  Unbound: (Not answered)
  Loan Period: N/A
  Renewable: N/A
  Will lend if article exceeds
    _____ number of pages (Not
    answered)

MICROFORMS:
  Will Lend: Do not own
  Specific Types of Microforms:
    N/A

GOVERNMENT PUBLICATIONS:
  Will Lend: Yes

DISSERTATIONS:
  Will Lend: Do not own

THESES:
  Will Lend: Do not own

AUDIO-VISUAL MATERIALS:
  Records: Will not lend
  Cassettes: Do not own
  Other (slides, filmstrips,
    etc.): Do not own

COMPUTER SOFTWARE:
  Will Lend: Do not own

PHOTODUPLICATION SERVICE:
  No charge up to unlimited
    exposures
  Charge Per Exposure: None
  Minimum/handling Fee: None
  Average Turnaround Time:
    3 days

MICROFILMING SERVICE:
  Service Available: No
  Charges: N/A

DO YOU CHARGE THE BORROWING
  LIBRARY FOR POSTAGE? No

FOR HOW LONG DO YOU SUSPEND ILL
  SERVICE OVER THE CHRISTMAS
  HOLIDAYS? No suspension

ARE THERE ANY GROUPS OF LIBRARIES
  FOR WHICH YOU WAIVE FEES? IF
  SO, PLEASE NAME THEM: None

TORRANCE PUBLIC LIBRARY

NUC CODE: (Not answered)

OCLC CODE: (Not answered)

ADDRESS: Interlibrary Loan
           Torrance Public Library
           3301 Torrance Blvd.
           Torrance, CA 90503

TELEPHONE: (213) 328-2251

LIST NAMES OF BRANCHES WITH
    SEPARATE POLICIES: None

BOOKS:
    Will Lend: Yes
    Length of Loan: 3 weeks
    Renewable: Yes
    Charges: (Not answered)
    Average Turnaround Time:
       1 working day
    If you have indicated that a
      book is not to be lent, will
      you on receipt of a letter
      from the requesting library
      search the index for given
      entries? (Not answered)

PERIODICALS:
    Bound: Will not lend
    Unbound: Will not lend
    Loan Period: N/A
    Renewable: N/A
    Will lend if article exceeds
       _____ number of pages (Not
    answered)

MICROFORMS:
    Will Lend: No
    Specific Types of Microforms:
    N/A

GOVERNMENT PUBLICATIONS:
    Will Lend: Yes

DISSERTATIONS:
    Will Lend: Yes

THESES:
    Will Lend: Yes

AUDIO-VISUAL MATERIALS:
    Records: Will lend
    Cassettes: Will lend
    Other (slides, filmstrips,
       etc.): Will lend

COMPUTER SOFTWARE:
    Will Lend: No

PHOTODUPLICATION SERVICE:
    No charge up to 20 exposures
    Charge Per Exposure: 30¢ per
       page after first 20
    Minimum/handling Fee: (Not
       answered)
    Average Turnaround Time:
       1 working day

MICROFILMING SERVICE:
    Service Available: No
    Charges: N/A

DO YOU CHARGE THE BORROWING LIBRARY
    FOR POSTAGE? No

FOR HOW LONG DO YOU SUSPEND ILL
    SERVICE OVER THE CHRISTMAS
    HOLIDAYS? No more than 4 days

ARE THERE ANY GROUPS OF LIBRARIES
    FOR WHICH YOU WAIVE FEES? IF
    SO, PLEASE NAME THEM: None

TULARE COUNTY FREE LIBRARY

SAN CODE: 335-2749

OCLC CODE: TCB

ADDRESS: Interlibrary Loan
           Tulare County Free
           Library
           200 W. Oak St.
           Visalia, CA 93291-4993

TELEPHONE: (209) 733-8440

LIST NAMES OF BRANCHES WITH
    SEPARATE POLICIES: None

BOOKS:
    Will Lend: Yes
    Length of Loan: 1 month
    Renewable: Yes
    Charges: (Not answered)
    Average Turnaround Time:
       3 days
    If you have indicated that a
      book is not to be lent, will
      you on receipt of a letter
      from the requesting library
      search the index for given
      entries? Yes

PERIODICALS:
    Bound: Will not lend
    Unbound: Will not lend
    Loan Period: N/A
    Renewable: N/A
    Will send photocopy of
       article cited

MICROFORMS:
    Will Lend: Yes
    Specific Types of Microforms:
    (Not answered)

GOVERNMENT PUBLICATIONS:
    Will Lend: Yes

DISSERTATIONS:
    Will Lend: Do not own

THESES:
    Will Lend: Do not own

AUDIO-VISUAL MATERIALS:
    Records: Will not lend
    Cassettes: Will not lend
    Other (slides, filmstrips,
       etc.): Will not lend

COMPUTER SOFTWARE:
    Will Lend: Do not own

PHOTODUPLICATION SERVICE:
    No charge up to 10 exposures
    Charge Per Exposure: 15¢
    Minimum/handling Fee: None
    Average Turnaround Time:
       3 days

MICROFILMING SERVICE:
    Service Available: No
    Charges: N/A

DO YOU CHARGE THE BORROWING LIBRARY
    FOR POSTAGE? No

FOR HOW LONG DO YOU SUSPEND ILL
    SERVICE OVER THE CHRISTMAS
    HOLIDAYS? No suspension

ARE THERE ANY GROUPS OF LIBRARIES
    FOR WHICH YOU WAIVE FEES? IF
    SO, PLEASE NAME THEM: Libraries
    of the San Joaquin Valley
    Library System

UNIVERSITY OF CALIFORNIA AT BERKELEY

NUC CODE: CU

OCLC CODE: CUY

ADDRESS: Interlibrary Lending
Service
General Library
University of
California
Berkeley, CA 94720

TELEPHONE: (415) 642-7367

LIST NAMES OF BRANCHES WITH
SEPARATE POLICIES:
Institute of Transportation
Studies Library
Lawrence Berkeley Laboratory
Earthquake Engineering
Research Center

BOOKS:
Will Lend: Yes, except for
current and past year U. S.
imprints; also, do not lend
to public libraries
outside California
Length of Loan: 7-21 days
from receipt
Renewable: No
Charges: $10.00 for filled
non-California requests;
$5.00 for unfilled non-
California requests; none
for California borrowers
Average Turnaround Time:
1-2 weeks
If you have indicated that a
book is not to be lent, will
you on receipt of a letter
from the requesting library
search the index for given
entries? Yes, if a photocopy is requested

PERIODICALS:
Bound: Will not lend
Unbound: Will not lend
Loan Period: N/A
Renewable: N/A
Will lend if article exceeds
_____ number of pages (Not
answered)

MICROFORMS:
Will Lend: Yes
Specific Types of Microforms:
(Not answered)

GOVERNMENT PUBLICATIONS:
Will Lend: Yes, depending on
the material

DISSERTATIONS:
Will Lend: Yes, if 2nd copy
available; library use only;
Sept. 1962-Dec. 1970 and
Dec. 1975 to present
available from University
Microfilms

THESES:
Will Lend: Yes, if 2nd copy
available; library use only

AUDIO-VISUAL MATERIALS:
Records: Will not lend
Cassettes: Will not lend
Other (slides, filmstrips,
etc.): Will not lend

COMPUTER SOFTWARE:
Will Lend: No

PHOTODUPLICATION SERVICE:
No charge up to 0 exposures
Charge Per Exposure: 15¢
Handling Fee: $5.00 per
volume
Average Turnaround Time:
2 weeks

MICROFILMING SERVICE:
Service Available: Yes
Charge Per Frame:
Negative: 15¢ (first 200),
then 14¢
Positive: 15¢ per foot
Processing Charge:
$5.00 per volume plus
special handling and
sales tax if applicable

DO YOU CHARGE THE BORROWING
LIBRARY FOR POSTAGE? Yes,
for special mailing and
insurance

FOR HOW LONG DO YOU SUSPEND ILL
SERVICE OVER THE CHRISTMAS
HOLIDAYS? 4 weeks

ARE THERE ANY GROUPS OF LIBRARIES
FOR WHICH YOU WAIVE FEES? IF
SO, PLEASE NAME THEM: RLG
member libraries

UNIVERSITY OF CALIFORNIA AT DAVIS

NUC CODE: CU-A

OCLC CODE: CUV

ADDRESS: Interlibrary Loan
Shields Library
University of
California at Davis
Davis, CA 95616

TELEPHONE: (916) 752-2251

LIST NAMES OF BRANCHES WITH
SEPARATE POLICIES:
Health Science Library

BOOKS:
Will Lend: Yes
Length of Loan: 3 weeks from
receipt
Renewable: Yes, sometimes
Charges: (Not answered)
Average Turnaround Time:
(Not answered)
If you have indicated that a
book is not to be lent, will
you on receipt of a letter
from the requesting library
search the index for given
entries? No

PERIODICALS:
Bound: Will not lend
Unbound: Will not lend
Loan Period: N/A
Renewable: N/A
Will lend if article exceeds
_____ number of pages (Will
not lend, regardless of
length of article)

MICROFORMS:
Will Lend: Yes, some of them
Specific Types of Microforms:
Government documents

GOVERNMENT PUBLICATIONS:
Will Lend: Yes, some of them

DISSERTATIONS:
Will Lend: Yes; available
from University Microfilms,
1964 to present

THESES:
Will Lend: Yes, if pre-1960

AUDIO-VISUAL MATERIALS:
Records: Will not lend
Cassettes: Will not lend
Other (slides, filmstrips,
etc.): Will not lend

COMPUTER SOFTWARE:
Will Lend: No

PHOTODUPLICATION SERVICE:
No charge up to 0 exposures
Charge Per Exposure: 15¢
Minimum/handling Fee: $5.00
Average Turnaround Time:
1 week

MICROFILMING SERVICE:
Service Available: No
Charges: N/A

DO YOU CHARGE THE BORROWING
LIBRARY FOR POSTAGE? Only
when special mailing is
requested

FOR HOW LONG DO YOU SUSPEND ILL
SERVICE OVER THE CHRISTMAS
HOLIDAYS? Dec.15-Jan.5

ARE THERE ANY GROUPS OF LIBRARIES
FOR WHICH YOU WAIVE FEES? IF
SO, PLEASE NAME THEM: RLG;
University of California
campuses; California public
libraries

UNIVERSITY OF CALIFORNIA AT IRVINE

NUC CODE: CU-I

OCLC CODE: CUI

ADDRESS: Interlibrary Loan
University of
   California at
   Irvine
General Library
P. O. Box 19557
Irvine, CA 92713

TELEPHONE: (714) 833-6839

LIST NAMES OF BRANCHES WITH
   SEPARATE POLICIES:
   Biomedical Library

BOOKS:
   Will Lend: Yes
   Length of Loan: 3 weeks use
   Renewable: Yes
   Charges: None
   Average Turnaround Time:
      1-2 days
   If you have indicated that a
      book is not to be lent, will
      you on receipt of a letter
      from the requesting library
      search the index for given
      entries? (Not answered)

PERIODICALS:
   Bound: Will not lend
   Unbound: Will not lend
   Loan Period: N/A
   Renewable: N/A
   Will lend if article exceeds
      _____ number of pages (Not
      answered)

MICROFORMS:
   Will Lend: Yes
   Specific Types of Microforms:
      Newspapers, dissertations

GOVERNMENT PUBLICATIONS:
   Will Lend: Yes

DISSERTATIONS:
   Will Lend: Yes

THESES:
   Will Lend: Yes

AUDIO-VISUAL MATERIALS:
   Records: Will not lend
   Cassettes: Will lend by
      special arrangement
   Other (slides, filmstrips,
      etc.): Will not lend

COMPUTER SOFTWARE:
   Will Lend: No

PHOTODUPLICATION SERVICE:
   No charge up to 0 exposures
   Charge Per Exposure: 10¢
   Minimum/handling Fee: $4.00
   Average Turnaround Time:
      2-3 days

MICROFILMING SERVICE:
   Service Available: Yes
   Charges: $4.00 minimum
      plus 15¢ per exposure

DO YOU CHARGE THE BORROWING
   LIBRARY FOR POSTAGE? No

FOR HOW LONG DO YOU SUSPEND ILL
   SERVICE OVER THE CHRISTMAS
   HOLIDAYS? Approximately
      Dec.10-Jan.2 (outside of
      California)

ARE THERE ANY GROUPS OF LIBRARIES
   FOR WHICH YOU WAIVE FEES? IF
   SO, PLEASE NAME THEM: None

UNIVERSITY OF CALIFORNIA AT LOS ANGELES

NUC CODE: CLU

OCLC CODE: CLU

ADDRESS: Interlibrary Loan
Reference Department
University Research
   Library
University of
   California
Los Angeles, CA 90024

TELEPHONE: (213) 825-1201

LIST NAMES OF BRANCHES WITH
   SEPARATE POLICIES:
   Biomedical Library
   Physical Sciences and
      Technology Library
   Law Library

BOOKS:
   Will Lend: Yes
   Length of Loan: 2 weeks
   Renewable: Yes
   Charges: None
   Average Turnaround Time:
      1-2 days
   If you have indicated that a
      book is not to be lent, will
      you on receipt of a letter
      from the requesting library
      search the index for given
      entries? (Not answered)

PERIODICALS:
   Bound: Will not lend
   Unbound: Will not lend
   Loan Period: N/A
   Renewable: N/A
   Will lend if article exceeds
      _____ number of pages (Not
      answered)

MICROFORMS:
   Will Lend: Yes
   Specific Types of Microforms:
      (Not answered)

GOVERNMENT PUBLICATIONS:
   Will Lend: Yes

DISSERTATIONS:
   Will Lend: Yes, but post-
      1963 lent on reciprocal
      basis only. 1963 to present
      available from University
      Microfilms

THESES:
   Will Lend: Yes

AUDIO-VISUAL MATERIALS:
   Records: Will not lend
   Cassettes: Will not lend
   Other (slides, filmstrips,
      etc.): Will not lend

COMPUTER SOFTWARE:
   Will Lend: No

PHOTODUPLICATION SERVICE:
   No charge up to 0 exposures
   Charge Per Exposure: (Not
      answered)
   Minimum Fee: $5.00
   Average Turnaround Time: (Not
      answered)

MICROFILMING SERVICE:
   Service Available: No
   Charges: N/A

DO YOU CHARGE THE BORROWING
   LIBRARY FOR POSTAGE? No

FOR HOW LONG DO YOU SUSPEND ILL
   SERVICE OVER THE CHRISTMAS
   HOLIDAYS? No suspension

ARE THERE ANY GROUPS OF LIBRARIES
   FOR WHICH YOU WAIVE FEES? IF
   SO, PLEASE NAME THEM: None

UNIVERSITY OF CALIFORNIA AT LOS ANGELES
CENTER FOR THE HEALTH SCIENCES

NUC CODE: CLU-M

OCLC CODE: CLU

ADDRESS: Interlibrary Loan
           UCLA Biomedical Library
           Center for the Health
             Sciences
           Los Angeles, CA 90024

TELEPHONE: (213) 825-4055

LIST NAMES OF BRANCHES WITH
  SEPARATE POLICIES:
    University Research Library
    Law Library
    Physical Science and
      Technical Libraries

BOOKS:
  Will Lend: Yes
  Length of Loan: 2 weeks from
    date of receipt
  Renewable: No
  Charges: $5.50
  Average Turnaround Time:
    2 weeks
  If you have indicated that a
    book is not to be lent, will
    you on receipt of a letter
    from the requesting library
    search the index for given
    entries? (Not answered)

PERIODICALS:
  Bound: Will lend those that
    are 10 years old
  Unbound: Will not lend
  Loan Period: 2 weeks
  Renewable: No
  Will lend if article exceeds
    _____ number of pages (Will
    not lend)

MICROFORMS:
  Will Lend: Yes, unless
    classified as periodicals
  Specific Types of Microforms:
    Microfilm, microfiche, and
    microcard

GOVERNMENT PUBLICATIONS:
  Will Lend: Yes

DISSERTATIONS:
  Will Lend: Yes, if library has
    2 copies

THESES:
  Will Lend: Yes, if library has
    2 copies

AUDIO-VISUAL MATERIALS:
  Records: Will not lend
  Cassettes: Will not lend
  Other (slides, filmstrips,
    etc.): Will not lend

COMPUTER SOFTWARE:
  Will Lend: No

PHOTODUPLICATION SERVICE:
  Charges are the same as book
    loans
  Average Turnaround Time:
    5 days

MICROFILMING SERVICE:
  Service Available: Yes

DO YOU CHARGE THE BORROWING LIBRARY
  FOR POSTAGE? No

FOR HOW LONG DO YOU SUSPEND ILL
  SERVICE OVER THE CHRISTMAS
  HOLIDAYS? Do not suspend
  services

ARE THERE ANY GROUPS OF LIBRARIES
  FOR WHICH YOU WAIVE FEES? IF
  SO, PLEASE NAME THEM: None

UNIVERSITY OF CALIFORNIA AT RIVERSIDE

NUC CODE: CU-Rir

OCLC CODE: CRU

ADDRESS: Interlibrary Loan
           University of
             California Library
           P. O. Box 5900
           Riverside, CA 92517

TELEPHONE: (714) 787-3234

LIST NAMES OF BRANCHES WITH
  SEPARATE POLICIES: None

BOOKS:
  Will Lend: Yes
  Length of Loan: Quarter
  Renewable: Yes
  Charges: (Not answered)
  Average Turnaround Time:
    (Not answered)
  If you have indicated that a
    book is not to be lent, will
    you on receipt of a letter
    from the requesting library
    search the index for given
    entries? (Not answered)

PERIODICALS:
  Bound: Will lend
  Unbound: Will lend
  Loan Period: Bound for
    1 month; unbound for
    1 week
  Renewable: Yes
  Will lend if article exceeds
    _____ number of pages (Not
    answered)

MICROFORMS:
  Will Lend: Yes
  Specific Types of Microforms:
    (Not answered)

GOVERNMENT PUBLICATIONS:
  Will Lend: Yes

DISSERTATIONS:
  Will Lend: Yes, if 2nd copy
    available; January 1963 to
    present available from
    University Microfilms

THESES:
  Will Lend: Yes, if 2nd copy
    available

AUDIO-VISUAL MATERIALS:
  Records: (Not answered)
  Cassettes: (Not answered)
  Other (slides, filmstrips,
    etc.): (Not answered)

COMPUTER SOFTWARE:
  Will Lend: (Not answered)

PHOTODUPLICATION SERVICE:
  No charge up to 0 exposures
  Charge Per Exposure: 20¢
  Minimum Fee: $4.00
  Average Turnaround Time:
    (Not answered)

MICROFILMING SERVICE:
  Service Available: No
  Charges: N/A

DO YOU CHARGE THE BORROWING
  LIBRARY FOR POSTAGE? (Not
  answered)

FOR HOW LONG DO YOU SUSPEND ILL
  SERVICE OVER THE CHRISTMAS
  HOLIDAYS? (Not answered)

ARE THERE ANY GROUPS OF LIBRARIES
  FOR WHICH YOU WAIVE FEES? IF
  SO, PLEASE NAME THEM: (Not
  answered)

UNIVERSITY OF CALIFORNIA AT SAN DIEGO

NUC CODE: CUS

OCLC CODE: CUS

ADDRESS: Interlibrary Loan
Central University
Library
University of
California at San
Diego
La Jolla, CA 92093

TELEPHONE: (714) 452-2528

LIST NAMES OF BRANCHES WITH
SEPARATE POLICIES:
Scripps Institute of
Oceanography
Biomedical Library
University Hosptial Library

BOOKS:
Will Lend: Yes
Length of Loan: 3-4 weeks
Renewable: Yes
Charges: None, except postage
reimbursement
Average Turnaround Time:
4 days
If you have indicated that a
book is not to be lent, will
you on receipt of a letter
from the requesting library
search the index for given
entries? (Not answered)

PERIODICALS:
Bound: Will not lend
Unbound: Will not lend
Loan Period: N/A
Renewable: N/A
Will lend if article exceeds
_____ number of pages (Not
answered)

MICROFORMS:
Will Lend: Yes
Specific Types of Microforms:
(Not answered)

GOVERNMENT PUBLICATIONS:
Will Lend: Yes

DISSERTATIONS:
Will Lend: Yes

THESES:
Will Lend: Yes

AUDIO-VISUAL MATERIALS:
Records: Will not lend
Cassettes: Will not lend
Other (slides, filmstrips,
etc.): Will not lend

COMPUTER SOFTWARE:
Will Lend: No

PHOTODUPLICATION SERVICE:
No charge up to 0 exposures
Charge Per Exposure: 25¢
Minimum/handling Fee: $2.50
min./ $3.00 handling
Average Turnaround Time:
4 days

MICROFILMING SERVICE:
Service Available: No
Charges: N/A

DO YOU CHARGE THE BORROWING
LIBRARY FOR POSTAGE? Yes

FOR HOW LONG DO YOU SUSPEND ILL
SERVICE OVER THE CHRISTMAS
HOLIDAYS? No suspension

ARE THERE ANY GROUPS OF LIBRARIES
FOR WHICH YOU WAIVE FEES? IF
SO, PLEASE NAME THEM: None

UNIVERSITY OF CALIFORNIA AT SANTA BARBARA

NUC CODE: CU-SB

OCLC CODE: CUT

ADDRESS: Interlibrary Loan
University Library
University of
California
Santa Barbara, CA
93106

TELEPHONE: (805) 961-3436

LIST NAMES OF BRANCHES WITH
SEPARATE POLICIES: None

BOOKS:
Will Lend: Yes
Length of Loan: 2 weeks
Renewable: Yes
Charges: (Not answered)
Average Turnaround Time:
2-3 weeks
If you have indicated that a
book is not to be lent, will
you on receipt of a letter
from the requesting library
search the index for given
entries? (Not answered)

PERIODICALS:
Bound: Will not lend
Unbound: Will not lend
Loan Period: N/A
Renewable: N/A
Will lend if article exceeds
_____ number of pages (Not
answered)

MICROFORMS:
Will Lend: (Not answered)
Specific Types of Microforms:
N/A

GOVERNMENT PUBLICATIONS:
Will Lend: Yes

DISSERTATIONS:
Will Lend: Yes

THESES:
Will Lend: Yes

AUDIO-VISUAL MATERIALS:
Records: Will not lend
Cassettes: Will not lend
Other (slides, filmstrips,
etc.): (Not answered)

COMPUTER SOFTWARE:
Will Lend: (Not answered)

PHOTODUPLICATION SERVICE:
No charge up to 20 exposures
Charge Per Exposure: 10¢
Minimum/handling Fee: None
Average Turnaround Time:
2 weeks

MICROFILMING SERVICE:
Service Available: (Not
answered)
Charges: N/A

DO YOU CHARGE THE BORROWING
LIBRARY FOR POSTAGE? No

FOR HOW LONG DO YOU SUSPEND ILL
SERVICE OVER THE CHRISTMAS
HOLIDAYS? No suspension

ARE THERE ANY GROUPS OF LIBRARIES
FOR WHICH YOU WAIVE FEES? IF
SO, PLEASE NAME THEM: None

UNIVERSITY OF CALIFORNIA AT SANTA CRUZ

NUC CODE: CU-SC

OCLC CODE: CUZ

ADDRESS: Interlibrary Loan
           The University Library
           University of
             California
           Santa Cruz, CA 95064

TELEPHONE: (408) 429-2234

LIST NAMES OF BRANCHES WITH
  SEPARATE POLICIES: None

BOOKS:
  Will Lend: Yes
  Length of Loan: 3 weeks from
    date of receipt
  Renewable: Yes
  Charges: None
  Average Turnaround Time:
    3-4 days
  If you have indicated that a
    book is not to be lent, will
    you on receipt of a letter
    from the requesting library
    search the index for given
    entries? No

PERIODICALS:
  Bound: Will lend,
    conditionally
  Unbound: Will not lend
  Loan Period: 1 week from
    date of receipt
  Renewable: No
  Will lend if article exceeds
    _____ number of pages (Not
    answered)

MICROFORMS:
  Will Lend: No
  Specific Types of Microforms:
    N/A

GOVERNMENT PUBLICATIONS:
  Will Lend: Yes

DISSERTATIONS:
  Will Lend: Yes

THESES:
  Will Lend: Yes

AUDIO-VISUAL MATERIALS:
  Records: Will not lend
  Cassettes: Will not lend
  Other (slides, filmstrips,
    etc.): Will not lend

COMPUTER SOFTWARE:
  Will Lend: No

PHOTODUPLICATION SERVICE:
  No charge up to 0 exposures
  Charge Per Exposure: 7¢
  Minimum/handling Fee: $4.00
  Average Turnaround Time:
    3-4 days

MICROFILMING SERVICE:
  Service Available: No
  Charges: N/A

DO YOU CHARGE THE BORROWING
  LIBRARY FOR POSTAGE? No

FOR HOW LONG DO YOU SUSPEND ILL
  SERVICE OVER THE CHRISTMAS
  HOLIDAYS? No suspension

ARE THERE ANY GROUPS OF LIBRARIES
  FOR WHICH YOU WAIVE FEES? IF
  SO, PLEASE NAME THEM: None

UNIVERSITY OF SAN DIEGO

NUC CODE: (Not answered)

OCLC CODE: CDU

ADDRESS: Interlibrary Loans
           James S. Copley
             Library
           University of San Diego
           Alcala Park
           San Diego, CA 92110

TELEPHONE: (714) 291-6480, X4312

LIST NAMES OF BRANCHES WITH
  SEPARATE POLICIES: None

BOOKS:
  Will Lend: Yes
  Length of Loan: 3 weeks
  Renewable: Yes
  Charges: None
  Average Turnaround Time:
    3 days
  If you have indicated that a
    book is not to be lent, will
    you on receipt of a letter
    from the requesting library
    search the index for given
    entries? (Not answered)

PERIODICALS:
  Bound: Will not lend
  Unbound: Will not lend
  Loan Period: N/A
  Renewable: N/A
  Will lend if article exceeds
    _____ number of pages (Not
    answered)

MICROFORMS:
  Will Lend: Yes
  Specific Types of Microforms:
    We have a limited number of
    National Archive microfilms.

GOVERNMENT PUBLICATIONS:
  Will Lend: No

DISSERTATIONS:
  Will Lend: Yes

THESES:
  Will Lend: Yes

AUDIO-VISUAL MATERIALS:
  Records: Will not lend
  Cassettes: Will not lend
  Other (slides, filmstrips,
    etc.): Will not lend

COMPUTER SOFTWARE:
  Will Lend: No

PHOTODUPLICATION SERVICE:
  No charge up to _____ exposures
    (Not answered)
  Charge Per Exposure: 15¢ per
    page above 10 pages
  Minimum/handling Fee: $2.00
    up to 10 pages
  Average Turnaround Time:
    3 days

MICROFILMING SERVICE:
  Service Available: No
  Charges: N/A

DO YOU CHARGE THE BORROWING LIBRARY
  FOR POSTAGE? No

FOR HOW LONG DO YOU SUSPEND ILL
  SERVICE OVER THE CHRISTMAS
  HOLIDAYS? 4 days

ARE THERE ANY GROUPS OF LIBRARIES
  FOR WHICH YOU WAIVE FEES? IF
  SO, PLEASE NAME THEM: None

UNIVERSITY OF SAN FRANCISCO

NUC CODE: CSfU

OCLC CODE: CUF

ADDRESS: Interlibrary Loan
Gleeson Library
University of San
Francisco
San Francisco, CA 94117

TELEPHONE: (415) 666-6686

LIST NAMES OF BRANCHES WITH
SEPARATE POLICIES: None

BOOKS:
Will Lend: Yes
Length of Loan: 4 weeks
Renewable: Yes
Charges: None
Average Turnaround Time:
3 days
If you have indicated that a
book is not to be lent, will
you on receipt of a letter
from the requesting library
search the index for given
entries? (Not answered)

PERIODICALS:
Bound: Will not lend
Unbound: Will not lend
Loan Period: N/A
Renewable: N/A
Will lend if article exceeds
_____ number of pages (Not
answered)

MICROFORMS:
Will Lend: No
Specific Types of Microforms:
N/A

GOVERNMENT PUBLICATIONS:
Will Lend: Yes

DISSERTATIONS:
Will Lend: No

THESES:
Will Lend: Yes

AUDIO-VISUAL MATERIALS:
Records: Will not lend
Cassettes: Will not lend
Other (slides, filmstrips,
etc.): Will not lend

COMPUTER SOFTWARE:
Will Lend: No

PHOTODUPLICATION SERVICE:
No charge up to 10 exposures
Charge Per Exposure: None
Minimum/handling Fee: None
Average Turnaround Time:
3 days

MICROFILMING SERVICE:
Service Available: No
Charges: N/A

DO YOU CHARGE THE BORROWING LIBRARY
FOR POSTAGE? Only if they
charge us.

FOR HOW LONG DO YOU SUSPEND ILL
SERVICE OVER THE CHRISTMAS
HOLIDAYS? No suspension

ARE THERE ANY GROUPS OF LIBRARIES
FOR WHICH YOU WAIVE FEES? IF
SO, PLEASE NAME THEM: N/A

UNIVERSITY OF SANTA CLARA

NUC CODE: CStclU

OCLC CODE: STA

ADDRESS: Interlibrary Loan
Orradre Library
University of Santa
Clara
Santa Clara, CA 95053

TELEPHONE: (408) 984-4415

LIST NAMES OF BRANCHES WITH
SEPARATE POLICIES: None

BOOKS:
Will Lend: Yes
Length of Loan: 3 weeks
Renewable: Yes
Charges: None
Average Turnaround Time:
2 days
If you have indicated that a
book is not to be lent, will
you on receipt of a letter
from the requesting library
search the index for given
entries? (Not answered)

PERIODICALS:
Bound: Will not lend
Unbound: Will not lend
Loan Period: N/A
Renewable: N/A
Will lend if article exceeds
_____ number of pages (Not
answered)

MICROFORMS:
Will Lend: Yes
Specific Types of Microforms:
Film, card, fiche

GOVERNMENT PUBLICATIONS:
Will Lend: Yes

DISSERTATIONS:
Will Lend: Yes, if second copy
is available

THESES:
Will Lend: Yes, if second copy
is available

AUDIO-VISUAL MATERIALS:
Records: Will not lend
Cassettes: Will not lend
Other (slides, filmstrips,
etc.): Will not lend

COMPUTER SOFTWARE:
Will Lend: No

PHOTODUPLICATION SERVICE:
No charge up to _____ exposures
(Not answered)
Charge Per Exposure: 10¢
Minimum/handling Fee: $2.10
Average Turnaround Time:
2 days

MICROFILMING SERVICE:
Service Available: No
Charges: N/A

DO YOU CHARGE THE BORROWING
LIBRARY FOR POSTAGE? No

FOR HOW LONG DO YOU SUSPEND ILL
SERVICE OVER THE CHRISTMAS
HOLIDAYS? Dec.15-Jan.1

ARE THERE ANY GROUPS OF LIBRARIES
FOR WHICH YOU WAIVE FEES? IF
SO, PLEASE NAME THEM: None

UNIVERSITY OF SOUTHERN CALIFORNIA

NUC CODE: CLSU

OCLC CODE: CSL

ADDRESS: Interlibrary Loan
Library
University of Southern
California
University Park
Los Angeles, CA 90007

TELEPHONE: (213) 743-2540

LIST NAMES OF BRANCHES WITH
SEPARATE POLICIES:
Law Library
Norris Medical
Hancock Library
Dentistry Library
Gerontology Library

BOOKS:
Will Lend: Yes
Length of Loan: 2 weeks
Renewable: Yes
Charges: (Not answered)
Average Turnaround Time:
(Not answered)
If you have indicated that a
book is not to be lent, will
you on receipt of a letter
from the requesting library
search the index for given
entries? (Not answered)

PERIODICALS:
Bound: Will not lend
Unbound: Will not lend
Loan Period: N/A
Renewable: N/A
Will lend if article exceeds
_____ number of pages (Not
answered)

MICROFORMS:
Will Lend: (Not answered)
Specific Types of Microforms:
N/A

GOVERNMENT PUBLICATIONS:
Will Lend: (Not answered)

DISSERTATIONS:
Will Lend: No

THESES:
Will Lend: No

AUDIO-VISUAL MATERIALS:
Records: (Not answered)
Cassettes: (Not answered)
Other (slides, filmstrips,
etc.): (Not answered)

COMPUTER SOFTWARE:
Will Lend: (Not answered)

PHOTODUPLICATION SERVICE:
No charge up to 0 exposures
Charges: Write for prices
Average Turnaround Time:
(Not answered)

MICROFILMING SERVICE:
Service Available: Yes
Charges: Write for prices

DO YOU CHARGE THE BORROWING
LIBRARY FOR POSTAGE? Yes

FOR HOW LONG DO YOU SUSPEND ILL
SERVICE OVER THE CHRISTMAS
HOLIDAYS? Dec.12-28

ARE THERE ANY GROUPS OF LIBRARIES
FOR WHICH YOU WAIVE FEES? IF
SO, PLEASE NAME THEM: (Not
answered)

UNIVERSITY OF THE PACIFIC

NUC CODE: CStoC

OCLC CODE: None

ADDRESS: Interlibrary Loan
University of the
Pacific Library
Stockton, CA 95211

TELEPHONE: (209) 946-2196

LIST NAMES OF BRANCHES WITH
SEPARATE POLICIES:
Music Library: most
material is non-
circulating
Stuart Library of Western
Americana: a non-
circulating collection

BOOKS:
Will Lend: Yes
Length of Loan: 2-3 weeks use
Renewable: Yes
Charges: None
Average Turnaround Time: As
soon as possible
If you have indicated that a
book is not to be lent, will
you on receipt of a letter
from the requesting library
search the index for given
entries? Yes

PERIODICALS:
Bound: Will lend
Unbound: Will lend
Loan Period: 1 week use
Renewable: Yes
Will lend if article exceeds
20 pages

MICROFORMS:
Will Lend: Yes
Specific Types of Microforms:
Film, fiche, cards

GOVERNMENT PUBLICATIONS:
Will Lend: Yes

DISSERTATIONS:
Will Lend: Yes

THESES:
Will Lend: Yes

AUDIO-VISUAL MATERIALS:
Records: Will not lend
Cassettes: Will not lend
Other (slides, filmstrips,
etc.): Will not lend

COMPUTER SOFTWARE:
Will Lend: No

PHOTODUPLICATION SERVICE:
No charge up to 20 exposures
Charge Per Exposure: 5¢
Minimum/handling Fee: None
Average Turnaround Time:
As soon as possible

MICROFILMING SERVICE:
Service Available: No
Charges: N/A

DO YOU CHARGE THE BORROWING
LIBRARY FOR POSTAGE? No,
unless first-class mailing
(books, etc.) is required

FOR HOW LONG DO YOU SUSPEND ILL
SERVICE OVER THE CHRISTMAS
HOLIDAYS? About 1 week

ARE THERE ANY GROUPS OF LIBRARIES
FOR WHICH YOU WAIVE FEES? IF
SO, PLEASE NAME THEM: 49-99/
CAL Library System

NOTE: ALL ILL'S ARE HANDLED
THROUGH THE MAIN (IRVING
MARTIN) LIBRARY

VENTURA COUNTY LIBRARY

NUC CODE: None

OCLC CODE: None

ADDRESS: Interlibrary Loan
          Ventura County Library
            Services Agency
          P. O. Box 771
          Ventura, CA 93002

TELEPHONE: (805) 654-2635

LIST NAMES OF BRANCHES WITH
  SEPARATE POLICIES: None

BOOKS:
  Will Lend: Yes
  Length of Loan: 1 month
  Renewable: Yes
  Charges: None
  Average Turnaround Time:
   1 week
  If you have indicated that a
    book is not to be lent, will
    you on receipt of a letter
    from the requesting library
    search the index for given
    entries? Yes, for genealogy,
     local history, and some
      reference titles.

PERIODICALS:
  Bound: Will not lend
  Unbound: Will not lend
  Loan Period: N/A
  Renewable: N/A
  Will lend if article exceeds
   _____ number of pages (Not
  answered)

MICROFORMS:
  Will Lend: No
  Specific Types of Microforms:
   N/A

GOVERNMENT PUBLICATIONS:
  Will Lend: Yes

DISSERTATIONS:
  Will Lend: No

THESES:
  Will Lend: No

AUDIO-VISUAL MATERIALS:
  Records: Will not lend
  Cassettes: Will not lend
  Other (slides, filmstrips,
    etc.): Will not lend

COMPUTER SOFTWARE:
  Will Lend: No

PHOTODUPLICATION SERVICE:
  No charge up to 10 exposures
  Charge Per Exposure: 10¢
  Minimum/handling Fee: None
  Average Turnaround Time:
   1 week

MICROFILMING SERVICE:
  Service Available: No
  Charges: N/A

DO YOU CHARGE THE BORROWING LIBRARY
FOR POSTAGE? No

FOR HOW LONG DO YOU SUSPEND ILL
  SERVICE OVER THE CHRISTMAS
  HOLIDAYS? No suspension

ARE THERE ANY GROUPS OF LIBRARIES
  FOR WHICH YOU WAIVE FEES? IF
  SO, PLEASE NAME THEM: None

AURARIA LIBRARY

NUC CODE: CoU-Da

OCLC CODE: COA

ADDRESS: Interlibrary Loan
           Auraria Library
           Lawrence at 11th
           Denver, CO 80204

TELEPHONE: (303) 629-2562

LIST NAMES OF BRANCHES WITH
   SEPARATE POLICIES: None

BOOKS:
   Will Lend: Yes
   Length of Loan: 3 weeks
   Renewable: Yes
   Charges: $8.00
   Average Turnaround Time:
   1 week
   If you have indicated that a
   book is not to be lent, will
   you on receipt of a letter
   from the requesting library
   search the index for given
   entries? No

PERIODICALS:
   Bound: Will not lend
   Unbound: Will not lend
   Loan Period: N/A
   Renewable: N/A
   Will lend if article exceeds
   _____ number of pages (Not
   answered)

MICROFORMS:
   Will Lend: Yes
   Specific Types of Microforms:
   Books in microform

GOVERNMENT PUBLICATIONS:
   Will Lend: Yes

DISSERTATIONS:
   Kept at CU-Boulder

THESES:
   Kept at CU-Boulder

AUDIO-VISUAL MATERIALS:
   Records: Will not lend
   Cassettes: Will not lend
   Other (slides, filmstrips,
   etc.): Will not lend

COMPUTER SOFTWARE:
   Will Lend: No

PHOTODUPLICATION SERVICE:
   No charge up to 0 exposures
   Charge Per Exposure: (Not
   answered)
   Minimum/handling Fee: $4.00
   per transaction
   Average Turnaround Time:
   1 week

MICROFILMING SERVICE:
   Service Available: No
   Charges: N/A

DO YOU CHARGE THE BORROWING
   LIBRARY FOR POSTAGE? No

FOR HOW LONG DO YOU SUSPEND ILL
   SERVICE OVER THE CHRISTMAS
   HOLIDAYS? Dec.23-Jan.2

ARE THERE ANY GROUPS OF LIBRARIES
   FOR WHICH YOU WAIVE FEES? IF
   SO, PLEASE NAME THEM: All in-
   state, except corporations.
   Out-of-state libraries from
   whom we borrow frequently.

COLORADO COLLEGE

NUC CODE: CoCC

OCLC CODE: COC

ADDRESS: Interlibrary Loan
           Tutt Library
           Colorado College
           Cascade and San Rafael
             Streets
           Colorado Springs, CO
           80903

TELEPHONE: (303) 473-2233, X664

LIST NAMES OF BRANCHES WITH
   SEPARATE POLICIES: (Not
   answered)

BOOKS:
   Will Lend: Yes
   Length of Loan: 2 weeks
   Renewable: Yes
   Charges: (Not answered)
   Average Turnaround Time: (Not
   answered)
   If you have indicated that a
   book is not to be lent, will
   you on receipt of a letter
   from the requesting library
   search the index for given
   entries? (Not answered)

PERIODICALS:
   Bound: Will not lend
   Unbound: Will not lend
   Loan Period: N/A
   Renewable: N/A
   Will lend if article exceeds
   _____ number of pages (Not
   answered)

MICROFORMS:
   Will Lend: No
   Specific Types of Microforms:
   N/A

GOVERNMENT PUBLICATIONS:
   Will Lend: Yes

DISSERTATIONS:
   Will Lend: (Not answered)

THESES:
   Will Lend: (Not answered)

AUDIO-VISUAL MATERIALS:
   Records: (Not answered)
   Cassettes: (Not answered)
   Other (slides, filmstrips,
   etc.): (Not answered)

COMPUTER SOFTWARE:
   Will Lend: (Not answered)

PHOTODUPLICATION SERVICE:
   No charge up to 10 exposures
   Charge Per Exposure: 10¢
   Minimum/handling Fee: None
   Average Turnaround Time: (Not
   answered)

MICROFILMING SERVICE:
   Service Available: No
   Charges: N/A

DO YOU CHARGE THE BORROWING LIBRARY
   FOR POSTAGE? (Not answered)

FOR HOW LONG DO YOU SUSPEND ILL
   SERVICE OVER THE CHRISTMAS
   HOLIDAYS? 2 weeks

ARE THERE ANY GROUPS OF LIBRARIES
   FOR WHICH YOU WAIVE FEES? IF
   SO, PLEASE NAME THEM: (Not
   answered)

COLORADO MOUNTAIN COLLEGE

NUC CODE: (Not answered)

OCLC CODE: (Not answered)

ADDRESS: Interlibrary Loan
Colorado Mountain
    College
West Campus Learning
    Center
3000 County Road 114
Glenwood Springs, CO
    81601

TELEPHONE: (303) 945-7481

LIST NAMES OF BRANCHES WITH
    SEPARATE POLICIES: None

BOOKS:
    Will Lend: Yes
    Length of Loan: 3 weeks
    Renewable: Yes
    Charges: None
    Average Turnaround Time:
        (Not answered)
    If you have indicated that a
        book is not to be lent, will
        you on receipt of a letter
        from the requesting library
        search the index for given
        entries? (Not answered)

PERIODICALS:
    Bound: Will not lend
    Unbound: Will not lend
    Loan Period: N/A
    Renewable: N/A
    Will lend if article exceeds
        _____ number of pages (Not
        answered)

MICROFORMS:
    Will Lend: No
    Specific Types of Microforms:
    N/A

GOVERNMENT PUBLICATIONS:
    Will Lend: No

DISSERTATIONS:
    Will Lend: No

THESES:
    Will Lend: No

AUDIO-VISUAL MATERIALS:
    Records: Will not lend
    Cassettes: Will not lend
    Other (slides, filmstrips,
        etc.): Will not lend

COMPUTER SOFTWARE:
    Will Lend: No

PHOTODUPLICATION SERVICE:
    No charge up to _____
        exposures (Not answered)
    Charge Per Exposure: (Not
        answered)
    Minimum/handling Fee: (Not
        answered)
    Average Turnaround Time:
        (Not answered)

MICROFILMING SERVICE:
    Service Available: No
    Charges: N/A

DO YOU CHARGE THE BORROWING
    LIBRARY FOR POSTAGE? No

FOR HOW LONG DO YOU SUSPEND ILL
    SERVICE OVER THE CHRISTMAS
    HOLIDAYS? No suspension

ARE THERE ANY GROUPS OF LIBRARIES
    FOR WHICH YOU WAIVE FEES? IF
    SO, PLEASE NAME THEM: (Not
        answered)

COLORADO STATE LIBRARY

NUC CODE: (Not answered)

OCLC CODE: (Not answered)

ADDRESS: Interlibrary Loan
Library Development
    Services
Colorado State Library
1362 Lincoln St.
Denver, CO 80203

TELEPHONE: (303) 866-2174

THIS LIBRARY LOANS ONLY COLORADO
GOVERNMENT DOCUMENTS

COLORADO STATE UNIVERSITY

NUC CODE:　CoFS

OCLC CODE:　COF

ADDRESS:　Interlibrary Loan
　　　　　Libraries
　　　　　Colorado State
　　　　　University
　　　　　Ft. Collins, CO 80523

TELEPHONE:　(303) 491-5911

LIST NAMES OF BRANCHES WITH
　SEPARATE POLICIES:　None

BOOKS:
　Will Lend:　Yes
　Length of Loan:　2 weeks
　Renewable:　Yes
　Charges:　(Not answered)
　Average Turnaround Time:
　　(Not answered)
　If you have indicated that a
　　book is not to be lent, will
　　you on receipt of a letter
　　from the requesting library
　　search the index for given
　　entries?　(Not answered)

PERIODICALS:
　Bound:　Will not lend
　Unbound:　Will not lend
　Loan Period:　N/A
　Renewable:　N/A
　Will lend if article exceeds
　　_____ number of pages (Not
　　answered)

MICROFORMS:
　Will Lend:　Yes
　Specific Types of Microforms:
　　(Not answered)

GOVERNMENT PUBLICATIONS:
　Will Lend:　Yes

DISSERTATIONS:
　Will Lend:　No.　Available
　　from University Microfilms

THESES:
　Will Lend:　Yes, if circulat-
　　ing copy available

AUDIO-VISUAL MATERIALS:
　Records:　(Not answered)
　Cassettes:　(Not answered)
　Other (slides, filmstrips,
　　etc.):　(Not answered)

COMPUTER SOFTWARE:
　Will Lend:　(Not answered)

PHOTODUPLICATION SERVICE:
　No charge up to 0 exposures
　Charges--Colorado libraries:
　　COLONET libraries:　15¢ per
　　copy plus a service and
　　handling fee of $4.00
　　Non-COLONET, non-profit:
　　$3.00 minimum charge; rate
　　of 15¢ per page
　　Non-COLONET, profit making:
　　20¢ per copy plus a
　　service and handling fee
　　of $5.00
　Charges--Non-Colorado U. S.
　　libraries;
　　Academic:　15¢ per copy plus
　　a service and handling fee
　　of $4.00
　　Non-academic, non-profit:
　　25¢ per copy plus a service
　　and handling fee of $5.00
　　Profit making:
　　25¢ per copy plus a service
　　and handling fee of $15.00

MICROFILMING SERVICE:
　Service Available:　(Not
　　answered)
　Charges:　(Not answered)

DO YOU CHARGE THE BORROWING
LIBRARY FOR POSTAGE? (Not
answered)

FOR HOW LONG DO YOU SUSPEND ILL
SERVICE OVER THE CHRISTMAS
HOLIDAYS?　(Not answered)

ARE THERE ANY GROUPS OF LIBRARIES
FOR WHICH YOU WAIVE FEES?　IF
SO, PLEASE NAME THEM:　(Not
answered)

FORT COLLINS PUBLIC LIBRARY

NUC CODE:　(Not answered)

OCLC CODE:　(Not answered)

ADDRESS:　Interlibrary Loan
　　　　　Fort Collins Public
　　　　　Library
　　　　　201 Peterson St.
　　　　　Fort Collins, CO　80524

TELEPHONE:　(303) 493-4422

LIST NAMES OF BRANCHES WITH
　SEPARATE POLICIES:　No branches

BOOKS:
　Will Lend:　Yes
　Length of Loan:　3 weeks
　Renewable:　Yes
　Charges:　(Not answered)
　Average Turnaround Time:
　　10 days-2 weeks.　It is usual
　　to have to place reserves for
　　Ill requests.
　If you have indicated that a
　　book is not to be lent, will
　　you on receipt of a letter
　　from the requesting library
　　search the index for given
　　entries?　(Not answered)

PERIODICALS:
　Bound:　Will not lend
　Unbound:　Will not lend
　Loan Period:　N/A
　Renewable:　N/A
　Will lend if article exceeds
　　_____ number of pages (Not
　　answered)
　Will photocopy if exact title,
　　date, page, article title, and
　　article author are given.

MICROFORMS:
　Will Lend:　No
　Specific Types of Microforms:
　　N/A

GOVERNMENT PUBLICATIONS:
　Will Lend:　Yes, but collection
　　is limited.

DISSERTATIONS:
　Will Lend:　Yes, but collection
　　is extremely limited.

THESES:
　Will Lend:　Yes, but collection
　　is extremely limited.

AUDIO-VISUAL MATERIALS:
　Records:　Will not lend
　Cassettes:　Will not lend
　Other (slides, filmstrips,
　　etc.):　(Not answered)

COMPUTER SOFTWARE:　N/A

PHOTODUPLICATION SERVICE:
　No charge unless search for
　　material is required.
　Charge Per Exposure:　(Not
　　answered)
　Minimum/handling Fee:　(Not
　　answered)
　Microform Search and Copy:
　　$5.00 minimum
　Average Turnaround Time:　1 day,
　　depending upon availability
　　of materials.

MICROFILMING SERVICE:
　Service Available:　No
　Charges:　N/A

DO YOU CHARGE THE BORROWING LIBRARY
FOR POSTAGE?　At present, no.

FOR HOW LONG DO YOU SUSPEND ILL
SERVICE OVER THE CHRISTMAS
HOLIDAYS?　Legal holidays only.

ARE THERE ANY GROUPS OF LIBRARIES
FOR WHICH YOU WAIVE FEES?　IF
SO, PLEASE NAME THEM:　(Not
answered)

JEFFERSON COUNTY PUBLIC LIBRARY

NUC CODE: COGJ

OCLC CODE: (Not answered)

ADDRESS: Interlibrary Loan
Jefferson County Public
Library
10200 W. 20th Ave.
Lakewood, CO 80215

TELEPHONE: (303) 238-8411, X292

LIST NAMES OF BRANCHES WITH
SEPARATE POLICIES: None

BOOKS:
Will Lend: Yes
Length of Loan: 3 weeks
Renewable: Yes
Charges: Only if lost or
damaged
Average Turnaround Time: 1 week
If you have indicated that a
book is not to be lent, will
you on receipt of a letter
from the requesting library
search the index for given
entries? Yes

PERIODICALS:
Bound: Will not lend
Unbound: Will lend
Loan Period: 3 weeks
Renewable: Yes
Will lend if article exceeds
_____ number of pages (Not
answered)

MICROFORMS:
Will Lend: No
Specific Types of Microforms:
N/A

GOVERNMENT PUBLICATIONS:
Will Lend: Yes

DISSERTATIONS:
Will Lend: No

THESES:
Will Lend: No

AUDIO-VISUAL MATERIALS
Records: Will not lend
Cassettes: Will not lend
Other (slides, filmstrips,
etc.): Will not lend

COMPUTER SOFTWARE:
Will Lend: No

PHOTODUPLICATION SERVICE:
No charge up to 10 exposures
Charge Per Exposure: 10¢
Minimum/handling Fee: None
Average Turnaround Time: 1 week

MICROFILMING SERVICE:
Service Available: No

DO YOU CHARGE THE BORROWING LIBRARY
FOR POSTAGE? No, but they pay
return postage

FOR HOW LONG DO YOU SUSPEND ILL
SERVICE OVER THE CHRISTMAS
HOLIDAYS? Not at all

ARE THERE ANY GROUPS OF LIBRARIES
FOR WHICH YOU WAIVE FEES? IF
SO, PLEASE NAME THEM: VA--waive
postage--they pay both ways

MESA COLLEGE

NUC CODE: CoGjM

OCLC CODE: COM

ADDRESS: Interlibrary Loan
Mesa College Library
P. O. Box 2647
Grand Junction, CO
81502

TELEPHONE: (303) 248-1244

LIST NAMES OF BRANCHES WITH
SEPARATE POLICIES: None

BOOKS:
Will Lend: Yes
Length of Loan: 3 weeks
Renewable: Yes
Charges: None
Average Turnaround Time:
48 hours
If you have indicated that a
book is not to be lent, will
you on receipt of a letter
from the requesting library
search the index for given
entries? (Not answered)

PERIODICALS:
Bound: Will lend in special
circumstances
Unbound: Will lend in special
circumstances
Loan Period: 1 week use
Renewable: No
Will lend if article exceeds
_____ number of pages (Not
answered)

MICROFORMS:
Will Lend: Yes
Specific Types of Microforms:
Magazines and newspapers,
Bendix field reports

GOVERNMENT PUBLICATIONS:
Will Lend: Yes

DISSERTATIONS:
Will Lend: (Not owned)

THESES:
Will Lend: (Not owned)

AUDIO-VISUAL MATERIALS:
Records: Will not lend
Cassettes: Will not lend
Other (slides, filmstrips,
etc.): Will not lend

COMPUTER SOFTWARE:
Will Lend: No

PHOTODUPLICATION SERVICE:
No charge up to 10 exposures
Charge Per Exposure: 10¢
Minimum/handling Fee: None
Average Turnaround Time:
48 hours

MICROFILMING SERVICE:
Service Available: No
Charges: N/A

DO YOU CHARGE THE BORROWING LIBRARY
FOR POSTAGE? No

FOR HOW LONG DO YOU SUSPEND ILL
SERVICE OVER THE CHRISTMAS
HOLIDAYS? 7-10 days

ARE THERE ANY GROUPS OF LIBRARIES
FOR WHICH YOU WAIVE FEES? IF
SO, PLEASE NAME THEM:
Consortium of State Colleges
in Colorado

PENROSE PUBLIC LIBRARY

NUC CODE: CoC

OCLC CODE: N/A

ADDRESS: Interlibrary Loan
Penrose Public Library
P. O. Box 1579
Colorado Springs, CO
80901

TELEPHONE: (303) 473-2080, X258

LIST NAMES OF BRANCHES WITH
SEPARATE POLICIES:
Pikes Peak Regional

BOOKS:
Will Lend: Yes
Length of Loan: 3 weeks use
Renewable: Yes
Charges: None for loans
Average Turnaround Time: 2 days
If you have indicated that a
book is not to be lent, will
you on receipt of a letter
from the requesting library
search the index for given
entries? (Not answered)

PERIODICALS:
Bound: Will not lend
Unbound: Will not lend
Loan Period: N/A
Renewable: N/A
Will lend if article exceeds
_____ number of pages (N/A)

MICROFORMS:
Will Lend: Yes
Specific Types of Microforms:
Some microfilm (newspapers,
etc.)

GOVERNMENT PUBLICATIONS:
Will Lend: Yes

DISSERTATIONS:
Will Lend: Yes

THESES:
Will Lend: Yes

AUDIO-VISUAL MATERIALS:
Records: Will not lend
Cassettes: Will not lend
Other (slides, filmstrips,
etc.): Will not lend

COMPUTER SOFTWARE:
Will Lend: No

PHOTODUPLICATION SERVICE:
No charge up to 10 exposures
Charge Per Exposure: 10¢
Minimum/handling Fee: None
Average Turnaround Time: 2 days

MICROFILMING SERVICE:
Service Available: No
Charges: N/A

DO YOU CHARGE THE BORROWING LIBRARY
FOR POSTAGE? No

FOR HOW LONG DO YOU SUSPEND ILL
SERVICE OVER THE CHRISTMAS
HOLIDAYS? One week

ARE THERE ANY GROUPS OF LIBRARIES
FOR WHICH YOU WAIVE FEES? IF
SO, PLEASE NAME THEM: (Not
answered)

UNITED STATES DEPARTMENT OF THE INTERIOR-- BUREAU OF RECLAMATION

NUC CODE: CoDBR

OCLC CODE: UDR

ADDRESS: Interlibrary Loan
Library
Bureau of Reclamation
Engineering and
Research Center
P. O. Box 25007
Denver Federal Center
Denver, CO 80225

TELEPHONE: (303) 234-3019

LIST NAMES OF BRANCHES WITH
SEPARATE POLICIES: None

BOOKS:
Will Lend: Yes
Length of Loan: 30 days
Renewable: Yes
Charges: None
Average Turnaround Time:
(Not answered)
If you have indicated that a
book is not to be lent, will
you on receipt of a letter
from the requesting library
search the index for given
entries? (Not answered)

PERIODICALS:
Bound: Will not lend
Unbound: Will not lend
Loan Period: N/A
Renewable: N/A
Will lend if article exceeds
_____ number of pages (Not
answered)

MICROFORMS:
Will Lend: (Not answered)
Specific Types of Microforms:
N/A

GOVERNMENT PUBLICATIONS:
Will Lend: Yes

DISSERTATIONS:
Will Lend: Yes

THESES:
Will Lend: Yes

AUDIO-VISUAL MATERIALS:
Records: Do not own
Cassettes: Do not own
Other (slides, filmstrips,
etc.): Do not own

COMPUTER SOFTWARE:
Will Lend: (Not answered)

PHOTODUPLICATION SERVICE:
We are not set up for this
service

MICROFILMING SERVICE:
Service Available: No
Charges: N/A

DO YOU CHARGE THE BORROWING
LIBRARY FOR POSTAGE? No

FOR HOW LONG DO YOU SUSPEND ILL
SERVICE OVER THE CHRISTMAS
HOLIDAYS? No suspension

ARE THERE ANY GROUPS OF LIBRARIES
FOR WHICH YOU WAIVE FEES? IF
SO, PLEASE NAME THEM: None

UNIVERSITY OF COLORADO

NUC CODE: CoU

OCLC CODE: COD

ADDRESS: Interlibrary Loan
University Libraries
Campus Box 184
University of Colorado
Boulder, CO 80309

TELEPHONE: (303) 492-6176

LIST NAMES OF BRANCHES WITH
SEPARATE POLICIES: None

BOOKS:
Will Lend: Yes
Length of Loan: 2 weeks use
Renewable: Yes
Charges: None
Average Turnaround Time:
(Not answered)
If you have indicated that a
book is not to be lent, will
you on receipt of a letter
from the requesting library
search the index for given
entries? Yes

PERIODICALS:
Bound: Will not lend
Unbound: Will not lend
Loan Period: N/A
Renewable: N/A
Will lend if article exceeds
10 pages

MICROFORMS:
Will lend microcards, microfilm, microprint. Will not
lend microfiche.

GOVERNMENT PUBLICATIONS:
Will Lend: Yes

DISSERTATIONS:
Will Lend: Yes, if pre-1955.
(1955 to present available
through University
Microfilms)

THESES:
Will Lend: Yes

AUDIO-VISUAL MATERIALS:
Records: Will not lend
Cassettes: Will not lend
Other (slides, filmstrips,
etc.): Will not lend

COMPUTER SOFTWARE:
Will Lend: No

PHOTODUPLICATION SERVICE:
In-State:
No charge up to 30 exposures
Charge Per Exposure: 10¢ for
each exposure after 1st 30
Minimum/handling Fee: None
Average Turnaround Time:
(Not answered)

Out-of-State:
No charge up to 0 exposures
Charge Per Exposure: 15¢
Minimum/handling Fee: $4.00
(includes 10 pages)
Average Turnaround Time:
(Not answered)

MICROFILMING SERVICE:
Service Available: Yes
Charges: Request charges
from library

DO YOU CHARGE THE BORROWING
LIBRARY FOR POSTAGE? No

FOR HOW LONG DO YOU SUSPEND ILL
SERVICE OVER THE CHRISTMAS
HOLIDAYS? Dec.10-Jan.5 for
books only

ARE THERE ANY GROUPS OF LIBRARIES
FOR WHICH YOU WAIVE FEES? IF
SO, PLEASE NAME THEM:
Photocopy agreements with
CARL, MASUA; 30 pages free
copy in Colorado for public
and non-profit institutions

UNIVERSITY OF COLORADO AT COLORADO SPRINGS

NUC CODE: CoU-CS

OCLC CODE: COX

ADDRESS: Interlibrary Loan
Library
University of Colorado
at Colorado Springs
Austin Bluffs Pkwy.
P. O. Box 7150
Colorado Springs, CO
80933-7150

TELEPHONE: (303) 593-3285

LIST NAMES OF BRANCHES WITH
SEPARATE POLICIES: (Not
answered)

BOOKS:
Will Lend: Yes
Length of Loan: 3-4 weeks
Renewable: Yes
Charges: None
Average Turnaround Time:
3 days
If you have indicated that a
book is not to be lent, will
you on receipt of a letter
from the requesting library
search the index for given
entries? (Not answered)

PERIODICALS:
Bound: Will not lend
Unbound: Will not lend
Loan Period: N/A
Renewable: N/A
Will lend if article exceeds
_____ number of pages (Not
answered)

MICROFORMS:
Will Lend: No
Specific Types of Microforms:
N/A

GOVERNMENT PUBLICATIONS:
Will Lend: Yes

DISSERTATIONS:
Will Lend: (Not owned)

THESES:
Will Lend: (Not owned)

AUDIO-VISUAL MATERIALS:
Records: (Not owned)
Cassettes: (Not owned)
Other (slides, filmstrips,
etc.): (Not owned)

COMPUTER SOFTWARE:
Will Lend: (Not owned)

PHOTODUPLICATION SERVICE:
No charge up to 10 exposures
Charge Per Exposure: 10¢
Minimum/handling Fee: None
Average Turnaround Time: 3 days

MICROFILMING SERVICE:
Service Available: Yes
Charges: 10¢ per copy

DO YOU CHARGE THE BORROWING LIBRARY
FOR POSTAGE? No

FOR HOW LONG DO YOU SUSPEND ILL
SERVICE OVER THE CHRISTMAS
HOLIDAYS? None

ARE THERE ANY GROUPS OF LIBRARIES
FOR WHICH YOU WAIVE FEES? IF
SO, PLEASE NAME THEM: Willing
to participate in reciprocal
borrowing and photocopying
privileges.

UNIVERSITY OF COLORADO HEALTH SCIENCES CENTER LIBRARY

NUC CODE: COU M

OCLC CODE: (Not answered)

ADDRESS: Interlibrary Loan
University of Colorado
    Health Sciences Center
    Library
4200 East Ninth Ave.
Denver, CO 80262

TELEPHONE: (Not answered)

LIST NAMES OF BRANCHES WITH
    SEPARATE POLICIES: (Not
    answered)

BOOKS:
    Will Lend: Yes
    Length of Loan: 4 weeks
    Renewable: No
    Charges: $3.00 within Colorado
        $4.50 outside of Colorado
    Average Turnaround Time: We
        mail within 1-3 days. Average
        return to us is 2 weeks.
    If you have indicated that a
        book is not to be lent, will
        you on receipt of a letter
        from the requesting library
        search the index for given
        entries? We will mail
        contents or sections of
        indexes pertaining to
        citations.

PERIODICALS:
    Bound: Will lend those 13 years
        or older
    Unbound: Will not lend unless
        13 years or older
    Loan Period: 1 week
    Renewable: No
    Will lend if article exceeds
        _____ number of pages (Will
        not lend unless in circulating
        holdings)

MICROFORMS:
    Will Lend: No
    Specific Types of Microforms: N/A

GOVERNMENT PUBLICATIONS:
    Will Lend: No

DISSERTATIONS:
    Will Lend: Yes

THESES:
    Will Lend: Yes

AUDIO-VISUAL MATERIALS:
    Records: Will not lend
    Cassettes: Will not lend
    Other (slides, filmstrips,
        etc.): Will not lend

COMPUTER SOFTWARE:
    Will Lend: No

PHOTODUPLICATION SERVICE:
    No charge up to _____ exposures
        (Not answered)
    Charge Per Exposure: (Not
        answered)
    Minimum/handling Fee: $3.00 in
        Colorado. $4.50 outside of
        Colorado.
    Average Turnaround Time: 1-3
        days

MICROFILMING SERVICE:
    Service available: No
    Charges: N/A

DO YOU CHARGE THE BORROWING LIBRARY
    FOR POSTAGE? No--just flat fee
    for borrowing

FOR HOW LONG DO YOU SUSPEND ILL
    SERVICE OVER THE CHRISTMAS
    HOLIDAYS? Did not suspend last
    year. One month in previous
    years.

ARE THERE ANY GROUPS OF LIBRARIES
    FOR WHICH YOU WAIVE FEES? IF
    SO, PLEASE NAME THEM: Only
    local ones with rotating
    teaching programs.

UNIVERSITY OF DENVER

NUC CODE: CoDU

OCLC CODE: DVP

ADDRESS: Interlibrary Loan
University of Denver
    Libraries
Denver, CO 80208

TELEPHONE: (303) 753-2117

LIST NAMES OF BRANCHES WITH
    SEPARATE POLICIES:
    University of Denver, Law
        Library
    Iliff School of Theology
        Library

BOOKS:
    Will Lend: Yes
    Length of Loan: 4 weeks
    Renewable: No
    Charges: Reciprocal
    Average Turnaround Time:
        1 week in-state; 2 weeks
        out-of-state
    If you have indicated that a
        book is not to be lent, will
        you on receipt of a letter
        from the requesting library
        search the index for given
        entries? (Not answered)

PERIODICALS:
    Bound: Will not lend
    Unbound: Will not lend
    Loan Period: N/A
    Renewable: N/A
    Will lend if article exceeds
        _____ number of pages (Not
        answered)

MICROFORMS:
    Will Lend: Yes
    Specific Types of Microforms:
        Some microfilm, all micro-
        fiche and microcards

GOVERNMENT PUBLICATIONS:
    Will Lend: No

DISSERTATIONS:
    Will Lend: Yes, only if
        pre-1960

THESES:
    Will Lend: Yes, only if
        pre-1960

AUDIO-VISUAL MATERIALS:
    Records: Will not lend
    Cassettes: Will not lend
    Other (slides, filmstrips,
        etc.): Will not lend

COMPUTER SOFTWARE:
    Will Lend: No

PHOTODUPLICATION SERVICE:
    No charge up to 0 exposures
    Charge Per Exposure: 10¢
    Minimum/handling Fee: $1.50
        for in-state; $3.00 for out-
        of-state
    Average Turnaround Time:
        1 week in-state; 2 weeks
        out-of-state

MICROFILMING SERVICE:
    Service Available: Yes
    Service Charges: $2.50
    Minimum Charges: $10.00 if
        we own negative; $25.00 if
        we do not
    Charge Per Frame: 6¢ negative,
        $.006 positive

DO YOU CHARGE THE BORROWING
    LIBRARY FOR POSTAGE? No

FOR HOW LONG DO YOU SUSPEND ILL
    SERVICE OVER THE CHRISTMAS
    HOLIDAYS? No suspension

ARE THERE ANY GROUPS OF LIBRARIES
    FOR WHICH YOU WAIVE FEES? IF
    SO, PLEASE NAME THEM: All
    CARL libraries, KU, WyU,
    AzTes, Vtu, Co, CoCC, Cou-CS

UNIVERSITY OF NORTHERN COLORADO

NUC CODE: CoGrU

OCLC CODE: COV

ADDRESS: Interlibrary Loan
Michener Library
University of Northern
Colorado
Greeley, CO 80639

TELEPHONE: (303) 351-2580

LIST NAMES OF BRANCHES WITH
SEPARATE POLICIES: None

BOOKS:
Will Lend: Yes
Length of Loan: 2 weeks
Renewable: Yes
Charges: (Not answered)
Average Turnaround Time:
(Not answered)
If you have indicated that a
book is not to be lent, will
you on receipt of a letter
from the requesting library
search the index for given
entries? (Not answered)

PERIODICALS:
Bound: Will not lend
Unbound: Will not lend
Loan Period: N/A
Renewable: N/A
Will lend if article exceeds
_____ number of pages (Not
answered)

MICROFORMS:
Will Lend: Yes
Specific Types of Microforms:
Microfilm, microcards,
microfiche

GOVERNMENT PUBLICATIONS:
Will Lend: (Not answered)

DISSERTATIONS:
Will lend within state. Will
lend out-of-state if
unavailable from University
Microfilms or if reciprocal
agreement exists.

THESES:
Will Lend: Yes

AUDIO-VISUAL MATERIALS:
Records: Will not lend
Cassettes: Will not lend
Other (slides, filmstrips,
etc.): (Not answered)

COMPUTER SOFTWARE:
Will Lend: (Not answered)

PHOTODUPLICATION SERVICE:
No charge up to 9 exposures
Charge Per Exposure: 10¢
Minimum/handling Fee: None
Average Turnaround Time:
(Not answered)

MICROFILMING SERVICE:
Service Available: No
Charges: N/A

DO YOU CHARGE THE BORROWING
LIBRARY FOR POSTAGE? No

FOR HOW LONG DO YOU SUSPEND ILL
SERVICE OVER THE CHRISTMAS
HOLIDAYS? (Not answered)

ARE THERE ANY GROUPS OF LIBRARIES
FOR WHICH YOU WAIVE FEES? IF
SO, PLEASE NAME THEM: (Not
answered)

UNIVERSITY OF SOUTHERN COLORADO

NUC CODE: CoPS

OCLC CODE: COS

ADDRESS: Interlibrary Loan
Library
University of Southern
Colorado
Pueblo, CO 81001

TELEPHONE: (303) 549-2451

LIST NAMES OF BRANCHES WITH
SEPARATE POLICIES: None

BOOKS:
Will Lend: Yes
Length of Loan: 3 weeks use
Renewable: Yes
Charges: None
Average Turnaround Time: 1 day
If you have indicated that a
book is not to be lent, will
you on receipt of a letter
from the requesting library
search the index for given
entries? Yes

PERIODICALS:
Bound: Will not lend
Unbound: (Not answered)
Loan Period: N/A
Renewable: N/A
Will lend if article exceeds
_____ number of pages (Not
answered)

MICROFORMS:
Will Lend: No
Specific Types of Microforms:
N/A

GOVERNMENT PUBLICATIONS:
Will Lend: Yes

DISSERTATIONS:
N/A

THESES:
N/A

AUDIO-VISUAL MATERIALS:
Records: Will not lend
Cassettes: Will not lend
Other (slides, filmstrips,
etc.): Will not lend

COMPUTER SOFTWARE:
Will Lend: No

PHOTODUPLICATION SERVICE:
No charge up to 10 exposures
Charge Per Exposure: 10¢
Minimum/handling Fee: None
Average Turnaround Time: 1 day

MICROFILMING SERVICE:
Service Available: No
Charges: N/A

DO YOU CHARGE THE BORROWING LIBRARY
FOR POSTAGE? No

FOR HOW LONG DO YOU SUSPEND ILL
SERVICE OVER THE CHRISTMAS
HOLIDAYS? 1 week (between
Christmas and New Year)

ARE THERE ANY GROUPS OF LIBRARIES
FOR WHICH YOU WAIVE FEES? IF
SO, PLEASE NAME THEM: (Not
answered)

CONNECTICUT COLLEGE

NUC CODE: CtN1C

OCLC CODE: CTL

ADDRESS: Interlibrary Loan
Connecticut College
Library
New London, CT 06320

TELEPHONE: (203) 447-1911, X7213

LIST NAMES OF BRANCHES WITH
SEPARATE POLICIES: None

BOOKS:
Will Lend: Yes
Length of Loan: 1 month from
receipt
Renewable: Yes
Charges: None
Average Turnaround Time:
5 days
If you have indicated that a
book is not to be lent, will
you on receipt of a letter
from the requesting library
search the index for given
entries? (Not answered)

PERIODICALS:
Bound: Will not lend
Unbound: Will not lend
Loan Period: N/A
Renewable: N/A
Will lend if article exceeds
75 pages

MICROFORMS:
Will Lend: Yes
Specific Types of Microforms:
Microfilm, microfiche

GOVERNMENT PUBLICATIONS:
Will Lend: No

DISSERTATIONS:
Will Lend: No

THESES:
Will Lend: No

AUDIO-VISUAL MATERIALS:
Records: Will not lend
Cassettes: Will not lend
Other (slides, filmstrips,
etc.): Will not lend

COMPUTER SOFTWARE:
Will Lend: No

PHOTODUPLICATION SERVICE:
No charge up to 0 exposures
Charge Per Exposure: 15¢
Minimum/handling Fee: None
Average Turnaround Time:
1 week

MICROFILMING SERVICE:
Service Available: No
Charges: N/A

DO YOU CHARGE THE BORROWING
LIBRARY FOR POSTAGE? No

FOR HOW LONG DO YOU SUSPEND
ILL SERVICE OVER THE
CHRISTMAS HOLIDAYS? No
suspension

ARE THERE ANY GROUPS OF LIBRARIES
FOR WHICH YOU WAIVE FEES? IF
SO, PLEASE NAME THEM: CTUW
libraries; NELINET ILL Code
signatories

CONNECTICUT STATE LIBRARY

NUC CODE: Ct

OCLC CODE: CZL

ADDRESS: Interlibrary Loan
Connecticut State
Library
90 Washington St.
Hartford, CT 06106

TELEPHONE: (203) 566-3024

LIST NAMES OF BRANCHES WITH
SEPARATE POLICIES: None

BOOKS:
Will Lend: Yes
Length of Loan: 1 month
from receipt
Renewable: Yes
Charges: None
Average Turnaround Time:
(Not answered)
If you have indicated that a
book is not to be lent, will
you on receipt of a letter
from the requesting library
search the index for given
entries? Yes

PERIODICALS:
Bound: Will not lend
Unbound: Will not lend
Loan Period: N/A
Renewable: N/A
Will lend if article exceeds
_____ number of pages (Not
answered)

MICROFORMS:
Will Lend: Yes
Specific Types of Microforms:
Film

GOVERNMENT PUBLICATIONS:
Will Lend: Yes

DISSERTATIONS:
Will Lend: Do not own

THESES:
Will Lend: Do not own

AUDIO-VISUAL MATERIALS:
Records: Will lend
Cassettes: Will lend
Other (slides, filmstrips,
etc.): Will lend

COMPUTER SOFTWARE:
Will Lend: Do not own

PHOTODUPLICATION SERVICE:
No charge up to 0 exposures
Charge Per Exposure: 25¢
Minimum/handling Fee: $1.25
Average Turnaround Time:
(Not answered)

MICROFILMING SERVICE:
Service Available: No
Charges: N/A

DO YOU CHARGE THE BORROWING
LIBRARY FOR POSTAGE? No

FOR HOW LONG DO YOU SUSPEND ILL
SERVICE OVER THE CHRISTMAS
HOLIDAYS? No suspension

ARE THERE ANY GROUPS OF LIBRARIES
FOR WHICH YOU WAIVE FEES? IF
SO, PLEASE NAME THEM: None

GREENWICH LIBRARY

NUC CODE: (Not answered)

OCLC CODE: GRN

ADDRESS: Interlibrary Loan
The Greenwich Library
101 West Putnam Ave.
Greenwich, CT 06830

TELEPHONE: (203) 622-7900

LIST NAMES OF BRANCHES WITH
SEPARATE POLICIES: None

BOOKS:
Will Lend: Yes
Length of Loan: 4 weeks from
shipment
Renewable: Yes, if no
reserves
Charges: None
Average Turnaround Time:
2 days
If you have indicated that a
book is not to be lent, will
you on receipt of a letter
from the requesting library
search the index for given
entries? Yes

PERIODICALS:
Bound: Will not lend
Unbound: Will not lend
Loan Period: N/A
Renewable: N/A
Will lend if article exceeds
_____ number of pages (Not
answered)

MICROFORMS:
Will Lend: No
Specific Types of Microforms:
N/A

GOVERNMENT PUBLICATIONS:
Will Lend: Yes

DISSERTATIONS:
Will Lend: Do not own

THESES:
Will Lend: Do not own

AUDIO-VISUAL MATERIALS:
Records: Will not lend
Cassettes: Will not lend
Other (slides, filmstrips,
etc.): Will not lend

COMPUTER SOFTWARE:
Will Lend: No

PHOTODUPLICATION SERVICE:
No charge up to a reasonable
number of exposures
Charge Per Exposure: None
Minimum/handling Fee: None
Average Turnaround Time:
2 days

MICROFILMING SERVICE:
Service Available: No
Charges: N/A

DO YOU CHARGE THE BORROWING
LIBRARY FOR POSTAGE? No

FOR HOW LONG DO YOU SUSPEND ILL
SERVICE OVER THE CHRISTMAS
HOLIDAYS? No suspension

ARE THERE ANY GROUPS OF LIBRARIES
FOR WHICH YOU WAIVE FEES? IF
SO, PLEASE NAME THEM: No
charges at present

HARTFORD GRADUATE CENTER

NUC CODE: (Not answered)

OCLC CODE: None

ADDRESS: Interlibrary Loan
Hartford Graduate
Center Library
275 Windsor St.
Hartford, CT 06120

TELEPHONE: (203) 549-3600

LIST NAMES OF BRANCHES WITH
SEPARATE POLICIES: None

BOOKS:
Will Lend: Yes
Length of Loan: 1 month
Renewable: Yes
Charges: Postage
Average Turnaround Time:
24 hours
If you have indicated that a
book is not to be lent, will
you on receipt of a letter
from the requesting library
search the index for given
entries? (Not answered)

PERIODICALS:
Bound: Will not lend
Unbound: Will not lend
Loan Period: N/A
Renewable: N/A
Will lend if article exceeds
50 pages

MICROFORMS:
Will Lend: No
Specific Types of Microforms:
N/A

GOVERNMENT PUBLICATIONS:
Will Lend: No

DISSERTATIONS:
Will Lend: No

THESES:
Will Lend: No

AUDIO-VISUAL MATERIALS:
Records: Will not lend
Cassettes: Will not lend
Other (slides, filmstrips,
etc.): Will not lend

COMPUTER SOFTWARE:
Will Lend: No

PHOTODUPLICATION SERVICE:
No charge up to 0 exposures
Charge Per Exposure: 10¢
Minimum/handling Fee: None
Average Turnaround Time:
24 hours

MICROFILMING SERVICE:
Service Available: No
Charges: N/A

DO YOU CHARGE THE BORROWING
LIBRARY FOR POSTAGE? Yes

FOR HOW LONG DO YOU SUSPEND ILL
SERVICE OVER THE CHRISTMAS
HOLIDAYS? No suspension

ARE THERE ANY GROUPS OF LIBRARIES
FOR WHICH YOU WAIVE FEES? IF
SO, PLEASE NAME THEM:
Greater Hartford Consortium
for Higher Education

TRINITY COLLEGE

NUC CODE: CtHT

OCLC CODE: TYC

ADDRESS: Interlibrary Loan
          Trinity College
          Library
          Hartford, CT 06106

TELEPHONE: (203) 527-3151, X303

LIST NAMES OF BRANCHES WITH
  SEPARATE POLICIES: None

BOOKS:
  Will Lend: Yes
  Length of Loan: 1 month
  Renewable: Yes, if not
    needed here
  Charges: None
  Average Turnaround Time:
    1 week
  If you have indicated that
    a book is not to be lent,
    will you on receipt of a
    letter from the
    requesting library search
    the index for given
    entries? (Not answered)

PERIODICALS:
  Bound: Will not lend
  Unbound: Will not lend
  Loan Period: N/A
  Renewable: N/A
  Will lend if article exceeds
    _____ number of pages (Not
    answered)

MICROFORMS:
  Will Lend: No
  Specific Types of Microforms:
    N/A

GOVERNMENT PUBLICATIONS:
  Will Lend: No

DISSERTATIONS:
  Will Lend: No

THESES:
  Will Lend: No

AUDIO-VISUAL MATERIALS:
  Records: Do not own
  Cassettes: Do not own
  Other (slides, filmstrips,
    etc.): Do not own

COMPUTER SOFTWARE:
  Will Lend: No

PHOTODUPLICATION SERVICE:
  No charge up to 0 exposures
  Charge Per Exposure: 10¢
  Minimum/handling Fee: $1.00
  Average Turnaround Time:
    1 week

MICROFILMING SERVICE:
  Service Available: Yes, but
    only in special instances
  Charges: $12.00 minimum plus
    10¢ per exposure

DO YOU CHARGE THE BORROWING
  LIBRARY FOR POSTAGE? No

FOR HOW LONG DO YOU SUSPEND ILL
  SERVICE OVER THE CHRISTMAS
  HOLIDAYS? No suspension

ARE THERE ANY GROUPS OF LIBRARIES
  FOR WHICH YOU WAIVE FEES? IF
  SO, PLEASE NAME THEM: Signers
  of the NELINET reciprocal
  agreement; Yale, Wesleyan,
  Connecticut College, and
  University of Connecticut

UNIVERSITY OF CONNECTICUT

NUC CODE: CtU

OCLC CODE: UCW

ADDRESS: Interlibrary Loan
          University of
            Connecticut
          Library
          Storrs, CT 06268

TELEPHONE: (203) 486-4974

LIST NAMES OF BRANCHES WITH
  SEPARATE POLICIES:
  UCONN Health Center
  UCONN Hartford Campus
  UCONN Law School
  UCONN School of Social Work
  UCONN School of Business
    Administration
  UCONN Stamford Campus
  UCONN Avery Point Campus
  UCONN Torrington Campus
  UCONN Waterbury Campus

BOOKS:
  Will Lend: Yes
  Length of Loan: 2 weeks
  Renewable: Yes
  Charges: (Not answered)
  Average Turnaround Time:
    1 day
  If you have indicated that a
    book is not to be lent, will
    you on receipt of a letter
    from the requesting library
    search the index for given
    entries? Yes

PERIODICALS:
  Bound: Will not lend
  Unbound: Will not lend
  Loan Period: N/A
  Renewable: N/A
  Will lend if article exceeds
    _____ number of pages (Not
    answered)

MICROFORMS:
  Will Lend: Yes
  Specific Types of Microforms:
    (Not answered)

GOVERNMENT PUBLICATIONS:
  Will Lend: Yes

DISSERTATIONS:
  Will Lend: Yes, stack copy
    only

THESES:
  Will Lend: Yes, stack copy
    only

AUDIO-VISUAL MATERIALS:
  Records: Will not lend
  Cassettes: Will lend
  Other (slides, filmstrips,
    etc.): Will not lend

COMPUTER SOFTWARE:
  Will Lend: No

PHOTODUPLICATION SERVICE:
  No charge up to 0 exposures
  Charge Per Exposure: 15¢
  Minimum/handling Fee: $2.00
  Average Turnaround Time:
    1 day

MICROFILMING SERVICE:
  Service Available: No
  Charges: N/A

DO YOU CHARGE THE BORROWING
  LIBRARY FOR POSTAGE? (Not
  answered)

FOR HOW LONG DO YOU SUSPEND ILL
  SERVICE OVER THE CHRISTMAS
  HOLIDAYS? No suspension

ARE THERE ANY GROUPS OF LIBRARIES
  FOR WHICH YOU WAIVE FEES? IF
  SO, PLEASE NAME THEM: None

UNIVERSITY OF CONNECTICUT HEALTH CENTER

NUC CODE: (Not answered)

OCLC CODE: UCH

ADDRESS: Interlibrary Loan Dept.
    Health Center Library
    University of
    Connecticut
    Farmington, CT 06032

TELEPHONE: (203) 674-2940

LIST NAMES OF BRANCHES WITH
    SEPARATE POLICIES: None

BOOKS:
    Will Lend: Yes
    Length of Loan: 3 weeks
    Renewable: Yes
    Charges: $5.00 per
    request
    Average Turnaround Time:
    Same day
    If you have indicated that a
    book is not to be lent, will
    you on receipt of a letter
    from the requesting library
    search the index for given
    entries? (Not answered)

PERIODICALS:
    Bound: Will not lend
    Unbound: Will not lend
    Loan Period: N/A
    Renewable: N/A
    Will lend if article exceeds
    _____ number of pages (Not
    answered)

MICROFORMS:
    Will Lend: No
    Specific Types of Microforms:
    N/A

GOVERNMENT PUBLICATIONS:
    Will Lend: Yes

DISSERTATIONS:
    Will Lend: No

THESES:
    Will Lend: No

AUDIO-VISUAL MATERIALS:
    Records: Do not own
    Cassettes: Will lend
    Other (slides, filmstrips,
    etc.): Will lend

COMPUTER SOFTWARE:
    Will Lend: Do not own

PHOTODUPLICATION SERVICE:
    No charge up to 0 exposures
    Charge Per Exposure: (Not
    answered)
    Minimum/handling Fee: $5.00
    per request
    Average Turnaround Time:
    Same day

MICROFILMING SERVICE:
    Service Available: Yes
    Charges: $5.00 per request

DO YOU CHARGE THE BORROWING
    LIBRARY FOR POSTAGE? No

FOR HOW LONG DO YOU SUSPEND ILL
    SERVICE OVER THE CHRISTMAS
    HOLIDAYS? No suspension

ARE THERE ANY GROUPS OF LIBRARIES
    FOR WHICH YOU WAIVE FEES? IF
    SO, PLEASE NAME THEM: None

UNIVERSITY OF CONNECTICUT SCHOOL OF PHARMACY

NUC CODE: CtU

OCLC CODE: UCW

ADDRESS: Interlibrary Loan
    Pharmacy Library, U-92
    University of
    Connecticut
    Storrs, CT 06268

TELEPHONE: (203) 486-2218

LIST NAMES OF BRANCHES WITH
    SEPARATE POLICIES: None

BOOKS:
    Will Lend: Yes
    Length of Loan: 2 weeks
    Renewable: Yes
    Charges: None
    Average Turnaround Time:
    2 days
    If you have indicated that a
    book is not to be lent, will
    you on receipt of a letter
    from the requesting library
    search the index for given
    entries? (Not answered)

PERIODICALS:
    Bound: Will not lend
    Unbound: Will not lend
    Loan Period: N/A
    Renewable: N/A
    Will lend if article exceeds
    _____ number of pages (Will
    not lend, regardless of
    length of article)

MICROFORMS:
    Will Lend: No
    Specific Types of Microforms:
    N/A

GOVERNMENT PUBLICATIONS:
    Will Lend: Yes

DISSERTATIONS:
    Will Lend: Yes

THESES:
    Will Lend: Yes

AUDIO-VISUAL MATERIALS:
    Records: Will not lend
    Cassettes: Will not lend
    Other (slides, filmstrips,
    etc.): Will not lend

COMPUTER SOFTWARE:
    Will Lend: No

PHOTODUPLICATION SERVICE:
    No charge up to 10 exposures
    Charge Per Exposure: 5¢
    Minimum/handling Fee: None
    Average Turnaround Time:
    2 days

MICROFILMING SERVICE:
    Service Available: No
    Charges: N/A

DO YOU CHARGE THE BORROWING
    LIBRARY FOR POSTAGE? No

FOR HOW LONG DO YOU SUSPEND ILL
    SERVICE OVER THE CHRISTMAS
    HOLIDAYS? No suspension

ARE THERE ANY GROUPS OF LIBRARIES
    FOR WHICH YOU WAIVE FEES? IF
    SO, PLEASE NAME THEM:
    University of Connecticut
    libraries

WESLEYAN UNIVERSITY

NUC CODE: CtW

OCLC CODE: WLU

ADDRESS: Interlibrary Loan
Wesleyan University
Library
Middleton, CT 06457

TELEPHONE: (203) 347-9411, X2134
or X2296

LIST NAMES OF BRANCHES WITH
SEPARATE POLICIES: None

BOOKS:
Will Lend: Yes
Length of Loan: 4 weeks from
receipt
Renewable: Yes, usually
Charges: Only to those who
charge us
Average Turnaround Time:
(Not answered)
If you have indicated that a
book is not to be lent, will
you on receipt of a letter
from the requesting library
search the index for given
entries? Yes

PERIODICALS:
Bound: Will not lend
Unbound: Will not lend
Loan Period: N/A
Renewable: N/A
Will sometimes lend if article
exceeds 50 pages

MICROFORMS:
Will Lend: Yes, some of them
Specific Types of Microforms:
Film, fiche, microcard; will
not loan New York Times and
other heavy-demand items.

GOVERNMENT PUBLICATIONS:
Will Lend: Yes

DISSERTATIONS:
Will Lend: Yes, if 2d copy
available

THESES:
Will Lend: Yes, if 2d copy
available

AUDIO-VISUAL MATERIALS:
Records: Will not lend
Cassettes: Will not lend
Other (slides, filmstrips,
etc.): Will not lend

COMPUTER SOFTWARE:
Will Lend: No

PHOTODUPLICATION SERVICE:
No charge up to 0 exposures
Charge Per Exposure: 15¢
each after 1st 16 pages
Minimum/handling Fee: $2.50
(covers 1-16 pages)
Average Turnaround Time:
(Not answered)

MICROFILMING SERVICE:
Service Available: Yes, but
from outside vendor, so
long time delays result
Charges: (Not answered)

DO YOU CHARGE THE BORROWING
LIBRARY FOR POSTAGE? Only
those who charge us

FOR HOW LONG DO YOU SUSPEND ILL
SERVICE OVER THE CHRISTMAS
HOLIDAYS? Mailing of books
suspended from mid-December
through New Year's Day;
mailing of photocopies not
suspended.

YALE UNIVERSITY

NUC CODE: CtY

OCLC CODE: YUS

ADDRESS: Interlibrary Loan
Yale University Library
130 Wall St.
Box 1603A Yale Station
New Haven, CT 06520

TELEPHONE: (203) 436-1972

LIST NAMES OF BRANCHES WITH
SEPARATE POLICIES:
Law Library
Medical Library
Kline Science Library
Divinity Library

BOOKS:
Will Lend: Yes
Length of Loan: 2 weeks
Renewable: No
Charges: $12.00 per
completed transaction. (A
completed transaction may
consist of 4 volumes of a
multivolume set or 4 reels
of microfilm.)
Average Turnaround Time:
2 days
If you have indicated that a
book is not to be lent, will
you on receipt of a letter
from the requesting library
search the index for given
entries? (Not answered)

PERIODICALS:
Bound: Will lend if 10 years
or older
Unbound: Will not lend
Loan Period: 2 weeks
Renewable: No
Will lend if article exceeds
_____ number of pages (N/A)

MICROFORMS:
Will Lend: Yes
Specific Types of Microforms:
Anything but negative
microfilm, spliced micro-
film, dissertations, or

material in special collections at Beinecke Rare Book
Library

GOVERNMENT PUBLICATIONS:
Will Lend: No

DISSERTATIONS:
Will Lend: Yes, with
restrictions

THESES:
Will Lend: Yes, with
restrictions

AUDIO-VISUAL MATERIALS:
Records: Do not own
Cassettes: Do not own
Other (slides, filmstrips,
etc.): Do not own

COMPUTER SOFTWARE:
Will Lend: Do not own

PHOTODUPLICATION SERVICE:
No charge up to 0 exposures
Charge Per Exposure: Write
for information
Minimum Fee: $8.00 plus
postage
Average Turnaround Time:
2 days

MICROFILMING SERVICE:
Service Available: Yes
Charges: Write for charges

DO YOU CHARGE THE BORROWING
LIBRARY FOR POSTAGE? Yes,
for photocopies and for
book loans outside the
continental U. S.

FOR HOW LONG DO YOU SUSPEND ILL
SERVICE OVER THE CHRISTMAS
HOLIDAYS? Approximately
Dec.10-Jan.5

ARE THERE ANY GROUPS OF LIBRARIES
FOR WHICH YOU WAIVE FEES? IF
SO, PLEASE NAME THEM: RLG,
Connecticut College,
Trinity College, University
of Connecticut, and
Wesleyan College (CTUW)

DELAWARE DIVISION OF LIBRARIES

NUC CODE: (Not answered)

OCLC CODE: DWA

ADDRESS: Interlibrary Loan
Delaware Division of
Libraries
P. O. Box 639
Dover, DE 19901

TELEPHONE: (302) 736-4748

LIST NAMES OF BRANCHES WITH
SEPARATE POLICIES: None

BOOKS:
Will Lend: Yes
Length of Loan: 1 month
Renewable: Yes
Charges: None
Average Turnaround Time:
Same day
If you have indicated that a
book is not to be lent, will
you on receipt of a letter
from the requesting library
search the index for given
entries? (Not answered)

PERIODICALS:
Bound: Will not lend
Unbound: Will not lend
Renewable: N/A
Loan Period: N/A
Will lend if article exceeds
_____ number of pages (Not
answered)

MICROFORMS:
Will Lend: No
Specific Types of Microforms:
N/A

GOVERNMENT PUBLICATIONS:
Will Lend: Yes

DISSERTATIONS:
Will Lend: Do not own

THESES:
Will Lend: Do not own

AUDIO-VISUAL MATERIALS:
Records: Will not lend
Cassettes: Will not lend
Other (slides, filmstrips,
etc.): Will not lend

COMPUTER SOFTWARE:
Will Lend: Do not own

PHOTODUPLICATION SERVICE:
No charge up to 10 exposures
Charge Per Exposure: 15¢
Minimum/handling Fee: None
Average Turnaround Time:
Same day

MICROFILMING SERVICE:
Service Available: No
Charges: N/A

DO YOU CHARGE THE BORROWING
LIBRARY FOR POSTAGE? No

FOR HOW LONG DO YOU SUSPEND ILL
SERVICE OVER THE CHRISTMAS
HOLIDAYS? No suspension

ARE THERE ANY GROUPS OF LIBRARIES
FOR WHICH YOU WAIVE FEES? IF
SO, PLEASE NAME THEM: None

UNIVERSITY OF DELAWARE AT NEWARK

NUC CODE: DeU

OCLC CODE: DLM

ADDRESS: Interlibrary Loan
University Library
University of Delaware
Newark, DE 19711

TELEPHONE: (302) 738-2236

LIST NAMES OF BRANCHES WITH
SEPARATE POLICIES: None

BOOKS:
Will Lend: Yes
Length of Loan: 2 weeks use
Renewable: Yes
Charges: (Not answered)
Average Turnaround Time:
Approximately 4 days
If you have indicated that a
book is not to be lent, will
you on receipt of a letter
from the requesting library
search the index for given
entries? Yes

PERIODICALS:
Bound: Will not lend
Unbound: Will not lend
Loan Period: N/A
Renewable: N/A
Will lend if article exceeds
_____ number of pages (Not
answered)

MICROFORMS:
Will Lend: Yes, in most cases
Specific Types of Microforms:
(Not answered)

GOVERNMENT PUBLICATIONS:
Will Lend: Yes, in most cases

DISSERTATIONS:
Will Lend: No; 1957 to present
available from University
Microfilms

THESES:
Will Lend: Yes

AUDIO-VISUAL MATERIALS:
Records: Will lend
Cassettes: Do not own
Other (slides, filmstrips,
etc.): Do not own

COMPUTER SOFTWARE:
Will Lend: Do not own

PHOTODUPLICATION SERVICE:
No charge up to 0 exposures
Charges: $5.00 for 1-20
exposures; 10¢ per each
additional exposure
Average Turnaround Time:
4 days

MICROFILMING SERVICE:
Service Available: No
Charges: N/A

DO YOU CHARGE THE BORROWING
LIBRARY FOR POSTAGE? No

FOR HOW LONG DO YOU SUSPEND ILL
SERVICE OVER THE CHRISTMAS
HOLIDAYS? Approximately
2 weeks

ARE THERE ANY GROUPS OF LIBRARIES
FOR WHICH YOU WAIVE FEES? IF
SO, PLEASE NAME THEM:
We have several reciprocal
agreements

WILMINGTON LIBRARY

NUC CODE: DeWI

OCLC CODE: DWW

ADDRESS: Interlibrary Loan
          Wilmington Library
          10th & Market Sts.
          Wilmington, DE 19801

TELEPHONE: (302) 571-7404

LIST NAMES OF BRANCHES WITH
    SEPARATE POLICIES: None

BOOKS:
    Will Lend: Yes
    Length of Loan: 4 weeks
    Renewable: Yes
    Charges: None
    Average Turnaround Time:
      2 days
    If you have indicated that a
      book is not to be lent, will
      you on receipt of a letter
      from the requesting library
      search the index for given
      entries? (Not answered)

PERIODICALS:
    Bound: Will not lend
    Unbound: Will not lend
    Loan Period: N/A
    Renewable: N/A
    Will lend if article exceeds
      _____ number of pages (Not
      answered)

MICROFORMS:
    Will Lend: No
    Specific Types of Microforms:
      N/A

GOVERNMENT PUBLICATIONS:
    Will Lend: Do not own

DISSERTATIONS:
    Will Lend: Do not own

THESES:
    Will Lend: Do not own

AUDIO-VISUAL MATERIALS:
    Records: Will lend
    Cassettes: Will not lend
    Other (slides, filmstrips,
      etc.): Will not lend

COMPUTER SOFTWARE:
    Will Lend: Do not own

PHOTODUPLICATION SERVICE:
    No charge up to 3 exposures
    Charge Per Exposure: 10¢
    Minimum/handling Fee: None
    Average Turnaround Time:
      2 days

MICROFILMING SERVICE:
    Service Available: No
    Charges: N/A

DO YOU CHARGE THE BORROWING
    LIBRARY FOR POSTAGE? No

FOR HOW LONG DO YOU SUSPEND ILL
    SERVICE OVER THE CHRISTMAS
    HOLIDAYS? No suspension

ARE THERE ANY GROUPS OF LIBRARIES
    FOR WHICH YOU WAIVE FEES? IF
    SO, PLEASE NAME THEM: New
    Castle County Public
    Libraries

AMERICAN UNIVERSITY LIBRARY

NUC CODE: DAU

OCLC CODE: EAU

ADDRESS: Interlibrary Loan
American University
Library
Massachusetts and
Nebraska, N.W.
Washington, D. C. 20016

TELEPHONE: (202) 686-5615

LIST NAMES OF BRANCHES WITH
SEPARATE POLICIES: (Not
answered)

BOOKS:
Will Lend: Yes
Length of Loan: 3 weeks use
Renewable: Yes
Charges: (Not answered)
Average Turnaround Time:
(Not answered)
If you have indicated that a
book is not to be lent, will
you on receipt of a letter
from the requesting library
search the index for given
entries? (Not answered)

PERIODICALS:
Bound: Will not lend
Unbound: Will not lend
Loan Period: N/A
Renewable: N/A
Will lend if article exceeds
_____ number of pages (Not
answered)

MICROFORMS:
Will Lend: (Not answered)
Specific Types of Microforms:
N/A

GOVERNMENT PUBLICATIONS:
Will Lend: (Not answered)

DISSERTATIONS:
Will Lend: Yes; 1958 to
present available from
University Microfilms

THESES:
Will Lend: Yes

AUDIO-VISUAL MATERIALS:
Records: (Not answered)
Cassettes: (Not answered)
Other (slides, filmstrips,
etc.): (Not answered)

COMPUTER SOFTWARE:
Will Lend: (Not answered)

PHOTODUPLICATION SERVICE:
No charge up to 0 exposures
Charge Per Exposure: 10¢
Minimum Fee: $2.50
Handling Fee: $1.50
Average Turnaround Time: (Not
answered)

MICROFILMING SERVICE:
Service Available: No
Charges: N/A

DO YOU CHARGE THE BORROWING
LIBRARY FOR POSTAGE? No

FOR HOW LONG DO YOU SUSPEND ILL
SERVICE OVER THE CHRISTMAS
HOLIDAYS? No suspension

ARE THERE ANY GROUPS OF LIBRARIES
FOR WHICH YOU WAIVE FEES? IF
SO, PLEASE NAME THEM: (Not
answered)

CATHOLIC UNIVERSITY OF AMERICA

NUC CODE: DCU

OCLC CODE: DCU

ADDRESS: Interlibrary Loan
Room 116 Mullen Library
Catholic University of
America
Washington, D. C. 20064

TELEPHONE: (202) 635-5055

LIST NAMES OF BRANCHES WITH
SEPARATE POLICIES: (Not
answered)

BOOKS:
Will Lend: Yes
Length of Loan: (Not answered)
Renewable: Yes
Charges: (Not answered)
Average Turnaround Time:
(Not answered)
If you have indicated that a
book is not to be lent, will
you on receipt of a letter
from the requesting library
search the index for given
entries? (Not answered)

PERIODICALS:
Bound: Will not lend
Unbound: Will not lend
Loan Period: N/A
Renewable: N/A
Will lend if article exceeds
_____ number of pages (Not
answered)

MICROFORMS:
Will Lend: Yes
Specific Types of Microforms:
Microfilm only

GOVERNMENT PUBLICATIONS:
Will Lend: (Not answered)

DISSERTATIONS:
Will Lend: Yes, if pre-1961;
1961 to present available
from University Microfilms

THESES:
Will Lend: Yes, if post-1957

AUDIO-VISUAL MATERIALS:
Records: (Not answered)
Cassettes: (Not answered)
Other (slides, filmstrips,
etc.): (Not answered)

COMPUTER SOFTWARE:
Will Lend: (Not answered)

PHOTODUPLICATION SERVICE:
No charge up to 0 exposures
Charge Per Exposure: 10¢
Minimum/handling Fee: $2.50
Average Turnaround Time:
(Not answered)

MICROFILMING SERVICE:
Service Available: (Not
answered)
Charges: N/A

DO YOU CHARGE THE BORROWING
LIBRARY FOR POSTAGE? No

FOR HOW LONG DO YOU SUSPEND ILL
SERVICE OVER THE CHRISTMAS
HOLIDAYS? (Not answered)

ARE THERE ANY GROUPS OF LIBRARIES
FOR WHICH YOU WAIVE FEES? IF
SO, PLEASE NAME THEM: (Not
answered)

FOLGER SHAKESPEARE LIBRARY

NUC CODE: DFo

OCLC CODE: None

ADDRESS: Interlibrary Loan
Folger Shakespeare
Library
201 E. Capitol St., S.E.
Washington, D.C. 20003

TELEPHONE: (202) 544-4600

LIST NAMES OF BRANCHES WITH
SEPARATE POLICIES: None

BOOKS:
Will Lend: No
Length of Loan: N/A
Renewable: N/A
Charges: N/A
Average Turnaround Time: N/A
If you have indicated that a
book is not to be lent, will
you on receipt of a letter
from the requesting library
search the index for given
entries? Generally yes--
depends upon the size of
the request

PERIODICALS:
Bound: Will not lend
Unbound: Will not lend
Loan Period: N/A
Renewable: N/A
Will lend if article exceeds
_____ number of pages (Will
not lend, regardless of
length of article)

MICROFORMS:
Will Lend: No
Specific Types of Microforms:
N/A

GOVERNMENT PUBLICATIONS:
Will Lend: No

DISSERTATIONS:
Will Lend: No

THESES:
Will Lend: No

AUDIO-VISUAL MATERIALS:
Records: Will not lend
Cassettes: Will not lend
Other (slides, filmstrips,
etc.): Will not lend

COMPUTER SOFTWARE:
Will Lend: No

PHOTODUPLICATION SERVICE:
No charge up to 0 exposures
Charge Per Exposure: 50¢--
will not copy pre-1800
books
Minimum/handling Fee: $5.00
Average Turnaround Time:
4-6 weeks

MICROFILMING SERVICE:
Service Available: Yes
Charges: 20¢ per exposure;
$5.00 minimum

DO YOU CHARGE THE BORROWING
LIBRARY FOR POSTAGE? Yes,
$1.50 minimum

FOR HOW LONG DO YOU SUSPEND ILL
SERVICE OVER THE CHRISTMAS
HOLIDAYS? No suspension

ARE THERE ANY GROUPS OF LIBRARIES
FOR WHICH YOU WAIVE FEES? IF
SO, PLEASE NAME THEM: None

GEORGE WASHINGTON UNIVERSITY

NUC CODE: DGW

OCLC CODE: DGW

ADDRESS: Interlibrary Loan
Gelman Library
George Washington
University
2130 H St., NW
Washington, D. C. 20402

TELEPHONE: (202) 676-6455

LIST NAMES OF BRANCHES WITH
SEPARATE POLICIES:
Law Library
Medical Library

BOOKS:
Will Lend: Yes
Length of Loan: 2 weeks
Renewable: Yes
Charges: None
Average Turnaround Time:
(Not answered)
If you have indicated that a
book is not to be lent, will
you on receipt of a letter
from the requesting library
search the index for given
entries? (Not answered)

PERIODICALS:
Bound: Will not lend
Unbound: Will not lend
Loan Period: N/A
Renewable: N/A
Will lend if article exceeds
_____ number of pages (Not
answered)

MICROFORMS:
Will Lend: No
Specific Types of Microforms:
N/A

GOVERNMENT PUBLICATIONS:
Will Lend: Yes

DISSERTATIONS:
Will Lend: Yes, if 2nd copy
available. 1966- available
from University Microfilms.

THESES:
Will Lend: Yes

AUDIO-VISUAL MATERIALS:
Records: Will not lend
Cassettes: Will not lend
Other (slides, filmstrips,
etc.): Will not lend

COMPUTER SOFTWARE:
Will Lend: No

PHOTODUPLICATION SERVICE:
No charge up to 0 exposures
Charge Per Exposure: 10¢
Minimum/handling Fee: $2.50
Average Turnaround Time:
(Not answered)

MICROFILMING SERVICE:
Service Available: No
Charges: N/A

DO YOU CHARGE THE BORROWING
LIBRARY FOR POSTAGE? No

FOR HOW LONG DO YOU SUSPEND ILL
SERVICE OVER THE CHRISTMAS
HOLIDAYS? Dec.15-Jan.5

ARE THERE ANY GROUPS OF LIBRARIES
FOR WHICH YOU WAIVE FEES? IF
SO, PLEASE NAME THEM:
Consortium of Universities
of the Washington Metro-
politan Area

GEORGETOWN UNIVERSITY

NUC CODE: DGU

OCLC CODE: DGU

ADDRESS: Interlibrary Loan
          Georgetown University
          Library
          P.O. Box 37445
          Washington, D.C. 20013

TELEPHONE: (202) 625-4138

LIST NAMES OF BRANCHES WITH
  SEPARATE POLICIES:
  Medical library
  Law Library
  Woodstock Library

BOOKS:
  Will Lend: Yes
  Length of Loan: 2 weeks
  Renewable: Yes
  Charges: Only to libraries
    who charge us
  Average Turnaround Time:
    1 week
  If you have indicated that a
    book is not to be lent, will
    you on receipt of a letter
    from the requesting library
    search the index for given
    entries? No

PERIODICALS:
  Bound: Will not lend
  Unbound: Will not lend
  Loan Period: N/A
  Renewable: N/A
  Will lend if article exceeds
    _____ number of pages (Will
    not lend, regardless of
    length of article)

MICROFORMS:
  Will Lend: No
  Specific Types of Microforms:
    N/A

GOVERNMENT PUBLICATIONS:
  Will Lend: Yes

DISSERTATIONS:
  Will Lend: Yes, if pre-1965

THESES:
  Will Lend: Yes, if pre-1965

AUDIO-VISUAL MATERIALS:
  Records: Will not lend
  Cassettes: Will not lend
  Other (slides, filmstrips,
    etc.): Will not lend

COMPUTER SOFTWARE:
  Will Lend: No

PHOTODUPLICATION SERVICE:
  No charge up to 0 exposures
  Charge Per Exposure: 10¢
  Minimum/handling Fee: $3.00
  Average Turnaround Time:
    1 week

MICROFILMING SERVICE:
  Service Available: Yes
  Charges: Depends upon
    request

DO YOU CHARGE THE BORROWING
  LIBRARY FOR POSTAGE? No

FOR HOW LONG DO YOU SUSPEND ILL
  SERVICE OVER THE CHRISTMAS
  HOLIDAYS? No suspension

ARE THERE ANY GROUPS OF LIBRARIES
  FOR WHICH YOU WAIVE FEES? IF
  SO, PLEASE NAME THEM: No
  fees charged except to
  libraries who charge us

LIBRARY OF CONGRESS

NUC CODE: DLC

OCLC CODE: DLC

ADDRESS: Loan Division
          Interlibrary Loans
          Library of Congress
          Washington, D.C. 20540

TELEPHONE: (202) 287-5444

LIST NAMES OF BRANCHES WITH
  SEPARATE POLICIES: None

BOOKS:
  Will Lend: Yes
  Length of Loan: 2 weeks
  Renewable: Yes, for 2 weeks
  Charges: None for loans
  Average Turnaround Time:
    2 weeks
  If you have indicated that a
    book is not to be lent, will
    you on receipt of a letter
    from the requesting library
    search the index for given
    entries? No

PERIODICALS:
  Bound: Will not lend
  Unbound: Will not lend
  Loan Period: N/A
  Renewable: N/A
  Will lend if article exceeds
    _____ number of pages (Will
    not lend, regardless of
    length of article)

MICROFORMS:
  Will Lend: Yes
  Specific Types of Microforms:
    Material for which LC owns
    negative microfilm and a
    positive (lendable) copy

GOVERNMENT PUBLICATIONS:
  Will Lend: Yes

DISSERTATIONS:
  Will Lend: Yes, bound only,
    and only if unavailable from
    University Microfilms or
    National Library of Canada

THESES:
  Will Lend: Yes, bound only,
    and only if unavailable from
    University Microfilms or
    National Library of Canada

AUDIO-VISUAL MATERIALS:
  Records: Will not lend
  Cassettes: Will not lend
  Other (slides, filmstrips,
    etc.): Will not lend

COMPUTER SOFTWARE:
  Will Lend: No

PHOTODUPLICATION SERVICE:
  No charge up to 10 exposures
  Charge Per Exposure: 25¢
    plus handling fee
  Minimum/handling Fee: $8.80
  Average Turnaround Time:
    Varies

MICROFILMING SERVICE:
  Service Available: Yes
  Charges: 20¢ per foot for
    positive; 14¢ per exposure
    for negative

DO YOU CHARGE THE BORROWING
  LIBRARY FOR POSTAGE? No

FOR HOW LONG DO YOU SUSPEND ILL
  SERVICE OVER THE CHRISTMAS
  HOLIDAYS? No suspension

ARE THERE ANY GROUPS OF LIBRARIES
  FOR WHICH YOU WAIVE FEES? IF
  SO, PLEASE NAME THEM: None

ORGANIZATION OF AMERICAN STATES

NUC CODE: DPU

OCLC OCDE: DOA

ADDRESS: Interlibrary Loan
           Columbus Memorial
           Library
           Organization of
           American States
           17th And Constitution
           Avenue NW
           Washington, D.C. 20006

TELEPHONE: (202) 789-6037

LIST NAMES OF BRANCHES WITH
   SEPARATE POLICIES: None

BOOKS:
   Will Lend: Yes, pre-1962
      imprint only
   Length of Loan: 1 month use
   Renewable: Yes
   Charges: None
   Average Turnaround Time:
      2 days
   If you have indicated that a
      book is not to be lent, will
      you on receipt of a letter
      from the requesting library
      search the index for given
      entries? (Not answered)

PERIODICALS:
   Bound: Will lend
   Unbound: Will not lend in
      local area
   Loan Period: 1 month use for
      bound volumes; 2 weeks use
      in local area
   Renewable: Yes
   Will lend if article exceeds
      _____ number of pages (Not
      answered)

MICROFORMS:
   Will Lend: No
   Specific Types of Microforms:
      N/A

GOVERNMENT PUBLICATIONS:
   Will Lend: Yes

DISSERTATIONS:
   Will Lend: No

THESES:
   Will Lend: No

AUDIO-VISUAL MATERIALS:
   Records: Do not own
   Cassettes: Do not own
   Other (slides, filmstrips,
      etc.): Do not own

COMPUTER SOFTWARE:
   Will Lend: No

PHOTODUPLICATION SERVICE:
   No charge up to 0 exposures
   Charge Per Exposure: 15¢
   Minimum/handling Fee: (Not
      answered)
   Average Turnaround Time:
      2 days

MICROFILMING SERVICE:
   Service Available: No
   Charges: N/A

DO YOU CHARGE THE BORROWING
   LIBRARY FOR POSTAGE? No

FOR HOW LONG DO YOU SUSPEND ILL
   SERVICE OVER THE CHRISTMAS
   HOLIDAYS? App. third week in
   Dec.-Jan.2

ARE THERE ANY GROUPS OF LIBRARIES
   FOR WHICH YOU WAIVE FEES? IF
   SO, PLEASE NAME THEM: None

UNITED STATES DEPARTMENT OF STATE

NUC CODE: DS

OCLC CODE: DOS

ADDRESS: Interlibrary Loan
           FAIM/LR, Room 3239 N.S.
           U. S. Dept. of State
           Library
           2201 C Street, N.W.
           Washington, D.C. 20520

TELEPHONE: (202) 632-0535

LIST NAMES OF BRANCHES WITH
   SEPARATE POLICIES: None

BOOKS:
   Will Lend: Yes
   Length of Loan: 2 weeks
   Renewable: Yes
   Charges: (Not answered)
   Average Turnaround Time:
      3 days
   If you have indicated that a
      book is not to be lent, will
      you on receipt of a letter
      from the requesting library
      search the index for given
      entries? (Not answered)

PERIODICALS:
   Bound: Will not lend
   Unbound: Will not lend
   Loan Period: N/A
   Renewable: N/A
   Will lend if article exceeds
      _____ number of pages (Not
      answered)

MICROFORMS:
   Will Lend: No
   Specific Types of Microforms:
      N/A

GOVERNMENT PUBLICATIONS:
   Will Lend: Yes

DISSERTATIONS:
   Will Lend: Do not own

THESES:
   Will Lend: Do not own

AUDIO-VISUAL MATERIALS:
   Records: Do not own
   Cassettes: Do not own
   Other (slides, filmstrips,
      etc.): Do not own

COMPUTER SOFTWARE:
   Will Lend: Do not own

PHOTODUPLICATION SERVICE:
   No charge up to 10 exposures
   Charge Per Exposure: 10¢
      per exposure after 1st 10
   Minimum/handling Fee: None
   Average Turnaround Time:
      3 days

MICROFILMING SERVICE:
   Service Available: No
   Charges: N/A

DO YOU CHARGE THE BORROWING
   LIBRARY FOR POSTAGE? No

FOR HOW LONG DO YOU SUSPEND ILL
   SERVICE OVER THE CHRISTMAS
   HOLIDAYS? No suspension

ARE THERE ANY GROUPS OF LIBRARIES
   FOR WHICH YOU WAIVE FEES? IF
   SO, PLEASE NAME THEM: None

UNITED STATES DEPARTMENT OF THE ARMY

NUC CODE: (Not answered)

OCLC CODE: (Not answered)

ADDRESS: Interlibrary Loan
The Army Library
1A518 Pentagon
Washington, D.C.   20310

TELEPHONE: (202) 697-4301

LIST NAMES OF BRANCHES WITH
SEPARATE POLICIES: None

BOOKS:
Will Lend: Yes
Length of Loan: 2 weeks
Renewable: Yes, once
Charges: None
Average Turnaround Time:
(Not answered)
If you have indicated that a
book is not to be lent, will
you on receipt of a letter
from the requesting library
search the index for given
entries? No

PERIODICALS:
Bound: Will lend
Unbound: Will lend
Loan Period: 1 week
Renewable: Yes, once
Will lend if article exceeds
_____ number of pages (Not
answered)

MICROFORMS:
Will Lend: No
Specific Types of Microforms:
N/A

GOVERNMENT PUBLICATIONS:
Will Lend: Yes

DISSERTATIONS:
Will Lend: Yes

THESES:
Will Lend: Yes

AUDIO-VISUAL MATERIALS:
Records: Will not lend
Cassettes: Will not lend
Other (slides, filmstrips,
etc.): Will not lend

COMPUTER SOFTWARE:
Will Lend: No

PHOTODUPLICATION SERVICE:
Not available

MICROFILMING SERVICE:
Service Available: No
Charges: N/A

DO YOU CHARGE THE BORROWING
LIBRARY FOR POSTAGE?
Require labels postage
paid

FOR HOW LONG DO YOU SUSPEND ILL
SERVICE OVER THE CHRISTMAS
HOLIDAYS? 1 month

ARE THERE ANY GROUPS OF LIBRARIES
FOR WHICH YOU WAIVE FEES? IF
SO, PLEASE NAME THEM: None

UNITED STATES DEPARTMENT OF THE NAVY

NUC CODE: DN

OCLC CODE: NHC

ADDRESS: Interlibrary Loan
Navy Department Library
Bldg. 220
Washington Navy Yard
Washington, D.C.   20374

TELEPHONE: (202) 433-4131

LIST NAMES OF BRANCHES WITH
SEPARATE POLICIES: None

BOOKS:
Will Lend: Yes
Length of Loan: 2 weeks use
Renewable: Yes, upon request
Charges: None
Average Turnaround Time:
1 day
If you have indicated that a
book is not to be lent, will
you on receipt of a letter
from the requesting library
search the index for given
entries? (Not answered)

PERIODICALS:
Bound: Will lend
Unbound: Will lend
Loan Period: 1 week use
Renewable: No
Will lend if article exceeds
_____ number of pages (Not
answered)

MICROFORMS:
Will Lend: Yes
Specific Types of Microforms:
Microfilm, microfiche

GOVERNMENT PUBLICATIONS:
Will Lend: Yes

DISSERTATIONS:
Will Lend: Do not own

THESES:
Will Lend: Do not own

AUDIO-VISUAL MATERIALS:
Records: Do not own
Cassettes: Do not own
Other (slides, filmstrips,
etc.): Do not own

COMPUTER SOFTWARE:
Will Lend: Do not own

PHOTODUPLICATION SERVICE:
No charge up to 0 exposures
Charge Per Exposure: 15¢
Minimum/handling Fee: None
Average Turnaround Time:
1 day

MICROFILMING SERVICE:
Service Available: Yes, but
only reproduction of
existing microfilm
Charges: $5.00 per
reproduced reel

DO YOU CHARGE THE BORROWING
LIBRARY FOR POSTAGE? No

FOR HOW LONG DO YOU SUSPEND ILL
SERVICE OVER THE CHRISTMAS
HOLIDAYS? No suspension

ARE THERE ANY GROUPS OF LIBRARIES
FOR WHICH YOU WAIVE FEES? IF
SO, PLEASE NAME THEM: None

UNITED STATES NATIONAL BUREAU OF STANDARDS

NUC CODE: DBS

OCLC CODE: NBS

ADDRESS: Interlibrary Loan
            National Bureau of
               Standards
            Library
            ILL - ADM E 106
            Washington, D.C. 20234

TELEPHONE: (301) 921-3410

LIST NAMES OF BRANCHES WITH
   SEPARATE POLICIES: None

BOOKS:
   Will Lend: Yes
   Length of Loan: 4 weeks
   Renewable: No
   Charges: None
   Average Turnaround Time:
      1 week
   If you have indicated that a
      book is not to be lent, will
      you on receipt of a letter
      from the requesting library
      search the index for given
      entries? (Not answered)

PERIODICALS:
   Bound: Will not lend
   Unbound: Will not lend
   Loan Period: N/A
   Renewable: N/A
   Will lend if article exceeds
      _____ number of pages (Not
      answered)

MICROFORMS:
   Will Lend: No
   Specific Types of Microforms:
      N/A

GOVERNMENT PUBLICATIONS:
   Will Lend: Yes, but National
      Bureau of Standards
      publications only

DISSERTATIONS:
   Will Lend: No

THESES:
   Will Lend: No

AUDIO-VISUAL MATERIALS:
   Records: Will not lend
   Cassettes: Will not lend
   Other (slides, filmstrips,
      etc.): Will not lend

COMPUTER SOFTWARE:
   Will Lend: No

PHOTODUPLICATION SERVICE:
   No charge up to 25 exposures
   Charge Per Exposure: None
   Minimum/handling Fee: None
   Average Turnaround Time:
      (Not answered)

MICROFILMING SERVICE:
   Service Available: No
   Charges: N/A

DO YOU CHARGE THE BORROWING
   LIBRARY FOR POSTAGE? No

FOR HOW LONG DO YOU SUSPEND ILL
   SERVICE OVER THE CHRISTMAS
   HOLIDAYS? 1 week

ARE THERE ANY GROUPS OF LIBRARIES
   FOR WHICH YOU WAIVE FEES? IF
   SO, PLEASE NAME THEM: No fees
   charged

NOTE: Limit number of requests
   to 6 per week

UNIVERSITY OF THE DISTRICT OF COLUMBIA

NUC CODE: DUDC

OCLC CODE: DDU

ADDRESS: Interlibrary Loan
            Learning Resources Div.
            University of the
               District of Columbia
            Bldg.41, Level A
            4200 Connecticut Ave.,
               N.W.
            Washington, D.C. 20008

TELEPHONE: (202) 282-7536

LIST NAMES OF BRANCHES WITH
   SEPARATE POLICIES: None

BOOKS:
   Will Lend: Yes
   Length of Loan: 4 weeks
   Renewable: Yes
   Charges: (Not answered)
   Average Turnaround Time:
      (Not answered)
   If you have indicated that a
      book is not to be lent, will
      you on receipt of a letter
      from the requesting library
      search the index for given
      entries? (Not answered)

PERIODICALS:
   Bound: Will not lend
   Unbound: Will not lend
   Loan Period: N/A
   Renewable: N/A
   Will lend if article exceeds
      _____ number of pages (Not
      answered)

MICROFORMS:
   Will Lend: (Not answered)
   Specific Types of Microforms:
      N/A

GOVERNMENT PUBLICATIONS:
   Will Lend: (Not answered)

DISSERTATIONS:
   Will Lend: No

THESES:
   Will Lend: No

AUDIO-VISUAL MATERIALS:
   Records: (Not answered)
   Cassettes: (Not answered)
   Other (slides, filmstrips,
      etc.): (Not answered)

COMPUTER SOFTWARE:
   Will Lend: (Not answered)

PHOTODUPLICATION SERVICE:
   No charge up to 0 exposures
   Charge Per Exposure: 10¢
   Minimum Fee: $2.50
   Average Turnaround Time:
      (Not answered)

MICROFILMING SERVICE:
   Service Available: No
   Charges: N/A

DO YOU CHARGE THE BORROWING
   LIBRARY FOR POSTAGE? No

FOR HOW LONG DO YOU SUSPEND ILL
   SERVICE OVER THE CHRISTMAS
   HOLIDAYS? Dec.18-Jan.3

ARE THERE ANY GROUPS OF LIBRARIES
   FOR WHICH YOU WAIVE FEES? IF
   SO, PLEASE NAME THEM: (Not
   answered)

BETHUNE-COOKMAN COLLEGE

NUC CODE: (Not answered)

OCLC CODE: (Not answered)

ADDRESS: Interlibrary Loan
Carl S. Swisher Library
Bethune-Cookman College
Daytona Beach, FL 32015

TELEPHONE: (904) 255-1401

LIST NAMES OF BRANCHES WITH
SEPARATE POLICIES: None

BOOKS:
Will Lend: Yes
Length of Loan: 2 weeks
Renewable: Yes
Charges: None
Average Turnaround Time:
1-3 days
If you have indicated that a
book is not to be lent, will
you on receipt of a letter
from the requesting library
search the index for given
entries? (Not answered)

PERIODICALS:
Bound: Will not lend
Unbound: Will not lend
Loan Period: N/A
Renewable: N/A
Will lend if article exceeds
_____ number of pages (Not
answered)

MICROFORMS:
Will Lend: No
Specific Types of Microforms:
N/A

GOVERNMENT PUBLICATIONS:
Will Lend: No

DISSERTATIONS:
Will Lend: No

THESES:
Will Lend: No

AUDIO-VISUAL MATERIALS:
Records: Will not lend
Cassettes: Will not lend
Other (slides, filmstrips,
etc.): Will lend

COMPUTER SOFTWARE:
Will Lend: No

PHOTODUPLICATION SERVICE:
No charge up to 0 exposures
Charge Per Exposure: 10¢
Minimum/handling Fee: $1.00
Average Turnaround Time:
1-3 days

MICROFILMING SERVICE:
Service Available: No
Charges: N/A

DO YOU CHARGE THE BORROWING
LIBRARY FOR POSTAGE? No

FOR HOW LONG DO YOU SUSPEND ILL
SERVICE OVER THE CHRISTMAS
HOLIDAYS? 3 weeks

ARE THERE ANY GROUPS OF LIBRARIES
FOR WHICH YOU WAIVE FEES? IF
SO, PLEASE NAME THEM: None

BREVARD COUNTY LIBRARY SYSTEM

NUC CODE: (Not answered)

OCLC CODE: (Not answered)

ADDRESS: Interlibrary Loan
Brevard County Library
System
2575 N. Courtenay Pkwy.
Merritt Island, FL
32952

TELEPHONE: (305) 453-9509

LIST NAMES OF BRANCHES WITH
SEPARATE POLICIES: None

BOOKS:
Will Lend: Yes
Length of Loan: 3 weeks
Renewable: Yes
Charges: (Not answered)
Average Turnaround Time:
4 days
If you have indicated that a
book is not to be lent, will
you on receipt of a letter
from the requesting library
search the index for given
entries? (Not answered)

PERIODICALS:
Bound: Will not lend
Unbound: Will not lend
Loan Period: N/A
Renewable: N/A
Will lend if article exceeds
_____ number of pages (Not
answered)

MICROFORMS:
Will Lend: No
Specific Types of Microforms:
N/A

GOVERNMENT PUBLICATIONS:
Will Lend: No; will photocopy if available

DISSERTATIONS:
Will Lend: Do not own

THESES:
Will Lend: Do not own

AUDIO-VISUAL MATERIALS:
Records: Will not lend
Cassettes: Will not lend
Other (slides, filmstrips,
etc.): Will not lend

COMPUTER SOFTWARE:
Will Lend: No

PHOTODUPLICATION SERVICE:
No charge up to 0 exposures
Charge Per Exposure: 10¢
from hardcopy; 25¢ from
microcopy
Minimum/handling Fee: $1.00
Average Turnaround Time:
3 days

MICROFILMING SERVICE:
Service Available: No
Charges: N/A

DO YOU CHARGE THE BORROWING
LIBRARY FOR POSTAGE? (Not
answered)

FOR HOW LONG DO YOU SUSPEND ILL
SERVICE OVER THE CHRISTMAS
HOLIDAYS? No suspension

ARE THERE ANY GROUPS OF LIBRARIES
FOR WHICH YOU WAIVE FEES? IF
SO, PLEASE NAME THEM: None

FLORIDA ATLANTIC UNIVERSITY

NUC CODE: FBrU

OCLC CODE: FGM

ADDRESS: Interlibrary Loan
Florida Atlantic
University Library
Boca Raton, FL 33431

TELEPHONE: (305) 393-3769

LIST NAMES OF BRANCHES WITH
SEPARATE POLICIES: None

BOOKS:
Will Lend: Yes
Length of Loan: 2 weeks
Renewable: Yes
Charges: None
Average Turnaround Time:
2 days
If you have indicated that a
book is not to be lent, will
you on receipt of a letter
from the requesting library
search the index for given
entries? Yes

PERIODICALS:
Bound: Will not lend
Unbound: Will not lend
Loan Period: N/A
Renewable: N/A
Will lend if article exceeds
_____ number of pages (Not
answered)

MICROFORMS:
Will Lend: No
Specific Types of Microforms:
N/A

GOVERNMENT PUBLICATIONS:
Will Lend: Yes

DISSERTATIONS:
Will Lend: Yes

THESES:
Will Lend: Yes

AUDIO-VISUAL MATERIALS:
Records: Will not lend
Cassettes: Will not lend
Other (slides, filmstrips,
etc.): Will not lend

COMPUTER SOFTWARE:
Will Lend: No

PHOTODUPLICATION SERVICE:
No charge up to 0 exposures
Charge Per Exposure: 10¢
Minimum/handling Fee: $1.00
Average Turnaround Time:
2 days

MICROFILMING SERVICE:
Service Available: No
Charges: N/A

DO YOU CHARGE THE BORROWING
LIBRARY FOR POSTAGE? No

FOR HOW LONG DO YOU SUSPEND ILL
SERVICE OVER THE CHRISTMAS
HOLIDAYS? No suspension

ARE THERE ANY GROUPS OF LIBRARIES
FOR WHICH YOU WAIVE FEES? IF
SO, PLEASE NAME THEM: Florida
State University System
libraries

FLORIDA INTERNATIONAL UNIVERSITY

NUC CODE: (Not answered)

OCLC CODE: FXG

ADDRESS: Interlibrary Loan
University Libraries
Florida International
University
Tamiami Campus
Miami, FL 33199

TELEPHONE: (305) 554-2459

LIST NAMES OF BRANCHES WITH
SEPARATE POLICIES:
University Libraries
Florida International
Library
North Campus
North Miami, FL 33181

BOOKS:
Will Lend: Yes
Length of Loan: 3 weeks
Renewable: Yes
Charges: (Not answered)
Average Turnaround Time:
2 days
If you have indicated that a
book is not to be lent, will
you on receipt of a letter
from the requesting library
search the index for given
entries? Yes

PERIODICALS:
Bound: Will not lend
Unbound: Will not lend
Loan Period: N/A
Renewable: N/A
Will lend if article exceeds
_____ number of pages (Will
not lend, regardless of
length of article)

MICROFORMS:
Will Lend: Yes
Specific Types of Microforms:
Film, fiche

GOVERNMENT PUBLICATIONS:
Will Lend: Yes

DISSERTATIONS:
Will Lend: Yes, if 2d copy
available

THESES:
Will Lend: Yes, if 2d copy
available

AUDIO-VISUAL MATERIALS:
Records: Will not lend
Cassettes: Will not lend
Other (slides, filmstrips,
etc.): Will not lend

COMPUTER SOFTWARE:
Will Lend: No

PHOTODUPLICATION SERVICE:
No charge up to 0 exposures
Charge Per Exposure: 10¢
Minimum Fee: $1.00
Average Turnaround Time:
2 days

MICROFILMING SERVICE:
Service Available: No
Charges: N/A

DO YOU CHARGE THE BORROWING
LIBRARY FOR POSTAGE? No

FOR HOW LONG DO YOU SUSPEND ILL
SERVICE OVER THE CHRISTMAS
HOLIDAYS? No suspension

ARE THERE ANY GROUPS OF LIBRARIES
FOR WHICH YOU WAIVE FEES? IF
SO, PLEASE NAME THEM: Florida
Atlantic University and Univ.
West Florida

FLORIDA STATE UNIVERSITY

NUC CODE: FTaSU

OCLC CODE: FDA

ADDRESS: Interlibrary Loan
Strozier Library
Florida State
University
Tallahassee, FL 32306

TELEPHONE: (904) 644-4466

LIST NAMES OF BRANCHES WITH
SEPARATE POLICIES:
Law Library
Instructional Systems
Development Center
(Educational films
library)

BOOKS:
Will Lend: Yes
Length of Loan: 3 weeks
Renewable: No
Charges: Reciprocal
Average Turnarond Time:
2-3 weeks
If you have indicated that a
book is not to be lent, will
you on receipt of a letter
from the requesting library
search the index for given
entries? Only if time
permits

PERIODICALS:
Bound: Will not lend
Unbound: Will not lend
Loan Period: N/A
Renewable: N/A
Will lend if article exceeds
_____ number of pages (Not
answered)

MICROFORMS:
Will Lend: Yes
Specific Types of Microforms:
Film, card, fiche

GOVERNMENT PUBLICATIONS:
Will Lend: Yes

DISSERTATIONS:
Will Lend: Yes; 1953 to
present available from
University Microfilms

THESES:
Will Lend: Yes

AUDIO-VISUAL MATERIALS:
Records: Will not lend
Cassettes: Will lend
Other (slides, filmstrips,
etc.): Do not own

COMPUTER SOFTWARE:
Will Lend: Do not own

PHOTODUPLICATION SERVICE:
No charge up to 0 exposures
Charge Per Exposure: 10¢
in-state; 20¢ out-of-state
Minimum/handling Fee: $1.00
in-state; $2.00 out-of-
state
Average Turnaround Time:
2-3 weeks

MICROFILMING SERVICE:
Service Available: Yes
Charges: 15¢ per frame,
$15.00 minimum

DO YOU CHARGE THE BORROWING
LIBRARY FOR POSTAGE? No

FOR HOW LONG DO YOU SUSPEND ILL
SERVICE OVER THE CHRISTMAS
HOLIDAYS? 2 weeks before
Christmas till January 2

ARE THERE ANY GROUPS OF LIBRARIES
FOR WHICH YOU WAIVE FEES? IF
SO, PLEASE NAME THEM: None

JACKSONVILLE PUBLIC LIBRARY

NUC CODE: FJ

OCLC CODE: JPL

ADDRESS: Interlibrary Loan
Jacksonville Public
Library
122 N. Ocean St.
Jacksonville, FL 32202

TELEPHONE: (904) 633-2087 or
633-2088

LIST NAMES OF BRANCHES WITH
SEPARATE POLICIES: None

BOOKS:
Will Lend: Yes
Length of Loan: 4 weeks
Renewable: Yes, if no
reserves
Charges: (Not answered)
Average Turnaround Time:
Depends on workload
If you have indicated that a
book is not to be lent, will
you on receipt of a letter
from the requesting library
search the index for given
entries? Depends on
individual situation

PERIODICALS:
Bound: Will not lend
Unbound: Will not lend
Loan Period: N/A
Renewable: N/A
Will lend if article exceeds
_____ number of pages (Will
not lend, regardless of
length of article. Will
photocopy article only.)

MICROFORMS:
Will Lend: No
Specific Types of Microforms:
N/A

GOVERNMENT PUBLICATIONS:
Will Lend: Yes, with
permission of department

DISSERTATIONS:
Will Lend: No

THESES:
Will Lend: No

AUDIO-VISUAL MATERIALS:
Records: Will not lend
Cassettes: Will not lend
Other (slides, filmstrips,
etc.): (Not answered)

COMPUTER SOFTWARE:
Will Lend: No

PHOTODUPLICATION SERVICE:
No charge up to 2 exposures
Charge Per Exposure: 10¢
Minimum/handling Fee: $1.00
Average Turnaround Time:
Depends on workload

MICROFILMING SERVICE:
Service Available: No
Charges: N/A

DO YOU CHARGE THE BORROWING
LIBRARY FOR POSTAGE? No

FOR HOW LONG DO YOU SUSPEND ILL
SERVICE OVER THE CHRISTMAS
HOLIDAYS? No suspension

ARE THERE ANY GROUPS OF LIBRARIES
FOR WHICH YOU WAIVE FEES? IF
SO, PLEASE NAME THEM: FLIN
(Florida Library
Information Network)

MIAMI-DADE PUBLIC LIBRARY

NUC CODE: FM

OCLC CODE: DZM

ADDRESS: Interlibrary Loan
          Miami-Dade Public
          Library
          One Biscayne Blvd.
          Miami, FL 33132

TELEPHONE: (305) 579-5023

LIST NAMES OF BRANCHES WITH
  SEPARATE POLICIES: None

BOOKS:
  Will Lend: Yes
  Length of Loan: 4 weeks
  Renewable: Yes
  Charges: (Not answered)
  Average Turnaround Time:
    (Not answered)
  If you have indicated that a
    book is not to be lent, will
    you on receipt of a letter
    from the requesting library
    search the index for given
    entries? (Not answered)

PERIODICALS:
  Bound: Will not lend
  Unbound: Will not lend
  Loan Period: N/A
  Renewable: N/A
  Will lend if article exceeds
    _____ number of pages (Not
    answered)

MICROFORMS:
  Will Lend: No
  Specific Types of Microforms:
    N/A

GOVERNMENT PUBLICATIONS:
  Will Lend: Yes

DISSERTATIONS:
  Will Lend: Yes

THESES:
  Will Lend: Yes

AUDIO-VISUAL MATERIALS:
  Records: Will not lend
  Cassettes: Will not lend
  Other (slides, filmstrips,
    etc.): (Not answered)

COMPUTER SOFTWARE:
  Will Lend: (Not answered)

PHOTODUPLICATION SERVICE:
  No charge up to 10 exposures
  Charge Per Exposure: 10¢
  Minimum/handling Fee: None
  Average Turnaround Time:
    1-5 days

MICROFILMING SERVICE:
  Service Available: No
  Charges: N/A

DO YOU CHARGE THE BORROWING
  LIBRARY FOR POSTAGE? No

FOR HOW LONG DO YOU SUSPEND ILL
  SERVICE OVER THE CHRISTMAS
  HOLIDAYS? (Not answered)

ARE THERE ANY GROUPS OF LIBRARIES
  FOR WHICH YOU WAIVE FEES? IF
  SO, PLEASE NAME THEM: (Not
  answered)

ORANGE LIBRARY SYSTEM

NUC CODE: FO

OCLC CODE: ORL

ADDRESS: Interlibrary Loan
          Orange Library System
          10 N. Rosalind
          Orlando, FL 32801

TELEPHONE: (305) 425-4694

LIST NAMES OF BRANCHES WITH
  SEPARATE POLICIES: None--
    ILL centralized in main
    library

BOOKS:
  Will Lend: Yes
  Length of Loan: 3-4 weeks
  Renewable: Yes
  Charges: None
  Average Turnaround Time:
    1 week
  If you have indicated that a
    book is not to be lent, will
    you on receipt of a letter
    from the requesting library
    search the index for given
    entries? Yes (including
    genealogy "name" searches
    in indexes)

PERIODICALS:
  Bound: Will not lend
  Unbound: Will not lend
  Loan Period: N/A
  Renewable: N/A
  Will lend if article exceeds
    _____ number of pages (Will
    not lend, regardless of
    length of article)

MICROFORMS:
  Will Lend: No
  Specific Types of Microforms:
    N/A

GOVERNMENT PUBLICATIONS:
  Will Lend: No

DISSERTATIONS:
  Will Lend: Do not own

THESES:
  Will Lend: Do not own

AUDIO-VISUAL MATERIALS:
  Records: Will not lend
  Cassettes: Will not lend
  Other (slides, filmstrips,
    etc.): Will not lend

COMPUTER SOFTWARE:
  Will Lend: No

PHOTODUPLICATION SERVICE:
  No charge up to 0 exposures
  Charge Per Exposure: 15¢
  Minimum/handling Fee: $1.00
  Average Turnaround Time:
    1 week

MICROFILMING SERVICE:
  Service Available: No
  Charges: N/A

DO YOU CHARGE THE BORROWING
  LIBRARY FOR POSTAGE? No

FOR HOW LONG DO YOU SUSPEND ILL
  SERVICE OVER THE CHRISTMAS
  HOLIDAYS? No suspension

ARE THERE ANY GROUPS OF LIBRARIES
  FOR WHICH YOU WAIVE FEES? IF
  SO, PLEASE NAME THEM: None

PALM BEACH COUNTY PUBLIC LIBRARY SYSTEM

NUC CODE: (Not answered)

OCLC CODE: (Not answered)

ADDRESS: Interlibrary Loan
          Palm Beach County
            Public Library System
          3650 Summit Blvd.
          West Palm Beach, FL
            33406

TELEPHONE: (305) 686-0895

LIST NAMES OF BRANCHES WITH
    SEPARATE POLICIES: None--
    all branches use one
    policy

BOOKS:
    Will Lend: Yes
    Length of Loan: 3 weeks
    Renewable: No
    Charges: None
    Average Turnaround Time:
      (Not answered)
    If you have indicated that a
      book is not to be lent, will
      you on receipt of a letter
      from the requesting library
      search the index for given
      entries? Yes

PERIODICALS:
    Bound: Will not lend
    Unbound: Will not lend
    Loan Period: N/A
    Renewable: N/A
    Will lend if article exceeds
      _____ number of pages (Not
      answered)

MICROFORMS:
    Will Lend: No
    Specific Types of Microforms:
      N/A

GOVERNMENT PUBLICATIONS:
    Will Lend: No

DISSERTATIONS:
    Will Lend: Do not own

THESES:
    Will Lend: Do not own

AUDIO-VISUAL MATERIALS:
    Records: Will not lend
    Cassettes: Will not lend
    Other (slides, filmstrips,
      etc.): Will not lend

COMPUTER SOFTWARE:
    Will Lend: No

PHOTODUPLICATION SERVICE:
    No charge up to 0 exposures
    Charge Per Exposure: 10¢
    Minimum/handling Fee: None
    Average Turnaround Time:
      (Not answered)

MICROFILMING SERVICE:
    Service Available: No
    Charges: N/A

DO YOU CHARGE THE BORROWING
    LIBRARY FOR POSTAGE? No

FOR HOW LONG DO YOU SUSPEND ILL
    SERVICE OVER THE CHRISTMAS
    HOLIDAYS? No suspension

ARE THERE ANY GROUPS OF LIBRARIES
    FOR WHICH YOU WAIVE FEES? IF
    SO, PLEASE NAME THEM: None

ST. PETERSBURG PUBLIC LIBRARY

NUC CODE: FSP

OCLC CODE: (Not answered)

ADDRESS: Interlibrary Loan
          Reference Dept.
          St. Petersburg Public
            Library
          3745 9 Ave. N.
          St. Petersburg, FL
            33713

TELEPHONE: (813) 893-7724

LIST NAMES OF BRANCHES WITH
    SEPARATE POLICIES: None

BOOKS:
    Will Lend: Yes
    Length of Loan: 4 weeks
    Renewable: No
    Charges: Postage
    Average Turnaround Time:
      (Not answered)
    If you have indicated that a
      book is not to be lent, will
      you on receipt of a letter
      from the requesting library
      search the index for given
      entries? (Not answered)

PERIODICALS:
    Bound: Will not lend
    Unbound: Will not lend
    Loan Period: N/A
    Renewable: N/A
    Will lend if article exceeds
      _____ number of pages (Not
      answered)

MICROFORMS:
    Will Lend: No
    Specific Types of Microforms:
      N/A

GOVERNMENT PUBLICATIONS:
    Will Lend: Yes

DISSERTATIONS:
    Will Lend: Yes

THESES:
    Will Lend: Yes

AUDIO-VISUAL MATERIALS:
    Records: Will not lend
    Cassettes: Will not lend
    Other (slides, filmstrips,
      etc.): Will not lend

COMPUTER SOFTWARE:
    Will Lend: No

PHOTODUPLICATION SERVICE:
    No charge up to 0 exposures
    Charge Per Exposure: $1.00
    Minimum/handling Fee: $2.00
    Average Turnaround Time:
      2 weeks

MICROFILMING SERVICE:
    Service Available: No
    Charges: N/A

DO YOU CHARGE THE BORROWING
    LIBRARY FOR POSTAGE? Yes

FOR HOW LONG DO YOU SUSPEND ILL
    SERVICE OVER THE CHRISTMAS
    HOLIDAYS? Dec.15-Jan.4

ARE THERE ANY GROUPS OF LIBRARIES
    FOR WHICH YOU WAIVE FEES? IF
    SO, PLEASE NAME THEM: None

STATE LIBRARY OF FLORIDA

NUC CODE: F

OCLC CODE: FBA

ADDRESS: Interlibrary Loan
State Library of
Florida
Gray Bldg.
Tallahassee, FL 32304

TELEPHONE: (904) 487-2651

LIST NAMES OF BRANCHES WITH
SEPARATE POLICIES: None

BOOKS:
Will Lend: Yes
Length of Loan: 4 weeks
Renewable: Yes
Charges: (Not answered)
Average Turnaround Time:
(Not answered)
If you have indicated that a
book is not to be lent, will
you on receipt of a letter
from the requesting library
search the index for given
entries? (Not answered)

PERIODICALS:
Bound: Will not lend
Unbound: Will not lend
Loan Period: N/A
Renewable: N/A
Will lend if article exceeds
_____ number of pages (Not
answered)

MICROFORMS:
Will Lend: Yes
Specific Types of Microforms:
All types

GOVERNMENT PUBLICATIONS:
Will Lend: Yes

DISSERTATIONS:
Will Lend: Yes

THESES:
Will Lend: Yes

AUDIO-VISUAL MATERIALS:
Records: (Not answered)
Cassettes: (Not answered)
Other (slides, filmstrips,
etc.): (Not answered)

COMPUTER SOFTWARE:
Will Lend: (Not answered)

PHOTODUPLICATION SERVICE:
No charge up to 25 exposures
Charge Per Exposure: 10¢
Minimum/handling Fee: None
Average Turnaround Time:
(Not answered)

MICROFILMING SERVICE:
Service Available: No
Charges: N/A

DO YOU CHARGE THE BORROWING
LIBRARY FOR POSTAGE? No

FOR HOW LONG DO YOU SUSPEND ILL
SERVICE OVER THE CHRISTMAS
HOLIDAYS? No suspension

ARE THERE ANY GROUPS OF LIBRARIES
FOR WHICH YOU WAIVE FEES? IF
SO, PLEASE NAME THEM: (Not
answered)

STATE UNIVERSITY SYSTEM OF FLORIDA

NUC CODE: (Not answered)

OCLC CODE: (Not answered)

ADDRESS: State University System
Extension Library
State University System
of Florida
1011 First Avenue North
St. Petersburg, FL
33705-1591

TELEPHONE: (813) 893-9120

LIST NAMES OF BRANCHES WITH
SEPARATE POLICIES: None

BOOKS:
Will Lend: No
Length of Loan: N/A
Renewable: N/A
Charges: N/A
Average Turnaround Time:
N/A
If you have indicated that a
book is not to be lent, will
you on receipt of a letter
from the requesting library
search the index for given
entries? No

PERIODICALS:
Bound: Will not lend
Unbound: Will not lend
Loan Period: N/A
Renewable: N/A
Will lend if article exceeds
_____ number of pages (Will
not lend, regardless of
length of article)

MICROFORMS:
Will Lend: No
Specific Types of Microforms:
N/A

GOVERNMENT PUBLICATIONS:
Will Lend: No

DISSERTATIONS:
Will Lend: Do not own

THESES:
Will Lend: Do not own

AUDIO-VISUAL MATERIALS:
Records: Will not lend
Cassettes: Will not lend
Other (slides, filmstrips,
etc.): Will not lend

COMPUTER SOFTWARE:
Will Lend: Do not own

PHOTODUPLICATION SERVICE:
Service not offered

MICROFILMING SERVICE:
Service Available: No
Charges: N/A

DO YOU CHARGE THE BORROWING
LIBRARY FOR POSTAGE? N/A

FOR HOW LONG DO YOU SUSPEND ILL
SERVICE OVER THE CHRISTMAS
HOLIDAYS? N/A

ARE THERE ANY GROUPS OF LIBRARIES
FOR WHICH YOU WAIVE FEES? IF
SO, PLEASE NAME THEM: N/A

TAMPA PUBLIC LIBRARY

NUC CODE: (Not answered)

OCLC CODE: TNH

ADDRESS: Interlibrary Loan
Tampa Public Library
900 N. Ashley St.
Tampa, FL 33602

TELEPHONE: (813) 223-8955

LIST NAMES OF BRANCHES WITH
SEPARATE POLICIES: None

BOOKS:
Will Lend: Yes
Length of Loan: 3 weeks
Renewable: Yes
Charges: Overdue fines,
10¢ per day
Average Turnaround Time:
(Not answered)
If you have indicated that a
book is not to be lent, will
you on receipt of a letter
from the requesting library
search the index for given
entries? Yes

PERIODICALS:
Bound: Will not lend
Unbound: Will not lend
Loan Period: N/A
Renewable: N/A
Will lend if article exceeds
_____ number of pages (Not
answered)

MICROFORMS:
Will Lend: No
Specific Types of Microforms:
N/A

GOVERNMENT PUBLICATIONS:
Will Lend: No

DISSERTATIONS:
Will Lend: No

THESES:
Will Lend: No

AUDIO-VISUAL MATERIALS:
Records: Will not lend
Cassettes: Will not lend
Other (slides, filmstrips,
etc.): Will not lend

COMPUTER SOFTWARE:
Will Lend: No

PHOTODUPLICATION SERVICE:
No charge up to 10 exposures
Charge Per Exposure: 10¢
Minimum/handling Fee: None
Average Turnaround Time:
10 days

MICROFILMING SERVICE:
Service Available: No
Charges: N/A

DO YOU CHARGE THE BORROWING
LIBRARY FOR POSTAGE? No

FOR HOW LONG DO YOU SUSPEND ILL
SERVICE OVER THE CHRISTMAS
HOLIDAYS? 2 weeks at most

ARE THERE ANY GROUPS OF LIBRARIES
FOR WHICH YOU WAIVE FEES? IF
SO, PLEASE NAME THEM: None

UNIVERSITY OF CENTRAL FLORIDA

NUC CODE: FOT

OCLC CODE: FTU

ADDRESS: Interlibrary Loan
University of Central
Florida
P. O. Box 25000
Orlando, FL 32816

TELEPHONE: (305) 275-2383

LIST NAMES OF BRANCHES WITH
SEPARATE POLICIES: None

BOOKS:
Will Lend: Yes
Length of Loan: 3 weeks
Renewable: Yes
Charges: None
Average Turnaround Time:
4 working days
If you have indicated that a
book is not to be lent, will
you on receipt of a letter
from the requesting library
search the index for given
entries? (Not answered)

PERIODICALS:
Bound: Will not lend
Unbound: Will not lend
Loan Period: N/A
Renewable: N/A
Will lend if article exceeds
50 pages

MICROFORMS:
Will Lend: No
Specific Types of Microforms:
N/A

GOVERNMENT PUBLICATIONS:
Will Lend: Yes

DISSERTATIONS:
Will Lend: Yes

THESES:
Will Lend: Yes

AUDIO-VISUAL MATERIALS:
Records: Will not lend
Cassettes: Will not lend
Other (slides, filmstrips,
etc.): Will not lend

COMPUTER SOFTWARE:
Will Lend: No

PHOTODUPLICATION SERVICE:
No charge up to 0 exposures
Charge Per Exposure: 10¢
Minimum/handling Fee: $1.00
up to 10 pages
Average Turnaround Time:
4 working days

MICROFILMING SERVICE:
Service Available: No
Charges: N/A

DO YOU CHARGE THE BORROWING
LIBRARY FOR POSTAGE? No

FOR HOW LONG DO YOU SUSPEND ILL
SERVICE OVER THE CHRISTMAS
HOLIDAYS? App. Dec.15-Jan.2

ARE THERE ANY GROUPS OF LIBRARIES
FOR WHICH YOU WAIVE FEES? IF
SO, PLEASE NAME THEM: None

UNIVERSITY OF FLORIDA

NUC CODE: FU

OCLC CODE: FUG

ADDRESS: Interlibrary Loan
           273 Library West
           University of Florida
           Gainesville, FL 32611

TELEPHONE: (904) 392-0311

LIST NAMES OF BRANCHES WITH
  SEPARATE POLICIES:
    Hume Library (Ag.)
    Legal Information Center
      (Law)
    Health Center Library
      (Med.)
    J. H. Miller Health Center

BOOKS:
  Will Lend: Yes
  Length of Loan: 1 month
  Renewable: Yes
  Charges: None
  Average Turnaround Time:
    1 week
  If you have indicated that a
    book is not to be lent, will
    you on receipt of a letter
    from the requesting library
    search the index for given
    entries? (Not answered)

PERIODICALS:
  Bound: Will not lend
  Unbound: Will not lend
  Loan Period: N/A
  Renewable: N/A
  Will lend if article exceeds
    _____ number of pages (Not
    answered)

MICROFORMS:
  Will Lend: Yes, some of them
  Specific Types of Microforms:
    Microfilm

GOVERNMENT PUBLICATIONS:
  Will Lend: Yes, some of them

DISSERTATIONS:
  Will Lend: Yes, pre-1954

THESES:
  Will Lend: Yes, pre-1954

AUDIO-VISUAL MATERIALS:
  Records: Will not lend
  Cassettes: Will not lend
  Other (slides, filmstrips,
    etc.): Will not lend

COMPUTER SOFTWARE:
  Will Lend: No

PHOTODUPLICATION SERVICE:
  No charge up to 0 exposures
  Charge Per Exposure: (Not
    answered)
  Minimum Fee: $2.00
  Average Turnaround Time:
    1 week

MICROFILMING SERVICE:
  Service Available: Yes
  Charges: 14¢ per frame +
    $13.50 per reel + $5.00
    service charge + postage

DO YOU CHARGE THE BORROWING
  LIBRARY FOR POSTAGE? No

FOR HOW LONG DO YOU SUSPEND ILL
  SERVICE OVER THE CHRISTMAS
  HOLIDAYS? No suspension

ARE THERE ANY GROUPS OF LIBRARIES
  FOR WHICH YOU WAIVE FEES? IF
  SO, PLEASE NAME THEM: None

UNIVERSITY OF FLORIDA--J. HILLIS MILLER HEALTH CENTER

NUC CODE: FU-HC

OCLC CODE: FUH

ADDRESS: Interlibrary Loan
           University of Florida
           J. Hillis Miller Health
             Center Library
           P. O. Box J-206, JHMHC
           Gainesville, FL 32610

TELEPHONE: (904) 392-4018

LIST NAMES OF BRANCHES WITH
  SEPARATE POLICIES: None

BOOKS:
  Will Lend: Yes
  Length of Loan: 1 week
  Renewable: No
  Charges: $4.75
  Average Turnaround Time:
    1 day
  If you have indicated that a
    book is not to be lent, will
    you on receipt of a letter
    from the requesting library
    search the index for given
    entries? (Not answered)

PERIODICALS:
  Bound: Yes, pre-1977 only
  Unbound: Yes, pre-1977 only
  Loan Period: 4 days,
    depending on condition and
    length of article
  Renewable: No
  Will lend if article exceeds
    50 pages and if pre-1977

MICROFORMS:
  Will Lend: No
  Specific Types of Microforms:
    N/A

GOVERNMENT PUBLICATIONS:
  Will Lend: No

DISSERTATIONS:
  Will Lend: No

THESES:
  Will Lend: No

AUDIO-VISUAL MATERIALS:
  Records: Will not lend
  Cassettes: Will not lend
  Other (slides, filmstrips,
    etc.): Will not lend

COMPUTER SOFTWARE:
  Will Lend: No

PHOTODUPLICATION SERVICE:
  No charge up to 0 exposures
  Charge Per Exposure: $4.75
    per article
  Minimum/handling Fee: $4.75
  Average Turnaround Time:
    1 day

MICROFILMING SERVICE:
  Service Available: No
  Charges: N/A

DO YOU CHARGE THE BORROWING
  LIBRARY FOR POSTAGE? No

FOR HOW LONG DO YOU SUSPEND ILL
  SERVICE OVER THE CHRISTMAS
  HOLIDAYS? 4 weeks, original
  materials only

ARE THERE ANY GROUPS OF LIBRARIES
  FOR WHICH YOU WAIVE FEES? IF
  SO, PLEASE NAME THEM: Only
  resource libraries in
  Southeastern region

UNIVERSITY OF SOUTH FLORIDA

NUC CODE: FSN

OCLC CODE: FHC

ADDRESS: Interlibrary Loan
University of South
Florida Library
5700 N. Tamiami Trail
Sarasota, FL 33580

TELEPHONE: (813) 355-7671, X214

LIST NAMES OF BRANCHES WITH
SEPARATE POLICIES: None

BOOKS:
Will Lend: Yes
Length of Loan: 2 weeks
Renewable: Yes
Charges: None
Average Turnaround Time:
1 week
If you have indicated that a
book is not to be lent, will
you on receipt of a letter
from the requesting library
search the index for given
entries? Yes

PERIODICALS:
Bound: Will lend
Unbound: Will not lend
Loan Period: 2 weeks
Renewable: No
Will lend if article exceeds
100 pages

MICROFORMS:
Will Lend: No
Specific Types of Microforms:
N/A

GOVERNMENT PUBLICATIONS:
Will Lend: Yes

DISSERTATIONS:
Will Lend: No

THESES:
Will Lend: No

AUDIO-VISUAL MATERIALS:
Records: Will not lend
Cassettes: Will not lend
Other (slides, filmstrips,
etc.): Will not lend

COMPUTER SOFTWARE:
Will Lend: No

PHOTODUPLICATION SERVICE:
No charge up to 5 exposures
Charge Per Exposure: 10¢
Minimum/handling Fee: None
Average Turnaround Time:
1 week

MICROFILMING SERVICE:
Service Available: No
Charges: N/A

DO YOU CHARGE THE BORROWING
LIBRARY FOR POSTAGE? No

FOR HOW LONG DO YOU SUSPEND ILL
SERVICE OVER THE CHRISTMAS
HOLIDAYS? No suspension

ARE THERE ANY GROUPS OF LIBRARIES
FOR WHICH YOU WAIVE FEES? IF
SO, PLEASE NAME THEM: None

UNIVERSITY OF WEST FLORIDA

NUC CODE: FPeU

OCLC CODE: FWA

ADDRESS: Interlibrary Loan
John C. Pace Library
University of West
Florida
Pensacola, FL 32504

TELEPHONE: (904) 476-9500, X2411

LIST NAMES OF BRANCHES WITH
SEPARATE POLICIES: None

BOOKS:
Will Lend: Yes
Length of Loan: 1 month
Renewable: Yes
Charges: None
Average Turnaround Time:
2 days
If you have indicated that a
book is not to be lent, will
you on receipt of a letter
from the requesting library
search the index for given
entries? (Not answered)

PERIODICALS:
Bound: Will not lend
Unbound: Will not lend
Loan Period: N/A
Renewable: N/A
Will lend if article exceeds
_____ number of pages (Not
answered)

MICROFORMS:
Will Lend: No
Specific Types of Microforms:
N/A

GOVERNMENT PUBLICATIONS:
Will Lend: Yes

DISSERTATIONS:
Will Lend: No

THESES:
Will Lend: Yes

AUDIO-VISUAL MATERIALS:
Records: Will not lend
Cassettes: Will not lend
Other (slides, filmstrips,
etc.): Will not lend

COMPUTER SOFTWARE:
Will Lend: No

PHOTODUPLICATION SERVICE:
No charge up to 0 exposures
Charge Per Exposure: 10¢
Minimum/handling Fee: $1.00
for up to 10 pages
Average Turnaround Time:
2 days

MICROFILMING SERVICE:
Service Available: No
Charges: N/A

DO YOU CHARGE THE BORROWING
LIBRARY FOR POSTAGE? No

FOR HOW LONG DO YOU SUSPEND ILL
SERVICE OVER THE CHRISTMAS
HOLIDAYS? App. 2 weeks

ARE THERE ANY GROUPS OF LIBRARIES
FOR WHICH YOU WAIVE FEES? IF
SO, PLEASE NAME THEM:
Participants in West Florida
Union List; all state
university system libraries
who enter into reciprocal
agreement

WEST FLORIDA REGIONAL LIBRARY

NUC CODE: (Not answered)

OCLC CODE: (Not answered)

ADDRESS: Interlibrary Loan
           West Florida Regional
             Library
           200 West Gregory St.
           Pensacola, FL   32501

TELEPHONE: (904) 436-4261

LIST NAMES OF BRANCHES WITH
  SEPARATE POLICIES: None

BOOKS:
  Will Lend: Yes, circulating
    collection only
  Length of Loan: 3 weeks
  Renewable: No
  Charges: None
  Average Turnaround Time:
    3 days
  If you have indicated that a
    book is not to be lent, will
    you on receipt of a letter
    from the requesting library
    search the index for given
    entries?   Yes

PERIODICALS:
  Bound: Will not lend
  Unbound: Will not lend
  Loan Period: N/A
  Renewable: N/A
  Will lend if article exceeds
    _____ number of pages   (Not
      answered)

MICROFORMS:
  Will Lend: Yes
  Specific Types of Microforms:
    Pensacola News-Journal on
    microfilm

GOVERNMENT PUBLICATIONS:
  Will Lend: Do not own

DISSERTATIONS:
  Will Lend: Do not own

THESES:
  Will Lend: Do not own

AUDIO-VISUAL MATERIALS:
  Records: Will not lend
  Cassettes: Will not lend
  Other (slides, filmstrips,
    etc.):   Will not lend

COMPUTER SOFTWARE:
  Will Lend: Do not own

PHOTODUPLICATION SERVICE:
  No charge up to 5 exposures
  Charge Per Exposure: 15¢
  Minimum/handling Fee: $1.00
  Average Turnaround Time:
    3 days

MICROFILMING SERVICE:
  Service Available: No
  Charges: N/A

DO YOU CHARGE THE BORROWING
  LIBRARY FOR POSTAGE?   No

FOR HOW LONG DO YOU SUSPEND ILL
  SERVICE OVER THE CHRISTMAS
  HOLIDAYS?   No suspension

ARE THERE ANY GROUPS OF LIBRARIES
  FOR WHICH YOU WAIVE FEES?   IF
  SO, PLEASE NAME THEM: None

ATLANTA PUBLIC LIBRARY

NUC CODE: GA

OCLC CODE: GAP

ADDRESS: Interlibrary Loan
Atlanta Public Library
One Margaret Mitchell
Square
Atlanta, GA 30303

TELEPHONE: (404) 688-4636, X245

LIST NAMES OF BRANCHES WITH
SEPARATE POLICIES: None

BOOKS:
Will Lend: Yes
Length of Loan: 3 weeks
Renewable: Yes
Charges: None
Average Turnaround Time:
(Not answered)
If you have indicated that a
book is not to be lent, will
you on receipt of a letter
from the requesting library
search the index for given
entries? Yes

PERIODICALS:
Bound: Will not lend
Unbound: Will not lend
Loan Period: N/A
Renewable: N/A
Will lend if article exceeds
_____ number of pages (Not
answered)

MICROFORMS:
Will Lend: No
Specific Types of Microforms:
N/A

GOVERNMENT PUBLICATIONS:
Will Lend: No

DISSERTATIONS:
Will Lend: No

THESES:
Will Lend: No

AUDIO-VISUAL MATERIALS:
Records: Will not lend
Cassettes: Will not lend
Other (slides, filmstrips,
etc.): Will not lend

COMPUTER SOFTWARE:
Will Lend: No

PHOTODUPLICATION SERVICE:
No charge up to 0 exposures
Charge Per Exposure: 10¢
Minimum/handling Fee: (Not
answered)
Average Turnaround Time:
(Not answered)

MICROFILMING SERVICE:
Service Available: Yes
Charges: 25¢ per exposure

DO YOU CHARGE THE BORROWING
LIBRARY FOR POSTAGE? No

FOR HOW LONG DO YOU SUSPEND ILL
SERVICE OVER THE CHRISTMAS
HOLIDAYS? No suspension

ARE THERE ANY GROUPS OF LIBRARIES
FOR WHICH YOU WAIVE FEES? IF
SO, PLEASE NAME THEM: Georgia
libraries participating in
GLIN (Georgia Library
Information Network)

ATLANTA UNIVERSITY

NUC CODE: (Not answered)

OCLC CODE: (Not answered)

ADDRESS: Interlibrary Loan
Atlanta University
Center
Robert W. Woodruff
Library
111 Chestnut St., SW
Atlanta, GA 30314

TELEPHONE: (404) 223-5378, X115

LIST NAMES OF BRANCHES WITH
SEPARATE POLICIES: None

BOOKS:
Will Lend: Yes, except for
special collection materials
Length of Loan: 3 weeks
Renewable: Yes
Charges: None
Average Turnaround Time:
(Not answered)
If you have indicated that a
book is not to be lent, will
you on receipt of a letter
from the requesting library
search the index for given
entries? Yes

PERIODICALS:
Bound: Will not lend
Unbound: Will not lend
Loan Period: N/A
Renewable: N/A
Will lend if article exceeds
_____ number of pages (Not
answered)

MICROFORMS:
Will Lend: Yes
Specific Types of Microforms:
Newspapers only

GOVERNMENT PUBLICATIONS:
Will Lend: Yes

DISSERTATIONS:
Will Lend: No

THESES:
Will Lend: No

AUDIO-VISUAL MATERIALS:
Records: Will not lend
Cassettes: (Not answered)
Other (slides, filmstrips,
etc.): Will lend

COMPUTER SOFTWARE:
Will Lend: (Not answered)

PHOTODUPLICATION SERVICE:
No charge up to indefinite
number of exposures
Charge Per Exposure: 10¢
Minimum/handling Fee: $2.00
Average Turnaround Time:
3 weeks

MICROFILMING SERVICE:
Service Available: Yes
Charges: 10¢ per exposure

DO YOU CHARGE THE BORROWING
LIBRARY FOR POSTAGE? No

FOR HOW LONG DO YOU SUSPEND ILL
SERVICE OVER THE CHRISTMAS
HOLIDAYS? 1 month

ARE THERE ANY GROUPS OF LIBRARIES
FOR WHICH YOU WAIVE FEES? IF
SO, PLEASE NAME THEM: Members
of the University Center in
Georgia

CHATTAHOOCHEE VALLEY REGIONAL LIBRARY

NUC CODE: GCOL

OCLC CODE: GCV

ADDRESS: Interlibrary Loan
Chattahoochee Valley
Regional Library
1120 Bradley Dr.
Columbus, GA
31995-1099

TELEPHONE: (404) 327-0211, X15

LIST NAMES OF BRANCHES WITH
SEPARATE POLICIES: None

BOOKS:
Will Lend: Yes
Length of Loan: 14 and 28
days
Renewable: Yes, under special
circumstances
Charges: None
Average Turnaround Time:
5 days
If you have indicated that a
book is not to be lent, will
you on receipt of a letter
from the requesting library
search the index for given
entries? Yes

PERIODICALS:
Bound: Will not lend
Unbound: Will not lend
Loan Period: N/A
Renewable: N/A
Will lend if article exceeds
_____ number of pages (Not
answered)

MICROFORMS:
Will Lend: No
Specific Types of Microforms:
N/A

GOVERNMENT PUBLICATIONS:
Will Lend: Do not own

DISSERTATIONS:
Will Lend: Do not own

THESES:
Will Lend: Do not own

AUDIO-VISUAL MATERIALS:
Records: Will not lend
Cassettes: Will not lend
Other (slides, filmstrips,
etc.): Will not lend

COMPUTER SOFTWARE:
Will Lend: No

PHOTODUPLICATION SERVICE:
No charge up to 5 exposures
Charge Per Exposure: 10¢
Minimum/handling Fee: None
Average Turnaround Time:
4 days

MICROFILMING SERVICE:
Service Available: No
Charges: N/A

DO YOU CHARGE THE BORROWING
LIBRARY FOR POSTAGE? No

FOR HOW LONG DO YOU SUSPEND ILL
SERVICE OVER THE CHRISTMAS
HOLIDAYS? Dec.20-Jan.3

ARE THERE ANY GROUPS OF LIBRARIES
FOR WHICH YOU WAIVE FEES? IF
SO, PLEASE NAME THEM: None

COBB COUNTY PUBLIC LIBRARY SYSTEM

NUC CODE: (Not answered)

OCLC CODE: (Not answered)

ADDRESS: Interlibrary Loan
Cobb County Public
Library System
30 Atlanta St.
Marietta, GA 30060

TELEPHONE: (404) 429-3029

LIST NAMES OF BRANCHES WITH
SEPARATE POLICIES: None

BOOKS:
Will Lend: Yes, from
circulating collection only
Length of Loan: 3 weeks
Renewable: No
Charges: None
Average Turnaround Time:
1-7 days, depending on
availability of book on
shelves
If you have indicated that a
book is not to be lent, will
you on receipt of a letter
from the requesting library
search the index for given
entries? Yes

PERIODICALS:
Bound: Will not lend
Unbound: Will not lend
Loan Period: N/A
Renewable: N/A
Will lend if article exceeds
_____ number of pages (Will
not lend, regardless of
length of article)

MICROFORMS:
Will Lend: No
Specific Types of Microforms:
N/A

GOVERNMENT PUBLICATIONS:
Will Lend: No

DISSERTATIONS:
Will Lend: No

THESES:
Will Lend: No

AUDIO-VISUAL MATERIALS:
Records: Will not lend
Cassettes: Will not lend
Other (slides, filmstrips,
etc.): Will not lend

COMPUTER SOFTWARE:
Will Lend: No

PHOTODUPLICATION SERVICE:
No charge up to 0 exposures
Charge Per Exposure: 10¢
Minimum/handling Fee: None
Average Turnaround Time:
1-3 days

MICROFILMING SERVICE:
Service Available: No
Charges: N/A

DO YOU CHARGE THE BORROWING
LIBRARY FOR POSTAGE? Yes

FOR HOW LONG DO YOU SUSPEND ILL
SERVICE OVER THE CHRISTMAS
HOLIDAYS? No suspension

ARE THERE ANY GROUPS OF LIBRARIES
FOR WHICH YOU WAIVE FEES? IF
SO, PLEASE NAME THEM: None

COLUMBUS COLLEGE

NUC CODE: GColuC

OCLC CODE: GCO

ADDRESS: Interlibrary Loan
Columbus College
Library
Columbus, GA 31907

TELEPHONE: (404) 568-2042

LIST NAMES OF BRANCHES WITH
SEPARATE POLICIES: None

BOOKS:
Will Lend: Yes
Length of Loan: 1 month from
date sent
Renewable: Yes
Charges: None
Average Turnaround Time:
2 days
If you have indicated that a
book is not to be lent, will
you on receipt of a letter
from the requesting library
search the index for given
entries? Depends upon the
complexity of the request

PERIODICALS:
Bound: Will not lend
Unbound: Will not lend
Loan Period: N/A
Renewable: N/A
Will lend if article exceeds
_____ number of pages

MICROFORMS:
Will Lend: Yes, selectively
Specific Types of Microforms:
Microfilm, microfiche

GOVERNMENT PUBLICATIONS:
Will Lend: Yes, selectively

DISSERTATIONS:
Will Lend: Do not own

THESES:
Will Lend: Do not own

AUDIO-VISUAL MATERIALS:
Records: Will not lend
Cassettes: Will not lend
Other (slides, filmstrips,
etc.): Will not lend

COMPUTER SOFTWARE:
Will Lend: No

PHOTODUPLICATION SERVICE:
No charge up to 0 exposures
Charge Per Exposure: 10¢
Minimum/handling Fee: $1.00
Average Turnaround Time:
2 days

MICROFILMING SERVICE:
Service Available: No
Charges: N/A

DO YOU CHARGE THE BORROWING
LIBRARY FOR POSTAGE? No

FOR HOW LONG DO YOU SUSPEND ILL
SERVICE OVER THE CHRISTMAS
HOLIDAYS? 3 weeks

ARE THERE ANY GROUPS OF LIBRARIES
FOR WHICH YOU WAIVE FEES? IF
SO, PLEASE NAME THEM: South
Georgia Associated
Libraries; Central Georgia
Associated Libraries; North
Georgia Associated
Libraries

DEKALB LIBRARY SYSTEM

NUC CODE: GD

OCLC CODE: (Not answered)

ADDRESS: Interlibrary Loan
DeKalb Library System
Maud Burrus Library
215 Sycamore St.
Decatur, GA 30030

TELEPHONE: (404) 378-7569

LIST NAMES OF BRANCHES WITH
SEPARATE POLICIES: None

BOOKS:
Will Lend: Yes
Length of Loan: 3 weeks
Renewable: No
Charges: None
Average Turnaround Time:
1 week
If you have indicated that a
book is not to be lent, will
you on receipt of a letter
from the requesting library
search the index for given
entries? Yes

PERIODICALS:
Bound: Will not lend
Unbound: Will not lend
Loan Period: N/A
Renewable: N/A
Will lend if article exceeds
_____ number of pages (Not
answered)

MICROFORMS:
Will Lend: No
Specific Types of Microforms:
N/A

GOVERNMENT PUBLICATIONS:
Will Lend: Do not own

DISSERTATIONS:
Will Lend: Do not own

THESES:
Will Lend: Do not own

AUDIO-VISUAL MATERIALS:
Records: Will not lend
Cassettes: Will not lend
Other (slides, filmstrips,
etc.): Will not lend

COMPUTER SOFTWARE:
Will Lend: Do not own

PHOTODUPLICATION SERVICE:
No charge up to 0 exposures
Charges Per Exposure: 15¢
from hardcopy; 25¢ from
microform
Minimum/handling Fee: (Not
answered)
Average Turnaround Time:
(Not answered)

MICROFILMING SERVICE:
Service Available: No
Charges: N/A

DO YOU CHARGE THE BORROWING
LIBRARY FOR POSTAGE? No

FOR HOW LONG DO YOU SUSPEND ILL
SERVICE OVER THE CHRISTMAS
HOLIDAYS? No suspension

ARE THERE ANY GROUPS OF LIBRARIES
FOR WHICH YOU WAIVE FEES? IF
SO, PLEASE NAME THEM: None

EMORY UNIVERSITY AT ATLANTA

NUC CODE: GEU

OCLC CODE: EMU

ADDRESS: Interlibrary Loan
Robert W. Woodruff
Library
Emory University
Atlanta, GA 30322

TELEPHONE: (404) 329-6875

LIST NAMES OF BRANCHES WITH
SEPARATE POLICIES:
Theology Library
Medical Library
Dental Library
Library School Library
Law Library

BOOKS:
Will Lend: Yes
Length of Loan: 4 weeks
Renewable: Yes
Charges: None
Average Turnaround Time:
2-4 days
If you have indicated that a
book is not to be lent, will
you on receipt of a letter
from the requesting library
search the index for given
entries? Yes

PERIODICALS:
Bound: Will not lend usually
Unbound: Will not lend usually
Loan Period: (Not answered)
Renewable: (Not answered)
Will lend if article exceeds
_____ number of pages (Not
answered)

MICROFORMS:
Will Lend: Yes
Specific Types of Microforms:
Cards, film, fiche

GOVERNMENT PUBLICATIONS:
Will Lend: Yes

DISSERTATIONS:
Will Lend: Yes; all years are
available from University
Microfilms

THESES:
Will Lend: Yes

AUDIO-VISUAL MATERIALS:
Records: Will not lend
Cassettes: Will not lend
Other (slides, filmstrips,
etc.): Will not lend

COMPUTER SOFTWARE:
Will Lend: No

PHOTODUPLICATION SERVICE:
No charge up to 0 exposures
Charge Per Exposure: 10¢
Minimum/handling Fee: $3.00
Average Turnaround Time:
2-4 days

MICROFILMING SERVICE:
Service Available: No
Charges: N/A

DO YOU CHARGE THE BORROWING
LIBRARY FOR POSTAGE? Only
non-academic libraries

FOR HOW LONG DO YOU SUSPEND ILL
SERVICE OVER THE CHRISTMAS
HOLIDAYS? No suspension

ARE THERE ANY GROUPS OF LIBRARIES
FOR WHICH YOU WAIVE FEES? IF
SO, PLEASE NAME THEM: ASERL,
University Center including
local academic and public
libraries

EMORY UNIVERSITY--SCHOOL OF MEDICINE

NUC CODE: GEU-M

OCLC CODE: EMM

ADDRESS: Interlibrary Loan
A. W. Calhoun Medical
Library
Woodruff Memorial Bldg.
Emory University
Atlanta, GA 30322

TELEPHONE: (404) 329-5816

LIST NAMES OF BRANCHES WITH
SEPARATE POLICIES:
Grady Branch

BOOKS:
Will Lend: Yes
Length of Loan: 28 days from
checkout date
Renewable: Yes
Charges: $4.75 (rate
established by SERMLP)
Average Turnaround Time:
1 day
If you have indicated that a
book is not to be lent, will
you on receipt of a letter
from the requesting library
search the index for given
entries? (Not answered)

PERIODICALS:
Bound: Will not lend
Unbound: Will not lend
Loan Period: N/A
Renewable: N/A
Will lend if article exceeds
_____ number of pages (Not
answered)

MICROFORMS:
Will Lend: Do not own
Specific Types of Microforms:
N/A

GOVERNMENT PUBLICATIONS:
Will Lend: No

DISSERTATIONS:
Will Lend: Yes

THESES:
Will Lend: Yes

AUDIO-VISUAL MATERIALS:
Records: Will lend
Cassettes: Will lend
Other (slides, filmstrips,
etc.): Will lend

COMPUTER SOFTWARE:
Will Lend: Do not own

PHOTODUPLICATION SERVICE:
No charge up to 0 exposures
Charges: $4.75 per
transaction (rate
established by SERMLP)
Average Turnaround Time:
1 day

MICROFILMING SERVICE:
Service Available: No
Charges: N/A

DO YOU CHARGE THE BORROWING
LIBRARY FOR POSTAGE? No

FOR HOW LONG DO YOU SUSPEND ILL
SERVICE OVER THE CHRISTMAS
HOLIDAYS? 2 days

ARE THERE ANY GROUPS OF LIBRARIES
FOR WHICH YOU WAIVE FEES? IF
SO, PLEASE NAME THEM:
University Center in
Georgia members

FLINT RIVER REGIONAL LIBRARY

NUC CODE: (Not answered)

OCLC CODE: (Not answered)

ADDRESS: Interlibrary Loan
Flint River Regional
Library
800 Memorial Dr.
Griffin, GA   30223

TELEPHONE: (404) 227-2756

LIST NAMES OF BRANCHES WITH
SEPARATE POLICIES: None

BOOKS:
Will Lend: Yes
Length of Loan: 1 month
Renewable: Yes
Charges: Postage
Average Turnaround Time:
(Not answered)
If you have indicated that a
book is not to be lent, will
you on receipt of a letter
from the requesting library
search the index for given
entries?   No

PERIODICALS:
Bound: Will not lend
Unbound: Will not lend
Loan Period: N/A
Renewable: N/A
Will lend if article exceeds
_____ number of pages   (Will
not lend, regardless of
length of article.   Will
photocopy articles)

MICROFORMS:
Will Lend: No
Specific Types of Microforms:
N/A

GOVERNMENT PUBLICATIONS:
Will Lend: No

DISSERTATIONS:
Will Lend: No

THESES:
Will Lend: No

AUDIO-VISUAL MATERIALS:
Records: Will not lend
Cassettes: Will not lend
Other (slides, filmstrips,
etc.):   Will not lend

COMPUTER SOFTWARE:
Will Lend: No

PHOTODUPLICATION SERVICE:
No charge up to 0 exposures
Charge Per Exposure: 15¢
Minimum/handling Fee:
Postage
Average Turnaround Time:
(Not answered)

MICROFILMING SERVICE:
Service Available: No
Charges: N/A

DO YOU CHARGE THE BORROWING
LIBRARY FOR POSTAGE?   Yes--
pay when materials are
returned

FOR HOW LONG DO YOU SUSPEND ILL
SERVICE OVER THE CHRISTMAS
HOLIDAYS?   1 week

ARE THERE ANY GROUPS OF LIBRARIES
FOR WHICH YOU WAIVE FEES?   IF
SO, PLEASE NAME THEM: None

GEORGIA DEPARTMENT OF EDUCATION

NUC CODE: GAE-P

OCLC CODE: GSL

ADDRESS: Interlibrary Loan
Readers Services
Division of Public
Library Services
Georgia Department of
Education
156 Trinity Ave., S.W.
Atlanta, GA   30303

TELEPHONE: (404) 656-2461

LIST NAMES OF BRANCHES WITH
SEPARATE POLICIES: None

BOOKS:
Will Lend: Yes
Length of Loan: 1 month
Renewable: Yes
Charges: Postage and
insurance (if necessary)
Average Turnaround Time:
As soon as possible
If you have indicated that a
book is not to be lent, will
you on receipt of a letter
from the requesting library
search the index for given
entries?   No

PERIODICALS:
Bound: Will lend, selectively
Unbound: Will lend,
selectively
Loan Period: 2 weeks
Renewable: Yes
May lend if article exceeds
5 pages

MICROFORMS:
Will Lend: Yes
Specific Types of Microforms:
Microfilm only

GOVERNMENT PUBLICATIONS:
Will Lend: Yes

DISSERTATIONS:
Will Lend: Yes

THESES:
Will Lend: Do not own

AUDIO-VISUAL MATERIALS:
Records: Do not own
Cassettes: Will not lend
Other (slides, filmstrips,
etc.):   Will not lend

COMPUTER SOFTWARE:
Will Lend: Do not own

PHOTODUPLICATION SERVICE:
No charge up to 10 exposures
Charge Per Exposure: 10¢
from hardcopy; 15¢ from
microfilm; 25¢ per fiche
Minimum/handling Fee: None
Average Turnaround Time:
As soon as possible

MICROFILMING SERVICE:
Service Available: No
Charges: N/A

DO YOU CHARGE THE BORROWING
LIBRARY FOR POSTAGE?   Only
when insured

FOR HOW LONG DO YOU SUSPEND ILL
SERVICE OVER THE CHRISTMAS
HOLIDAYS?   No suspension

ARE THERE ANY GROUPS OF LIBRARIES
FOR WHICH YOU WAIVE FEES?   IF
SO, PLEASE NAME THEM: None

GEORGIA INSTITUTE OF TECHNOLOGY

NUC CODE: GAT

OCLC CODE: GAT

ADDRESS: Interlibrary Loan
Price Gilbert Memorial
Library
Georgia Institute of
Technology
Atlanta, GA 30332

TELEPHONE: (404) 894-4511

LIST NAMES OF BRANCHES WITH
SEPARATE POLICIES: None

BOOKS:
Will Lend: Yes
Length of Loan: 1 month
Renewable: Yes, for 2 weeks
Charges: $8.00 to commercial
libraries only; others none
Average Turnaround Time:
1 week
If you have indicated that a
book is not to be lent, will
you on receipt of a letter
from the requesting library
search the index for given
entries? (Not answered)

PERIODICALS:
Bound: Will not lend
Unbound: Will not lend
Loan Period: N/A
Renewable: N/A
Will lend if article exceeds
_____ number of pages (Not
answered)

MICROFORMS:
Will Lend: No
Specific Types of Microforms:
N/A
Will make fiche-to-fiche
copies

GOVERNMENT PUBLICATIONS:
Will Lend: Yes, except
periodicals

DISSERTATIONS:
Will Lend: Yes; 1969 to
present available from
University Microfilms

THESES:
Will Lend: Yes

AUDIO-VISUAL MATERIALS:
Records: Do not own
Cassettes: Do not own
Other (slides, filmstrips,
etc.): Do not own

COMPUTER SOFTWARE:
Will Lend: Do not own

PHOTODUPLICATION SERVICE:
No charge up to 0 exposures
Charge Per Exposure: 25¢
from hardcopy; 50¢ for
fiche-to-fiche
Minimum/handling Fee: $4.00
Southeastern academic and
public libraries: 20¢
paper, 40¢ fiche-to-fiche,
$3.00 handling fee
Average Turnaround Time:
1-2 weeks

MICROFILMING SERVICE:
Service Available: No
Charges: N/A

DO YOU CHARGE THE BORROWING
LIBRARY FOR POSTAGE? No,
unless special postage
requested

FOR HOW LONG DO YOU SUSPEND ILL
SERVICE OVER THE CHRISTMAS
HOLIDAYS? Books loans only
suspended from Dec.15-
Jan.2

ARE THERE ANY GROUPS OF LIBRARIES
FOR WHICH YOU WAIVE FEES? IF
SO, PLEASE NAME THEM:
University Center and
University System libraries
(Georgia)

GEORGIA SOUTHERN COLLEGE

NUC CODE: (Not answered)

OCLC CODE: GPM

ADDRESS: Interlibrary Loan
Georgia Southern
College
Library
P. O. Box 8074
Statesboro, GA 30460

TELEPHONE: (912) 681-5645

LIST NAMES OF BRANCHES WITH
SEPARATE POLICIES: None

BOOKS:
Will Lend: Yes
Length of Loan: 2 weeks
Renewable: Yes
Charges: (Not answered)
Average Turnaround Time:
(Not answered)
If you have indicated that a
book is not to be lent, will
you on receipt of a letter
from the requesting library
search the index for given
entries? (Not answered)

PERIODICALS:
Bound: Will not lend
Unbound: Will not lend
Loan Period: N/A
Renewable: N/A
Will lend if article exceeds
_____ number of pages (Not
answered)

MICROFORMS:
Will Lend: Yes
Specific Types of Microforms:
(Not answered)

GOVERNMENT PUBLICATIONS:
Will Lend: Yes

DISSERTATIONS:
Will Lend: Yes

THESES:
Will Lend: Yes

AUDIO-VISUAL MATERIALS:
Records: Will lend
Cassettes: Will lend
Other (slides, filmstrips,
etc.): Will lend

COMPUTER SOFTWARE:
Will Lend: (Not answered)

PHOTODUPLICATION SERVICE:
No charge up to 20 exposures
Charge Per Exposure: 5¢
Minimum/handling Fee: (Not
answered)
Average Turnaround Time:
(Not answered)

MICROFILMING SERVICE:
Service Available: No
Charges: N/A

DO YOU CHARGE THE BORROWING
LIBRARY FOR POSTAGE? No

FOR HOW LONG DO YOU SUSPEND ILL
SERVICE OVER THE CHRISTMAS
HOLIDAYS? Dec.24-Jan.2

ARE THERE ANY GROUPS OF LIBRARIES
FOR WHICH YOU WAIVE FEES? IF
SO, PLEASE NAME THEM: (Not
answered)

GEORGIA STATE UNIVERSITY

NUC CODE: GASU

OCLC CODE: GSU

ADDRESS: Interlibrary Loan
William R. Pullen
Library
Georgia State
University
100 Decatur St. S.E.
Atlanta, GA 30303

TELEPHONE: (404) 658-2475

LIST NAMES OF BRANCHES WITH
SEPARATE POLICIES: None

BOOKS:
Will Lend: Yes
Length of Loan: 2 weeks
Renewable: Yes
Charges: None
Average Turnaround Time:
3 days
If you have indicated that a
book is not to be lent, will
you on receipt of a letter
from the requesting library
search the index for given
entries?   (Not answered)

PERIODICALS:
Bound: Will not lend
Unbound: Will not lend
Loan Period: N/A
Renewable: N/A
Will lend if article exceeds
_____ number of pages (Not
answered)

MICROFORMS:
Will Lend: Yes
Specific Types of Microforms:
Will generally not lend
periodicals and newspapers
in microform

GOVERNMENT PUBLICATIONS:
Will Lend: Yes

DISSERTATIONS:
Will Lend: Yes; 1965 to
present available from
University Microfilms

THESES:
Will Lend: Yes

AUDIO-VISUAL MATERIALS:
Records: Will not lend
Cassettes: Will not lend
Other (slides, filmstrips,
etc.):   Will not lend

COMPUTER SOFTWARE:
Will Lend: No

PHOTODUPLICATION SERVICE:
No charge up to 0 exposures
Charge Per Exposure: 10¢
from hardcopy; 25¢ from
microforms
Minimum/handling Fee: $2.00
Average Turnaround Time:
3 days

MICROFILMING SERVICE:
Service Available: No
Charges: N/A

DO YOU CHARGE THE BORROWING
LIBRARY FOR POSTAGE?
Approximately 2 weeks

ARE THERE ANY GROUPS OF LIBRARIES
FOR WHICH YOU WAIVE FEES?   IF
SO, PLEASE NAME THEM:
University Center in Georgia,
Inc.

KENNESAW COLLEGE

NUC CODE: G-MARK

OCLC CODE: GKJ

ADDRESS: Interlibrary Loan
Kennesaw College
Library
Marietta, GA 30061

TELEPHONE: (404) 422-8770

LIST NAMES OF BRANCHES WITH
SEPARATE POLICIES: None

BOOKS:
Will Lend: Yes
Length of Loan: 2 weeks
Renewable: Yes
Charges: None
Average Turnaround Time:
2 days
If you have indicated that a
book is not to be lent, will
you on receipt of a letter
from the requesting library
search the index for given
entries?   (Not answered)

PERIODICALS:
Bound: Will not lend
Unbound: (Not answered)
Loan Period: N/A
Renewable: N/A
Will lend if article exceeds
_____ number of pages (Not
answered)

MICROFORMS:
Will Lend: No
Specific Types of Microforms:
N/A

GOVERNMENT PUBLICATIONS:
Will Lend: No

DISSERTATIONS:
Will Lend: Do not own

THESES:
Will Lend: Do not own

AUDIO-VISUAL MATERIALS:
Records: Will not lend
Cassettes: Will not lend
Other (slides, filmstrips,
etc.):   Will not lend

COMPUTER SOFTWARE:
Will Lend: No

PHOTODUPLICATION SERVICE:
No charge up to 10 exposures
Charge Per Exposure: 10¢
Minimum/handling Fee: (Not
answered)
Average Turnaround Time:
2 days

MICROFILMING SERVICE:
Service Available: (Not
answered)
Charges: (Not answered)

DO YOU CHARGE THE BORROWING
LIBRARY FOR POSTAGE?   No

FOR HOW LONG DO YOU SUSPEND ILL
SERVICE OVER THE CHRISTMAS
HOLIDAYS?   1 week

ARE THERE ANY GROUPS OF LIBRARIES
FOR WHICH YOU WAIVE FEES?   IF
SO, PLEASE NAME THEM: None

MEDICAL COLLEGE OF GEORGIA

NUC CODE: GAU-M

OCLC CODE: GXM

ADDRESS: Interlibrary Loan
Library
Medical College of
Georgia
Augusta, GA   30912

TELEPHONE: (404) 828-3441

LIST NAMES OF BRANCHES WITH
SEPARATE POLICIES: None

BOOKS:
Will Lend: Yes
Length of Loan: 2 weeks
Renewable: Yes
Charges: $4.75
Average Turnaround Time:
1 week
If you have indicated that a
book is not to be lent, will
you on receipt of a letter
from the requesting library
search the index for given
entries?   (Not answered)

PERIODICALS:
Bound: Will lend
Unbound: Will lend
Loan Period: 2 weeks
Renewable: No
Will lend if article exceeds
25 pages

MICROFORMS:
Will Lend: No
Specific Types of Microforms:
N/A

GOVERNMENT PUBLICATIONS:
Will Lend: Yes

DISSERTATIONS:
Will Lend: Yes

THESES:
Will Lend: Yes

AUDIO-VISUAL MATERIALS:
Records: Will not lend
Cassettes: Will not lend
Other (slides, filmstrips,
etc.):   Will not lend

COMPUTER SOFTWARE:
Will Lend: No

PHOTODUPLICATION SERVICE:
No charge up to 0 exposures
Charge Per Exposure: (Not
answered)
Minimum/handling Fee: $4.75
Average Turnaround Time:
1 week

MICROFILMING SERVICE:
Service Available: No
Charges: N/A

DO YOU CHARGE THE BORROWING
LIBRARY FOR POSTAGE?   No

FOR HOW LONG DO YOU SUSPEND ILL
SERVICE OVER THE CHRISTMAS
HOLIDAYS?   Dec.20-Jan.2

ARE THERE ANY GROUPS OF LIBRARIES
FOR WHICH YOU WAIVE FEES?   IF
SO, PLEASE NAME THEM: None

UNIVERSITY OF GEORGIA

NUC CODE: GU

OCLC CODE: GUA

ADDRESS: Interlibrary Loan
University of Georgia
Libraries
Athens, GA   30602

TELEPHONE: (404) 542-3274

LIST NAMES OF BRANCHES WITH
SEPARATE POLICIES: None

BOOKS:
Will Lend: Yes
Length of Loan: 2 weeks use
Renewable: Yes
Charges: We charge those
libraries which charge us
Average Turnaround Time:
(Not answered)
If you have indicated that a
book is not to be lent, will
you on receipt of a letter
from the requesting library
search the index for given
entries?   (Not answered)

PERIODICALS:
Bound: Will rarely lend
Unbound: Will not lend
Loan Period: 1 week use
Renewable: No
Will lend if article exceeds
_____ number of pages
(Length of article not
a factor)

MICROFORMS:
Will Lend: Yes
Specific Types of Microforms:
Microfilm, microfiche

GOVERNMENT PUBLICATIONS:
Will Lend: Yes

DISSERTATIONS:
Will Lend: Yes, pre-1956
dissertations

THESES:
Will Lend: Yes

AUDIO-VISUAL MATERIALS:
Records: Will not lend
Cassettes: Will not lend
Other (slides, filmstrips,
etc.):   Will not lend

COMPUTER SOFTWARE:
Will Lend: No

PHOTODUPLICATION SERVICE:
No charge up to 0 exposures
Charge Per Exposure: 10¢
Handling Fee: $3.00 per
request
Average Turnaround Time:
(Not answered)

MICROFILMING SERVICE:
Service Available: Yes
Charges: Upon request to
Photographic Services/
Univ. of Georgia Libraries/
Athens, GA   30620

DO YOU CHARGE THE BORROWING
LIBRARY FOR POSTAGE?   Only
for extraordinary charges

FOR HOW LONG DO YOU SUSPEND ILL
SERVICE OVER THE CHRISTMAS
HOLIDAYS?   App. 2 weeks

ARE THERE ANY GROUPS OF LIBRARIES
FOR WHICH YOU WAIVE FEES?   IF
SO, PLEASE NAME THEM: Members
of the University Center in
Georgia

WEST GEORGIA COLLEGE

NUC CODE: GCarrWG

OCLC CODE: GWC

ADDRESS: Interlibrary Loan
           Irving Sullivan Ingram
             Library
           West Georgia College
           Carrollton, GA 30118

TELEPHONE: (404) 834-1371

LIST NAMES OF BRANCHES WITH
  SEPARATE POLICIES: None

BOOKS:
  Will Lend: Yes
  Length of Loan: 2 weeks
  Renewable: Yes
  Charges: None
  Average Turnaround Time:
    2 weeks
  If you have indicated that a
    book is not to be lent, will
    you on receipt of a letter
    from the requesting library
    search the index for given
    entries? (Not answered)

PERIODICALS:
  Bound: Will usually lend
  Unbound: Will lend old
    issues only
  Loan Period: 1 week
  Renewable: No
  Will lend if article exceeds
    50 pages

MICROFORMS:
  Will Lend: Yes
  Specific Types of Microforms:
    Microfilm, microfiche,
    microcard

GOVERNMENT PUBLICATIONS:
  Will Lend: Yes

DISSERTATIONS:
  Will Lend: Yes

THESES:
  Will Lend: Yes

AUDIO-VISUAL MATERIALS
  Records: Will lend
  Cassettes: Will lend
  Other (slides, filmstrips,
    etc.): Will lend

COMPUTER SOFTWARE:
  Will Lend: Do not own

PHOTODUPLICATION SERVICE:
  No charge up to 10 exposures
  Charge Per Exposure: 10¢
  Minimum/handling Fee: None
  Average Turnaround Time:
    1 week

MICROFILMING SERVICE:
  Service Available: No
  Charges: N/A

DO YOU CHARGE THE BORROWING
  LIBRARY FOR POSTAGE? No

FOR HOW LONG DO YOU SUSPEND ILL
  SERVICE OVER THE CHRISTMAS
  HOLIDAYS? 3 weeks

ARE THERE ANY GROUPS OF LIBRARIES
  FOR WHICH YOU WAIVE FEES? IF
  SO, PLEASE NAME THEM: State
  of Georgia libraries

HAWAII STATE LIBRARY

NUC CODE: HH

OCLC CODE: (Not answered)

ADDRESS: Interlibrary Loan
Hawaii State Library
478 South King St.
Honolulu, HI 96813

TELEPHONE: (808) 548-4166

LIST NAMES OF BRANCHES WITH
SEPARATE POLICIES: None

BOOKS:
Will Lend: Yes
Length of Loan: 3 weeks from
receipt
Renewable: Yes
Charges: (Not answered)
Average Turnaround Time:
24 hours
If you have indicated that a
book is not to be lent, will
you on receipt of a letter
from the requesting library
search the index for given
entries? Yes, for any
work classed non-circulating

PERIODICALS:
Bound: Will not lend,
usually
Unbound: Will not lend,
usually
(Most serials are classed
non-circulating. Would lend
those few which circulate.)
Loan Period: 1 week
Renewable: Yes
Will lend if article exceeds
_____ number of pages (Not
answered)

MICROFORMS:
Will Lend: Yes
Specific Types of Microforms:
Will lend those classed
circulating.

GOVERNMENT PUBLICATIONS:
Will Lend: Yes, but most of
the federal collection is
non-circulating.

DISSERTATIONS:
Will Lend: Yes

THESES:
Will Lend: Yes

AUDIO-VISUAL MATERIALS:
Records: Will not lend usually
Cassettes: Will lend if
circulating
Other (slides, filmstrips,
etc.): Will lend if
circulating

COMPUTER SOFTWARE:
Will Lend: (Not answered)

PHOTODUPLICATION SERVICE:
No charge up to 0 exposures
Charge Per Exposure: 25¢
Minimum/handling Fee: (Not
answered)
Average Turnaround Time:
24 hours

MICROFILMING SERVICE:
Service Available: No
Charges: N/A

DO YOU CHARGE THE BORROWING
LIBRARY FOR POSTAGE? No

FOR HOW LONG DO YOU SUSPEND ILL
SERVICE OVER THE CHRISTMAS
HOLIDAYS? (Not answered)

ARE THERE ANY GROUPS OF LIBRARIES
FOR WHICH YOU WAIVE FEES? IF
SO, PLEASE NAME THEM: None

UNIVERSITY OF HAWAII

NUC CODE: HU

OCLC CODE: HUH

ADDRESS: Interlibrary Loan
University of Hawaii
Library
2550 The Mall
Honolulu, HI 96822

TELEPHONE: (808) 943-8568

LIST NAMES OF BRANCHES WITH
SEPARATE POLICIES: None

BOOKS:
Will Lend: Yes
Length of Loan: 2 weeks from
receipt
Renewable: Yes
Charges: Postage for first-
class mail
Average Turnaround Time:
(Not answered)
If you have indicated that a
book is not to be lent, will
you on receipt of a letter
from the requesting library
search the index for given
entries? (Not answered)

PERIODICALS:
Bound: Will not lend
Unbound: Will not lend
Loan Period: N/A
Renewable: N/A
Will lend if article exceeds
_____ number of pages (Not
answered)

MICROFORMS:
Will Lend: Yes, microfilm
only

GOVERNMENT PUBLICATIONS:
Will Lend: No

DISSERTATIONS:
Will Lend: Yes, if 2nd copy
available

THESES:
Will Lend: Yes, if 2nd copy
available

AUDIO-VISUAL MATERIALS:
Records: Will not lend
Cassettes: Will not lend
Other (slides, filmstrips,
etc.): Will not lend

COMPUTER SOFTWARE:
Will Lend: No

PHOTODUPLICATION SERVICE:
No charge up to 0 exposures
Charge Per Exposure: 10¢
Minimum/handling Fee: $1.00
plus postage
Average Turnaround Time:
(Not answered)

MICROFILMING SERVICE:
Service Available: Yes
Charges: (Positive) $6.30
for first 50 feet, $12.30
for 50-100 feet, plus
postage

DO YOU CHARGE THE BORROWING
LIBRARY FOR POSTAGE? For
first-class mail only

FOR HOW LONG DO YOU SUSPEND ILL
SERVICE OVER THE CHRISTMAS
HOLIDAYS? No suspension

ARE THERE ANY GROUPS OF LIBRARIES
FOR WHICH YOU WAIVE FEES? IF
SO, PLEASE NAME THEM:
Reciprocal agreements with
the Hawaii State and local
medical libraries

UNIVERSITY OF HAWAII AT HILO

NUC CODE: (Not answered)

OCLC CODE: (Not answered)

ADDRESS: Interlibrary Loan
          Library
          University of Hawaii
             at Hilo
          1400 Kapiolani St.
          Hilo, HI 96720

TELEPHONE: (808) 961-9346

LIST NAMES OF BRANCHES WITH
    SEPARATE POLICIES:
       University of Hawaii at
       Manoa

BOOKS:
   Will Lend: Yes
   Length of Loan: 4 weeks use
   Renewable: No
   Charges: Insurance
   Average Turnaround Time:
      (Not answered)
   If you have indicated that a
      book is not to be lent, will
      you on receipt of a letter
      from the requesting library
      search the index for given
      entries? (Not answered)

PERIODICALS:
   Bound: Will not lend
   Unbound: Will not lend
   Loan Period: N/A
   Renewable: N/A
   Will lend if article exceeds
      _____ number of pages (Not
      answered)

MICROFORMS:
   Will Lend: Yes
   Specific Types of Microforms:
      (Not answered)

GOVERNMENT PUBLICATIONS:
   Will Lend: Yes

DISSERTATIONS:
   Will Lend: Yes

THESES:
   Will Lend: Yes

AUDIO-VISUAL MATERIALS:
   Records: Will not lend
   Cassettes: Will not lend
   Other (slides, filmstrips,
      etc.): Will not lend

COMPUTER SOFTWARE:
   Will Lend: No

PHOTODUPLICATION SERVICE:
   No charge up to 0 exposures
   Charge Per Exposure: 15¢
   Minimum/handling Fee: (Not
      answered)
   Average Turnaround Time:
      (Not answered)

MICROFILMING SERVICE:
   Service Available: Yes
   Charges: 15¢ per frame

DO YOU CHARGE THE BORROWING
   LIBRARY FOR POSTAGE? No

FOR HOW LONG DO YOU SUSPEND ILL
   SERVICE OVER THE CHRISTMAS
   HOLIDAYS? (Not answered)

ARE THERE ANY GROUPS OF LIBRARIES
   FOR WHICH YOU WAIVE FEES? IF
   SO, PLEASE NAME THEM: None

BOISE PUBLIC LIBRARY

NUC CODE: (Not answered)

OCLC CODE: (Not answered)

ADDRESS: Interlibrary Loan
           Boise Public Library
           715 S. Capitol Blvd.
           Boise, ID 83702

TELEPHONE: (208) 384-4078

LIST NAMES OF BRANCHES WITH
   SEPARATE POLICIES: None

BOOKS:
   Will Lend: Yes
   Length of Loan: 4 weeks
   Renewable: Yes
   Charges: Postage
   Average Turnaround Time:
      24 hours
   If you have indicated that a
      book is not to be lent, will
      you on receipt of a letter
      from the requesting library
      search the index for given
      entries? (Not answered)

PERIODICALS:
   Bound: Will not lend
   Unbound: Will not lend
   Loan Period: N/A
   Renewable: N/A
   Will lend if article exceeds
      _____ number of pages (Not
      answered)

MICROFORMS:
   Will Lend: No
   Specific Types of Microforms:
      N/A

GOVERNMENT PUBLICATIONS:
   Will Lend: Yes

DISSERTATIONS:
   N/A

THESES:
   N/A

AUDIO-VISUAL MATERIALS:
   Records: Will not lend
   Cassettes: Will not lend
   Other (slides, filmstrips,
      etc.): (Not answered)

COMPUTER SOFTWARE:
   Will Lend: No

PHOTODUPLICATION SERVICE:
   No charge up to 50 exposures
   Charge Per Exposure: (Not
      answered)
   Minimum/handling Fee: None
   Average Turnaround Time:
      48 hours

MICROFILMING SERVICE:
   Service Available: No
   Charges: N/A

DO YOU CHARGE THE BORROWING LIBRARY
   FOR POSTAGE? Yes

FOR HOW LONG DO YOU SUSPEND ILL
   SERVICE OVER THE CHRISTMAS
   HOLIDAYS? Dec.10-Jan.7

ARE THERE ANY GROUPS OF LIBRARIES
   FOR WHICH YOU WAIVE FEES? IF
   SO, PLEASE NAME THEM: (Not
   answered)

BOISE STATE UNIVERSITY

NUC CODE: IdBB

OCLC CODE: (Not answered)

ADDRESS: Interlibrary Loan
           Boise State University
           Library
           Boise, ID 83725

TELEPHONE: (208) 385-3756

LIST NAMES OF BRANCHES WITH
   SEPARATE POLICIES: (Not
   answered)

BOOKS:
   Will Lend: Yes, except for
      reference books
   Length of Loan: 4 weeks
   Renewable: Yes
   Charges: Postage refund
   Average Turnaround Time:
      We answer within 48 hours
   If you have indicated that a
      book is not to be lent, will
      you on receipt of a letter
      from the requesting library
      search the index for given
      entries? (Not answered)

PERIODICALS:
   Bound: Will lend
   Unbound: Will not lend
   Loan Period: 2 weeks
   Renewable: No
   Will lend if article exceeds
      20 pages

MICROFORMS:
   Will Lend: Yes
   Specific Types of Microforms:
      Microfilm, microfiche,
      microcards

GOVERNMENT PUBLICATIONS:
   Will Lend: Yes, sometimes

DISSERTATIONS:
   Will Lend: Yes

THESES:
   Will Lend: Yes

AUDIO-VISUAL MATERIALS:
   Records: Will not lend
   Cassettes: Will not lend
   Other (slides, filmstrips,
      etc.): Will not lend

COMPUTER SOFTWARE:
   Will Lend: No

PHOTODUPLICATION SERVICE:
   No charge up to _____ exposure
      (Not answered)
   Charge Per Exposure: 10¢
   Minimum/handling Fee: None
   Average Turnaround Time:
      48 hours

MICROFILMING SERVICE:
   Service Available: No
   Charges: N/A

DO YOU CHARGE THE BORROWING LIBRA
   FOR POSTAGE? Yes

FOR HOW LONG DO YOU SUSPEND ILL
   SERVICE OVER THE CHRISTMAS
   HOLIDAYS? Christmas week only

ARE THERE ANY GROUPS OF LIBRARIES
   FOR WHICH YOU WAIVE FEES? IF
   SO, PLEASE NAME THEM: Hospita
   libraries

IDAHO STATE LIBRARY

NUC CODE: Id

OCLC CODE: (Not answered)

ADDRESS: Interlibrary Loan
Idaho State Library
325 West State St.
Boise, ID 83702

TELEPHONE: (208) 334-2150

LIST NAMES OF BRANCHES WITH
SEPARATE POLICIES: (Not
answered)

BOOKS:
Will Lend: Yes
Length of Loan: 4 weeks use
Renewable: Yes
Charges: Insurance for rare
items
Average Turnaround Time: 1 day
If you have indicated that a
book is not to be lent, will
you on receipt of a letter
from the requesting library
search the index for given
entries? Yes

PERIODICALS:
Bound: Will lend, depending
on journal title and article
contents
Unbound: Will lend, depending
on journal title and article
contents
Loan Period: 4 weeks use
Renewable: No
Will lend if article exceeds
_____ number of pages (Not
answered)

MICROFORMS:
Will Lend: Yes
Specific Types of Microforms:
Very few owned at this time.
Newspapers on microfilm are
available from Idaho State
Historical Society Library.

GOVERNMENT PUBLICATIONS:
Will Lend: Yes

DISSERTATIONS:
Will Lend: Yes, but very few
owned

THESES:
Will Lend: Yes, but very few
owned

AUDIO-VISUAL MATERIALS:
Records: Will not lend
Cassettes: Will not lend
Other (slides, filmstrips,
etc.): Will not lend

COMPUTER SOFTWARE:
N/A

PHOTODUPLICATION SERVICE:
No charge up to 10 exposures
Charge Per Exposure: 10¢
Minimum/handling Fee: None
Average Turnaround Time: 1 day

MICROFILMING SERVICE:
Service Available: No
Charges: N/A

DO YOU CHARGE THE BORROWING LIBRARY
FOR POSTAGE? No

FOR HOW LONG DO YOU SUSPEND ILL
SERVICE OVER THE CHRISTMAS
HOLIDAYS? Not at all. Closed
only for state/federal
holidays.

ARE THERE ANY GROUPS OF LIBRARIES
FOR WHICH YOU WAIVE FEES? IF
SO, PLEASE NAME THEM: Generally
no charge to other state
libraries. Photocopy charges
are very lenient and depend on
nature of the document
requested.

IDAHO STATE UNIVERSITY

NUC CODE: IdPI

OCLC CODE: None

ADDRESS: Interlibrary Loan
Idaho State University
Library
Pocatello, ID
83209-0009

TELEPHONE: (208) 236-3127
(prefer no phone requests)

LIST NAMES OF BRANCHES WITH
SEPARATE POLICIES:
Audio-Visual Services

BOOKS:
Will Lend: Yes
Length of Loan: 4 weeks
from receipt
Renewable: Yes
Charges: $2.00 per book plus
postage
Average Turnaround Time:
3 working days
If you have indicated that a
book is not to be lent, will
you on receipt of a letter
from the requesting library
search the index for given
entries? (Not answered)

PERIODICALS:
Bound: Will not lend
Unbound: Will not lend
Loan Period: N/A
Renewable: N/A
Will lend if article exceeds
_____ number of pages (Will
not lend, regardless of
length of article)

MICROFORMS:
Will Lend: Yes
Specific Types of Microforms:
Microfilm and microcards
only

GOVERNMENT PUBLICATIONS:
Will Lend: Yes

DISSERTATIONS:
Will Lend: Yes

THESES:
Will Lend: Yes

AUDIO-VISUAL MATERIALS:
Address inquiries to
Audio-Visual Services at ISU

COMPUTER SOFTWARE:
Will Lend: No

PHOTODUPLICATION SERVICE:
No charge up to 0 exposures
Charge Per Exposure: 10¢
after first 10
Minimum/handling Fee: $2.00
for 1-10 pages
Average Turnaround Time:
3 working days

MICROFILMING SERVICE:
Service Available: No
Charges: N/A

DO YOU CHARGE THE BORROWING
LIBRARY FOR POSTAGE? Yes

FOR HOW LONG DO YOU SUSPEND ILL
SERVICE OVER THE CHRISTMAS
HOLIDAYS? Dec.13-Jan.3

ARE THERE ANY GROUPS OF LIBRARIES
FOR WHICH YOU WAIVE FEES? IF
SO, PLEASE NAME THEM: Idaho
Council of State Academic
Libraries

SOUTHWESTERN IDAHO REGIONAL LIBRARY SYSTEM

NUC CODE: (Not answered)

WLN CODE: IdB

ADDRESS: Interlibrary Loan
Southwestern Idaho
Regional Library
System
715 So. Capitol Blvd.
Boise, ID 83702

TELEPHONE: (208) 384-4269

LIST NAMES OF BRANCHES WITH
SEPARATE POLICIES:
Boise Public Library
Caldwell Public Library
Nampa Public Library

BOOKS:
Will Lend: Yes
Length of Loan: 28 days
Renewable: Yes
Charges: Postage
Average Turnaround Time:
24 hours
If you have indicated that a
book is not to be lent, will
you on receipt of a letter
from the requesting library
search the index for given
entries? (Not answered)

PERIODICALS:
Bound: Will not lend
Unbound: Will not lend
Loan Period: N/A
Renewable: N/A
Will lend if article exceeds
_____ number of pages (Not
answered)

MICROFORMS:
Will Lend: No
Specific Types of Microforms:
N/A

GOVERNMENT PUBLICATIONS:
Will Lend: No

DISSERTATIONS:
Will Lend: No

THESES:
Will Lend: No

AUDIO-VISUAL MATERIALS:
Records: Will lend
Cassettes: Will lend
Other (slides, filmstrips,
etc.): Will lend

COMPUTER SOFTWARE:
Will Lend: No

PHOTODUPLICATION SERVICE:
No charge up to 10 exposures
Charge Per Exposure: 10¢
Minimum/handling Fee: None
Average Turnaround Time:
24 hours

MICROFILMING SERVICE:
Service Available: No
Charges: N/A

DO YOU CHARGE THE BORROWING LIBRARY
FOR POSTAGE? Yes

FOR HOW LONG DO YOU SUSPEND ILL
SERVICE OVER THE CHRISTMAS
HOLIDAYS? Not suspended

ARE THERE ANY GROUPS OF LIBRARIES
FOR WHICH YOU WAIVE FEES? IF
SO, PLEASE NAME THEM: None
except system members.

UNIVERSITY OF IDAHO

NUC CODE: IdU

OCLC CODE: (Not answered)

ADDRESS: Interlibrary Loan
University of Idaho
Library
Moscow, ID 83843

TELEPHONE: (208) 885-6559

LIST NAMES OF BRANCHES WITH
SEPARATE POLICIES:
Law Library

BOOKS:
Will Lend: Yes
Length of Loan: 4 weeks
Renewable: Yes
Charges: $5.00
Average Turnaround Time:
(Not answered)
If you have indicated that a
book is not to be lent, will
you on receipt of a letter
from the requesting library
search the index for given
entries? (Not answered)

PERIODICALS:
Bound: Will not lend
Unbound: Will not lend
Loan Period: N/A
Renewable: N/A
Will lend if article exceeds
_____ number of pages (Not
answered)

MICROFORMS:
Will Lend: Yes
Specific Types of Microforms:
All types

GOVERNMENT PUBLICATIONS:
Will Lend: Yes

DISSERTATIONS:
Will Lend: Yes; 1959 to
present available from
University Microfilms

THESES:
Will Lend: Yes

AUDIO-VISUAL MATERIALS:
Records: Will not lend
Cassettes: Will not lend
Other (slides, filmstrips,
etc.): (Not answered)

COMPUTER SOFTWARE:
Will Lend: (Not answered)

PHOTODUPLICATION SERVICE:
No charge up to 0 exposures
Charge Per Exposure: 10¢
Handling Fee: $2.00
Average Turnaround Time:
(Not answered)

MICROFILMING SERVICE:
Service Available: (Not
answered)
Charges: N/A

DO YOU CHARGE THE BORROWING
LIBRARY FOR POSTAGE? No

FOR HOW LONG DO YOU SUSPEND ILL
SERVICE OVER THE CHRISTMAS
HOLIDAYS? No suspension

ARE THERE ANY GROUPS OF LIBRARIES
FOR WHICH YOU WAIVE FEES? IF
SO, PLEASE NAME THEM: (Not
answered)

AMERICAN DENTAL ASSOCIATION

NUC CODE: ICADA

OCLC CODE: JAA

ADDRESS: Interlibrary Loan
          American Dental
            Association
          Bureau of Library
            Services
          211 E. Chicago Ave.
          Chicago, IL 60611

TELEPHONE: (312) 440-2642

LIST NAMES OF BRANCHES WITH
  SEPARATE POLICIES: None

BOOKS:
  Will Lend: Yes
  Length of Loan: 4 weeks
  Renewable: Yes
  Charges: Return postage
  Average Turnaround Time:
    2 days
  If you have indicated that a
    book is not to be lent, will
    you on receipt of a letter
    from the requesting library
    search the index for given
    entries? (Not answered)

PERIODICALS:
  Bound: Will not lend
  Unbound: Will lend
  Loan Period: 4 weeks
  Renewable: Yes
  Will lend if article exceeds
    _____ number of pages (Not
    answered)

MICROFORMS:
  Will Lend: Yes
  Specific Types of Microforms:
    (Not answered)

GOVERNMENT PUBLICATIONS:
  Will Lend: Yes

DISSERTATIONS:
  Will Lend: Yes

THESES:
  Will Lend: Yes

AUDIO-VISUAL MATERIALS:
  Records: (Not answered)
  Cassettes: (Not answered)
  Other (slides, filmstrips,
    etc.): (Not answered)

COMPUTER SOFTWARE:
  Will Lend: (Not answered)

PHOTODUPLICATION SERVICE:
  No charge up to 0 exposures
  Charge Per Exposure: 10¢
  Minimum/handling Fee: (Not
    answered)
  Average Turnaround Time:
    2 days

MICROFILMING SERVICE:
  Service Available: No
  Charges: N/A

DO YOU CHARGE THE BORROWING
  LIBRARY FOR POSTAGE? No

FOR HOW LONG DO YOU SUSPEND ILL
  SERVICE OVER THE CHRISTMAS
  HOLIDAYS? No suspension

ARE THERE ANY GROUPS OF LIBRARIES
  FOR WHICH YOU WAIVE FEES? IF
  SO, PLEASE NAME THEM: None

AMERICAN LIBRARY ASSOCIATION

NUC CODE: ICALA

OCLC CODE: IEH

ADDRESS: Interlibrary Loan
          Headquarters Library
          American Library
            Association
          50 E. Huron St.
          Chicago, IL 60611

TELEPHONE: (312) 944-6780

LIST NAMES OF BRANCHES WITH
  SEPARATE POLICIES: None

BOOKS:
  Will Lend: Yes
  Length of Loan: 3 days
  Renewable: Yes
  Charges: None
  Average Turnaround Time:
    5 days maximum
  If you have indicated that a
    book is not to be lent, will
    you on receipt of a letter
    from the requesting library
    search the index for given
    entries? (Not answered)

PERIODICALS:
  Bound: Will not lend
  Unbound: Will not lend
  Loan Period: N/A
  Renewable: N/A
  Will lend if article exceeds
    _____ number of pages (Not
    answered)

MICROFORMS:
  Will Lend: No
  Specific Types of Microforms:
    N/A

GOVERNMENT PUBLICATIONS:
  Will Lend: No

DISSERTATIONS:
  Will Lend: Yes

THESES:
  Will Lend: Yes

AUDIO-VISUAL MATERIALS:
  Records: Will not lend
  Cassettes: Will not lend
  Other (slides, filmstrips,
    etc.): Will not lend

COMPUTER SOFTWARE:
  Will Lend: No

PHOTODUPLICATION SERVICE:
  No charge up to 0 exposures
  Charge Per Exposure: 15¢
  Minimum/handling Fee: $1.00
  Average Turnaround Time:
    5 days maximum

MICROFILMING SERVICE:
  Service Available: No
  Charges: N/A

DO YOU CHARGE THE BORROWING
  LIBRARY FOR POSTAGE? Yes

FOR HOW LONG DO YOU SUSPEND ILL
  SERVICE OVER THE CHRISTMAS
  HOLIDAYS? No suspension

ARE THERE ANY GROUPS OF LIBRARIES
  FOR WHICH YOU WAIVE FEES? IF
  SO, PLEASE NAME THEM: None

ARGONNE NATIONAL LABORATORY

NUC CODE: IArg

OCLC CODE: None

ADDRESS: Interlibrary Loan
Central Library Bldg.
203
Argonne National
Laboratory
9700 S. Cass Ave.
Argonne, IL 60439

TELEPHONE: (312) 972-4223

LIST NAMES OF BRANCHES WITH
SEPARATE POLICIES: None

BOOKS:
Will Lend: Yes
Length of Loan: 2 weeks
Renewable: Yes
Charges: $5.00 per
transaction
Average Turnaround Time:
(Not answered)
If you have indicated that a
book is not to be lent, will
you on receipt of a letter
from the requesting library
search the index for given
entries? Yes

PERIODICALS:
Bound: Will not lend
Unbound: Will not lend
Loan Period: N/A
Renewable: N/A
Will lend if article exceeds
_____ number of pages (Will
not lend, regardless of
length of article)

MICROFORMS:
Will Lend: Do not own
Specific Types of Microforms:
N/A

GOVERNMENT PUBLICATIONS:
Will Lend: Yes

DISSERTATIONS:
Will Lend: Do not own

THESES:
Will Lend: Do not own

AUDIO-VISUAL MATERIALS:
Records: Will lend
Cassettes: (Not answered)
Other (slides, filmstrips,
etc.): Do not own

COMPUTER SOFTWARE:
Will Lend: No

PHOTODUPLICATION SERVICE:
No charge up to 0 exposures
Charges: $5.00 per
transaction
Minimum/handling Fee: $5.00
Average Turnaround Time:
As soon as possible

MICROFILMING SERVICE:
Service Available: No
Charges: N/A

DO YOU CHARGE THE BORROWING
LIBRARY FOR POSTAGE? No

FOR HOW LONG DO YOU SUSPEND ILL
SERVICE OVER THE CHRISTMAS
HOLIDAYS? No suspension

ARE THERE ANY GROUPS OF LIBRARIES
FOR WHICH YOU WAIVE FEES? IF
SO, PLEASE NAME THEM: None

ARLINGTON HEIGHTS MEMORIAL LIBRARY

NUC CODE: (Not answered)

OCLC CODE: (Not answered)

ADDRESS: Interlibrary Loan
Arlington Heights
Memorial Library
500 N. Dunton
Arlington Heights, IL
60004

TELEPHONE: (312) 392-0100

LIST NAMES OF BRANCHES WITH
SEPARATE POLICIES: None

BOOKS:
Will Lend: Yes
Length of Loan: 3 weeks
Renewable: Yes, if no
reserves
Charges: (Not answered)
Average Turnaround Time:
(Not answered)
If you have indicated that a
book is not to be lent, will
you on receipt of a letter
from the requesting library
search the index for given
entries? No

PERIODICALS:
Bound: Will lend
Unbound: (Not answered)
Loan Period: (Not answered)
Renewable: No
Will lend if article exceeds
_____ number of pages (Not
answered)

MICROFORMS:
Will Lend: No
Specific Types of Microforms:
N/A

GOVERNMENT PUBLICATIONS:
Will Lend: Yes

DISSERTATIONS:
Will Lend: Do not own

THESES:
Will Lend: Do not own

AUDIO-VISUAL MATERIALS:
Records: Will lend
Cassettes: Will lend
Other (slides, filmstrips,
etc.): Will lend

COMPUTER SOFTWARE:
Will Lend: No

PHOTODUPLICATION SERVICE:
Service not available

MICROFILMING SERVICE:
Service Available: No
Charges: N/A

DO YOU CHARGE THE BORROWING
LIBRARY FOR POSTAGE? Yes

FOR HOW LONG DO YOU SUSPEND ILL
SERVICE OVER THE CHRISTMAS
HOLIDAYS? No suspension

ARE THERE ANY GROUPS OF LIBRARIES
FOR WHICH YOU WAIVE FEES? IF
SO, PLEASE NAME THEM: None

CENTER FOR RESEARCH LIBRARIES

NUC CODE: ICRL

OCLC CODE: CRL

ADDRESS: Interlibrary Loan
          Circulation Dept.
          Center for Research
          Libraries
          6050 S. Kenwood Ave.
          Chicago, IL 60637

TELEPHONE: (312) 955-4545

LIST NAMES OF BRANCHES WITH
   SEPARATE POLICIES: None

NON-MEMBERS MAY BORROW
   OCCASIONALLY FROM THE CENTER,
   BUT NOT ON A REGULAR AND
   CONTINUING BASIS. THE
   FOLLOWING POLICIES ARE FOR
   NON-MEMBERS:

BOOKS:
   Will Lend: Yes
   Length of Loan: 2 weeks
   Renewable: (Not answered)
   Charges: $20.00 per title
   Average Turnaround Time:
      (Not answered)
   If you have indicated that a
      book is not to be lent, will
      you on receipt of a letter
      from the requesting library
      search the index for given
      entries? (Not answered)

PERIODICALS:
   Bound: Will lend
   Unbound: Will lend
   Loan Period: 2 weeks
   Renewable: (Not answered)
   Will lend if article exceeds
      _____ number of pages (Not
      answered)

MICROFORMS:
   Will Lend: Yes, except for
      newspapers on microfilm
   Specific Types of Microforms:
      Microfilm

GOVERNMENT PUBLICATIONS:
   Will Lend: (Not answered)

DISSERTATIONS:
   Will Lend: Yes

THESES:
   Will Lend: Yes

AUDIO-VISUAL MATERIALS:
   Records: (Not answered)
   Cassettes: (Not answered)
   Other (slides, filmstrips,
      etc.): (Not answered)

COMPUTER SOFTWARE:
   Will Lend: (Not answered)

PHOTODUPLICATION SERVICE:
   No charge up to _____
      exposures (Not answered)
   Charge Per Exposure: (Not
      answered)
   Minimum/handling Fee: (Not
      answered)
   Average Turnaround Time:
      (Not answered)

MICROFILMING SERVICE:
   Service Available: Yes
   Charges: Write for charges

DO YOU CHARGE THE BORROWING
   LIBRARY FOR POSTAGE? No,
   up to $50.00

FOR HOW LONG DO YOU SUSPEND ILL
   SERVICE OVER THE CHRISTMAS
   HOLIDAYS? No suspension

ARE THERE ANY GROUPS OF LIBRARIES
   FOR WHICH YOU WAIVE FEES? IF
   SO, PLEASE NAME THEM: CRL
   member libraries

CHAMPAIGN PUBLIC LIBRARY AND INFORMATION CENTER

NUC CODE: None

OCLC CODE: IHI

ADDRESS: Interlibrary Loan
          Champaign Public
          Library and
          Information Center
          505 S. Randolph
          Champaign, IL 61820

TELEPHONE: (217) 356-7243

LIST NAMES OF BRANCHES WITH
   SEPARATE POLICIES: None

BOOKS:
   Will Lend: Yes
   Length of Loan: 28 days
   Renewable: No
   Charges: (Not answered)
   Average Turnaround Time:
      3 days
   If you have indicated that a
      book is not to be lent, will
      you on receipt of a letter
      from the requesting library
      search the index for given
      entries? (Not answered)

PERIODICALS:
   Bound: Will not lend
   Unbound: Will not lend
   Loan Period: N/A
   Renewable: N/A
   Will lend if article exceeds
      _____ number of pages (Will
      not lend, regardless of
      length of article)

MICROFORMS:
   Will Lend: No
   Specific Types of Microforms:
      N/A

GOVERNMENT PUBLICATIONS:
   Will Lend: No

DISSERTATIONS:
   Will Lend: Do not own

THESES:
   Will Lend: Do not own

AUDIO-VISUAL MATERIALS:
   Records: Will not lend
   Cassettes: Will not lend
   Other (slides, filmstrips,
      etc.): Will lend

COMPUTER SOFTWARE:
   Will Lend: Do not own

PHOTODUPLICATION SERVICE:
   No charge up to 10 exposures
   Charge Per Exposure: 10¢
      after 1st 10
   Minimum/handling Fee: None
   Average Turnaround Time:
      3 days

MICROFILMING SERVICE:
   Service Available: No
   Charges: N/A

DO YOU CHARGE THE BORROWING
   LIBRARY FOR POSTAGE? No

FOR HOW LONG DO YOU SUSPEND ILL
   SERVICE OVER THE CHRISTMAS
   HOLIDAYS? No suspension

ARE THERE ANY GROUPS OF LIBRARIES
   FOR WHICH YOU WAIVE FEES? IF
   SO, PLEASE NAME THEM: None

CHICAGO PUBLIC LIBRARY

NUC CODE: IC

OCLC CODE: CGP

ADDRESS: Chicago Public Library
          Bibliographic and
            Interlibrary Loan
            Center
          425 N. Michigan Ave.
          Chicago, IL 60611

TELEPHONE: (312) 269-2823

BOOKS:
  Will Lend: Yes
  Length of Loan: 4 weeks
  Renewable: Yes
  Charges: None
  Average Turnaround Time:
    14 days
  If you have indicated that a
    book is not to be lent, will
    you on receipt of a letter
    from the requesting library
    search the index for given
    entries? (Not answered)

PERIODICALS:
  Bound: Will not lend
  Unbound: Will not lend
  Loan Period: N/A
  Renewable: N/A
  Will lend if article exceeds
    _____ number of pages (Not
    answered)

MICROFORMS:
  Will Lend: Yes
  Specific Types of Microforms:
    Will not lend Chicago
    Tribune or current 2 years
    of Chicago Sun Times

GOVERNMENT PUBLICATIONS:
  Will Lend: Yes

DISSERTATIONS:
  Will Lend: Yes

THESES:
  Will Lend: Yes

AUDIO-VISUAL MATERIALS:
  Records: Will not lend
  Cassettes: Will not lend
  Other (slides, filmstrips,
    etc.): Will not lend

COMPUTER SOFTWARE:
  Will Lend: No

PHOTODUPLICATION SERVICE:
  ILLINET:
    No charge up to 10
      exposures
    Charge Per Exposure: 10¢
      for Xerox copies; 30¢ for
      microform copies; 50¢ for
      fiche-to-fiche copies
  NON-ILLINET:
    No charge up to 0 exposures
    Charge Per Exposure: 10¢
      for Xerox copies; 30¢ for
      microform copies; 50¢ for
      fiche-to-fiche copies
    Minimum/handling Fee: None
    Average Turnaround Time:
      5 days

MICROFILMING SERVICE:
  Service Available: No
  Charges: N/A

DO YOU CHARGE THE BORROWING
  LIBRARY FOR POSTAGE? No

FOR HOW LONG DO YOU SUSPEND ILL
  SERVICE OVER THE CHRISTMAS
  HOLIDAYS? No suspension

ARE THERE ANY GROUPS OF LIBRARIES
  FOR WHICH YOU WAIVE FEES? IF
  SO, PLEASE NAME THEM: None

DEPAUL UNIVERSITY

NUC CODE: ICD

OCLC CODE: IAC

ADDRESS: Interlibrary Loan
          Lewis Center Library
          DePaul University
          25 E. Jackson
          Chicago, IL 60604

TELEPHONE: (312) 321-7619

LIST NAMES OF BRANCHES WITH
  SEPARATE POLICIES:
  Law Library
  Lincoln Park Campus

BOOKS:
  Will Lend: Yes
  Length of Loan: 3 weeks
  Renewable: Yes
  Charges: (Not answered)
  Average Turnaround Time:
    (Not answered)
  If you have indicated that a
    book is not to be lent, will
    you on receipt of a letter
    from the requesting library
    search the index for given
    entries? (Not answered)

PERIODICALS:
  Bound: Will not lend
  Unbound: Will not lend
  Loan Period: N/A
  Renewable: N/A
  Will lend if article exceeds
    _____ number of pages (Not
    answered)

MICROFORMS:
  Will Lend: No
  Specific Types of Microforms:
    N/A

GOVERNMENT PUBLICATIONS:
  Will Lend: (Not answered)

DISSERTATIONS:
  Will Lend: Yes

THESES:
  Will Lend: Yes

AUDIO-VISUAL MATERIALS:
  Records: (Not answered)
  Cassettes: (Not answered)
  Other (slides, filmstrips,
    etc.): (Not answered)

COMPUTER SOFTWARE:
  Will Lend: (Not answered)

PHOTODUPLICATION SERVICE:
  No charge up to 0 exposures
  Charge Per Exposures: 10¢
  Minimum Fee: $1.00
  Handling Fee: $1.00
  Average Turnaround Time:
    (Not answered)

MICROFILMING SERVICE:
  Service Available: No
  Charges: N/A

DO YOU CHARGE THE BORROWING
  LIBRARY FOR POSTAGE? No

FOR HOW LONG DO YOU SUSPEND ILL
  SERVICE OVER THE CHRISTMAS
  HOLIDAYS? (Not answered)

ARE THERE ANY GROUPS OF LIBRARIES
  FOR WHICH YOU WAIVE FEES? IF
  SO, PLEASE NAME THEM: (Not
  answered)

EASTERN ILLINOIS UNIVERSITY

NUC OCDE: ICharE

OCLC CODE: IAD

ADDRESS: Interlibrary Loan
Library
Eastern Illinois
University
Charleston, IL
61920-3099

TELEPHONE: (217) 581-6072

LIST NAMES OF BRANCHES WITH
SEPARATE POLICIES: None

BOOKS:
Will Lend: Yes
Length of Loan: 30 days
Renewable: Yes
Charges: None
Average Turnaround Time:
1-3 days
If you have indicated that a
book is not to be lent, will
you on receipt of a letter
from the requesting library
search the index for given
entries? (Not answered)

PERIODICALS:
Bound: Will not lend
Unbound: Will not lend
Loan Period: N/A
Renewable: N/A
Will lend if article exceeds
_____ number of pages (Not
answered)

MICROFORMS:
Will Lend: No
Specific Types of Microforms:
N/A

GOVERNMENT PUBLICATIONS:
Will Lend: Yes

DISSERTATIONS:
Will Lend: Yes

THESES:
Will Lend: Yes

AUDIO-VISUAL MATERIALS:
Records: Will not lend
Cassettes: Will not lend
Other (slides, filmstrips,
etc.): Will not lend

COMPUTER SOFTWARE:
Will Lend: No

PHOTODUPLICATION SERVICE:
No charge up to 10 exposures
Charge Per Exposure: 10¢
Minimum/handling Fee: None
Average Turnaround Time:
1-3 days

MICROFILMING SERVICE:
Service Available: No
Charges: N/A

DO YOU CHARGE THE BORROWING
LIBRARY FOR POSTAGE? No

FOR HOW LONG DO YOU SUSPEND ILL
SERVICE OVER THE CHRISTMAS
HOLIDAYS? Week between

ARE THERE ANY GROUPS OF LIBRARIES
FOR WHICH YOU WAIVE FEES? IF
SO, PLEASE NAME THEM: None

ELMHURST COLLEGE

NUC CODE: IE1mC

OCLC CODE: ICV

ADDRESS: Interlibrary Loan
A. C. Buehler Library
Elmhurst College
190 Prospect
Elmhurst, IL 60126

TELEPHONE: (312) 279-4100, X255

LIST NAMES OF BRANCHES WITH
SEPARATE POLICIES: None

BOOKS:
Will Lend: Yes
Length of Loan: 1 month
Renewable: Yes
Charges: Postage for out-
of-state libraries
Average Turnaround Time:
1-2 days
If you have indicated that a
book is not to be lent, will
you on receipt of a letter
from the requesting library
search the index for given
entries? (Not answered)

PERIODICALS:
Bound: Will lend in unusual
circumstances
Unbound: Will not lend
Loan Period: 1 week
Renewable: No
Will lend if article exceeds
35 pages

MICROFORMS:
Will Lend: No
Specific Types of Microforms:
N/A

GOVERNMENT PUBLICATIONS:
Will Lend: Yes

DISSERTATIONS:
Will Lend: Do not own

THESES:
Will Lend: Do not own

AUDIO-VISUAL MATERIALS:
Records: Will not lend
Cassettes: Will not lend
Other (slides, filmstrips,
etc.): Will not lend

COMPUTER SOFTWARE:
Will Lend: Do not own

PHOTODUPLICATION SERVICE:
No charge up to 3 exposures
Charge Per Exposure: 10¢
Minimum/handling Fee: None
Average Turnaround Time:
1-2 days

MICROFILMING SERVICE:
Service Available: No
Charges: N/A

DO YOU CHARGE THE BORROWING
LIBRARY FOR POSTAGE? Only
for out-of-state book
loans

FOR HOW LONG DO YOU SUSPEND ILL
SERVICE OVER THE CHRISTMAS
HOLIDAYS? No suspension

ARE THERE ANY GROUPS OF LIBRARIES
FOR WHICH YOU WAIVE FEES? IF
SO, PLEASE NAME THEM: None

GOVERNORS STATE UNIVERSITY

NUC CODE: (Not answered)

OCLC CODE: IAF

ADDRESS: Interlibrary Loan
University Library
Governors State
University
Park Forest South, IL
60466

TELEPHONE: (312) 534-5000, X2574

LIST NAMES OF BRANCHES WITH
SEPARATE POLICIES: None

BOOKS:
Will Lend: Yes
Length of Loan: 2-4 weeks
Renewable: Yes
Charges: None
Average Turnaround Time:
2 working days
If you have indicated that a
book is not to be lent, will
you on receipt of a letter
from the requesting library
search the index for given
entries? Yes, time
permitting

PERIODICALS:
Bound: Will not lend
Unbound: Will not lend
Loan Period: N/A
Renewable: N/A
Will lend if article exceeds
_____ number of pages (Not
answered)

MICROFORMS:
Will Lend: No
Specific Types of Microforms:
N/A

GOVERNMENT PUBLICATIONS:
Will Lend: Yes

DISSERTATIONS:
Will Lend: Do not own

THESES:
Will Lend: Yes

AUDIO-VISUAL MATERIALS:
Records: Will not lend
Cassettes: Will not lend
Other (slides, filmstrips,
etc.): Will not lend

COMPUTER SOFTWARE:
Will Lend: No

PHOTODUPLICATION SERVICE:
No charge up to 0 exposures
Charge Per Exposure: 10¢
Minimum/handling Fee: $1.00
Average Turnaround Time:
2 working days

MICROFILMING SERVICE:
Service Available: No
Charges: N/A

DO YOU CHARGE THE BORROWING
LIBRARY FOR POSTAGE? No

FOR HOW LONG DO YOU SUSPEND ILL
SERVICE OVER THE CHRISTMAS
HOLIDAYS? Usually 1 week

ARE THERE ANY GROUPS OF LIBRARIES
FOR WHICH YOU WAIVE FEES? IF
SO, PLEASE NAME THEM:
Chicago Academic Library
Counsel; Chicago and South
(Medical) Consortium

ILLINOIS STATE UNIVERSITY

NUC CODE: 1

OCLC CODE: SPI

ADDRESS: Interlibrary Loan
Illinois State Library
Centennial Bldg.
Springfield, IL 62756

TELEPHONE: (217) 782-5823

LIST NAMES OF BRANCHES WITH
SEPARATE POLICIES: None

BOOKS:
Will Lend: Yes
Length of Loan: 6 weeks
Renewable: Yes
Charges: (Not answered)
Average Turnaround Time:
(Not answered)
If you have indicated that a
book is not to be lent, will
you on receipt of a letter
from the requesting library
search the index for given
entries? (Not answered)

PERIODIDALS:
Bound: Will not lend
Unbound: Will not lend
Loan Period: N/A
Renewable: N/A
Will lend if article exceeds
40 pages

MICROFORMS:
Will Lend: Yes
Specific Types of Microforms:
Film, except periodicals

GOVERNMENT PUBLICATIONS:
Will Lend: Yes

DISSERTATIONS:
Will Lend: Yes

THESES:
Will Lend: Yes

AUDIO-VISUAL MATERIALS:
Records: (Not answered)
Cassettes: (Not answered)
Other (slides, filmstrips,
etc.): (Not answered)

COMPUTER SOFTWARE:
Will Lend: (Not answered)

PHOTODUPLICATION SERVICE:
No charge up to 10 exposures
Charge Per Exposure: (Not
answered)
Minimum/handling Fee: $1.00
Average Turnaround Time:
(Not answered)

MICROFILMING SERVICE:
Service Available: No
Charges: N/A

DO YOU CHARGE THE BORROWING
LIBRARY FOR POSTAGE? No

FOR HOW LONG DO YOU SUSPEND ILL
SERVICE OVER THE CHRISTMAS
HOLIDAYS? No suspension

ARE THERE ANY GROUPS OF LIBRARIES
FOR WHICH YOU WAIVE FEES? IF
SO, PLEASE NAME THEM: None

JOHN CRERAR LIBRARY

NUC CODE: ICJ

OCLC CODE: IAB

ADDRESS: Extramural Circulation
Service
John Crerar Library
35 W. 33rd St.
Chicago, IL 60616

Photoduplication
Service
John Crerar Library
35 W. 33rd St.
Chicago, IL 60616

TELEPHONE: (312) 225-2526

LIST NAMES OF BRANCHES WITH
SEPARATE POLICIES: None

NOTE: JOHN CRERAR LIBRARY LENDS
MATERIAL ONLY TO CONTRIBUTING
INDUSTRIAL AND INSTITUTIONAL
MEMBERS

BOOKS:
Will Lend: Yes
Length of Loan: 3 weeks
Renewable: Yes
Charges: (Not answered)
Average Turnaround Time:
5-7 days
If you have indicated that a
book is not to be lent, will
you on receipt of a letter
from the requesting library
search the index for given
entries? Yes

PERIODICALS:
Bound: Will lend
Unbound: Will lend if older
than 1 year
Loan Period: 3 weeks
Renewable: Yes
Will lend if article exceeds
_____ number of pages (Not
answered)

MICROFORMS:
Will Lend: Yes
Specific Types of Microforms:
Microcards, microfiche,
microfilm

GOVERNMENT PUBLICATIONS:
Will Lend: Yes

DISSERTATIONS:
Will Lend: Do not own

THESES:
Will Lend: Do not own

AUDIO-VISUAL MATERIALS:
Records: Do not own
Cassettes: Do not own
Other (slides, filmstrips,
etc.): Do not own

PHOTODUPLICATION SERVICE:
Service available to any
requester
No charge up to 0 exposures
Charge Per Page: 30¢
Handling Fee: $2.00 per item
Average Turnaround Time:
10 days; rush orders filled
within 24-36 hours (Rush
surcharge, $1.50)

MICROFILMING SERVICE:
Service Available: Yes
Charges: 5¢ per page plus
$2.00 per item

DO YOU CHARGE THE BORROWING
LIBRARY FOR POSTAGE? Not to
members

FOR HOW LONG DO YOU SUSPEND ILL
SERVICE OVER THE CHRISTMAS
HOLIDAYS? No suspension

ARE THERE ANY GROUPS OF LIBRARIES
FOR WHICH YOU WAIVE FEES? IF
SO, PLEASE NAME THEM: None

LOYOLA UNIVERSITY OF CHICAGO

NUC CODE: (Not answered)

OCLC CODE: (Not answered)

ADDRESS: Interlibrary Loan
E. M. Cudahy Memorial
Library
Loyola University of
Chicago
6525 N. Sheridan Rd.
Chicago, IL 60626

TELEPHONE: (312) 274-3000, X791

LIST NAMES OF BRANCHES WITH
SEPARATE POLICIES: None

BOOKS:
Will Lend: Yes
Length of Loan: 1 month
Renewable: Yes
Charges: (Not answered)
Average Turnaround Time:
(Not answered)
If you have indicated that a
book is not to be lent, will
you on receipt of a letter
from the requesting library
search the index for given
entries? Yes

PERIODICALS:
Bound: Will not lend
Unbound: Will not lend
Loan Period: N/A
Renewable: N/A
Will lend if article exceeds
_____ number of pages (Not
answered)

MICROFORMS:
Will Lend: No
Specific Types of Microforms:
N/A

GOVERNMENT PUBLICATIONS:
Will Lend: No

DISSERTATIONS:
Will Lend: Yes

THESES:
Will Lend: Yes

AUDIO-VISUAL MATERIALS:
Records: Will not lend
Cassettes: Will not lend
Other (slides, filmstrips,
etc.): Will not lend

COMPUTER SOFTWARE:
Will Lend: (Not answered)

PHOTODUPLICATION SERVICE:
No charge up to 0 exposures
Charge Per Exposure: 10¢
Minimum/handling Fee: $1.00
Average Turnaround Time:
1 week

MICROFILMING SERVICE:
Service Available: No
Charges: N/A

DO YOU CHARGE THE BORROWING
LIBRARY FOR POSTAGE? (Not
answered)

FOR HOW LONG DO YOU SUSPEND ILL
SERVICE OVER THE CHRISTMAS
HOLIDAYS? (Not answered)

ARE THERE ANY GROUPS OF LIBRARIES
FOR WHICH YOU WAIVE FEES? IF
SO, PLEASE NAME THEM: State
institutions

MONMOUTH COLLEGE

NUC CODE: (Not answered)

OCLC CODE: ICL

ADDRESS: Interlibrary Loan
Monmouth College
Library
Monmouth, IL 61462

TELEPHONE: (309) 457-2031

LIST NAMES OF BRANCHES WITH
SEPARATE POLICIES: None

BOOKS:
Will Lend: Yes
Length of Loan: Usually
1 month
Renewable: Yes
Charges: None at this time
Average Turnaround Time:
4-5 days
If you have indicated that a
book is not to be lent, will
you on receipt of a letter
from the requesting library
search the index for given
entries? (Not answered)

PERIODICALS:
Bound: Will not lend
Unbound: Will not lend
Loan Period: N/A
Renewable: N/A
Will lend if article exceeds
_____ number of pages (Not
answered)

MICROFORMS:
Will Lend: Yes, sometimes
Specific Types of Microforms:
Some microfiche

GOVERNMENT PUBLICATIONS:
Will Lend: Yes

DISSERTATIONS:
Will Lend: Yes

THESES:
Will Lend: Yes

AUDIO-VISUAL MATERIALS:
Records: Will not lend
Cassettes: Will not lend
Other (slides, filmstrips,
etc.): Will not lend

COMPUTER SOFTWARE:
Will Lend: No

PHOTODUPLICATION SERVICE:
No charge up to any exposures
Charge Per Exposure: None
at this time
Minimum/handling Fee: None
Average Turnaround Time:
4-5 days

MICROFILMING SERVICE:
Service Available: No
Charges: N/A

DO YOU CHARGE THE BORROWING
LIBRARY FOR POSTAGE? No

FOR HOW LONG DO YOU SUSPEND ILL
SERVICE OVER THE CHRISTMAS
HOLIDAYS? No suspension

ARE THERE ANY GROUPS OF LIBRARIES
FOR WHICH YOU WAIVE FEES? IF
SO, PLEASE NAME THEM: None

NEWBERRY LIBRARY

NUC CODE: ICN

OCLC CODE: IBV

ADDRESS: Interlibrary Loan
The Newberry Library
60 W. Walton St.
Chicago, IL 60610

TELEPHONE: (312) 943-9090, X220

LIST NAMES OF BRANCHES WITH
SEPARATE POLICIES: None

BOOKS:
Will Lend: No
Length of Loan: N/A
Renewable: N/A
Charges: N/A
Average Turnaround Time:
N/A
If you have indicated that a
book is not to be lent, will
you on receipt of a letter
from the requesting library
search the index for given
entries? Yes, within
reason

PERIODICALS:
Bound: Will not lend
Unbound: Will not lend
Loan Period: N/A
Renewable: N/A
Will lend if article exceeds
_____ number of pages (Not
answered)

MICROFORMS:
Will Lend: No
Specific Types of Microforms:
N/A

GOVERNMENT PUBLICATIONS:
Will Lend: No

DISSERTATIONS:
Will Lend: No

THESES:
Will Lend: No

AUDIO-VISUAL MATERIALS:
Records: Will not lend
Cassettes: Will not lend
Other (slides, filmstrips,
etc.): Will not lend

COMPUTER SOFTWARE:
Will Lend: No

PHOTODUPLICATION SERVICE:
No charge up to 0 exposures
Charge Per Exposure: 20¢
Minimum/handling Fee: $3.00
Average Turnaround Time:
2 weeks

MICROFILMING SERVICE:
Service Available: Yes
Charges: 10¢ per exposure,
$3.00 handling

DO YOU CHARGE THE BORROWING
LIBRARY FOR POSTAGE? Yes

FOR HOW LONG DO YOU SUSPEND ILL
SERVICE OVER THE CHRISTMAS
HOLIDAYS? No suspension

ARE THERE ANY GROUPS OF LIBRARIES
FOR WHICH YOU WAIVE FEES? IF
SO, PLEASE NAME THEM: None

NORTHEAST ILLINOIS UNIVERSITY

NUC CODE: ICNE

OCLC CODE: IAO

ADDRESS: Interlibrary Loan
            Library--Reference
            Northeast Illinois
            University
            5500 N. St. Louis Ave.
            Chicago, IL 60625

TELEPHONE: (312) 583-4050, X8174

LIST NAMES OF BRANCHES WITH
  SEPARATE POLICIES: None

BOOKS:
  Will Lend: Yes
  Length of Loan: 3 weeks
  Renewable: Yes
  Charges: (Not answered)
  Average Turnaround Time:
    (Not answered)
  If you have indicated that a
    book is not to be lent, will
    you on receipt of a letter
    from the requesting library
    search the index for given
    entries? (Not answered)

PERIODICALS:
  Bound: Will not lend
  Unbound: Will not lend
  Loan Period: N/A
  Renewable: N/A
  Will lend if article exceeds
    _____ number of pages (Not
    answered)

MICROFORMS:
  Will Lend: No
  Specific Types of Microforms:
    N/A

GOVERNMENT PUBLICATIONS:
  Will Lend: Yes

DISSERTATIONS:
  Will Lend: Yes

THESES:
  Will Lend: Yes

AUDIO-VISUAL MATERIALS:
  Records: (Not answered)
  Cassettes: (Not answered)
  Other (slides, filmstrips,
    etc.): (Not answered)

COMPUTER SOFTWARE:
  Will Lend: (Not answered)

PHOTODUPLICATION SERVICE:
  No charge up to 0 exposures
  Charge Per Exposure: 10¢
  Minimum Fee: $2.00
  Average Turnaround Time:
    (Not answered)

MICROFILMING SERVICE:
  Service Available: (Not
    answered)
  Charges: N/A

DO YOU CHARGE THE BORROWING
  LIBRARY FOR POSTAGE? No

FOR HOW LONG DO YOU SUSPEND ILL
  SERVICE OVER THE CHRISTMAS
  HOLIDAYS? Dec.20-Jan.4

ARE THERE ANY GROUPS OF LIBRARIES
  FOR WHICH YOU WAIVE FEES? IF
  SO, PLEASE NAME THEM: (Not
  answered)

NORTHERN ILLINOIS UNIVERSITY AT DEKALB

NUC CODE: IDeKN

OCLC CODE: JNA

ADDRESS: Interlibrary Loan
            University Libraries
            Northern Illinois
            University
            De Kalb, IL 60115

TELEPHONE: (815) 753-1094

LIST NAMES OF BRANCHES WITH
  SEPARATE POLICIES: None

BOOKS:
  Will Lend: Yes
  Length of Loan: 2 weeks use
  Renewable: Yes
  Charges: None
  Average Turnaround Time:
    1 day
  If you have indicated that a
    book is not to be lent, will
    you on receipt of a letter
    from the requesting library
    search the index for given
    entries? (Not answered)

PERIODICALS:
  Bound: Will not lend
  Unbound: Will not lend
  Loan Period: N/A
  Renewable: N/A
  Will lend if article exceeds
    _____ number of pages (Not
    answered)

MICROFORMS:
  Will Lend: Yes
  Specific Types of Microforms:
    (Not answered)

GOVERNMENT PUBLICATIONS:
  Will Lend: Yes

DISSERTATIONS:
  Will Lend: Yes; 1956 to
    present also available from
    University Microfilms

THESES:
  Will Lend: Yes

AUDIO-VISUAL MATERIALS:
  Records: Will not lend
  Cassettes: Will lend
  Other (slides, filmstrips,
    etc.): Will lend

COMPUTER SOFTWARE:
  Will Lend: Yes

PHOTODUPLICATION SERVICE:
  No charge up to 0 exposures
  Charge Per Exposure: 10¢
  Minimum/handling Fee: $2.00
    handling fee
  Average Turnaround Time:
    2 days

MICROFILMING SERVICE:
  Service Available: Yes
  Charges: (Not answered)

DO YOU CHARGE THE BORROWING
  LIBRARY FOR POSTAGE?
  Reciprocal

FOR HOW LONG DO YOU SUSPEND ILL
  SERVICE OVER THE CHRISTMAS
  HOLIDAYS? Dec.10-Jan.3

ARE THERE ANY GROUPS OF LIBRARIES
  FOR WHICH YOU WAIVE FEES? IF
  SO, PLEASE NAME THEM:
  Reciprocal

ROCKFORD PUBLIC LIBRARY

NUC CODE: IRO

OCLC CODE: JBO

ADDRESS: Interlibrary Loan
Rockford Public Library
215 N. Wyman St.
Rockford, IL 61103

TELEPHONE: (815) 965-6731

LIST NAMES OF BRANCHES WITH
SEPARATE POLICIES: None

BOOKS:
Will Lend: Yes
Length of Loan: 3 weeks
Renewable: No
Charges: None
Average Turnaround Time:
2-3 days
If you have indicated that a
book is not to be lent, will
you on receipt of a letter
from the requesting library
search the index for given
entries? No

PERIODICALS:
Bound: Will not lend
Unbound: Will not lend
Loan Period: 2 weeks to NILS
Renewable: No
Will lend if article exceeds
_____ number of pages (Not
answered)

MICROFORMS:
Will Lend: No
Specific Types of Microforms:
Microfilm, microfiche

GOVERNMENT PUBLICATIONS:
Will Lend: Yes

DISSERTATIONS:
Will Lend: No

THESES:
Will Lend: No

AUDIO-VISUAL MATERIALS:
Records: Will lend
Cassettes: Will lend
Other (slides, filmstrips,
etc.): Will lend

COMPUTER SOFTWARE:
Will Lend: No

PHOTODUPLICATION SERVICE:
No charge up to 0 exposures
Charge Per Exposure: 25¢
Minimum/handling Fee: (Not
answered)
Average Turnaround Time:
Same day service

MICROFILMING SERVICE:
Service Available: Yes
Charges: 25¢

DO YOU CHARGE THE BORROWING
LIBRARY FOR POSTAGE? No

FOR HOW LONG DO YOU SUSPEND ILL
SERVICE OVER THE CHRISTMAS
HOLIDAYS? No suspension

ARE THERE ANY GROUPS OF LIBRARIES
FOR WHICH YOU WAIVE FEES? IF
SO, PLEASE NAME THEM: NILS
libraries

SANGAMON STATE UNIVERSITY

NUC CODE: None

OCLC CODE: IAS

ADDRESS: Interlibrary Loan
Sangamon State
University
Springfield, IL 62708

TELEPHONE: (217) 786-6601

LIST NAMES OF BRANCHES WITH
SEPARATE POLICIES: None

BOOKS:
Will Lend: Yes
Length of Loan: 4 weeks
Renewable: Yes
Charges: None
Average Turnaround Time:
24-36 hours
If you have indicated that a
book is not to be lent, will
you on receipt of a letter
from the requesting library
search the index for given
entries? Yes

PERIODICALS:
Bound: Will not lend
Unbound: Will not lend
Loan Period: N/A
Renewable: N/A
Will lend if article exceeds
_____ number of pages (Will
not lend, regardless of
length of article)

MICROFORMS:
Will Lend: Yes
Specific Types of Microforms:
Microfiche, microfilm,
microprint

GOVERNMENT PUBLICATIONS:
Will Lend: Yes

DISSERTATIONS:
Will Lend: No

THESES:
Will Lend: No

AUDIO-VISUAL MATERIALS:
Records: Will not lend
Cassettes: Will lend if
circulating
Other (slides, filmstrips,
etc.): Will lend if
circulating

COMPUTER SOFTWARE:
Will Lend: No

PHOTODUPLICATION SERVICE:
No charge up to 10 exposures
Charge Per Exposure: 10¢
Minimum/handling Fee: None
Average Turnaround Time:
24-36 hours

MICROFILMING SERVICE:
Service Available: No
Charges: N/A

DO YOU CHARGE THE BORROWING
LIBRARY FOR POSTAGE? No

FOR HOW LONG DO YOU SUSPEND ILL
SERVICE OVER THE CHRISTMAS
HOLIDAYS? Dec.15-Jan.3

ARE THERE ANY GROUPS OF LIBRARIES
FOR WHICH YOU WAIVE FEES? IF
SO, PLEASE NAME THEM: None

SHAWNEE LIBRARY SYSTEM

NUC CODE: (Not answered)

OCLC CODE: IUI

ADDRESS: Interlibrary Loan
Shawnee Library System
Greenbriar Rd.
Carterville, IL   62918

TELEPHONE:

LIST NAMES OF BRANCHES WITH
SEPARATE POLICIES: None

BOOKS:
Will Lend: Yes
Length of Loan: 30 days
from receipt
Renewable: Yes
Charges: (Not answered)
Average Turnaround Time:
(Not answered)
If you have indicated that a
book is not to be lent, will
you on receipt of a letter
from the requesting library
search the index for given
entries?   (Not answered)

PERIODICALS:
Bound: Will not lend
Unbound: Will not lend
Loan Period: N/A
Renewable: N/A
Will lend if article exceeds
_____ number of pages (Not
answered)

MICROFORMS:
Will Lend: Yes
Specific Types of Microforms:
Fiche, in-state only

GOVERNMENT PUBLICATIONS:
Will Lend: Yes

DISSERTATIONS:
Will Lend: (Not answered)

THESES:
Will Lend: (Not answered)

AUDIO-VISUAL MATERIALS:
Records: Will lend
Cassettes: Will lend
Other (slides, filmstrips,
etc.):   Will lend, in-
state only

COMPUTER SOFTWARE:
Will Lend: (Not answered)

PHOTODUPLICATION SERVICE:
No charge up to 0 exposures
Charge Per Exposure: 10¢
Minimum/handling Fee: (Not
answered)
Average Turnaround Time:
(Not answered)

MICROFILMING SERVICE:
Service Available: (Not
answered)
Charges: N/A

DO YOU CHARGE THE BORROWING
LIBRARY FOR POSTAGE?   (Not
answered)

FOR HOW LONG DO YOU SUSPEND ILL
SERVICE OVER THE CHRISTMAS
HOLIDAYS?   (Not answered)

ARE THERE ANY GROUPS OF LIBRARIES
FOR WHICH YOU WAIVE FEES?   IF
SO, PLEASE NAME THEM: None

SKOKIE PUBLIC LIBRARY

NUC CODE: (Not answered)

OCLC CODE: IHG

ADDRESS: Interlibrary Loan
Skokie Public Library
5215 Oakton St.
Skokie, IL   60077

TELEPHONE: (312) 673-7774

LIST NAMES OF BRANCHES WITH
SEPARATE POLICIES: None

BOOKS:
Will Lend: Yes
Length of Loan: 3 weeks
Renewable: Yes, for 1 week,
if no reserves
Charges: None
Average Turnaround Time:
(Not answered)
If you have indicated that a
book is not to be lent, will
you on receipt of a letter
from the requesting library
search the index for given
entries?   (Not answered)

PERIODICALS:
Bound: Will not lend
Unbound: Will not lend
Loan Period: N/A
Renewable: N/A
Will lend if article exceeds
_____ number of pages (Not
answered)

MICROFORMS:
Will Lend: No
Specific Types of Microforms:
N/A

GOVERNMENT PUBLICATIONS:
Will Lend: Yes

DISSERTATIONS:
Will Lend: (Not answered)

THESES:
Will Lend: (Not answered)

AUDIO-VISUAL MATERIALS:
Records: Will not lend
Cassettes: Will not lend
Other (slides, filmstrips,
etc.):   Will not lend

COMPUTER SOFTWARE:
Will Lend: No

PHOTODUPLICATION SERVICE:
No charge up to _____
exposures   (Not answered)
Charge Per Exposure: (Not
answered)
Minimum/handling Fee: (Not
answered)
Average Turnaround Time:
(Not answered)

MICROFILMING SERVICE:
Service Available: No
Charges: N/A

DO YOU CHARGE THE BORROWING
LIBRARY FOR POSTAGE?   No

FOR HOW LONG DO YOU SUSPEND ILL
SERVICE OVER THE CHRISTMAS
HOLIDAYS?   No suspension

ARE THERE ANY GROUPS OF LIBRARIES
FOR WHICH YOU WAIVE FEES?   IF
SO, PLEASE NAME THEM: None

SOUTHERN ILLINOIS UNIVERSITY AT CARBONDALE

NUC CODE: ICarbS

OCLC CODE: SOI

ADDRESS: Interlibrary Loan
          Morris Library
          Southern Illinois
          University
          Carbondale, IL 62901

TELEPHONE: (618) 453-3374

LIST NAMES OF BRANCHES WITH
    SEPARATE POLICIES: None

BOOKS
    Will Lend: Yes
    Length of Loan: 4 weeks
    Renewable: Yes
    Charges: Postage reimbursement
    Average Turnaround Time:
        1 week
    If you have indicated that a
        book is not to be lent, will
        you on receipt of a letter
        from the requesting library
        search the index for given
        entries? (Not answered)

PERIODICALS:
    Bound: Will not lend
    Unbound: Will not lend
    Loan Period: N/A
    Renewable: N/A
    Will lend if article exceeds
        _____ number of pages (Not
        answered)

MICROFORMS:
    Will Lend: Yes
    Specific Types of Microforms:
        (Not answered)

GOVERNMENT PUBLICATIONS:
    Will Lend: Yes

DISSERTATIONS:
    Will Lend: Yes

THESES:
    Will Lend: Yes

AUDIO-VISUAL MATERIALS:
    Records: Will lend
    Cassettes: Will not lend
    Other (slides, filmstrips,
        etc.): (Not answered)

COMPUTER SOFTWARE:
    Will Lend: (Not answered)

PHOTODUPLICATION SERVICE:
    No charge up to 0 exposures
    Charge Per Exposure: 15¢
    Minimum/handling Fee: $3.00
        for 1-5 exposures
    Average Turnaround Time:
        1 week

MICROFILMING SERVICE:
    Service Available: No
    Charges: N/A

DO YOU CHARGE THE BORROWING
    LIBRARY FOR POSTAGE? Yes

FOR HOW LONG DO YOU SUSPEND ILL
    SERVICE OVER THE CHRISTMAS
    HOLIDAYS? 3 weeks for out-
    of-state requests

ARE THERE ANY GROUPS OF LIBRARIES
    FOR WHICH YOU WAIVE FEES? IF
    SO, PLEASE NAME THEM:
    ILLINET libraries

SOUTHERN ILLINOIS UNIVERSITY AT EDWARDSVILLE

NUC CODE: IEdS

OCLC CODE: IAT

ADDRESS: Interlibrary Loan
          Lovejoy Library
          Southern Illinois
          University
          Edwardsville, IL
          62026-1001

TELEPHONE: (618) 692-2174

LIST NAMES OF BRANCHES WITH
    SEPARATE POLICIES: None

BOOKS:
    Will Lend: Yes
    Length of Loan: 2 weeks use
    Renewable: Yes
    Charges: None
    Average Turnaround Time:
        24 hours
    If you have indicated that a
        book is not to be lent, will
        you on receipt of a letter
        from the requesting library
        search the index for given
        entries? Occasionally

PERIODICALS:
    Bound: Will not lend
    Unbound: Will not lend
    Loan Period: N/A
    Renewable: N/A
    Will lend if article exceeds
        _____ number of pages (Will
        not lend, regardless of
        length of article)

MICROFORMS:
    Will Lend: Yes, sometimes
    Specific Types of Microforms:
        Cards, film, and fiche

GOVERNMENT PUBLICATIONS:
    Will Lend: Yes

DISSERTATIONS:
    Will Lend: Yes

THESES:
    Will Lend: Yes

AUDIO-VISUAL MATERIALS:
    Records: Will not lend
    Cassettes: Will not lend
    Other (slides, filmstrips,
        etc.): Will not lend

COMPUTER SOFTWARE:
    Will Lend: No

PHOTODUPLICATION SERVICE:
    No charge up to 0 exposures
    Charge Per Exposure: 10¢
    Minimum/handling Fee: $3.00
    Average Turnaround Time:
        24 hours

MICROFILMING SERVICE:
    Service Available: No
    Charges: N/A

DO YOU CHARGE THE BORROWING
    LIBRARY FOR POSTAGE? No

FOR HOW LONG DO YOU SUSPEND ILL
    SERVICE OVER THE CHRISTMAS
    HOLIDAYS? No suspension

ARE THERE ANY GROUPS OF LIBRARIES
    FOR WHICH YOU WAIVE FEES? IF
    SO, PLEASE NAME THEM: ILLINET

UNIVERSITY OF CHICAGO

NUC CODE: ICU

OCLC CODE: None

ADDRESS: Interlibrary Loan
University of Chicago
Library
1100 E. 57th St.
Chicago, IL 60637

TELEPHONE: (312) 962-8706

LIST NAMES OF BRANCHES WITH
SEPARATE POLICIES: None

BOOKS:
Will Lend: Yes
Length of Loan: 4 weeks
Renewable: No
Charges: None
Average Turnaround Time:
2 weeks
If you have indicated that a
book is not to be lent, will
you on receipt of a letter
from the requesting library
search the index for given
entries? Address to
Reference Dept.

PERIODICALS:
Bound: Will not usually lend
Unbound: Will not lend
Loan Period: 4 weeks
Renewable: No
Will lend if article exceeds
50 pages

MICROFORMS:
Will Lend: Yes
Specific Types of Microforms:
Microfilm, microfiche,
microcard (positive only)

GOVERNMENT PUBLICATIONS:
Will Lend: Yes

DISSERTATIONS:
Will Lend: Yes, if pre-1964
and 2d copy available

THESES:
Will Lend: Yes, if pre-1964
and 2d copy available

AUDIO-VISUAL MATERIALS:
Records: Will not lend
Cassettes: Will not lend
Other (slides, filmstrips,
etc.): Will not lend

COMPUTER SOFTWARE:
Will Lend: No

PHOTODUPLICATION SERVICE:
No charge up to 0 exposures
Charge Per Exposure: 15¢
Minimum Fee: $4.00 per item
Handling Fee: $1.00
Average Turnaround Time:
(Not answered)

MICROFILMING SERVICE:
Service Available: (Not
answered)
Charges: N/A

DO YOU CHARGE THE BORROWING
LIBRARY FOR POSTAGE? No

FOR HOW LONG DO YOU SUSPEND ILL
SERVICE OVER THE CHRISTMAS
HOLIDAYS? App. 3 weeks

ARE THERE ANY GROUPS OF LIBRARIES
FOR WHICH YOU WAIVE FEES? IF
SO, PLEASE NAME THEM: None

UNIVERSITY OF ILLINOIS AT CHICAGO CIRCLE

NUC CODE: ICIU

OCLC CODE: IAY

ADDRESS: Interlibrary Loan
University of Illinois
at Chicago Circle
P. O. Box 8198
Chicago, IL 60680

TELEPHONE: (312) 996-4886

LIST NAMES OF BRANCHES WITH
SEPARATE POLICIES: None

BOOKS:
Will Lend: Yes
Length of Loan: 3 weeks use
Renewable: Yes
Charges: (Not answered)
Average Turnaround Time:
1 day
If you have indicated that a
book is not to be lent, will
you on receipt of a letter
from the requesting library
search the index for given
entries? (Not answered)

PERIODICALS:
Bound: Will not lend
Unbound: Will not lend
Loan Period: N/A
Renewable: N/A
Will lend if article exceeds
_____ number of pages (Not
answered)

MICROFORMS:
Will Lend: No
Specific Types of Microforms:
N/A

GOVERNMENT PUBLICATIONS:
Will Lend: Yes

DISSERTATIONS:
Will Lend: Yes

THESES:
Will Lend: Yes

AUDIO-VISUAL MATERIALS:
Records: Will not lend
Cassettes: Will not lend
Other (slides, filmstrips,
etc.): Will not lend

COMPUTER SOFTWARE:
Will Lend: Do not own

PHOTODUPLICATION SERVICE:
No charge up to 0 exposures
Charge Per Exposure: 10¢
Minimum/handling Fee: $5.00
Average Turnaround Time:
2 days

MICROFILMING SERVICE:
Service Available: No
Charges: N/A

DO YOU CHARGE THE BORROWING
LIBRARY FOR POSTAGE? No

FOR HOW LONG DO YOU SUSPEND ILL
SERVICE OVER THE CHRISTMAS
HOLIDAYS? 1 week

ARE THERE ANY GROUPS OF LIBRARIES
FOR WHICH YOU WAIVE FEES? IF
SO, PLEASE NAME THEM: Univer-
sity of Illinois Libraries;
CALC Libraries; ILLINET
Libraries

UNIVERSITY OF ILLINOIS AT THE MEDICAL CENTER

NUC CODE: IU-M

OCLC CODE: (Not answered)

ADDRESS: Interlibrary Loan
          Library of the Health
          Sciences
          University of Illinois
          at the Medical Center
          P. O. Box 7509
          Chicago, IL 60680

TELEPHONE: (312) 996-8991

LIST NAMES OF BRANCHES WITH
  SEPARATE POLICIES: None

BOOKS:
  Will Lend: Yes
  Length of Loan: 4 weeks
  Renewable: (Not answered)
  Charges: $5.00
  Average Turnaround Time:
    (Not answered)
  If you have indicated that a
    book is not to be lent, will
    you on receipt of a letter
    from the requesting library
    search the index for given
    entries? (Not answered)

PERIODICALS:
  Bound: (Not answered)
  Unbound: (Not answered)
  Loan Period: (Not answered)
  Renewable: (Not answered)
  Will lend if article exceeds
    50 pages

MICROFORMS:
  Will Lend: (Not answered)
  Specific Types of Microforms:
    (Not answered)

GOVERNMENT PUBLICATIONS:
  Will Lend: (Not answered)

DISSERTATIONS:
  Will Lend: Yes

THESES:
  Will Lend: Yes

AUDIO-VISUAL MATERIALS:
  Records: (Not answered)
  Cassettes: (Not answered)
  Other (slides, filmstrips,
    etc.): (Not answered)

COMPUTER SOFTWARE:
  Will Lend: (Not answered)

PHOTODUPLICATION SERVICE:
  No charge up to 0 exposures
  Charge Per Exposure: 10¢
  Minimum Fee: $5.00
  Average Turnaround Time:
    (Not answered)

MICROFILMING SERVICE:
  Service Available: No
  Charges: N/A

DO YOU CHARGE THE BORROWING
  LIBRARY FOR POSTAGE? No

FOR HOW LONG DO YOU SUSPEND ILL
  SERVICE OVER THE CHRISTMAS
  HOLIDAYS? (Not answered)

ARE THERE ANY GROUPS OF LIBRARIES
  FOR WHICH YOU WAIVE FEES? IF
  SO, PLEASE NAME THEM: (Not
  answered)

UNIVERSITY OF ILLINOIS AT URBANA-CHAMPAIGN

NUC CODE: IU

OCLC CODE: UIU

ADDRESS: Interlibrary Loan
          Library 128
          University of Illinois
          at Urbana-Champaign
          1408 W. Gregory Dr.
          Urbana, IL 61801

TELEPHONE: (217) 333-1958

LIST NAMES OF BRANCHES WITH
  SEPARATE POLICIES: None

BOOKS:
  Will Lend: Yes
  Length of Loan: 2 weeks
  Renewable: Yes
  Charges: Postage
  Average Turnaround Time:
    1 day
  If you have indicated that a
    book is not to be lent, will
    you on receipt of a letter
    from the requesting library
    search the index for given
    entries? (Not answered)

PERIODICALS:
  Bound: Will lend
  Unbound: (Not answered)
  Loan Period: 2 weeks
  Renewable: Yes
  Will lend if article exceeds
    70 pages

MICROFORMS:
  Will Lend: Yes
  Specific Types of Microforms:
    (Not answered)

GOVERNMENT PUBLICATIONS:
  Will Lend: Yes

DISSERTATIONS:
  Will Lend: Yes, if pre-1954.
    1954- available from
    University Microfilms

THESES:
  Will Lend: Yes, if pre-1954.
    1954- available from
    University Microfilms

AUDIO-VISUAL MATERIALS:
  Records: (Not answered)
  Cassettes: (Not answered)
  Other (slides, filmstrips,
    etc.): (Not answered)

COMPUTER SOFTWARE:
  Will Lend: (Not answered)

PHOTODUPLICATION SERVICE:
  No charge up to 0 exposures
  Charge Per Exposure: 50¢
  Handling Fee: $4.00
  Average Turnaround Time:
    2 days

MICROFILMING SERVICE:
  Service Available: Yes
  Charges: $4.00 plus 15¢ per
    exposure

DO YOU CHARGE THE BORROWING
  LIBRARY FOR POSTAGE? (Not
  answered)

FOR HOW LONG DO YOU SUSPEND ILL
  SERVICE OVER THE CHRISTMAS
  HOLIDAYS? Dec. 15-Jan. 2

ARE THERE ANY GROUPS OF LIBRARIES
  FOR WHICH YOU WAIVE FEES? IF
  SO, PLEASE NAME THEM: None

WESTERN ILLINOIS UNIVERSITY

NUC CODE: IMacoW

OCLC CODE: IAZ

ADDRESS: Interlibrary Loan
          University Library
          Western Illinois
          University
          Macomb, IL 61455

TELEPHONE: (309) 298-2411

LIST NAMES OF BRANCHES WITH
  SEPARATE POLICIES: None

BOOKS:
  Will Lend: Yes
  Length of Loan: 2 weeks
  Renewable: Yes
  Charges: None
  Average Turnaround Time:
    1 week
  If you have indicated that a
    book is not to be lent, will
    you on receipt of a letter
    from the requesting library
    search the index for given
    entries? (Not answered)

PERIODICALS:
  Bound: Will not lend
  Unbound: Will not lend
  Loan Period: N/A
  Renewable: N/A
  Will lend if article exceeds
    _____ number of pages (Will
    not lend, regardless of
    length of article)

MICROFORMS:
  Will Lend: Yes
  Specific Types of Microforms:
    ERIC, master's theses,
    dissertations

GOVERNMENT PUBLICATIONS:
  Will Lend: Yes

DISSERTATIONS:
  Will Lend: Yes

THESES:
  Will Lend: Yes

AUDIO-VISUAL MATERIALS:
  Records: Will not lend
  Cassettes: Will not lend
  Other (slides, filmstrips,
    etc.): Will not lend

COMPUTER SOFTWARE:
  Will Lend: No

PHOTODUPLICATION SERVICE:
  No charge up to 0 exposures
  Charge Per Exposure: 10¢
  Minimum/handling Fee: $1.00
  Average Turnaround Time:
    1 week

MICROFILMING SERVICE:
  Service Available: No
  Charges: N/A

DO YOU CHARGE THE BORROWING
  LIBRARY FOR POSTAGE? No

FOR HOW LONG DO YOU SUSPEND ILL
  SERVICE OVER THE CHRISTMAS
  HOLIDAYS? 1 week

ARE THERE ANY GROUPS OF LIBRARIES
  FOR WHICH YOU WAIVE FEES? IF
  SO, PLEASE NAME THEM: None

ALLEN COUNTY PUBLIC LIBRARY

NUC CODE: None

OCLC CODE: IMF

ADDRESS: Interlibrary Loan
Allen County Public
Library
P. O. Box 2270
900 Webster St.
Fort Wayne, IN 46801

TELEPHONE: (219) 424-7241, X216

LIST NAMES OF BRANCHES WITH
SEPARATE POLICIES: None

BOOKS:
Will Lend: Yes
Length of Loan: 2 weeks use
Renewable: Yes
Charges: Postage and
insurance cost if needed
Average Turnaround Time:
2 days
If you have indicated that a
book is not to be lent, will
you on receipt of a letter
from the requesting library
search the index for given
entries? Yes

PERIODICALS:
Bound: Will not lend
Unbound: Will not lend
Loan Period: N/A
Renewable: N/A
Will lend if article exceeds
_____ number of pages (Will
not lend, regardless of
length of article)

MICROFORMS:
Will Lend: No
Specific Types of Microforms:
N/A

GOVERNMENT PUBLICATIONS:
Will Lend: Yes

DISSERTATIONS:
Will Lend: Do not own

THESES:
Will Lend: Do not own

AUDIO-VISUAL MATERIALS:
Records: Will not lend
Cassettes: Will not lend
Other (slides, filmstrips,
etc.): Will not lend

COMPUTER SOFTWARE:
Will Lend: No

PHOTODUPLICATION SERVICE:
No charge up to 0 exposures
Charge Per Exposure: 10¢-
25¢
Minimum/handling Fee: $1.00
plus postage
Average Turnaround Time:
2 days

MICROFILMING SERVICE:
Service Available: No
Charges: N/A

DO YOU CHARGE THE BORROWING
LIBRARY FOR POSTAGE? Yes

FOR HOW LONG DO YOU SUSPEND ILL
SERVICE OVER THE CHRISTMAS
HOLIDAYS? No suspension

ARE THERE ANY GROUPS OF LIBRARIES
FOR WHICH YOU WAIVE FEES? IF
SO, PLEASE NAME THEM: None

BALL STATE UNIVERSITY

NUC CODE: InMB

OCLC CODE: IBS

ADDRESS: Interlibrary Loan
Ball State University
Library
Muncie, IN 47306

TELEPHONE: (317) 285-1779

LIST NAMES OF BRANCHES WITH
SEPARATE POLICIES: None

BOOKS:
Will Lend: Yes
Length of Loan: 2 weeks
Renewable: Yes, usually
Charges: None
Average Turnaround Time:
3 days
If you have indicated that a
book is not to be lent, will
you on receipt of a letter
from the requesting library
search the index for given
entries? (Not answered)

PERIODICALS:
Bound: Will not lend
Unbound: Will not lend
Loan Period: N/A
Renewable: N/A
Will lend if article exceeds
_____ number of pages (Will
not lend, regardless of
length of article)

MICROFORMS:
Will Lend: Yes
Specific Types of Microforms:
(Not answered)

GOVERNMENT PUBLICATIONS:
Will Lend: Yes

DISSERTATIONS:
Will Lend: No. Available
from University Microfilms

THESES:
Will Lend: Yes

AUDIO-VISUAL MATERIALS:
Records: Will not lend
Cassettes: Will not lend
Other (slides, filmstrips,
etc.): Will not lend

COMPUTER SOFTWARE:
Will Lend: No

PHOTODUPLICATION SERVICE:
No charge up to 15 exposures
Charge Per Additional
Exposure: 10¢ if over 15
(e.g., 16 exposures=$1.60)
Minimum/handling Fee: None
Average Turnaround Time:
3 days

MICROFILMING SERVICE:
Service Available: No
Charges: N/A

DO YOU CHARGE THE BORROWING
LIBRARY FOR POSTAGE? Postage
reimbursement appreciated

FOR HOW LONG DO YOU SUSPEND ILL
SERVICE OVER THE CHRISTMAS
HOLIDAYS? Dec.10-Dec.30

ARE THERE ANY GROUPS OF LIBRARIES
FOR WHICH YOU WAIVE FEES? IF
SO, PLEASE NAME THEM: Those
which have specific
reciprocal agreements with
us

EARLHAM COLLEGE

NUC CODE: InRE

OCLC CODE: IEC

ADDRESS: Interlibrary Loan
Earlham College Library
Richmond, IN 47374

TELEPHONE: (317) 962-6561, X307

LIST NAMES OF BRANCHES WITH
SEPARATE POLICIES: None

BOOKS:
Will Lend: Yes
Length of Loan: Usually
1 month
Renewable: Yes
Charges: None
Average Turnaround Time:
5 days
If you have indicated that a
book is not to be lent, will
you on receipt of a letter
from the requesting library
search the index for given
entries? (Not answered)

PERIODICALS:
Bound: Will not lend
Unbound: May lend
Loan Period: 1 week
Renewable: No
Will lend if article exceeds
_____ number of pages (Not
answered)

MICROFORMS:
Will Lend: Yes, except for
periodicals on microfilm
Specific Types of Microforms:
Microfilm

GOVERNMENT PUBLICATIONS:
Will Lend: Yes

DISSERTATIONS:
Will Lend: Yes

AUDIO-VISUAL MATERIALS:
Records: Will not lend
Cassettes: Will lend
Other (slides, filmstrips,
etc.): Will not lend

COMPUTER SOFTWARE:
Will Lend: No

PHOTODUPLICATION SERVICE:
No charge up to 0 exposures
Charge Per Exposure: 10¢
Minimum Fee: $1.00
Average Turnaround Time:
5 days

MICROFILMING SERVICE:
Service Available: No
Charges: N/A

DO YOU CHARGE THE BORROWING
LIBRARY FOR POSTAGE? Not
usually

FOR HOW LONG DO YOU SUSPEND ILL
SERVICE OVER THE CHRISTMAS
HOLIDAYS? 2 weeks

ARE THERE ANY GROUPS OF LIBRARIES
FOR WHICH YOU WAIVE FEES? IF
SO, PLEASE NAME THEM:
Photocopy is free within
the state

EVANSVILLE-VANDERBURGH COUNTY PUBLIC LIBRARY

NUC CODE: InE

OCLC CODE: IEP

ADDRESS: Interlibrary Loan
Evansville-Vanderburgh
County Public Library
22 S. E. Fifth St.
Evansville, IN
47708-1694

TELEPHONE: (812) 425-2621

LIST NAMES OF BRANCHES WITH
SEPARATE POLICIES: None

BOOKS:
Will Lend: Yes
Length of Loan: 4 weeks from
date of mailing
Renewable: Sometimes
Charges: Postage (and
insurance when deemed
appropriate)
Average Turnaround Time:
4-8 days
If you have indicated that a
book is not to be lent, will
you on receipt of a letter
from the requesting library
search the index for given
entries? Yes

PERIODICALS:
Bound: Will not lend
Unbound: Will not lend
Loan Period: N/A
Renewable: N/A
Will lend if article exceeds
_____ number of pages (Not
answered)

MICROFORMS:
Will Lend: No
Specific Types of Microforms:
N/A

GOVERNMENT PUBLICATIONS:
Will Lend: Sometimes

DISSERTATIONS:
Will Lend: Do not own

THESES:
Will Lend: Do not own

AUDIO-VISUAL MATERIALS:
Records: Will not lend
Cassettes: Will not lend
Other (slides, filmstrips,
etc.): Will not lend

COMPUTER SOFTWARE:
Will Lend: No

PHOTODUPLICATION SERVICE:
No charge up to 0 exposures
Charge Per Exposure: 10¢
from hard copy; 15¢ from
microfilm
Minimum/handling Fee: Postage
plus exposure charge
Average Turnaround Time:
4-8 days

MICROFILMING SERVICE:
Service Available: No
Charges: N/A

DO YOU CHARGE THE BORROWING
LIBRARY FOR POSTAGE? Yes

FOR HOW LONG DO YOU SUSPEND ILL
SERVICE OVER THE CHRISTMAS
HOLIDAYS? No suspension

ARE THERE ANY GROUPS OF LIBRARIES
FOR WHICH YOU WAIVE FEES? IF
SO, PLEASE NAME THEM: None

HAMMOND PUBLIC LIBRARY

NUC CODE: (Not answered)

OCLC CODE: IHP

ADDRESS: Interlibrary Loan
            Hammond Public Library
            564 State St.
            Hammond, IN 46320

TELEPHONE: (219) 931-5100

LIST NAMES OF BRANCHES WITH
    SEPARATE POLICIES: None

BOOKS:
    Will Lend: Yes
    Length of Loan: 4 weeks
    Renewable: Yes
    Charges: Postage
    Average Turnaround Time:
      (Not answered)
    If you have indicated that a
      book is not to be lent, will
      you on receipt of a letter
      from the requesting library
      search the index for given
      entries? Yes

PERIODICALS:
    Bound: Will not lend
    Unbound: Will lend
    Loan Period: 2 weeks
    Renewable: No
    Will lend if article exceeds
      _____ number of pages (Not
      answered)

MICROFORMS:
    Will Lend: Yes
    Specific Types of Microforms:
      Microfilm

GOVERNMENT PUBLICATIONS:
    Will Lend: Yes

DISSERTATIONS:
    Will Lend: (Not answered)

THESES:
    Will Lend: (Not answered)

AUDIO-VISUAL MATERIALS:
    Records: Will not lend
    Cassettes: Will not lend
    Other (slides, filmstrips,
      etc.): Will not lend

COMPUTER SOFTWARE:
    Will Lend: No

PHOTODUPLICATION SERVICE:
    No charge up to 0 exposures
    Charge Per Exposure: 10¢
    Minimum/handling Fee:
      (Not answered)
    Average Turnaround Time:
      (Not answered)

MICROFILMING SERVICE:
    Service Available: No
    Charges: N/A

DO YOU CHARGE THE BORROWING
    LIBRARY FOR POSTAGE? Yes

FOR HOW LONG DO YOU SUSPEND ILL
    SERVICE OVER THE CHRISTMAS
    HOLIDAYS? No suspension

ARE THERE ANY GROUPS OF LIBRARIES
    FOR WHICH YOU WAIVE FEES? IF
    SO, PLEASE NAME THEM: None

INDIANA STATE LIBRARY

NUC CODE: In

OCLC CODE: ISL

ADDRESS: Interlibrary Loan
            Indiana State Library
            140 N. Senate Ave.
            Indianapolis, IN 46204

TELEPHONE: (317) 232-3728

LIST NAMES OF BRANCHES WITH
    SEPARATE POLICIES: None

BOOKS:
    Will Lend: Yes
    Length of Loan: 30 days
    Renewable: Yes
    Charges: Out-of-state
    Average Turnaround Time:
      (Not answered)
    If you have indicated that a
      book is not to be lent, will
      you on receipt of a letter
      from the requesting library
      search the index for given
      entries? (Not answered)

PERIODICALS:
    Bound: Will lend in-state
      only
    Unbound: Will not lend
    Loan Period: 30 days
    Renewable: Yes
    Will lend if article exceeds
      _____ number of pages (Not
      answered)

MICROFORMS:
    Will Lend: Yes
    Specific Types of Microforms:
      (Not answered)

GOVERNMENT PUBLICATIONS:
    Will Lend: Yes

DISSERTATIONS:
    Will Lend: Yes

THESES:
    Will Lend: Yes

AUDIO-VISUAL MATERIALS:
    Records: (Not answered)
    Cassettes: (Not answered)
    Other (slides, filmstrips,
      etc.): (Not answered)

COMPUTER SOFTWARE:
    Will Lend: (Not answered)

PHOTODUPLICATION SERVICE:
    No charge up to 0 exposures
    Charge Per Exposure: 25¢
    Minimum/handling Fee:
      Minimal
    Average Turnaround Time:
      (Not answered)

MICROFILMING SERVICE:
    Service Available: (Not
      answered)
    Charges: N/A

DO YOU CHARGE THE BORROWING
    LIBRARY FOR POSTAGE? (Not
    answered)

FOR HOW LONG DO YOU SUSPEND ILL
    SERVICE OVER THE CHRISTMAS
    HOLIDAYS? Dec.15-Jan.5

ARE THERE ANY GROUPS OF LIBRARIES
    FOR WHICH YOU WAIVE FEES? IF
    SO, PLEASE NAME THEM: (Not
    answered)

INDIANA STATE UNIVERSITY

NUC CODE: InTI

OCLC CODE: ISU

ADDRESS: Interlibrary Loan
Indiana State University
Library
Terre Haute, IN 47809

TELEPHONE: (812) 232-6311, X2451

LIST NAMES OF BRANCHES WITH
SEPARATE POLICIES: None

BOOKS:
Will Lend: Yes
Length of Loan: 2 weeks
Renewable: (Not answered)
Charges: None
Average Turnaround Time:
(Not answered)
If you have indicated that a
book is not to be lent, will
you on receipt of a letter
from the requesting library
search the index for given
entries? (Not answered)

PERIODICALS:
Bound: Will not lend
Unbound: Will not lend
Loan Period: N/A
Renewable: N/A
Will lend if article exceeds
_____ number of pages (Not
answered)

MICROFORMS:
Will Lend: (Not answered)
Specific Types of Microforms:
N/A

GOVERNMENT PUBLICATIONS:
Will Lend: Yes

DISSERTATIONS:
Will Lend: Yes

THESES:
Will Lend: Yes

AUDIO-VISUAL MATERIALS:
Records: (Not answered)
Cassettes: (Not answered)
Other (slides, filmstrips,
etc.): (Not answered)

COMPUTER SOFTWARE:
Will Lend: (Not answered)

PHOTODUPLICATION SERVICE:
No charge up to 0 exposures
Charge Per Exposure: 10¢
Minimum/handling Fee: $1.00
Average Turnaround Time:
(Not answered)

MICROFILMING SERVICE:
Service Available: No
Charges: N/A

DO YOU CHARGE THE BORROWING
LIBRARY FOR POSTAGE? (Not
answered)

FOR HOW LONG DO YOU SUSPEND ILL
SERVICE OVER THE CHRISTMAS
HOLIDAYS? (Not answered)

ARE THERE ANY GROUPS OF LIBRARIES
FOR WHICH YOU WAIVE FEES? IF
SO, PLEASE NAME THEM: (Not
answered)

INDIANA UNIVERSITY AT BLOOMINGTON

NUC CODE: InU

OCLC CODE: IUL

ADDRESS: Interlibrary Loan
Indiana University
Libraries
Bloomington, IN 47405

TELEPHONE: (812) 335-7746

LIST NAMES OF BRANCHES WITH
SEPARATE POLICIES: None

BOOKS:
Will Lend: Yes
Length of Loan: 3 weeks use
Renewable: No
Charges: None
Average Turnaround Time:
24 hours
If you have indicated that a
book is not to be lent, will
you on receipt of a letter
from the requesting library
search the index for given
entries? No

PERIODICALS:
Bound: Will not lend
Unbound: Will not lend
Loan Period: N/A
Renewable: N/A
Will lend if article exceeds
_____ number of pages (Not
answered)

MICROFORMS:
Will Lend: Yes
Specific Types of Microforms:
Microfiche, microfilm,
microprint, microcard

GOVERNMENT PUBLICATIONS:
Will Lend: Yes, selectively

DISSERTATIONS:
Will Lend: Yes, if 2nd copy
available; 1952 to present
available from University
Microfilms

THESES:
Will Lend: Yes, if 2nd copy
available

AUDIO-VISUAL MATERIALS:
Records: Will not lend
Cassettes: Will not lend
Other (slides, filmstrips,
etc.): Will not lend

COMPUTER SOFTWARE:
Will Lend: No

PHOTODUPLICATION SERVICE:
No charge up to 0 exposures
Charge Per Exposure: 10¢
Minimum Charge: $4.00
Handling Fee: $1.50
Average Turnaround Time:
48 hours

MICROFILMING SERVICE:
Service Available: Yes
Charges: 8¢ per frame for
negative; positive not
available; minimum charge
$7.50 plus $3.75 handling;
diazo only

DO YOU CHARGE THE BORROWING
LIBRARY FOR POSTAGE? No

FOR HOW LONG DO YOU SUSPEND ILL
SERVICE OVER THE CHRISTMAS
HOLIDAYS? Dec.12-Jan.2

ARE THERE ANY GROUPS OF LIBRARIES
FOR WHICH YOU WAIVE FEES? IF
SO, PLEASE NAME THEM: None

INDIANA UNIVERSITY-PURDUE UNIVERSITY AT FORT WAYNE

NUC CODE: None

OCLC CODE: None

ADDRESS: Interlibrary Loan
           Indiana-Purdue
             University Library
           2101 Coliseum Blvd.
             East
           Fort Wayne, IN 46805

TELEPHONE: (219) 482-5593

LIST NAMES OF BRANCHES WITH
  SEPARATE POLICIES: None

BOOKS:
  Will Lend: Yes
  Length of Loan: 1 month
  Renewable: Yes, unless
    specified otherwise
  Charges: None
  Average Turnaround Time:
    10 days
  If you have indicated that a
    book is not to be lent, will
    you on receipt of a letter
    from the requesting library
    search the index for given
    entries? (Not answered)

PERIODICALS:
  Bound: Will not lend
  Unbound: Will not lend
  Loan Period: N/A
  Renewable: N/A
  Will lend if article exceeds
    _____ number of pages (Will
    not lend, regardless of
    length of article)

MICROFORMS:
  Will Lend: Yes, some of them
  Specific Types of Microforms:
    Some newspapers

GOVERNMENT PUBLICATIONS:
  Will Lend: Yes, most of them

DISSERTATIONS:
  Will Lend: Yes

THESES:
  Will Lend: Yes

AUDIO-VISUAL MATERIALS:
  Records: Will not lend
  Cassettes: Will not lend
  Other (slides, filmstrips,
    etc.): Will not lend

COMPUTER SOFTWARE:
  Will Lend: No

PHOTODUPLICATION SERVICE:
  No charge up to 20 exposures
  Charge Per Exposure: None
  Minimum/handling Fee: None
  Average Turnaround Time:
    10 days

MICROFILMING SERVICE:
  Service Available: No
  Charges: N/A

DO YOU CHARGE THE BORROWING
  LIBRARY FOR POSTAGE? No

FOR HOW LONG DO YOU SUSPEND ILL
  SERVICE OVER THE CHRISTMAS
  HOLIDAYS? Dec.15-Jan.2

ARE THERE ANY GROUPS OF LIBRARIES
  FOR WHICH YOU WAIVE FEES? IF
  SO, PLEASE NAME THEM: None

INDIANA UNIVERSITY-PURDUE UNIVERSITY AT INDIANAPOLIS

NUC CODE: InIU

OCLC CODE: IUP

ADDRESS: Interlibrary Loan
           Indiana University/
             Purdue University at
             Indianapolis
           815 W. Michigan
           IUPUI Libraries
           Indianapolis, IN 46202

TELEPHONE: (317) 264-8278

LIST NAMES OF BRANCHES WITH
  SEPARATE POLICIES:
    IUPUI-38th Street Campus
    IUPUI-Herron School of Art

BOOKS:
  Will Lend: Yes
  Length of Loan: 4 weeks
  Renewable: Yes, once
  Charges: None
  Average Turnaround Time:
    4 days
  If you have indicated that a
    book is not to be lent, will
    you on receipt of a letter
    from the requesting library
    search the index for given
    entries? (Not answered)

PERIODICALS:
  Bound: Will not lend
  Unbound: Will not lend
  Loan Period: N/A
  Renewable: N/A
  Will lend if article exceeds
    _____ number of pages (Will
    not lend, regardless of
    length of article)

MICROFORMS:
  Will Lend: No
  Specific Types of Microforms:
    N/A

GOVERNMENT PUBLICATIONS:
  Will Lend: Yes

DISSERTATIONS:
  Will Lend: Do not own

THESES:
  Will Lend: Do not own

AUDIO-VISUAL MATERIALS:
  Records: Will not lend
  Cassettes: Will not lend
  Other (slides, filmstrips,
    etc.): Will not lend

COMPUTER SOFTWARE:
  Will Lend: No

PHOTODUPLICATION SERVICE:
  No charge up to 25 exposures
  Charge Per Exposure: 10¢
  Minimum/handling Fee: None
  Average Turnaround Time:
    4 days

MICROFILMING SERVICE:
  Service Available: No
  Charges: N/A

DO YOU CHARGE THE BORROWING
  LIBRARY FOR POSTAGE? No

FOR HOW LONG DO YOU SUSPEND ILL
  SERVICE OVER THE CHRISTMAS
  HOLIDAYS? Dec.25-Jan.3

ARE THERE ANY GROUPS OF LIBRARIES
  FOR WHICH YOU WAIVE FEES? IF
  SO, PLEASE NAME THEM: None

INDIANAPOLIS-MARION COUNTY PUBLIC LIBRARY

NUC CODE: InI

OCLC CODE: IMD

ADDRESS: Interlibrary Loan
Indianapolis-Marion
  County Public Library
40 E. St. Clair St.
Indianapolis, IN 46204

TELEPHONE: (317) 269-1729

LIST NAMES OF BRANCHES WITH
  SEPARATE POLICIES: None

BOOKS:
  Will Lend: Yes
  Length of Loan: 4 weeks use
  Renewable: No
  Charges: $5.00 loan fee
  Average Turnaround Time:
  2 days
  If you have indicated that a
  book is not to be lent, will
  you on receipt of a letter
  from the requesting library
  search the index for given
  entries? N/A

PERIODICALS:
  Bound: Will not lend
  Unbound: Will not lend
  Loan Period: N/A
  Renewable: N/A
  Will lend if article exceeds
  _____ number of pages (Will
  not lend, regardless of
  length of article)

MICROFORMS:
  Will Lend: No
  Specific Types of Microforms:
  N/A

GOVERNMENT PUBLICATIONS:
  Will Lend: No

DISSERTATIONS:
  Will Lend: No

THESES:
  Will Lend: No

AUDIO-VISUAL MATERIALS:
  Records: Will not lend
  Cassettes: Will not lend
  Other (slides, filmstrips,
  etc.): Will not lend

COMPUTER SOFTWARE:
  Will Lend: No

PHOTODUPLICATION SERVICE:
  No charge up to 0 exposures
  Charge Per Exposure: $1.00
  Minimum/handling Fee: $6.00
  Average Turnaround Time:
  3 days

MICROFILMING SERVICE:
  Service Available: No
  Charges: N/A

DO YOU CHARGE THE BORROWING
  LIBRARY FOR POSTAGE? No

FOR HOW LONG DO YOU SUSPEND ILL
  SERVICE OVER THE CHRISTMAS
  HOLIDAYS? No suspension

ARE THERE ANY GROUPS OF LIBRARIES
  FOR WHICH YOU WAIVE FEES? IF
  SO, PLEASE NAME THEM:
  CIAISA (Central Indiana
  Area Library Service
  Authority)

LAKE COUNTY PUBLIC LIBRARY

NUC CODE: None

OCLC CODE: ILC

ADDRESS: Interlibrary Loan
Lake County Public
  Library
1919 W. Lincoln Hwy.
Merrillville, IN 46410

TELEPHONE: (219) 769-3541

LIST NAMES OF BRANCHES WITH
  SEPARATE POLICIES: None

BOOKS:
  Will Lend: Yes
  Length of Loan: 2 weeks use
  Renewable: Yes
  Charges: Postage
  Average Turnaround Time:
  10 days
  If you have indicated that a
  book is not to be lent, will
  you on receipt of a letter
  from the requesting library
  search the index for given
  entries? (Not answered)

PERIODICALS:
  Bound: Will not lend
  Unbound: Will not lend
  Loan Period: N/A
  Renewable: N/A
  Will lend if article exceeds
  _____ number of pages (Not
  answered)

MICROFORMS:
  Will Lend: No
  Specific Types of Microforms:
  N/A

GOVERNMENT PUBLICATIONS:
  Will Lend: No

DISSERTATIONS:
  Will Lend: No

THESES:
  Will Lend: No

AUDIO-VISUAL MATERIALS:
  Records: Will not lend
  Cassettes: Will not lend
  Other (slides, filmstrips,
  etc.): Will not lend

COMPUTER SOFTWARE:
  Will Lend: No

PHOTODUPLICATION SERVICE:
  No charge up to 0 exposures
  Charge Per Exposure: 15¢
  Minimum/handling Fee: (Not
  answered)
  Average Turnaround Time:
  5 days

MICROFILMING SERVICE:
  Service Available: No
  Charges: N/A

DO YOU CHARGE THE BORROWING
  LIBRARY FOR POSTAGE? Yes

FOR HOW LONG DO YOU SUSPEND ILL
  SERVICE OVER THE CHRISTMAS
  HOLIDAYS? No suspension

ARE THERE ANY GROUPS OF LIBRARIES
  FOR WHICH YOU WAIVE FEES? IF
  SO, PLEASE NAME THEM: None

MICHIGAN CITY PUBLIC LIBRARY

NUC CODE: (Not answered)

OCLC CODE: IMY

ADDRESS: Interlibrary Loan
           Michigan City Public
           Library
           100 E. Fourth St.
           Michigan City, IN 46360

TELEPHONE: (219) 879-4561

LIST NAMES OF BRANCHES WITH
   SEPARATE POLICIES: None

BOOKS:
   Will Lend: Yes
   Length of Loan: 1 month
   Renewable: Yes, possibly
   Charges: None
   Average Turnaround Time:
      (Not answered)
   If you have indicated that a
      book is not to be lent, will
      you on receipt of a letter
      from the requesting library
      search the index for given
      entries?   (Not answered)

PERIODICALS:
   Bound: Will not lend
   Unbound: Will not lend
   Loan Period: N/A
   Renewable: N/A
   Will lend if article exceeds
      _____ number of pages (Not
      answered)

MICROFORMS:
   Will Lend: No
   Specific Types of Microforms:
      N/A

GOVERNMENT PUBLICATIONS:
   Will Lend: No

DISSERTATIONS:
   Will Lend: No

THESES:
   Will Lend: No

AUDIO-VISUAL MATERIALS:
   Records: Will not lend
   Cassettes: Will not lend
   Other (slides, filmstrips,
      etc.):   Will not lend

COMPUTER SOFTWARE:
   Will Lend: No

PHOTODUPLICATION SERVICE:
   No charge up to 20 exposures
   Charge Per Exposure: 15¢
   Minimum/handling Fee: $1.00
   Average Turnaround Time:
      (Not answered)

MICROFILMING SERVICE:
   Service Available: Yes
   Charges: Minimum of $1.00,
      20¢ additional exposures

DO YOU CHARGE THE BORROWING
   LIBRARY FOR POSTAGE?   No

FOR HOW LONG DO YOU SUSPEND ILL
   SERVICE OVER THE CHRISTMAS
   HOLIDAYS?   No suspension

ARE THERE ANY GROUPS OF LIBRARIES
   FOR WHICH YOU WAIVE FEES?   IF
   SO, PLEASE NAME THEM: NIALA

PURDUE UNIVERSITY

NUC CODE: InLP

OCLC CODE: IPL

ADDRESS: Interlibrary Loan
           Stewart Center
           Purdue University
           Libraries
           West Lafayette, IN
           47906

TELEPHONE: (317) 743-3156

LIST NAMES OF BRANCHES WITH
   SEPARATE POLICIES:
      Purdue Calumet Campus,
      Hammond, IN
      Purdue North Central
      Campus, Westville, IN

BOOKS:
   Will Lend: Yes
   Length of Loan: 2 weeks use
   Renewable: Yes, usually
   Charges: $5.00 out-of-state;
      $3.00 in-state
   Average Turnaround Time:
      4-5 days
   If you have indicated that a
      book is not to be lent, will
      you on receipt of a letter
      from the requesting library
      search the index for given
      entries?   Varies according
      to department library

PERIODICALS:
   Bound: Will not lend
   Unbound: Will not lend
   Loan Period: N/A
   Renewable: N/A
   Will lend if article exceeds
      _____ number of pages (Will
      not lend, regardless of
      length of article)

MICROFORMS:
   Will Lend: Yes, selectively
   Specific Types of Microforms:
      Will not lend newspapers

GOVERNMENT PUBLICATIONS:
   Will Lend: Yes, some of them

DISSERTATIONS:
   Will Lend: No. 1954-
      available from University
      Microfilms

THESES:
   Will Lend: No; will photocopy

AUDIO-VISUAL MATERIALS:
   Records: (Not answered)
   Cassettes: (Not answered)
   Other (slides, filmstrips,
      etc.):   (Not answered)

COMPUTER SOFTWARE:
   Will Lend: (Not answered)

PHOTODUPLICATION SERVICE:
   No charge up to 0 exposures
   Charges: $5.00 for 1-10
      exposures; $5.65 for 11
      exposures plus 15¢ for each
      additional exposure
   Average Turnaround Time:
      4-6 days

MICROFILMING SERVICE:
   Service Available: No
   Charges: N/A

DO YOU CHARGE THE BORROWING
   LIBRARY FOR POSTAGE?   Included
   in minimum fee

FOR HOW LONG DO YOU SUSPEND ILL
   SERVICE OVER THE CHRISTMAS
   HOLIDAYS?   Dec.10-Jan.2

ARE THERE ANY GROUPS OF LIBRARIES
   FOR WHICH YOU WAIVE FEES?   IF
   SO, PLEASE NAME THEM:
      Approximately 14 reciprocal
      agreements both in-state and
      out-of-state

UNIVERSITY OF NOTRE DAME

NUC CODE: InND

OCLC CODE: IND

ADDRESS: Interlibrary Loan
Memorial Library
University of Notre Dame
Notre Dame, IN 46556

TELEPHONE: (219) 239-6260

LIST NAMES OF BRANCHES WITH
SEPARATE POLICIES: None

BOOKS:
Will Lend: Yes
Length of Loan: 2 weeks from
receipt
Renewable: Yes, usually
Charges: Only to those
libraries that charge us
Average Turnaround Time:
2-4 days
If you have indicated that a
book is not to be lent, will
you on receipt of a letter
from the requesting library
search the index for given
entries? Yes

PERIODICALS:
Bound: Will not lend
Unbound: Will not lend
Loan Period: N/A
Renewable: N/A
May lend if article exceeds
a certain number of pages

MICROFORMS:
Will Lend: Yes
Specific Types of Microforms:
Cards, film, fiche

GOVERNMENT PUBLICATIONS:
Will Lend: Yes

DISSERTATIONS:
Will Lend: Maybe, if
circulating copy available

THESES:
Will Lend: Maybe, if
circulating copy available

AUDIO-VISUAL MATERIALS:
Records: Will not lend
Cassettes: Will not lend
Other (slides, filmstrips,
etc.): Will not lend

COMPUTER SOFTWARE:
Will Lend: No

PHOTODUPLICATION SERVICE:
No charge up to 0 exposures
Charge Per Exposure: 10¢
Minimum/handling Fee: $2.00
Average Turnaround Time:
2-4 days

MICROFILMING SERVICE:
Service Available: No
Charges: N/A

DO YOU CHARGE THE BORROWING
LIBRARY FOR POSTAGE? No

FOR HOW LONG DO YOU SUSPEND ILL
SERVICE OVER THE CHRISTMAS
HOLIDAYS? Dec.10-Jan.5

ARE THERE ANY GROUPS OF LIBRARIES
FOR WHICH YOU WAIVE FEES? IF
SO, PLEASE NAME THEM: None

COE COLLEGE

NUC CODE: IaCrC

OCLC CODE: ION

ADDRESS: Interlibrary Loan
           Stewart Memorial
           Library
           Coe College
           Cedar Rapids, IA 52402

TELEPHONE: (319) 399-8585

LIST NAMES OF BRANCHES WITH
  SEPARATE POLICIES: None

BOOKS:
  Will Lend: Yes
  Length of Loan: 3 weeks
  Renewable: Yes
  Charges: None
  Average Turnaround Time:
    1 day
  If you have indicated that a
    book is not to be lent, will
    you on receipt of a letter
    from the requesting library
    search the index for given
    entries? Yes

PERIODICALS:
  Bound: Will not lend
  Unbound: Will not lend
  Loan Period: N/A
  Renewable: N/A
  Will lend if article exceeds
    _____ number of pages (Not
    answered)

MICROFORMS:
  Will Lend: Yes, selectively
  Specific Types of Microforms:
    Microfilm, microcard

GOVERNMENT PUBLICATIONS:
  Will Lend: Yes

DISSERTATIONS:
  Will Lend: Yes

THESES:
  Will Lend: Yes

AUDIO-VISUAL MATERIALS:
  Records: Will lend,
    selectively
  Cassettes: Will lend,
    selectively
  Other (slides, filmstrips,
    etc.): Will lend
    selectively

COMPUTER SOFTWARE:
  Will Lend: Do not own

PHOTODUPLICATION SERVICE:
  No charge up to 0 exposures
  Charge Per Exposure: 10¢
  Minimum/handling Fee: None
  Average Turnaround Time:
    1 day

MICROFILMING SERVICE:
  Service Available: No
  Charges: N/A

DO YOU CHARGE THE BORROWING
  LIBRARY FOR POSTAGE? No

FOR HOW LONG DO YOU SUSPEND ILL
  SERVICE OVER THE CHRISTMAS
  HOLIDAYS? 2-5 days

ARE THERE ANY GROUPS OF LIBRARIES
  FOR WHICH YOU WAIVE FEES? IF
  SO, PLEASE NAME THEM: Linn
  County (Iowa) Library
  Consortium

CORNELL COLLEGE

NUC CODE: (Not answered)

OCLC CODE: IMV

ADDRESS: Interlibrary Loan
           Russell D. Cole Library
           Cornell College
           Mt. Vernon, IA 52314

TELEPHONE: (319) 895-8811, X271

LIST NAMES OF BRANCHES WITH
  SEPARATE POLICIES: None

BOOKS:
  Will Lend: Yes
  Length of Loan: 3 weeks
  Renewable: Yes, if no
    reserves
  Charges: None
  Average Turnaround Time:
    2 days
  If you have indicated that a
    book is not to be lent, will
    you on receipt of a letter
    from the requesting library
    search the index for given
    entries? No

PERIODICALS:
  Bound: Will not lend
  Unbound: Will not lend
  Loan Period: N/A
  Renewable: N/A
  Will lend if article exceeds
    _____ number of pages (Not
    answered)

MICROFORMS:
  Will Lend: No
  Specific Types of Microforms:
    N/A

GOVERNMENT PUBLICATIONS:
  Will Lend: Yes

DISSERTATIONS:
  Will Lend: No

THESES:
  Will Lend: No

AUDIO-VISUAL MATERIALS:
  Records: Will not lend
  Cassettes: Will not lend
  Other (slides, filmstrips,
    etc.): Will not lend

COMPUTER SOFTWARE:
  Will Lend: No

PHOTODUPLICATION SERVICE:
  No charge up to 0 exposures
  Charge Per Exposure: 10¢
  Minimum/handling Fee: None
  Average Turnaround Time:
    2 days

MICROFILMING SERVICE:
  Service Available: No
  Charges: N/A

DO YOU CHARGE THE BORROWING
  LIBRARY FOR POSTAGE? No

FOR HOW LONG DO YOU SUSPEND ILL
  SERVICE OVER THE CHRISTMAS
  HOLIDAYS? About 1 week

ARE THERE ANY GROUPS OF LIBRARIES
  FOR WHICH YOU WAIVE FEES? IF
  SO, PLEASE NAME THEM: Cedar
  Rapids Library Consortium,
  Iowa Libraries Inter-
  library Loan Teletype
  System, ACM School

DRAKE UNIVERSITY

NUC CODE: IaDmD

OCLC CODE: IOD

ADDRESS: Interlibrary Loan
Cowles Library
Drake University
Des Moines, IA 50311

TELEPHONE: (515) 271-2113

LIST NAMES OF BRANCHES WITH
SEPARATE POLICIES: None

BOOKS:
Will Lend: Yes
Length of Loan: 4 weeks
Renewable: Yes
Charges: Reciprocal
Average Turnaround Time:
(Not answered)
If you have indicated that a
book is not to be lent, will
you on receipt of a letter
from the requesting library
search the index for given
entries? (Not answered)

PERIODICALS:
Bound: Will not lend
Unbound: Will not lend
Loan Period: N/A
Renewable: N/A
Will lend if article exceeds
_____ number of pages (Not
answered)

MICROFORMS:
Will Lend: Yes
Specific Types of Microforms:
(Not answered)

GOVERNMENT PUBLICATIONS:
Will Lend: Yes

DISSERTATIONS:
Will Lend: Do not own

THESES:
Will Lend: Yes

AUDIO-VISUAL MATERIALS:
Records: (Not answered)
Cassettes: (Not answered)
Other (slides, filmstrips,
etc.): (Not answered)

COMPUTER SOFTWARE:
Will Lend: (Not answered)

PHOTODUPLICATION SERVICE:
No charge up to 0 exposures
Charge Per Exposure: 10¢
Minimum Fee: $1.00
Average Turnaround Time:
(Not answered)

MICROFILMING SERVICE:
Service Available: (Not
answered)
Charges: N/A

DO YOU CHARGE THE BORROWING
LIBRARY FOR POSTAGE? No

FOR HOW LONG DO YOU SUSPEND ILL
SERVICE OVER THE CHRISTMAS
HOLIDAYS? Dec.20-Jan.5

ARE THERE ANY GROUPS OF LIBRARIES
FOR WHICH YOU WAIVE FEES? IF
SO, PLEASE NAME THEM: I-LITE,
PCBC

GRACELAND COLLEGE

NUC CODE: IaLG

OCLC CODE: IOF

ADDRESS: Interlibrary Loan
Smith Library
Graceland College
Lamoni, IA 50140

TELEPHONE: (515) 784-5306

LIST NAMES OF BRANCHES WITH
SEPARATE POLICIES: None

BOOKS:
Will Lend: Yes
Length of Loan: 3 weeks
Renewable: No
Charges: (Not answered)
Average Turnaround Time:
(Not answered)
If you have indicated that a
book is not to be lent, will
you on receipt of a letter
from the requesting library
search the index for given
entries? (Not answered)

PERIODICALS:
Bound: Will not lend
Unbound: Will not lend
Loan Period: N/A
Renewable: N/A
Will lend if article exceeds
_____ number of pages (Not
answered)

MICROFORMS:
Will Lend: Yes, selectively
Specific Types of Microforms:
(Not answered)

GOVERNMENT PUBLICATIONS:
Will Lend: Yes

DISSERTATIONS:
Will Lend: No

THESES:
Will Lend: No

AUDIO-VISUAL MATERIALS:
Records: (Not answered)
Cassettes: (Not answered)
Other (slides, filmstrips,
etc.): (Not answered)

COMPUTER SOFTWARE:
Will Lend: (Not answered)

PHOTODUPLICATION SERVICE:
No charge up to 0 exposures
Charge Per Exposure: 10¢
Minimum/handling Fee: (Not
answered)
Average Turnaround Time:
(Not answered)

MICROFILMING SERVICE:
Service Available: No
Charges: N/A

DO YOU CHARGE THE BORROWING
LIBRARY FOR POSTAGE? Yes

FOR HOW LONG DO YOU SUSPEND ILL
SERVICE OVER THE CHRISTMAS
HOLIDAYS? Dec.15-Jan.2

ARE THERE ANY GROUPS OF LIBRARIES
FOR WHICH YOU WAIVE FEES? IF
SO, PLEASE NAME THEM: None

GRINNELL COLLEGE

NUC CODE: Iagg

OCLC CODE: IOG

ADDRESS: Interlibrary Loan
Burling Library
Grinnell College
Grinnell, IA 50112

TELEPHONE: (515) 236-6181, X697

LIST NAMES OF BRANCHES WITH
SEPARATE POLICIES: None

BOOKS:
Will Lend: Yes
Length of Loan: 4 weeks
Renewable: Yes
Charges: (Not answered)
Average Turnaround Time:
(Not answered)
If you have indicated that a
book is not to be lent, will
you on receipt of a letter
from the requesting library
search the index for given
entries? (Not answered)

PERIODICALS:
Bound: Will not lend
Unbound: Will not lend
Loan Period: N/A
Renewable: N/A
Will lend if article exceeds
_____ number of pages (Not
answered)

MICROFORMS:
Will Lend: Yes
Specific Types of Microforms:
(Not answered)

GOVERNMENT PUBLICATIONS:
Will Lend: Yes

DISSERTATIONS:
Will Lend: Yes

THESES:
Will Lend: Yes

AUDIO-VISUAL MATERIALS:
Records: (Not answered)
Cassettes: (Not answered)
Other (slides, filmstrips,
etc.): (Not answered)

COMPUTER SOFTWARE:
Will Lend: (Not answered)

PHOTODUPLICATION SERVICE:
No charge up to 0 exposures
Charge Per Exposure: 10¢
Minimum/handling Fee: None
Average Turnaround Time:
(Not answered)

MICROFILMING SERVICE:
Service Available: No
Charges: N/A

DO YOU CHARGE THE BORROWING
LIBRARY FOR POSTAGE? (Not
answered)

FOR HOW LONG DO YOU SUSPEND ILL
SERVICE OVER THE CHRISTMAS
HOLIDAYS? (Not answered)

ARE THERE ANY GROUPS OF LIBRARIES
FOR WHICH YOU WAIVE FEES? IF
SO, PLEASE NAME THEM: (Not
answered)

IOWA STATE UNIVERSITY

NUC CODE: IaAS

OCLC CODE: IWA

ADDRESS: Interlibrary Loan
Iowa State University
Library
Ames, IA 50011

TELEPHONE: (515) 294-3642

LIST NAMES OF BRANCHES WITH
SEPARATE POLICIES: None

BOOKS:
Will Lend: Yes
Length of Loan: 2 weeks
Renewable: (Not answered)
Charges: (Not answered)
Average Turnaround Time:
(Not answered)
If you have indicated that a
book is not to be lent, will
you on receipt of a letter
from the requesting library
search the index for given
entries? (Not answered)

PERIODICALS:
Bound: Will not lend
Unbound: Will not lend
Loan Period: N/A
Renewable: N/A
Will lend if article exceeds
_____ number of pages (Not
answered)

MICROFORMS:
Will Lend: Yes
Specific Types of Microforms:
Fiche, film, print

GOVERNMENT PUBLICATIONS:
Will Lend: Yes

DISSERTATIONS:
Will Lend: No; 1959 to
present available from
University Microfilms

THESES:
Will Lend: Yes

AUDIO-VISUAL MATERIALS:
Records: Will not lend
Cassettes: Will not lend
Other (slides, filmstrips,
etc.): Will not lend

COMPUTER SOFTWARE:
Will Lend: No

PHOTODUPLICATION SERVICE:
No charge up to 0 exposures
Charge Per Exposure: 15¢
Minimum/handling Fee: $2.00
Average Turnaround Time:
(Not answered)

MICROFILMING SERVICE:
Service Available: No
Charges: N/A

DO YOU CHARGE THE BORROWING
LIBRARY FOR POSTAGE? No

FOR HOW LONG DO YOU SUSPEND ILL
SERVICE OVER THE CHRISTMAS
HOLIDAYS? 2-3 weeks

ARE THERE ANY GROUPS OF LIBRARIES
FOR WHICH YOU WAIVE FEES? IF
SO, PLEASE NAME THEM:
University of Iowa; Univer-
sity of Northern Iowa; Uni-
versity of Nebraska; Univer-
sity of Kansas; Kansas State;
Oklahoma State; University
of Oklahoma; University of
Missouri; University of
Colorado; Colorado State

MORNINGSIDE COLLEGE

NUC CODE: (Not answered)

OCLC CODE: IOM

ADDRESS: Interlibrary Loan
           Morningside College
           Library
           Sioux City, IA 51106

TELEPHONE: (712) 274-5248

LIST NAMES OF BRANCHES WITH
   SEPARATE POLICIES: None

BOOKS:
   Will Lend: Yes
   Length of Loan: 1 month
   Renewable: Yes
   Charges: None
   Average Turnaround Time:
   (Not answered)
   If you have indicated that a
   book is not to be lent, will
   you on receipt of a letter
   from the requesting library
   search the index for given
   entries? (Not answered)

PERIODICALS:
   Bound: Will not lend
   Unbound: Will not lend
   Loan Period: N/A
   Renewable: N/A
   Will lend if article exceeds
   _____ number of pages (Not
   answered)

MICROFORMS:
   Will Lend: No
   Specific Types of Microforms:
   N/A

GOVERNMENT PUBLICATIONS:
   Will Lend: No

DISSERTATIONS:
   Will Lend: No

THESES:
   Will Lend: No

AUDIO-VISUAL MATERIALS:
   Records: Will not lend
   Cassettes: Will not lend
   Other (slides, filmstrips,
   etc.): Will not lend

COMPUTER SOFTWARE:
   Will Lend: No

PHOTODUPLICATION SERVICE:
   No charge up to 5 exposures
   Charge Per Exposure: 10¢
   Minimum/handling Fee: None
   Average Turnaround Time:
   (Not answered)

MICROFILMING SERVICE:
   Service Available: No
   Charges: N/A

DO YOU CHARGE THE BORROWING
   LIBRARY FOR POSTAGE? No

FOR HOW LONG DO YOU SUSPEND ILL
   SERVICE OVER THE CHRISTMAS
   HOLIDAYS? 3 weeks

ARE THERE ANY GROUPS OF LIBRARIES
   FOR WHICH YOU WAIVE FEES? IF
   SO, PLEASE NAME THEM: None

NORTHWESTERN COLLEGE

NUC CODE: (Not answered)

OCLC CODE: IOO

ADDRESS: Interlibrary Loan
           Ramaker Library
           Northwestern College
           Orange City, IA 51041

TELEPHONE: (712) 737-4821, X144

LIST NAMES OF BRANCHES WITH
   SEPARATE POLICIES: None

BOOKS:
   Will Lend: Yes
   Length of Loan: 1 month
   Renewable: Yes
   Charges: None
   Average Turnaround Time:
   2 days
   If you have indicated that a
   book is not to be lent, will
   you on receipt of a letter
   from the requesting library
   search the index for given
   entries? Yes

PERIODICALS:
   Bound: Will not lend
   Unbound: Will not lend
   Loan Period: N/A
   Renewable: N/A
   Will lend if article exceeds
   _____ number of pages (Not
   answered)

MICROFORMS:
   Will Lend: No
   Specific Types of Microforms:
   N/A

GOVERNMENT PUBLICATIONS:
   Will Lend: Yes

DISSERTATIONS:
   Will Lend: Do not own

THESES:
   Will Lend: Do not own

AUDIO-VISUAL MATERIALS:
   Records: Will not lend
   Cassettes: Will not lend
   Other (slides, filmstrips,
   etc.): Will not lend

COMPUTER SOFTWARE:
   Will Lend: No

PHOTODUPLICATION SERVICE:
   No charge up to 10 exposures
   Charge Per Exposure: 10¢
   Minimum/handling Fee: None
   Average Turnaround Time:
   2 days

MICROFILMING SERVICE:
   Service Available: Yes
   Charges: 10¢ per page

DO YOU CHARGE THE BORROWING
   LIBRARY FOR POSTAGE? No

FOR HOW LONG DO YOU SUSPEND ILL
   SERVICE OVER THE CHRISTMAS
   HOLIDAYS? No suspension

ARE THERE ANY GROUPS OF LIBRARIES
   FOR WHICH YOU WAIVE FEES? IF
   SO, PLEASE NAME THEM: None

STATE LIBRARY OF IOWA

NUC CODE: IA

OCLC CODE: IOZ

ADDRESS: Interlibrary Loan
State Library of Iowa
Historical Bldg.
E. 12th and Grand
Des Moines, IA 50319

TELEPHONE: (515) 281-4111

LIST NAMES OF BRANCHES WITH
SEPARATE POLICIES: None

BOOKS:
Will Lend: Yes
Length of Loan: 4 weeks
Renewable: Yes
Charges: None
Average Turnaround Time:
24-48 hours
If you have indicated that a
book is not to be lent, will
you on receipt of a letter
from the requesting library
search the index for given
entries? (Not answered)

PERIODICALS:
Bound: Will lend
Unbound: Will lend
Loan Period: 2 weeks
Renewable: Yes
Will lend if article exceeds
_____ number of pages (Will
not lend, regardless of
length of article)

MICROFORMS:
Will Lend: No
Specific Types of Microforms:
N/A

GOVERNMENT PUBLICATIONS:
Will Lend: Yes

DISSERTATIONS:
Will Lend: Do not own

THESES:
Will Lend: Do not own

AUDIO-VISUAL MATERIALS:
Records: Yes, within state
Cassettes: Yes, within state
Other (slides, filmstrips,
etc.): Yes, within state

COMPUTER SOFTWARE:
Will Lend: No

PHOTODUPLICATION SERVICE:
No charge up to 0 exposures
Charge Per Exposure: 10¢
Minimum/handling Fee: None
Average Turnaround Time:
1 week

MICROFILMING SERVICE:
Service Available: No
Charges: N/A

DO YOU CHARGE THE BORROWING
LIBRARY FOR POSTAGE? No

FOR HOW LONG DO YOU SUSPEND ILL
SERVICE OVER THE CHRISTMAS
HOLIDAYS? No suspension

ARE THERE ANY GROUPS OF LIBRARIES
FOR WHICH YOU WAIVE FEES? IF
SO, PLEASE NAME THEM: None

UNIVERSITY OF IOWA

NUC CODE: IaU

OCLC CODE: None

ADDRESS: Interlibrary Loan
University of Iowa
Libraries
Iowa City, IA 52242

TELEPHONE: (319) 353-4210

LIST NAMES OF BRANCHES WITH
SEPARATE POLICIES:
Health Sciences Library
Law Library

BOOKS:
Will Lend: Yes
Length of Loan: 4 weeks
Renewable: No
Charges: None
Average Turnaround Time:
5 days
If you have indicated that a
book is not to be lent, will
you on receipt of a letter
from the requesting library
search the index for given
entries? Yes

PERIODICALS:
Bound: Will not lend
Unbound: Will not lend
Loan Period: N/A
Renewable: N/A
Will lend if article exceeds
_____ number of pages (Not
answered)

MICROFORMS:
Will Lend: Yes
Specific Types of Microforms:
(Not answered)

GOVERNMENT PUBLICATIONS:
Will Lend: Yes, selectively

DISSERTATIONS:
Will Lend: Yes, if 2nd copy
available; August 1952 to
present available from
University Microfilms

THESES:
Will Lend: Yes, if 2nd copy
available

AUDIO-VISUAL MATERIALS:
Records: Will not lend
Cassettes: Will not lend
Other (slides, filmstrips,
etc.): Will not lend

COMPUTER SOFTWARE:
Will Lend: No

PHOTODUPLICATION SERVICE:
No charge up to 0 exposures
Charge Per Exposure: 15¢
each after first 10
Minimum Fee: $4.00 for
1-10 exposures
Average Turnaround Time:
7-10 days

MICROFILMING SERVICE:
Service Available: Yes
Charges: Write for charges

DO YOU CHARGE THE BORROWING
LIBRARY FOR POSTAGE? No

FOR HOW LONG DO YOU SUSPEND ILL
SERVICE OVER THE CHRISTMAS
HOLIDAYS? No suspension

ARE THERE ANY GROUPS OF LIBRARIES
FOR WHICH YOU WAIVE FEES? IF
SO, PLEASE NAME THEM: None

UNIVERSITY OF NORTHERN IOWA

NUC CODE: IaCfT

OCLC CODE: NIU

ADDRESS: Interlibrary Loan
          University of Northern
            Iowa Library
          Cedar Falls, IA 50613

TELEPHONE: (319) 273-2838

LIST NAMES OF BRANCHES WITH
  SEPARATE POLICIES: None

BOOKS:
  Will Lend: Yes
  Length of Loan: 2 weeks use
  Renewable: Yes
  Charges: None
  Average Turnaround Time:
    3 days
  If you have indicated that a
    book is not to be lent, will
    you on receipt of a letter
    from the requesting library
    search the index for given
    entries? (Not answered)

PERIODICALS:
  Bound: Will not lend
  Unbound: Will not lend
  Loan Period: N/A
  Renewable: N/A
  Will lend if article exceeds
  _____ number of pages (Will
    not lend, regardless of
    length of article)

MICROFORMS:
  Will Lend: Yes
  Specific Types of Microforms:
    Newspapers (selectively);
    ERIC microfiche

GOVERNMENT PUBLICATIONS:
  Will Lend: Yes

DISSERTATIONS:
  Will Lend: Yes

THESES:
  Will Lend: Yes

AUDIO-VISUAL MATERIALS:
  Records: Will not lend
  Cassettes: Will not lend
  Other (slides, filmstrips,
    etc.): Will not lend

COMPUTER SOFTWARE:
  Will Lend: No

PHOTODUPLICATION SERVICE:
  No charge up to 0 exposures
  Charge Per Exposure: 10¢
  Minimum/handling Fee: $2.00
    for out-of-state; $1.00
    for in-Iowa
  Average Turnaround Time:
    3 days

MICROFILMING SERVICE:
  Service Available: Yes
  Charges: Request estimate

DO YOU CHARGE THE BORROWING
  LIBRARY FOR POSTAGE? No

FOR HOW LONG DO YOU SUSPEND ILL
  SERVICE OVER THE CHRISTMAS
  HOLIDAYS? No suspension

ARE THERE ANY GROUPS OF LIBRARIES
  FOR WHICH YOU WAIVE FEES? IF
  SO, PLEASE NAME THEM: None

BETHANY COLLEGE

NUC CODE: KLindB

OCLC CODE: KFB

ADDRESS: Interlibrary Loan
Wallerstedt Library
Bethany College
Lindsborg, KS 67456

TELEPHONE: (913) 227-3311, X166

LIST NAMES OF BRANCHES WITH
SEPARATE POLICIES:
Kansas Wesleyan College

BOOKS:
Will Lend: Yes
Length of Loan: 4 weeks
Renewable: Yes
Charges: None
Average Turnaround Time:
2 days
If you have indicated that a
book is not to be lent, will
you on receipt of a letter
from the requesting library
search the index for given
entries? (Not answered)

PERIODICALS:
Bound: Will not lend
Unbound: Will not lend
Loan Period: N/A
Renewable: N/A
Will lend if article exceeds
_____ number of pages (Will
not lend, regardless of
length of article)

MICROFORMS:
Will Lend: No
Specific Types of Microforms:
N/A

GOVERNMENT PUBLICATIONS:
Will Lend: No

DISSERTATIONS:
Will Lend: No

THESES:
Will Lend: No

AUDIO-VISUAL MATERIALS:
Records: Will not lend
Cassettes: Will not lend
Other (slides, filmstrips,
etc.): Will not lend

COMPUTER SOFTWARE:
Will Lend: No

PHOTODUPLICATION SERVICE:
No charge up to 10 exposures
Charge Per Exposure: 10¢
Minimum/handling Fee: $3.00
Average Turnaround Time:
2 days

MICROFILMING SERVICE:
Service Available: No
Charges: N/A

DO YOU CHARGE THE BORROWING
LIBRARY FOR POSTAGE? No

FOR HOW LONG DO YOU SUSPEND ILL
SERVICE OVER THE CHRISTMAS
HOLIDAYS? 3 weeks

ARE THERE ANY GROUPS OF LIBRARIES
FOR WHICH YOU WAIVE FEES? IF
SO, PLEASE NAME THEM:
Nebraska, BCR, Kansas,
Colorado

CLENDENING LIBRARY

NUC CODE: KU-M

OCLC CODE: KKP

ADDRESS: Interlibrary Loan
Clendening Library
39th and Rainbow Blvd.
Kansas City, KS 66103

TELEPHONE: (913) 588-5072

LIST NAMES OF BRANCHES WITH
SEPARATE POLICIES:
History of Medicine
Educational Resource
Center (Audiovisual)

BOOKS:
Will Lend: Yes
Length of Loan: 3 weeks
Renewable: Yes
Charges: $6.00
Average Turnaround Time:
3 days
If you have indicated that a
book is not to be lent, will
you on receipt of a letter
from the requesting library
search the index for given
entries? Yes

PERIODICALS:
Bound: Will lend
Unbound: Will lend
Loan Period: 3 weeks
Renewable: Yes
Will lend if article exceeds
_____ number of pages (Not
answered)

MICROFORMS:
Will Lend: No
Specific Types of Microforms:
N/A

GOVERNMENT PUBLICATIONS:
Will Lend: Yes

DISSERTATIONS:
Will Lend: Yes

THESES:
Will Lend: Yes

AUDIO-VISUAL MATERIALS:
Records: Will lend
Cassettes: Will lend
Other (slides, filmstrips,
etc.): Will lend

COMPUTER SOFTWARE:
Will Lend: No

PHOTODUPLICATION SERVICE:
No charge up to 0 exposures
Charge Per Exposure: N/A
Minimum/handling Fee: $6.00
Average Turnaround Time:
3 days

MICROFILMING SERVICE:
Service Available: No
Charges: N/A

DO YOU CHARGE THE BORROWING
LIBRARY FOR POSTAGE? No

FOR HOW LONG DO YOU SUSPEND ILL
SERVICE OVER THE CHRISTMAS
HOLIDAYS? No suspension

ARE THERE ANY GROUPS OF LIBRARIES
FOR WHICH YOU WAIVE FEES? IF
SO, PLEASE NAME THEM: Kansas
Regent Schools

EMPORIA STATE UNIVERSITY

NUC CODE: KEmU (formerly KEmT)

OCLC CODE: KKR

ADDRESS: Interlibrary Loan
William Allen White
Library
Emporia State
University
Emporia, KS 66801

TELEPHONE: (316) 343-1200, X205

LIST NAMES OF BRANCHES WITH
SEPARATE POLICIES: None

BOOKS:
Will Lend: Yes
Length of Loan: 3 weeks
Renewable: Yes
Charges: None
Average Turnaround Time:
3-5 days
If you have indicated that a
book is not to be lent, will
you on receipt of a letter
from the requesting library
search the index for given
entries? No

PERIODICALS:
Bound: Will not lend
Unbound: Will not lend
Loan Period: N/A
Renewable: N/A
Will lend if article exceeds
_____ number of pages (Will
not lend, regardless of
length of article)

MICROFORMS:
Will Lend: Yes
Specific Types of Microforms:
(Not answered)

GOVERNMENT PUBLICATIONS:
Will Lend: Yes

DISSERTATIONS:
Will Lend: Yes

THESES:
Will Lend: Yes

AUDIO-VISUAL MATERIALS:
Records: Will not lend
Cassettes: Will not lend
Other (slides, filmstrips,
etc.): Will not lend

COMPUTER SOFTWARE:
Will Lend: No

PHOTODUPLICATION SERVICE:
No charge up to 0 exposures
Charge Per Exposure: 15¢
Minimum/handling Fee: $3.00
Average Turnaround Time:
3-5 days

MICROFILMING SERVICE:
Service Available: No
Charges: N/A

DO YOU CHARGE THE BORROWING
LIBRARY FOR POSTAGE? No

FOR HOW LONG DO YOU SUSPEND ILL
SERVICE OVER THE CHRISTMAS
HOLIDAYS? No suspension

ARE THERE ANY GROUPS OF LIBRARIES
FOR WHICH YOU WAIVE FEES? IF
SO, PLEASE NAME THEM: None

FORT HAYS STATE UNIVERSITY

NUC CODE: None

OCLC CODE: KFH

ADDRESS: Interlibrary Loan
Forsyth Library
Fort Hays State
University
Hays, KS 67601

TELEPHONE: (913) 628-4351

LIST NAMES OF BRANCHES WITH
SEPARATE POLICIES: None

BOOKS:
Will Lend: Yes
Length of Loan: 3 weeks
Renewable: Yes
Charges: None
Average Turnaround Time:
(Not answered)
If you have indicated that a
book is not to be lent, will
you on receipt of a letter
from the requesting library
search the index for given
entries? Yes

PERIODICALS:
Bound: Will not lend
Unbound: Will not lend
Loan Period: N/A
Renewable: N/A
Will lend if article exceeds
_____ number of pages (Will
not lend, regardless of
length of article. Will
photocopy article)

MICROFORMS:
Will Lend: Yes
Specific Types of Microforms:
Kansas newspapers and state
censuses

GOVERNMENT PUBLICATIONS:
Will Lend: Yes

DISSERTATIONS:
Will Lend: No

THESES:
Will Lend: Yes

AUDIO-VISUAL MATERIALS:
Records: Will lend
Cassettes: (Not answered)
Other (slides, filmstrips,
etc.): (Not answered)

COMPUTER SOFTWARE:
Will Lend: No

PHOTODUPLICATION SERVICE:
No charge up to 0 exposures
Charge Per Exposure: 10¢
Minimum/handling Fee: $1.00
Average Turnaround Time:
(Not answered)

MICROFILMING SERVICE:
Service Available: No
Charges: N/A

DO YOU CHARGE THE BORROWING
LIBRARY FOR POSTAGE? We
charge oil companies

FOR HOW LONG DO YOU SUSPEND ILL
SERVICE OVER THE CHRISTMAS
HOLIDAYS? 2 weeks

ARE THERE ANY GROUPS OF LIBRARIES
FOR WHICH YOU WAIVE FEES? IF
SO, PLEASE NAME THEM:
Libraries in the Kansas
Regents System

JOHNSON COUNTY LIBRARY

NUC CODE: KSHM

OCLC CODE: KKC

ADDRESS: Interlibrary Loan
Johnson County Library
8700 W. 63rd St.
P. O. Box 2901
Shawnee Mission, KS
66201

TELEPHONE: (913) 831-1550

LIST NAMES OF BRANCHES WITH
SEPARATE POLICIES: None

BOOKS:
Will Lend: Yes
Length of Loan: 5 weeks
Renewable: Yes, if no
reserves
Charges: None
Average Turnaround Time:
3 days
If you have indicated that a
book is not to be lent, will
you on receipt of a letter
from the requesting library
search the index for given
entries? Yes

PERIODICALS:
Bound: Will not lend
Unbound: Will not lend
Loan Period: N/A
Renewable: N/A
Will lend if article exceeds
_____ number of pages (Will
not lend, regardless of
length of article)

MICROFORMS:
Will Lend: No
Specific Types of Microforms:
N/A

GOVERNMENT PUBLICATIONS:
Will Lend: Yes

DISSERTATIONS:
Will Lend: Do not own

THESES:
Will Lend: Do not own

AUDIO-VISUAL MATERIALS:
Records: Do not own
Cassettes: Do not own
Other (slides, filmstrips,
etc.): Do not own

COMPUTER SOFTWARE:
Will Lend: No

PHOTODUPLICATION SERVICE:
No charge up to 10 exposures
Charge Per Exposure: 10¢
Minimum/handling Fee: None
Average Turnaround Time:
3 days

MICROFILMING SERVICE:
Service Available: No
Charges: N/A

DO YOU CHARGE THE BORROWING
LIBRARY FOR POSTAGE? No

FOR HOW LONG DO YOU SUSPEND ILL
SERVICE OVER THE CHRISTMAS
HOLIDAYS? None

ARE THERE ANY GROUPS OF LIBRARIES
FOR WHICH YOU WAIVE FEES? IF
SO, PLEASE NAME THEM: None

KANSAS CITY KANSAS PUBLIC LIBRARY

NUC CODE: (Not answered)

OCLC CODE: (Not answered)

ADDRESS: Interlibrary Loan
Kansas City Kansas
Public Library
Main Library
625 Minnesota
Kansas City, KS 66101

TELEPHONE: (913) 621-3073

LIST NAMES OF BRANCHES WITH
SEPARATE POLICIES: None

BOOKS:
Will Lend: Yes
Length of Loan: 1 month
Renewable: No
Charges: None
Average Turnaround Time:
3-4 days
If you have indicated that a
book is not to be lent, will
you on receipt of a letter
from the requesting library
search the index for given
entries? (Not answered)

PERIODICALS:
Bound: Will not lend
Unbound: Will not lend
Loan Period: N/A
Renewable: N/A
Will lend if article exceeds
_____ number of pages (Not
answered)

MICROFORMS:
Will Lend: No
Specific Types of Microforms:
N/A

GOVERNMENT PUBLICATIONS:
Will Lend: No

DISSERTATIONS:
Will Lend: No

THESES:
Will Lend: No

AUDIO-VISUAL MATERIALS:
Records: Will not lend
Cassettes: Will not lend
Other (slides, filmstrips,
etc.): Will not lend

COMPUTER SOFTWARE:
Will Lend: No

PHOTODUPLICATION SERVICE:
No charge up to 10 exposures
Charge Per Exposure: 10¢
Minimum/handling Fee: None
Average Turnaround Time:
3-4 days

MICROFILMING SERVICE:
Service Available: No
Charges: N/A

DO YOU CHARGE THE BORROWING
LIBRARY FOR POSTAGE? No

FOR HOW LONG DO YOU SUSPEND ILL
SERVICE OVER THE CHRISTMAS
HOLIDAYS? No suspension

ARE THERE ANY GROUPS OF LIBRARIES
FOR WHICH YOU WAIVE FEES? IF
SO, PLEASE NAME THEM: None

KANSAS STATE UNIVERSITY

NUC CODE: KMK

OCLC CODE: KKS

ADDRESS: Interlibrary Loan
Farrell Library
Kansas State
University
Manhattan, KS 66506

TELEPHONE: (913) 532-6598

LIST NAMES OF BRANCHES WITH
SEPARATE POLICIES: None

BOOKS:
Will Lend: Yes
Length of Loan: 3 weeks use
Renewable: Yes, sometimes
Charges: None
Average Turnaround Time:
2 days
If you have indicated that a
book is not to be lent, will
you on receipt of a letter
from the requesting library
search the index for given
entries? (Not answered)

PERIODICALS:
Bound: Will not lend (with
some exceptions)
Unbound: Will not lend
Loan Period: 3-7 days
Renewable: No
Will lend if article exceeds
_____ number of pages (Not
answered)

MICROFORMS:
Will Lend: Yes
Specific Types of Microforms:
Cards, film, and fiche
(except ERIC)

GOVERNMENT PUBLICATIONS:
Will Lend: Yes

DISSERTATIONS:
Will Lend: Yes; 1955 to
present available from
University Microfilms

THESES:
Will Lend: Yes

AUDIO-VISUAL MATERIALS:
Records: Will not lend
Cassettes: Will lend
Other (slides, filmstrips,
etc.): Will lend some of
them

COMPUTER SOFTWARE:
Will Lend: No

PHOTODUPLICATION SERVICE:
No charge up to 0 exposures
Charge Per Exposure: 10¢
Minimum/handling Fee: $2.00
Average Turnaround Time:
2-3 days

MICROFILMING SERVICE:
Service Available: No
Charges: N/A

DO YOU CHARGE THE BORROWING
LIBRARY FOR POSTAGE? No,
unless first-class or
air-mail

FOR HOW LONG DO YOU SUSPEND ILL
SERVICE OVER THE CHRISTMAS
HOLIDAYS? Dec.15-Jan.1

ARE THERE ANY GROUPS OF LIBRARIES
FOR WHICH YOU WAIVE FEES? IF
SO, PLEASE NAME THEM: Kansas
Regent Schools; MASUA Schools

MC PHERSON COLLEGE

NUC CODE: None

OCLC CODE: KKQ

ADDRESS: Interlibrary Loan
Miller Library
McPherson College
1600 E. Euclid
McPherson, KS 67460

TELEPHONE: (316) 241-0731, X216

LIST NAMES OF BRANCHES WITH
SEPARATE POLICIES: None

BOOKS:
Will Lend: Yes
Length of Loan: 1 month
Renewable: Yes
Charges: None
Average Turnaround Time:
2 days
If you have indicated that a
book is not to be lent, will
you on receipt of a letter
from the requesting library
search the index for given
entries? (Not answered)

PERIODICALS:
Bound: Will not lend
Unbound: Will not lend
Loan Period: N/A
Renewable: N/A
Will lend if article exceeds
_____ number of pages (Not
answered)

MICROFORMS:
Will Lend: Yes
Specific Types of Microforms:
Microfiche, microfilm

GOVERNMENT PUBLICATIONS:
Will Lend: Yes

DISSERTATIONS:
Will Lend: Yes

THESES:
Will Lend: Yes

AUDIO-VISUAL MATERIALS:
Records: Will lend
Cassettes: Will lend
Other (slides, filmstrips,
etc.): Will lend

COMPUTER SOFTWARE:
No policy as yet

PHOTODUPLICATION SERVICE:
No charge up to 11 exposures
Charge Per Exposure: 15¢
from film; 10¢ from paper;
10¢ from fiche
Minimum/handling Fee: None
Average Turnaround Time:
2 days

MICROFILMING SERVICE:
Service Available: No
Charges: N/A

DO YOU CHARGE THE BORROWING
LIBRARY FOR POSTAGE? No

FOR HOW LONG DO YOU SUSPEND ILL
SERVICE OVER THE CHRISTMAS
HOLIDAYS? 2-3 days

ARE THERE ANY GROUPS OF LIBRARIES
FOR WHICH YOU WAIVE FEES? IF
SO, PLEASE NAME THEM: Member
libraries of Associated
Colleges of Central Kansas

STATE LIBRARY OF KANSAS

NUC CODE: K

OCLC CODE: KKC

ADDRESS: Interlibrary Loan
           State Library of Kansas
           Third Floor, Statehouse
           Topeka, KS 66612

TELEPHONE: (913) 296-3296

LIST NAMES OF BRANCHES WITH
  SEPARATE POLICIES: None

BOOKS:
  Will Lend: Yes
  Length of Loan: 4 weeks
  Renewable: Yes
  Charges: None
  Average Turnaround Time:
  1 day
  If you have indicated that a
  book is not to be lent, will
  you on receipt of a letter
  from the requesting library
  search the index for given
  entries? Yes

PERIODICALS:
  Bound: Will lend
  Unbound: Will lend
  Loan Period: 4 weeks
  Renewable: Yes
  Will lend if article exceeds
  _____ number of pages (Will
  not lend, regardless of
  length of article)

MICROFORMS:
  Will Lend: No
  Specific Types of Microforms:
  Fiche, roll film

GOVERNMENT PUBLICATIONS:
  Will Lend: Yes

DISSERTATIONS:
  Will Lend: Do not own

THESES:
  Will Lend: Do not own

AUDIO-VISUAL MATERIALS:
  Records: Do not own
  Cassettes: Do not own
  Other (slides, filmstrips,
    etc.): Do not own

COMPUTER SOFTWARE:
  Will Lend: Do not own

PHOTODUPLICATION SERVICE:
  No charge up to 10 exposures
  Charge Per Exposure: 10¢
  Minimum/handling Fee: None
  Average Turnaround Time:
  1 day

MICROFILMING SERVICE:
  Service Available: No
  Charges: N/A

DO YOU CHARGE THE BORROWING
  LIBRARY FOR POSTAGE? No

FOR HOW LONG DO YOU SUSPEND ILL
  SERVICE OVER THE CHRISTMAS
  HOLIDAYS? No suspension

ARE THERE ANY GROUPS OF LIBRARIES
  FOR WHICH YOU WAIVE FEES? IF
  SO, PLEASE NAME THEM: None

PITTSBURG STATE UNIVERSITY

NUC CODE: KPT

OCLC CODE: KFP

ADDRESS: Interlibrary Loan
           Leonard H. Axe
           Library
           Pittsburg State
           University
           Pittsburg, KS 66762

TELEPHONE: (316) 231-7000, X431

LIST NAMES OF BRANCHES WITH
  SEPARATE POLICIES: None

BOOKS:
  Will Lend: Yes
  Length of Loan: 3 weeks use
  Renewable: Yes
  Charges: None
  Average Turnaround Time:
  2 days
  If you have indicated that a
  book is not to be lent, will
  you on receipt of a letter
  from the requesting library
  search the index for given
  entries? (Not answered)

PERIODICALS:
  Bound: Will lend in special
  circumstances
  Unbound: Will lend in
  special circumstances
  Loan Period: 1 weeks use
  Renewable: No
  Will lend if article exceeds
  _____ number of pages (Not
  answered)

MICROFORMS:
  Will Lend: Yes
  Specific Types of Microforms:
  Microfilm, microfiche,
  microcards

GOVERNMENT PUBLICATIONS:
  Will Lend: Yes

DISSERTATIONS:
  Will Lend: Do not own

THESES:
  Will Lend: Yes

AUDIO-VISUAL MATERIALS:
  Records: Will lend
  Cassettes: Will lend
  Other (slides, filmstrips,
    etc.): Will not lend

COMPUTER SOFTWARE:
  Will Lend: No

PHOTODUPLICATION SERVICE:
  No charge up to 0 exposures
  Charge Per Exposure: 10¢
  Minimum/handling Fee: None
  Average Turnaround Time:
  2 days

MICROFILMING SERVICE:
  Service Available: No
  Charges: N/A

DO YOU CHARGE THE BORROWING
  LIBRARY FOR POSTAGE? No

FOR HOW LONG DO YOU SUSPEND ILL
  SERVICE OVER THE CHRISTMAS
  HOLIDAYS? No suspension

ARE THERE ANY GROUPS OF LIBRARIES
  FOR WHICH YOU WAIVE FEES? IF
  SO, PLEASE NAME THEM: Kansas
  Regents Libraries; Kansas-
  Nebraska Project Libraries;
  BCR-ILL Code signers

UNIVERSITY OF KANSAS

NUC CODE: KU

OCLC CODE: KKU

ADDRESS: Interlibrary Loan
          Services
          University of Kansas
          Libraries
          Lawrence, KS 66045

TELEPHONE: (913) 864-3960

LIST NAMES OF BRANCHES WITH
  SEPARATE POLICIES:
    Law Library
    Medical Center, Kansas City

BOOKS:
  Will Lend: Yes
  Length of Loan: 3 weeks
  Renewable: No
  Charges: None
  Average Turnaround Time:
    24 hours
  If you have indicated that a
    book is not to be lent, will
    you on receipt of a letter
    from the requesting library
    search the index for given
    entries? Yes

PERIODICALS:
  Bound: Will lend occasionally
  Unbound: Will not lend
  Loan Period: 3 weeks
  Renewable: No
  Will lend if article exceeds
    _____ number of pages (Not
    answered)

MICROFORMS:
  Will Lend: Yes
  Specific Types of Microforms:
    Microfilm, microfiche,
    microcards, microprint

GOVERNMENT PUBLICATIONS:
  Will Lend: Yes, occasionally

DISSERTATIONS:
  Will Lend: Yes; 1959 to
    present available from
    University Microfilms

THESES:
  Will Lend: Yes

AUDIO-VISUAL MATERIALS:
  Reocrds: Will not lend
  Cassettes: Do not own
  Other (slides, filmstrips,
    etc.): Will not lend

COMPUTER SOFTWARE:
  Will Lend: Yes

PHOTODUPLICATION SERVICE:
  No charge up to 1 exposure
  Charge Per Exposure: 20¢
    per page after first 15
  Minimum/handling Fee: $3.00
    for 1-15 pages
  Average Turnaround Time:
    24 hours

MICROFILMING SERVICE:
  Service Available: Yes
    (takes 2 months)
  Charges: 10¢ per frame

DO YOU CHARGE THE BORROWING
  LIBRARY FOR POSTAGE? No,
    if sent library rate

FOR HOW LONG DO YOU SUSPEND ILL
  SERVICE OVER THE CHRISTMAS
  HOLIDAYS? Approximately
    Dec.12-26

ARE THERE ANY GROUPS OF LIBRARIES
  FOR WHICH YOU WAIVE FEES? IF
  SO, PLEASE NAME THEM: MASUA
    libraries; we will
    reciprocally charge
    libraries that charge us

WASHBURN UNIVERSITY

NUC CODE: KTW

OCLC CODE: KKW

ADDRESS: Interlibrary Loan
          Mabee Library
          Washburn University
          Topeka, KS 66621

TELEPHONE: (913) 295-6479

LIST NAMES OF BRANCHES WITH
  SEPARATE POLICIES: None

BOOKS:
  Will Lend: Yes
  Length of Loan: 4 weeks
  Renewable: Yes
  Charges: None
  Average Turnaround Time:
    1 week
  If you have indicated that a
    book is not to be lent, will
    you on receipt of a letter
    from the requesting library
    search the index for given
    entries? (Not answered)

PERIODICALS:
  Bound: Will not lend
  Unbound: Will not lend
  Loan Period: N/A
  Renewable: N/A
  Will lend if article exceeds
    20 pages

MICROFORMS:
  Will Lend: No
  Specific Types of Microforms:
    N/A

GOVERNMENT PUBLICATIONS:
  Will Lend: Yes

DISSERTATIONS:
  Will Lend: No

THESES:
  Will Lend: Yes

AUDIO-VISUAL MATERIALS:
  Records: Will not lend
  Cassettes: Will not lend
  Other (slides, filmstrips,
    etc.): Will not lend

COMPUTER SOFTWARE:
  Will Lend: No

PHOTODUPLICATION SERVICE:
  No charge up to 10 exposures
  Charge Per Exposure:
    (Not answered)
  Minimum/handling Fee: None
  Average Turnaround Time:
    1 week

MICROFILMING SERVICE:
  Service Available: No
  Charges: N/A

DO YOU CHARGE THE BORROWING
  LIBRARY FOR POSTAGE? No

FOR HOW LONG DO YOU SUSPEND ILL
  SERVICE OVER THE CHRISTMAS
  HOLIDAYS? 1 week

ARE THERE ANY GROUPS OF LIBRARIES
  FOR WHICH YOU WAIVE FEES? IF
  SO, PLEASE NAME THEM: BCR
    and Kansas

WICHITA PUBLIC LIBRARY

NUC CODE: (Not answered)

OCLC CODE: KFW

ADDRESS: Interlibrary Loan
           Wichita Public Library
           223 S. Main
           Wichita, KS   67202

TELEPHONE: (316) 262-0611

LIST NAMES OF BRANCHES WITH
  SEPARATE POLICIES: None

BOOKS:
  Will Lend: Yes
  Length of Loan: 3 weeks
  Renewable: Yes
  Charges: None
  Average Turnaround Time:
  1 day
  If you have indicated that a
  book is not to be lent, will
  you on receipt of a letter
  from the requesting library
  search the index for given
  entries? (Not answered)

PERIODICALS:
  Bound: Will not lend
  Unbound: Will not lend
  Loan Period: N/A
  Renewable: N/A
  Will lend if article exceeds
  _____ number of pages (Not
  answered)

MICROFORMS:
  Will Lend: No
  Specific Types of Microforms:
  N/A
  Photoduplication charges: 25¢
  to 50¢

GOVERNMENT PUBLICATIONS:
  Will Lend: No

DISSERTATIONS:
  Will Lend: Do not own

THESES:
  Will Lend: Do not own

AUDIO-VISUAL MATERIALS:
  Records: Will not lend
  Cassettes: Will not lend
  Other (slides, filmstrips,
    etc.): Will not lend

COMPUTER SOFTWARE:
  Will Lend: No

PHOTODUPLICATION SERVICE:
  No charge up to 0 exposures
  Charge Per Exposure: 20¢
  Minimum/handling Fee: None
  Average Turnaround Time:
  1 day

MICROFILMING SERVICE:
  Service Available: No
  Charges: N/A

DO YOU CHARGE THE BORROWING
  LIBRARY FOR POSTAGE? No

FOR HOW LONG DO YOU SUSPEND ILL
  SERVICE OVER THE CHRISTMAS
  HOLIDAYS? No suspension

ARE THERE ANY GROUPS OF LIBRARIES
  FOR WHICH YOU WAIVE FEES? IF
  SO, PLEASE NAME THEM: Kansas
  and Nebraska libraries
  receive the first 10 photocopies free

WICHITA STATE UNIVERSITY

NUC CODE: KWiU

OCLC CODE: KSW

ADDRESS: Interlibrary Loan
           Wichita State Univer-
           sity Library
           Wichita, KS   67208

TELEPHONE: (316) 689-3591

LIST NAMES OF BRANCHES WITH
  SEPARATE POLICIES: None

BOOKS:
  Will Lend: Yes
  Length of Loan: 3 weeks
  Renewable: Yes, for 2 weeks
  Charges: None
  Average Turnaround Time:
  (Not answered)
  If you have indicated that a
  book is not to be lent, will
  you on receipt of a letter
  from the requesting library
  search the index for given
  entries? (Not answered)

PERIODICALS:
  Bound: Will seldom lend
  Unbound: Will seldom lend
  Loan Period: (Not answered)
  Renewable: (Not answered)
  Will lend if article exceeds
  _____ number of pages (Not
  answered)

MICROFORMS:
  Will Lend: Yes
  Specific Types of Microforms:
  Cards, films fiche

GOVERNMENT PUBLICATIONS:
  Will Lend: Yes

DISSERTATIONS:
  Will Lend: Yes

THESES:
  Will Lend: Yes

AUDIO-VISUAL MATERIALS:
  Records: Will not lend
  Cassettes: Will not lend
  Other (slides, filmstrips,
    etc.): Will not lend

COMPUTER SOFTWARE:
  Will Lend: No

PHOTODUPLICATION SERVICE:
  No charge up to 20 exposures
  Charge Per Exposure: 10¢
  Minimum/handling Fee: None
  Average Turnaround Time:
  (Not answered)

MICROFILMING SERVICE:
  Service Available: No
  Charges: N/A

DO YOU CHARGE THE BORROWING
  LIBRARY FOR POSTAGE? No

FOR HOW LONG DO YOU SUSPEND ILL
  SERVICE OVER THE CHRISTMAS
  HOLIDAYS? Dec.15-Jan.2

ARE THERE ANY GROUPS OF LIBRARIES
  FOR WHICH YOU WAIVE FEES? IF
  SO, PLEASE NAME THEM: None

EASTERN KENTUCKY UNIVERSITY

NUC CODE: KYRE

OCLC CODE: KEU

ADDRESS: Interlibrary Loan
John Grant Crabbe
Library
Eastern Kentucky
University
Rickmond, KY   40475

TELEPHONE: (606) 622-3360

LIST NAMES OF BRANCHES WITH
SEPARATE POLICIES: None

BOOKS:
Will Lend: Yes
Length of Loan: 1 month
from shipping date
Renewable: Yes
Charges: None
Average Turnaround Time:
Within the week
If you have indicated that a
book is not to be lent, will
you on receipt of a letter
from the requesting library
search the index for given
entries? (Not answered)

PERIODICALS:
Bound: Will not lend
Unbound: Will not lend
Loan Period: N/A
Renewable: N/A
Will lend if article exceeds
_____ number of pages (Not
answered)

MICROFORMS:
Will Lend: Yes
Specific Types of Microforms:
Fiche and film

GOVERNMENT PUBLICATIONS:
Will Lend: Yes, occasionally

DISSERTATIONS:
Will Lend: No

THESES:
Will Lend: Yes

AUDIO-VISUAL MATERIALS:
Records: Will not lend
Cassettes: Will not lend
Other (slides, filmstrips,
etc.): Will not lend

COMPUTER SOFTWARE:
Will Lend: No

PHOTODUPLICATION SERVICE:
No charge up to 0 exposures
Charge Per Exposure: 10¢
Minimum/handling Fee: $2.00
Average Turnaround Time:
Within the week

MICROFILMING SERVICE:
Service Available: No
Charges: N/A

DO YOU CHARGE THE BORROWING
LIBRARY FOR POSTAGE? No

FOR HOW LONG DO YOU SUSPEND ILL
SERVICE OVER THE CHRISTMAS
HOLIDAYS? 2 weeks

ARE THERE ANY GROUPS OF LIBRARIES
FOR WHICH YOU WAIVE FEES? IF
SO, PLEASE NAME THEM: We
have reciprocal agreements
with many libraries, both
in-state and out

KENTON COUNTY PUBLIC LIBRARY

NUC CODE: (Not answered)

OCLC CODE: (Not answered)

ADDRESS: Interlibrary Loan
Kenton County Public
Library
502 Scott Blvd.
Covington, KY   41011

TELEPHONE: (606) 491-7610

LIST NAMES OF BRANCHES WITH
SEPARATE POLICIES: None

BOOKS:
Will Lend: Yes
Length of Loan: 28 days
Renewable: No
Charges: None
Average Turnaround Time:
24 hours
If you have indicated that a
book is not to be lent, will
you on receipt of a letter
from the requesting library
search the index for given
entries? Yes

PERIODICALS:
Bound: Will not lend
Unbound: Will not lend
Loan Period: N/A
Renewable: N/A
Will lend if article exceeds
_____ number of pages (Not
answered)

MICROFORMS:
Will Lend: No
Specific Types of Microforms:
N/A

GOVERNMENT PUBLICATIONS:
Will Lend: Do not own

DISSERTATIONS:
Will Lend: Do not own

THESES:
Will Lend: Do not own

AUDIO-VISUAL MATERIALS:
Records: Will not lend
Cassettes: Will not lend
Other (slides, filmstrips,
etc.): Will not lend

COMPUTER SOFTWARE:
Will Lend: Do not own

PHOTODUPLICATION SERVICE:
No charge up to 0 exposures
Charge Per Exposure: 10¢
Minimum/handling Fee: $1.00
Average Turnaround Time:
24 hours on books, maga-
zines, etc.; 2 weeks on
genealogical/historical
queries

MICROFILMING SERVICE:
Service Available: No
Charges: N/A

DO YOU CHARGE THE BORROWING
LIBRARY FOR POSTAGE? Yes

FOR HOW LONG DO YOU SUSPEND ILL
SERVICE OVER THE CHRISTMAS
HOLIDAYS? No suspension

ARE THERE ANY GROUPS OF LIBRARIES
FOR WHICH YOU WAIVE FEES? IF
SO, PLEASE NAME THEM: None

LEXINGTON PUBLIC LIBRARY

NUC CODE: KyLx

OCLC CODE: (Not answered)

ADDRESS: Interlibrary Loan
Lexington Public
Library
251 W. Second St.
Lexington, KY
40507-1187

TELEPHONE: (606) 253-1750 or
254-8347

LIST NAMES OF BRANCHES WITH
SEPARATE POLICIES: None

BOOKS:
Will Lend: Yes
Length of Loan: 1 month
Renewable: Yes
Charges: None
Average Turnaround Time:
2-5 days
If you have indicated that a
book is not to be lent, will
you on receipt of a letter
from the requesting library
search the index for given
entries? (Not answered)

PERIODICALS:
Bound: Will not lend
Unbound: Will not lend
Loan Period: N/A
Renewable: N/A
Will lend if article exceeds
_____ number of pages (Not
answered)

MICROFORMS:
Will Lend: No
Specific Types of Microforms:
N/A

GOVERNMENT PUBLICATIONS:
Will Lend: No

DISSERTATIONS:
Will Lend: Do not own

THESES:
Will Lend: Do not own

AUDIO-VISUAL MATERIALS:
Records: Will not lend
Cassettes: Will lend
foreign language
materials only
Other (slides, filmstrips,
etc.): Will not lend

COMPUTER SOFTWARE:
Will Lend: No

PHOTODUPLICATION SERVICE:
No charge up to 0 exposures
Charge Per Exposure: 10¢
from hard copy; 20¢ from
microfilm
Minimum/handling Fee: $1.00
Average Turnaround Time:
3-6 days

MICROFILMING SERVICE:
Service Available: No
Charges: N/A

DO YOU CHARGE THE BORROWING
LIBRARY FOR POSTAGE? No

FOR HOW LONG DO YOU SUSPEND ILL
SERVICE OVER THE CHRISTMAS
HOLIDAYS? No suspension

ARE THERE ANY GROUPS OF LIBRARIES
FOR WHICH YOU WAIVE FEES? IF
SO, PLEASE NAME THEM: None

LOUISVILLE FREE PUBLIC LIBRARY

NUC CODE: KyLo

OCLC CODE: KLP

ADDRESS: Interlibrary Loan
Louisville Free Public
Library
Fourth and York Sts.
Louisville, KY 40203

TELEPHONE: (502) 584-4154

LIST NAMES OF BRANCHES WITH
SEPARATE POLICIES: None

BOOKS:
Will Lend: Yes
Length of Loan: 2 weeks use
Renewable: Yes
Charges: Postage
Average Turnaround Time:
3 days
If you have indicated that a
book is not to be lent, will
you on receipt of a letter
from the requesting library
search the index for given
entries? Yes

PERIODICALS:
Bound: Will not lend
Unbound: Will not lend
Loan Period: N/A
Renewable: N/A
Will lend if article exceeds
_____ number of pages (Not
answered)

MICROFORMS:
Will Lend: No
Specific Types of Microforms:
N/A

GOVERNMENT PUBLICATIONS:
Will Lend: No

DISSERTATIONS:
Will Lend: Do not own

THESES:
Will Lend: Do not own

AUDIO-VISUAL MATERIALS:
Records: Will not lend
Cassettes: Do not own
Other (slides, filmstrips,
etc.): Will not lend

COMPUTER SOFTWARE:
Will Lend: Do not own

PHOTODUPLICATION SERVICE:
No charge up to 0 exposures
Charge Per Exposure: 10¢
from hard copy; 20¢ from
microform
Minimum/handling Fee: 50¢
minimum
Average Turnaround Time:
3 days

MICROFILMING SERVICE:
Service Available: No
Charges: N/A

DO YOU CHARGE THE BORROWING
LIBRARY FOR POSTAGE? Yes

FOR HOW LONG DO YOU SUSPEND ILL
SERVICE OVER THE CHRISTMAS
HOLIDAYS? No suspension

ARE THERE ANY GROUPS OF LIBRARIES
FOR WHICH YOU WAIVE FEES? IF
SO, PLEASE NAME THEM: None

MOREHEAD STATE UNIVERSITY

NUC CODE: KyMoreU

OCLC CODE: KMM

ADDRESS: Interlibrary Loan
Camden-Carroll Library
Morehead State
University
Morehead, KY 40351

TELEPHONE: (606) 783-2251

LIST NAMES OF BRANCHES WITH
SEPARATE POLICIES: None

BOOKS:
Will Lend: Yes
Length of Loan: 1 month from
date sent
Renewable: Yes, if not needed
here
Charges: None
Average Turnaround Time:
2 days
If you have indicated that a
book is not to be lent, will
you on receipt of a letter
from the requesting library
search the index for given
entries? Yes, if request
is not for extensive
research and staff time
allows

PERIODICALS:
Bound: Will not lend
Unbound: Will not lend
Loan Period: N/A
Renewable: N/A
Will lend if article exceeds
_____ number of pages (Not
answered)

MICROFORMS:
Will Lend: Yes
Specific Types of Microforms:
Newspapers on microfilm,
with some exceptions

GOVERNMENT PUBLICATIONS:
Will Lend: Yes

DISSERTATIONS:
Will Lend: Yes

THESES:
Will Lend: Yes

AUDIO-VISUAL MATERIALS:
Records: Will not lend
Cassettes: Will not lend
Other (slides, filmstrips,
etc.): Will not lend

COMPUTER SOFTWARE:
Will Lend: No

PHOTODUPLICATION SERVICE:
No charge up to 5 exposures
Charge Per Exposure: 10¢
Minimum/handling Fee: $1.00
Average Turnaround Time:
2 days

MICROFILMING SERVICE:
Service Available: No
Charges: N/A

DO YOU CHARGE THE BORROWING
LIBRARY FOR POSTAGE? No

FOR HOW LONG DO YOU SUSPEND ILL
SERVICE OVER THE CHRISTMAS
HOLIDAYS? Dec.15-Jan.2

ARE THERE ANY GROUPS OF LIBRARIES
FOR WHICH YOU WAIVE FEES? IF
SO, PLEASE NAME THEM:
Kentucky libraries

MURRAY STATE UNIVERSITY

NUC CODE: KyMurt

OCLC CODE: KMS

ADDRESS: Interlibrary Loan
Waterfield Library
Murray State
University
Murray, KY 42071

TELEPHONE: (502) 762-4298

LIST NAMES OF BRANCHES WITH
SEPARATE POLICIES: None

BOOKS:
Will Lend: Yes
Length of Loan: 2 weeks from
date of receipt
Renewable: Yes
Charges: Postage
Average Turnaround Time:
Same day
If you have indicated that a
book is not to be lent, will
you on receipt of a letter
from the requesting library
search the index for given
entries? (Not answered)

PERIODICALS:
Bound: Will not lend
Unbound: Will not lend
Loan Period: N/A
Renewable: N/A
Will lend if article exceeds
_____ number of pages (Not
answered)

MICROFORMS:
Will Lend: Yes
Specific Types of Microforms:
Microfilm

GOVERNMENT PUBLICATIONS:
Will Lend: Yes

DISSERTATIONS:
Will Lend: Do not own

THESES:
Will Lend: Yes

AUDIO-VISUAL MATERIALS:
Records: Will not lend
Cassettes: Will not lend
Other (slides, filmstrips,
etc.): Will not lend

COMPUTER SOFTWARE:
Will Lend: No

PHOTODUPLICATION SERVICE:
No charge up to 0 exposures
Charge Per Exposure: 10¢
Minimum/handling Fee: $1.00
Average Turnaround Time:
Same day

MICROFILMING SERVICE:
Service Available: No
Charges: N/A

DO YOU CHARGE THE BORROWING
LIBRARY FOR POSTAGE? Yes

FOR HOW LONG DO YOU SUSPEND ILL
SERVICE OVER THE CHRISTMAS
HOLIDAYS? Mid-December to
2nd week in January

ARE THERE ANY GROUPS OF LIBRARIES
FOR WHICH YOU WAIVE FEES? IF
SO, PLEASE NAME THEM: SAALCK
libraries of Kentucky

NORTHERN KENTUCKY UNIVERSITY

NUC CODE: KyHhn

OCLC CODE: KHN

ADDRESS: Interlibrary Loan
          Northern Kentucky
            University Library
          Highland Heights, KY
            41076

TELEPHONE: (606) 572-6365

LIST NAMES OF BRANCHES WITH
  SEPARATE POLICIES: None

BOOKS:
  Will Lend: Yes
  Length of Loan: 3 weeks
  Renewable: Yes
  Charges: None
  Average Turnaround Time:
    2 days
  If you have indicated that a
    book is not to be lent, will
    you on receipt of a letter
    from the requesting library
    search the index for given
    entries? (Not answered)

PERIODICALS:
  Bound: Will not lend
  Unbound: Will not lend
  Loan Period: N/A
  Renewable: N/A
  Will lend if article exceeds
    _____ number of pages (Not
    answered)

MICROFORMS:
  Will Lend: No
  Specific Types of Microforms:
    N/A

GOVERNMENT PUBLICATIONS:
  Will Lend: Yes

DISSERTATIONS:
  Will Lend: No

THESES:
  Will Lend: No

AUDIO-VISUAL MATERIALS:
  Records: Will not lend
  Cassettes: Will lend
  Other (slides, filmstrips,
    etc.): Will not lend

COMPUTER SOFTWARE:
  Will Lend: Do not own

PHOTODUPLICATION SERVICE:
  No charge up to 3 exposures
  Charge Per Exposure: 10¢
    from hard copy; 15¢ from
    microforms
  Minimum/handling Fee: $3.00
  Average Turnaround Time:
    2 days

MICROFILMING SERVICE:
  Service Available: No
  Charges: N/A

DO YOU CHARGE THE BORROWING
  LIBRARY FOR POSTAGE? No

FOR HOW LONG DO YOU SUSPEND ILL
  SERVICE OVER THE CHRISTMAS
  HOLIDAYS? 2 weeks

ARE THERE ANY GROUPS OF LIBRARIES
  FOR WHICH YOU WAIVE FEES? IF
  SO, PLEASE NAME THEM: All
    Kentucky state universities

TRANSYLVANIA UNIVERSITY

NUC CODE: KYLXT

OCLC CODE: KTU

ADDRESS: Interlibrary Loan
          Transylvania University
            Library
          Lexington, KY 40508

TELEPHONE: (606) 233-8225

LIST NAMES OF BRANCHES WITH
  SEPARATE POLICIES: None

BOOKS:
  Will Lend: Yes
  Length of Loan: 1 month
  Renewable: Yes
  Charges: None, unless some
    special collection
  Average Turnaround Time:
    4 days
  If you have indicated that a
    book is not to be lent, will
    you on receipt of a letter
    from the requesting library
    search the index for given
    entries? (Not answered)

PERIODICALS:
  Bound: Will not lend
  Unbound: Will not lend
  Loan Period: N/A
  Renewable: N/A
  Will lend if article exceeds
    _____ number of pages (Not
    answered)

MICROFORMS:
  Will Lend: (Not answered)
  Specific Types of Microforms:
    N/A

GOVERNMENT PUBLICATIONS:
  Will Lend: Do not own

DISSERTATIONS:
  Will Lend: Do not own

THESES:
  Will Lend: Do not own

AUDIO-VISUAL MATERIALS:
  Records: Do not own
  Cassettes: Do not own
  Other (slides, filmstrips,
    etc.): Do not own

COMPUTER SOFTWARE:
  Will Lend: Do not own

PHOTODUPLICATION SERVICE:
  No charge up to 20 exposures
  Charge Per Exposure: 5¢
    after 1st 20
  Minimum/handling Fee: None
  Average Turnaround Time:
    2 days

MICROFILMING SERVICE:
  Service Available: No
  Charges: N/A

DO YOU CHARGE THE BORROWING
  LIBRARY FOR POSTAGE? No

FOR HOW LONG DO YOU SUSPEND ILL
  SERVICE OVER THE CHRISTMAS
  HOLIDAYS? 1 week

ARE THERE ANY GROUPS OF LIBRARIES
  FOR WHICH YOU WAIVE FEES? IF
  SO, PLEASE NAME THEM: None

UNIVERSITY OF KENTUCKY

NUC CODE: KyU

OCLC CODE: KUK

ADDRESS: Interlibrary Loan
University of Kentucky
Libraries
Lexington, KY
40506-0039

TELEPHONE: (606) 257-3353

LIST NAMES OF BRANCHES WITH
SEPARATE POLICIES:
Medical Center Library
Agriculture Library
Law Library

BOOKS:
Will Lend: Yes
Length of Loan: 2 weeks use
Renewable: Yes
Charges: Only to libraries
that charge us
Average Turnaround Time:
1 week
If you have indicated that a
book is not to be lent, will
you on receipt of a letter
from the requesting library
search the index for given
entries? Yes

PERIODICALS:
Bound: Will not lend
Unbound: Will not lend
Loan Period: N/A
Renewable: N/A
Will lend if article exceeds
_____ number of pages (Not
answered)

MICROFORMS:
Will Lend: Yes
Specific Types of Microforms:
Microfilm, microfiche

GOVERNMENT PUBLICATIONS:
Will Lend: Yes, except for
Census and Serial Set

DISSERTATIONS:
Will Lend: Yes, if 2nd copy
available (Engineering
dissertations are non-
circulating)

THESES:
Will Lend: Yes, if 2nd copy
available

AUDIO-VISUAL MATERIALS:
Records: Will not lend
Cassettes: Will not lend
Other (slides, filmstrips,
etc.): Will not lend

COMPUTER SOFTWARE:
Will Lend: Do not own

PHOTODUPLICATION SERVICE:
No charge up to 0 exposures
Charge Per Exposure: 15¢
Handling Fee: $3.00
Average Turnaround Time:
1 week

MICROFILMING SERVICE:
Service Available: Yes
Charges: 20¢ per foot,
50¢ per reel

DO YOU CHARGE THE BORROWING
LIBRARY FOR POSTAGE? No

FOR HOW LONG DO YOU SUSPEND ILL
SERVICE OVER THE CHRISTMAS
HOLIDAYS? Approximately
3 weeks

ARE THERE ANY GROUPS OF LIBRARIES
FOR WHICH YOU WAIVE FEES? IF
SO, PLEASE NAME THEM: Miami
of Ohio, Purdue, Vermont,
University of Dayton

UNIVERSITY OF LOUISVILLE

NUC CODE: KyLoU

OCLC CODE: KLG

ADDRESS: Interlibrary Loan
Ekstrom Library
University of
Louisville
Louisville, KY 40292

TELEPHONE: (502) 588-6749

LIST NAMES OF BRANCHES WITH
SEPARATE POLICIES:
Health Sciences Library
Law Library

BOOKS:
Will Lend: Yes
Length of Loan: 2 weeks
Renewable: Yes
Charges: None
Average Turnaround Time:
2-3 days
If you have indicated that a
book is not to be lent, will
you on receipt of a letter
from the requesting library
search the index for given
entries? Yes

PERIODICALS:
Bound: Will not lend
Unbound: Will not lend
Loan Period: N/A
Renewable: N/A
Will lend if article exceeds
_____ number of pages (Not
answered)

MICROFORMS:
Will Lend: Yes, occasionally
Specific Types of Microforms:
Do not lend newspapers on
film

GOVERNMENT PUBLICATIONS:
Will Lend: Yes

DISSERTATIONS:
Will Lend: Yes; July 1968 to
present available from
University Microfilms

THESES:
Will Lend: Yes; 1969 to
present available from
University Microfilms

AUDIO-VISUAL MATERIALS:
Records: Do not own
Cassettes: Do not own
Other (slides, filmstrips,
etc.): Do not own

COMPUTER SOFTWARE:
Will Lend: Do not own

PHOTODUPLICATION SERVICE:
No charge up to 0 exposures
Charge Per Exposure: 20¢
Handling Fee: $2.50
Average Turnaround Time:
2-3 days

MICROFILMING SERVICE:
Service Available: No
Charges: N/A

DO YOU CHARGE THE BORROWING
LIBRARY FOR POSTAGE? No

FOR HOW LONG DO YOU SUSPEND ILL
SERVICE OVER THE CHRISTMAS
HOLIDAYS? 3 weeks

ARE THERE ANY GROUPS OF LIBRARIES
FOR WHICH YOU WAIVE FEES? IF
SO, PLEASE NAME THEM:
We have reciprocal
agreements with some
libraries

WESTERN KENTUCKY UNIVERSITY

NUC CODE: KyBgW

OCLC CODE: None

ADDRESS: Interlibrary Loan
           Helm-Cravens Library
           Western Kentucky
             University
           Bowling Green, KY
             42101

TELEPHONE: (502) 745-3951

LIST NAMES OF BRANCHES WITH
  SEPARATE POLICIES: None

BOOKS:
   Will Lend: Yes
   Length of Loan: 3 weeks use
   Renewable: Yes
   Charges: None
   Average Turnaround Time:
     2 days
   If you have indicated that a
     book is not to be lent, will
     you on receipt of a letter
     from the requesting library
     search the index for given
     entries? Yes

PERIODICALS:
   Bound: Will not lend
   Unbound: Will not lend
   Loan Period: N/A
   Renewable: N/A
   Will lend if article exceeds
     _____ number of pages (Will
       not lend, regardless of
       length of article)

MICROFORMS:
   Will Lend: Yes
   Specific Types of Microforms:
     Newspapers, etc.

GOVERNMENT PUBLICATIONS:
   Will Lend: Yes

DISSERTATIONS:
   Will Lend: Do not own

THESES:
   Will Lend: Yes

AUDIO-VISUAL MATERIALS:
   Records: Will not lend
   Cassettes: Will not lend
   Other (slides, filmstrips,
     etc.): Will not lend

COMPUTER SOFTWARE:
   Will Lend: No

PHOTODUPLICATION SERVICE:
   No charge up to 0 exposures
   Charge Per Exposure: 15¢
   Minimum/handling Fee: $2.00
   Average Turnaround Time:
     2 days

MICROFILMING SERVICE:
   Service Available: No
   Charges: N/A

DO YOU CHARGE THE BORROWING
   LIBRARY FOR POSTAGE? No

FOR HOW LONG DO YOU SUSPEND ILL
   SERVICE OVER THE CHRISTMAS
   HOLIDAYS? 2 weeks

ARE THERE ANY GROUPS OF LIBRARIES
   FOR WHICH YOU WAIVE FEES? IF
   SO, PLEASE NAME THEM: In-
     state libraries that do not
     charge us

EAST BATON ROUGE PARISH LIBRARY

NUC CODE: LBr

OCLC CODE: LFB

ADDRESS: Interlibrary Loan
East Baton Rouge
  Parish Library
7711 Goodwood Blvd.
Baton Rouge, LA 70806

TELEPHONE: (504) 389-3370

LIST NAMES OF BRANCHES WITH
  SEPARATE POLICIES: None

BOOKS:
  Will Lend: Yes
  Length of Loan: 3 weeks
  Renewable: Yes
  Charges: (Not answered)
  Average Turnaround Time:
    1 week
  If you have indicated that a
    book is not to be lent, will
    you on receipt of a letter
    from the requesting library
    search the index for given
    entries? Yes

PERIODICALS:
  Bound: Will not lend
  Unbound: Will lend
  Loan Period: 3 weeks
  Renewable: Yes
  Will lend if article exceeds
    _____ number of pages (Not
    answered)

MICROFORMS:
  Will Lend: No
  Specific Types of Microforms:
    N/A

GOVERNMENT PUBLICATIONS:
  Will Lend: Yes, if circulating

DISSERTATIONS:
  Will Lend: Do not own

THESES:
  Will Lend: Do not own

AUDIO-VISUAL MATERIALS:
  Records: Do not own
  Cassettes: Do not own
  Other (slides, filmstrips,
    etc.): Do not own

COMPUTER SOFTWARE:
  Will Lend: Do not own

PHOTODUPLICATION SERVICE:
  No charge up to 0 exposures
  Charge Per Exposure: 10¢
  Minimum/handling Fee: $1.00
  Average Turnaround Time:
    1 week

MICROFILMING SERVICE:
  Service Available: No
  Charges: N/A

DO YOU CHARGE THE BORROWING
  LIBRARY FOR POSTAGE? Yes

FOR HOW LONG DO YOU SUSPEND ILL
  SERVICE OVER THE CHRISTMAS
  HOLIDAYS? No suspension

ARE THERE ANY GROUPS OF LIBRARIES
  FOR WHICH YOU WAIVE FEES? IF
  SO, PLEASE NAME THEM: None

GRAMBLING STATE UNIVERSITY

NUC CODE: (Not answered)

OCLC CODE: LGS

ADDRESS: Interlibrary Loan
Lewis Library
Grambling State
  University
P. O. Box 3
Grambling, LA 71245

TELEPHONE: (318) 274-6941, X227

LIST NAMES OF BRANCHES WITH
  SEPARATE POLICIES: None

BOOKS:
  Will Lend: Yes
  Length of Loan: 3-4 weeks
  Renewable: Yes
  Charges: None
  Average Turnaround Time:
    (Not answered)
  If you have indicated that a
    book is not to be lent, will
    you on receipt of a letter
    from the requesting library
    search the index for given
    entries? Afro-American
    books in restricted
    collection

PERIODICALS:
  Bound: (Not answered)
  Unbound: Will lend, except
    for current issues
  Loan Period: 2 weeks
  Renewable: Yes
  Will lend if article exceeds
    15 pages

MICROFORMS:
  Will Lend: Yes
  Specific Types of Microforms:
    (Not answered)

GOVERNMENT PUBLICATIONS:
  Will Lend: Yes

DISSERTATIONS:
  Will Lend: No

THESES:
  Will Lend: No

AUDIO-VISUAL MATERIALS:
  Records: Will lend
  Cassettes: Will lend
  Other (slides, filmstrips,
    etc.): Will lend

COMPUTER SOFTWARE:
  Will Lend: Do not own

PHOTODUPLICATION SERVICE:
  No charge up to 10 exposures
  Charge Per Exposure: (Not
    answered)
  Minimum/handling Fee: None
  Average Turnaround Time:
    (Not answered)

MICROFILMING SERVICE:
  Service Available: No
  Charges: N/A

DO YOU CHARGE THE BORROWING
  LIBRARY FOR POSTAGE? No

FOR HOW LONG DO YOU SUSPEND ILL
  SERVICE OVER THE CHRISTMAS
  HOLIDAYS? 1 week

ARE THERE ANY GROUPS OF LIBRARIES
  FOR WHICH YOU WAIVE FEES? IF
  SO, PLEASE NAME THEM: None

JEFFERSON PARISH LIBRARY

NUC CODE: None

OCLC CODE: None

ADDRESS: Interlibrary Loan
         Jefferson Parish
         Library
         P. O. Box 7490
         Metairie, LA   70010

TELEPHONE: (504) 834-5850

LIST NAMES OF BRANCHES WITH
   SEPARATE POLICIES: None

BOOKS:
   Will Lend: Yes
   Length of Loan: 4 weeks
   Renewable: Yes
   Charges: None
   Average Turnaround Time:
     24 hours
   If you have indicated that a
     book is not to be lent, will
     you on receipt of a letter
     from the requesting library
     search the index for given
     entries? Yes

PERIODICALS:
   Bound: Will not lend
   Unbound: Will lend
   Loan Period: 4 weeks
   Renewable: Yes
   Will lend if article exceeds
     _____ number of pages   (Not
     answered)

MICROFORMS:
   Will Lend: No
   Specific Types of Microforms:
     Microfilm periodicals;
     microfilm Louisiana census

GOVERNMENT PUBLICATIONS:
   Will Lend: Yes

DISSERTATIONS:
   Will Lend: Yes

THESES:
   Will Lend: Yes

AUDIO-VISUAL MATERIALS:
   Records: Will lend
   Cassettes: Will lend
   Other (slides, filmstrips,
     etc.):   Will lend

COMPUTER SOFTWARE:
   Will Lend: Do not own

PHOTODUPLICATION SERVICE:
   No charge up to 5 exposures
   Charge Per Exposure: 15¢ to
     25¢
   Minimum/handling Fee: None
   Average Turnaround Time:
     2 days

MICROFILMING SERVICE:
   Service Available: No
   Charges: N/A

DO YOU CHARGE THE BORROWING
   LIBRARY FOR POSTAGE?   No

FOR HOW LONG DO YOU SUSPEND ILL
   SERVICE OVER THE CHRISTMAS
   HOLIDAYS?   No suspension

ARE THERE ANY GROUPS OF LIBRARIES
   FOR WHICH YOU WAIVE FEES?   IF
   SO, PLEASE NAME THEM:
     Louisiana libraries, except
     photoduplication charges

LAW LIBRARY OF LOUISIANA

NUC CODE: None

OCLC CODE: LNL

ADDRESS: Interlibrary Loan
         Law Library of
         Louisiana
         301 Loyola Ave.
         Room 100
         New Orleans, LA   70112

TELEPHONE: (504) 568-5705

LIST NAMES OF BRANCHES WITH
   SEPARATE POLICIES: None

BOOKS:
   Will Lend: Yes, sometimes
   Length of Loan:
     Approximately 2 weeks
   Renewable: Yes, sometimes
   Charges: None
   Average Turnaround Time:
     24 hours
   If you have indicated that a
     book is not to be lent, will
     you on receipt of a letter
     from the requesting library
     search the index for given
     entries? Yes

PERIODICALS:
   Bound: Will sometimes lend
   Unbound: Will sometimes
     lend
   Loan Period: Depends upon
     the situation
   Renewable: Not usually
   Will lend if article exceeds
     _____ number of pages   (No
     set length)

MICROFORMS:
   Will Lend: Yes, sometimes
   Specific Types of Microforms:
     Microfiche

GOVERNMENT PUBLICATIONS:
   Will Lend: Yes, sometimes

DISSERTATIONS:
   Will Lend: Do not own

THESES:
   Will Lend: Do not own

AUDIO-VISUAL MATERIALS:
   Records: Do not own
   Cassettes: Will not lend
   Other (slides, filmstrips,
     etc.):   Do not own

COMPUTER SOFTWARE:
   Will Lend: Do not own

PHOTODUPLICATION SERVICE:
   No charge up to 0 exposures
   Charge Per Exposure: 20¢
     from hardcopy; 25¢ from
     microcopy
   Minimum/handling Fee: None
   Average Turnaround Time:
     24 hours

MICROFILMING SERVICE:
   Service Available: No
   Charges: N/A

DO YOU CHARGE THE BORROWING
   LIBRARY FOR POSTAGE?   Yes,
   for photocopies and for
   first-class book loans

FOR HOW LONG DO YOU SUSPEND ILL
   SERVICE OVER THE CHRISTMAS
   HOLIDAYS?   No suspension

ARE THERE ANY GROUPS OF LIBRARIES
   FOR WHICH YOU WAIVE FEES?   IF
   SO, PLEASE NAME THEM: Some
   Louisiana law libraries

LOUISIANA STATE UNIVERSITY

NUC CODE: (Not answered)

OCLC CODE: LUU

ADDRESS: Interlibrary Loan
Middleton Library
Louisiana State
University
Baton Rouge, LA   70803

TELEPHONE: (504) 388-2138

LIST NAMES OF BRANCHES WITH
SEPARATE POLICIES: None

BOOKS:
Will Lend: Yes
Length of Loan: 1 month
Renewable: Yes
Charges: $4.00 for out-of-
state
Average Turnaround Time:
(Not answered)
If you have indicated that a
book is not to be lent, will
you on receipt of a letter
from the requesting library
search the index for given
entries?   (Not answered)

PERIODICALS:
Bound: Will not lend
Unbound: Will not lend
Loan Period: N/A
Renewable: N/A
Will lend if article exceeds
100 pages

MICROFORMS:
Will Lend: Yes
Specific Types of Microforms:
All types

GOVERNMENT PUBLICATIONS:
Will Lend: Yes

DISSERTATIONS:
Will Lend: Yes, if 2nd copy
available; 1955 to present
available from University
Microfilms

THESES:
Will Lend: Yes, if 2nd copy
available

AUDIO-VISUAL MATERIALS:
Records: (Not answered)
Cassettes: (Not answered)
Other (slides, filmstrips,
etc.):   (Not answered)

COMPUTER SOFTWARE:
Will Lend: (Not answered)

PHOTODUPLICATION SERVICE:
No charge up to 0 exposures
Charge Per Exposure: 15¢
Minimum/handling Fee: $3.50
for 1-20 pages
Average Turnaround Time:
(Not answered)

MICROFILMING SERVICE:
Service Available: (Not
answered)
Charges: N/A

DO YOU CHARGE THE BORROWING
LIBRARY FOR POSTAGE?   (Not
answered)

FOR HOW LONG DO YOU SUSPEND ILL
SERVICE OVER THE CHRISTMAS
HOLIDAYS?   Dec.10-Jan.4

ARE THERE ANY GROUPS OF LIBRARIES
FOR WHICH YOU WAIVE FEES?   IF
SO, PLEASE NAME THEM: ARL,
ASERL

LOUISIANA STATE UNIVERSITY MEDICAL CENTER

NUC CODE: LU-M

OCLC CODE: (Not answered)

ADDRESS: Interlibrary Loan
Louisiana State
University Medical
Center Library
1542 Tulane Ave.
New Orleans, LA   70112

TELEPHONE: (504) 568-6101

LIST NAMES OF BRANCHES WITH
SEPARATE POLICIES: None

BOOKS:
Will Lend: Yes
Length of Loan: 2 weeks
Renewable: Yes
Charges: $4.00
Average Turnaround Time:
(Not answered)
If you have indicated that a
book is not to be lent, will
you on receipt of a letter
from the requesting library
search the index for given
entries?   No

PERIODICALS:
Bound: Will lend with
special permission
Unbound: (Not answered)
Loan Period: (Not answered)
Renewable: (Not answered)
Will lend if article exceeds
_____ number of pages (Not
answered)

MICROFORMS:
Will Lend: No
Specific Types of Microforms:
N/A

GOVERNMENT PUBLICATIONS:
Will Lend: Yes

DISSERTATIONS:
Will Lend: Yes

THESES:
Will Lend: Yes

AUDIO-VISUAL MATERIALS:
Records: Will not lend
Cassettes: Will not lend
Other (slides, filmstrips,
etc.):   Will not lend

COMPUTER SOFTWARE:
Will Lend: No

PHOTODUPLICATION SERVICE:
No charge up to 0 exposures
Charge Per Exposure: 10¢
after 25
Minimum/handling Fee: $4.00
Average Turnaround Time:
(Not answered)

MICROFILMING SERVICE:
Service Available: No
Charges: N/A

DO YOU CHARGE THE BORROWING
LIBRARY FOR POSTAGE?   No

FOR HOW LONG DO YOU SUSPEND ILL
SERVICE OVER THE CHRISTMAS
HOLIDAYS?   Varies (no hard
copy after Dec.1)

ARE THERE ANY GROUPS OF LIBRARIES
FOR WHICH YOU WAIVE FEES?   IF
SO, PLEASE NAME THEM: None

MCNEESE STATE UNIVERSITY

NUC CODE: LLcM

OCLC CODE: LHA

ADDRESS: Interlibrary Loan
Frazar Memorial Library
McNeese State
University
Lake Charles, LA 70609

TELEPHONE: (318) 477-2520,
X454/270

LIST NAMES OF BRANCHES WITH
SEPARATE POLICIES: None

BOOKS:
Will Lend: Yes
Length of Loan: 4 weeks
Renewable: Yes, for 1 week
Charges: None
Average Turnaround Time:
1-3 days
If you have indicated that a
book is not to be lent, will
you on receipt of a letter
from the requesting library
search the index for given
entries? (Not answered)

PERIODICALS:
Bound: Will not lend
Unbound: Will not lend
Loan Period: N/A
Renewable: N/A
May lend if article exceeds
50 pages

MICROFORMS:
Will Lend: Yes
Specific Types of Microforms:
Film, fiche, cards

GOVERNMENT PUBLICATIONS:
Will Lend: Yes

DISSERTATIONS:
Will Lend: Yes, on microfilm

THESES:
Will Lend: Yes, on microfilm

AUDIO-VISUAL MATERIALS:
Records: Will not lend
Cassettes: Will not lend
Other (slides, filmstrips,
etc.): Will not lend

COMPUTER SOFTWARE:
Will Lend: No

PHOTODUPLICATION SERVICE:
No charge up to 0 exposures
Charge Per Exposure: 10¢
Minimum/handling Fee: $1.50
minimum; no handling fee
Average Turnaround Time:
1-3 days

MICROFILMING SERVICE:
Service Available: No
Charges: N/A

DO YOU CHARGE THE BORROWING
LIBRARY FOR POSTAGE? No

FOR HOW LONG DO YOU SUSPEND ILL
SERVICE OVER THE CHRISTMAS
HOLIDAYS? Dec.15-Jan.5

ARE THERE ANY GROUPS OF LIBRARIES
FOR WHICH YOU WAIVE FEES? IF
SO, PLEASE NAME THEM:
Louisiana OCLC data base
users--reciprocal agreement
which includes xeroxing up
to $100.00 assessed at 10¢
per exposure

NEW ORLEANS PUBLIC LIBRARY

NUC CODE: LN

OCLC CODE: LNC

ADDRESS: Interlibrary Loan
New Orleans Public
Library
219 Loyola Ave.
New Orleans, LA 70140

TELEPHONE: (504) 524-7382

LIST NAMES OF BRANCHES WITH
SEPARATE POLICIES:
Louisiana Division has
special regulations
regarding loan of archival
and genealogical materials

BOOKS:
Will Lend: Yes
Length of Loan: 3 weeks
Renewable: Yes
Charges: None
Average Turnaround Time:
1 week
If you have indicated that a
book is not to be lent, will
you on receipt of a letter
from the requesting library
search the index for given
entries? Yes, staff time
permitting

PERIODICALS:
Bound: Will lend
Unbound: Will not lend
Loan Period: 1 week
Renewable: No
Will lend if article exceeds
50 pages

MICROFORMS:
Will Lend: Yes
Specific Types of Microforms:
U. S. Census tracts except
for Louisiana; newspapers;
theses; dissertations

GOVERNMENT PUBLICATIONS:
Will Lend: Yes

DISSERTATIONS:
Will Lend: Yes

THESES:
Will Lend: Yes

AUDIO-VISUAL MATERIALS:
Records: Will not lend
Cassettes: Will not lend
Other (slides, filmstrips,
etc.): Will not lend

COMPUTER SOFTWARE:
Will Lend: No

PHOTODUPLICATION SERVICE:
No charge up to 25 exposures
Charge Per Exposure: 25¢
Minimum/handling Fee: None
Average Turnaround Time:
1 week

MICROFILMING SERVICE:
Service Available: No
Charges: N/A

DO YOU CHARGE THE BORROWING
LIBRARY FOR POSTAGE? No

FOR HOW LONG DO YOU SUSPEND ILL
SERVICE OVER THE CHRISTMAS
HOLIDAYS? No suspension

ARE THERE ANY GROUPS OF LIBRARIES
FOR WHICH YOU WAIVE FEES? IF
SO, PLEASE NAME THEM: None

SHREVE MEMORIAL LIBRARY

NUC CODE: None

OCLC CODE: None

ADDRESS: Interlibrary Loan
            Shreve Memorial Library
            P. O. Box 21523
            424 Texas St.
            Shreveport, LA 71120

TELEPHONE: (318) 226-5878

LIST NAMES OF BRANCHES WITH
   SEPARATE POLICIES: None

BOOKS:
   Will Lend: Yes
   Length of Loan: 1 month
   Renewable: Yes
   Charges: None
   Average Turnaround Time:
      (Not answered)
   If you have indicated that a
      book is not to be lent, will
      you on receipt of a letter
      from the requesting library
      search the index for given
      entries? Yes

PERIODICALS:
   Bound: Will not lend
   Unbound: Will not lend
   Loan Period: N/A
   Renewable: N/A
   Will lend if article exceeds
   _____ number of pages (Will
      not lend, regardless of
      length of article)

MICROFORMS:
   Will Lend: No
   Specific Types of Microforms:
   N/A

GOVERNMENT PUBLICATIONS:
   Will Lend: No

DISSERTATIONS:
   Will Lend: No

THESES:
   Will Lend: No

AUDIO-VISUAL MATERIALS:
   Records: Will not lend
   Cassettes: Will not lend
   Other (slides, filmstrips,
      etc.): Will not lend

COMPUTER SOFTWARE:
   Will Lend: No

PHOTODUPLICATION SERVICE:
   No charge up to 10 exposures
   Charge Per Exposure: 10¢
   Minimum/handling Fee: None
   Average Turnaround Time:
      (Not answered)

MICROFILMING SERVICE:
   Service Available: Yes
   Charges: 25¢ per page

DO YOU CHARGE THE BORROWING
   LIBRARY FOR POSTAGE? No

FOR HOW LONG DO YOU SUSPEND ILL
   SERVICE OVER THE CHRISTMAS
   HOLIDAYS? No suspension

ARE THERE ANY GROUPS OF LIBRARIES
   FOR WHICH YOU WAIVE FEES? IF
   SO, PLEASE NAME THEM: None

SOUTHEASTERN LOUISIANA UNIVERSITY

NUC CODE: LHS

OCLC CODE: LSH

ADDRESS: Interlibrary Loan
            Southeastern Louisiana
               University Library
            P. O. Drawer 896
            Hammond, LA 70402

TELEPHONE: (504) 549-2027

LIST NAMES OF BRANCHES WITH
   SEPARATE POLICIES:
   SLU Nursing Library
   Baton Rouge Nursing Center
   4849 Essen Lane
   Baton Rouge, LA 70809

BOOKS:
   Will Lend: Yes
   Length of Loan: 28 days
   Renewable: Yes
   Charges: None
   Average Turnaround Time:
      1 week
   If you have indicated that a
      book is not to be lent, will
      you on receipt of a letter
      from the requesting library
      search the index for given
      entries? Will photocopy in
      non-circulating books

PERIODICALS:
   Bound: Will not lend
   Unbound: Will not lend
   Loan Period: N/A
   Renewable: N/A
   Will lend if article exceeds
      50 pages. Exceptions are
      made on an individual basis

MICROFORMS:
   Will Lend: Yes
   Specific Types of Microforms:
   Microfiche, microcard,
   microfilm, PCMI

GOVERNMENT PUBLICATIONS:
   Will Lend: Yes

DISSERTATIONS:
   Will Lend: No

THESES:
   Will Lend: Yes

AUDIO-VISUAL MATERIALS:
   Records: Will lend
   Cassettes: Will lend
   Other (slides, filmstrips,
      etc.): Will lend

COMPUTER SOFTWARE:
   Will Lend: Do not own

PHOTODUPLICATION SERVICE:
   No charge up to 10 exposures
   Charge Per Exposure: 15¢
   Minimum/handling Fee: None
   Average Turnaround Time:
      1 week

MICROFILMING SERVICE:
   Service Available: No
   Charges: N/A

DO YOU CHARGE THE BORROWING
   LIBRARY FOR POSTAGE? No

FOR HOW LONG DO YOU SUSPEND ILL
   SERVICE OVER THE CHRISTMAS
   HOLIDAYS? No suspension

ARE THERE ANY GROUPS OF LIBRARIES
   FOR WHICH YOU WAIVE FEES? IF
   SO, PLEASE NAME THEM: SOLINET
   participants; basically, we
   will not charge anyone who
   does not charge us

TULANE UNIVERSITY

NUC CODE: LNT

OCLC CODE: LRU

ADDRESS: Interlibrary Loan
Tulane University
Library
New Orleans, LA 70118

TELEPHONE: (504) 865-5608

LIST NAMES OF BRANCHES WITH
SEPARATE POLICIES:
Tulane Law School Library
Tulane Medical School
Library
Norman Mayer Library

BOOKS:
Will Lend: Yes
Length of Loan: 2 weeks
Renewable: Yes
Charges: None
Average Turnaround Time:
3 days
If you have indicated that a
book is not to be lent, will
you on receipt of a letter
from the requesting library
search the index for given
entries? (Not answered)

PERIODICALS:
Bound: Will not lend
Unbound: Will not lend
Loan Period: N/A
Renewable: N/A
Will lend if article exceeds
50 pages

MICROFORMS:
Will Lend: Yes
Specific Types of Microforms:
(Not answered)

GOVERNMENT PUBLICATIONS:
Will Lend: Yes

DISSERTATIONS:
Will Lend: Yes, pre-1956

THESES:
Will Lend: Yes, pre-1956

AUDIO-VISUAL MATERIALS:
Records: Will not lend
Cassettes: Will not lend
Other (slides, filmstrips,
etc.): Will not lend

COMPUTER SOFTWARE:
Will Lend: No

PHOTODUPLICATION SERVICE:
No charge up to 0 exposures
Charge Per Exposure: 10¢
Minimum/handling Fee: $1.50
Average Turnaround Time:
3 days

MICROFILMING SERVICE:
Service Available: No
Charges: N/A

DO YOU CHARGE THE BORROWING
LIBRARY FOR POSTAGE? No

FOR HOW LONG DO YOU SUSPEND ILL
SERVICE OVER THE CHRISTMAS
HOLIDAYS? Dec.14-Jan.4

ARE THERE ANY GROUPS OF LIBRARIES
FOR WHICH YOU WAIVE FEES? IF
SO, PLEASE NAME THEM: RLG

TULANE UNIVERSITY MEDICAL CENTER

NUC CODE: LNT-M

OCLC CODE: (Not answered)

ADDRESS: Interlibrary Loan
Medical Library
Tulane University
Medical Center
1430 Tulane Ave.
New Orleans, LA 70112

TELEPHONE: (504) 588-5155

LIST NAMES OF BRANCHES WITH
SEPARATE POLICIES: None

BOOKS:
Will Lend: Yes
Length of Loan: 2 weeks
Renewable: Yes
Charges: $4.00
Average Turnaround Time:
2 days
If you have indicated that a
book is not to be lent, will
you on receipt of a letter
from the requesting library
search the index for given
entries? (Not answered)

PERIODICALS:
Bound: Will lend for special
reasons only
Unbound: Will lend for
special reasons only
Loan Period: 1 week
Renewable: Yes, for special
reasons only
Will lend if article exceeds
40 pages

MICROFORMS:
Will Lend: No
Specific Types of Microforms:
N/A

GOVERNMENT PUBLICATIONS:
Will Lend: Yes

DISSERTATIONS:
Will Lend: Yes

THESES:
Will Lend: Yes

AUDIO-VISUAL MATERIALS:
Records: Will not lend
Cassettes: Will not lend
Other (slides, filmstrips,
etc.): Will not lend

COMPUTER SOFTWARE:
Will Lend: No

PHOTODUPLICATION SERVICE:
No charge up to 0 exposures
Charges: $4.00
Average Turnaround Time:
2 days

MICROFILMING SERVICE:
Service Available: No
Charges: N/A

DO YOU CHARGE THE BORROWING
LIBRARY FOR POSTAGE?
Is included in $4.00 charge

FOR HOW LONG DO YOU SUSPEND ILL
SERVICE OVER THE CHRISTMAS
HOLIDAYS? 3 weeks

ARE THERE ANY GROUPS OF LIBRARIES
FOR WHICH YOU WAIVE FEES? IF
SO, PLEASE NAME THEM: None

UNIVERSITY OF NEW ORLEANS

NUC CODE: LNU

OCLC CODE: LNU

ADDRESS: Interlibrary Loan
Earl K. Long Library
University of New
Orleans
Lake Front
New Orleans, LA 70148

TELEPHONE: (504) 286-6548

LIST NAMES OF BRANCHES WITH
SEPARATE POLICIES: None

BOOKS:
Will Lend: Yes
Length of Loan: 4 weeks
Renewable: Yes, for 2 weeks
Charges: (Not answered)
Average Turnaround Time:
3 days
If you have indicated that a
book is not to be lent, will
you on receipt of a letter
from the requesting library
search the index for given
entries? (Not answered)

PERIODICALS:
Bound: Will not lend
Unbound: Will not lend
Loan Period: N/A
Renewable: N/A
Will lend if article exceeds
50 pages and journal is not
in demand here

MICROFORMS:
Will Lend: Yes
Specific Types of Microforms:
Film, fiche, card

GOVERNMENT PUBLICATIONS:
Will Lend: Yes

DISSERTATIONS:
Will Lend: Yes, if 2nd copy
available

THESES:
Will Lend: Yes, if 2nd copy
available

AUDIO-VISUAL MATERIALS:
Records: Will not lend
Cassettes: Will not lend
Other (slides, filmstrips,
etc.): Will not lend

COMPUTER SOFTWARE:
Will Lend: No

PHOTODUPLICATION SERVICE:
No charge up to 0 exposures
Charge Per Exposure: 10¢
Minimum/handling Fee: $1.00
in-state; $2.00 out-of-
state
Average Turnaround Time:
4 days

MICROFILMING SERVICE:
Service Available: No
Charges: N/A

DO YOU CHARGE THE BORROWING
LIBRARY FOR POSTAGE? Only
for first-class

FOR HOW LONG DO YOU SUSPEND ILL
SERVICE OVER THE CHRISTMAS
HOLIDAYS? Dec.15-Jan.4

ARE THERE ANY GROUPS OF LIBRARIES
FOR WHICH YOU WAIVE FEES? IF
SO, PLEASE NAME THEM:
Louisiana SOLINET member
libraries per OCLC-Ill
Agreement, 1980

UNIVERSITY OF SOUTHWESTERN LOUISIANA

NUC CODE: LLafS

OCLC CODE: LWA

ADDRESS: Interlibrary Loan
Dupre Library
University of South-
western Louisiana
302 E. St. Mary Blvd.
Lafayette, LA 70504

TELEPHONE: (318) 231-6035

LIST NAMES OF BRANCHES WITH
SEPARATE POLICIES: None

BOOKS:
Will Lend: Yes
Length of Loan: 1 month
Renewable: Yes
Charges: None
Average Turnaround Time:
2 days
If you have indicated that a
book is not to be lent, will
you on receipt of a letter
from the requesting library
search the index for given
entries? Yes

PERIODICALS:
Bound: Will not lend
Unbound: Will not lend
Loan Period: N/A
Renewable: N/A
Will lend if article exceeds
_____ number of pages (Not
answered)

MICROFORMS:
Will Lend: Yes, sometimes
Specific Types of Microforms:
Microfiche, microcard

GOVERNMENT PUBLICATIONS:
Will Lend: Yes

DISSERTATIONS:
Will Lend: Yes

THESES:
Will Lend: Yes

AUDIO-VISUAL MATERIALS:
Records: Will not lend
Cassettes: Will not lend
Other (slides, filmstrips,
etc.): Will not lend

COMPUTER SOFTWARE:
Will Lend: No

PHOTODUPLICATION SERVICE:
No charge up to 0 exposures
Charge Per Exposure: 10¢
Minimum/handling Fee: $1.00
Average Turnaround Time:
2 days

MICROFILMING SERVICE:
Service Available: Yes
Charges: $8.00 per roll

DO YOU CHARGE THE BORROWING
LIBRARY FOR POSTAGE? No

FOR HOW LONG DO YOU SUSPEND ILL
SERVICE OVER THE CHRISTMAS
HOLIDAYS? Dec.18-Jan.2

ARE THERE ANY GROUPS OF LIBRARIES
FOR WHICH YOU WAIVE FEES? IF
SO, PLEASE NAME THEM:
Libraries with whom we have
reciprocal agreements;
Louisiana SOLINET libraries

XAVIER UNIVERSITY

NUC CODE: None

OCLC CODE: LNX

ADDRESS: Interlibrary Loan
          Xavier University
            Library
          Pine & Palmetto Sts.
          New Orleans, LA 70125

TELEPHONE: (504) 483-7304

LIST NAMES OF BRANCHES WITH
  SEPARATE POLICIES: None

BOOKS:
    Will Lend: Yes
    Length of Loan: 4 weeks
    Renewable: Yes
    Charges: Charge libraries
      that charge us
    Average Turnaround Time:
      2 days
    If you have indicated that a
      book is not to be lent, will
      you on receipt of a letter
      from the requesting library
      search the index for given
      entries? Yes

PERIODICALS:
    Bound: Will not lend
    Unbound: Will not lend
    Loan Period: N/A
    Renewable: N/A
    Will lend if article exceeds
      _____ number of pages (Will
      not lend, regardless of
      length of article)

MICROFORMS:
    Will Lend: Yes
    Specific Types of Microforms:
      (Not answered)

GOVERNMENT PUBLICATIONS:
    Will Lend: Yes

DISSERTATIONS:
    Will Lend: No

THESES:
    Will Lend: No

AUDIO-VISUAL MATERIALS:
    Records: Will not lend
    Cassettes: Will not lend
    Other (slides, filmstrips,
      etc.): Will not lend

COMPUTER SOFTWARE:
    Will Lend: Do not own

PHOTODUPLICATION SERVICE:
    No charge up to 20 exposures
    Charge Per Exposure: Charge
      libraries that charge us
    Minimum/handling Fee: None
    Average Turnaround Time:
      2 days

MICROFILMING SERVICE:
    Service Available: No
    Charges: N/A

DO YOU CHARGE THE BORROWING
  LIBRARY FOR POSTAGE? No

FOR HOW LONG DO YOU SUSPEND ILL
  SERVICE OVER THE CHRISTMAS
  HOLIDAYS? Dec.18-Jan.5

ARE THERE ANY GROUPS OF LIBRARIES
  FOR WHICH YOU WAIVE FEES? IF
  SO, PLEASE NAME THEM: AMIGOS;
  Louisiana SOLINET

BANGOR PUBLIC LIBRARY

NUC CODE: MeBa

OCLC CODE: BYN

ADDRESS: Interlibrary Loan
           Bangor Public Library
           145 Harlow St.
           Bangor, ME 04401

TELEPHONE: (207) 947-8336

LIST NAMES OF BRANCHES WITH
   SEPARATE POLICIES: None

BOOKS:
   Will Lend: Yes
   Length of Loan: 3 weeks
   Renewable: Yes
   Charges: (Not answered)
   Average Turnaround Time:
   48 hours
   If you have indicated that a
   book is not to be lent, will
   you on receipt of a letter
   from the requesting library
   search the index for given
   entries? Yes

PERIODICALS:
   Bound: Will not lend
   Unbound: Will lend
   Loan Period: 1 week
   Renewable: Yes
   Will lend if article exceeds
   _____ number of pages (Not
   answered)

MICROFORMS:
   Will Lend: No
   Specific Types of Microforms:
   N/A

GOVERNMENT PUBLICATIONS:
   Will Lend: Yes

DISSERTATIONS:
   Will Lend: Do not own

THESES:
   Will lend: Do not own

AUDIO-VISUAL MATERIALS:
   Records: (Not answered)
   Cassettes: (Not answered)
   Other (slides, filmstrips,
   etc.): (Not answered)

COMPUTER SOFTWARE:
   Will Lend: (Not answered)

PHOTODUPLICATION SERVICE:
   No charge up to 10 exposures
   Charge Per Exposure: 10¢
   Minimum/handling Fee: (Not
   answered)
   Average Turnaround Time:
   48 hours

MICROFILMING SERVICE:
   Service Available: No
   Charges: N/A

DO YOU CHARGE THE BORROWING
   LIBRARY FOR POSTAGE? No

FOR HOW LONG DO YOU SUSPEND ILL
   SERVICE OVER THE CHRISTMAS
   HOLIDAYS? No suspension

ARE THERE ANY GROUPS OF LIBRARIES
   FOR WHICH YOU WAIVE FEES? IF
   SO, PLEASE NAME THEM: NELINET
   reciprocal borrowing
   agreement

BATES COLLEGE

NUC CODE: MeLB

OCLC CODE: BTS

ADDRESS: Interlibrary Loan
           Bates College
           Library
           Lewiston, ME 04240

TELEPHONE: (207) 784-2949

LIST NAMES OF BRANCHES WITH
   SEPARATE POLICIES: None

BOOKS:
   Will Lend: Yes
   Length of Loan: 4 weeks
   Renewable: Not usually
   Charges: (Not answered)
   Average Turnaround Time:
   2 days
   If you have indicated that a
   book is not to be lent, will
   you on receipt of a letter
   from the requesting library
   search the index for given
   entries? Yes

PERIODICALS:
   Bound: Will lend
   Unbound: Will occasionally
   lend
   Loan Period: 1 week
   Renewable: Not usually
   Will lend if article exceeds
   30 pages

MICROFORMS:
   Will Lend: Yes
   Specific Types of Microforms:
   Microfilm, microfiche,
   ultrafiche, microcard

GOVERNMENT PUBLICATIONS:
   Will Lend: Yes

DISSERTATIONS:
   Will Lend: No

THESES:
   Will Lend: No

AUDIO-VISUAL MATERIALS:
   Records: Will not lend
   Cassettes: Will not lend
   Other (slides, filmstrips,
   etc.): Will not lend

COMPUTER SOFTWARE:
   Will Lend: No

PHOTODUPLICATION SERVICE:
   No charge up to 0 exposures
   Charge Per Exposure: 10¢
   Minimum/handling Fee: $1.00
   Average Turnaround Time:
   2 days

MICROFILMING SERVICE:
   Service Available: No
   Charges: N/A

DO YOU CHARGE THE BORROWING
   LIBRARY FOR POSTAGE? Only if
   other than library rate.

FOR HOW LONG DO YOU SUSPEND ILL
   SERVICE OVER THE CHRISTMAS
   HOLIDAYS? 2-3 weeks, but
   still handle photocopy
   requests

ARE THERE ANY GROUPS OF LIBRARIES
   FOR WHICH YOU WAIVE FEES? IF
   SO, PLEASE NAME THEM:
   Reciprocating libraries in
   the state of Maine; NELINET
   ILL agreement signatories

BOWDOIN COLLEGE

NUC CODE: MeB

OCLC CODE: BBH

ADDRESS: Interlibrary Loan
Bowdoin College
Library
Brunswick, ME 04011

TELEPHONE: (207) 725-8731, X283

LIST NAMES OF BRANCHES WITH
SEPARATE POLICIES: None

BOOKS:
Will Lend: Yes
Length of Loan: 4 weeks use
Renewable: No
Charges: None, or based on
reciprocity
Average Turnaround Time:
3 days
If you have indicated that a
book is not to be lent, will
you on receipt of a letter
from the requesting library
search the index for given
entries? Yes

PERIODICALS:
Bound: Will lend
Unbound: Will not lend
Loan Period: 2 weeks use
Renewable: No
Will lend if article exceeds
_____ number of pages (Not
answered)

MICROFORMS:
Will Lend: Yes
Specific Types of Microforms:
35 mm reel, fiche

GOVERNMENT PUBLICATIONS:
Will Lend: Yes

DISSERTATIONS:
Will Lend: Do not own

THESES:
Will Lend: Do not own

AUDIO-VISUAL MATERIALS:
Records: Will not lend
Cassettes: Do not own
Other (slides, filmstrips,
etc.): Do not own

COMPUTER SOFTWARE:
Will Lend: Do not own

PHOTODUPLICATION SERVICE:
No charge up to 0 exposures
Charge Per Exposure: 10¢ (or
reciprocal costs)
Minimum/handling Fee: $1.00
(or reciprocal costs)
Average Turnaround Time:
3 days

MICROFILMING SERVICE:
Service Available: No
Charges: N/A

DO YOU CHARGE THE BORROWING
LIBRARY FOR POSTAGE? No

FOR HOW LONG DO YOU SUSPEND ILL
SERVICE OVER THE CHRISTMAS
HOLIDAYS? Mid-December to
mid-January

ARE THERE ANY GROUPS OF LIBRARIES
FOR WHICH YOU WAIVE FEES? IF
SO, PLEASE NAME THEM: Signa-
tories of NELINET ILL Code

MAINE STATE LIBRARY

NUC CODE: ME

OCLC CODE: MEA

ADDRESS: Interlibrary Loan
Maine State Library
Cultural Bldg. Sta. 64
Augusta, ME 04333

TELEPHONE: (207) 289-3328

LIST NAMES OF BRANCHES WITH
SEPARATE POLICIES: None

BOOKS:
Will Lend: Yes
Length of Loan: 2 weeks
Renewable: No
Charges: None
Average Turnaround Time:
(Not answered)
If you have indicated that a
book is not to be lent, will
you on receipt of a letter
from the requesting library
search the index for given
entries? Yes

PERIODICALS:
Bound: Will not lend
Unbound: Will lend
Loan Period: 2 weeks
Renewable: No
Will lend if article exceeds
_____ number of pages (Not
answered)

MICROFORMS:
Will Lend: No
Specific Types of Microforms:
N/A

GOVERNMENT PUBLICATIONS:
Will Lend: Yes

DISSERTATIONS:
Will Lend: Do not own

THESES:
Will Lend: Do not own

AUDIO-VISUAL MATERIALS:
Records: Do not own
Cassettes: Do not own
Other (slides, filmstrips,
etc.): Do not own

COMPUTER SOFTWARE:
Will Lend: Do not own

PHOTODUPLICATION SERVICE:
No charge up to 10 exposures
Charge Per Exposure: 10¢
Minimum/handling Fee: None
Average Turnaround Time:
3 weeks

MICROFILMING SERVICE:
Service Available: No
Charges: N/A

DO YOU CHARGE THE BORROWING
LIBRARY FOR POSTAGE? No

FOR HOW LONG DO YOU SUSPEND ILL
SERVICE OVER THE CHRISTMAS
HOLIDAYS? No suspension

ARE THERE ANY GROUPS OF LIBRARIES
FOR WHICH YOU WAIVE FEES? IF
SO, PLEASE NAME THEM: Members
of NELINET

UNIVERSITY OF MAINE

NUC CODE: MeU

OCLC CODE: MEU

ADDRESS: Interlibrary Loan
Fogler Library
University of Maine
Orono, ME 04469

TELEPHONE: (207) 581-7451

LIST NAMES OF BRANCHES WITH
SEPARATE POLICIES: None

BOOKS:
Will Lend: Yes
Length of Loan: 4 weeks,
subject to recall after
2 weeks
Renewable: No
Charges: None
Average Turnaround Time:
24 hours
If you have indicated that a
book is not to be lent, will
you on receipt of a letter
from the requesting library
search the index for given
entries? (Not answered)

PERIODICALS:
Bound: Will not lend
Unbound: Will not lend
Loan Period: N/A
Renewable: N/A
Will lend if article exceeds
_____ number of pages (Will
not lend, regardless of
length of article)

MICROFORMS:
Will Lend: Yes
Specific Types of Microforms:
Will loan cards and film for
4 weeks. Do not loan fiche,
but will reproduce fiche at
35¢ per sheet, plus handling
charge of $2.50

GOVERNMENT PUBLICATIONS:
Will Lend: Yes, for 2 weeks
in-library use only

DISSERTATIONS:
Will Lend: No

THESES:
Will Lend: Yes, for 4 weeks
in-library use only

AUDIO-VISUAL MATERIALS:
Records: Will not lend
Cassettes: Will not lend
Other (slides, filmstrips,
etc.): Will not lend

COMPUTER SOFTWARE:
Will Lend: Do not own

PHOTODUPLICATION SERVICE:
No charge up to 0 exposures
Charge Per Exposure: 10¢
Handling Fee: $2.50
Average Turnaround Time:
24 hours

MICROFILMING SERVICE:
Service Available: No
Charges: N/A

DO YOU CHARGE THE BORROWING
LIBRARY FOR POSTAGE? No

FOR HOW LONG DO YOU SUSPEND ILL
SERVICE OVER THE CHRISTMAS
HOLIDAYS? No suspension

ARE THERE ANY GROUPS OF LIBRARIES
FOR WHICH YOU WAIVE FEES? IF
SO, PLEASE NAME THEM: None

UNIVERSITY OF SOUTHERN MAINE

NUC CODE: MeU-P

OCLC CODE: PGP

ADDRESS: Interlibrary Loan
Gorham Campus Library
University of Southern
Maine
Gorham, ME 04038
(207) 780-5344

and

Interlibrary Loan
Portland Campus Library
University of Southern
Maine
96 Falmouth St.
Portland, ME 04103
(207) 780-5379

LIST NAMES OF BRANCHES WITH
SEPARATE POLICIES: None

BOOKS:
Will Lend: Yes
Length of Loan: 4 weeks,
including mailing
Renewable: No
Charges: None
Average Turnaround Time:
4 days maximum
If you have indicated that a
book is not to be lent, will
you on receipt of a letter
from the requesting library
search the index for given
entries? (Not answered)

PERIODICALS:
Bound: Will not lend
Unbound: Will not lend
Loan Period: N/A
Renewable: N/A
Will lend if article exceeds
20 pages

MICROFORMS:
Will Lend: No
Specific Types of Microforms:
N/A

GOVERNMENT PUBLICATIONS:
Will Lend: (Not answered)

DISSERTATIONS:
Will Lend: Yes

THESES:
Will Lend: Yes

AUDIO-VISUAL MATERIALS:
Records: Will not lend
Cassettes: Will not lend
Other (slides, filmstrips,
etc.): Will not lend

COMPUTER SOFTWARE:
Will Lend: No

PHOTODUPLICATION SERVICE:
No charge up to 0 exposures
Charge Per Exposure: 10¢
Minimum/handling Fee: $1.50
including 10 pages
Average Turnaround Time:
4 days maximum

MICROFILMING SERVICE:
Service Available: Yes
Charges: 10¢ per page

DO YOU CHARGE THE BORROWING
LIBRARY FOR POSTAGE? No

FOR HOW LONG DO YOU SUSPEND ILL
SERVICE OVER THE CHRISTMAS
HOLIDAYS? 10 days

ARE THRERE ANY GROUPS OF LIBRARIES
FOR WHICH YOU WAIVE FEES? IF
SO, PLEASE NAME THEM:
Reciprocal agreements; health/
hospital libraries in Maine

ANNAPOLIS AREA LIBRARY

NUC CODE: (Not answered)

OCLC CODE: (Not answered)

ADDRESS: Interlibrary Loan
Annapolis Area Library
1410 West St.
Annapolis, MD 21401

TELEPHONE: (301) 224-7501

LIST NAMES OF BRANCHES WITH
SEPARATE POLICIES: None

BOOKS:
Will Lend: Yes
Length of Loan: 3-4 weeks
Renewable: Yes
Charges: (Not answered)
Average Turnaround Time:
(Not answered)
If you have indicated that a
book is not to be lent, will
you on receipt of a letter
from the requesting library
search the index for given
entries? (Not answered)

PERIODICALS:
Bound: Will not lend
Unbound: Will not lend
Loan Period: N/A
Renewable: N/A
Will lend if article exceeds
_____ number of pages (Not
answered)

MICROFORMS:
Will Lend: No
Specific Types of Microforms:
N/A

GOVERNMENT PUBLICATIONS:
Will Lend: Do not own

DISSERTATIONS:
Will Lend: Do not own

THESES:
Will Lend: Do not own

AUDIO-VISUAL MATERIALS:
Records: Will lend
Cassettes: Will lend
Other (slides, filmstrips,
etc.): Will lend

COMPUTER SOFTWARE:
Will Lend: Do not lend

PHOTODUPLICATION SERVICE:
No charge up to 50 exposures
Charge Per Exposure: 10¢
Minimum/handling Fee: None
Average Turnaround Time:
1 week

MICROFILMING SERVICE:
Service Available: No
Charges: N/A

DO YOU CHARGE THE BORROWING
LIBRARY FOR POSTAGE? No

FOR HOW LONG DO YOU SUSPEND ILL
SERVICE OVER THE CHRISTMAS
HOLIDAYS? No suspension

ARE THERE ANY GROUPS OF LIBRARIES
FOR WHICH YOU WAIVE FEES? IF
SO, PLEASE NAME THEM: None

COPPIN STATE COLLEGE

NUC CODE: (Not answered)

OCLC CODE: MDP

ADDRESS: Interlibrary Loan
Parlett Moore Library
Coppin State College
2500 West North Ave.
Baltimore, MD 21216

TELEPHONE: (301) 383-5926

LIST NAMES OF BRANCHES WITH
SEPARATE POLICIES: None

BOOKS:
Will Lend: Yes
Length of Loan: 4 weeks
Renewable: Yes
Charges: None
Average Turnaround Time:
(Not answered)
If you have indicated that a
book is not to be lent, will
you on receipt of a letter
from the requesting library
search the index for given
entries? Yes

PERIODICALS:
Bound: Will not lend
Unbound: Will not lend
Loan Period: N/A
Renewable: N/A
Will lend if article exceeds
_____ number of pages (Will
not lend, regardless of
length of article)

MICROFORMS:
Will Lend: No
Specific Types of Microforms:
N/A

GOVERNMENT PUBLICATIONS:
Will Lend: No

DISSERTATIONS:
Will Lend: No

THESES:
Will Lend: No

AUDIO-VISUAL MATERIALS:
Records: Will not lend
Cassettes: Will not lend
Other (slides, filmstrips,
etc.): Will not lend

COMPUTER SOFTWARE:
Will Lend: No

PHOTODUPLICATION SERVICE:
No charge up to any exposures
Charge Per Exposure: None
Minimum/handling Fee: None
Average Turnaround Time:
(Not answered)

MICROFILMING SERVICE:
Service Available: No
Charges: N/A

DO YOU CHARGE THE BORROWING
LIBRARY FOR POSTAGE? No

FOR HOW LONG DO YOU SUSPEND ILL
SERVICE OVER THE CHRISTMAS
HOLIDAYS? 2 weeks

ARE THERE ANY GROUPS OF LIBRARIES
FOR WHICH YOU WAIVE FEES? IF
SO, PLEASE NAME THEM: None

ENOCH PRATT FREE LIBRARY

NUC CODE: MdBE

OCLC CODE: (Not answered)

ADDRESS: MILO-Central
Enoch Pratt Free
Library
400 Cathedral St.
Baltimore, MD 21201

TELEPHONE: (301) 396-5498

LIST NAMES OF BRANCHES WITH
SEPARATE POLICIES: None

BOOKS:
Will Lend: Yes
Length of Loan: 3 weeks
Renewable: No
Charges: (Not answered)
Average Turnaround Time:
(Not answered)
If you have indicated that a
book is not to be lent, will
you on receipt of a letter
from the requesting library
search the index for given
entries? (Not answered)

PERIODICALS:
Bound: Will not lend
Unbound: Will not lend
Loan Period: N/A
Renewable: N/A
Will lend if article exceeds
_____ number of pages (Not
answered)

MICROFORMS:
Will Lend: No
Specific Types of Microforms:
N/A

GOVERNMENT PUBLICATIONS:
Will Lend: (Not answered)

DISSERTATIONS:
Will Lend: (Not answered)

THESES:
Will Lend: (Not answered)

AUDIO-VISUAL MATERIALS:
Records: (Not answered)
Cassettes: (Not answered)
Other (slides, filmstrips,
etc.): (Not answered)

COMPUTER SOFTWARE:
Will Lend: (Not answered)

PHOTODUPLICATION SERVICE:
No charge up to 7 exposures
Charge Per Exposure: 15¢
Minimum Fee: $1.00
Average Turnaround Time:
(Not answered)

MICROFILMING SERVICE:
Service Available: Yes
Charges: Varies

DO YOU CHARGE THE BORROWING
LIBRARY FOR POSTAGE? Yes

FOR HOW LONG DO YOU SUSPEND ILL
SERVICE OVER THE CHRISTMAS
HOLIDAYS? (Not answered)

ARE THERE ANY GROUPS OF LIBRARIES
FOR WHICH YOU WAIVE FEES? IF
SO, PLEASE NAME THEM: (Not
answered)

JOHNS HOPKINS UNIVERSITY

NUC CODE: MdBJ

OCLC CODE: JHE

ADDRESS: Interlibrary Loan
Milton S. Eisenhower
Library
Johns Hopkins
University
Baltimore, MD 21218

TELEPHONE: (301) 338-8358

LIST NAMES OF BRANCHES WITH
SEPARATE POLICIES: (Not
answered)

BOOKS:
Will Lend: Yes
Length of Loan: 2 weeks
Renewable: Yes, once
Charges: $10.00 (up to 4
volumes per title)
Average Turnaround Time:
(Not answered)
If you have indicated that a
book is not to be lent, will
you on receipt of a letter
from the requesting library
search the index for given
entries? (Not answered)

PERIODICALS:
Bound: Will not lend
Unbound: Will not lend
Loan Period: N/A
Renewable: N/A
Will lend if article exceeds
_____ number of pages (Not
answered)

MICROFORMS:
Will Lend: No
Specific Types of Microforms:
N/A

GOVERNMENT PUBLICATIONS:
Will Lend: (Not answered)

DISSERTATIONS:
Will Lend: No; 1965 to
present available from
University Microfilms

THESES:
Will Lend: No

AUDIO-VISUAL MATERIALS:
Records: (Not answered)
Cassettes: (Not answered)
Other (slides, filmstrips,
etc.): (Not answered)

COMPUTER SOFTWARE:
Will Lend: (Not answered)

PHOTODUPLICATION SERVICE:
No charge up to 0 exposures
Charge Per Exposure: 15¢
Minimum Fee: $5.00 for 1-20
exposures
Average Turnaround Time:
(Not answered)

MICROFILMING SERVICE:
Service Available: Yes
Charges: 10¢ per frame plus
$7.50 handling charge

DO YOU CHARGE THE BORROWING
LIBRARY FOR POSTAGE? (Not
answered)

FOR HOW LONG DO YOU SUSPEND ILL
SERVICE OVER THE CHRISTMAS
HOLIDAYS? (Not answered)

ARE THERE ANY GROUPS OF LIBRARIES
FOR WHICH YOU WAIVE FEES? IF
SO, PLEASE NAME THEM: RLG;
MILO

JOHNS HOPKINS UNIVERSITY--MEDICAL SCHOOL

NUC CODE: MDBJW

OCLC CODE: JHW

ADDRESS: Interlibrary Loan
          Welch Medical Library
          Johns Hopkins
          University
          1900 E. Monument St.
          Baltimore, MD 21205

TELEPHONE: (301) 955-3596

LIST NAMES OF BRANCHES WITH
  SEPARATE POLICIES: None

BOOKS:
  Will Lend: Yes
  Length of Loan: 4 weeks
  Renewable: Yes
  Charges: $5.00 per request;
    $10.00 per request for
    commercial groups
  Average Turnaround Time:
    3-5 days
  If you have indicated that a
    book is not to be lent, will
    you on receipt of a letter
    from the requesting library
    search the index for given
    entries? (Not answered)

PERIODICALS:
  Bound: Will not lend
  Unbound: Will not lend
  Loan Period: N/A
  Renewable: N/A
  Will lend if article exceeds
    _____ number of pages (Not
    answered)

MICROFORMS:
  Will Lend: No
  Specific Types of Microforms:
    N/A

GOVERNMENT PUBLICATIONS:
  Will Lend: Yes

DISSERTATIONS:
  Will Lend: Yes, hardcopy
    format only

THESES:
  Will Lend: Yes, hardcopy
    format only

AUDIO-VISUAL MATERIALS:
  Records: Will lend in-state
    only
  Cassettes: Will lend in-
    state only
  Other (slides, filmstrips,
    etc.): Will lend in-state
    only

COMPUTER SOFTWARE:
  Will Lend: No

PHOTODUPLICATION SERVICE:
  No charge up to 0 exposures
  Charge Per Exposure: (Not
    answered)
  Minimum/handling Fee: $5.00
  Average Turnaround Time:
    (Not answered)

MICROFILMING SERVICE:
  Service Available: No
  Charges: N/A

DO YOU CHARGE THE BORROWING
  LIBRARY FOR POSTAGE? No

FOR HOW LONG DO YOU SUSPEND ILL
  SERVICE OVER THE CHRISTMAS
  HOLIDAYS? Approximately
  3 weeks

ARE THERE ANY GROUPS OF LIBRARIES
  FOR WHICH YOU WAIVE FEES? IF
  SO, PLEASE NAME THEM: None

NATIONAL AGRICULTURAL LIBRARY

NUC CODE: DNAL

OCLC CODE: AGL

ADDRESS: Interlibrary Loan
          National Agricultural
            Library
          Utilization Section
          Beltsville, MD 20705

TELEPHONE: (301) 344-3755

LIST NAMES OF BRANCHES WITH
  SEPARATE POLICIES: None

BOOKS:
  Will Lend: Yes
  Length of Loan: 1 month
  Renewable: Yes
  Charges: None
  Average Turnaround Time:
    2 weeks
  If you have indicated that a
    book is not to be lent, will
    you on receipt of a letter
    from the requesting library
    search the index for given
    entries? (Not answered)

PERIODICALS:
  Bound: Will not lend
  Unbound: Will not lend
  Loan Period: N/A
  Renewable: N/A
  Will lend if article exceeds
    _____ number of pages (Not
    answered)

MICROFORMS:
  Will Lend: No
  Specific Types of Microforms:
    N/A

GOVERNMENT PUBLICATIONS:
  Will Lend: Yes

DISSERTATIONS:
  Will Lend: Yes

THESES:
  Will Lend: Yes

AUDIO-VISUAL MATERIALS:
  Records: Will not lend
  Cassettes: Will not lend
  Other (slides, filmstrips,
    etc.): Will not lend

COMPUTER SOFTWARE:
  Will Lend: No

PHOTODUPLICATION SERVICE:
  No charge up to 0 exposures
  Charges:
    Electrostatic copy, micro-
    film and microfiche,
    $3.00 for up to 10 pages
    from single article or
    publication
  Minimum/handling Fee: $3.00
  Average Turnaround Time:
    2 weeks

MICROFILMING SERVICE:
  Service Available: Yes
  Charges: Duplication of
    NAL-owned microfilm, $10.00
    per reel; duplication of
    NAL-owned microfiche, $3.00
    for the first fiche and 50¢
    for each additional fiche

DO YOU CHARGE THE BORROWING
  LIBRARY FOR POSTAGE? No

FOR HOW LONG DO YOU SUSPEND ILL
  SERVICE OVER THE CHRISTMAS
  HOLIDAYS? No suspension

ARE THERE ANY GROUPS OF LIBRARIES
  FOR WHICH YOU WAIVE FEES? IF
  SO, PLEASE NAME THEM: Local
  Federal libraries

NATIONAL LIBRARY OF MEDICINE--HISTORY OF MEDICINE DIVISION

NUC CODE: DNLM

OCLC CODE: (Not answered)

ADDRESS: Interlibrary Loan
History of Medicine
Division
National Library of
Medicine
8600 Rockville Pike
Bethesda, MD 20209

TELEPHONE: (301) 496-5405

LIST NAMES OF BRANCHES WITH
SEPARATE POLICIES:
General Collection

BOOKS:
Will Lend: Yes, some 19th
century materials; will not
lend earlier materials
Length of Loan: 1 month
Renewable: No
Charges: (Not answered)
Average Turnaround Time:
(Not answered)
If you have indicated that a
book is not to be lent, will
you on receipt of a letter
from the requesting library
search the index for given
entries? Yes

PERIODICALS:
Bound: Will not lend
Unbound: Will not lend
Loan Period: N/A
Renewable: N/A
Will lend if article exceeds
_____ number of pages (Not
answered)

MICROFORMS:
Will Lend: Yes
Specific Types of Microforms:
Microfilm

GOVERNMENT PUBLICATIONS:
Will Lend: Do not own

DISSERTATIONS:
Will Lend: Judgment made on
individual basis

THESES:
Will Lend: Judgment made on
individual basis

AUDIO-VISUAL MATERIALS:
Records: (Not answered)
Cassettes: (Not answered)
Other (slides, filmstrips,
etc.): (Not answered)

COMPUTER SOFTWARE:
Will Lend: Do not own

PHOTODUPLICATION SERVICE:
No charge up to 50 exposures
Charge Per Additional
Exposure: 10¢ from hard-
copy; 5¢ from microcopy
Minimum/handling Fee: None
Average Turnaround Time:
(Not answered)

MICROFILMING SERVICE:
Service Available: Yes
Charges: $8.00 per reel

DO YOU CHARGE THE BORROWING
LIBRARY FOR POSTAGE? No

FOR HOW LONG DO YOU SUSPEND ILL
SERVICE OVER THE CHRISTMAS
HOLIDAYS? 1 month

ARE THERE ANY GROUPS OF LIBRARIES
FOR WHICH YOU WAIVE FEES? IF
SO, PLEASE NAME THEM:
Government agencies

NATIONAL OCEANIC AND ATMOSPHERIC ADMINISTRATION

NUC CODE: DWB, DAS, DME

OCLC CODE: OLA

ADDRESS: Interlibrary Loan
National Oceanic and
Atmospheric
Administration
LISD OA/D822
6009 Executive Blvd.
Rockville, MD 20852

TELEPHONE: (301) 443-8334

LIST NAMES OF BRANCHES WITH
SEPARATE POLICIES: None

BOOKS:
Will Lend: Yes
Length of Loan: 4 weeks
Renewable: Yes
Charges: None
Average Turnaround Time:
1 week
If you have indicated that a
book is not to be lent, will
you on receipt of a letter
from the requesting library
search the index for given
entries? (Not answered)

PERIODICALS:
Bound: Will lend
Unbound: Will lend
Loan Period: 2 weeks
Renewable: Yes
Will lend if article exceeds
20 pages

MICROFORMS:
Will Lend: Yes
Specific Types of Microforms:
(Not answered)

GOVERNMENT PUBLICATIONS:
Will Lend: Yes

DISSERTATIONS:
Will Lend: Yes

THESES:
Will Lend: Yes

AUDIO-VISUAL MATERIALS:
Records: (Not answered)
Cassettes: (Not answered)
Other (slides, filmstrips,
etc.): (Not answered)

COMPUTER SOFTWARE:
Will Lend: (Not answered)

PHOTODUPLICATION SERVICE:
No charge up to any exposures
Charge Per Exposure: None
Minimum/handling Fee: None
Average Turnaround Time:
1 week

MICROFILMING SERVICE:
Service Available: No
Charges: N/A

DO YOU CHARGE THE BORROWING
LIBRARY FOR POSTAGE? No

FOR HOW LONG DO YOU SUSPEND ILL
SERVICE OVER THE CHRISTMAS
HOLIDAYS? No suspension

ARE THERE ANY GROUPS OF LIBRARIES
FOR WHICH YOU WAIVE FEES? IF
SO, PLEASE NAME THEM: No fees
charged

PRINCE GEORGE'S COUNTY MEMORIAL LIBRARY

NUC CODE: (Not answered)

OCLC CODE: (Not answered)

ADDRESS: Interlibrary Loan
Prince George's County
Memorial Library
6532 Adelphi Rd.
Hyattsville, MD   20782

TELEPHONE: (301) 699-3500, X268

LIST NAMES OF BRANCHES WITH
SEPARATE POLICIES: None

BOOKS:
Will Lend: Yes
Length of Loan: 6 weeks
Renewable: Yes
Charges: None
Average Turnaround Time:
(Not answered)
If you have indicated that a
book is not to be lent, will
you on receipt of a letter
from the requesting library
search the index for given
entries?   (Not answered)

PERIODICALS:
Bound: Will not lend
Unbound: Will lend
Loan Period: 6 weeks
Renewable: Yes
Will lend if article exceeds
_____ number of pages (Not
answered)

MICROFORMS:
Will Lend: No
Specific Types of Microforms:
N/A

GOVERNMENT PUBLICATIONS:
Will Lend: (Not answered)

DISSERTATIONS:
Will Lend: Do not own

THESES:
Will Lend: Do not own

AUDIO-VISUAL MATERIALS:
Records: Will not lend
Cassettes: Will not lend
Other (slides, filmstrips,
etc.):   (Not answered)

COMPUTER SOFTWARE:
Will Lend: (Not answered)

PHOTODUPLICATION SERVICE:
No charge up to any exposures
Charge Per Exposure: None
Minimum/handling Fee: None
Average Turnaround Time:
(Not answered)

MICROFILMING SERVICE:
Service Available: (Not
answered)
Charges: (Not answered)

DO YOU CHARGE THE BORROWING
LIBRARY FOR POSTAGE?   No

FOR HOW LONG DO YOU SUSPEND ILL
SERVICE OVER THE CHRISTMAS
HOLIDAYS?   No suspension

ARE THERE ANY GROUPS OF LIBRARIES
FOR WHICH YOU WAIVE FEES?   IF
SO, PLEASE NAME THEM:
No fees charged

TOWSON STATE UNIVERSITY

NUC CODE: (Not answered)

OCLC CODE: TSC

ADDRESS: Interlibrary Loan
Albert S. Cook Library
Towson State University
Baltimore, MD 21204

TELEPHONE (301) 321-3292

LIST NAMES OF BRANCHES WITH
SEPARATE POLICIES: None

BOOKS:
Will Lend: Yes
Length of Loan: 2 weeks
Renewable: Yes
Charges: Not at this time
Average Turnaround Time:
3 days
If you have indicated that a
book is not to be lent, will
you on receipt of a letter
from the requesting library
search the index for given
entries?   No.   Will only
send copies if specific
pages given.

PERIODICALS:
Bound: Will not lend
Unbound: Will not lend
Loan Period: N/A
Renewable: N/A
Will lend if article exceeds
_____ number of pages (Will
not lend, regardless of
length of article)

MICROFORMS:
Will Lend: Yes
Specific Types of Microforms:
Microfilm, microfiche

GOVERNMENT PUBLICATIONS:
Will Lend: Yes

DISSERTATIONS:
Will Lend: No

THESES:
Will Lend: Yes

AUDIO-VISUAL MATERIALS:
Records: Will not lend
Cassettes: Will lend
Other (slides, filmstrips,
etc.):   Will lend

COMPUTER SOFTWARE:
Will Lend: No

PHOTODUPLICATION SERVICE:
No charge up to 50 exposures
Charge Per Exposure: 10¢
over 1st 50 pages
Minimum/handling Fee: None
at this time
Average Turnaround Time:
3 days

MICROFILMING SERVICE:
Service Available: No
Charges: N/A

DO YOU CHARGE THE BORROWING
LIBRARY FOR POSTAGE?   No

FOR HOW LONG DO YOU SUSPEND ILL
SERVICE OVER THE CHRISTMAS
HOLIDAYS?   Dec.24-Jan.2

ARE THERE ANY GROUPS OF LIBRARIES
FOR WHICH YOU WAIVE FEES?   IF
SO, PLEASE NAME THEM: Member
libraries of the Maryland
ILL organization

UNITED STATES NAVAL ACADEMY

NUC CODE: MdAN

OCLC CODE: UNA

ADDRESS: Interlibrary Loan
Nimitz Library
U. S. Naval Academy
Annapolis, MD 21402

TELEPHONE: (301) 267-2233

LIST NAMES OF BRANCHES WITH
SEPARATE POLICIES: None

BOOKS:
Will Lend: Yes
Length of Loan: 4 weeks
Renewable: Yes
Charges: None
Average Turnaround Time:
2 weeks
If you have indicated that a
book is not to be lent, will
you on receipt of a letter
from the requesting library
search the index for given
entries? Yes

PERIODICALS:
Bound: Will not lend
Unbound: Will not lend
Loan Period: N/A
Renewable: N/A
Will lend if article exceeds
_____ number of pages (Not
answered)

MICROFORMS:
Will Lend: No
Specific Types of Microforms:
N/A

GOVERNMENT PUBLICATIONS:
Will Lend: Yes

DISSERTATIONS:
Will Lend: Do not own

THESES:
Will Lend: Do not own

AUDIO-VISUAL MATERIALS:
Records: Do not own
Cassettes: Do not own
Other (slides, filmstrips,
etc.): Do not own

COMPUTER SOFTWARE:
Will Lend: Do not own

PHOTODUPLICATION SERVICE:
No charge up to 15 exposures
Charge Per Exposure: 10¢
Minimum/handling Fee: None
Average Turnaround Time:
2 weeks

MICROFILMING SERVICE:
Service Available: No
Charges: N/A

DO YOU CHARGE THE BORROWING
LIBRARY FOR POSTAGE? No

FOR HOW LONG DO YOU SUSPEND ILL
SERVICE OVER THE CHRISTMAS
HOLIDAYS? Dec.5-Jan.5

ARE THERE ANY GROUPS OF LIBRARIES
FOR WHICH YOU WAIVE FEES? IF
SO, PLEASE NAME THEM: None

UNIVERSITY OF MARYLAND

NUC CODE: MdU

OCLC CODE: UMC

ADDRESS: Interlibrary Loan
McKeldin Library
University of Maryland
College Park, MD 20742

TELEPHONE: (301) 454-2816

LIST NAMES OF BRANCHES WITH
SEPARATE POLICIES: None

BOOKS:
Will Lend: Yes
Length of Loan: 28 days
including traveling
time
Renewable: Yes
Charges: None
Average Turnaround Time:
4 days
If you have indicated that a
book is not to be lent, will
you on receipt of a letter
from the requesting library
search the index for given
entries? No

PERIODICALS:
Bound: Will not lend
Unbound: Will not lend
Loan Period: N/A
Renewable: N/A
Will lend if article exceeds
_____ number of pages (Will
not lend, regardless of
length of article)

MICROFORMS:
Will Lend: Yes, except fiche
Specific Types of Microforms:
Old newspapers for 2 weeks
loan; will make fiche to
fiche copies for 30¢ each
plus $3.00 handling.

GOVERNMENT PUBLICATIONS:
Will Lend: Yes

DISSERTATIONS:
Will Lend: Yes, if 2d copy
available

THESES:
Will Lend: No

AUDIO-VISUAL MATERIALS:
Records: Will not lend
Cassettes: Will not lend
Other (slides, filmstrips,
etc.): Will not lend

COMPUTER SOFTWARE:
Will Lend: No

PHOTODUPLICATION SERVICE:
No charge up to 0 exposures
Charge Per Exposure: 20¢
Handling Fee: $3.00
Minimum Fee: $5.00 for
academic libraries; $7.00
for others
Average Turnaround Time:
4 days

MICROFILMING SERVICE:
Service Available: Yes
Charges: 8¢ per frame for
negative plus $3.00 handling
fee

DO YOU CHARGE THE BORROWING
LIBRARY FOR POSTAGE? No

FOR HOW LONG DO YOU SUSPEND ILL
SERVICE OVER THE CHRISTMAS
HOLIDAYS? 3 weeks (books only)

ARE THERE ANY GROUPS OF LIBRARIES
FOR WHICH YOU WAIVE FEES? IF
SO, PLEASE NAME THEM: MILO
(Maryland State Network)

UNIVERSITY OF MARYLAND AT BALTIMORE COUNTY

NUC CODE: MdU-BC

OCLC CODE: MUB

ADDRESS: Interlibrary Loan
University Library
University of Maryland
at Baltimore County
Catonsville, MD 21228

TELEPHONE: (301) 455-2234

LIST NAMES OF BRANCHES WITH
SEPARATE POLICIES: None

BOOKS:
Will Lend: Yes
Length of Loan: 2 weeks
Renewable: Yes
Charges: (Not answered)
Average Turnaround Time:
1-3 days
If you have indicated that a
book is not to be lent, will
you on receipt of a letter
from the requesting library
search the index for given
entries? (Not answered)

PERIODICALS:
Bound: Will not lend
Unbound: Will not lend
Loan Period: N/A
Renewable: N/A
Will lend if article exceeds
_____ number of pages (Not
answered)

MICROFORMS:
Will Lend: Yes
Specific Types of Microforms:
Microfilm, microfiche

GOVERNMENT PUBLICATIONS:
Will Lend: Yes, if non-
reference materials

DISSERTATIONS:
Will Lend: Yes

THESES:
Will Lend: Yes

AUDIO-VISUAL MATERIALS:
Records: Will not lend
Cassettes: Will not lend
Other (slides, filmstrips,
etc.): Will not lend

COMPUTER SOFTWARE:
Will Lend: No

PHOTODUPLICATION SERVICE:
No charge up to 0 exposures
Charges: $2.50 for 1-25
exposures; 10¢ each
additional exposure
Average Turnaround Time:
1-3 days

MICROFILMING SERVICE:
Service Available: No
Charges: N/A

DO YOU CHARGE THE BORROWING
LIBRARY FOR POSTAGE? For
multi-volumes or
excessively large books

FOR HOW LONG DO YOU SUSPEND ILL
SERVICE OVER THE CHRISTMAS
HOLIDAYS? Approximately
Dec.13-Jan.3

ARE THERE ANY GROUPS OF LIBRARIES
FOR WHICH YOU WAIVE FEES? IF
SO, PLEASE NAME THEM: None

WASHINGTON COUNTY FREE LIBRARY

NUC CODE: None

OCLC CODE: None

ADDRESS: Interlibrary Loan
Washington County Free
Library
100 S. Potomac St.
Hagerstown, MD 21740

TELEPHONE: (301) 739-3250

LIST NAMES OF BRANCHES WITH
SEPARATE POLICIES: None

BOOKS:
Will Lend: Yes
Length of Loan: Usually
3 weeks
Renewable: No
Charges: None at this time
Average Turnaround Time:
5-7 days
If you have indicated that a
book is not to be lent, will
you on receipt of a letter
from the requesting library
search the index for given
entries? Lends books

PERIODICALS:
Bound: Will not lend
Unbound: Will lend
Loan Period: 3 weeks
Renewable: No
Will lend if article exceeds
10 pages

MICROFORMS:
Will Lend: Yes
Specific Types of Microforms:
Newspapers on microfilm and
their indexes

GOVERNMENT PUBLICATIONS:
Will Lend: Yes

DISSERTATIONS:
Will Lend: No

THESES:
Will Lend: No

AUDIO-VISUAL MATERIALS:
Records: Will not lend
Cassettes: Will not lend
Other (slides, filmstrips,
etc.): Will not lend

COMPUTER SOFTWARE:
Will Lend: No

PHOTODUPLICATION SERVICE:
No charge up to 10 exposures
Charge Per Exposure: 10¢
Minimum/handling Fee: Not
determined
Average Turnaround Time:
5-7 days

MICROFILMING SERVICE:
Service Available: No
Charges: N/A

DO YOU CHARGE THE BORROWING
LIBRARY FOR POSTAGE?
Depends on materials being
loaned

FOR HOW LONG DO YOU SUSPEND ILL
SERVICE OVER THE CHRISTMAS
HOLIDAYS? App. 4 days

ARE THERE ANY GROUPS OF LIBRARIES
FOR WHICH YOU WAIVE FEES? IF
SO, PLEASE NAME THEM: None

AMHERST COLLEGE

NUC CODE: MA

OCLC CODE: (Not answered)

ADDRESS: Interlibrary Loan
Amherst College
Amherst, MA 01002

TELEPHONE: (413) 542-2319

LIST NAMES OF BRANCHES WITH
SEPARATE POLICIES: None

BOOKS:
Will Lend: Yes
Length of Loan: 3 weeks
Renewable: Yes
Charges: (Not answered)
Average Turnaround Time:
(Not answered)
If you have indicated that a
book is not to be lent, will
you on receipt of a letter
from the requesting library
search the index for given
entries? (Not·answered)

PERIODICALS:
Bound: (Not answered)
Unbound: (Not answered)
Loan Period: (Not answered)
Renewable: (Not answered)
Will lend if article exceeds
30 pages

MICROFORMS:
Will Lend: Yes
Specific Types of Microforms:
(Not answered)

GOVERNMENT PUBLICATIONS:
Will Lend: Yes

DISSERTATIONS:
Will Lend: No

THESES:
Will Lend: No

AUDIO-VISUAL MATERIALS:
Records: Will not lend
Cassettes: Will not lend
Other (slides, filmstrips,
etc.): Will not lend

COMPUTER SOFTWARE:
Will Lend: (Not answered)

PHOTODUPLICATION SERVICE:
No charge up to 0 exposures
Charge Per Exposure: 20¢
Minimum Fee: $3.00
Average Turnaround Time:
(Not answered)

MICROFILMING SERVICE:
Service Available: No
Charges: N/A

DO YOU CHARGE THE BORROWING
LIBRARY FOR POSTAGE? No

FOR HOW LONG DO YOU SUSPEND ILL
SERVICE OVER THE CHRISTMAS
HOLIDAYS? Dec.15-Jan.2

ARE THERE ANY GROUPS OF LIBRARIES
FOR WHICH YOU WAIVE FEES? IF
SO, PLEASE NAME THEM: (Not
answered)

BOSTON COLLEGE

NUC CODE: MChB

OCLC CODE: BXM

ADDRESS: Interlibrary Loan
Bapst Library
Boston College
Chestnut Hill, MA 02167

TELEPHONE: (617) 969-0100, X3209

LIST NAMES OF BRANCHES WITH
SEPARATE POLICIES:
Nursing Library
Social Work Library
School of Management
Library
Science Library
Law School Library

BOOKS:
Will Lend: Yes, but
pre-1972 only
Length of Loan: 1 month
Renewable: Yes
Charges: $6.00 for those
libraries which charge us
Average Turnaround Time:
1 day
If you have indicated that a
book is not to be lent, will
you on receipt of a letter
from the requesting library
search the index for given
entries? Yes

PERIODICALS:
Bound: Will not lend
Unbound: Will not lend
Loan Period: N/A
Renewable: N/A
Will lend if article exceeds
_____ number of pages (Will
not lend, regardless of
length of article)

MICROFORMS:
Will Lend: Yes
Specific Types of Microforms:
Any except Boston Globe,
Boston Pilot, and last 6
months of other newspapers

GOVERNMENT PUBLICATIONS:
Will Lend: Yes

DISSERTATIONS:
Will Lend: Yes, if pre-1968
and if circulating copy
available

THESES:
Will Lend: Yes, if pre-1968
and if circulating copy
available

AUDIO-VISUAL MATERIALS:
Records: Will not lend
Cassettes: Will not lend
Other (slides, filmstrips,
etc.): (Not answered)

COMPUTER SOFTWARE:
Will Lend: No

PHOTODUPLICATION SERVICE:
No charge up to 0 exposures
Charge Per Exposure: 10¢
Minimum/handling Fee: $1.00
($4.00 for profit
organizations)
Average Turnaround Time:
1 day

MICROFILMING SERVICE:
Service Available: No
Charges: N/A

DO YOU CHARGE THE BORROWING
LIBRARY FOR POSTAGE? No

FOR HOW LONG DO YOU SUSPEND ILL
SERVICE OVER THE CHRISTMAS
HOLIDAYS? No suspension

ARE THERE ANY GROUPS OF LIBRARIES
FOR WHICH YOU WAIVE FEES? IF
SO, PLEASE NAME THEM:
Boston Library Consortium
Libraries; Boston Theological
Institute Libraries

BOSTON PUBLIC LIBRARY

NUC CODE: MB

OCLC CODE: (Not answered)

ADDRESS: Interlibrary Loan
Boston Public Library
Boston, MA 02117

TELEPHONE: (617) 536-5400, X343

LIST NAMES OF BRANCHES WITH
SEPARATE POLICIES: None

BOOKS:
Will Lend: Yes, if 2d copy
Length of Loan: 3 weeks
Renewable: No
Charges: None
Average Turnaround Time:
2 weeks
If you have indicated that a
book is not to be lent, will
you on receipt of a letter
from the requesting library
search the index for given
entries? Yes

PERIODICALS:
Bound: Will not lend
Unbound: Will not lend
Loan Period: N/A
Renewable: N/A
Will lend if article exceeds
_____ number of pages (Not
answered)

MICROFORMS:
Will Lend: No
Specific Types of Microforms:
N/A

GOVERNMENT PUBLICATIONS:
Will Lend: Yes, some of
them

DISSERTATIONS:
Will Lend: Do not own

THESES:
Will Lend: Do not own

AUDIO-VISUAL MATERIALS:
Records: Will not lend
Cassettes: Will not lend
Other (slides, filmstrips,
etc.): Will not lend

COMPUTER SOFTWARE:
Will Lend: No

PHOTODUPLICATION SERVICE:
No charge up to 0 exposures
Charge Per Exposure: 20¢
Minimum/handling Fee: $5.00
Average Turnaround Time:
2 weeks

MICROFILMING SERVICE:
Service Available: Yes
Charges: 15¢ per exposure,
$10.00 minimum

DO YOU CHARGE THE BORROWING
LIBRARY FOR POSTAGE? No

FOR HOW LONG DO YOU SUSPEND ILL
SERVICE OVER THE CHRISTMAS
HOLIDAYS? No suspension

ARE THERE ANY GROUPS OF LIBRARIES
FOR WHICH YOU WAIVE FEES? IF
SO, PLEASE NAME THEM: None

BOSTON UNIVERSITY

NUC CODE: MBU

OCLC CODE: BOS

ADDRESS: Interlibrary Loan
Mugar Memorial Library
771 Commonwealth Ave.
Boston University
Boston, MA 02215

TELEPHONE: (617) 353-3706

LIST NAMES OF BRANCHES WITH
SEPARATE POLICIES:
Law Library
Theology Library
Medical Library

BOOKS:
Will Lend: Yes
Length of Loan: 4 weeks
Renewable: Yes
Charges: $5.00
Average Turnaround Time:
1 week
If you have indicated that a
book is not to be lent, will
you on receipt of a letter
from the requesting library
search the index for given
entries? Yes

PERIODICALS:
Bound: Will not lend
Unbound: Will not lend
Loan Period: N/A
Renewable: N/A
Will lend if article exceeds
_____ number of pages (Not
answered)

MICROFORMS:
Will Lend: Yes
Specific Types of Microforms:
(Not answered)

GOVERNMENT PUBLICATIONS:
Will Lend: Yes

DISSERTATIONS:
Will Lend: Yes, if 2nd copy
available and dissertation
not available from University
Microfilms; various schools
available from University
Microfilms since 1957

THESES:
Will Lend: Yes, if 2nd copy
available

AUDIO-VISUAL MATERIALS:
Records: Will not lend
Cassettes: Will not lend
Other (slides, filmstrips,
etc.): Will not lend

COMPUTER SOFTWARE:
Will Lend: No

PHOTODUPLICATION SERVICE:
No charge up to 0 exposures
Charge Per Exposure: 10¢
after first 30
Minimum/handling Fee: $5.00
for 1-30 exposures
Average Turnaround Time:
(Not answered)

MICROFILMING SERVICE:
Service Available: No
Charges: N/A

DO YOU CHARGE THE BORROWING
LIBRARY FOR POSTAGE? No

FOR HOW LONG DO YOU SUSPEND ILL
SERVICE OVER THE CHRISTMAS
HOLIDAYS? (Not answered)

ARE THERE ANY GROUPS OF LIBRARIES
FOR WHICH YOU WAIVE FEES? IF
SO, PLEASE NAME THEM: Boston
Library Consortium

BRIDGEWATER STATE COLLEGE

NUC CODE: (Not answered)

OCLC CODE: (Not answered)

ADDRESS: Interlibrary Loan
Clement C. Maxwell
Library
Bridgewater State
College
Bridgewater, MA   02324

TELEPHONE: (617) 697-8321, X448

LIST NAMES OF BRANCHES WITH
SEPARATE POLICIES: None

BOOKS:
Will Lend: Yes
Length of Loan: 3 weeks
Renewable: No
Charges: None
Average Turnaround Time:
2-3 days
If you have indicated that a
book is not to be lent, will
you on receipt of a letter
from the requesting library
search the index for given
entries? (Not answered)

PERIODICALS:
Bound: Will not lend
Unbound: Will not lend
Loan Period: N/A
Renewable: N/A
Will lend if article exceeds
_____ number of pages (Not
answered)

MICROFORMS:
Will Lend: No
Specific Types of Microforms:
N/A

GOVERNMENT PUBLICATIONS:
Will Lend: Yes

DISSERTATIONS:
Will Lend: Yes

THESES:
Will Lend: Yes

AUDIO-VISUAL MATERIALS:
Records: Do not own
Cassettes: Do not own
Other (slides, filmstrips,
etc.): Do not own

COMPUTER SOFTWARE:
Will Lend: Do not own

PHOTODUPLICATION SERVICE:
No charge up to 9 exposures
Charge Per Exposure: 10¢
Minimum/handling Fee: None
Average Turnaround Time:
2-3 days

MICROFILMING SERVICE:
Service Available: Yes
Charges: 15¢ per fiche

DO YOU CHARGE THE BORROWING
LIBRARY FOR POSTAGE? No

FOR HOW LONG DO YOU SUSPEND ILL
SERVICE OVER THE CHRISTMAS
HOLIDAYS? Dec.15-Jan.1

ARE THERE ANY GROUPS OF LIBRARIES
FOR WHICH YOU WAIVE FEES? IF
SO, PLEASE NAME THEM: Those
who have signed the NELINET
agreement

CAMBRIDGE PUBLIC LIBRARY

NUC CODE: (Not answered)

OCLC CODE: (Not answered)

ADDRESS: Interlibrary Loan
Cambridge Public
Library
449 Broadway
Cambridge, MA   02138

TELEPHONE: (617) 498-9080

LIST NAMES OF BRANCHES WITH
SEPARATE POLICIES: None

BOOKS:
Will Lend: Yes
Length of Loan: 2 weeks
Renewable: Yes
Charges: None
Average Turnaround Time:
(Not answered)
If you have indicated that a
book is not to be lent, will
you on receipt of a letter
from the requesting library
search the index for given
entries? (Not answered)

PERIODICALS:
Bound: Will not lend
Unbound: Will lend
Loan Period: 2 weeks
Renewable: Yes
Will lend if article exceeds
_____ number of pages (Not
answered)

MICROFORMS:
Will Lend: No
Specific Types of Microforms:
N/A

GOVERNMENT PUBLICATIONS:
Will Lend: No

DISSERTATIONS:
Will Lend: Do not own

THESES:
Will Lend: Do not own

AUDIO-VISUAL MATERIALS:
Records: Will not lend
Cassettes: Will not lend
Other (slides, filmstrips,
etc.): Will not lend

COMPUTER SOFTWARE:
Will Lend: No

PHOTODUPLICATION SERVICE:
No charge up to 0 exposures
Charge Per Exposure: 20¢
Minimum/handling Fee: None
Average Turnaround Time:
(Not answered)

MICROFILMING SERVICE:
Service Available: Yes
Charges: (Not answered)

DO YOU CHARGE THE BORROWING
LIBRARY FOR POSTAGE? No

FOR HOW LONG DO YOU SUSPEND ILL
SERVICE OVER THE CHRISTMAS
HOLIDAYS? No suspension

ARE THERE ANY GROUPS OF LIBRARIES
FOR WHICH YOU WAIVE FEES? IF
SO, PLEASE NAME THEM: None

CLARK UNIVERSITY

NUC CODE: MWC

OCLC CODE: CKM

ADDRESS: Interlibrary Loan
           Robert Hutchings
             Goddard Library
           Clark University
           Worcester, MA 01610

TELEPHONE: (617) 793-7578

LIST NAMES OF BRANCHES WITH
  SEPARATE POLICIES: None

BOOKS:
  Will Lend: Yes
  Length of Loan: 2 weeks use
  Renewable: Yes
  Charges: (Not answered)
  Average Turnaround Time:
    (Not answered)
  If you have indicated that a
    book is not to be lent, will
    you on receipt of a letter
    from the requesting library
    search the index for given
    entries? Yes

PERIODICALS:
  Bound: Will not lend
  Unbound: (Not answered)
  Loan Period: N/A
  Renewable: N/A
  Will lend if article exceeds
    unusually lengthy number of
    pages

MICROFORMS:
  Will Lend: Yes
  Specific Types of Microforms:
    (Not answered)

GOVERNMENT PUBLICATIONS:
  Will Lend: Yes

DISSERTATIONS:
  Will Lend: Yes, but pre-1956
    only

THESES:
  Will Lend: Yes, but pre-1956
    only

AUDIO-VISUAL MATERIALS:
  Records: (Not answered)
  Cassettes: (Not answered)
  Other (slides, filmstrips,
    etc.): (Not answered)

COMPUTER SOFTWARE:
  Will Lend: (Not answered)

PHOTODUPLICATION SERVICE:
  No charge up to 0 exposures
  Charge Per Exposure: 10¢
  Minimum/handling Fee: (Not
    answered)
  Average Turnaround Time:
    (Not answered)

MICROFILMING SERVICE:
  Service Available: (Not
    answered)
  Charges: N/A

DO YOU CHARGE THE BORROWING
  LIBRARY FOR POSTAGE? No

FOR HOW LONG DO YOU SUSPEND ILL
  SERVICE OVER THE CHRISTMAS
  HOLIDAYS? 3 weeks

ARE THERE ANY GROUPS OF LIBRARIES
  FOR WHICH YOU WAIVE FEES? IF
  SO, PLEASE NAME THEM: None

EASTERN MASSACHUSETTS REGIONAL LIBRARY SYSTEM

ADDRESS: Eastern Massachusetts
           Regional Library
           System
           Boston Public Library
           Boston, MA 02117

Eastern Massachusetts Regional Library System administers
an interlibrary loan program for member libraries with loans
supplied by the Boston Public Library and other member libraries.
It is not a separate collection; interlibrary loan policies of
member libraries are established by member libraries.

FALL RIVER PUBLIC LIBRARY

NUC CODE: (Not answered)

OCLC CODE: (Not answered)

ADDRESS: Interlibrary Loan
Fall River Public
Library
104 North Main St.
Fall River, MA 02720

TELEPHONE: (617) 676-8541

LIST NAMES OF BRANCHES WITH
SEPARATE POLICIES: None

BOOKS:
Will Lend: Yes, except for
reference and Fall River
history materials
Length of Loan: 2 weeks
Renewable: Yes
Charges: None
Average Turnaround Time:
(Not answered)
If you have indicated that a
book is not to be lent, will
you on receipt of a letter
from the requesting library
search the index for given
entries? Yes

PERIODICALS:
Bound: Will not lend
Unbound: Will not lend
Loan Period: N/A
Renewable: N/A
Will lend if article exceeds
_____ number of pages (Not
answered)

MICROFORMS:
Will Lend: No
Specific Types of Microforms:
N/A

GOVERNMENT PUBLICATIONS:
Will Lend: No

DISSERTATIONS:
Will Lend: No

THESES:
Will Lend: No

AUDIO-VISUAL MATERIALS:
Records: Will lend to city
residents
Cassettes: Will lend to city
residents
Other (slides, filmstrips,
etc.): Will not lend

COMPUTER SOFTWARE:
Will Lend: No

PHOTODUPLICATION SERVICE:
No charge up to 0 exposures
Charge Per Exposure: 10¢
Minimum/handling Fee: (Not
answered)
Average Turnaround Time:
(Not answered)

MICROFILMING SERVICE:
Service Available: No
Charges: N/A

DO YOU CHARGE THE BORROWING
LIBRARY FOR POSTAGE? (Not
answered)

FOR HOW LONG DO YOU SUSPEND ILL
SERVICE OVER THE CHRISTMAS
HOLIDAYS? (Not answered)

ARE THERE ANY GROUPS OF LIBRARIES
FOR WHICH YOU WAIVE FEES? IF
SO, PLEASE NAME THEM: None

FRAMINGHAM PUBLIC LIBRARY

NUC CODE: None

OCLC CODE: FRM

ADDRESS: Interlibrary Loan
Framingham Public
Library
49 Lexington St.
Framingham, MA 01701

TELEPHONE: (617) 879-3570

LIST NAMES OF BRANCHES WITH
SEPARATE POLICIES: None

BOOKS:
Will Lend: Yes, within
Massachusetts
Length of Loan: 1 month
Renewable: Not generally
Charges: None
Average Turnaround Time:
(Not answered)
If you have indicated that a
book is not to be lent, will
you on receipt of a letter
from the requesting library
search the index for given
entries? (Not answered)

PERIODICALS:
Bound: Will not lend
Unbound: Will not lend
Loan Period: N/A
Renewable: N/A
Will lend if article exceeds
_____ number of pages (Not
answered)

MICROFORMS:
Will Lend: No
Specific Types of Microforms:
N/A

GOVERNMENT PUBLICATIONS:
Will Lend: (Not answered)

DISSERTATIONS:
Will Lend: (Not answered)

THESES:
Will Lend: (Not answered)

AUDIO-VISUAL MATERIALS:
Records: Will lend within
Massachusetts
Cassettes: (Not answered)
Other (slides, filmstrips,
etc.): (Not answered)

COMPUTER SOFTWARE:
Will Lend: No

PHOTODUPLICATION SERVICE:
No charge up to 0 exposures
Charge Per Exposure: 10¢
Minimum/handling Fee: None
Average Turnaround Time:
(Not answered)

MICROFILMING SERVICE:
Service Available: No
Charges: N/A

DO YOU CHARGE THE BORROWING
LIBRARY FOR POSTAGE? No

FOR HOW LONG DO YOU SUSPEND ILL
SERVICE OVER THE CHRISTMAS
HOLIDAYS? No suspension

ARE THERE ANY GROUPS OF LIBRARIES
FOR WHICH YOU WAIVE FEES? IF
SO, PLEASE NAME THEM: None

HARVARD UNIVERSITY

NUC CODE: MH

OCLC CODE: HLS

ADDRESS: Interlibrary Loan
Harvard University
Widener Library
Cambridge, MA 02138

TELEPHONE: (617) 495-3650

LIST NAMES OF BRANCHES WITH
SEPARATE POLICIES: (Not
answered)

BOOKS:
Will Lend: Yes
Length of Loan: 1 month from
date sent
Renewable: Yes
Charges: $10.00 per title
(includes 4 volumes or 6
reels of the title)
Average Turnaround Time:
(Not answered)
If you have indicated that a
book is not to be lent, will
you on receipt of a letter
from the requesting library
search the index for given
entries? (Not answered)

PERIODICALS:
Bound: (Not answered)
Unbound: (Not answered)
Loan Period: (Not answered)
Renewable: (Not answered)
Will lend if article exceeds
_____ number of pages (Not
answered)

MICROFORMS:
Will Lend: Yes
Specific Types of Microforms:
(Not answered)

GOVERNMENT PUBLICATIONS:
Will Lend: (Not answered)

DISSERTATIONS:
Will Lend: (Not answered)

THESES:
Will Lend: (Not answered)

AUDIO-VISUAL MATERIALS:
Records: (Not answered)
Cassettes: (Not answered)
Other (slides, filmstrips,
etc.): (Not answered)

COMPUTER SOFTWARE:
Will Lend: (Not answered)

PHOTODUPLICATION SERVICE:
Mail requests only
No charge up to 0 exposures
Charge Per Exposure: Write
for charges
Minimum Fee: $8.00
Handling Fee: At least $2.00
Average Turnaround Time:
(Not answered)

MICROFILMING SERVICE:
Service Available: Yes
Charges: Write for charges

DO YOU CHARGE THE BORROWING
LIBRARY FOR POSTAGE? No

FOR HOW LONG DO YOU SUSPEND ILL
SERVICE OVER THE CHRISTMAS
HOLIDAYS? Dec.10-Jan.2

ARE THERE ANY GROUPS OF LIBRARIES
FOR WHICH YOU WAIVE FEES? IF
SO, PLEASE NAME THEM: (Not
answered)

HARVARD UNIVERSITY--GRADUATE SCHOOL OF BUSINESS ADMINISTRATION

NUC CODE: MH-BA

OCLC CODE: HBS

ADDRESS: Interlibrary Loan
Baker Library
Harvard Business
School
Boston, MA 02163

TELEPHONE: (617) 495-6533

LIST NAMES OF BRANCHES WITH
SEPARATE POLICIES: (Not
answered)

BOOKS:
Will Lend: Yes
Length of Loan: (Not
answered)
Renewable: (Not answered)
Charges: $10.00 non-profit;
$15.00 profit
Average Turnaround Time:
(Not answered)
If you have indicated that a
book is not to be lent, will
you on receipt of a letter
from the requesting library
search the index for given
entries? (Not answered)

PERIODICALS:
Bound: (Not answered)
Unbound: (Not answered)
Loan Period: (Not answered)
Renewable: (Not answered)
Will lend if article exceeds
_____ number of pages (Not
answered)

MICROFORMS:
Will Lend: (Not answered)
Specific Types of Microforms:
(Not answered)

GOVERNMENT PUBLICATIONS:
Will Lend: (Not answered)

DISSERTATIONS:
Will Lend: Yes, if pre-1972;
1972 to present available
from University Microfilms

THESES:
Will Lend: Do not own

AUDIO-VISUAL MATERIALS:
Records: (Not answered)
Cassettes: (Not answered)
Other (slides, filmstrips,
etc.): (Not answered)

COMPUTER SOFTWARE:
Will Lend: (Not answered)

PHOTODUPLICATION SERVICE:
No charge up to 0 exposures
Charges: $10.00 non-profit,
$15.00 profit, for 1-25
exposures; 10¢ each
additional exposures

MICROFILMING SERVICE:
Service Available: (Not
answered)
Charges: N/A

DO YOU CHARGE THE BORROWING
LIBRARY FOR POSTAGE? No

FOR HOW LONG DO YOU SUSPEND ILL
SERVICE OVER THE CHRISTMAS
HOLIDAYS? (Not answered)

ARE THERE ANY GROUPS OF LIBRARIES
FOR WHICH YOU WAIVE FEES? IF
SO, PLEASE NAME THEM: (Not
answered)

MARINE BIOLOGICAL LIBRARY

NUC CODE: MWhB

OCLC CODE: (Not answered)

ADDRESS: Interlibrary Loan
Marine Biological
Library
Woods Hole, MA   02543

TELEPHONE: (617) 548-3705, X436

LIST NAMES OF BRANCHES WITH
SEPARATE POLICIES: None

BOOKS:
Will Lend: Yes
Length of Loan: (Not
answered)
Renewable: (Not answered)
Charges: (Not answered)
Average Turnaround Time:
(Not answered)
If you have indicated that a
book is not to be lent, will
you on receipt of a letter
from the requesting library
search the index for given
entries?   (Not answered)

PERIODICALS:
Bound: Will lend
Unbound: Will not lend
Loan Period: (Not answered)
Renewable: (Not answered)
Will lend if article exceeds
50 pages

MICROFORMS:
Will Lend: (Not answered)
Specific Types of Microforms:
N/A

GOVERNMENT PUBLICATIONS:
Will Lend: (Not answered)

DISSERTATIONS:
Will Lend: (Not answered)

THESES:
Will Lend: (Not answered)

AUDIO-VISUAL MATERIALS:
Records: (Not answered)
Cassettes: (Not answered)
Other (slides, filmstrips,
etc.):   (Not answered)

COMPUTER SOFTWARE:
Will Lend: (Not answered)

PHOTODUPLICATION SERVICE:
No charge up to 0 exposures
Charge Per Exposure: 1-10
pages, $3.00
Minimum/handling Fee: $3.00
Average Turnaround Time:
(Not answered)

MICROFILMING SERVICE:
Service Available: (Not
answered)
Charges: N/A

DO YOU CHARGE THE BORROWING
LIBRARY FOR POSTAGE?   (Not
answered)

FOR HOW LONG DO YOU SUSPEND ILL
SERVICE OVER THE CHRISTMAS
HOLIDAYS?   December

ARE THERE ANY GROUPS OF LIBRARIES
FOR WHICH YOU WAIVE FEES?   IF
SO, PLEASE NAME THEM: (Not
answered)

MASSACHUSETTS BOARD OF LIBRARY COMMISSIONERS

NUC CODE: (Not answered)

OCLC CODE: (Not answered)

ADDRESS: Interlibrary Loan
Massachusetts Board of
Library Commissioners
648 Beacon St.
Boston, MA   02215

TELEPHONE: (617) 267-9400

LIST NAMES OF BRANCHES WITH
SEPARATE POLICIES: None

BOOKS:
Will Lend: Yes
Length of Loan: 1 month
Renewable: Yes
Charges: None
Average Turnaround Time:
2 days
If you have indicated that a
book is not to be lent, will
you on receipt of a letter
from the requesting library
search the index for given
entries?   (Not answered)

PERIODICALS:
Bound: Will not lend
Unbound: Will not lend
Loan Period: N/A
Renewable: N/A
Will lend if article exceeds
_____ number of pages (Not
answered)

MICROFORMS:
Will Lend: No
Specific Types of Microforms:
N/A

GOVERNMENT PUBLICATIONS
Will Lend: Yes

DISSERTATIONS:
Will Lend: No

THESES:
Will Lend: No

AUDIO-VISUAL MATERIALS:
Records: (Not answered)
Cassettes: Will lend
Other (slides, filmstrips,
etc.):   Will lend

COMPUTER SOFTWARE:
Will Lend: No

PHOTODUPLICATION SERVICE:
No charge up to 30 exposures
Charge Per Exposure: None
Minimum/handling Fee: None
Average Turnaround Time:
2 days

MICROFILMING SERVICE:
Service Available: No
Charges: N/A

DO YOU CHARGE THE BORROWING
LIBRARY FOR POSTAGE?   No

FOR HOW LONG DO YOU SUSPEND ILL
SERVICE OVER THE CHRISTMAS
HOLIDAYS?   No suspension

ARE THERE ANY GROUPS OF LIBRARIES
FOR WHICH YOU WAIVE FEES?   IF
SO, PLEASE NAME THEM: No fees
charged

MASSACHUSETTS INSTITUTE OF TECHNOLOGY AT CAMBRIDGE

NUC CODE: MCM

OCLC CODE: MYG

ADDRESS: Interlibrary Loan
            Massachusetts Institute
            of Technology
            M.I.T. 145-234
            Cambridge, MA 02139

TELEPHONE: (617) 253-5682

LIST NAMES OF BRANCHES WITH
  SEPARATE POLICIES: (Not
  answered)

BOOKS:
  Will Lend: Yes
  Length of Loan: (Not
    answered)
  Renewable: Yes
  Charges: (Not answered)
  Average Turnaround Time:
    (Not answered)
  If you have indicated that a
    book is not to be lent, will
    you on receipt of a letter
    from the requesting library
    search the index for given
    entries? (Not answered)

PERIODICALS:
  Bound: Will not lend
  Unbound: Will not lend
  Loan Period: N/A
  Renewable: N/A
  Will lend if article exceeds
    _____ number of pages (Not
    answered)

MICROFORMS:
  Will Lend: No
  Specific Types of Microforms:
    N/A; will provide microcopy

GOVERNMENT PUBLICATIONS:
  Will Lend: Yes

DISSERTATIONS:
  Will Lend: No; order from
    MIT Reproduction Laboratory

THESES:
  Will Lend: No

AUDIO-VISUAL MATERIALS:
  Records: (Not answered)
  Cassettes: (Not answered)
  Other (slides, filmstrips,
    etc.): (Not answered)

COMPUTER SOFTWARE:
  Will Lend: (Not answered)

PHOTODUPLICATION SERVICE:
  No charge up to 0 exposures
  Charge Per Exposure: (Not
    answered)
  Handling Fee: $4.50 per
    volume
  Write for price list
  Average Turnaround Time:
    (Not answered)

MICROFILMING SERVICE:
  Service Available: (Not
    answered)
  Charges: N/A

DO YOU CHARGE THE BORROWING
  LIBRARY FOR POSTAGE? (Not
  answered)

FOR HOW LONG DO YOU SUSPEND ILL
  SERVICE OVER THE CHRISTMAS
  HOLIDAYS? (Not answered)

ARE THERE ANY GROUPS OF LIBRARIES
  FOR WHICH YOU WAIVE FEES? IF
  SO, PLEASE NAME THEM: (Not
  answered)

MOUNT HOLYOKE COLLEGE

NUC CODE: MshM

OCLC CODE: MTH

ADDRESS: Interlibrary Loan
            Mt. Holyoke College
            Williston Library
            South Hadley, MA 01033

TELEPHONE: (413) 538-2423

LIST NAMES OF BRANCHES WITH
  SEPARATE POLICIES: None

BOOKS:
  Will Lend: Yes
  Length of Loan: 3 weeks
  Renewable: Yes
  Charges: None
  Average Turnaround Time:
    2 days
  If you have indicated that a
    book is not to be lent, will
    you on receipt of a letter
    from the requesting library
    search the index for given
    entries? (Not answered)

PERIODICALS:
  Bound: Will not lend
  Unbound: (Not answered)
  Loan Period: (Not answered)
  Renewable: (Not answered)
  Will lend if article exceeds
    _____ number of pages (Not
    answered)

MICROFORMS:
  Will Lend: Yes
  Specific Types of Microforms:
    (Not answered)

GOVERNMENT PUBLICATIONS:
  Will Lend: Yes

DISSERTATIONS:
  Will Lend: No

THESES:
  Will Lend: No

AUDIO-VISUAL MATERIALS:
  Records: Will not lend
  Cassettes: Will not lend
  Other (slides, filmstrips,
    etc.): Will not lend

COMPUTER SOFTWARE:
  Will Lend: No

PHOTODUPLICATION SERVICE:
  No charge up to 30 exposures
  Charge Per Exposure: 10¢
  Minimum/handling Fee: None
  Average Turnaround Time:
    1 day

MICROFILMING SERVICE:
  Service Available: No
  Charges: N/A

DO YOU CHARGE THE BORROWING
  LIBRARY FOR POSTAGE? No

FOR HOW LONG DO YOU SUSPEND ILL
  SERVICE OVER THE CHRISTMAS
  HOLIDAYS? No suspension

ARE THERE ANY GROUPS OF LIBRARIES
  FOR WHICH YOU WAIVE FEES? IF
  SO, PLEASE NAME THEM: None

NEWTON FREE LIBRARY

NUC CODE: (Not answered)

OCLC CODE: (Not answered)

ADDRESS: Interlibrary Loan
Newton Free Library
414 Centre St.
Newton, MA 02158

TELEPHONE: (617) 552-7152

LIST NAMES OF BRANCHES WITH
SEPARATE POLICIES: None

BOOKS:
Will Lend: Yes
Length of Loan: 3 weeks
Renewable: Yes
Charges: Mailing costs
Average Turnaround Time:
1 day
If you have indicated that a
book is not to be lent, will
you on receipt of a letter
from the requesting library
search the index for given
entries? Yes, for books in
our Rare Book Room or our
Newton Collection.

PERIODICALS:
Bound: Will not lend
Unbound: Will not lend
Loan Period: N/A
Renewable: N/A
Will lend if article exceeds
_____ number of pages (Not
answered)

MICROFORMS:
Will Lend: No
Specific Types of Microforms:
N/A

GOVERNMENT PUBLICATIONS:
Will Lend: No

DISSERTATIONS:
Will Lend: Do not own

THESES:
Will Lend: Do not own

AUDIO-VISUAL MATERIALS:
Records: Will not lend
Cassettes: Will not lend
Other (slides, filmstrips,
etc.): Will not lend

COMPUTER SOFTWARE:
Will Lend: (Not answered)

PHOTODUPLICATION SERVICE:
No charge up to 0 exposures
Charge Per Exposure: 10¢
Minimum/handling Fee: None
Average Turnaround Time:
1 day

MICROFILMING SERVICE:
Service Available: Yes
Charges: 15¢ per page

DO YOU CHARGE THE BORROWING
LIBRARY FOR POSTAGE? Yes

FOR HOW LONG DO YOU SUSPEND ILL
SERVICE OVER THE CHRISTMAS
HOLIDAYS? Christmas Day only

ARE THERE ANY GROUPS OF LIBRARIES
FOR WHICH YOU WAIVE FEES? IF
SO, PLEASE NAME THEM: None

NORTHEASTERN UNIVERSITY

NUC CODE: MBNU

OCLC CODE: NED

ADDRESS: Interlibrary Loan
Northeastern University
Library
360 Huntington Ave.
Boston, MA 02115

TELEPHONE: (617) 437-3198

LIST NAMES OF BRANCHES WITH
SEPARATE POLICIES:
Law Library

BOOKS:
Will Lend: Yes
Length of Loan: 4 weeks from
date sent
Renewable: Yes
Charges: None
Average Turnaround Time:
1-2 days
If you have indicated that a
book is not to be lent, will
you on receipt of a letter
from the requesting library
search the index for given
entries? (Not answered)

PERIODICALS:
Bound: Will not lend
Unbound: Will not lend
Loan Period: N/A
Renewable: N/A
Will lend if article exceeds
_____ number of pages (Not
answered)

MICROFORMS:
Will Lend: No
Specific Types of Microforms:
N/A
Will make fiche-to-fiche copies
at $1.00 per request

GOVERNMENT PUBLICATIONS:
Will Lend: Yes

DISSERTATIONS:
Will Lend: No

THESES:
Will Lend: No

AUDIO-VISUAL MATERIALS:
Records: Will not lend
Cassettes: Will not lend
Other (slides, filmstrips,
etc.): Will not lend

COMPUTER SOFTWARE:
Will Lend: No

PHOTODUPLICATION SERVICE:
No charge up to 10 exposures
Charge Per Exposure: 10¢
(e.g., 11 exposures=$1.10)
Minimum/handling Fee: None
Average Turnaround Time:
1-2 days

MICROFILMING SERVICE:
Service Available: No
Charges: N/A

DO YOU CHARGE THE BORROWING
LIBRARY FOR POSTAGE? No

FOR HOW LONG DO YOU SUSPEND ILL
SERVICE OVER THE CHRISTMAS
HOLIDAYS? No suspension

ARE THERE ANY GROUPS OF LIBRARIES
FOR WHICH YOU WAIVE FEES? IF
SO, PLEASE NAME THEM: Boston
Library Consortium NELINET
members participating in
NELINET photocopy agreement

PUBLIC LIBRARY OF BROOKLINE

NUC CODE: (Not answered)

OCLC CODE: (Not answered)

ADDRESS: Interlibrary Loan
          Public Library of
          Brookline
          361 Washington St.
          Brookline, MA 02146

TELEPHONE: (617) 734-0100

LIST NAMES OF BRANCHES WITH
  SEPARATE POLICIES: None

BOOKS:
  Will Lend: Yes
  Length of Loan: 4 weeks
  Renewable: Yes
  Charges: None
  Average Turnaround Time:
    2 days
  If you have indicated that a
    book is not to be lent, will
    you on receipt of a letter
    from the requesting library
    search the index for given
    entries? Yes

PERIODICALS:
  Bound: Will not lend
  Unbound: Will not lend
  Loan Period: N/A
  Renewable: N/A
  Will lend if article exceeds
    _____ number of pages (Will
    not lend, regardless of
    length of article)

MICROFORMS:
  Will Lend: No
  Specific Types of Microforms:
    N/A

GOVERNMENT PUBLICATIONS:
  Will Lend: No

DISSERTATIONS:
  Will Lend: Do not own

THESES:
  Will Lend: Do not own

AUDIO-VISUAL MATERIALS:
  Records: Will lend
  Cassettes: Will lend
  Other (slides, filmstrips,
    etc.): Will not lend

COMPUTER SOFTWARE:
  Will Lend: Do not own

PHOTODUPLICATION SERVICE:
  No charge up to 0 exposures
  Charge Per Exposure: 10¢
  Minimum/handling Fee: (Not
    answered)
  Average Turnaround Time:
    2 days

MICROFILMING SERVICE:
  Service Available: No
  Charges: N/A

DO YOU CHARGE THE BORROWING
  LIBRARY FOR POSTAGE? No

FOR HOW LONG DO YOU SUSPEND ILL
  SERVICE OVER THE CHRISTMAS
  HOLIDAYS? No suspension

ARE THERE ANY GROUPS OF LIBRARIES
  FOR WHICH YOU WAIVE FEES? IF
  SO, PLEASE NAME THEM: None

SMITH COLLEGE

NUC CODE: MNS

OCLC CODE: SNN

ADDRESS: Interlibrary Loan
          Smith College Library
          Northhampton, MA 01063

TELEPHONE: (413) 584-2700, X501

LIST NAMES OF BRANCHES WITH
  SEPARATE POLICIES: None

BOOKS:
  Will Lend: Yes
  Length of Loan: 2 weeks
  Renewable: Yes
  Charges: Reciprocal
  Average Turnaround Time:
    (Not answered)
  If you have indicated that a
    book is not to be lent, will
    you on receipt of a letter
    from the requesting library
    search the index for given
    entries? (Not answered)

PERIODICALS:
  Bound: Will not lend
  Unbound: Will not lend
  Loan Period: N/A
  Renewable: N/A
  Will lend if article exceeds
    _____ number of pages (Not
    answered)

MICROFORMS:
  Will Lend: Yes
  Specific Types of Microforms:
    (Not answered)

GOVERNMENT PUBLICATIONS:
  Will Lend: Yes

DISSERTATIONS:
  Will Lend: Yes. Also
    available from University
    Microfilms since 1970.

THESES:
  Will Lend: Yes

AUDIO-VISUAL MATERIALS:
  Records: (Not answered)
  Cassettes: (Not answered)
  Other (slides, filmstrips,
    etc.): (Not answered)

COMPUTER SOFTWARE:
  Will Lend: (Not answered)

PHOTODUPLICATION SERVICE:
  No charge up to 0 exposures
  Charges: $4.00 for 1-20
    exposures; 10¢ each
    additional exposure
  Average Turnaround Time:
    (Not answered)

MICROFILMING SERVICE:
  Service Available: No
  Charges: N/A

DO YOU CHARGE THE BORROWING
  LIBRARY FOR POSTAGE? No

FOR HOW LONG DO YOU SUSPEND ILL
  SERVICE OVER THE CHRISTMAS
  HOLIDAYS? Dec.15-Jan.3

ARE THERE ANY GROUPS OF LIBRARIES
  FOR WHICH YOU WAIVE FEES? IF
  SO, PLEASE NAME THEM: (Not
  answered)

STONEHILL COLLEGE

NUC CODE: MNoeS

OCLC CODE: STO

ADDRESS: Interlibrary Loan
Cushing-Martin Library
Stonehill College
North Easton, MA 02356

TELEPHONE: (Not answered)

LIST NAMES OF BRANCHES WITH
SEPARATE POLICIES: None

BOOKS:
Will Lend: Yes
Length of Loan: 4 weeks
Renewable: Yes
Charges: None
Average Turnaround Time:
1 working day
If you have indicated that a
book is not to be lent, will
you on receipt of a letter
from the requesting library
search the index for given
entries? (Not answered)

PERIODICALS:
Bound: Will not lend
Unbound: Will not lend
Loan Period: N/A
Renewable: N/A
Will lend if article exceeds
_____ number of pages (Will
not lend, regardless of
length of article)

MICROFORMS:
Will Lend: Yes
Specific Types of Microforms:
Government document fiche,
if more than 20 frames

GOVERNMENT PUBLICATIONS:
Will Lend: Yes

DISSERTATIONS:
Will Lend: Do not own

THESES:
Will Lend: Do not own

AUDIO-VISUAL MATERIALS:
Records: Will not lend
Cassettes: Will not lend
Other (slides, filmstrips,
etc.): Will not lend

COMPUTER SOFTWARE:
Will Lend: Do not own

PHOTODUPLICATION SERVICE:
No charge up to 0 exposures
Charge Per Exposure: 10¢
Minimum/handling Fee: $1.00
Average Turnaround Time:
1 day

MICROFILMING SERVICE:
Service Available: No
Charges: N/A

DO YOU CHARGE THE BORROWING
LIBRARY FOR POSTAGE? Only
postage that is above
library rate

FOR HOW LONG DO YOU SUSPEND ILL
SERVICE OVER THE CHRISTMAS
HOLIDAYS? Dec.15-Jan.7

ARE THERE ANY GROUPS OF LIBRARIES
FOR WHICH YOU WAIVE FEES? IF
SO, PLEASE NAME THEM: NELINET
reciprocal ILL agreement

SUFFOLK UNIVERSITY

NUC CODE: (Not answered)

OCLC CODE: SUF

ADDRESS: Interlibrary Loan
Mildred F. Sawyer
Library
Suffolk University
Beacon Hill
Boston, MA 02108

TELEPHONE: (617) 723-4700, X532

LIST NAMES OF BRANCHES WITH
SEPARATE POLICIES: None

BOOKS:
Will Lend: Yes
Length of Loan: 30 days
Renewable: Yes
Charges: Only replacement if
lost
Average Turnaround Time:
10-14 days
If you have indicated that a
book is not to be lent, will
you on receipt of a letter
from the requesting library
search the index for given
entries? (Not answered)

PERIODICALS:
Bound: Will not lend
Unbound: Will not lend
Loan Period: N/A
Renewable: N/A
Will lend if article exceeds
_____ number of pages (Not
answered)

MICROFORMS:
Will Lend: No
Specific Types of Microforms:
N/A

GOVERNMENT PUBLICATIONS:
Will Lend: Yes

DISSERTATIONS:
Will Lend: No

THESES:
Will Lend: No

AUDIO-VISUAL MATERIALS:
Records: Will not lend
Cassettes: Will not lend
Other (slides, filmstrips,
etc.): Will not lend

COMPUTER SOFTWARE:
Will Lend: No

PHOTODUPLICATION SERVICE:
No charge up to any
exposures
Charge Per Exposure: None
Minimum/handling Fee: None
Average Turnaround Time:
(Not answered)

MICROFILMING SERVICE:
Service Available: No
Charges: N/A

DO YOU CHARGE THE BORROWING
LIBRARY FOR POSTAGE? No

FOR HOW LONG DO YOU SUSPEND ILL
SERVICE OVER THE CHRISTMAS
HOLIDAYS? About 2 weeks

ARE THERE ANY GROUPS OF LIBRARIES
FOR WHICH YOU WAIVE FEES? IF
SO, PLEASE NAME THEM: No fees
charged at this time

THOMAS CRANE PUBLIC LIBRARY

NUC CODE: MQ

OCLC CODE: QUI

ADDRESS: Interlibrary Loan
           Thomas Crane Public
           Library
           Quincy, MA 02269-0379

TELEPHONE: (617) 471-2400, X49

LIST NAMES OF BRANCHES WITH
   SEPARATE POLICIES: None

BOOKS:
   Will Lend: Yes
   Length of Loan: 28 days
   Renewable: No
   Charges: None
   Average Turnaround Time:
   Varies
   If you have indicated that a
   book is not to be lent, will
   you on receipt of a letter
   from the requesting library
   search the index for given
   entries? (Not answered)

PERIODICALS:
   Bound: Will not lend
   Unbound: Will not lend
   Loan Period: N/A
   Renewable: N/A
   Will lend if article exceeds
   _____ number of pages (Not
   answered)

MICROFORMS:
   Will Lend: No
   Specific Types of Microforms:
   N/A

GOVERNMENT PUBLICATIONS:
   Will Lend: No

DISSERTATIONS:
   Will Lend: No

THESES:
   Will Lend: No

AUDIO-VISUAL MATERIALS:
   Records: Will lend
   Cassettes: Will lend
   Other (slides, filmstrips,
   etc.): Will lend

COMPUTER SOFTWARE:
   Will Lend: No

PHOTODUPLICATION SERVICE:
   No charge up to 0 exposures
   Charge Per Exposure: 10¢
   Minimum/handling Fee: (Not
   answered)
   Average Turnaround Time:
   Varies

MICROFILMING SERVICE:
   Service Available: No
   Charges: N/A

DO YOU CHARGE THE BORROWING
   LIBRARY FOR POSTAGE? No

FOR HOW LONG DO YOU SUSPEND ILL
   SERVICE OVER THE CHRISTMAS
   HOLIDAYS? No suspension

ARE THERE ANY GROUPS OF LIBRARIES
   FOR WHICH YOU WAIVE FEES? IF
   SO, PLEASE NAME THEM: NELINET
   (per NELINET ILL code)

TUFTS UNIVERSITY

NUC CODE: MMeT

OCLC CODE: TFW

ADDRESS: Interlibrary Loan
           Tufts University
           Library
           Medford, MA 02155

TELEPHONE: (617) 381-3460

LIST NAMES OF BRANCHES WITH
   SEPARATE POLICIES:
   Ginn Library, Fletcher
   School of Law and
   Diplomacy
   Tufts Health Sciences
   Library

BOOKS:
   Will Lend: Yes
   Length of Loan: 2 weeks
   Renewable: Yes
   Charges: Only to libraries
   that charge us
   Average Turnaround Time:
   3 days
   If you have indicated that a
   book is not to be lent, will
   you on receipt of a letter
   from the requesting library
   search the index for given
   entries? Yes, normally

PERIODICALS:
   Bound: Will not lend
   Unbound: Will not lend
   Loan Period: N/A
   Renewable: N/A
   Will lend if article exceeds
   _____ number of pages (Not
   answered)

MICROFORMS:
   Will Lend: Yes, selectively
   Specific Types of Microforms:
   Will not lend newspapers on
   microfilm

GOVERNMENT PUBLICATIONS:
   Will Lend: Yes

DISSERTATIONS:
   Will Lend: Yes

THESES:
   Will Lend: Yes

AUDIO-VISUAL MATERIALS:
   Records: Will not lend
   Cassettes: Will not lend
   Other (slides, filmstrips,
   etc.): Will not lend

COMPUTER SOFTWARE:
   Will Lend: No

PHOTODUPLICATION SERVICE:
   No charge up to 0 exposures
   Charge Per Exposure: 10¢
   for hardcopy; 15¢ for
   microcopy
   Minimum Fee: $1.50 at this
   time
   Average Turnaround Time:
   5-7 days

MICROFILMING SERVICE:
   Service Available: No
   Charges: N/A

DO YOU CHARGE THE BORROWING
   LIBRARY FOR POSTAGE? No

FOR HOW LONG DO YOU SUSPEND ILL
   SERVICE OVER THE CHRISTMAS
   HOLIDAYS? No suspension

ARE THERE ANY GROUPS OF LIBRARIES
   FOR WHICH YOU WAIVE FEES? IF
   SO, PLEASE NAME THEM:
   Libraries in Boston Library
   Consortium (no fee for
   photocopies up to 30
   exposures)

UNIVERSITY OF MASSACHUSETTS

NUC CODE: MU

OCLC CODE: AUM

ADDRESS: Interlibrary Loan
University Library
University of
Massachusetts
Amherst, MA 01003

TELEPHONE: (413) 545-0553

LIST NAMES OF CAMPUSES WITH
SEPARATE POLICIES:
University of Massachusetts
at Boston
University of Massachusetts
Medical School at
Worcester

BOOKS:
Will Lend: Yes
Length of Loan: 3 weeks use
Renewable: Yes
Charges: Reciprocal
Average Turnaround Time:
3 days
If you have indicated that a
book is not to be lent, will
you on receipt of a letter
from the requesting library
search the index for given
entries? As time allows

PERIODICALS:
Bound: Will rarely lend
Unbound: Will not lend
Loan Period: 1 weeks use
Renewable: No
May lend if article exceeds
50 pages; each request is
considered individually

MICROFORMS:
Will Lend: Yes
Specific Types of Microforms:
Microfilm, microfiche,
microcards (except for
selected newspapers on film)

GOVERNMENT PUBLICATIONS:
Will Lend: Yes

DISSERTATIONS:
Will Lend: Yes, if pre-1961
and 2nd copy available;
will not lend post-1961 if
available from University
Microfilms

THESES:
Will lend: Yes, if 2nd copy
available

AUDIO-VISUAL MATERIALS:
Records: Will not lend
Cassettes: Will not lend
Other (slides, filmstrips,
etc.): Will not lend

COMPUTER SOFTWARE:
Will Lend: No

PHOTODUPLICATION SERVICE:
No charge up to 0 exposures
Charge Per Exposure: 15¢
from paper copy; 20¢ from
microcopy
Handling Fee: $3.00 per
request
Minimum Fee: $4.00
Invoiced with material

MICROFILMING SERVICE:
Service Available: No
Charges: N/A

DO YOU CHARGE THE BORROWING
LIBRARY FOR POSTAGE? Not
usually, unless first-
class requested

FOR HOW LONG DO YOU SUSPEND ILL
SERVICE OVER THE CHRISTMAS
HOLIDAYS? No suspension

ARE THERE ANY GROUPS OF LIBRARIES
FOR WHICH YOU WAIVE FEES? IF
SO, PLEASE NAME THEM:
5-College Libraries;
Boston Library Consortium;
Massachusetts State
institutions; New England
State Universities; signers
of NELINET reciprocal
agreement

UNIVERSITY OF MASSACHUSETTS--MEDICAL SCHOOL

NUC CODE: (Not answered)

OCLC CODE: WQM

ADDRESS: Interlibrary Loan
University of
Massachusetts Medical
School Library
55 N. Lake Ave.
Worcester, MA 01605

TELEPHONE: (617) 856-3302

LIST NAMES OF BRANCHES WITH
SEPARATE POLICIES: None

BOOKS:
Will Lend: Yes
Length of Loan: 3 weeks
Renewable: Yes
Charges: Reciprocal
Average Turnaround Time:
1 day
If you have indicated that a
book is not to be lent, will
you on receipt of a letter
from the requesting library
search the index for given
entries? (Not answered)

PERIODICALS:
Bound: Will not lend
Unbound: Will not lend
Loan Period: N/A
Renewable: N/A
Will lend if article exceeds
_____ number of pages (Not
answered)

MICROFORMS:
Will Lend: Yes
Specific Types of Microforms:
(Not answered)

GOVERNMENT PUBLICATIONS:
Will Lend: No

DISSERTATIONS:
Will Lend: Do not own

THESES:
Will Lend: Do not own

AUDIO-VISUAL MATERIALS:
Records: (Not answered)
Cassettes: Will lend
Other (slides, filmstrips,
etc.): (Not answered)

COMPUTER SOFTWARE:
Will Lend: (Not answered)

PHOTDUPLICATION SERVICE:
No charge up to any exposures
for Massachusetts
institutions
Charge Per Exposure: 10¢
Minimum Fee: $2.00
Average Turnaround Time:
1 day

MICROFILMING SERVICE:
Service Available: Yes
Charges: 10¢ per frame

DO YOU CHARGE THE BORROWING
LIBRARY FOR POSTAGE? No

FOR HOW LONG DO YOU SUSPEND ILL
SERVICE OVER THE CHRISTMAS
HOLIDAYS? (Not answered)

ARE THERE ANY GROUPS OF LIBRARIES
FOR WHICH YOU WAIVE FEES? IF
SO, PLEASE NAME THEM: (Not
answered)

WELLESLEY COLLEGE

NUC CODE: WelC

OCLC CODE: WEL

ADDRESS: Interlibrary Loan
Wellesley College
Library
Wellesley, MA 02181

TELEPHONE: (617) 235-0320, X2101

LIST NAMES OF BRANCHES WITH
SEPARATE POLICIES: None

BOOKS:
Will Lend: Yes
Length of Loan: 1 month
Renewable: Yes, if local
demand allows
Charges: None
Average Turnaround Time:
4 days
If you have indicated that a
book is not to be lent, will
you on receipt of a letter
from the requesting library
search the index for given
entries? Yes

PERIODICALS:
Bound: Will not lend
Unbound: Will not lend
Loan Period: N/A
Renewable: N/A
Will usually lend if
article exceeds 50 pages,
but loan is non-renewable,
10 days, in-library use
only.

MICROFORMS:
Will Lend: Not usually
Specific Types of Microforms:
N/A

GOVERNMENT PUBLICATIONS:
Will Lend: Yes, at discre-
tion of Documents
Librarian

DISSERTATIONS:
Will Lend: Yes, if 2d copy
available

THESES:
Will Lend: Yes, if 2d copy
available

AUDIO-VISUAL MATERIALS:
Records: Will not lend
Cassettes: Will lend
Other (slides, filmstrips,
etc.): Will not lend

COMPUTER SOFTWARE:
Will Lend: Do not own

PHOTODUPLICATION SERVICE:
No charge up to 10 exposures
Charge Per Exposure: 10¢
Minimum/handling Fee: None
Average Turnaround Time:
4-7 days

MICROFILMING SERVICE:
Service Available: No
Charges: N/A

DO YOU CHARGE THE BORROWING
LIBRARY FOR POSTAGE? No

FOR HOW LONG DO YOU SUSPEND ILL
SERVICE OVER THE CHRISTMAS
HOLIDAYS? Dec.13-Jan.1
(parcels only)

ARE THERE ANY GROUPS OF LIBRARIES
FOR WHICH YOU WAIVE FEES? IF
SO, PLEASE NAME THEM: Boston
Library Consortium: Boston
College, Boston Public,
Boston University, Brandeis
University, MIT, Northeastern
University, Massachusetts
State Library, Tufts Univer-
sity, University of Massachu-
setts

WELLESLEY FREE LIBRARY

NUC CODE: (Not answered)

OCLC CODE: (Not answered)

ADDRESS: Interlibrary Loan
Wellesley Free Library
530 Washington St.
Wellesley, MA 02181

TELEPHONE: (617) 235-1896

LIST NAMES OF BRANCHES WITH
SEPARATE POLICIES: None

BOOKS:
Will Lend: Yes
Length of Loan: 3 weeks
Renewable: Yes
Charges: 5¢ per day
overdue
Average Turnaround Time:
(Not answered)
If you have indicated that a
book is not to be lent, will
you on receipt of a letter
from the requesting library
search the index for given
entries? (Not answered)

PERIODICALS:
Bound: Will not lend
Unbound: Will lend
Loan Period: 2 days
Renewable: No
Will lend if article exceeds
_____ number of pages (Not
answered)

MICROFORMS:
Will Lend: No
Specific Types of Microforms:
N/A

GOVERNMENT PUBLICATIONS:
Will Lend: Yes

DISSERTATIONS:
Will Lend: Do not own

THESES:
Will Lend: Do not own

AUDIO-VISUAL MATERIALS:
Records: Will lend
Cassettes: Will lend
Other (slides, filmstrips,
etc.): Will lend

COMPUTER SOFTWARE:
Will Lend: Do not own

PHOTODUPLICATION SERVICE:
No charge up to 0 exposures
Charge Per Exposure: 10¢
Minimum/handling Fee: (Not
answered)
Average Turnaround Time:
(Not answered)

MICROFILMING SERVICE:
Service Available: No
Charges: N/A

DO YOU CHARGE THE BORROWING
LIBRARY FOR POSTAGE? No

FOR HOW LONG DO YOU SUSPEND ILL
SERVICE OVER THE CHRISTMAS
HOLIDAYS? No suspension

ARE THERE ANY GROUPS OF LIBRARIES
FOR WHICH YOU WAIVE FEES? IF
SO, PLEASE NAME THEM: None

WHEATON COLLEGE

NUC CODE: MNoW

OCLC CODE: WHE

ADDRESS: Interlibrary Loan
          Wheaton College
          Library
          Norton, MA 02766

TELEPHONE: (617) 285-7722, X506

LIST NAMES OF BRANCHES WITH
  SEPARATE POLICIES: None

BOOKS:
  Will Lend: Yes
  Length of Loan: 1 month
  Renewable: Yes
  Charges: None
  Average Turnaround Time:
    2 days
  If you have indicated that a
  book is not to be lent, will
  you on receipt of a letter
  from the requesting library
  search the index for given
  entries? (Not answered)

PERIODICALS:
  Bound: Will not lend
  Unbound: Will not lend
  Loan Period: N/A
  Renewable: N/A
  Will lend if article exceeds
  _____ number of pages (Will
    not lend, regardless of
    length of article)

MICROFORMS:
  Will Lend: No
  Specific Types of Microforms:
    N/A

GOVERNMENT PUBLICATIONS:
  Will Lend: Do not own

DISSERTATIONS:
  Will Lend: Do not own

THESES:
  Will Lend: Do not own

AUDIO-VISUAL MATERIALS:
  Records: Will not lend
  Cassettes: Will not lend
  Other (slides, filmstrips,
    etc.): Will not lend

COMPUTER SOFTWARE:
  Will Lend: Do not own

PHOTODUPLICATION SERVICE:
  No charge up to 15 exposures
  Charge Per Exposure: 10¢
  Minimum/handling Fee: None
  Average Turnaround Time:
    2 days

MICROFILMING SERVICE:
  Service Available: No
  Charges: N/A

DO YOU CHARGE THE BORROWING
  LIBRARY FOR POSTAGE? No

FOR HOW LONG DO YOU SUSPEND ILL
  SERVICE OVER THE CHRISTMAS
  HOLIDAYS? Dec.15-Jan.1

ARE THERE ANY GROUPS OF LIBRARIES
  FOR WHICH YOU WAIVE FEES? IF
  SO, PLEASE NAME THEM:
    Libraries which have signed
    the NELINET ILL Code, 1981

WORCESTER POLYTECHNIC INSTITUTE

NUC CODE: MWP

OCLC CODE: WPG

ADDRESS: Interlibrary Loan
          Gordon Library
          Worcester Polytechnic
            Institute
          Worcester, MA 01609

TELEPHONE: (617) 793-5411

LIST NAMES OF BRANCHES WITH
  SEPARATE POLICIES: None

BOOKS:
  Will Lend: Yes
  Length of Loan: 4 weeks
  Renewable: Yes
  Charges: None
  Average Turnaround Time:
    5 days; we ship UPS
  If you have indicated that a
  book is not to be lent, will
  you on receipt of a letter
  from the requesting library
  search the index for given
  entries? Yes

PERIODICALS:
  Bound: Will not lend
  Unbound: Will not lend
  Loan Period: N/A
  Renewable: N/A
  Will lend if article exceeds
  _____ number of pages (Not
    answered)

MICROFORMS:
  Will Lend: No
  Specific Types of Microforms:
    Microfiche; we can dupli-
    cate microfiche at $1.00
    per set.

GOVERNMENT PUBLICATIONS:
  Will Lend: Yes

DISSERTATIONS:
  Will Lend: Yes, microfilm
    copy only, 1978-

THESES:
  Will Lend: Yes, if 2d copy
    available

AUDIO-VISUAL MATERIALS:
  Records: Will not lend
  Cassettes: Will not lend
  Other (slides, filmstrips,
    etc.): Will not lend

COMPUTER SOFTWARE:
  Will Lend: No

PHOTODUPLICATION SERVICE:
  No charge up to 0 exposures
  Charge Per Exposure: 20¢
  Minimum/handling Fee: $2.50
  Average Turnaround Time:
    5 days

MICROFILMING SERVICE:
  Service Available: No
  Charges: N/A

DO YOU CHARGE THE BORROWING
  LIBRARY FOR POSTAGE? No

FOR HOW LONG DO YOU SUSPEND ILL
  SERVICE OVER THE CHRISTMAS
  HOLIDAYS? Dec.15-Jan.5

ARE THERE ANY GROUPS OF LIBRARIES
  FOR WHICH YOU WAIVE FEES? IF
  SO, PLEASE NAME THEM: None

WORCESTER STATE COLLEGE

NUC CODE: None

OCLC CODE: WRM

ADDRESS: Interlibrary Loan
          Learning Resources
            Center
          Worcester State
            College
          486 Chandler St.
          Worcester, MA 01602

TELEPHONE: (617) 793-8000, X8523

LIST NAMES OF BRANCHES WITH
   SEPARATE POLICIES: None

BOOKS:
   Will Lend: Yes
   Length of Loan: 3-4 weeks
   Renewable: No
   Charges: None
   Average Turnaround Time:
     2 days
   If you have indicated that a
     book is not to be lent, will
     you on receipt of a letter
     from the requesting library
     search the index for given
     entries? (Not answered)

PERIODICALS:
   Bound: Will not lend
   Unbound: Will not lend
   Loan Period: 1 week
   Renewable: No
   Will lend if article exceeds
     50 pages

MICROFORMS:
   Will Lend: No
   Specific Types of Microforms:
     Journals, theses

GOVERNMENT PUBLICATIONS:
   Will Lend: Yes

DISSERTATIONS:
   Will Lend: Yes

THESES:
   Will Lend: Yes

AUDIO-VISUAL MATERIALS:
   Records: Will not lend
   Cassettes: Will not lend
   Other (slides, filmstrips,
     etc.): Will not lend

COMPUTER SOFTWARE:
   Will Lend: No

PHOTODUPLICATION SERVICE:
   No charge up to 35 exposures
   Charge Per Exposure: 10¢
   Minimum/handling Fee: None
   Average Turnaround Time:
     2 days

MICROFILMING SERVICE:
   Service Available: Yes

DO YOU CHARGE THE BORROWING
   LIBRARY FOR POSTAGE? No

FOR HOW LONG DO YOU SUSPEND ILL
   SERVICE OVER THE CHRISTMAS
   HOLIDAYS? No suspension

ARE THERE ANY GROUPS OF LIBRARIES
   FOR WHICH YOU WAIVE FEES? IF
   SO, PLEASE NAME THEM: WACL
     (Worcester Area Co-operating
     Libraries); NELINET
     reciprocal agreement
     libraries.

ANDREWS UNIVERSITY

NUC CODE: MiBsA

OCLC CODE: EXN

ADDRESS: Interlibrary Loan
James White Library
Andrews University
Berrien Springs, MI
49104

TELEPHONE: (616) 471-3506

LIST NAMES OF BRANCHES WITH
SEPARATE POLICIES: None

BOOKS:
Will Lend: Yes
Length of Loan: 3 weeks
Renewable: Yes
Charges: None
Average Turnaround Time:
1 week
If you have indicated that a
book is not to be lent, will
you on receipt of a letter
from the requesting library
search the index for given
entries? Yes

PERIODICALS:
Bound: Will not lend
Unbound: Will not lend
Loan Period: N/A
Renewable: N/A
Will lend if article exceeds
_____ number of pages (Will
not lend, regardless of
length of article)

MICROFORMS:
Will Lend: Yes, microfilm
only

GOVERNMENT PUBLICATIONS:
Will Lend: Yes

DISSERTATIONS:
Will Lend: No

THESES:
Will Lend: Yes

AUDIO-VISUAL MATERIALS:
Records: Will not lend
Cassettes: Will not lend
Other (slides, filmstrips,
etc.): Will not lend

COMPUTER SOFTWARE:
Will Lend: No

PHOTODUPLICATION SERVICE:
No charge up to 10 exposures
Charge Per Exposure: 10¢
Minimum/handling Fee: None
Average Turnaround Time:
1 week

MICROFILMING SERVICE:
Service Available: No
Charges: N/A

DO YOU CHARGE THE BORROWING
LIBRARY FOR POSTAGE? No

FOR HOW LONG DO YOU SUSPEND ILL
SERVICE OVER THE CHRISTMAS
HOLIDAYS? Dec.15-Jan.2

ARE THERE ANY GROUPS OF LIBRARIES
FOR WHICH YOU WAIVE FEES? IF
SO, PLEASE NAME THEM: None

ANN ARBOR PUBLIC LIBRARY

NUC CODE: (Not answered)

OCLC CODE: EYH

ADDRESS: Interlibrary Loan
Ann Arbor Public
Library
c/o Huron Valley
Library System
4133 Washtenaw Ave.
Ann Arbor, MI 48104
THE HURON VALLEY LIBRARY
SYSTEM IS OUR ILL CLEARING
HOUSE. ADDRESS REQUESTS
THERE.

TELEPHONE: (313) 994-2352

LIST NAMES OF BRANCHES WITH
SEPARATE POLICIES: None

BOOKS:
Will Lend: Yes
Length of Loan: 3 weeks
Renewable: No
Charges: None
Average Turnaround Time:
3 days
If you have indicated that a
book is not to be lent, will
you on receipt of a letter
from the requesting library
search the index for given
entries? (Not answered)

PERIODICALS:
Bound: Will not lend
Unbound: Will not lend
Loan Period: N/A
Renewable: N/A
Will lend if article exceeds
_____ number of pages (Not
answered)

MICROFORMS:
Will Lend: No
Specific Types of Microforms:
N/A

GOVERNMENT PUBLICATIONS:
Will Lend: No

DISSERTATIONS:
Will Lend: No

THESES:
Will Lend: No

AUDIO-VISUAL MATERIALS:
Records: Will not lend
Cassettes: Will not lend
Other (slides, filmstrips,
etc.): (Not answered)

COMPUTER SOFTWARE:
Will Lend: (Not answered)

PHOTODUPLICATION SERVICE:
No charge up to 0 exposures
Charge Per Exposure: 30¢
Minimum/handling Fee: $1.00
Average Turnaround Time:
1 week

MICROFILMING SERVICE:
Service Available: No
Charges: N/A

DO YOU CHARGE THE BORROWING
LIBRARY FOR POSTAGE? No

FOR HOW LONG DO YOU SUSPEND ILL
SERVICE OVER THE CHRISTMAS
HOLIDAYS? (Not answered)

ARE THERE ANY GROUPS OF LIBRARIES
FOR WHICH YOU WAIVE FEES? IF
SO, PLEASE NAME THEM: None

CALVIN COLLEGE AND SEMINARY

NUC CODE: MiGrC

OCLC CODE: EXC

ADDRESS: Interlibrary Loan
           Calvin College and
           Seminary Library
           3207 Burton St. S.E.
           Grand Rapids, MI 49506

TELEPHONE: (616) 949-4000, X310

LIST NAMES OF BRANCHES WITH
   SEPARATE POLICIES: None

BOOKS:
   Will Lend: Yes
   Length of Loan: 2 weeks
     from receipt
   Renewable: Yes, upon request
     before due date
   Charges: Reciprocal
   Average Turnaround Time:
     1 day
   If you have indicated that a
     book is not to be lent, will
     you on receipt of a letter
     from the requesting library
     search the index for given
     entries? (Not answered)

PERIODICALS:
   Bound: Will not lend
   Unbound: Will not lend
   Loan Period: N/A
   Renewable: N/A
   Will lend if article exceeds
     _____ number of pages (Not
     answered)

MICROFORMS:
   Will Lend: No
   Specific Types of Microforms:
     N/A

GOVERNMENT PUBLICATIONS:
   Will Lend: Yes

DISSERTATIONS:
   Will Lend: Yes

THESES:
   Will Lend: Yes

AUDIO-VISUAL MATERIALS:
   Records: Will not lend
   Cassettes: Will not lend
   Other (slides, filmstrips,
     etc.): Will not lend

COMPUTER SOFTWARE:
   Will Lend: (Not answered)

PHOTODUPLICATION SERVICE:
   No charge up to 0 exposures
   Charge Per Exposure: 25¢
   Minimum/handling Fee: None
   Average Turnaround Time:
     1 day

MICROFILMING SERVICE:
   Service Available: No
   Charges: N/A

DO YOU CHARGE THE BORROWING
   LIBRARY FOR POSTAGE? No

FOR HOW LONG DO YOU SUSPEND ILL
   SERVICE OVER THE CHRISTMAS
   HOLIDAYS? Dec.15-Jan.5

ARE THERE ANY GROUPS OF LIBRARIES
   FOR WHICH YOU WAIVE FEES? IF
   SO, PLEASE NAME THEM:
     Lakeland Library Coop (Area)
     ATLA and those that are good
     to us

CAPITAL LIBRARY COOPERATIVE

NUC CODE: None

OCLC CODE: EEJ

ADDRESS: Interlibrary Loan
           Capital Library
           Cooperative
           Library Service Center
           407 N. Cedar St.
           Mason, MI 48854

LIST NAMES OF BRANCHES WITH
   SEPARATE POLICIES: Capital
   Library Cooperative is a
   library service center that
   processes books for over 40
   libraries

BOOKS:
   Will Lend: Yes
   Length of Loan: 4 weeks
   Renewable: Yes
   Charges: None
   Average Turnaround Time:
     Varies greatly
   If you have indicated that a
     book is not to be lent, will
     you on receipt of a letter
     from the requesting library
     search the index for given
     entries?

PERIODICALS:
   Bound: (Not answered)
   Unbound: Will lend
   Loan Period: 3-4 weeks
   Renewable: Yes
   Will lend if article exceeds
     _____ number of pages (Not
     answered)

MICROFORMS:
   Will Lend: Do not own
   Specific Types of Microforms:
     N/A

GOVERNMENT PUBLICATIONS:
   Will Lend: Do not own

DISSERTATIONS:
   Will Lend: Do not own

THESES:
   Will Lend: Do not own

AUDIO-VISUAL MATERIALS:
   Records: Do not own
   Cassettes: Do not own
   Other (slides, filmstrips,
     etc.): Do not own

COMPUTER SOFTWARE:
   Will Lend: Do not own

PHOTODUPLICATION SERVICE:
   No charge up to 20 exposures
   Charge Per Exposure: 10¢
   Minimum/handling Fee: None
   Average Turnaround Time:
     (Not answered)

MICROFILMING SERVICE:
   Service Available: No
   Charges: N/A

DO YOU CHARGE THE BORROWING
   LIBRARY FOR POSTAGE? No

FOR HOW LONG DO YOU SUSPEND ILL
   SERVICE OVER THE CHRISTMAS
   HOLIDAYS? No suspension

ARE THERE ANY GROUPS OF LIBRARIES
   FOR WHICH YOU WAIVE FEES? IF
   SO, PLEASE NAME THEM: None

CENTRAL MICHIGAN UNIVERSITY

NUC CODE: MiMtpT

OCLC CODE: EZC

ADDRESS: Interlibrary Loan
Charles V. Park
Library
Central Michigan
University
Mt. Pleasant, MI 48859

TELEPHONE: (517) 774-3244 or
774-3470

LIST NAMES OF BRANCHES WITH
SEPARATE POLICIES: None

BOOKS:
Will Lend: Yes
Length of Loan: 2 weeks use
Renewable: Yes
Charges: None
Average Turnaround Time:
2-3 days
If you have indicated that a
book is not to be lent, will
you on receipt of a letter
from the requesting library
search the index for given
entries? Yes; we will
photocopy specific
references

PERIODICALS:
Bound: Will not lend
Unbound: Will not lend
Loan Period: N/A
Renewable: N/A
Will lend if article exceeds
50 pages

MICROFORMS:
Will Lend: Yes
Specific Types of Microforms:
Most of them

GOVERNMENT PUBLICATIONS:
Will Lend: Yes

DISSERTATIONS:
Will Lend: Do not own

THESES:
Will Lend: Yes

AUDIO-VISUAL MATERIALS:
Records: Will not lend
Cassettes: Will not lend
Other (slides, filmstrips,
etc.): Will not lend

COMPUTER SOFTWARE:
Will Lend: No

PHOTODUPLICATION SERVICE:
No charge up to 50 exposures
Charge Per Exposure: 10¢
for out-of-state
Minimum/handling Fee: $1.50
for out-of-state
Average Turnaround Time:
2-3 days

MICROFILMING SERVICE:
Service Available: No
Charges: N/A

DO YOU CHARGE THE BORROWING
LIBRARY FOR POSTAGE? No

FOR HOW LONG DO YOU SUSPEND ILL
SERVICE OVER THE CHRISTMAS
HOLIDAYS? Approximately
Dec.15-Jan.5

ARE THERE ANY GROUPS OF LIBRARIES
FOR WHICH YOU WAIVE FEES? IF
SO, PLEASE NAME THEM: None

DETROIT PUBLIC LIBRARY

NUC CODE: MD

OCLC CODE: EYP

ADDRESS: Interlibrary Loan
Detroit Public Library
5201 Woodward
Detroit, MI 48202

TELEPHONE: (313) 833-1423

LIST NAMES OF BRANCHES WITH
SEPARATE POLICIES: None

BOOKS:
Will Lend: Yes
Length of Loan: 1-4 weeks
Renewable: Yes
Charges: (Not answered)
Average Turnaround Time:
4-7 days
If you have indicated that a
book is not to be lent, will
you on receipt of a letter
from the requesting library
search the index for given
entries? Yes, but not for
genealogical inquiries.
These must be made
directly by patron in
letter form to our Burton
Historical Collection.

PERIODICALS:
Bound: Will not usually lend
Unbound: Will not usually
lend
Loan Period: N/A
Renewable: N/A
Will lend if article exceeds
_____ number of pages (Will
not lend, regardless of
length of article)

MICROFORMS:
Will Lend: Yes
Specific Types of Microforms:
Film, fiche, cards

GOVERNMENT PUBLICATIONS:
Will Lend: Yes

DISSERTATIONS:
Will Lend: Do not own

THESES:
Will Lend: Do not own

AUDIO-VISUAL MATERIALS:
Records: Will not lend
Cassettes: Will lend
Other (slides, filmstrips,
etc.): Will not lend

COMPUTER SOFTWARE:
Will Lend: Do not own

PHOTODUPLICATION SERVICE:
No charge up to 0 exposures
Charge Per Exposure: 15¢
Minimum/handling Fee: Postage
35¢ per each 10 pages
Average Turnaround Time:
4-10 days

MICROFILMING SERVICE:
Service Available: Yes,
through outside source
Charges: Must be determined
by item

DO YOU CHARGE THE BORROWING
LIBRARY FOR POSTAGE? Only
for photocopies for for
oversized or very heavy
monograph loans

FOR HOW LONG DO YOU SUSPEND ILL
SERVICE OVER THE CHRISTMAS
HOLIDAYS? Book loans
suspended Dec.17-Jan.2

ARE THERE ANY GROUPS OF LIBRARIES
FOR WHICH YOU WAIVE FEES? IF
SO, PLEASE NAME THEM:
Michigan non-profit
libraries

EASTERN MICHIGAN UNIVERSITY

NUC CODE: Miyem

OCLC CODE: EYE

ADDRESS: Interlibrary Loan
Center of Educational
Resources
Eastern Michigan
University
Ypsilanti, MI 48197

TELEPHONE: (313) 487-3191

LIST NAMES OF BRANCHES WITH
SEPARATE POLICIES: None

BOOKS:
Will Lend: Yes
Length of Loan: 2 weeks
Renewable: Yes
Charges: None
Average Turnaround Time:
2 days
If you have indicated that a
book is not to be lent, will
you on receipt of a letter
from the requesting library
search the index for given
entries? No

PERIODICALS:
Bound: Will not lend
Unbound: Will not lend
Loan Period: N/A
Renewable: N/A
Will lend if article exceeds
_____ number of pages (Will
not lend, regardless of
length of article)

MICROFORMS:
Will Lend: No
Specific Types of Microforms:
N/A

GOVERNMENT PUBLICATIONS:
Will Lend: Yes

DISSERTATIONS:
Will Lend: No

THESES:
Will Lend: Yes

AUDIO-VISUAL MATERIALS:
Records: Will not lend
Cassettes: Will not lend
Other (slides, filmstrips,
etc.): Will not lend

COMPUTER SOFTWARE:
Will Lend: No

PHOTODUPLICATION SERVICE:
No charge up to 0 exposures
Charges: $4.00 up to 30
pages plus $1.00 if not
prepaid
Minimum Fee: $4.00
Average Turnaround Time:
2 days

MICROFILMING SERVICE:
Service Available: Yes
Charges: Same as photo-
duplication

DO YOU CHARGE THE BORROWING
LIBRARY FOR POSTAGE? No

FOR HOW LONG DO YOU SUSPEND ILL
SERVICE OVER THE CHRISTMAS
HOLIDAYS? 3 weeks

ARE THERE ANY GROUPS OF LIBRARIES
FOR WHICH YOU WAIVE FEES? IF
SO, PLEASE NAME THEM: None

FERRIS STATE COLLEGE

NUC CODE: MiBrF

OCLC CODE: EZF

ADDRESS: Interlibrary Loan
Ferris State College
Library
Big Rapids, MI 49307

TELEPHONE: (616) 796-0461, X5433

LIST NAMES OF BRANCHES WITH
SEPARATE POLICIES:
School of Pharmacy Reading
Room (contact Main
Library for loans)

BOOKS:
Will Lend: Yes
Length of Loan: 4 weeks
Renewable: Yes
Charges: Reciprocal
Average Turnaround Time:
2 days
If you have indicated that a
book is not to be lent, will
you on receipt of a letter
from the requesting library
search the index for given
entries? (Not answered)

PERIODICALS:
Bound: Will not lend
Unbound: Will not lend
Loan Period: N/A
Renewable: N/A
Will lend if article exceeds
_____ number of pages (Not
answered)

MICROFORMS:
Will Lend: No
Specific Types of Microforms:
N/A

GOVERNMENT PUBLICATIONS:
Will Lend: Yes

DISSERTATIONS:
Will Lend: Do not own

THESES:
Will Lend: Do not own

AUDIO-VISUAL MATERIALS:
Records: Will not lend
Cassettes: Will not lend
Other (slides, filmstrips,
etc.): Will not lend

COMPUTER SOFTWARE:
Will Lend: No

PHOTODUPLICATION SERVICE:
No charge up to 10 exposures
Charge Per Exposure: Based
on charges for photocopying
of requesting library. We
try to have reciprocal
agreements
Minimum/handling Fee: None
Average Turnaround Time:
2 days

MICROFILMING SERVICE:
Service Available: No
Charges: N/A

DO YOU CHARGE THE BORROWING
LIBRARY FOR POSTAGE? No

FOR HOW LONG DO YOU SUSPEND ILL
SERVICE OVER THE CHRISTMAS
HOLIDAYS? Dec.15-Jan.2

ARE THERE ANY GROUPS OF LIBRARIES
FOR WHICH YOU WAIVE FEES? IF
SO, PLEASE NAME THEM:
Michigan Academic Libraries
Association of Visual
Science Librarians

FLINT PUBLIC LIBRARY

NUC CODE: (Not answered)

OCLC CODE: (Not answered)

ADDRESS: Interlibrary Loan
Flint Public Library
1026 E. Kearsley St.
Flint, MI 48502

TELEPHONE: (313) 232-7111, X254
and 255

LIST NAMES OF BRANCHES WITH
SEPARATE POLICIES: None

BOOKS:
Will Lend: Yes
Length of Loan: 2 weeks
Renewable: No
Charges: None
Average Turnaround Time:
1 week
If you have indicated that a
book is not to be lent, will
you on receipt of a letter
from the requesting library
search the index for given
entries? Yes

PERIODICALS:
Bound: Will not lend
Unbound: Will not lend
Loan Period: N/A
Renewable: N/A
Will lend if article exceeds
_____ number of pages (Not
answered)

MICROFORMS:
Will Lend: Rarely
Specific Types of Microforms:
Film

GOVERNMENT PUBLICATIONS:
Will Lend: Yes

DISSERTATIONS:
Will Lend: Do not own

THESES:
Will Lend: Do not own

AUDIO-VISUAL MATERIALS:
Records: Will not lend
Cassettes: Will not lend
Other (slides, filmstrips,
etc.): Will not lend

COMPUTER SOFTWARE:
Will Lend: Do not own

PHOTODUPLICATION SERVICE:
No charge up to 0 exposures
Charge Per Exposure: 5¢ from
hard copy; 10¢ from
microfilm
Minimum/handling Fee: (Not
answered)
Average Turnaround Time:
1 week

MICROFILMING SERVICE:
Service Available: No
Charges: N/A

DO YOU CHARGE THE BORROWING
LIBRARY FOR POSTAGE? Yes

FOR HOW LONG DO YOU SUSPEND ILL
SERVICE OVER THE CHRISTMAS
HOLIDAYS? 15 days

ARE THERE ANY GROUPS OF LIBRARIES
FOR WHICH YOU WAIVE FEES? IF
SO, PLEASE NAME THEM:
Michigan libraries

GENERAL MOTORS INSTITUTE

NUC CODE: (Not answered)

OCLC CODE: (Not answered)

ADDRESS: Interlibrary Loan
General Motors
Institute
GMI Engineering and
Management Institute
Library
1700 W. 3rd Avenue
Flint, MI 48502

TELEPHONE: (313) 762-7812

LIST NAMES OF BRANCHES WITH
SEPARATE POLICIES: None

BOOKS:
Will Lend: Yes
Length of Loan: 1 month
Renewable: Yes
Charges: None
Average Turnaround Time:
1 week
If you have indicated that a
book is not to be lent, will
you on receipt of a letter
from the requesting library
search the index for given
entries? (Not answered)

PERIODICALS:
Bound: Will not lend
Unbound: Will not lend
Loan Period: N/A
Renewable: N/A
Will lend if article exceeds
_____ number of pages (Not
answered)

MICROFORMS:
Will Lend: No
Specific Types of Microforms:
N/A

GOVERNMENT PUBLICATIONS:
Will Lend: No

DISSERTATIONS:
Will Lend: No

THESES:
Will Lend: No

AUDIO-VISUAL MATERIALS:
Records: Will not lend
Cassettes: Will not lend
Other (slides, filmstrips,
etc.): Will not lend

COMPUTER SOFTWARE:
Will Lend: No

PHOTODUPLICATION SERVICE:
No charge up to any exposures
Charge Per Exposure: None
Minimum/handling Fee: None
Average Turnaround Time:
1 week

MICROFILMING SERVICE:
Service Available: No
Charges: N/A

DO YOU CHARGE THE BORROWING
LIBRARY FOR POSTAGE? No

FOR HOW LONG DO YOU SUSPEND ILL
SERVICE OVER THE CHRISTMAS
HOLIDAYS? 3 weeks

ARE THERE ANY GROUPS OF LIBRARIES
FOR WHICH YOU WAIVE FEES? IF
SO, PLEASE NAME THEM: No fees
charged

GENESEE DISTRICT LIBRARY

NUC CODE: (Not answered)

OCLC CODE: (Not answered)

ADDRESS: Interlibrary Loan
Genesee District
Library
4195 W. Pasadena
Flint, MI 48504

TELEPHONE: (313) 732-0110

LIST NAMES OF BRANCHES WITH
SEPARATE POLICIES: None

BOOKS:
Will Lend: Yes
Length of Loan: 3 weeks
Renewable: No
Charges: None
Average Turnaround Time:
3 days
If you have indicated that a
book is not to be lent, will
you on receipt of a letter
from the requesting library
search the index for given
entries? Yes

PERIODICALS:
Bound: Will not lend
Unbound: Will not lend
Loan Period: N/A
Renewable: N/A
Will lend if article exceeds
_____ number of pages (Will
not lend, regardless of
length of article)

MICROFORMS:
Will Lend: No
Specific Types of Microforms:
N/A

GOVERNMENT PUBLICATIONS:
Will Lend: Yes

DISSERTATIONS:
Will Lend: (Not answered)

THESES:
Will Lend: (Not answered)

AUDIO-VISUAL MATERIALS:
Records: Will lend
Cassettes: (Not answered)
Other (slides, filmstrips,
etc.): (Not answered)

COMPUTER SOFTWARE:
Will Lend: (Not answered)

PHOTODUPLICATION SERVICE:
No charge up to 0 exposures
Charge Per Exposure: 10¢
Minimum/handling Fee: $1.00
Average Turnaround Time:
5 days

MICROFILMING SERVICE:
Service Available: No
Charges: N/A

DO YOU CHARGE THE BORROWING
LIBRAR FOR POSTAGE? No

FOR HOW LONG DO YOU SUSPEND ILL
SERVICE OVER THE CHRISTMAS
HOLIDAYS? No suspension

ARE THERE ANY GROUPS OF LIBRARIES
FOR WHICH YOU WAIVE FEES? IF
SO, PLEASE NAME THEM: None

HENRY FORD CENTENNIAL LIBRARY

NUC CODE: None

OCLC CODE: None

ADDRESS: Interlibrary Loan
Henry Ford Centennial
Library
16301 Michigan Ave.
Dearborn, MI 48126

TELEPHONE: (313) 943-2084

LIST NAMES OF BRANCHES WITH
SEPARATE POLICIES: None

BOOKS:
Will Lend: Yes
Length of Loan: 1 month
from date sent
Renewable: No
Charges: (Not answered)
Average Turnaround Time:
10 days
If you have indicated that a
book is not to be lent, will
you on receipt of a letter
from the requesting library
search the index for given
entries? (Not answered)

PERIODICALS:
Bound: Will not lend
Unbound: Will lend
Loan Period: 5 days use
Renewable: (Not answered)
Will lend if article exceeds
5 pages

MICROFORMS:
Will Lend: No
Specific Types of Microforms:
N/A

GOVERNMENT PUBLICATIONS:
Will Lend: No

DISSERTATIONS:
Will Lend: Do not own

THESES:
Will Lend: Do not own

AUDIO-VISUAL MATERIALS:
Records: Will not lend
Cassettes: Will not lend
Other (slides, filmstrips,
etc.): Will not lend

COMPUTER SOFTWARE:
Will Lend: Do not own

PHOTODUPLICATION SERVICE:
No charge up to 5 exposures
Charge Per Exposure: (Not
answered)
Minimum/handling Fee: None
Average Turnaround Time:
10 days

MICROFILMING SERVICE:
Service Available: No
Charges: N/A

DO YOU CHARGE THE BORROWING
LIBRARY FOR POSTAGE? No

FOR HOW LONG DO YOU SUSPEND ILL
SERVICE OVER THE CHRISTMAS
HOLIDAYS? No suspension

ARE THERE ANY GROUPS OF LIBRARIES
FOR WHICH YOU WAIVE FEES? IF
SO, PLEASE NAME THEM: None

JACKSON DISTRICT LIBRARY

NUC CODE: (Not answered)

OCLC CODE: EEJ

ADDRESS: Interlibrary Loan
Jackson District
Library
244 W. Michigan Ave.
Jackson, MI 49201

TELEPHONE: (517) 788-4313

LIST NAMES OF BRANCHES WITH
SEPARATE POLICIES: None

BOOKS:
Will Lend: Yes
Length of Loan: 3 weeks
Renewable: Yes
Charges: None
Average Turnaround Time:
(Not answered)
If you have indicated that a
book is not to be lent, will
you on receipt of a letter
from the requesting library
search the index for given
entries? Yes

PERIODICALS:
Bound: Will not lend
Unbound: Will not lend
Loan Period: N/A
Renewable: N/A
Will lend if article exceeds
_____ number of pages (Not
answered)

MICROFORMS:
Will Lend: No
Specific Types of Microforms:
N/A

GOVERNMENT PUBLICATIONS:
Will Lend: Yes

DISSERTATIONS:
Will Lend: No

THESES:
Will Lend: No

AUDIO-VISUAL MATERIALS:
Records: Will not lend
Cassettes: Will not lend
Other (slides, filmstrips,
etc.): Will not lend

COMPUTER SOFTWARE:
Will Lend: No

PHOTODUPLICATION SERVICE:
No charge up to 5 exposures
Charge Per Exposure: 10¢
Minimum/handling Fee: $1.00
Average Turnaround Time:
2 weeks

MICROFILMING SERVICE:
Service Available: No
Charges: N/A

DO YOU CHARGE THE BORROWING
LIBRARY FOR POSTAGE? Yes

FOR HOW LONG DO YOU SUSPEND ILL
SERVICE OVER THE CHRISTMAS
HOLIDAYS? No suspension

ARE THERE ANY GROUPS OF LIBRARIES
FOR WHICH YOU WAIVE FEES? IF
SO, PLEASE NAME THEM: None

KALAMAZOO PUBLIC LIBRARY

NUC CODE: MiK

OCLC CODE: EXZ

ADDRESS: Interlibrary Loan
Kalamazoo Public
Library
315 S. Rose St.
Kalamazoo, MI 49007

TELEPHONE: (616) 342-9837, X61

LIST NAMES OF BRANCHES WITH
SEPARATE POLICIES: None

BOOKS:
Will Lend: Yes
Length of Loan: (Not
answered)
Renewable: Yes
Charges: (Not answered)
Average Turnaround Time:
7 days
If you have indicated that a
book is not to be lent, will
you on receipt of a letter
from the requesting library
search the index for given
entries? (Not answered)

PERIODICALS:
Bound: Will not lend
Unbound: Will not lend
Loan Period: N/A
Renewable: N/A
Will lend if article exceeds
_____ number of pages (Not
answered)

MICROFORMS:
Will Lend: No
Specific Types of Microforms:
N/A

GOVERNMENT PUBLICATIONS:
Will Lend: No

DISSERTATIONS:
Will Lend: No

THESES:
Will Lend: No

AUDIO-VISUAL MATERIALS:
Records: Will not lend
Cassettes: Will not lend
Other (slides, filmstrips,
etc.): Will not lend

COMPUTER SOFTWARE:
Will Lend: No

PHOTODUPLICATION SERVICE:
No charge up to 10 exposures
Charge Per Exposure: 10¢.
Prepaid MLC coupons are
accepted
Minimum/handling Fee: None
Average Turnaround Time:
7 days

MICROFILMING SERVICE:
Service Available: No
Charges: N/A

DO YOU CHARGE THE BORROWING
LIBRARY FOR POSTAGE? No

FOR HOW LONG DO YOU SUSPEND ILL
SERVICE OVER THE CHRISTMAS
HOLIDAYS? No suspension

ARE THERE ANY GROUPS OF LIBRARIES
FOR WHICH YOU WAIVE FEES? IF
SO, PLEASE NAME THEM: None

KENT COUNTY LIBRARY SYSTEM

NUC CODE: (Not answered)

OCLC CODE: EXE

ADDRESS: Interlibrary Loan
Kent County Library
System
775 Ball N.E.
Grand Rapids, MI 49503

TELEPHONE: (616) 774-3255

LIST NAMES OF BRANCHES WITH
SEPARATE POLICIES: None

BOOKS:
Will Lend: Yes
Length of Loan: 4 weeks
Renewable: No
Charges: (Not answered)
Average Turnaround Time:
(Not answered)
If you have indicated that a
book is not to be lent, will
you on receipt of a letter
from the requesting library
search the index for given
entries? (Not answered)

PERIODICALS:
Bound: Will not lend
Unbound: Will not lend
Loan Period: N/A
Renewable: N/A
Will lend if article exceeds
_____ number of pages (Not
answered)

MICROFORMS:
Will Lend: No
Specific Types of Microforms:
N/A

GOVERNMENT PUBLICATIONS:
Will Lend: No

DISSERTATIONS:
Will Lend: No

THESES:
Will Lend: No

AUDIO-VISUAL MATERIALS:
Records: Will not lend
Cassettes: Will not lend
Other (slides, filmstrips,
etc.): (Not answered)

COMPUTER SOFTWARE:
Will Lend: No

PHOTODUPLICATION SERVICE:
No charge up to 0 exposures
Charge Per Exposure: 10¢
Minimum/handling Fee: $3.00
Average Turnaround Time:
(Not answered)

MICROFILMING SERVICE:
Service Available: No
Charges: N/A

DO YOU CHARGE THE BORROWING
LIBRARY FOR POSTAGE? Yes

FOR HOW LONG DO YOU SUSPEND ILL
SERVICE OVER THE CHRISTMAS
HOLIDAYS? No suspension

ARE THERE ANY GROUPS OF LIBRARIES
FOR WHICH YOU WAIVE FEES? IF
SO, PLEASE NAME THEM: None

MICHIGAN STATE LIBRARY

NUC CODE: Mi

OCLC CODE: EEX

ADDRESS: Interlibrary Loan
Michigan State Library
P. O. Box 30007
Lansing, MI 48909

TELEPHONE: (517) 373-9197

LIST NAMES OF BRANCHES WITH
SEPARATE POLICIES: None

BOOKS:
Will Lend: Yes
Length of Loan: 1 month
Renewable: Yes
Charges: None
Average Turnaround Time:
4 days
If you have indicated that a
book is not to be lent, will
you on receipt of a letter
from the requesting library
search the index for given
entries? (Not answered)

PERIODICALS:
Bound: Will not lend
Unbound: Will not lend
Loan Period: N/A
Renewable: N/A
Will lend if article exceeds
_____ number of pages (Not
answered)

MICROFORMS:
Will Lend: Yes
Specific Types of Microforms:
Microfiche

GOVERNMENT PUBLICATIONS:
Will Lend: Yes

DISSERTATIONS:
Will Lend: Do not own

THESES:
Will Lend: Do not own

AUDIO-VISUAL MATERIALS:
Records: Will lend
Cassettes: Will lend
Other (slides, filmstrips,
etc.): Will lend

COMPUTER SOFTWARE:
Will Lend: No

PHOTODUPLICATION SERVICE:
No charge up to 10 exposures
Charge Per Exposure: 10¢
Minimum/handling Fee: $1.00
Average Turnaround Time:
(Not answered)

MICROFILMING SERVICE:
Service Available: No
Charges: N/A

DO YOU CHARGE THE BORROWING
LIBRARY FOR POSTAGE? No

FOR HOW LONG DO YOU SUSPEND ILL
SERVICE OVER THE CHRISTMAS
HOLIDAYS? No suspension

ARE THERE ANY GROUPS OF LIBRARIES
FOR WHICH YOU WAIVE FEES? IF
SO, PLEASE NAME THEM: None

MICHIGAN STATE UNIVERSITY

NUC CODE: MiEM

OCLC CODE: EEM

ADDRESS: Document Delivery
Service
Michigan State Univer-
sity Libraries
East Lansing, MI   48824

TELEPHONE: (517) 355-7641

LIST NAMES OF BRANCHES WITH
SEPARATE POLICIES: None

BOOKS:
Will Lend: Yes
Length of Loan: 2 weeks
Renewable: Yes
Charges: $7.00 prepaid;
$8.00 invoiced
Average Turnaround Time:
(Not answered)
If you have indicated that a
book is not to be lent, will
you on receipt of a letter
from the requesting library
search the index for given
entries? (Not answered)

PERIODICALS:
Bound: Will not lend
Unbound: Will not lend
Loan Period: N/A
Renewable: N/A
Will lend if article exceeds
_____ number of pages (Not
answered)

MICROFORMS:
Will Lend: Yes
Specific Types of Microforms:
All types

GOVERNMENT PUBLICATIONS:
Will Lend: (Not answered)

DISSERTATIONS:
Will Lend: Yes, with
reciprocal agreement and if
2nd copy available. 1960 to
present available from
University Microfilms

THESES:
Will Lend: Yes, with
reciprocal agreement and if
2nd copy available. 1978 to
present available from
University Microfilms

COMPUTER SOFTWARE:
Will Lend: (Not answered)

PHOTODUPLICATION SERVICE:
No charge up to 0 exposures
Charges: $7.00 up to 30
exposures; $8.00 if
invoiced
Average Turnaround Time:
(Not answered)

MICROFILMING SERVICE:
Service Available: (Not
answered)
Charges: N/A

DO YOU CHARGE THE BORROWING
LIBRARY FOR POSTAGE? (Not
answered)

FOR HOW LONG DO YOU SUSPEND ILL
SERVICE OVER THE CHRISTMAS
HOLIDAYS? Dec.15-Jan.3

ARE THERE ANY GROUPS OF LIBRARIES
FOR WHICH YOU WAIVE FEES? IF
SO, PLEASE NAME THEM: (Not
answered)

MONROE COUNTY LIBRARY SYSTEM

NUC CODE: (Not answered)

OCLC CODE: EXY

ADDRESS: Interlibrary Loan
Monroe County Library
System
3700 S. Custer Rd.
Monroe, MI   48161

TELEPHONE: (313) 241-5277

LIST NAMES OF BRANCHES WITH
SEPARATE POLICIES: None

BOOKS:
Will Lend: Yes
Length of Loan: 2 weeks
Renewable: Yes, upon
request
Charges: None
Average Turnaround Time:
1 month
If you have indicated that a
book is not to be lent, will
you on receipt of a letter
from the requesting library
search the index for given
entries? (Not answered)

PERIODICALS:
Bound: Will not lend
Unbound: Will lend
Loan Period: 2 weeks
Renewable: Yes, upon
request
Will lend if article exceeds
_____ number of pages (Not
answered)

MICROFORMS:
Will Lend: No
Specific Types of Microforms:
N/A

GOVERNMENT PUBLICATIONS:
Will Lend: Yes

DISSERTATIONS:
Will Lend: Do not own

THESES:
Will Lend: Do not own

AUDIO-VISUAL MATERIALS:
Records: Will lend
Cassettes: Will lend
Other (slides, filmstrips,
etc.): Will lend

COMPUTER SOFTWARE:
Will Lend: Do not own

PHOTODUPLICATION SERVICE:
No charge up to any exposures
Charge Per Exposure: None
Minimum/handling Fee: None
Average Turnaround Time:
(Not answered)

MICROFILMING SERVICE:
Service Available: No
Charges: N/A

DO YOU CHARGE THE BORROWING
LIBRARY FOR POSTAGE? No

FOR HOW LONG DO YOU SUSPEND ILL
SERVICE OVER THE CHRISTMAS
HOLIDAYS? 4 days

ARE THERE ANY GROUPS OF LIBRARIES
FOR WHICH YOU WAIVE FEES? IF
SO, PLEASE NAME THEM: None

OAKLAND UNIVERSITY

NUC CODE: MiRochOU

OCLC CODE: EYR

ADDRESS: Interlibrary Loan
          Kresge Library
          Oakland University
          Rochester, MI 48063

TELEPHONE: (313) 377-2473

LIST NAMES OF BRANCHES WITH
  SEPARATE POLICIES: None

BOOKS:
  Will Lend: Yes
  Length of Loan: 3 weeks
  Renewable: Yes
  Charges: $1.00 per title
  Average Turnaround Time:
    48 hours
  If you have indicated that a
    book is not to be lent, will
    you on receipt of a letter
    from the requesting library
    search the index for given
    entries? (Not answered)

PERIODICALS:
  Bound: Will not lend
  Unbound: Will not lend
  Loan Period: N/A
  Renewable: N/A
  Will lend if article exceeds
        _____ number of pages (Will
    not lend, regardless of
    length of article)

MICROFORMS:
  Will Lend: No
  Specific Types of Microforms:
    N/A

GOVERNMENT PUBLICATIONS:
  Will Lend: Yes

DISSERTATIONS:
  Will Lend: No

THESES:
  Will Lend: No

AUDIO-VISUAL MATERIALS:
  Records: Will not lend
  Cassettes: Will not lend
  Other (slides, filmstrips,
    etc.): Will not lend

COMPUTER SOFTWARE:
  Will Lend: Do not own

PHOTODUPLICATION SERVICE:
  No charge up to 0 exposures
  Charges: $4.00 for 1-30
    exposures
  Average Turnaround Time:
    72 hours

MICROFILMING SERVICE:
  Service Available: No
  Charges: N/A

DO YOU CHARGE THE BORROWING
  LIBRARY FOR POSTAGE? No

FOR HOW LONG DO YOU SUSPEND ILL
  SERVICE OVER THE CHRISTMAS
  HOLIDAYS? Approximately 19
  days

ARE THERE ANY GROUPS OF LIBRARIES
  FOR WHICH YOU WAIVE FEES? IF
  SO, PLEASE NAME THEM:
    Academic Libraries funded by
    the state of Michigan

SAGINAW VALLEY STATE COLLEGE

NUC CODE: None

OCLC CODE: EZS

ADDRESS: Interlibrary Loan
          Saginaw Valley State
            College Library
          2250 Pierce Rd.
          University Center, MI
            48710

TELEPHONE: (517) 790-4241 or
                  790-4242

LIST NAMES OF BRANCHES WITH
  SEPARATE POLICIES: None

BOOKS:
  Will Lend: Yes
  Length of Loan: 3 weeks
  Renewable: Yes
  Charges: None
  Average Turnaround Time:
    5-6 days
  If you have indicated that a
    book is not to be lent, will
    you on receipt of a letter
    from the requesting library
    search the index for given
    entries? (Not answered)

PERIODICALS:
  Bound: Will not lend
  Unbound: Will not lend
  Loan Period: N/A
  Renewable: N/A
  Will lend if article exceeds
        _____ number of pages (Will
    not lend, regardless of
    length of article)

MICROFORMS:
  Will Lend: No
  Specific Types of Microforms:
    N/A

GOVERNMENT PUBLICATIONS:
  Will Lend: Yes

DISSERTATIONS:
  Will Lend: No

THESES:
  Will Lend: No

AUDIO-VISUAL MATERIALS:
  Records: Will not lend
  Cassettes: Will not lend
  Other (slides, filmstrips,
    etc.): Will not lend

COMPUTER SOFTWARE:
  Will Lend: No

PHOTODUPLICATION SERVICE:
  No charge up to 15 exposures
  Charge Per Exposure: None
  Minimum/handling Fee: None
  Average Turnaround Time:
    4-5 days

MICROFILMING SERVICE:
  Service Available: No
  Charges: N/A

DO YOU CHARGE THE BORROWING
  LIBRARY FOR POSTAGE? No

FOR HOW LONG DO YOU SUSPEND ILL
  SERVICE OVER THE CHRISTMAS
  HOLIDAYS? No suspension

ARE THERE ANY GROUPS OF LIBRARIES
  FOR WHICH YOU WAIVE FEES? IF
  SO, PLEASE NAME THEM: No fees
  charged

TROY PUBLIC LIBRARY

NUC CODE: None

OCLC CODE: None

ADDRESS: Interlibrary Loan
Troy Public Library
510 W. Big Beaver Rd.
Troy, MI 48084

TELEPHONE: (313) 524-3539

LIST NAMES OF BRANCHES WITH
SEPARATE POLICIES: None

BOOKS:
Will Lend: Yes
Length of Loan: 4 weeks
Renewable: Yes
Charges: None
Average Turnaround Time:
1 day
If you have indicated that a
book is not to be lent, will
you on receipt of a letter
from the requesting library
search the index for given
entries? (Not answered)

PERIODICALS:
Bound: Will not lend
Unbound: Will not lend
Loan Period: N/A
Renewable: N/A
Will lend if article exceeds
_____ number of pages (Not
answered)

MICROFORMS:
Will Lend: No
Specific Types of Microforms:
N/A

GOVERNMENT PUBLICATIONS:
Will Lend: Yes

DISSERTATIONS:
Will Lend: Do not own

THESES:
Will Lend: Do not own

AUDIO-VISUAL MATERIALS:
Records: Will not lend
Cassettes: Will not lend
Other (slides, filmstrips,
etc.): Will not lend

COMPUTER SOFTWARE:
Will Lend: No

PHOTODUPLICATION SERVICE:
No charge up to 20 exposures
Charge Per Exposure: (Not
answered)
Minimum/handling Fee: (Not
answered)
Average Turnaround Time:
1 day

MICROFILMING SERVICE:
Service Available: No
Charges: N/A

DO YOU CHARGE THE BORROWING
LIBRARY FOR POSTAGE? No

FOR HOW LONG DO YOU SUSPEND ILL
SERVICE OVER THE CHRISTMAS
HOLIDAYS? No suspension

ARE THERE ANY GROUPS OF LIBRARIES
FOR WHICH YOU WAIVE FEES? IF
SO, PLEASE NAME THEM: None

UNIVERSITY OF DETROIT

NUC CODE: MiDU

OCLC CODE: EYU

ADDRESS: Interlibrary Loan
University of Detroit
Main Library
4001 W. McNichols Rd.
Detroit, MI 48221

TELEPHONE: (313) 927-1971 or
927-1078

LIST NAMES OF BRANCHES WITH
SEPARATE POLICIES:
University of Detroit
Dental Library

BOOKS:
Will Lend: Yes
Length of Loan: 2 weeks
Renewable: Yes
Charges: $3.00 for out-
of-state loans
Average Turnaround Time:
1 day
If you have indicated that a
book is not to be lent, will
you on receipt of a letter
from the requesting library
search the index for given
entries? (Not answered)

PERIODICALS:
Bound: Will not lend
Unbound: Will not lend
Loan Period: N/A
Renewable: N/A
Will lend if article exceeds
_____ number of pages (Will
not lend, regardless of
length of article)

MICROFORMS:
Will Lend: No
Specific Types of Microforms:
Card, film, fiche

GOVERNMENT PUBLICATIONS:
Will Lend: Yes

DISSERTATIONS:
Will Lend: No

THESES:
Will Lend: Yes

AUDIO-VISUAL MATERIALS:
Records: Will not lend
Cassettes: Will lend
Other (slides, filmstrips,
etc.): Will lend

COMPUTER SOFTWARE:
Will Lend: Do not own

PHOTODUPLICATION SERVICE:
No charge up to 0 exposures
Charges: $3.00 for 1-30
exposures; $1.00 each
additional 10 or fraction
Average Turnaround Time:
1 day

MICROFILMING SERVICE:
Service Available: No
Charges: N/A

DO YOU CHARGE THE BORROWING
LIBRARY FOR POSTAGE? No

FOR HOW LONG DO YOU SUSPEND ILL
SERVICE OVER THE CHRISTMAS
HOLIDAYS? Dec.15-Jan.5

ARE THERE ANY GROUPS OF LIBRARIES
FOR WHICH YOU WAIVE FEES? IF
SO, PLEASE NAME THEM:
Metropolitan Detroit
Medical Library Group

UNIVERSITY OF DETROIT DENTAL SCHOOL

NUC CODE: MiDU-D

OCLC CODE: EYU

ADDRESS: Interlibrary Loan
           University of Detroit
           Dental Library
           2931 E. Jefferson Ave.
           Detroit, MI 48207

TELEPHONE: (313) 446-1817

LIST NAMES OF BRANCHES WITH
   SEPARATE POLICIES:
   University of Detroit Main
   Library

BOOKS:
   Will Lend: Yes
   Length of Loan: 1 month
   Renewable: No
   Charges: $4.50/title
   Average Turnaround Time:
   2 days
   If you have indicated that a
   book is not to be lent, will
   you on receipt of a letter
   from the requesting library
   search the index for given
   entries? (Not answered)

PERIODICALS:
   Bound: Will not lend
   Unbound: Will not lend
   Loan Period: N/A
   Renewable: N/A
   Will lend if article exceeds
   _____ number of pages (Will
   not lend, regardless of
   length of article)

MICROFORMS:
   Will Lend: Do not own
   Specific Types of Microforms:
   N/A

GOVERNMENT PUBLICATIONS:
   Will Lend: Yes

DISSERTATIONS:
   Will Lend: Do not own

THESES:
   Will Lend: Do not own

AUDIO-VISUAL MATERIALS:
   Records: Do not own
   Cassettes: Do not own
   Other (slides, filmstrips,
   etc.): Do not own

COMPUTER SOFTWARE:
   Will Lend: No

PHOTODUPLICATION SERVICE:
   No charge up to 0 exposures
   Charges: $4.50 per request
   Average Turnaround Time:
   2 days

MICROFILMING SERVICE:
   Service Available: No
   Charges: N/A

DO YOU CHARGE THE BORROWING
   LIBRARY FOR POSTAGE? No

FOR HOW LONG DO YOU SUSPEND ILL
   SERVICE OVER THE CHRISTMAS
   HOLIDAYS? Dec.15-Jan.5

ARE THERE ANY GROUPS OF LIBRARIES
   FOR WHICH YOU WAIVE FEES? IF
   SO, PLEASE NAME THEM:
   Metropolitan Detroit Medical
   Library Group

UNIVERSITY OF MICHIGAN AT ANN ARBOR

NUC CODE: MiU

OCLC CODE: EYM

ADDRESS: Interlibrary Loan
           Hatcher Graduate
           Library
           University of Michigan
           Ann Arbor, MI 48109

TELEPHONE: (313) 764-8584

LIST NAMES OF BRANCHES WITH
   SEPARATE POLICIES:
   Taubman Medical Library
   Law Library

BOOKS:
   Will Lend: Yes
   Length of Loan: 2 weeks use
   Renewable: Yes
   Charges: $10.00 per loan,
   up to 4 volumes
   Average Turnaround Time:
   (Not answered)
   If you have indicated that a
   book is not to be lent, will
   you on receipt of a letter
   from the requesting library
   search the index for given
   entries? (Not answered)

PERIODICALS:
   Bound: Will not lend
   Unbound: Will not lend
   Loan Period: N/A
   Renewable: N/A
   Will lend if article exceeds
   _____ number of pages (Not
   answered)

MICROFORMS:
   Will Lend: Yes, some of them
   Specific Types of Microforms:
   (Not answered)

GOVERNMENT PUBLICATIONS:
   Will Lend: Yes, some of them

DISSERTATIONS:
   Will Lend: No; 1950 to
   present available from
   University Microfilms

THESES:
   Will Lend: No

AUDIO-VISUAL MATERIALS:
   Records: Will not lend
   Cassettes: Will not lend
   Other (slides, filmstrips,
   etc.): Will not lend

COMPUTER SOFTWARE:
   Will Lend: No

PHOTODUPLICATION SERVICE:
   No charge up to 0 exposures
   Charge Per Exposure: 15¢
   Minimum/handling Fee: $3.50
   Average Turnaround Time:
   (Not answered)

MICROFILMING SERVICE:
   Service Available: Yes
   Charges: Depends on nature
   of material

DO YOU CHARGE THE BORROWING
   LIBRARY FOR POSTAGE? Yes,
   for photocopies

FOR HOW LONG DO YOU SUSPEND ILL
   SERVICE OVER THE CHRISTMAS
   HOLIDAYS? 2 weeks

ARE THERE ANY GROUPS OF LIBRARIES
   FOR WHICH YOU WAIVE FEES? IF
   SO, PLEASE NAME THEM: RLG

UNIVERSITY OF MICHIGAN AT DEARBORN

NUC CODE: MiDbU

OCLC CODE: EYD

ADDRESS: Interlibrary Loan
           University of Michigan
           at Dearborn
           Library
           4901 Evergreen
           Dearborn, MI 48128

TELEPHONE: (313) 593-5400

LIST NAMES OF BRANCHES WITH
   SEPARATE POLICIES:
      University of Michigan at
      Ann Arbor
      University of Michigan at
      Flint

BOOKS:
   Will Lend: Yes
   Length of Loan: 1 month
     from shipping date
   Renewable: Yes
   Charges: None
   Average Turnaround Time:
     2 days
   If you have indicated that a
     book is not to be lent, will
     you on receipt of a letter
     from the requesting library
     search the index for given
     entries? (Not answered)

PERIODICALS:
   Bound: Will not lend
   Unbound: Will not lend
   Loan Period: N/A
   Renewable: N/A
   Will lend if article exceeds
     _____ number of pages (Will
     not lend, regardless of
     length of article)

MICROFORMS:
   Will Lend: No
   Specific Types of Microforms:
     N/A

GOVERNMENT PUBLICATIONS:
   Will Lend: No

DISSERTATIONS:
   Will Lend: No

THESES:
   Will Lend: No

AUDIO-VISUAL MATERIALS:
   Records: Will not lend
   Cassettes: Will not lend
   Other (slides, filmstrips,
     etc.): Will not lend

COMPUTER SOFTWARE:
   Will Lend: No

PHOTODUPLICATION SERVICE:
   No charge up to 0 exposures
   Charge Per Exposure: 5¢
   Minimum/handling Fee: $2.00
   Average Turnaround Time:
     2 days

MICROFILMING SERVICE:
   Service Available: No
   Charges: N/A

DO YOU CHARGE THE BORROWING
   LIBRARY FOR POSTAGE? No

FOR HOW LONG DO YOU SUSPEND ILL
   SERVICE OVER THE CHRISTMAS
   HOLIDAYS? Dec.23-Jan.5

ARE THERE ANY GROUPS OF LIBRARIES
   FOR WHICH YOU WAIVE FEES? IF
   SO, PLEASE NAME THEM: None

WARREN PUBLIC LIBRARY

NUC CODE: (Not answered)

OCLC CODE: (Not answered)

ADDRESS: Interlibrary Loan
           Arthur J. Miller
           Branch
           Warren Public Library
           4700 E. 13 Mile Rd.
           Warren, MI 48092

TELEPHONE: (313) 264-8720

LIST NAMES OF BRANCHES WITH
   SEPARATE POLICIES: All
   branches have same policy

BOOKS:
   Will Lend: Yes
   Length of Loan: 4 weeks
   Renewable: No
   Charges: None
   Average Turnaround Time:
     3 days
   If you have indicated that a
     book is not to be lent, will
     you on receipt of a letter
     from the requesting library
     search the index for given
     entries? (Not answered)

PERIODICALS:
   Bound: Will not lend
   Unbound: Will not lend
   Loan Period: N/A
   Renewable: N/A
   Will lend if article exceeds
     _____ number of pages (Not
     answered)

MICROFORMS:
   Will Lend: No
   Specific Types of Microforms:
     N/A

GOVERNMENT PUBLICATIONS:
   Will Lend: No

DISSERTATIONS:
   Will Lend: No

THESES:
   Will Lend: No

AUDIO-VISUAL MATERIALS:
   Records: Will not lend
   Cassettes: Will not lend
   Other (slides, filmstrips,
     etc.): Will not lend

COMPUTER SOFTWARE:
   Will Lend: No

PHOTODUPLICATION SERVICE:
   No charge up to 0 exposures
   Charge Per Exposure: 10¢
   Minimum/handling Fee: $3.00
   Average Turnaround Time:
     5 days

MICROFILMING SERVICE:
   Service Available: No
   Charges: N/A

DO YOU CHARGE THE BORROWING
   LIBRARY FOR POSTAGE? No

FOR HOW LONG DO YOU SUSPEND ILL
   SERVICE OVER THE CHRISTMAS
   HOLIDAYS? 2 weeks

ARE THERE ANY GROUPS OF LIBRARIES
   FOR WHICH YOU WAIVE FEES? IF
   SO, PLEASE NAME THEM: Member
   libraries of the Library
   Cooperative of Macomb

WAYNE OAKLAND LIBRARY FEDERATION

NUC CODE: (Not answered)

OCLC CODE: (Not answered)

ADDRESS: Interlibrary Loan
Wayne Oakland Library
Federation
33030 Van Born
Wayne, MI 48184

TELEPHONE: (313) 326-8910

LIST NAMES OF BRANCHES WITH
SEPARATE POLICIES: None

BOOKS:
Will Lend: Yes
Length of Loan: 4 weeks
Renewable: Yes
Charges: None
Average Turnaround Time:
7 days
If you have indicated that a
book is not to be lent, will
you on receipt of a letter
from the requesting library
search the index for given
entries? (Not answered)

PERIODICALS:
Bound: Will not lend
Unbound: Will not lend
Loan Period: N/A
Renewable: N/A
Will lend if article exceeds
_____ number of pages (Not
answered)

MICROFORMS:
Will Lend: No
Specific Types of Microforms:
N/A

GOVERNMENT PUBLICATIONS:
Will Lend: Yes

DISSERTATIONS:
Will Lend: Do not own

THESES:
Will Lend: Do not own

AUDIO-VISUAL MATERIALS:
Records: Will not lend
Cassettes: Will not lend
Other (slides, filmstrips,
etc.): Will not lend

COMPUTER SOFTWARE:
Will Lend: No

PHOTODUPLICATION SERVICE:
No charge up to 30 exposures
Charge Per Exposure: 10¢
Minimum/handling Fee: None
Average Turnaround Time:
3 days

MICROFILMING SERVICE:
Service Available: No
Charges: N/A

DO YOU CHARGE THE BORROWING
LIBRARY FOR POSTAGE? No

FOR HOW LONG DO YOU SUSPEND ILL
SERVICE OVER THE CHRISTMAS
HOLIDAYS? 1 week

ARE THERE ANY GROUPS OF LIBRARIES
FOR WHICH YOU WAIVE FEES? IF
SO, PLEASE NAME THEM: None

WAYNE STATE UNIVERSITY

NUC CODE: MIDW

OCLC CODE: EYW

ADDRESS: Document Delivery
University Libraries
Wayne State University
Detroit, MI 48202

TELEPHONE: (313) 577-4011

LIST NAMES OF BRANCHES WITH
SEPARATE POLICIES: None

BOOKS:
Will Lend: Yes
Length of Loan: 2 weeks plus
mailing time
Renewable: Yes
Charges: $4.00 plus $1.00
for invoice
Average Turnaround Time:
2-3 days
If you have indicated that a
book is not to be lent, will
you on receipt of a letter
from the requesting library
search the index for given
entries? (Not answered)

PERIODICALS:
Bound: Will not lend
Unbound: Will not lend
Loan Period: N/A
Renewable: N/A
Will lend if article exceeds
_____ number of pages (Not
answered)

MICROFORMS:
Will Lend: No
Specific Types of Microforms:
N/A

GOVERNMENT PUBLICATIONS:
Will Lend: Yes

DISSERTATIONS:
Will Lend: Yes, if not
available from UMI and if
2nd copy available; 1955 to
present available from
University Microfilms

THESES:
Will Lend: Yes

AUDIO-VISUAL MATERIALS:
Records: Will not lend
Cassettes: Will not lend
Other (slides, filmstrips,
etc.): Will not lend

COMPUTER SOFTWARE:
Will Lend: No

PHOTODUPLICATION SERVICE:
No charge up to 0 exposures
Charges: $4.00 handling
fee plus $1.00 invoice fee
per request
Average Turnaround Time:
3 days

MICROFILMING SERVICE:
Service Available: (Not
answered)
Charges: (Not answered)

DO YOU CHARGE THE BORROWING
LIBRARY FOR POSTAGE? Yes,
for photocopies

FOR HOW LONG DO YOU SUSPEND ILL
SERVICE OVER THE CHRISTMAS
HOLIDAYS? Dec.15-Jan.7

ARE THERE ANY GROUPS OF LIBRARIES
FOR WHICH YOU WAIVE FEES? IF
SO, PLEASE NAME THEM: Waive
loan fees only for ARL
members that do not charge
us

WESTERN MICHIGAN UNIVERSITY

NUC CODE: MiKW

OCLC CODE: EXW

ADDRESS: Interlibrary Loan
          Waldo Library
          Western Michigan
            University
          Kalamazoo, MI 49008

TELEPHONE: (616) 383-6054

LIST NAMES OF BRANCHES WITH
  SEPARATE POLICIES: None

BOOKS:
  Will Lend: Yes
  Length of Loan: 2 weeks
  Renewable: Yes
  Charges: Reciprocal charges
  Average Turnaround Time:
    24 hours
  If you have indicated that a
    book is not to be lent, will
    you on receipt of a letter
    from the requesting library
    search the index for given
    entries? (Not answered)

PERIODICALS:
  Bound: Will not lend
  Unbound: Will not lend
  Loan Period: N/A
  Renewable: N/A
  Will lend if article exceeds
    _____ number of pages (Not
    answered)

MICROFORMS:
  Will Lend: Yes, selectively
  Specific Types of Microforms:
    Microfilms and microfiche

GOVERNMENT PUBLICATIONS:
  Will Lend: Yes

DISSERTATIONS:
  Will Lend: Yes; 1968 to
    present available from
    University Microfilms

THESES:
  Will Lend: Yes

AUDIO-VISUAL MATERIALS:
  Records: Will not lend
  Cassettes: Will not lend
  Other (slides, filmstrips,
    etc.): Will not lend

COMPUTER SOFTWARE:
  Will Lend: No

PHOTODUPLICATION SERVICE:
  No charge up to 0 exposures
  Charge Per Exposure: 10¢
  Minimum/handling Fee: $2.00
    for out-of-state
  Average Turnaround Time:
    24 hours

MICROFILMING SERVICE:
  Service Available: No
  Charges: N/A

DO YOU CHARGE THE BORROWING
  LIBRARY FOR POSTAGE? No

FOR HOW LONG DO YOU SUSPEND ILL
  SERVICE OVER THE CHRISTMAS
  HOLIDAYS? Dec.15-Jan.4

ARE THERE ANY GROUPS OF LIBRARIES
  FOR WHICH YOU WAIVE FEES? IF
  SO, PLEASE NAME THEM:
    Southwest Michigan
    libraries; Michigan libraries
    (reciprocal charges when
    necessary)

ANOKA COUNTY LIBRARY

NUC CODE: MnMAC

OCLC CODE: (Not answered)

ADDRESS: Interlibrary Loan
           Anoka County Library
           1100 90th Ave. N.E.
           Blaine, MN 55434

TELEPHONE: (612) 784-1100

LIST NAMES OF BRANCHES WITH
  SEPARATE POLICIES: None

BOOKS:
  Will Lend: Yes
  Length of Loan: 3 weeks
  Renewable: No
  Charges: None
  Average Turnaround Time:
    (Not answered)
  If you have indicated that a
    book is not to be lent, will
    you on receipt of a letter
    from the requesting library
    search the index for given
    entries? (Not answered)

PERIODICALS:
  Bound: Will not lend
  Unbound: Will not lend
  Loan Period: N/A
  Renewable: N/A
  Will lend if article exceeds
    _____ number of pages (Not
    answered)

MICROFORMS:
  Will Lend: No
  Specific Types of Microforms:
    N/A

GOVERNMENT PUBLICATIONS:
  Will Lend: No

DISSERTATIONS:
  Will Lend: No

THESES:
  Will Lend: No

AUDIO-VISUAL MATERIALS:
  Records: Will not lend
  Cassettes: Will not lend
  Other (slides, filmstrips,
    etc.): Will not lend

COMPUTER SOFTWARE:
  Will Lend: No

PHOTODUPLICATION SERVICE:
  No charge up to 3 exposures
  Charge Per Exposure: 15¢
  Minimum/handling Fee: $5.00
  Average Turnaround Time:
    2 days

MICROFILMING SERVICE:
  Service Available: No
  Charges: N/A

DO YOU CHARGE THE BORROWING
  LIBRARY FOR POSTAGE? No

FOR HOW LONG DO YOU SUSPEND ILL
  SERVICE OVER THE CHRISTMAS
  HOLIDAYS? No suspension

ARE THERE ANY GROUPS OF LIBRARIES
  FOR WHICH YOU WAIVE FEES? IF
  SO, PLEASE NAME THEM: MINITEX
  or MELSA requests

BETHEL COLLEGE

NUC CODE: (Not answered)

OCLC CODE: MNK

ADDRESS: Interlibrary Loan
           Bethel College Library
           3900 Bethel Dr.
           St. Paul, MN 55112

TELEPHONE: (612) 638-6220

LIST NAMES OF BRANCHES WITH
  SEPARATE POLICIES: None

BOOKS:
  Will Lend: Yes
  Length of Loan: 4 weeks
  Renewable: No
  Charges: None
  Average Turnaround Time:
    (Not answered)
  If you have indicated that a
    book is not to be lent, will
    you on receipt of a letter
    from the requesting library
    search the index for given
    entries? Yes

PERIODICALS:
  Bound: Will not lend
  Unbound: Will not lend
  Loan Period: N/A
  Renewable: N/A
  Will lend if article exceeds
    _____ number of pages (Not
    answered)

MICROFORMS:
  Will Lend: Yes
  Specific Types of Microforms:
    Microfilm, microfiche

GOVERNMENT PUBLICATIONS:
  Will Lend: No

DISSERTATIONS:
  Will Lend: No

THESES:
  Will Lend: No

AUDIO-VISUAL MATERIALS:
  Records: Will not lend
  Cassettes: Will lend
  Other (slides, filmstrips,
    etc.): Will lend

COMPUTER SOFTWARE:
  Will Lend: No

PHOTODUPLICATION SERVICE:
  No charge up to 10 exposures
  Charge Per Exposure: 10¢
  Minimum/handling Fee: None
  Average Turnaround Time:
    3 days

MICROFILMING SERVICE:
  Service Available: No
  Charges: N/A

DO YOU CHARGE THE BORROWING
  LIBRARY FOR POSTAGE? No

FOR HOW LONG DO YOU SUSPEND ILL
  SERVICE OVER THE CHRISTMAS
  HOLIDAYS? 2 weeks

ARE THERE ANY GROUPS OF LIBRARIES
  FOR WHICH YOU WAIVE FEES? IF
  SO, PLEASE NAME THEM: None

COLLEGE OF ST. SCHOLASTICA

NUC CODE: MdDuStS

OCLC CODE: MNS

ADDRESS: Interlibrary Loan
           College of St.
             Scholastica Library
           1200 Kenwood Ave.
           Duluth, MN 55811

TELEPHONE: (218) 723-6140

LIST NAMES OF BRANCHES WITH
  SEPARATE POLICIES: None

BOOKS:
  Will Lend: Yes
  Length of Loan: 4 weeks
  Renewable: Yes
  Charges: None
  Average Turnaround Time:
    1-2 days
  If you have indicated that a
    book is not to be lent, will
    you on receipt of a letter
    from the requesting library
    search the index for given
    entries? Yes

PERIODICALS:
  Bound: Will not lend
  Unbound: Will not lend
  Loan Period: N/A
  Renewable: N/A
  Will lend if article exceeds
    _____ number of pages (Not
    answered)

MICROFORMS:
  Will Lend: No, but will copy
  Specific Types of Microforms:
    (Not answered)

GOVERNMENT PUBLICATIONS:
  Will Lend: Yes

DISSERTATIONS:
  Will Lend: Yes, if
    cataloged

THESES:
  Will Lend: Yes if
    cataloged

AUDIO-VISUAL MATERIALS:
  Records: Will not lend
  Cassettes: Will not lend
  Other (slides, filmstrips,
    etc.): Will not lend

COMPUTER SOFTWARE:
  Will Lend: No

PHOTODUPLICATION SERVICE:
  No charge up to _____
    exposures
  Charge Per Exposure: (Not
    answered)
  Minimum/handling Fee: (Not
    answered)
  Average Turnaround Time:
    1-2 days

MICROFILMING SERVICE:
  Service Available: No
  Charges: N/A

DO YOU CHARGE THE BORROWING
  LIBRARY FOR POSTAGE? No

FOR HOW LONG DO YOU SUSPEND ILL
  SERVICE OVER THE CHRISTMAS
  HOLIDAYS? No suspension

ARE THERE ANY GROUPS OF LIBRARIES
  FOR WHICH YOU WAIVE FEES? IF
  SO, PLEASE NAME THEM: N/A

CONCORDIA COLLEGE

NUC CODE: (Not answered)

OCLC CODE: TRI

ADDRESS: Interlibrary Loan
           Library
           Condordia College
           Moorhead, MN 56560

TELEPHONE: (218) 299-4641

LIST NAMES OF BRANCHES WITH
  SEPARATE POLICIES: None

BOOKS:
  Will Lend: Yes
  Length of Loan: 1 month
  Renewable: No
  Charges: Postage and
    insurance
  Average Turnaround Time:
    (Not answered)
  If you have indicated that a
    book is not to be lent, will
    you on receipt of a letter
    from the requesting library
    search the index for given
    entries? (Not answered)

PERIODICALS:
  Bound: Will not lend
  Unbound: Will not lend
  Loan Period: N/A
  Renewable: N/A
  Will lend if article exceeds
    _____ number of pages (Not
    answered)

MICROFORMS:
  Will Lend: No
  Specific Types of Microforms:
    N/A

GOVERNMENT PUBLICATIONS:
  Will Lend: No

DISSERTATIONS:
  Will Lend: No

THESES:
  Will Lend: No

AUDIO-VISUAL MATERIALS:
  Records: Will not lend
  Cassettes: Will not lend
  Other (slides, filmstrips,
    etc.): Will not lend

COMPUTER SOFTWARE:
  Will Lend: No

PHOTODUPLICATION SERVICE:
  No charge up to 0 exposures
  Charge Per Exposure: 10¢
  Minimum/handling Fee: $2.00
  Average Turnaround Time:
    (Not answered)

MICROFILMING SERVICE:
  Service Available: No
  Charges: N/A

DO YOU CHARGE THE BORROWING
  LIBRARY FOR POSTAGE? Yes

FOR HOW LONG DO YOU SUSPEND ILL
  SERVICE OVER THE CHRISTMAS
  HOLIDAYS? 2 weeks

ARE THERE ANY GROUPS OF LIBRARIES
  FOR WHICH YOU WAIVE FEES? IF
  SO, PLEASE NAME THEM: MINITEX

DAKOTA COUNTY LIBRARY SYSTEM

NUC CODE: None

OCLC CODE: None

ADDRESS: Interlibrary Loan
Dakota County Library
System
1101 West County Rd. 42
Burnsville, MN 55337

TELEPHONE: (612) 435-8111

LIST NAMES OF BRANCHES WITH
SEPARATE POLICIES: None

BOOKS:
Will Lend: Yes
Length of Loan: 4 weeks
Renewable: No
Charges: None
Average Turnaround Time:
4 days
If you have indicated that a
book is not to be lent, will
you on receipt of a letter
from the requesting library
search the index for given
entries? Yes

PERIODICALS:
Bound: Will not lend
Unbound: Will not lend
Loan Period: N/A
Renewable: N/A
Will lend if article exceeds
_____ number of pages (Will
not lend, regardless of
length of article)

MICROFORMS:
Will Lend: No
Specific Types of Microforms:
N/A

GOVERNMENT PUBLICATIONS:
Will Lend: Do not own

DISSERTATIONS:
Will Lend: Do not own

THESES:
Will Lend: Do not own

AUDIO-VISUAL MATERIALS:
Records: Will not lend
Cassettes: Will not lend
Other (slides, filmstrips,
etc.): Will not lend

COMPUTER SOFTWARE:
Will Lend: Do not own

PHOTODUPLICATION SERVICE:
No charge up to any exposures
Charge Per Exposure: None
Minimum/handling Fee: None
Average Turnaround Time:
(Not answered)

MICROFILMING SERVICE:
Service Available: No
Charges: N/A

DO YOU CHARGE THE BORROWING
LIBRARY FOR POSTAGE? No

FOR HOW LONG DO YOU SUSPEND ILL
SERVICE OVER THE CHRISTMAS
HOLIDAYS? No suspension

ARE THERE ANY GROUPS OF LIBRARIES
FOR WHICH YOU WAIVE FEES? IF
SO, PLEASE NAME THEM: No fees
charged

DULUTH PUBLIC LIBRARY

NUC CODE: None

OCLC CODE: None

ADDRESS: Interlibrary Loan
Duluth Public Library
520 W. Superior St.
Duluth, MN 55802

TELEPHONE: (218) 723-3828

LIST NAMES OF BRANCHES WITH
SEPARATE POLICIES: None

BOOKS:
Will Lend: Yes
Length of Loan: 4 weeks
Renewable: No
Charges: None
Average Turnaround Time:
2 days
If you have indicated that a
book is not to be lent, will
you on receipt of a letter
from the requesting library
search the index for given
entries? Yes

PERIODICALS:
Bound: Will not lend
Unbound: Will not lend
Loan Period: N/A
Renewable: N/A
Will lend if article exceeds
_____ number of pages (Will
not lend, regardless of
length of article)

MICROFORMS:
Will Lend: Yes
Specific Types of Microforms:
Local newspapers on
microfilm

GOVERNMENT PUBLICATIONS:
Will Lend: Yes

DISSERTATIONS:
Will Lend: Do not own

THESES:
Will Lend: Do not own

AUDIO-VISUAL MATERIALS:
Records: Will not lend
Cassettes: Will not lend
Other (slides, filmstrips,
etc.): Will not lend

COMPUTER SOFTWARE:
Will Lend: No

PHOTODUPLICATION SERVICE:
No charge up to 0 exposures
Charge Per Exposure: 25¢
Minimum/handling Fee: None
Average Turnaround Time:
3-5 days

MICROFILMING SERVICE:
Service Available: No
Charges: N/A

DO YOU CHARGE THE BORROWING
LIBRARY FOR POSTAGE? Yes

FOR HOW LONG DO YOU SUSPEND ILL
SERVICE OVER THE CHRISTMAS
HOLIDAYS? No suspension

ARE THERE ANY GROUPS OF LIBRARIES
FOR WHICH YOU WAIVE FEES? IF
SO, PLEASE NAME THEM:
Arrowhead Library System;
Public Library Access
Network of Minnesota;
MINITEX

GREAT RIVER REGIONAL LIBRARY

NUC CODE: (Not answered)

OCLC CODE: (Not answered)

ADDRESS: Interlibrary Loan
Great River Regional
Library
405 St. Germain
St. Cloud, MN 56301

TELEPHONE: (612) 251-7282

LIST NAMES OF BRANCHES WITH
SEPARATE POLICIES: None

BOOKS:
Will Lend: Yes
Length of Loan: 4 weeks
Renewable: No
Charges: None
Average Turnaround Time:
2 weeks
If you have indicated that a
book is not to be lent, will
you on receipt of a letter
from the requesting library
search the index for given
entries? (Not answered)

PERIODICALS:
Bound: Will not lend
Unbound: Will not lend
Loan Period: N/A
Renewable: N/A
Will lend if article exceeds
_____ number of pages (Not
answered)

MICROFORMS:
Will Lend: No
Specific Types of Microforms:
N/A

GOVERNMENT PUBLICATIONS:
Will Lend: No

DISSERTATIONS:
Will Lend: No

THESES:
Will Lend: No

AUDIO-VISUAL MATERIALS:
Records: Will not lend
Cassettes: Will not lend
Other (slides, filmstrips,
etc.): Will not lend

COMPUTER SOFTWARE:
Will Lend: No

PHOTODUPLICATION SERVICE:
No charge up to any exposures
Charge Per Exposure: 10¢
Minimum/handling Fee: None
Average Turnaround Time:
1 week

MICROFILMING SERVICE:
Service Available: No
Charges: N/A

DO YOU CHARGE THE BORROWING
LIBRARY FOR POSTAGE? No

FOR HOW LONG DO YOU SUSPEND ILL
SERVICE OVER THE CHRISTMAS
HOLIDAYS? (Not answered)

ARE THERE ANY GROUPS OF LIBRARIES
FOR WHICH YOU WAIVE FEES? IF
SO, PLEASE NAME THEM: None

HAMLINE UNIVERSITY

NUC CODE: MNSH

OCLC CODE: MHA

ADDRESS: Interlibrary Loan
Hamline University
Library
1536 Hewitt Ave.
St. Paul, MN 55104

TELEPHONE: (612) 641-2372

LIST NAMES OF BRANCHES WITH
SEPARATE POLICIES:
Hamline University Law
Library

BOOKS:
Will Lend: Yes
Length of Loan: 4 weeks
Renewable: Yes, if no
reserves
Charges: None at this time
Average Turnaround Time:
Same day
If you have indicated that a
book is not to be lent, will
you on receipt of a letter
from the requesting library
search the index for given
entries? Yes

PERIODICALS:
Bound: Will not lend
Unbound: Will not lend
Loan Period: N/A
Renewable: N/A
Will lend if article exceeds
_____ number of pages (Not
answered)

MICROFORMS:
Will Lend: No
Specific Types of Microforms:
N/A

GOVERNMENT PUBLICATIONS:
Will Lend: Yes

DISSERTATIONS:
Will Lend: Yes

THESES:
Will Lend: Yes

AUDIO-VISUAL MATERIALS:
Records: Will not lend
Cassettes: Will not lend
Other (slides, filmstrips,
etc.): Will not lend

COMPUTER SOFTWARE:
Will Lend: No

PHOTODUPLICATION SERVICE:
No charge up to 25 exposures
Charge Per Exposure: 10¢
Minimum/handling Fee: None
Average Turnaround Time:
Same day

MICROFILMING SERVICE:
Service Available: No
Charges: N/A

DO YOU CHARGE THE BORROWING
LIBRARY FOR POSTAGE? No

FOR HOW LONG DO YOU SUSPEND ILL
SERVICE OVER THE CHRISTMAS
HOLIDAYS? Closed only a few
days

ARE THERE ANY GROUPS OF LIBRARIES
FOR WHICH YOU WAIVE FEES? IF
SO, PLEASE NAME THEM: No fees
charged at this time, but
this policy is subject to
change if ILL load increases

HENNEPIN COUNTY LIBRARY

NUC CODE: None

OCLC CODE: None

ADDRESS: Interlibrary Loan
Hennepin County Library
Materials Selection
    Section
Ridgedale Drive at
    Plymouth Road
Mennetonka, MN 55343

TELEPHONE: (612) 541-8589

LIST NAMES OF BRANCHES WITH
SEPARATE POLICIES: None

BOOKS:
Will Lend: Yes
Length of Loan: 1 month
Renewable: Yes
Charges: None
Average Turnaround Time:
2 days
If you have indicated that a
book is not to be lent, will
you on receipt of a letter
from the requesting library
search the index for given
entries? (Not answered)

PERIODICALS:
Bound: Will not lend
Unbound: Will not lend
Loan Period: N/A
Renewable: N/A
Will lend if article exceeds
_____ number of pages (Not
answered)

MICROFORMS:
Will Lend: No
Specific Types of Microforms:
N/A

GOVERNMENT PUBLICATIONS:
Will Lend: Yes

DISSERTATIONS:
Will Lend: No

THESES:
Will Lend: No

AUDIO-VISUAL MATERIALS:
Records: Will not lend
Cassettes: Will not lend
Other (slides, filmstrips,
etc.): Will not lend

COMPUTER SOFTWARE:
Will Lend: No

PHOTODUPLICATION SERVICE:
No charge up to any exposures
Charge Per Exposure: None
Minimum/handling Fee: None
Average Turnaround Time:
2 days

MICROFILMING SERVICE:
Service Available: No
Charges: N/A

DO YOU CHARGE THE BORROWING
LIBRARY FOR POSTAGE? No

FOR HOW LONG DO YOU SUSPEND ILL
SERVICE OVER THE CHRISTMAS
HOLIDAYS? No suspension

ARE THERE ANY GROUPS OF LIBRARIES
FOR WHICH YOU WAIVE FEES? IF
SO, PLEASE NAME THEM: None

MACALESTER COLLEGE

NUC CODE: MnSM

OCLC CODE: MAC

ADDRESS: Interlibrary Loan
Macalester College
Library
1600 Grand Ave.
St. Paul, MN 55105

TELEPHONE: (612) 696-6546

LIST NAMES OF BRANCHES WITH
SEPARATE POLICIES: None

BOOKS:
Will Lend: Yes
Length of Loan: 4 weeks
Renewable: No
Charges: Postage for over-
size or multi-volume sets
Average Turnaround Time:
1 day
If you have indicated that a
book is not to be lent, will
you on receipt of a letter
from the requesting library
search the index for given
entries? (Not answered)

PERIODICALS:
Bound: Will not lend
Unbound: Will not lend
Loan Period: N/A
Renewable: N/A
Will lend if article exceeds
_____ number of pages (Not
answered)

MICROFORMS:
Will Lend: No
Specific Types of Microforms:
Microfilm and microfiche.
Will make copies if possible

GOVERNMENT PUBLICATIONS:
Will Lend: No

DISSERTATIONS:
Will Lend: No

THESES:
Will Lend: No

AUDIO-VISUAL MATERIALS:
Records: Will not lend
Cassettes: Will not lend
Other (slides, filmstrips,
etc.): Will not lend

COMPUTER SOFTWARE:
Will Lend: No

PHOTODUPLICATION SERVICE:
No charge up to 0 exposures
Charge Per Exposure: 10¢
Minimum/handling Fee: $1.50
Average Turnaround Time:
1 day

MICROFILMING SERVICE:
Service Available: No
Charges: N/A

DO YOU CHARGE THE BORROWING
LIBRARY FOR POSTAGE? No

FOR HOW LONG DO YOU SUSPEND ILL
SERVICE OVER THE CHRISTMAS
HOLIDAYS? Dec.1-Jan.8

ARE THERE ANY GROUPS OF LIBRARIES
FOR WHICH YOU WAIVE FEES? IF
SO, PLEASE NAME THEM: None

MANKATO STATE UNIVERSITY

NUC CODE: (Not answered)

OCLC CODE: MNM

ADDRESS: Interlibrary Loan
Memorial Library
2-12001
Mankato State University
Mankato, MN 56001

TELEPHONE: (507) 389-6201

LIST NAMES OF BRANCHES WITH
SEPARATE POLICIES: None

BOOKS:
Will Lend: Yes
Length of Loan: 1 month
Renewable: Yes
Charges: None
Average Turnaround Time:
48 hours
If you have indicated that a
book is not to be lent, will
you on receipt of a letter
from the requesting library
search the index for given
entries? (Not answered)

PERIODICALS:
Bound: Will not lend
Unbound: Will not lend
Loan Period: N/A
Renewable: N/A
Will lend if article exceeds
_____ number of pages (Not
answered)

MICROFORMS:
Will Lend: Yes, some of them
Specific Types of Microforms:
Monographs; some newspapers

GOVERNMENT PUBLICATIONS:
Will Lend: Yes

DISSERTATIONS:
Will Lend: Yes

THESES:
Will Lend: Yes

AUDIO-VISUAL MATERIALS:
Records: Will not lend
Cassettes: Will not lend
Other (slides, filmstrips,
etc.): Will not lend

COMPUTER SOFTWARE:
Will Lend: No

PHOTODUPLICATION SERVICE:
No charge up to 0 exposures
Charge Per Exposure: 10¢
Minimum/handling Fee: $2.00
Average Turnaround Time:
48 hours

MICROFILMING SERVICE:
Service Available: No
Charges: N/A

DO YOU CHARGE THE BORROWING
LIBRARY FOR POSTAGE? No

FOR HOW LONG DO YOU SUSPEND ILL
SERVICE OVER THE CHRISTMAS
HOLIDAYS? No suspension

ARE THERE ANY GROUPS OF LIBRARIES
FOR WHICH YOU WAIVE FEES? IF
SO, PLEASE NAME THEM: None

MINNEAPOLIS PUBLIC LIBRARY

NUC CODE: MnM

OCLC CODE: MPI

ADDRESS: Interlibrary Loan
Minneapolis Public
Library
300 Nicollet Mall
Minneapolis, MN 55401

TELEPHONE: (612) 372-6531

LIST NAMES OF BRANCHES WITH
SEPARATE POLICIES: None

BOOKS:
Will Lend: Yes
Length of Loan: 3 weeks use
Renewable: Yes, if not
on reserve
Charges: $10.00 to out-of-
state institutions
Average Turnaround Time:
(Not answered)
If you have indicated that a
book is not to be lent, will
you on receipt of a letter
from the requesting library
search the index for given
entries? (Not answered)

PERIODICALS:
Bound: Will not lend
Unbound: Will not lend
Loan Period: N/A
Renewable: N/A
Will lend if article exceeds
_____ number of pages (Not
answered)

MICROFORMS:
Will Lend: No
Specific Types of Microforms:
N/A

GOVERNMENT PUBLICATIONS:
Will Lend: No

DISSERTATIONS:
Will Lend: Do not own

THESES:
Will Lend: Do not own

AUDIO-VISUAL MATERIALS
Records: Will not lend
Cassettes: Will not lend
Other (slides, filmstrips,
etc.): Will not lend

COMPUTER SOFTWARE:
Will Lend: No

PHOTODUPLICATION SERVICE:
No charge up to _____ expo-
sures (Not answered)
Charge Per Exposure: (Not
answered)
Minimum/handling Fee:
(Not answered)
Average Turnaround Time:
(Not answered)

MICROFILMING SERVICE:
Service Available: No
Charges: N/A

DO YOU CHARGE THE BORROWING
LIBRARY FOR POSTAGE? No

FOR HOW LONG DO YOU SUSPEND ILL
SERVICE OVER THE CHRISTMAS
HOLIDAYS? No suspension

ARE THERE ANY GROUPS OF LIBRARIES
FOR WHICH YOU WAIVE FEES? IF
SO, PLEASE NAME THEM:
International Members of
Minitex

MINNESOTA STATE DEPARTMENT OF EDUCATION

NUC CODE: (Not answered)

OCLC CODE: MIL

ADDRESS: Interlibrary Loan
            Minnesota State
            Department of
            Education
            Office of Public
            Libraries and Inter-
            library Cooperation
            301 Hanover Bldg.
            480 Cedar St.
            St. Paul, MN 55101

TELEPHONE: (612) 296-2821

LIST NAMES OF BRANCHES WITH
  SEPARATE POLICIES: None

BOOKS:
  Will Lend: Yes
  Length of Loan: 3 weeks
    average
  Renewable: Yes
  Charges: None
  Average Turnaround Time:
    Varies
  If you have indicated that a
    book is not to be lent, will
    you on receipt of a letter
    from the requesting library
    search the index for given
    entries? (Not answered)

PERIODICALS:
  Bound: Will lend
  Unbound: Will lend
  Loan Period: 1-2 weeks
  Renewable: Yes
  Will lend if article exceeds
    _____ number of pages (Not
    answered)

MICROFORMS:
  Will Lend: Yes
  Specific Types of Microforms:
    Fiche and film

GOVERNMENT PUBLICATIONS:
  Will Lend: Yes

DISSERTATIONS:
  Will Lend: No

THESES:
  Will Lend: No

AUDIO-VISUAL MATERIALS:
  Records: Will lend
  Cassettes: Will lend
  Other (slides, filmstrips,
    etc.): Will lend

COMPUTER SOFTWARE:
  Will Lend: No

PHOTODUPLICATION SERVICE:
  No charge up to any exposures
  Charge Per Exposure: None
  Minimum/handling Fee: None
  Average Turnaround Time:
    Varies

MICROFILMING SERVICE:
  Service Available: No
  Charges: N/A

DO YOU CHARGE THE BORROWING
LIBRARY FOR POSTAGE? No

FOR HOW LONG DO YOU SUSPEND ILL
SERVICE OVER THE CHRISTMAS
HOLIDAYS? No suspension

ARE THERE ANY GROUPS OF LIBRARIES
FOR WHICH YOU WAIVE FEES? IF
SO, PLEASE NAME THEM: No fees
charged

RAMSEY COUNTY PUBLIC LIBRARY

NUC CODE: (Not answered)

OCLC CODE: RCL

ADDRESS: Interlibrary Loan
            Ramsey County Public
            Library
            1910 W. County Rd. B
            Roseville, MN 55113

TELEPHONE: (612) 636-6747, X10

LIST NAMES OF BRANCHES WITH
  SEPARATE POLICIES: None

BOOKS:
  Will Lend: Yes
  Length of Loan: 3 weeks
  Renewable: No
  Charges: None
  Average Turnaround Time:
    1 week
  If you have indicated that a
    book is not to be lent, will
    you on receipt of a letter
    from the requesting library
    search the index for given
    entries? Yes

PERIODICALS:
  Bound: Will not lend
  Unbound: Will not lend
  Loan Period: N/A
  Renewable: N/A
  Will lend if article exceeds
    _____ number of pages (Not
    answered)

MICROFORMS:
  Will Lend: No
  Specific Types of Microforms:
    N/A

GOVERNMENT PUBLICATIONS:
  Will Lend: (Not answered)

DISSERTATIONS:
  Will Lend: Do not own

THESES:
  Will Lend: Do not own

AUDIO-VISUAL MATERIALS:
  Records: Will not lend
  Cassettes: Will not lend
  Other (slides, filmstrips,
    etc.): Will not lend

COMPUTER SOFTWARE:
  Will Lend: No

PHOTODUPLICATION SERVICE:
  No charge for reasonable
    requests
  Minimum/handling Fee: None
  Average Turnaround Time:
    1 week

MICROFILMING SERVICE:
  Service Available: No
  Charges: N/A

DO YOU CHARGE THE BORROWING
LIBRARY FOR POSTAGE? No

FOR HOW LONG DO YOU SUSPEND ILL
SERVICE OVER THE CHRISTMAS
HOLIDAYS? No suspension

ARE THERE ANY GROUPS OF LIBRARIES
FOR WHICH YOU WAIVE FEES? IF
SO, PLEASE NAME THEM: No fees
charged

ST. OLAF COLLEGE

NUC CODE: MnNS

OCLC CODE: MNO

ADDRESS: Interlibrary Loan
           Rolvaag Memorial
           Library
           St. Olaf College
           Northfield, MN 55057

TELEPHONE: (507) 633-3223

LIST NAMES OF BRANCHES WITH
  SEPARATE POLICIES: None

BOOKS:
  Will Lend: Yes
  Length of Loan: 1 month
  Renewable: No
  Charges: (Not answered)
  Average Turnaround Time:
    2-3 days
  If you have indicated that a
    book is not to be lent, will
    you on receipt of a letter
    from the requesting library
    search the index for given
    entries? (Not answered)

PERIODICALS:
  Bound: Will not usually lend
  Unbound: Will not usually
    lend
  Loan Period: (Not answered)
  Renewable: (Not answered)
  PERIODICALS ARE NOT ROUTINELY
    LENT, BUT EXCEPTIONS ARE
    MADE FOR OLDER AND
    SPECIALIZED PERIODICALS

MICROFORMS:
  Will Lend: Yes
  Specific Types of Microforms:
    (Not answered)

GOVERNMENT PUBLICATIONS:
  Will Lend: Yes

DISSERTATIONS:
  Will Lend: Yes

THESES:
  Will Lend: Yes

AUDIO-VISUAL MATERIALS:
  Records: Will not lend
  Cassettes: Will not lend
  Other (slides, filmstrips,
    etc.): Will not lend

COMPUTER SOFTWARE:
  Will Lend: No

PHOTODUPLICATION SERVICE:
  No charge up to 0 exposures
  Charge Per Exposure: 10¢
  Minimum/handling Fee: $3.00
  Average Turnaround Time:
    2-3 days

MICROFILMING SERVICE:
  Service Available: No
  Charges: N/A

DO YOU CHARGE THE BORROWING
  LIBRARY FOR POSTAGE? No

FOR HOW LONG DO YOU SUSPEND ILL
  SERVICE OVER THE CHRISTMAS
  HOLIDAYS? (Not answered)

ARE THERE ANY GROUPS OF LIBRARIES
  FOR WHICH YOU WAIVE FEES? IF
  SO, PLEASE NAME THEM:
    Libraries in the Minitex
    System, (Minnesota,
    Wisconsin, North Dakota,
    South Dakota, Iowa)

ST. PAUL PUBLIC LIBRARY

NUC CODE: (Not answered)

OCLC CODE: SPP

ADDRESS: Interlibrary Loan
           St. Paul Public Library
           90 W. 4th St.
           St. Paul, MN 55102

TELEPHONE: (612) 292-6210

LIST NAMES OF BRANCHES WITH
  SEPARATE POLICIES: None

BOOKS:
  Will Lend: Yes
  Length of Loan: 2-3 weeks
  Renewable: No
  Charges: $5.00/loan
  Average Turnaround Time:
    1 day
  If you have indicated that a
    book is not to be lent, will
    you on receipt of a letter
    from the requesting library
    search the index for given
    entries? Yes

PERIODICALS:
  Bound: Will not lend
  Unbound: Will lend
  Loan Period: 2-3 weeks
  Renewable: No
  Will lend if article exceeds
    _____ number of pages (Not
    answered)

MICROFORMS:
  Will Lend: No
  Specific Types of Microforms:
    N/A

GOVERNMENT PUBLICATIONS:
  Will Lend: Yes

DISSERTATIONS:
  Will Lend: Do not own

THESES:
  Will Lend: Do not own

AUDIO-VISUAL MATERIALS:
  Records: Will not lend
  Cassettes: Will not lend
  Other (slides, filmstrips,
    etc.): Will not lend

COMPUTER SOFTWARE:
  Will Lend: No

PHOTODUPLICATION SERVICE:
  No charge up to 25 exposures
  Charge Per Additional
    Exposure: 15¢
  Minimum/handling Fee: $5.00
  Average Turnaround Time:
    1 day

MICROFILMING SERVICE:
  Service Available: No
  Charges: N/A

DO YOU CHARGE THE BORROWING
  LIBRARY FOR POSTAGE? No

FOR HOW LONG DO YOU SUSPEND ILL
  SERVICE OVER THE CHRISTMAS
  HOLIDAYS? No suspension

ARE THERE ANY GROUPS OF LIBRARIES
  FOR WHICH YOU WAIVE FEES? IF
  SO, PLEASE NAME THEM:
    MINITEX and Minnesota
    libraries that are members
    of Minnesota regional
    networks

UNIVERSITY OF MINNESOTA AT DULUTH

NUC CODE: MnDuU

OCLC CODE: MND

ADDRESS: Interlibrary Loan
University of Minnesota
at Duluth
Duluth Campus Library
Duluth, MN 55812

TELEPHONE: (218) 726-8100

LIST NAMES OF BRANCHES WITH
SEPARATE POLICIES: None

BOOKS:
Will Lend: Yes
Length of Loan: 2 weeks use
Renewable: Yes
Charges: (Not answered)
Average Turnaround Time:
(Not answered)
If you have indicated that a
book is not to be lent, will
you on receipt of a letter
from the requesting library
search the index for given
entries? (Not answered)

PERIODICALS:
Bound: Will not lend
Unbound: Will not lend
Loan Period: N/A
Renewable: N/A
Will lend if article exceeds
_____ number of pages (Not
answered)

MICROFORMS:
Will Lend: Yes
Specific Types of Microforms:
(Not answered)

GOVERNMENT PUBLICATIONS:
Will Lend: Yes

DISSERTATIONS:
Will Lend: Yes

THESES:
Will Lend: Yes

AUDIO-VISUAL MATERIALS:
Records: Will not lend
Cassettes: Will not lend
Other (slides, filmstrips,
etc.): Will not lend

COMPUTER SOFTWARE:
Will Lend: No

PHOTODUPLICATION SERVICE:
No charge up to 10 exposures
Charge Per Exposure: 10¢
Minimum/handling Fee: None
Average Turnaround Time:
(Not answered)

MICROFILMING SERVICE:
Service Available: No
Charges: N/A

DO YOU CHARGE THE BORROWING
LIBRARY FOR POSTAGE? No

FOR HOW LONG DO YOU SUSPEND ILL
SERVICE OVER THE CHRISTMAS
HOLIDAYS? No suspension

ARE THERE ANY GROUPS OF LIBRARIES
FOR WHICH YOU WAIVE FEES? IF
SO, PLEASE NAME THEM: None

UNIVERSITY OF MINNESOTA AT MINNEAPOLIS

NUC CODE: MnU

OCLC CODE: MNU

ADDRESS: Interlibrary Loan
179 Wilson Library
309 19th Ave. So.
University of Minnesota
Minneapolis, MN 55455

TELEPHONE: (612) 373-3259

LIST NAMES OF BRANCHES WITH
SEPARATE POLICIES:
Law School Library
St. Paul Campus Library
Bio-Medical Library

BOOKS:
Will Lend: Yes
Length of Loan: Usually
4 weeks
Renewable: Yes
Charges: Reciprocal
Average Turnaround Time:
3-5 days
If you have indicated that a
book is not to be lent, will
you on receipt of a letter
from the requesting library
search the index for given
entries? Yes

PERIODICALS:
Bound: Judged on case-by-case
basis
Unbound: Judged on case-by-
case basis
Loan Period: 1-4 weeks, case-
by-case basis
Renewable: Maybe
Will lend if article exceeds
_____ number of pages (Not
answered)

MICROFORMS:
Will Lend: Yes, microfilm
and microcards; no,
microfiche

GOVERNMENT PUBLICATIONS:
Will Lend: Yes

DISSERTATIONS:
Will Lend: We will lend on
reciprocal basis only

THESES:
Will Lend: We will lend on
reciprocal basis only

AUDIO-VISUAL MATERIALS:
Records: Will not lend
Cassettes: Will not lend
Other (slides, filmstrips,
etc.): Will not lend

COMPUTER SOFTWARE:
Will Lend: No

PHOTODUPLICATION SERVICE:
No charge up to 0 exposures
Charges: $3.50 for 1-10
exposures (includes
postage and handling);
10¢ each additional
exposure
Average Turnaround Time:
3-5 days

MICROFILMING SERVICE:
Service Available: Yes
Charges: Minimum charge,
$12.50; cost estimates by
request

DO YOU CHARGE THE BORROWING
LIBRARY FOR POSTAGE? No

FOR HOW LONG DO YOU SUSPEND ILL
SERVICE OVER THE CHRISTMAS
HOLIDAYS? No suspension

ARE THERE ANY GROUPS OF LIBRARIES
FOR WHICH YOU WAIVE FEES? IF
SO, PLEASE NAME THEM: RLG
members

UNIVERSITY OF MINNESOTA AT MINNEAPOLIS BIO-MEDICAL SCHOOL

NUC CODE: MnU-B

OCLC CODE:

ADDRESS: Interlibrary Loan
University of Minnesota
Bio-Medical Library
Diehl Hall
505 Essex Street S.E.
Minneapolis, MN 55455

TELEPHONE: (612) 376-3523

LIST NAMES OF BRANCHES WITH
SEPARATE POLICIES: None

BOOKS:
Will Lend: Yes
Length of Loan: 2 weeks
Renewable: Yes
Charges: $5.00
Average Turnaround Time:
1 day
If you have indicated that a
book is not to be lent, will
you on receipt of a letter
from the requesting library
search the index for given
entries? (Not answered)

PERIODICALS:
Bound: Will not lend
Unbound: Will not lend
Loan Period: N/A
Renewable: N/A
Will lend if article exceeds
_____ number of pages (Will
not lend, regardless of
length of article)

MICROFORMS:
Will Lend: Yes, some of them
Specific Types of Microforms:
Microfilm

GOVERNMENT PUBLICATIONS:
Will Lend: Yes

DISSERTATIONS:
Will Lend: Yes

THESES:
Will Lend: Yes

AUDIO-VISUAL MATERIALS:
Records: Will lend in-state
only
Cassettes: Will lend in-
state only
Other (slides, filmstrips,
etc.): Will lend in-state
only

COMPUTER SOFTWARE:
Will Lend: No

PHOTODUPLICATION SERVICE:
No charge up to 0 exposures
Charges: In-state=$2.00 per
item plus 10¢ a page plus
postage; Out-of-state=
$5.00 for 1-10 pages plus
10¢ per additional page
Average Turnaround Time:
1 day

MICROFILMING SERVICE:
Service Available: No
Charges: N/A

DO YOU CHARGE THE BORROWING
LIBRARY FOR POSTAGE? No

FOR HOW LONG DO YOU SUSPEND ILL
SERVICE OVER THE CHRISTMAS
HOLIDAYS? No suspension

ARE THERE ANY GROUPS OF LIBRARIES
FOR WHICH YOU WAIVE FEES? IF
SO, PLEASE NAME THEM: RLG
members

UNIVERSITY OF MINNESOTA AT MINNEAPOLIS LAW SCHOOL

NUC CODE: MnU-L

OCLC CODE: MLL

ADDRESS: Interlibrary Loan
University of Minnesota
Law Library
Law Center
229 19th Avenue So.
Minneapolis, MN 55455

TELEPHONE: (612) 376-2351

LIST NAMES OF BRANCHES WITH
SEPARATE POLICIES:
Wilson Library-ILL

BOOKS:
Will Lend: Yes
Length of Loan: 6 weeks
Renewable: Yes
Charges: None
Average Turnaround Time:
2-3 days
If you have indicated that a
book is not to be lent, will
you on receipt of a letter
from the requesting library
search the index for given
entries? (Not answered)

PERIODICALS:
Bound: Will not lend
Unbound: Will not lend
Loan Period: N/A
Renewable: N/A
Will lend if article exceeds
_____ number of pages (Not
answered)

MICROFORMS:
Will Lend: No
Specific Types of Microforms:
N/A

GOVERNMENT PUBLICATIONS:
Will Lend: Yes

DISSERTATIONS:
Will Lend: No

THESES:
Will Lend: No

AUDIO-VISUAL MATERIALS:
Records: Will not lend
Cassettes: Will not lend
Other (slides, filmstrips,
etc.): Will not lend

COMPUTER SOFTWARE:
Will Lend: No

PHOTODUPLICATION SERVICE:
No charge up to 0 exposures
Charge Per Exposure: 10¢
Minimum/handling Fee: $5.00
Average Turnaround Time:
2-3 days

MICROFILMING SERVICE:
Service Available: (Not
answered)
Charges: N/A

DO YOU CHARGE THE BORROWING
LIBRARY FOR POSTAGE? Only
for photoduplication
material

FOR HOW LONG DO YOU SUSPEND ILL
SERVICE OVER THE CHRISTMAS
HOLIDAYS? No suspension

ARE THERE ANY GROUPS OF LIBRARIES
FOR WHICH YOU WAIVE FEES? IF
SO, PLEASE NAME THEM: RLG

UNIVERSITY OF MINNESOTA AT SAINT PAUL

NUC CODE: MnSU

OCLC CODE: MNP

ADDRESS: Interlibrary Loan
University of Minnesota
St. Paul Campus
  Libraries
1984 Buford Ave.
St. Paul, MN 55108

TELEPHONE: (612) 373-0949

LIST NAMES OF BRANCHES WITH
  SEPARATE POLICIES: None

BOOKS:
  Will Lend: Yes
  Length of Loan: 4 weeks
  Renewable: Yes, if not in
    demand
  Charges: None, unless we are
    charged
  Average Turnaround Time:
    3 days
  If you have indicated that a
    book is not to be lent, will
    you on receipt of a letter
    from the requesting library
    search the index for given
    entries? (Not answered)

PERIODICALS:
  Bound: Will not usually lend
  Unbound: Will not usually
    lend
  Loan Period: 1 week, if
    loaned
  Renewable: No
  Will lend if article exceeds
    _____ number of pages (Not
    answered)

MICROFORMS:
  Will Lend: Yes
  Specific Types of Microforms:
    (Not answered)

GOVERNMENT PUBLICATIONS:
  Will Lend: Yes, at discretion
    of librarian

DISSERTATIONS:
  Will Lend: Yes, reciprocally
    only

THESES:
  Will Lend: Yes

AUDIO-VISUAL MATERIALS:
  Records: Do not own
  Cassettes: Do not own
  Other (slides, filmstrips,
    etc.): Do not own

COMPUTER SOFTWARE:
  Will Lend: Do not own

PHOTODUPLICATION SERVICE:
  No charge up to 0 exposures
  Charges: $3.50 for 1-10
    exposures; 10¢ each
    additional exposure
  Average Turnaround Time:
    (Not answered)

MICROFILMING SERVICE:
  Service Available: No
  Charges: N/A

DO YOU CHARGE THE BORROWING
  LIBRARY FOR POSTAGE? No

FOR HOW LONG DO YOU SUSPEND ILL
  SERVICE OVER THE CHRISTMAS
  HOLIDAYS? No suspension

ARE THERE ANY GROUPS OF LIBRARIES
  FOR WHICH YOU WAIVE FEES? IF
  SO, PLEASE NAME THEM: We
    charge reciprocally

DELTA STATE UNIVERSITY

NUC CODE: (Not answered)

OCLC CODE: (Not answered)

ADDRESS: Interlibrary Loan
Delta State University
W. B. Roberts Library
Cleveland, MS   38733

TELEPHONE: (601) 843-2483 or
843-2484

LIST NAMES OF BRANCHES WITH
SEPARATE POLICIES: None

BOOKS:
Will Lend: Yes
Length of Loan: 3 weeks
Renewable: Varies
Charges: None
Average Turnaround Time:
1 day
If you have indicated that a
book is not to be lent, will
you on receipt of a letter
from the requesting library
search the index for given
entries?   (Not answered)

PERIODICALS:
Bound: Will not lend
Unbound: Will not lend
Loan Period: N/A
Renewable: N/A
Will lend if article exceeds
_____ number of pages (Will
not lend, regardless of
length of article)

MICROFORMS:
Will Lend: No
Specific Types of Microforms:
Microfilm, microfiche,
microcard

GOVERNMENT PUBLICATIONS:
Will Lend: No

DISSERTATIONS:
Will Lend: Yes

THESES:
Will Lend: Yes

AUDIO-VISUAL MATERIALS:
Records: Will not lend
Cassettes: Will not lend
Other (slides, filmstrips,
etc.):   Will not lend

COMPUTER SOFTWARE:
Will Lend: Do not own

PHOTODUPLICATION SERVICE:
No charge up to 0 exposures
Charge Per Exposure: 10¢
Minimum/handling Fee: (Not
answered)
Average Turnaround Time:
1 day

MICROFILMING SERVICE:
Service Available: No
Charges: N/A

DO YOU CHARGE THE BORROWING
LIBRARY FOR POSTAGE?   No

FOR HOW LONG DO YOU SUSPEND ILL
SERVICE OVER THE CHRISTMAS
HOLIDAYS?   Dec.8-Jan.15

ARE THERE ANY GROUPS OF LIBRARIES
FOR WHICH YOU WAIVE FEES?   IF
SO, PLEASE NAME THEM: None

JACKSON METROPOLITAN LIBRARY

NUC CODE: (Not answered)

OCLC CODE: MJP

ADDRESS: Interlibrary Loan
Reference and Informa-
tion Dept.
Jackson Metro Library
301 N. State St.
Jackson, MS   39201

TELEPHONE: (601) 944-1120

LIST NAMES OF BRANCHES WITH
SEPARATE POLICIES: None

BOOKS:
Will Lend: Yes
Length of Loan: 4 weeks
Renewable: Yes
Charges: (Not answered)
Average Turnaround Time:
5 days
If you have indicated that a
book is not to be lent, will
you on receipt of a letter
from the requesting library
search the index for given
entries?   (Not answered)

PERIODICALS:
Bound: Will not lend
Unbound: Will not lend
Loan Period: N/A
Renewable: N/A
Will lend if article exceeds
_____ number of pages (Will
not lend, regardless of
length of article)

MICROFORMS:
Will Lend: No
Specific Types of Microforms:
N/A

GOVERNMENT PUBLICATIONS:
Will Lend: No

DISSERTATIONS:
Will Lend: No

THESES:
Will Lend: No

AUDIO-VISUAL MATERIALS:
Records: Will not lend
Cassettes: Will not lend
Other (slides, filmstrips,
etc.):   Will not lend

COMPUTER SOFTWARE:
Will Lend: No

PHOTODUPLICATION SERVICE:
No charge up to 0 exposures
Charge Per Exposure: 10¢
Minimum/handling Fee: Postage
Average Turnaround Time:
5 days

MICROFILMING SERVICE:
Service Available: No
Charges: N/A

DO YOU CHARGE THE BORROWING
LIBRARY FOR POSTAGE?   Yes

FOR HOW LONG DO YOU SUSPEND ILL
SERVICE OVER THE CHRISTMAS
HOLIDAYS?   No suspension

ARE THERE ANY GROUPS OF LIBRARIES
FOR WHICH YOU WAIVE FEES?   IF
SO, PLEASE NAME THEM: No
charge to libraries who do
not charge us

MISSISSIPPI STATE UNIVERSITY

NUC CODE: MSSM

OCLC CODE: MFM

ADDRESS: Interlibrary Loan
           Mitchell Memorial
             Library
           Mississippi State
             University
           Mississippi State, MS
             39762

TELEPHONE: (601) 325-3060

LIST NAMES OF BRANCHES WITH
  SEPARATE POLICIES: None

BOOKS:
  Will Lend: Yes
  Length of Loan: 1 month
    usually
  Renewable: Yes
  Charges: None
  Average Turnaround Time:
    7-10 days
  If you have indicated that a
    book is not to be lent, will
    you on receipt of a letter
    from the requesting library
    search the index for given
    entries? Yes

PERIODICALS:
  Bound: Will not lend
  Unbound: Will not lend
  Loan Period: N/A
  Renewable: N/A
  Will lend if article exceeds
    _____ number of pages (We
      do make exceptions)

MICROFORMS:
  Will Lend: No
  Specific Types of Microforms:
    N/A

GOVERNMENT PUBLICATIONS:
  Will Lend: Yes

DISSERTATIONS:
  Will Lend: Yes

AUDIO-VISUAL MATERIALS:
  Records: Will lend
  Cassettes: Will not lend
  Other (slides, filmstrips,
    etc.): Will not lend

COMPUTER SOFTWARE:
  Will Lend: No

PHOTODUPLICATION SERVICE:
  No charge up to 0 exposures
  Charge Per Exposure: 10¢
  Minimum Fee: $1.00
  Average Turnaround Time:
    7-10 days

MICROFILMING SERVICE:
  Service Available: Yes
  Charges: N/A

DO YOU CHARGE THE BORROWING
  LIBRARY FOR POSTAGE? Only
    if sent first-class

FOR HOW LONG DO YOU SUSPEND ILL
  SERVICE OVER THE CHRISTMAS
  HOLIDAYS? Dec.23-Jan.5

ARE THERE ANY GROUPS OF LIBRARIES
  FOR WHICH YOU WAIVE FEES? IF
  SO, PLEASE NAME THEM:
    Mississippi medical
    libraries

UNITED STATES ARMY ENGINEER WATERWAYS EXPERIMENT STATION

NUC CODE: None

OCLC CODE: AFM

ADDRESS: Interlibrary Loan
           U. S. Army Engineer
             Waterways Experiment
             Station
           ATTN: Technical
             Library
           P. O. Box 631
           Vicksburg, MS 39180

TELEPHONE: (601) 634-2355

LIST NAMES OF BRANCHES WITH
  SEPARATE POLICIES: None

BOOKS:
  Will Lend: Yes
  Length of Loan: 30 days
  Renewable: Yes, if no
    reserves
  Charges: None
  Average Turnaround Time:
    10 days
  If you have indicated that a
    book is not to be lent, will
    you on receipt of a letter
    from the requesting library
    search the index for given
    entries? (Not answered)

PERIODICALS:
  Bound: Will not lend
  Unbound: Will not lend
  Loan Period: N/A
  Renewable: N/A
  Will lend if article exceeds
    _____ number of pages (Not
      answered)

MICROFORMS:
  Will Lend: No
  Specific Types of Microforms:
    N/A

GOVERNMENT PUBLICATIONS:
  Will Lend: Yes

DISSERTATIONS:
  Will Lend: Yes

THESES:
  Will Lend: Yes

AUDIO-VISUAL MATERIALS:
  Records: Will not lend
  Cassettes: Will not lend
  Other (slides, filmstrips,
    etc.): Will not lend

COMPUTER SOFTWARE:
  Will Lend: Yes

PHOTODUPLICATION SERVICE:
  No charge ever
  Charge Per Exposure: None
  Minimum/handling Fee: None
  Average Turnaround Time:
    (Not answered)

MICROFILMING SERVICE:
  Service Available: Yes
  Charges: None

DO YOU CHARGE THE BORROWING
  LIBRARY FOR POSTAGE? No

FOR HOW LONG DO YOU SUSPEND ILL
  SERVICE OVER THE CHRISTMAS
  HOLIDAYS? No suspension

ARE THERE ANY GROUPS OF LIBRARIES
  FOR WHICH YOU WAIVE FEES? IF
  SO, PLEASE NAME THEM: No fees
    charged

UNIVERSITY OF MISSISSIPPI

NUC CODE: MsU

OCLC CODE: MUM

ADDRESS: Interlibrary Loan
John D. Williams
Library
University of
Mississippi
University, MS 38677

TELEPHONE: (601) 232-7091

LIST NAMES OF BRANCHES WITH
SEPARATE POLICIES:
A. A. Dodge Pharmacy Library

BOOKS:
Will Lend: Yes
Length of Loan: 1 month from
date mailed
Renewable: Yes
Charges: None
Average Turnaround Time:
2 days
If you have indicated that a
book is not to be lent, will
you on receipt of a letter
from the requesting library
search the index for given
entries? (Not answered)

PERIODICALS:
Bound: Will not lend
Unbound: Will not lend
Loan Period: N/A
Renewable: N/A
Will lend if article exceeds
_____ number of pages (Not
answered)

MICROFORMS:
Will Lend: Yes
Specific Types of Microforms:
Film, fiche, cards

GOVERNMENT PUBLICATIONS:
Will Lend: Yes

DISSERTATIONS:
Will Lend: Yes, if 2nd copy
available

THESES:
Will Lend: Yes, if 2nd copy
available

AUDIO-VISUAL MATERIALS:
Records: Will not lend
Cassettes: Will not lend
Other (slides, filmstrips,
etc.): Will not lend

COMPUTER SOFTWARE:
Will Lend: (Not answered)

PHOTODUPLICATION SERVICE:
No charge up to 2 exposures
Charge Per Exposure: 10¢
Minimum/handling Fee: $1.50
for out-of-state requests
Average Turnaround Time:
3 days

MICROFILMING SERVICE:
Service Available: No
Charges: N/A

DO YOU CHARGE THE BORROWING
LIBRARY FOR POSTAGE? No

FOR HOW LONG DO YOU SUSPEND ILL
SERVICE OVER THE CHRISTMAS
HOLIDAYS? Approximately
3 weeks

ARE THERE ANY GROUPS OF LIBRARIES
FOR WHICH YOU WAIVE FEES? IF
SO, PLEASE NAME THEM: Memphis
State University; Eastern
Kentucky University

UNIVERSITY OF MISSISSIPPI MEDICAL CENTER

NUC CODE: (Not answered)

OCLC CODE: (Not answered)

ADDRESS: Interlibrary Loan
University of
Mississippi Medical
Center
Rowland Medical Library
2500 North State St.
Jackson, MS 39216

TELEPHONE: (601) 987-4620

LIST NAMES OF BRANCHES WITH
SEPARATE POLICIES: None

BOOKS:
Will Lend: Yes
Length of Loan: 2 weeks
Renewable: No
Charges: $4.75 at this
time
Average Turnaround Time:
(Not answered)
If you have indicated that a
book is not to be lent, will
you on receipt of a letter
from the requesting library
search the index for given
entries? (Not answered)

PERIODICALS:
Bound: Will not lend
Unbound: Will not lend
Loan Period: N/A
Renewable: N/A
Will lend if article exceeds
_____ number of pages (Not
answered)

MICROFORMS:
Will Lend: No
Specific Types of Microforms:
N/A

GOVERNMENT PUBLICATIONS:
Will Lend: No

DISSERTATIONS:
Will Lend: No

THESES:
Will Lend: No

AUDIO-VISUAL MATERIALS:
Records: Will not lend
Cassettes: Will not lend
Other (slides, filmstrips,
etc.): Will not lend

COMPUTER SOFTWARE:
Will Lend: No

PHOTODUPLICATION SERVICE:
No charge up to 0 exposures
Charges: $4.75 per article
at this time
Average Turnaround Time:
(Not answered)

MICROFILMING SERVICE:
Service Available: No
Charges: N/A

DO YOU CHARGE THE BORROWING
LIBRARY FOR POSTAGE? No

FOR HOW LONG DO YOU SUSPEND ILL
SERVICE OVER THE CHRISTMAS
HOLIDAYS? 3 days

ARE THERE ANY GROUPS OF LIBRARIES
FOR WHICH YOU WAIVE FEES? IF
SO, PLEASE NAME THEM: None

UNIVERSITY OF SOUTHERN MISSISSIPPI

NUC CODE: (Not answered)

OCLC CODE: (Not answered)

ADDRESS: Interlibrary Loan
     Service
    University of Southern
    Mississippi Library
    Southern Station Box
    5053
    Hattiesburg, MS   39406

TELEPHONE: (601) 266-7011

LIST NAMES OF BRANCHES WITH
  SEPARATE POLICIES: None

BOOKS:
  Will Lend: Yes
  Length of Loan: 2 weeks
  Renewable: Yes
  Charges: $2.00 for out-of-
  state
  Average Turnaround Time:
  (Not answered)
  If you have indicated that a
  book is not to be lent, will
  you on receipt of a letter
  from the requesting library
  search the index for given
  entries?   (Not answered)

PERIODICALS:
  Bound: Will not lend
  Unbound: Will not lend
  Loan Period: N/A
  Renewable: N/A
  Will lend if article exceeds
  _____ number of pages   (Not
  answered)

MICROFORMS:
  Will Lend: Yes
  Specific Types of Microforms:
  (Not answered)

GOVERNMENT PUBLICATIONS:
  Will Lend: Yes

DISSERTATIONS:
  Will Lend: Yes, if microfiche available from USM;
  copying not permitted

THESES:
  Will Lend: No

AUDIO-VISUAL MATERIALS:
  Records: Will not lend
  Cassettes: Will not lend
  Other (slides, filmstrips,
  etc.):   (Not answered)

COMPUTER SOFTWARE:
  Will Lend: (Not answered)

PHOTODUPLICATION SERVICE:
  No charge up to 0 exposures
  Charge Per Exposure: 10¢
  Handling Fee: $2.00 for
  out-of-state
  Average Turnaround Time:
  (Not answered)

MICROFILMING SERVICE:
  Service Available: (Not
  answered)
  Charges: N/A

DO YOU CHARGE THE BORROWING
  LIBRARY FOR POSTAGE?   No

FOR HOW LONG DO YOU SUSPEND ILL
  SERVICE OVER THE CHRISTMAS
  HOLIDAYS?   (Not answered)

ARE THERE ANY GROUPS OF LIBRARIES
  FOR WHICH YOU WAIVE FEES?   IF
  SO, PLEASE NAME THEM: (Not
  answered)

CENTRAL MISSOURI STATE UNIVERSITY

NUC CODE: (Not answered)

OCLC CODE: MCW

ADDRESS: Interlibrary Loan
Ward Edwards Library
Central Missouri State
University
Warrensburg, MO 64093

TELEPHONE: (816) 429-4154

LIST NAMES OF BRANCHES WITH
SEPARATE POLICIES: None

BOOKS:
Will Lend: Yes
Length of Loan: 4 weeks
Renewable: Yes
Charges: None
Average Turnaround Time:
2 days
If you have indicated that a
book is not to be lent, will
you on receipt of a letter
from the requesting library
search the index for given
entries? (Not answered)

PERIODICALS:
Bound: Will not lend
Unbound: Will not lend
Loan Period: N/A
Renewable: N/A
Will lend if article exceeds
_____ number of pages (Not
answered)

MICROFORMS:
Will Lend: Yes, some of them
Specific Types of Microforms:
Dissertations

GOVERNMENT PUBLICATIONS:
Will Lend: Yes

DISSERTATIONS:
Will Lend: Yes

THESES:
Will Lend: Yes

AUDIO-VISUAL MATERIALS:
Records: Will not lend
Cassettes: Will not lend
Other (slides, filmstrips,
etc.): Will not lend

COMPUTER SOFTWARE:
Will Lend: No

PHOTODUPLICATION SERVICE:
No charge up to 0 exposures
Charge Per Exposure: 10¢
Minimum/handling Fee: $1.00
Average Turnaround Time:
1-2 days

MICROFILMING SERVICE:
Service Available: No
Charges: N/A

DO YOU CHARGE THE BORROWING
LIBRARY FOR POSTAGE? No

FOR HOW LONG DO YOU SUSPEND ILL
SERVICE OVER THE CHRISTMAS
HOLIDAYS? 1 week

ARE THERE ANY GROUPS OF LIBRARIES
FOR WHICH YOU WAIVE FEES? IF
SO, PLEASE NAME THEM: None

DANIEL BOONE REGIONAL LIBRARY

NUC CODE: (Not answered)

OCLC CODE: (Not answered)

ADDRESS: Interlibrary Loan
Daniel Boone Regional
Library
100 W. Broadway
Columbia, MO 65201

TELEPHONE: (314) 443-3161, X231

LIST NAMES OF BRANCHES WITH
SEPARATE POLICIES: None

BOOKS:
Will Lend: Yes
Length of Loan: 3 weeks
Renewable: Yes, if not
on reserve
Charges: None
Average Turnaround Time:
(Not answered)
If you have indicated that a
book is not to be lent, will
you on receipt of a letter
from the requesting library
search the index for given
entries? (Not answered)

PERIODICALS:
Bound: Will not lend
Unbound: Will lend
Loan Period: 3 weeks
Renewable: No
Will lend if article exceeds
_____ number of pages (Not
answered)

MICROFORMS:
Will Lend: No
Specific Types of Microforms:
N/A

GOVERNMENT PUBLICATIONS:
Will Lend: Yes, if
circulating

DISSERTATIONS:
Will Lend: Yes

THESES:
Will Lend: Yes

AUDIO-VISUAL MATERIALS:
Records: Will not lend
Cassettes: Will not lend
Other (slides, filmstrips,
etc.): Will not lend

COMPUTER SOFTWARE:
Will Lend: No

PHOTODUPLICATION SERVICE:
No charge up to 5 exposures
on automobile repair manuals
Charge Per Exposure: 10¢
Minimum/handling Fee: None
Average Turnaround Time:
(Not answered)

MICROFILMING SERVICE:
Service Available: No
Charges: N/A

DO YOU CHARGE THE BORROWING
LIBRARY FOR POSTAGE? No

FOR HOW LONG DO YOU SUSPEND ILL
SERVICE OVER THE CHRISTMAS
HOLIDAYS? 5-7 days

ARE THERE ANY GROUPS OF LIBRARIES
FOR WHICH YOU WAIVE FEES? IF
SO, PLEASE NAME THEM: None

DRURY COLLEGE

NUC CODE: MoSpD

OCLC CODE: MOD

ADDRESS: Interlibrary Loan
Walker Library
Drury College
Springfield, MO   65802

TELEPHONE: (417) 865-8731

LIST NAMES OF BRANCHES WITH
SEPARATE POLICIES: None

BOOKS:
Will Lend: Yes
Length of Loan: 1 month
Renewable: Yes
Charges: None
Average Turnaround Time:
2 days
If you have indicated that a
book is not to be lent, will
you on receipt of a letter
from the requesting library
search the index for given
entries? (Not answered)

PERIODICALS:
Bound: Will not lend
Unbound: Will not lend
Loan Period: N/A
Renewable: N/A
Will lend if article exceeds
_____ number of pages (Not
answered)

MICROFORMS:
Will Lend: No
Specific Types of Microforms:
N/A

GOVERNMENT PUBLICATIONS:
Will Lend: Yes

DISSERTATIONS:
Will Lend: Do not own

THESES:
Will Lend: Do not own

AUDIO-VISUAL MATERIALS:
Records: Will not lend
Cassettes: Will not lend
Other (slides, filmstrips,
etc.): Will not lend

COMPUTER SOFTWARE:
Will Lend: Do not own

PHOTODUPLICATION SERVICE:
No charge up to 1 exposure
Charge Per Exposure: 20¢
Minimum/handling Fee: $1.00
Average Turnaround Time:
2 days

MICROFILMING SERVICE:
Service Available: No
Charges: N/A

DO YOU CHARGE THE BORROWING
LIBRARY FOR POSTAGE? No

FOR HOW LONG DO YOU SUSPEND ILL
SERVICE OVER THE CHRISTMAS
HOLIDAYS? Dec.1-Jan.1

ARE THERE ANY GROUPS OF LIBRARIES
FOR WHICH YOU WAIVE FEES? IF
SO, PLEASE NAME THEM: None

KANSAS CITY PUBLIC LIBRARY

NUC CODE: MoK

OCLC CODE: KCP

ADDRESS: Interlibrary Loan
Kansas City Public
Library
311 E. 12th St.
Kansas City, MO   64106

TELEPHONE: (816) 221-2685

LIST NAMES OF BRANCHES WITH
SEPARATE POLICIES: None

BOOKS:
Will Lend: Yes
Length of Loan: 3 weeks use
Renewable: No
Charges: None
Average Turnaround Time:
(Not answered)
If you have indicated that a
book is not to be lent, will
you on receipt of a letter
from the requesting library
search the index for given
entries? (Not answered)

PERIODICALS:
Bound: Will not lend
Unbound: Will not lend
Loan Period: N/A
Renewable: N/A
Will lend if article exceeds
_____ number of pages (Not
answered)

MICROFORMS:
Will Lend: No
Specific Types of Microforms:
N/A

GOVERNMENT PUBLICATIONS:
Will Lend: Yes, with
approval of documents
librarian

DISSERTATIONS:
Will Lend: Do not own

THESES:
Will Lend: Do not own

AUDIO-VISUAL MATERIALS:
Records: Will not lend
Cassettes: Will not lend
Other (slides, filmstrips,
etc.): Will not lend

COMPUTER SOFTWARE:
Will Lend: No

PHOTODUPLICATION SERVICE:
No charge up to 0 exposures
Charge Per Exposure: 10¢
Minimum/handling Fee: $1.00
Average Turnaround Time:
1 week

MICROFILMING SERVICE:
Service Available: No
Charges: N/A

DO YOU CHARGE THE BORROWING
LIBRARY FOR POSTAGE? Yes

FOR HOW LONG DO YOU SUSPEND ILL
SERVICE OVER THE CHRISTMAS
HOLIDAYS? No suspension

ARE THERE ANY GROUPS OF LIBRARIES
FOR WHICH YOU WAIVE FEES? IF
SO, PLEASE NAME THEM: None

LINDA HALL LIBRARY

NUC CODE: MoKL

OCLC CODE: LHL

ADDRESS: Interlibrary Loan
Linda Hall Library
5109 Cherry St.
Kansas City, MO 64110

TELEPHONE: (816) 363-4600

LIST NAMES OF BRANCHES WITH
SEPARATE POLICIES: None

BOOKS:
Will Lend: Yes
Length of Loan: 2 weeks
Renewable: Yes, for 1 week
Charges: Postage
Average Turnaround Time:
1 week
If you have indicated that a
book is not to be lent, will
you on receipt of a letter
from the requesting library
search the index for given
entries? (Not answered)

PERIODICALS:
Bound: Will not lend
Unbound: Will not lend
Loan Period: N/A
Renewable: N/A
Will lend if article exceeds
_____ number of pages (Will
not lend, regardless of
length of article)

MICROFORMS:
Will Lend: Yes
Specific Types of Microforms:
Monographs

GOVERNMENT PUBLICATIONS:
Will Lend: No

DISSERTATIONS:
Will Lend: Do not own

THESES:
Will Lend: Do not own

AUDIO-VISUAL MATERIALS
Records: Do not own
Cassettes: Do not own
Other (slides, filmstrips,
etc.): Do not own

COMPUTER SOFTWARE:
Will Lend: Do not own

PHOTODUPLICATION SERVICE:
No charge up to 0 exposures
Charge Per Exposure: 40¢
Minimum/handling Fee: $2.00
per item or $4.00 per item
if ordered by mail
Average Turnaround Time:
1-3 weeks

MICROFILMING SERVICE:
Service Available: Yes
Charges: Same as photocopy
charges

DO YOU CHARGE THE BORROWING
LIBRARY FOR POSTAGE? Yes

FOR HOW LONG DO YOU SUSPEND ILL
SERVICE OVER THE CHRISTMAS
HOLIDAYS? No suspension

ARE THERE ANY GROUPS OF LIBRARIES
FOR WHICH YOU WAIVE FEES? IF
SO, PLEASE NAME THEM: None

MID-CONTINENT PUBLIC LIBRARY SYSTEM

NUC CODE: None

OCLC CODE: None

ADDRESS: Interlibrary Loan
Mid-Continent Public
Library System
15616 East 24 Hwy.
Independence, MO 64050

TELEPHONE: (816) 836-5200

LIST NAMES OF BRANCHES WITH
SEPARATE POLICIES: None

BOOKS:
Will Lend: Yes
Length of Loan: 28 days
Renewable: No
Charges: None
Average Turnaround Time:
(Not answered)
If you have indicated that a
book is not to be lent, will
you on receipt of a letter
from the requesting library
search the index for given
entries? (Not answered)

PERIODICALS:
Bound: Will not lend
Unbound: (Not answered)
Loan Period: N/A
Renewable: N/A
Will lend if article exceeds
_____ number of pages (Not
answered)

MICROFORMS:
Will Lend: No
Specific Types of Microforms:
N/A

GOVERNMENT PUBLICATIONS:
Will Lend: No

DISSERTATIONS:
Will Lend: No

THESES:
Will Lend: No

AUDIO-VISUAL MATERIALS:
Records: Will not lend
Cassettes: Will not lend
Other (slides, filmstrips,
etc.): Will not lend

COMPUTER SOFTWARE:
Will Lend: No

PHOTODUPLICATION SERVICE:
No charge up to 5 exposures
Charge Per Exposure: 10¢
after 1st 5
Minimum/handling Fee: None
Average Turnaround Time:
(Not answered)

MICROFILMING SERVICE:
Service Available: (Not
answered)
Charges: N/A

DO YOU CHARGE THE BORROWING
LIBRARY FOR POSTAGE? No

FOR HOW LONG DO YOU SUSPEND ILL
SERVICE OVER THE CHRISTMAS
HOLIDAYS? No suspension

ARE THERE ANY GROUPS OF LIBRARIES
FOR WHICH YOU WAIVE FEES? IF
SO, PLEASE NAME THEM: (Not
answered)

MISSOURI STATE LIBRARY

NUC CODE: LU

OCLC CODE: LUU

ADDRESS: Interlibrary Loan
Missouri State Library
308 E. High St.
Jefferson City, MO
65101

TELEPHONE: (910) 760-2455

LIST NAMES OF BRANCHES WITH
SEPARATE POLICIES: None

BOOKS:
Will Lend: Yes
Length of Loan: 1 month
Renewable: No
Charges: (Not answered)
Average Turnaround Time:
1 week
If you have indicated that a
book is not to be lent, will
you on receipt of a letter
from the requesting library
search the index for given
entries? (Not answered)

PERIODICALS:
Bound: Will not lend
Unbound: Will not lend
Loan Period: N/A
Renewable: N/A
Will lend if article exceeds
_____ number of pages (Not
answered)

MICROFORMS:
Will Lend: No
Specific Types of Microforms:
N/A

GOVERNMENT PUBLICATIONS:
Will Lend: Yes

DISSERTATIONS:
Will Lend: (Not answered)

THESES:
Will Lend: (Not answered)

AUDIO-VISUAL MATERIALS:
Records: Will not lend
Cassettes: Will not lend
Other (slides, filmstrips,
etc.): Will not lend

PHOTODUPLICATION SERVICE:
No charge up to 0 exposures
Charge Per Exposure: 20¢
Minimum/handling Fee: $2.00
Average Turnaround Time:
1 week

MICROFILMING SERVICE:
Service Available: No
Charges: N/A

DO YOU CHARGE THE BORROWING
LIBRARY FOR POSTAGE? No

FOR HOW LONG DO YOU SUSPEND ILL
SERVICE OVER THE CHRISTMAS
HOLIDAYS? No suspension

ARE THERE ANY GROUPS OF LIBRARIES
FOR WHICH YOU WAIVE FEES? IF
SO, PLEASE NAME THEM:
Missouri libraries

NORTHEAST MISSOURI STATE UNIVERSITY

NUC CODE: MoKiU

OCLC CODE: MKN

ADDRESS: Interlibrary Loan
Pickler Memorial
Library
Northeast Missouri
State University
Kirksville, MO 63501

TELEPHONE: (816) 785-4534

LIST NAMES OF BRANCHES WITH
SEPARATE POLICIES: None

BOOKS:
Will Lend: Yes
Length of Loan: 4 weeks
Renewable: No
Charges: Postage and
insurance fee
Average Turnaround Time:
1-2 days
If you have indicated that a
book is not to be lent, will
you on receipt of a letter
from the requesting library
search the index for given
entries? No

PERIODICALS:
Bound: Will not lend
Unbound: Will not lend
Loan Period: N/A
Renewable: N/A
Will lend if article exceeds
_____ number of pages (Not
answered)

MICROFORMS:
Will Lend: No
Specific Types of Microforms:
N/A

GOVERNMENT PUBLICATIONS:
Will Lend: Yes

DISSERTATIONS:
Will Lend: Yes

THESES:
Will Lend: Yes

AUDIO-VISUAL MATERIALS:
Records: Will not lend
Cassettes: Will not lend
Other (slides, filmstrips,
etc.): Will not lend

COMPUTER SOFTWARE:
Will Lend: No

PHOTODUPLICATION SERVICE:
No charge up to 0 exposures
Charge Per Exposure: 10¢
Minimum/handling Fee: None
Average Turnaround Time:
1-2 days

MICROFILMING SERVICE:
Service Available: No
Charges: N/A

DO YOU CHARGE THE BORROWING
LIBRARY FOR POSTAGE? Yes

FOR HOW LONG DO YOU SUSPEND ILL
SERVICE OVER THE CHRISTMAS
HOLIDAYS? Dec.15-Jan.2

ARE THERE ANY GROUPS OF LIBRARIES
FOR WHICH YOU WAIVE FEES? IF
SO, PLEASE NAME THEM: None

PARK COLLEGE

NUC CODE: MoPa

OCLC CODE: (Not answered)

ADDRESS: Interlibrary Loan
Park College
Parkville, MO 64152

TELEPHONE: (816) 741-2000

LIST NAMES OF BRANCHES WITH
SEPARATE POLICIES: None

BOOKS:
Will Lend: Yes
Length of Loan: 4 weeks
Renewable: Yes
Charges: Postage
Average Turnaround Time:
1 week
If you have indicated that a
book is not to be lent, will
you on receipt of a letter
from the requesting library
search the index for given
entries? (Not answered)

PERIODICALS:
Bound: Will not lend
Unbound: Will not lend
Loan Period: N/A
Renewable: N/A
Will lend if article exceeds
_____ number of pages (Not
answered)

MICROFORMS:
Will Lend: No
Specific Types of Microforms:
N/A

GOVERNMENT PUBLICATIONS:
Will Lend: Do not own

DISSERTATIONS:
Will Lend: Do not own

THESES:
Will Lend: Do not own

AUDIO-VISUAL MATERIALS:
Records: Will not lend
Cassettes: Will not lend
Other (slides, filmstrips,
etc.): Will not lend

COMPUTER SOFTWARE:
Will Lend: Do not own

PHOTODUPLICATION SERVICE:
No charge up to 0 exposures
Charge Per Exposure: (Not
answered)
Minimum/handling Fee: (Not
answered)
Average Turnaround Time:
(Not answered)

MICROFILMING SERVICE:
Service Available: No
Charges: N/A

DO YOU CHARGE THE BORROWING
LIBRARY FOR POSTAGE? Yes

FOR HOW LONG DO YOU SUSPEND ILL
SERVICE OVER THE CHRISTMAS
HOLIDAYS? 2 weeks

ARE THERE ANY GROUPS OF LIBRARIES
FOR WHICH YOU WAIVE FEES? IF
SO, PLEASE NAME THEM: None

ST. CHARLES CITY-COUNTY LIBRARY

NUC CODE: (Not answered)

OCLC CODE: (Not answered)

ADDRESS: Interlibrary Loan
St. Charles City-County
Library
1900 Merrill Dr.
St. Charles, MO 63301

TELEPHONE: (314) 723-0232

LIST NAMES OF BRANCHES WITH
SEPARATE POLICIES: None

BOOKS:
Will Lend: Yes
Length of Loan: 14 days
Renewable: Yes, upon
request
Charges: (Not answered)
Average Turnaround Time:
3 days
If you have indicated that a
book is not to be lent, will
you on receipt of a letter
from the requesting library
search the index for given
entries? (Not answered)

PERIODICALS:
Bound: Will not lend
Unbound: Will not lend
Loan Period: N/A
Renewable: N/A
Will lend if article exceeds
_____ number of pages (Not
answered)

MICROFORMS:
Will Lend: No
Specific Types of Microforms:
N/A

GOVERNMENT PUBLICATIONS:
Will Lend: No

DISSERTATIONS:
Will Lend: Do not own

THESES:
Will Lend: Do not own

AUDIO-VISUAL MATERIALS:
Records: Will not lend
Cassettes: Will not lend
Other (slides, filmstrips,
etc.): Will not lend

COMPUTER SOFTWARE:
Will Lend: No

PHOTODUPLICATION SERVICE:
No charge up to 0 exposures
Charge Per Exposure: 10¢
Minimum/handling Fee: None
Average Turnaround Time:
3 days

MICROFILMING SERVICE:
Service Available: No
Charges: N/A

DO YOU CHARGE THE BORROWING
LIBRARY FOR POSTAGE? No

FOR HOW LONG DO YOU SUSPEND ILL
SERVICE OVER THE CHRISTMAS
HOLIDAYS? 2 weeks

ARE THERE ANY GROUPS OF LIBRARIES
FOR WHICH YOU WAIVE FEES? IF
SO, PLEASE NAME THEM: None

ST. LOUIS COUNTY LIBRARY

NUC CODE: None

OCLC CODE: None

ADDRESS: Interlibrary Loan
St. Louis County
Library
1640 S. Lindbergh Blvd.
St. Louis, MO 63131

TELEPHONE: (314) 994-3300

LIST NAMES OF BRANCHES WITH
SEPARATE POLICIES: None

BOOKS:
Will Lend: Yes
Length of Loan: 4 weeks
Renewable: Yes, upon
request
Charges: None
Average Turnaround Time:
1-3 days
If you have indicated that a
book is not to be lent, will
you on receipt of a letter
from the requesting library
search the index for given
entries? Yes

PERIODICALS:
Bound: Will not lend
Unbound: Will not lend
Loan Period: N/A
Renewable: N/A
Will lend if article exceeds
_____ number of pages (Not
answered)

MICROFORMS:
Will Lend: No
Specific Types of Microforms:
N/A

GOVERNMENT PUBLICATIONS:
Will Lend: Yes

DISSERTATIONS:
Will Lend: Do not own

THESES:
Will Lend: Do not own

AUDIO-VISUAL MATERIALS:
Records: Will not lend
Cassettes: Will lend
Other (slides, filmstrips,
etc.): Will lend

COMPUTER SOFTWARE:
Will Lend: No

PHOTODUPLICATION SERVICE:
No charge up to 0 exposures
Charge Per Exposure: 1-5
exposures = 10¢/exposure;
6 exposures and up = 25¢/
exposure
Minimum/handling Fee: 50¢
Average Turnaround Time:
1-3 days

MICROFILMING SERVICE:
Service Available: No
Charges: N/A

DO YOU CHARGE THE BORROWING
LIBRARY FOR POSTAGE? No

FOR HOW LONG DO YOU SUSPEND ILL
SERVICE OVER THE CHRISTMAS
HOLIDAYS? No suspension

ARE THERE ANY GROUPS OF LIBRARIES
FOR WHICH YOU WAIVE FEES? IF
SO, PLEASE NAME THEM: None

ST. LOUIS PUBLIC LIBRARY

NUC CODE: MoS

OCLC CODE: SVP

ADDRESS: Interlibrary Loan
St. Louis Public
Library
1301 Olive St.
St. Louis, MO 63103

TELEPHONE: (314) 241-2288, X379

LIST NAMES OF BRANCHES WITH
SEPARATE POLICIES: None

BOOKS:
Will Lend: Yes
Length of Loan: 3 weeks
Renewable: No
Charges: None
Average Turnaround Time:
2 days
If you have indicated that a
book is not to be lent, will
you on receipt of a letter
from the requesting library
search the index for given
entries? Yes

PERIODICALS:
Bound: Will not lend
Unbound: Will not lend
Loan Period: N/A
Renewable: N/A
Will lend if article exceeds
_____ number of pages (Not
answered)

MICROFORMS:
Will Lend: No
Specific Types of Microforms:
N/A

GOVERNMENT PUBLICATIONS:
Will Lend: Yes

DISSERTATIONS:
Will Lend: No

THESES:
Will Lend: No

AUDIO-VISUAL MATERIALS:
Records: Will not lend
Cassettes: Will not lend
Other (slides, filmstrips,
etc.): Will not lend

COMPUTER SOFTWARE:
Will Lend: No

PHOTODUPLICATION SERVICE:
No charge up to 0 exposures
Charge Per Exposure: 25¢ for
xerox; 75¢ and up for copy
from microfilm
Minimum/handling Fee: $1.00
Average Turnaround Time:
48 hours

MICROFILMING SERVICE:
Service Available: No
Charges: N/A

DO YOU CHARGE THE BORROWING
LIBRARY FOR POSTAGE? No

FOR HOW LONG DO YOU SUSPEND ILL
SERVICE OVER THE CHRISTMAS
HOLIDAYS? No suspension

ARE THERE ANY GROUPS OF LIBRARIES
FOR WHICH YOU WAIVE FEES? IF
SO, PLEASE NAME THEM: None

ST. LOUIS UNIVERSITY

NUC CODE: MoSU

OCLC CODE: None

ADDRESS: Interlibrary Loan
Pius XII Memorial
Library
Saint Louis University
3655 W. Pine Blvd.
St. Louis, MO 63108

TELEPHONE: (314) 658-3104

LIST NAMES OF BRANCHES WITH
SEPARATE POLICIES:
School of Divinity Library
Medical Center Library
Omer Poos Law Library
Parks College

BOOKS:
Will Lend: Yes
Length of Loan: 2 weeks
Renewable: Yes
Charges: Reciprocal to fee-
charging libraries
Average Turnaround Time:
(Not answered)
If you have indicated that a
book is not to be lent, will
you on receipt of a letter
from the requesting library
search the index for given
entries? Yes

PERIODICALS:
Bound: Will not lend
Unbound: Will not lend
Loan Period: N/A
Renewable: N/A
Will lend if article exceeds
_____ number of pages (Not
answered)

MICROFORMS:
Will Lend: Yes
Specific Types of Microforms:
(Not answered)

GOVERNMENT PUBLICATIONS:
Will Lend: Yes

DISSERTATIONS:
Will Lend: No; 1957 to
present available from
University Microfilms

THESES:
Will Lend: No

AUDIO-VISUAL MATERIALS:
Records: Will not lend
Cassettes: Will not lend
Other (slides, filmstrips,
etc.): (Not answered)

COMPUTER SOFTWARE:
Will Lend: No

PHOTODUPLICATION SERVICE:
No charge up to 0 exposures
Charge Per Exposure: 10¢
Minimum Fee: $1.00 in-state
Handling Fee: 35¢ in-state
Minimum/handling Fee: $2.50
for out-of-state
Average Turnaround Time:
(Not answered)

MICROFILMING SERVICE:
Service Available: Yes
Charges: 10¢; $4.00 minimum/
handling fee

DO YOU CHARGE THE BORROWING
LIBRARY FOR POSTAGE? No

FOR HOW LONG DO YOU SUSPEND ILL
SERVICE OVER THE CHRISTMAS
HOLIDAYS? Dec.15-Jan.2

ARE THERE ANY GROUPS OF LIBRARIES
FOR WHICH YOU WAIVE FEES? IF
SO, PLEASE NAME THEM: None

ST. MARY'S COLLEGE

NUC CODE: (Not answered)

OCLC CODE: (Not answered)

ADDRESS: Interlibrary Loan
St. Mary's College
Library
200 North Main St.
O'Fallon, MO 63366

TELEPHONE: (314) 272-6171, X41

LIST NAMES OF BRANCHES WITH
SEPARATE POLICIES: None

BOOKS:
Will Lend: Yes
Length of Loan: 28 days
Renewable: Yes
Charges: Postage one way
Average Turnaround Time:
3 days
If you have indicated that a
book is not to be lent, will
you on receipt of a letter
from the requesting library
search the index for given
entries? Yes

PERIODICALS:
Bound: Will lend exception-
ally
Unbound: Will lend
Loan Period: 7 days
Renewable: Yes
Will lend if article exceeds
_____ number of pages (Not
answered)

MICROFORMS:
Will Lend: Yes
Specific Types of Microforms:
Fiche and reels

GOVERNMENT PUBLICATIONS:
Will Lend: No

DISSERTATIONS:
Will Lend: Yes

THESES:
Will Lend: Yes

AUDIO-VISUAL MATERIALS:
Records: Will lend
Cassettes: Will lend
Other (slides, filmstrips,
etc.): Will lend

COMPUTER SOFTWARE:
Will Lend: (Not answered)

PHOTODUPLICATION SERVICE:
No charge up to 0 exposures
Charge Per Exposure: 15¢
Minimum/handling Fee: $1.00
Average Turnaround Time:
3 days

MICROFILMING SERVICE:
Service Available: No
Charges: N/A

DO YOU CHARGE THE BORROWING
LIBRARY FOR POSTAGE? Yes,
if in excess of $1.00

FOR HOW LONG DO YOU SUSPEND ILL
SERVICE OVER THE CHRISTMAS
HOLIDAYS? No suspension

ARE THERE ANY GROUPS OF LIBRARIES
FOR WHICH YOU WAIVE FEES? IF
SO, PLEASE NAME THEM:
Usually none

SOUTHWEST MISSOURI STATE UNIVERSITY

NUC CODE: MoSpS

OCLC CODE: MOU

ADDRESS: Interlibrary Loan
           Southwest Missouri
             State University
             Library
           Springfield, MO 65804

TELEPHONE: (417) 836-5104

LIST NAMES OF BRANCHES WITH
  SEPARATE POLICIES: None

BOOKS:
  Will Lend: Yes
  Length of Loan: 4 weeks
  Renewable: Yes, once
  Charges: None
  Average Turnaround Time:
    5 days
  If you have indicated that a
    book is not to be lent, will
    you on receipt of a letter
    from the requesting library
    search the index for given
    entries? No

PERIODICALS:
  Bound: Will not lend
  Unbound: Will not lend
  Loan Period: N/A
  Renewable: N/A
  Will lend if article exceeds
    _____ number of pages (Not
    answered)

MICROFORMS:
  Will Lend: No
  Specific Types of Microforms:
    N/A

GOVERNMENT PUBLICATIONS:
  Will Lend: Yes

DISSERTATIONS:
  Will Lend: Do not own

THESES:
  Will Lend: Yes

AUDIO-VISUAL MATERIALS:
  Records: Will not lend
  Cassettes: Will not lend
  Other (slides, filmstrips,
    etc.): Will not lend

COMPUTER SOFTWARE:
  Will Lend: No

PHOTODUPLICATION SERVICE:
  No charge up to 0 exposures
  Charges: $2.50 for 1-5
    exposures; 10¢ each
    additional exposure
  Average Turnaround Time:
    1 week

MICROFILMING SERVICE:
  Service Available: No
  Charges: N/A

DO YOU CHARGE THE BORROWING
  LIBRARY FOR POSTAGE? No

FOR HOW LONG DO YOU SUSPEND ILL
  SERVICE OVER THE CHRISTMAS
  HOLIDAYS? No suspension

ARE THERE ANY GROUPS OF LIBRARIES
  FOR WHICH YOU WAIVE FEES? IF
  SO, PLEASE NAME THEM: None

UNIVERSITY OF MISSOURI AT KANSAS CITY

NUC CODE: MoKU

OCLC CODE: UMK

ADDRESS: Interlibrary Loan
           University of Missouri
             at Kansas City
           5100 Rockhill Rd.
           Kansas City, MO 64110

TELEPHONE: (816) 276-1586,
             276-1534, or 276-1535

LIST NAMES OF BRANCHES WITH
  SEPARATE POLICIES:
    Leon E. Bloch Law Library
    UMKC Health Sciences Library

BOOKS:
  Will Lend: Yes
  Length of Loan: 4 weeks
  Renewable: Yes
  Charges: None
  Average Turnaround Time:
    2 weeks
  If you have indicated that a
    book is not to be lent, will
    you on receipt of a letter
    from the requesting library
    search the index for given
    entries? (Not answered)

PERIODICALS:
  Bound: Will not lend
  Unbound: Will not lend
  Loan Period: N/A
  Renewable: N/A
  Will lend if article exceeds
    _____ number of pages (Not
    answered)

MICROFORMS:
  Will Lend: Yes, sometimes
  Specific Types of Microforms:
    Fiche, ultrafiche, microcard,
    microfiche

GOVERNMENT PUBLICATIONS:
  Will Lend: Yes

DISSERTATIONS:
  Will Lend: Yes

THESES:
  Will Lend: Yes

AUDIO-VISUAL MATERIALS:
  Records: Will sometimes lend
  Cassettes: Will sometimes
    lend
  Other (slides, filmstrips,
    etc.): Will sometimes lend

COMPUTER SOFTWARE:
  Will Lend: No

PHOTODUPLICATION SERVICE:
  No charge up to 0 exposures
  Charge Per Exposure: 10¢
  Minimum/handling Fee: $2.00
  Average Turnaround Time:
    2 weeks

MICROFILMING SERVICE:
  Service Available: No
  Charges: N/A

DO YOU CHARGE THE BORROWING
  LIBRARY FOR POSTAGE? No

FOR HOW LONG DO YOU SUSPEND ILL
  SERVICE OVER THE CHRISTMAS
  HOLIDAYS? No suspension

ARE THERE ANY GROUPS OF LIBRARIES
  FOR WHICH YOU WAIVE FEES? IF
  SO, PLEASE NAME THEM: None

UNIVERSITY OF MISSOURI AT ROLLA

NUC CODE: MoRM

OCLC CODE: UMR

ADDRESS: Interlibrary Loan
University of Missouri
at Rolla
Curtis Laws Wilson
Library
Rolla, MO 65401

TELEPHONE: (314) 341-4006

LIST NAMES OF BRANCHES WITH
SEPARATE POLICIES: None

BOOKS:
Will Lend: Yes
Length of Loan: 4 weeks
Renewable: (Not answered)
Charges: (Not answered)
Average Turnaround Time:
(Not answered)
If you have indicated that a
book is not to be lent, will
you on receipt of a letter
from the requesting library
search the index for given
entries? (Not answered)

PERIODICALS:
Bound: Will not lend
Unbound: Will not lend
Loan Period: N/A
Renewable: N/A
Will lend if article exceeds
_____ number of pages (Not
answered)

MICROFORMS:
Will Lend: Yes
Specific Types of Microforms:
(Not answered)

GOVERNMENT PUBLICATIONS:
Will Lend: Yes

DISSERTATIONS:
Will Lend: Yes, if pre-1967

THESES:
Will Lend: Yes, if pre-1967

AUDIO-VISUAL MATERIALS:
Records: Will not lend
Cassettes: Will not lend
Other (slides, filmstrips,
etc.): Will not lend

COMPUTER SOFTWARE:
Will Lend: No

PHOTODUPLICATION SERVICE:
No charge up to 0 exposures
Charge Per Exposure: 10¢
Minimum/handling Fee: $1.50
Average Turnaround Time:
(Not answered)

MICROFILMING SERVICE:
Service Available: No
Charges: N/A

DO YOU CHARGE THE BORROWING
LIBRARY FOR POSTAGE? No

FOR HOW LONG DO YOU SUSPEND ILL
SERVICE OVER THE CHRISTMAS
HOLIDAYS? No suspension

ARE THERE ANY GROUPS OF LIBRARIES
FOR WHICH YOU WAIVE FEES? IF
SO, PLEASE NAME THEM:
Other University of
Missouri campuses

UNIVERSITY OF MISSOURI AT ST. LOUIS

NUC CODE: MoU-St

OCLC CODE: UMS

ADDRESS: Interlibrary Loan
Thomas Jefferson
Library
University of Missouri
at St. Louis
8001 Natural Bridge Rd.
St. Louis, MO 63121

TELEPHONE: (314) 553-5066

LIST NAMES OF BRANCHES WITH
SEPARATE POLICIES:
Health Sciences Library

BOOKS:
Will Lend: Yes
Length of Loan: 4 weeks
Renewable: Yes
Charges: None
Average Turnaround Time:
2 days
If you have indicated that a
book is not to be lent, will
you on receipt of a letter
from the requesting library
search the index for given
entries? (Not answered)

PERIODICALS:
Bound: Will not lend
Unbound: Will not lend
Loan Period: N/A
Renewable: N/A
Will lend if article exceeds
_____ number of pages (Not
answered)

MICROFORMS:
Will Lend: Yes
Specific Types of Microforms:
Readex and microfilm lent
for Library Use only.
Microfiche originals not
lent, but fiche copies
made for 25¢ each.

GOVERNMENT PUBLICATIONS:
Will Lend: Yes

DISSERTATIONS:
Will Lend: Yes

THESES:
Will Lend: Yes

AUDIO-VISUAL MATERIALS:
Records: Will not lend
Cassettes: Will not lend
Other (slides, filmstrips,
etc.): Will not lend

COMPUTER SOFTWARE:
Will Lend: Do not own

PHOTODUPLICATION SERVICE:
No charge up to 0 exposures
Charge Per Exposure: 10¢
Minimum/handling Fee: $1.00
service charge
Average Turnaround Time:
2 days

MICROFILMING SERVICE:
Service Available: No
Charges: N/A

DO YOU CHARGE THE BORROWING
LIBRARY FOR POSTAGE? No

FOR HOW LONG DO YOU SUSPEND ILL
SERVICE OVER THE CHRISTMAS
HOLIDAYS? No suspension

ARE THERE ANY GROUPS OF LIBRARIES
FOR WHICH YOU WAIVE FEES? IF
SO, PLEASE NAME THEM: Univer-
sity of Missouri Libraries
at Columbia, Rolla and
Kansas City; Missouri
Institute of Psychiatry

WASHINGTON UNIVERSITY

NUC CODE: MoSW

OCLC CODE: WTU

ADDRESS: Interlibrary Loan
          Washington University
            Libraries
          St. Louis, MO 63130

TELEPHONE: (314) 889-5442

LIST NAMES OF BRANCHES WITH
  SEPARATE POLICIES: None

BOOKS:
  Will Lend: Yes
  Length of Loan: 2 weeks
  Renewable: Yes
  Charges: (Not answered)
  Average Turnaround Time:
    (Not answered)
  If you have indicated that a
    book is not to be lent, will
    you on receipt of a letter
    from the requesting library
    search the index for given
    entries? (Not answered)

PERIODICALS:
  Bound: Will not lend
  Unbound: Will not lend
  Loan Period: N/A
  Renewable: N/A
  Will lend if article exceeds
    _____ number of pages (Not
    answered)

MICROFORMS:
  Will Lend: Yes
  Specific Types of Microforms:
    Film only

GOVERNMENT PUBLICATIONS:
  Will Lend: (Not answered)

DISSERTATIONS:
  Will Lend: Yes. Available
    from University Microfilms
    since 1954

THESES:
  Will Lend: Yes

AUDIO-VISUAL MATERIALS:
  Records: Will not lend
  Cassettes: Will not lend
  Other (slides, filmstrips,
    etc.): (Not answered)

COMPUTER SOFTWARE:
  Will Lend: (Not answered)

PHOTODUPLICATION SERVICE:
  No charge up to _____
    exposures (Not answered)
  Charge Per Exposure: (Not
    answered)
  Minimum/handling Fee: (Not
    answered)
  Average Turnaround Time: (Not
    answered)

MICROFILMING SERVICE:
  Service Available: Yes
  Charges: 8¢-10¢ ($5.00
    minimum)

DO YOU CHARGE THE BORROWING
  LIBRARY FOR POSTAGE? No

FOR HOW LONG DO YOU SUSPEND ILL
  SERVICE OVER THE CHRISTMAS
  HOLIDAYS? (Not answered)

ARE THERE ANY GROUPS OF LIBRARIES
  FOR WHICH YOU WAIVE FEES? IF
  SO, PLEASE NAME THEM: (Not
  answered)

MONTANA STATE LIBRARY

NUC CODE: Mt

OCLC CODE: (Not answered)

ADDRESS: Interlibrary Loan
           Montana State Library
           930 E. Lyndale Ave.
           Helena, MT 59620

TELEPHONE: (406) 449-3004

LIST NAMES OF BRANCHES WITH
   SEPARATE POLICIES: None

BOOKS:
   Will Lend: Yes
   Length of Loan: 1 month
   Renewable: Yes
   Charges: Postage
   Average Turnaround Time:
      3 days
   If you have indicated that a
      book is not to be lent, will
      you on receipt of a letter
      from the requesting library
      search the index for given
      entries? (Not answered)

PERIODICALS:
   Bound: Will not lend
   Unbound: Will not lend
   Loan Period: N/A
   Renewable: N/A
   Will lend if article exceeds
   _____ number of pages (Not
      answered)

MICROFORMS:
   Will Lend: Yes
   Specific Types of Microforms:
      Federal document fiche

GOVERNMENT PUBLICATIONS:
   Will Lend: Yes

DISSERTATIONS:
   Will Lend: Do not own

THESES:
   Will Lend: Do not own

AUDIO-VISUAL MATERIALS:
   Records: Do not own
   Cassettes: Do not own
   Other (slides, filmstrips,
      etc.): Do not own

COMPUTER SOFTWARE:
   Will Lend: Do not own

PHOTODUPLICATION SERVICE:
   No charge up to 30 exposures
   Charge Per Exposure: (Not
      answered)
   Minimum/handling Fee: None
   Average Turnaround Time:
      3 days

MICROFILMING SERVICE:
   Service Available: No
   Charges: N/A

DO YOU CHARGE THE BORROWING
   LIBRARY FOR POSTAGE? Yes

FOR HOW LONG DO YOU SUSPEND ILL
   SERVICE OVER THE CHRISTMAS
   HOLIDAYS? No suspension

ARE THERE ANY GROUPS OF LIBRARIES
   FOR WHICH YOU WAIVE FEES? IF
   SO, PLEASE NAME THEM: None

MONTANA STATE UNIVERSITY

NUC CODE: MtBC

OCLC CODE: (Not answered)

ADDRESS: Interlibrary Loan
           Roland R. Renne
           Library
           Montana State
           University
           Bozeman, MT 59717

TELEPHONE: (406) 994-3161

LIST NAMES OF BRANCHES WITH
   SEPARATE POLICIES: None

BOOKS:
   Will Lend: Yes
   Length of Loan: 1 month
   Renewable: Yes, if no
      reserves, for 2 weeks
   Charges: Postage, if first-
      class, priority, or other
      special handling requested
   Average Turnaround Time:
      1-3 days
   If you have indicated that a
      book is not to be lent, will
      you on receipt of a letter
      from the requesting library
      search the index for given
      entries? (Not answered)

PERIODICALS:
   Bound: Will not lend
   Unbound: Will not lend
   Loan Period: N/A
   Renewable: N/A
   May lend if article exceeds
      30 pages (1 week use,
      library use only, no
      renewal)

MICROFORMS:
   Will Lend: Yes
   Specific Types of Microforms:
      Film, fiche, and cards,
      except for periodicals

GOVERNMENT PUBLICATIONS:
   Will Lend: Yes

DISSERTATIONS:
   Will Lend: Yes (library use
      only, 2 weeks use, copying
      not permitted)

THESES:
   Will Lend: Yes (library use
      only, 2 weeks use, copying
      not permitted)

AUDIO-VISUAL MATERIALS:
   Records: Will lend
   Cassettes: Will lend
   Other (slides, filmstrips,
      etc.): Will lend

COMPUTER SOFTWARE:
   Will Lend: Do not own

PHOTODUPLICATION SERVICE:
   No charge up to 0 exposures
   Charges: $1.00 for 1-9 pages,
      10¢ each additional page
      plus 25¢ handling
   Average Turnaround Time:
      1-3 days

MICROFILMING SERVICE:
   Service Available: No
   Charges: N/A

DO YOU CHARGE THE BORROWING
   LIBRARY FOR POSTAGE? Only
      for first-class, priority,
      or special handling

FOR HOW LONG DO YOU SUSPEND ILL
   SERVICE OVER THE CHRISTMAS
   HOLIDAYS? No suspension

ARE THERE ANY GROUPS OF LIBRARIES
   FOR WHICH YOU WAIVE FEES? IF
   SO, PLEASE NAME THEM: None

NORTHERN MONTANA COLLEGE

NUC CODE: MtHaN

OCLC CODE: (Not answered)

ADDRESS: Interlibrary Loan
Library
Northern Montana College
Havre, MT 59501

TELEPHON:E (406) 265-7821, X3306

LIST NAMES OF BRANCHES WITH
SEPARATE POLICIES: None

BOOKS:
Will Lend: Yes
Length of Loan: 4 weeks
Renewable: No
Charges: None
Average Turnaround Time:
2 days
If you have indicated that a
book is not to be lent, will
you on receipt of a letter
from the requesting library
search the index for given
entries? (Not answered)

PERIODICALS:
Bound: Will not lend
Unbound: Will not lend
Loan Period: N/A
Renewable: N/A
Will lend if article exceeds
_____ number of pages (Not
answered)

MICROFORMS:
Will Lend: No
Specific Types of Microforms:
N/A

GOVERNMENT PUBLICATIONS:
Will Lend: Yes

DISSERTATIONS:
Will Lend: No

THESES:
Will Lend: No

AUDIO-VISUAL MATERIALS:
Records: Will not lend
Cassettes: Will not lend
Other (slides, filmstrips,
etc.): Will not lend

COMPUTER SOFTWARE:
Will Lend: No

PHOTODUPLICATION SERVICE:
No charge up to 0 exposures
Charge Per Exposure: 10¢
Minimum/handling Fee: $1.00
Average Turnaround Time:
2 days

MICROFILMING SERVICE:
Service Available: Yes
(microfiche only)
Charges: $1.00 for first
fiche, 50¢ each additional
fiche

DO YOU CHARGE THE BORROWING
LIBRARY FOR POSTAGE? No

FOR HOW LONG DO YOU SUSPEND ILL
SERVICE OVER THE CHRISTMAS
HOLIDAYS? (Not answered)

ARE THERE ANY GROUPS OF LIBRARIES
FOR WHICH YOU WAIVE FEES? IF
SO, PLEASE NAME THEM: None

UNIVERSITY OF MONTANA

NUC CODE: MtU

OCLC CODE: (Not answered)

ADDRESS: Interlibrary Loan
University of Montana
Mansfield Library
Missoula, MT 59812

TELEPHONE: (406) 243-6736

LIST NAMES OF BRANCHES WITH
SEPARATE POLICIES: None

BOOKS:
Will Lend: Yes
Length of Loan: 4 weeks
Renewable: Yes
Charges: Postage
Average Turnaround Time:
(Not answered)
If you have indicated that a
book is not to be lent, will
you on receipt of a letter
from the requesting library
search the index for given
entries? Yes

PERIODICALS:
Bound: Will lend
Unbound: Will not lend
Loan Period: 2 weeks
Renewable: Yes
Will lend if article exceeds
30 pages

MICROFORMS:
Will Lend: Yes
Specific Types of Microforms:
(Not answered)

GOVERNMENT PUBLICATIONS:
Will Lend: Yes

DISSERTATIONS:
Will Lend: No

THESES:
Will Lend: Yes

AUDIO-VISUAL MATERIALS:
Records: Will not lend
Cassettes: Will not lend
Other (slides, filmstrips,
etc.): Will lend

COMPUTER SOFTWARE:
Will Lend: No

PHOTODUPLICATION SERVICE:
No charge up to 0 exposures
Charges: $1.00 for 1-5
exposures; 10¢ each
additional exposure
Average Turnaround Time:
(Not answered)

MICROFILMING SERVICE:
Service Available: Yes
Charges: Write for prices

DO YOU CHARGE THE BORROWING
LIBRARY FOR POSTAGE? Yes

FOR HOW LONG DO YOU SUSPEND ILL
SERVICE OVER THE CHRISTMAS
HOLIDAYS? No suspension

ARE THERE ANY GROUPS OF LIBRARIES
FOR WHICH YOU WAIVE FEES? IF
SO, PLEASE NAME THEM: None

CHADRON STATE COLLEGE

NUC CODE: NbChS

OCLC CODE: NCC

ADDRESS: Interlibrary Loan
          College Library
          Chadron State College
          Chadron, NE 69337

TELEPHONE: (308) 432-6271

LIST NAMES OF BRANCHES WITH
    SEPARATE POLICIES: None

BOOKS:
    Will Lend: Yes
    Length of Loan: 4 weeks
    Renewable: No
    Charges: Postage
    Average Turnaround Time:
      48 hours
    If you have indicated that a
      book is not to be lent, will
      you on receipt of a letter
      from the requesting library
      search the index for given
      entries? Depends on length
      of search and turnaround
      time desired; it's
      negotiable

PERIODICALS:
    Bound: Will not lend
    Unbound: Will not lend
    Loan Period: N/A
    Renewable: N/A
    Will lend if article exceeds
      _____ number of pages (Not
      answered)

MICROFORMS:
    Will Lend: No
    Specific Types of Microforms:
      N/A

GOVERNMENT PUBLICATIONS:
    Will Lend: Yes

DISSERTATIONS:
    Will Lend: Yes

THESES:
    Will Lend: Yes

AUDIO-VISUAL MATERIALS:
    Records: Will not lend
    Cassettes: Will not lend
    Other (slides, filmstrips,
      etc.): Will not lend

COMPUTER SOFTWARE:
    Will Lend: No

PHOTODUPLICATION SERVICE:
    No charge up to 5 exposures
    Charge Per Exposure: 15¢
    Minimum/handling Fee:
      $2.00 for out-of-state
    Average Turnaround Time:
      48 hours

MICROFILMING SERVICE:
    Service Available: No
    Charges: N/A

DO YOU CHARGE THE BORROWING
    LIBRARY FOR POSTAGE? Only
    for out-of-state

FOR HOW LONG DO YOU SUSPEND ILL
    SERVICE OVER THE CHRISTMAS
    HOLIDAYS? Dec.15-Jan.1

ARE THERE ANY GROUPS OF LIBRARIES
    FOR WHICH YOU WAIVE FEES? IF
    SO, PLEASE NAME THEM:
      PELARCON Members (Nebraska
      only); others by mutual
      consent or negotiation

CREIGHTON UNIVERSITY

NUC CODE: NbOc

OCLC CODE: OCA

ADDRESS: Interlibrary Loan
          Alumni Memorial
            Library
          Creighton University
          2500 California St.
          Omaha, NE 68178

TELEPHONE: (402) 280-2705

LIST NAMES OF BRANCHES WITH
    SEPARATE POLICIES: None

BOOKS:
    Will Lend: Yes
    Length of Loan: 1 months use
    Renewable: Yes, once
    Charges: $1.00 service fee
      plus postage
    Average Turnaround Time:
      1-3 days
    If you have indicated that a
      book is not to be lent, will
      you on receipt of a letter
      from the requesting library
      search the index for given
      entries? (Not answered)

PERIODICALS:
    Bound: Will not lend
    Unbound: Will not lend
    Loan Period: N/A
    Renewable: N/A
    Will lend if article exceeds
      _____ number of pages (Not
      answered)

MICROFORMS:
    Will Lend: (Not answered)
    Specific Types of Microforms:
      N/A

GOVERNMENT PUBLICATIONS:
    Will Lend: Yes, 2 weeks use

DISSERTATIONS:
    Will Lend: (Not answered)

THESES:
    Will Lend: Yes, 2 weeks use

AUDIO-VISUAL MATERIALS:
    Records: Will not lend
    Cassettes: Will not lend
    Other (slides, filmstrips,
      etc.): Will not lend

COMPUTER SOFTWARE:
    Will Lend: Do not own

PHOTODUPLICATION SERVICE:
    No charge up to 0 exposures
    Charge Per Exposure: 20¢
    Minimum/handling Fee: $1.00
    Average Turnaround Time:
      1-3 days

MICROFILMING SERVICE:
    Service Available: No
    Charges: N/A

DO YOU CHARGE THE BORROWING
    LIBRARY FOR POSTAGE? Yes,
    except PELARCON members

FOR HOW LONG DO YOU SUSPEND ILL
    SERVICE OVER THE CHRISTMAS
    HOLIDAYS? Approximately
    1 month

ARE THERE ANY GROUPS OF LIBRARIES
    FOR WHICH YOU WAIVE FEES? IF
    SO, PLEASE NAME THEM:
      PELARCON members

KEARNEY STATE COLLEGE

NUC CODE: (Not answered)

OCLC CODE: KRS

ADDRESS: Interlibrary Loan
           Calvin T. Ryan Library
           Kearney State College
           Kearney, NE 68847

TELEPHONE: (308) 236-4218

LIST NAMES OF BRANCHES WITH
  SEPARATE POLICIES: None

BOOKS:
  Will Lend: Yes
  Length of Loan: 4 weeks
  Renewable: No
  Charges: None
  Average Turnaround Time:
    3 days
  If you have indicated that a
  book is not to be lent, will
  you on receipt of a letter
  from the requesting library
  search the index for given
  entries? (Not answered)

PERIODICALS:
  Bound: Will not lend
  Unbound: Will not lend
  Loan Period: N/A
  Renewable: N/A
  Will lend if article exceeds
  _____ number of pages (Will
     not lend, regardless of
     length of article)

MICROFORMS:
  Will Lend: Yes
  Specific Types of Microforms:
    Microfilm, microfiche,
    ultrafiche

GOVERNMENT PUBLICATIONS:
  Will Lend: Yes

DISSERTATIONS:
  Will Lend: Yes

THESES:
  Will Lend: Yes

AUDIO-VISUAL MATERIALS:
  Records: Will not lend
  Cassettes: Will not lend
  Other (slides, filmstrips,
    etc.): Will not lend

COMPUTER SOFTWARE:
  Will Lend: No

PHOTODUPLICATION SERVICE:
  No charge up to 3 exposures
  Charge Per Exposure: 10¢
  Minimum/handling Fee: None
  Average Turnaround Time:
    3 days

MICROFILMING SERVICE:
  Service Available: No
  Charges: N/A

DO YOU CHARGE THE BORROWING
  LIBRARY FOR POSTAGE? No

FOR HOW LONG DO YOU SUSPEND ILL
  SERVICE OVER THE CHRISTMAS
  HOLIDAYS? 1 week

ARE THERE ANY GROUPS OF LIBRARIES
  FOR WHICH YOU WAIVE FEES? IF
  SO, PLEASE NAME THEM:
    PELARCON

LINCOLN CITY LIBRARIES

NUC CODE: (Not answered)

OCLC CODE: NLN

ADDRESS: Interlibrary Loan
           Lincoln City Libraries
           136 S. 14th St.
           Lincoln, NE 68508

TELEPHONE: (402) 435-2146

LIST NAMES OF BRANCHES WITH
  SEPARATE POLICIES: None

BOOKS:
  Will Lend: Yes
  Length of Loan: 1 month
  Renewable: Yes
  Charges: (Not answered)
  Average Turnaround Time:
    (Not answered)
  If you have indicated that a
  book is not to be lent, will
  you on receipt of a letter
  from the requesting library
  search the index for given
  entries? (Not answered)

PERIODICALS:
  Bound: Will not lend
  Unbound: Will not lend
  Loan Period: N/A
  Renewable: N/A
  Will lend if article exceeds
  _____ number of pages (Not
    answered)

MICROFORMS:
  Will Lend: No
  Specific Types of Microforms:
    N/A

GOVERNMENT PUBLICATIONS:
  Will Lend: Yes, if cataloged

DISSERTATIONS:
  Will Lend: Do not own

THESES:
  Will Lend: Do not own

AUDIO-VISUAL MATERIALS:
  Records: Will not lend
  Cassettes: Will not lend
  Other (slides, filmstrips,
    etc.): Will not lend

COMPUTER SOFTWARE:
  Will Lend: No

PHOTODUPLICATION SERVICE:
  No charge up to 10 exposures
  Charge Per Exposure: 10¢
  Minimum/handling Fee: None
  Average Turnaround Time:
    (Not answered)

MICROFILMING SERVICE:
  Service Available: No
  Charges: N/A

DO YOU CHARGE THE BORROWING
  LIBRARY FOR POSTAGE? No

FOR HOW LONG DO YOU SUSPEND ILL
  SERVICE OVER THE CHRISTMAS
  HOLIDAYS? No suspension

ARE THERE ANY GROUPS OF LIBRARIES
  FOR WHICH YOU WAIVE FEES? IF
  SO, PLEASE NAME THEM: None

NEBRASKA LIBRARY COMMISSION

NUC CODE: Nb-LC

OCLC CODE: NBL

ADDRESS: Interlibrary Loan
Nebraska Library
Commission
1420 P Street
Lincoln, NE 68502

TELEPHONE: (402) 471-2045

LIST NAMES OF BRANCHES WITH
SEPARATE POLICIES: None

BOOKS:
Will Lend: Yes
Length of Loan: 4 weeks,
reference--2 weeks
Renewable: Yes
Charges: None
Average Turnaround Time:
1 day
If you have indicated that a
book is not to be lent, will
you on receipt of a letter
from the requesting library
search the index for given
entries? (Not answered)

PERIODICALS:
Bound: Will not lend
Unbound: Will not lend
Loan Period: N/A
Renewable: N/A
Will lend if article exceeds
_____ number of pages (Will
not lend, regardless of
length of article. Will
photocopy)

MICROFORMS:
Will Lend: No
Specific Types of Microforms:
Microfiche. We will
duplicate these.

GOVERNMENT PUBLICATIONS:
Will Lend: Yes

DISSERTATIONS:
Will Lend: Do not own

THESES:
Will Lend: Do not own

AUDIO-VISUAL MATERIALS:
Records: Will lend
Cassettes: Will lend
Other (slides, filmstrips,
etc.): Will lend

COMPUTER SOFTWARE:
Will Lend: Do not own

PHOTODUPLICATION SERVICE:
No charge up to 0 exposures
Charges: $5.00
Average Turnaround Time:
Same day

MICROFILMING SERVICE:
Service Available: No
Charges: N/A

DO YOU CHARGE THE BORROWING
LIBRARY FOR POSTAGE? No

FOR HOW LONG DO YOU SUSPEND ILL
SERVICE OVER THE CHRISTMAS
HOLIDAYS? No suspension

ARE THERE ANY GROUPS OF LIBRARIES
FOR WHICH YOU WAIVE FEES? IF
SO, PLEASE NAME THEM: None

UNION COLLEGE

NUC CODE: NbLU

OCLC CODE: NCU

ADDRESS: Interlibrary Loan
Union College Library
Lincoln, NE 68506

TELEPHONE: (402) 488-2331, X316

LIST NAMES OF BRANCHES WITH
SEPARATE POLICIES: None

BOOKS:
Will Lend: Yes, if
circulating
Length of Loan: 4 weeks
Renewable: Yes
Charges: None
Average Turnaround Time:
1-2 days
If you have indicated that a
book is not to be lent, will
you on receipt of a letter
from the requesting library
search the index for given
entries? Yes

PERIODICALS:
Bound: Will not lend
Unbound: Will not lend
Loan Period: N/A
Renewable: N/A
Will lend if article exceeds
_____ number of pages (Will
not lend, regardless of
length of article. Will
photocopy)

MICROFORMS:
Will Lend: No
Specific Types of Microforms:
N/A

GOVERNMENT PUBLICATIONS:
Will Lend: Yes

DISSERTATIONS:
Will Lend: Yes

THESES:
Will Lend: Yes

AUDIO-VISUAL MATERIALS:
Records: Will not lend
Cassettes: Will not lend
Other (slides, filmstrips,
etc.): Will not lend

COMPUTER SOFTWARE:
Will Lend: No

PHOTODUPLICATION SERVICE:
No charge up to 10 exposures
Charge Per Exposure: 10¢
from paper; 25¢ from
reader-printer
Minimum/handling Fee: None
at this time
Average Turnaround Time:
1-2 days

MICROFILMING SERVICE:
Service Available: No
Charges: N/A

DO YOU CHARGE THE BORROWING
LIBRARY FOR POSTAGE? No

FOR HOW LONG DO YOU SUSPEND ILL
SERVICE OVER THE CHRISTMAS
HOLIDAYS? No suspension

ARE THERE ANY GROUPS OF LIBRARIES
FOR WHICH YOU WAIVE FEES? IF
SO, PLEASE NAME THEM:
Nebraska libraries; Kansas
libraries in KS/NE Project

UNIVERSITY OF NEBRASKA AT OMAHA

NUC CODE: NbOU

OCLC CODE: NBU

ADDRESS: Interlibrary Loan
University Library
University of Nebraska
at Omaha
Omaha, NE 68182-0237

TELEPHONE: (402) 554-3209

LIST NAMES OF BRANCHES WITH
SEPARATE POLICIES: None

BOOKS:
Will Lend: Yes
Length of Loan: 1 month
Renewable: Yes
Charges: None
Average Turnaround Time:
3 days
If you have indicated that a
book is not to be lent, will
you on receipt of a letter
from the requesting library
search the index for given
entries? Usually

PERIODICALS:
Bound: Will not lend
Unbound: Will not lend
Loan Period: N/A
Renewable: N/A
Will lend if article exceeds
_____ number of pages (Not
answered)

MICROFORMS:
Will Lend: Yes, on occasion
Specific Types of Microforms:
Film, cards; will make fiche-
to-fiche copies for 25¢ each
plus handling charge

GOVERNMENT PUBLICATIONS:
Will Lend: Yes

DISSERTATIONS:
Will Lend: Do not own

THESES:
Will Lend: Yes, if 2nd copy
available

AUDIO-VISUAL MATERIALS:
Records: Will not lend
Cassettes: Will not lend
Other (slides, filmstrips,
etc.): Will not lend

COMPUTER SOFTWARE:
Will Lend: No

PHOTODUPLICATION SERVICE:
No charge up to 0 exposures
Charge Per Exposure: 10¢
Minimum/handling Fee: 50¢
to NE public and college
libraries; $2.00 to others
Average Turnaround Time:
3 working days

MICROFILMING SERVICE:
Service Available: No
Charges: N/A

DO YOU CHARGE THE BORROWING
LIBRARY FOR POSTAGE? No

FOR HOW LONG DO YOU SUSPEND ILL
SERVICE OVER THE CHRISTMAS
HOLIDAYS? 10 days

ARE THERE ANY GROUPS OF LIBRARIES
FOR WHICH YOU WAIVE FEES? IF
SO, PLEASE NAME THEM: None

UNIVERSITY OF NEBRASKA-LINCOLN

NUC CODE: NbU

OCLC CODE: LDL

ADDRESS: Interlibrary Loan
University Libraries
University of Nebraska-
Lincoln
Lincoln, NE 68588-0410

TELEPHONE: (402) 472-2522

LIST NAMES OF BRANCHES WITH
SEPARATE POLICIES:
College of Law Library

BOOKS:
Will Lend: Yes, usually
Length of Loan: 2 weeks
Renewable: No
Charges: $5.00 for 4
volumes of a title or less
Average Turnaround Time:
2 days
If you have indicated that a
book is not to be lent, will
you on receipt of a letter
from the requesting library
search the index for given
entries? (Not answered)

PERIODICALS:
Bound: Will not lend
Unbound: Will not lend
Loan Period: N/A
Renewable: N/A
Will lend if article exceeds
_____ number of pages (Not
answered)

MICROFORMS:
Will Lend: Yes, film only
Specific Types of Microforms:
Will not lend journals on
film published within the
last 20 years

GOVERNMENT PUBLICATIONS:
Will Lend: Yes, except for
those on fiche

DISSERTATIONS:
Will Lend: Yes, if 1939-1954

THESES:
Will Lend: Yes, if 1939 to
present

AUDIO-VISUAL MATERIALS:
Records: Will not lend
Cassettes: Will not lend
Other (slides, filmstrips,
etc.): Will not lend

COMPUTER SOFTWARE:
Will Lend: No

PHOTODUPLICATION SERVICE:
No charge up to 0 exposures
Charge Per Exposure: 10¢
Minimum/handling Fee: $5.00
Average Turnaround Time:
72 hours

MICROFILMING SERVICE:
Service Available: Yes
Charges: Available upon
request

DO YOU CHARGE THE BORROWING
LIBRARY FOR POSTAGE? Only if
1st-class postage is
requested

FOR HOW LONG DO YOU SUSPEND ILL
SERVICE OVER THE CHRISTMAS
HOLIDAYS? 2 weeks

ARE THERE ANY GROUPS OF LIBRARIES
FOR WHICH YOU WAIVE FEES? IF
SO, PLEASE NAME THEM:
PELARCON; Nebraska
libraries; MASUA; ARL

NEVADA STATE LIBRARY

NUC CODE: Nv

OCLC CODE: (Not answered)

ADDRESS: Interlibrary Loan
Nevada State Library
Capitol Complex
Carson City, NV 89710

TELEPHONE: (702) 885-5165 or
885-4178

LIST NAMES OF BRANCHES WITH
SEPARATE POLICIES: None

BOOKS:
Will Lend: Yes
Length of Loan: 3 weeks from
receipt
Renewable: Yes
Charges: None
Average Turnaround Time:
48 hours
If you have indicated that a
book is not to be lent, will
you on receipt of a letter
from the requesting library
search the index for given
entries? (Not answered)

PERIODICALS:
Bound: Will lend
Unbound: Will lend
Loan Period: 3 weeks
Renewable: Yes
Will lend if article exceeds
25 pages

MICROFORMS:
Will Lend: Yes
Specific Types of Microforms:
Microfilm, microfiche

GOVERNMENT PUBLICATIONS:
Will Lend: Yes

DISSERTATIONS:
Will Lend: Do not own

THESES:
Will Lend: Do not own

AUDIO-VISUAL MATERIALS:
Records: Do not own
Cassettes: Do not own
Other (slides, filmstrips,
etc.): Do not own

COMPUTER SOFTWARE:
Will Lend: Do not own

PHOTODUPLICATION SERVICE:
No charge up to 25 exposures
Charge Per Exposure: None
Minimum/handling Fee: None
Average Turnaround Time:
48 hours

MICROFILMING SERVICE:
Service Available: No
Charges: N/A

DO YOU CHARGE THE BORROWING
LIBRARY FOR POSTAGE? Yes

FOR HOW LONG DO YOU SUSPEND ILL
SERVICE OVER THE CHRISTMAS
HOLIDAYS? No suspension

ARE THERE ANY GROUPS OF LIBRARIES
FOR WHICH YOU WAIVE FEES? IF
SO, PLEASE NAME THEM: None

UNIVERSITY OF NEVADA

NUC CODE: NvU

OCLC CODE: None

ADDRESS: Interlibrary Loan
University of Nevada
Library
Reno, NV 89557

TELEPHONE: (702) 784-6500

LIST NAMES OF BRANCHES WITH
SEPARATE POLICIES: None

BOOKS:
Will Lend: Yes
Length of Loan: 3 weeks use;
2 weeks use of books from
branch libraries
Renewable: Yes
Charges: None
Average Turnaround Time:
2 days
If you have indicated that a
book is not to be lent, will
you on receipt of a letter
from the requesting library
search the index for given
entries? (Not answered)

PERIODICALS:
Bound: Will not lend
Unbound: Will not lend
Loan Period: N/A
Renewable: N/A
Will lend if article exceeds
_____ number of pages (Not
answered)

MICROFORMS:
Will Lend: Yes
Specific Types of Microforms:
Microfilm (4 reels at a
time), microfiche, micro-
print, for 1 weeks loan

GOVERNMENT PUBLICATIONS:
Will Lend: Yes

DISSERTATIONS:
Will Lend: Yes; 1964 to
present available from
University Microfilm

THESES:
Will Lend: Yes; 1976 to
present available from
University Microfilm

AUDIO-VISUAL MATERIALS:
Records: Will not lend
Cassettes: Will not lend
Other (slides, filmstrips,
etc.): Will not lend

COMPUTER SOFTWARE:
Will Lend: No

PHOTODUPLICATION SERVICE:
No charge up to 30 exposures
Charge Per Exposure: 15¢
after first 30 pages
Minimum/handling Fee: $1.50
Average Turnaround Time:
2 days

MICROFILMING SERVICE:
Service Available: No
Charges: N/A

DO YOU CHARGE THE BORROWING
LIBRARY FOR POSTAGE? No

FOR HOW LONG DO YOU SUSPEND ILL
SERVICE OVER THE CHRISTMAS
HOLIDAYS? No suspension

ARE THERE ANY GROUPS OF LIBRARIES
FOR WHICH YOU WAIVE FEES? IF
SO, PLEASE NAME THEM:
Libraries in Nevada

UNIVERSITY OF NEVADA AT LAS VEGAS

NUC CODE: NvLN

OCLC CODE: (Not answered)

ADDRESS: Interlibrary Loan
University of Nevada
at Las Vegas
Library
Las Vegas, NV 89154

TELEPHONE: (702) 739-3864

LIST NAMES OF BRANCHES WITH
SEPARATE POLICIES: None

BOOKS:
Will Lend: Yes
Length of Loan: Usually 2
weeks use
Renewable: Yes, unless stated
otherwise
Charges: None
Average Turnaround Time:
(Not answered)
If you have indicated that a
book is not to be lent, will
you on receipt of a letter
from the requesting library
search the index for given
entries? Yes, within reason

PERIODICALS:
Bound: Will not lend
Unbound: Will not lend
Loan Period: N/A
Renewable: N/A
Will lend if article exceeds
_____ number of pages (Not
answered)

MICROFORMS:
Will Lend: No
Specific Types of Microforms:
N/A

GOVERNMENT PUBLICATIONS:
Will Lend: Yes

DISSERTATIONS:
Will Lend: Yes, if circulating

THESES:
Will Lend: Yes, if circulating

AUDIO-VISUAL MATERIALS:
Records: Will not lend
Cassettes: Will not lend
Other (slides, filmstrips,
etc.): Will not lend

COMPUTER SOFTWARE:
Will Lend: No

PHOTODUPLICATION SERVICE:
No charge up to 0 exposures
Charge Per Exposure: 15¢
Minimum/handling Fee: (Not
answered)
Average Turnaround Time:
(Not answered)

MICROFILMING SERVICE:
Service Available: No
Charges: N/A

DO YOU CHARGE THE BORROWING
LIBRARY FOR POSTAGE? Yes

FOR HOW LONG DO YOU SUSPEND ILL
SERVICE OVER THE CHRISTMAS
HOLIDAYS? No suspension

ARE THERE ANY GROUPS OF LIBRARIES
FOR WHICH YOU WAIVE FEES? IF
SO, PLEASE NAME THEM: None

WASHOE COUNTY LIBRARY

NUC CODE: (Not answered)

OCLC CODE: (Not answered)

ADDRESS: Interlibrary Loan
Washoe County Library
P. O. Box 2151
Reno, NV 89505

TELEPHONE: (702) 785-4008

LIST NAMES OF BRANCHES WITH
SEPARATE POLICIES: None.
We handle the interlibrary
loans for all our branches.

BOOKS:
Will Lend: Yes
Length of Loan: 4 weeks
Renewable: Yes
Charges: None
Average Turnaround Time:
3 days
If you have indicated that a
book is not to be lent, will
you on receipt of a letter
from the requesting library
search the index for given
entries? (Not answered)

PERIODICALS:
Bound: Will not lend
Unbound: Will not lend
Loan Period: N/A
Renewable: N/A
Will lend if article exceeds
_____ number of pages (Will
not lend)

MICROFORMS:
Will Lend: No
Specific Types of Microforms:
N/A

GOVERNMENT PUBLICATIONS:
Will Lend: Yes

DISSERTATIONS:
Will Lend: Do not own

THESES:
Will Lend: Do not own

AUDIO-VISUAL MATERIALS:
Records: Will lend, to Nevada
libraries only
Cassettes: Will lend, to
Nevada libraries only
Other (slides, filmstrips,
etc.): Will lend, to Nevada
libraries only

COMPUTER SOFTWARE:
Will Lend: No

PHOTODUPLICATION SERVICE:
No charge up to unlimited
number of exposures at this
time
Charge Per Exposure: None at
this time
Minimum/handling Fee: None
Average Turnaround Time:
3 days

MICROFILMING SERVICE:
Service Available: No
Charges: N/A

DO YOU CHARGE THE BORROWING LIBRARY
FOR POSTAGE? No

FOR HOW LONG DO YOU SUSPEND ILL
SERVICE OVER THE CHRISTMAS
HOLIDAYS? No suspension

ARE THERE ANY GROUPS OF LIBRARIES
FOR WHICH YOU WAIVE FEES? IF
SO, PLEASE NAME THEM: At this
time we do not charge any
fees. This situation is
being evaluated, however.

DARTMOUTH COLLEGE

NUC CODE: NhD

OCLC CODE: DRB

ADDRESS: Interlibrary Loan
Baker Library
Dartmouth College
Hanover, NH 03755

TELEPHONE: (603) 646-2596

LIST NAMES OF BRANCHES WITH
SEPARATE POLICIES:
Dana BioMedical Library
Kresge Physical Sciences
Library
Feldberg Library (Business
and Engineering)
Sherman Art Library

BOOKS:
Will Lend: Yes
Length of Loan: 4 weeks use
Renewable: Yes
Charges: $5.00
Average Turnaround Time:
(Not answered)
If you have indicated that a
book is not to be lent, will
you on receipt of a letter
from the requesting library
search the index for given
entries? (Not answered)

PERIODICALS:
Bound: Will lend sometimes
Unbound: Will lend sometimes
Loan Period: 2 weeks use
Renewable: Yes
Will lend if article exceeds
25 pages

MICROFORMS:
Will Lend: Yes, usually
Specific Types of Microforms:
Fiche, film, microcards

GOVERNMENT PUBLICATIONS:
Will Lend: Yes, some of them

DISSERTATIONS:
Will Lend: Yes, if 2nd copy
available; 1964 to present
available from University
Microfilms

THESES:
Will Lend: Yes

AUDIO-VISUAL MATERIALS:
Records: Will not lend
Cassettes: Will not lend
Other (slides, filmstrips,
etc.): Will not lend

COMPUTER SOFTWARE:
Will Lend: No

PHOTODUPLICATION SERVICE:
No charge up to 0 exposures
Charge Per Exposure: (Not
answered)
Minimum/handling Fee: $5.00
Average Turnaround Time:
3 days

MICROFILMING SERVICE:
Service Available: No
Charges: N/A

DO YOU CHARGE THE BORROWING
LIBRARY FOR POSTAGE? No

FOR HOW LONG DO YOU SUSPEND ILL
SERVICE OVER THE CHRISTMAS
HOLIDAYS? No suspension

ARE THERE ANY GROUPS OF LIBRARIES
FOR WHICH YOU WAIVE FEES? IF
SO, PLEASE NAME THEM: N.H.S.
Library system; Vermont
Department of Libraries;
RLG members

KEENE STATE COLLEGE

NUC CODE: (Not answered)

OCLC CODE: KNM

ADDRESS: Interlibrary Loan
Mason Library
Keene State College
Keene, NH 03431

TELEPHONE: (603) 352-1909, X520

LIST NAMES OF BRANCHES WITH
SEPARATE POLICIES: None

BOOKS:
Will Lend: Yes
Length of Loan: 1 month
Renewable: Yes, if not
needed here
Charges: None
Average Turnaround Time:
2-3 days
If you have indicated that a
book is not to be lent, will
you on receipt of a letter
from the requesting library
search the index for given
entries? Will do some
searching

PERIODICALS:
Bound: Will not lend
Unbound: Will not lend
Loan Period: N/A
Renewable: N/A
Will lend if article exceeds
_____ number of pages (Not
answered)

MICROFORMS:
Will Lend: No
Specific Types of Microforms:
N/A

GOVERNMENT PUBLICATIONS:
Will Lend: Yes, state
publications

DISSERTATIONS:
Will Lend: Yes

THESES:
Will Lend: Yes

AUDIO-VISUAL MATERIALS:
Records: Will not lend
Cassettes: Will not lend
Other (slides, filmstrips,
etc.): Will not lend

COMPUTER SOFTWARE:
Will Lend: No

PHOTODUPLICATION SERVICE:
No charge up to 10 exposures
Charge Per Exposure: 10¢
Minimum/handling Fee: None
Average Turnaround Time:
2-3 days

MICROFILMING SERVICE:
Service Available: No
Charges: N/A

DO YOU CHARGE THE BORROWING
LIBRARY FOR POSTAGE? No

FOR HOW LONG DO YOU SUSPEND ILL
SERVICE OVER THE CHRISTMAS
HOLIDAYS? 1-2 weeks

ARE THERE ANY GROUPS OF LIBRARIES
FOR WHICH YOU WAIVE FEES? IF
SO, PLEASE NAME THEM: New
Hampshire College and
University Consortium;
reciprocal agreements with
other libraries

NEW HAMPSHIRE STATE LIBRARY

NUC CODE: Nh

OCLC CODE: NHS

ADDRESS: Interlibrary Loan
New Hampshire State
Library
20 Park St.
Concord, NH 03301

TELEPHONE: (603) 271-2144

LIST NAMES OF BRANCHES WITH
SEPARATE POLICIES: None

BOOKS:
Will Lend: Yes
Length of Loan: 4 weeks
Renewable: Yes
Charges: None
Average Turnaround Time:
(Not answered)
If you have indicated that a
book is not to be lent, will
you on receipt of a letter
from the requesting library
search the index for given
entries? (Not answered)

PERIODICALS:
Bound: Will not lend
Unbound: Will lend 12
current issues
Loan Period: 4 weeks
Renewable: Yes
Will lend if article exceeds
_____ number of pages (Not
answered)

MICROFORMS:
Will Lend: No
Specific Types of Microforms:
N/A

GOVERNMENT PUBLICATIONS:
Will Lend: Yes

DISSERTATIONS:
Will Lend: (Not answered)

THESES:
Will Lend: (Not answered)

AUDIO-VISUAL MATERIALS:
Records: Will lend
Cassettes: (Not answered)
Other (slides, filmstrips,
etc.): (Not answered)

COMPUTER SOFTWARE:
Will Lend: (Not answered)

PHOTODUPLICATION SERVICE:
No charge up to 0 exposures
Charge Per Exposure: 10¢
Minimum/handling Fee: 50¢
Average Turnaround Time:
(Not answered)

MICROFILMING SERVICE:
Service Available: Yes
Charges: 25¢ per frame

DO YOU CHARGE THE BORROWING
LIBRARY FOR POSTAGE? No

FOR HOW LONG DO YOU SUSPEND ILL
SERVICE OVER THE CHRISTMAS
HOLIDAYS? No suspension

ARE THERE ANY GROUPS OF LIBRARIES
FOR WHICH YOU WAIVE FEES? IF
SO, PLEASE NAME THEM: None

PLYMOUTH STATE COLLEGE

NUC CODE: (Not answered)

OCLC CODE: PSM

ADDRESS: Interlibrary Loan
Lamson Library
Plymouth State College
Plymouth, NH 03264

TELEPHONE: (603) 636-1550, X257

LIST NAMES OF BRANCHES WITH
SEPARATE POLICIES: None

BOOKS:
Will Lend: Yes
Length of Loan: 4 weeks
Renewable: Yes
Charges: None
Average Turnaround Time:
2-3 days
If you have indicated that a
book is not to be lent, will
you on receipt of a letter
from the requesting library
search the index for given
entries? (Not answered)

PERIODICALS:
Bound: Will not lend
Unbound: Will not lend
Loan Period: N/A
Renewable: N/A
Will lend if article exceeds
_____ number of pages (Not
answered)

MICROFORMS:
Will Lend: Yes
Specific Types of Microforms:
Microfiche, ultrafiche

GOVERNMENT PUBLICATIONS:
Will Lend: Yes

DISSERTATIONS:
Will Lend: Do not own

THESES:
Will Lend: Do not own

AUDIO-VISUAL MATERIALS:
Records: Will not lend
Cassettes: Will lend
Other (slides, filmstrips,
etc.): Will lend

COMPUTER SOFTWARE:
Will Lend: Do not own

PHOTODUPLICATION SERVICE:
No charge up to 50 exposures
Charge Per Exposure: (Not
answered)
Minimum/handling Fee: None
Average Turnaround Time:
(Not answered)

MICROFILMING SERVICE:
Service Available: No
Charges: N/A

DO YOU CHARGE THE BORROWING
LIBRARY FOR POSTAGE? No

FOR HOW LONG DO YOU SUSPEND ILL
SERVICE OVER THE CHRISTMAS
HOLIDAYS? 7 days

ARE THERE ANY GROUPS OF LIBRARIES
FOR WHICH YOU WAIVE FEES? IF
SO, PLEASE NAME THEM: NELINET
New Hampshire Consortium

RIVIER COLLEGE

NUC CODE: RC

OCLC CODE: None

ADDRESS: Interlibrary Loan
Regina Library
Rivier College
Nashua, NH 03060

TELEPHONE: (603) 888-1311

LIST NAMES OF BRANCHES WITH
SEPARATE POLICIES: None

BOOKS:
Will Lend: Yes
Length of Loan: 1 month
Renewable: Yes, if not
reserved
Charges: If not a member
of consortium
Average Turnaround Time:
2 days
If you have indicated that a
book is not to be lent, will
you on receipt of a letter
from the requesting library
search the index for given
entries? (Not answered)

PERIODICALS:
Bound: Will not lend
Unbound: Will not lend
Loan Period: N/A
Renewable: N/A
Will lend if article exceeds
_____ number of pages (Will
not lend; will photocopy
articles)

MICROFORMS:
Will Lend: No
Specific Types of Microforms:
N/A

GOVERNMENT PUBLICATIONS:
Will Lend: Yes

DISSERTATIONS:
Will Lend: Yes

THESES:
Will Lend: Yes

AUDIO-VISUAL MATERIALS:
Records: Will not lend
Cassettes: Will not lend
Other (slides, filmstrips,
etc.): Do not own

COMPUTER SOFTWARE:
Will Lend: Do not own

PHOTODUPLICATION SERVICE:
No charge up to 0 exposures
Charge Per Exposure: 10¢
Minimum/handling Fee: $1.50
Average Turnaround Time:
2 days

MICROFILMING SERVICE:
Service Available: Yes
Charges: 10¢

DO YOU CHARGE THE BORROWING
LIBRARY FOR POSTAGE? Yes,
if outside New Hampshire

FOR HOW LONG DO YOU SUSPEND ILL
SERVICE OVER THE CHRISTMAS
HOLIDAYS? Mid-December-Jan.10

ARE THERE ANY GROUPS OF LIBRARIES
FOR WHICH YOU WAIVE FEES? IF
SO, PLEASE NAME THEM:
Consortium

ST. ANSELM COLLEGE

NUC CODE: NhMSA

OCLC CODE: SAC

ADDRESS: Interlibrary Loan
Geisel Library
St. Anselm College
Manchester, NH 03102

TELEPHONE: (603) 669-1030, X240

LIST NAMES OF BRANCHES WITH
SEPARATE POLICIES: None

BOOKS:
Will Lend: Yes
Length of Loan: 4 weeks
Renewable: Yes
Charges: None
Average Turnaround Time:
(Not answered)
If you have indicated that a
book is not to be lent, will
you on receipt of a letter
from the requesting library
search the index for given
entries? (Not answered)

PERIODICALS:
Bound: Will not lend
Unbound: Will lend
selectively
Loan Period: 2 weeks
Renewable: Yes
Will lend if article exceeds
25 pages

MICROFORMS:
Will Lend: Yes
Specific Types of Microforms:
Cards, fiche

GOVERNMENT PUBLICATIONS:
Will Lend: Yes

DISSERTATIONS:
Will Lend: Do not own

THESES:
Will Lend: Do not own

AUDIO-VISUAL MATERIALS:
Records: Will not lend
Cassettes: Will not lend
Other (slides, filmstrips,
etc.): Do not own

COMPUTER SOFTWARE:
Will Lend: No

PHOTODUPLICATION SERVICE:
No charge up to 0 exposures
Charge Per Exposure: 10¢
Minimum/handling Fee: (Not
answered)
Average Turnaround Time:
(Not answered)

MICROFILMING SERVICE:
Service Available: No
Charges: N/A

DO YOU CHARGE THE BORROWING
LIBRARY FOR POSTAGE? Yes

FOR HOW LONG DO YOU SUSPEND ILL
SERVICE OVER THE CHRISTMAS
HOLIDAYS? No suspension

ARE THERE ANY GROUPS OF LIBRARIES
FOR WHICH YOU WAIVE FEES? IF
SO, PLEASE NAME THEM: None

UNIVERSITY OF NEW HAMPSHIRE

NUC CODE: NhU

OCLC CODE: NHM

ADDRESS: Interlibrary Loan
          Dimond Library
          University of New
            Hampshire
          Durham, NH 03824

TELEPHONE: (603) 862-1173

LIST NAMES OF BRANCHES WITH
  SEPARATE POLICIES: None

BOOKS
  Will Lend: Yes
  Length of Loan: 4 weeks
  Renewable: Yes, if not
    needed
  Charges: Only to libraries
    which charge us
  Average Turnaround Time:
    2 days
  If you have indicated that a
    book is not to be lent, will
    you on receipt of a letter
    from the requesting library
    search the index for given
    entries? (Not answered)

PERIODICALS:
  Bound: Will lend
  Unbound: Will not lend
  Loan Period: 2 weeks
  Renewable: Yes, usually
  Will lend if article exceeds
    30 pages

MICROFORMS:
  Will Lend: Yes
  Specific Types of Microforms:
    Film, fiche, cards for in-
    library use only

GOVERNMENT PUBLICATIONS:
  Will Lend: Yes

DISSERTATIONS:
  Will Lend: Yes, if pre-1958

THESES:
  Will Lend: Yes

AUDIO-VISUAL MATERIALS:
  Records: Will not lend
  Cassettes: Will not lend
  Other (slides, filmstrips,
    etc.): Will usually lend

COMPUTER SOFTWARE:
  Will Lend: No

PHOTODUPLICATION SERVICE:
  No charge up to 0 exposures
  Charge Per Exposure: 15¢
  Minimum/handling Fee: $1.50
  Average Turnaround Time:
    2 days

MICROFILMING SERVICE:
  Service Available: No
  Charges: N/A

DO YOU CHARGE THE BORROWING
  LIBRARY FOR POSTAGE? No

FOR HOW LONG DO YOU SUSPEND ILL
  SERVICE OVER THE CHRISTMAS
  HOLIDAYS? Dec.15-Jan.5

ARE THERE ANY GROUPS OF LIBRARIES
  FOR WHICH YOU WAIVE FEES? IF
  SO, PLEASE NAME THEM: NELINET
  reciprocal agreement
  libraries; New England state
  universities; University
  System of New Hampshire

ATLANTIC COUNTY LIBRARY

NUC CODE: (Not answered)

OCLC CODE: (Not answered)

ADDRESS: Interlibrary Loan
Atlantic County Library
134 Philadelphia Ave.
Egg Harbor City, NJ
08215

TELEPHONE: (609) 625-2776

LIST NAMES OF BRANCHES WITH
SEPARATE POLICIES: None

BOOKS:
Will Lend: Yes
Length of Loan: 3 weeks
Renewable: No
Charges: (Not answered)
Average Turnaround Time:
5 days
If you have indicated that a
book is not to be lent, will
you on receipt of a letter
from the requesting library
search the index for given
entries?   (Not answered)

PERIODICALS:
Bound: Will not lend
Unbound: Will not lend
Loan Period: N/A
Renewable: N/A
Will lend if article exceeds
_____ number of pages (Will
not lend, regardless of
length of article, but
will photocopy material)

MICROFORMS:
Will Lend: No
Specific Types of Microforms:
N/A

GOVERNMENT PUBLICATIONS:
Will Lend: Yes

DISSERTATIONS:
Will Lend: Do not own

THESES:
Will Lend: Do not own

AUDIO-VISUAL MATERIALS:
Records: Will lend
Cassettes: Will lend
Other (slides, filmstrips,
etc.):   (Not answered)

COMPUTER SOFTWARE:
Will Lend: Do not own

PHOTODUPLICATION SERVICE:
No charge up to 20 exposures
Charge Per Exposure: 10¢
Minimum/handling Fee: None
Average Turnaround Time:
5 days

MICROFILMING SERVICE:
Service Available: No
Charges: N/A

DO YOU CHARGE THE BORROWING
LIBRARY FOR POSTAGE?   No

FOR HOW LONG DO YOU SUSPEND ILL
SERVICE OVER THE CHRISTMAS
HOLIDAYS?   No suspension

ARE THERE ANY GROUPS OF LIBRARIES
FOR WHICH YOU WAIVE FEES?   IF
SO, PLEASE NAME THEM: None

BURLINGTON COUNTY LIBRARY

NUC CODE: (Not answered)

OCLC CODE: (Not answered)

ADDRESS: Interlibrary Loan
Burlington County
Library
Woodlane Rd.
Mt. Holly, NJ   08060

TELEPHONE: (609) 267-9660

LIST NAMES OF BRANCHES WITH
SEPARATE POLICIES: None

BOOKS:
Will Lend: Yes
Length of Loan: 2 weeks
Renewable: No
Charges: None
Average Turnaround Time:
(Not answered)
If you have indicated that a
book is not to be lent, will
you on receipt of a letter
from the requesting library
search the index for given
entries?   Yes

PERIODICALS:
Bound: Will not lend
Unbound: Will not lend
Loan Period: N/A
Renewable: N/A
Will lend if article exceeds
_____ number of pages (Will
not lend, regardless of
length of article, but
will photocopy)

MICROFORMS:
Will Lend: No
Specific Types of Microforms:
Census of Burlington County,
New Jersey; County church
records

GOVERNMENT PUBLICATIONS:
Will Lend: No

DISSERTATIONS:
Will Lend: No

THESES:
Will Lend: No

AUDIO-VISUAL MATERIALS:
Records: Will not lend
Cassettes: Will not lend
Other (slides, filmstrips,
etc.):   Will not lend

COMPUTER SOFTWARE:
Will Lend: No

PHOTODUPLICATION SERVICE:
No charge up to 0 exposures
Charge Per Exposure: 15¢ for
Xerox; 25¢ for microfilm
Minimum/handling Fee: $2.00
Average Turnaround Time:
2 weeks

MICROFILMING SERVICE:
Service Available: No
Charges: N/A

DO YOU CHARGE THE BORROWING
LIBRARY FOR POSTAGE?   No

FOR HOW LONG DO YOU SUSPEND ILL
SERVICE OVER THE CHRISTMAS
HOLIDAYS?   No suspension

ARE THERE ANY GROUPS OF LIBRARIES
FOR WHICH YOU WAIVE FEES?   IF
SO, PLEASE NAME THEM:
Libraries in New Jersey

CAMDEN COUNTY LIBRARY

NUC CODE: None

OCLC CODE: NCL

ADDRESS: Interlibrary Loan
           Camden County Library
           Echelon Urban Center
           Voorhees, NJ 08043

TELEPHONE: (609) 772-1636

LIST NAMES OF BRANCHES WITH
  SEPARATE POLICIES: None

BOOKS:
  Will Lend: Yes
  Length of Loan: 4 weeks
  Renewable: No
  Charges: None
  Average Turnaround Time:
    12 days from receipt of
    request to receiving of
    book
  If you have indicated that a
  book is not to be lent, will
  you on receipt of a letter
  from the requesting library
  search the index for given
  entries? Yes

PERIODICALS:
  Bound: Will not lend
  Unbound: Will not lend
  Loan Period: N/A
  Renewable: N/A
  Will lend if article exceeds
  _____ number of pages (Will
    not lend, regardless of
    length of article)

MICROFORMS:
  Will Lend: No
  Specific Types of Microforms:
    N/A

GOVERNMENT PUBLICATIONS:
  Will Lend: No

DISSERTATIONS:
  Will Lend: No

THESES:
  Will Lend: No

AUDIO-VISUAL MATERIALS:
  Records: Will not lend
  Cassettes: Will not lend
  Other (slides, filmstrips,
    etc.): Will not lend

COMPUTER SOFTWARE:
  Will Lend: No

PHOTODUPLICATION SERVICE:
  No charge up to 20 exposures
  Charge Per Exposure: 10¢ per
    exposure, after 1st 20
  Minimum/handling Fee: None
  Average Turnaround Time:
    8 days

MICROFILMING SERVICE:
  Service Available: No
  Charges: N/A

DO YOU CHARGE THE BORROWING
  LIBRARY FOR POSTAGE? No

FOR HOW LONG DO YOU SUSPEND ILL
  SERVICE OVER THE CHRISTMAS
  HOLIDAYS? No suspension

ARE THERE ANY GROUPS OF LIBRARIES
  FOR WHICH YOU WAIVE FEES? IF
  SO, PLEASE NAME THEM: None

CAPE MAY COUNTY LIBRARY

NUC CODE: (Not answered)

OCLC CODE: None at this time

ADDRESS: Interlibrary Loan
           Cape May County
           Library
           Mechanic Street
           Cape May Court House,
           NJ 08210

TELEPHONE: (609) 465-7111

LIST NAMES OF BRANCHES WITH
  SEPARATE POLICIES: None

BOOKS:
  Will Lend: Yes
  Length of Loan: 2 weeks from
    day of receipt
  Renewable: Yes, if no
    reserves
  Charges: None
  Average Turnaround Time:
    4 days
  If you have indicated that a
  book is not to be lent, will
  you on receipt of a letter
  from the requesting library
  search the index for given
  entries? Yes

PERIODICALS:
  Bound: Will not lend
  Unbound: Will not lend
  Loan Period: N/A
  Renewable: N/A
  Will lend if article exceeds
  _____ number of pages (Not
    answered)

MICROFORMS:
  Will Lend: No
  Specific Types of Microforms:
    N/A

GOVERNMENT PUBLICATIONS:
  Will Lend: Yes

DISSERTATIONS:
  Will Lend: Yes

THESES:
  Will Lend: Yes

AUDIO-VISUAL MATERIALS:
  Records: Will lend
  Cassettes: Will lend
  Other (slides, filmstrips,
    etc.): Will lend

COMPUTER SOFTWARE:
  Will Lend: Do not own

PHOTODUPLICATION SERVICE:
  No charge up to 20 exposures
  Charge Per Exposure: 10¢ each,
    after first 20
  Minimum/handling Fee: None
  Average Turnaround Time:
    2 days

MICROFILMING SERVICE:
  Service Available: No
  Charges: N/A

DO YOU CHARGE THE BORROWING
  LIBRARY FOR POSTAGE? No

FOR HOW LONG DO YOU SUSPEND ILL
  SERVICE OVER THE CHRISTMAS
  HOLIDAYS? No suspension

ARE THERE ANY GROUPS OF LIBRARIES
  FOR WHICH YOU WAIVE FEES? IF
  SO, PLEASE NAME THEM: No
    fees except for photo-
    duplication

DREW UNIVERSITY

NUC CODE: NjMD

OCLC CODE: DRU

ADDRESS: Interlibrary Loan
Drew University
Library
Madison, NJ 07940

TELEPHONE: (201) 377-3000, X469

LIST NAMES OF BRANCHES WITH
SEPARATE POLICIES: None

BOOKS:
Will Lend: Yes
Length of Loan: 1 month
Renewable: Yes
Charges: (Not answered)
Average Turnaround Time:
(Not answered)
If you have indicated that a
book is not to be lent, will
you on receipt of a letter
from the requesting library
search the index for given
entries? (Not answered)

PERIODICALS:
Bound: Will lend
Unbound: Will lend
Loan Period: (Not answered)
Renewable: (Not answered)
Will lend if article exceeds
30 pages

MICROFORMS:
Will Lend: (Not answered)
Specific Types of Microforms:
N/A

GOVERNMENT PUBLICATIONS:
Will Lend: (Not answered)

DISSERTATIONS:
Will Lend: Yes

THESES:
Will Lend: Yes

AUDIO-VISUAL MATERIALS:
Records: (Not answered)
Cassettes: (Not answered)
Other (slides, filmstrips,
etc.): (Not answered)

COMPUTER SOFTWARE:
Will Lend: (Not answered)

PHOTODUPLICATION SERVICE:
No charge up to 0 exposures
Charge Per Exposure: 10¢
Minimum Fee: $1.00 out-of-
state
Handling Fee: $2.00 out-of-
state
Average Turnaround Time:
(Not answered)

MICROFILMING SERVICE:
Service Available: No
Charges: N/A

DO YOU CHARGE THE BORROWING
LIBRARY FOR POSTAGE? No

FOR HOW LONG DO YOU SUSPEND ILL
SERVICE OVER THE CHRISTMAS
HOLIDAYS? (Not answered)

ARE THERE ANY GROUPS OF LIBRARIES
FOR WHICH YOU WAIVE FEES? IF
SO, PLEASE NAME THEM: None

FAIRLEIGH DICKINSON UNIVERSITY

NUC CODE: (Not answered)

OCLC CODE: (Not answered)

ADDRESS: Interlibrary Loan
Fairleigh Dickinson
University
Florham-Madison Campus
Library
285 Madison Ave.
Madison, NJ 07940

TELEPHONE: (210) 377-4700, X335

LIST NAMES OF BRANCHES WITH
SEPARATE POLICIES: None

BOOKS:
Will Lend: Yes
Length of Loan: 4 weeks
Renewable: Yes
Charges: $5.00 for out-of-
state libraries only
Average Turnaround Time:
1 day
If you have indicated that a
book is not to be lent, will
you on receipt of a letter
from the requesting library
search the index for given
entries? (Not answered)

PERIODICALS:
Bound: Will not lend
Unbound: Will not lend
Loan Period: N/A
Renewable: N/A
Will lend if article exceeds
_____ number of pages (Not
answered)

MICROFORMS:
Will Lend: No
Specific Types of Microforms:
N/A

GOVERNMENT PUBLICATIONS:
Will Lend: Yes

DISSERTATIONS:
Will Lend: Yes, with
author's permission; 1975 to
present available from
University Microfilms

THESES:
Will Lend: No

AUDIO-VISUAL MATERIALS:
Records: Do not own
Cassettes: Do not own
Other (slides, filmstrips,
etc.): Will lend

COMPUTER SOFTWARE:
Will Lend: Do not own

PHOTODUPLICATION SERVICE:
No charge up to 0 exposures
Charge Per Exposure: 15¢
after first 6
Minimum/handling Fee: $2.00
for 1-6 exposures
Average Turnaround Time:
1 day

MICROFILMING SERVICE:
Service Available: No
Charges: N/A

DO YOU CHARGE THE BORROWING
LIBRARY FOR POSTAGE? No

FOR HOW LONG DO YOU SUSPEND ILL
SERVICE OVER THE CHRISTMAS
HOLIDAYS? 2 weeks

ARE THERE ANY GROUPS OF LIBRARIES
FOR WHICH YOU WAIVE FEES? IF
SO, PLEASE NAME THEM: New
Jersey libraries; other
Fairleigh Dickinson campus
libraries; Morris Union
Federation libraries; Morris
County Free Library

FREE PUBLIC LIBRARY OF WOODBRIDGE

NUC CODE: (Not answered)

OCLC CODE: (Not answered)

ADDRESS: Interlibrary Loan
Free Public Library of
Woodbridge
George Frederick Plaza
Woodbridge, NJ 07095

TELEPHONE: (201) 634-4450

LIST NAMES OF BRANCHES WITH
SEPARATE POLICIES: None

BOOKS:
Will Lend: Yes
Length of Loan: 2 weeks
Renewable: Yes, if no
reserves
Charges: None
Average Turnaround Time:
App. 1 month
If you have indicated that a
book is not to be lent, will
you on receipt of a letter
from the requesting library
search the index for given
entries? (Not answered)

PERIODICALS:
Bound: Will not lend
Unbound: Will lend if in
circulating collection
Loan Period: 2 weeks
Renewable: Yes
Will lend if article exceeds
_____ number of pages (Not
answered)

MICROFORMS:
Will Lend: No
Specific Types of Microforms:
N/A

GOVERNMENT PUBLICATIONS:
Will Lend: Yes, if in
circulating collection

DISSERTATIONS:
Will Lend: Do not own

THESES:
Will Lend: Do not own

AUDIO-VISUAL MATERIALS:
Records: Will not lend
Cassettes: Will not lend
Other (slides, filmstrips,
etc.): Will not lend

COMPUTER SOFTWARE:
Will Lend: Do not own

PHOTODUPLICATION SERVICE:
No charge for any exposures
Minimum/handling Fee: None
Average Turnaround Time:
2 weeks

MICROFILMING SERVICE:
Service Available: No
Charges: N/A

DO YOU CHARGE THE BORROWING
LIBRARY FOR POSTAGE? No

FOR HOW LONG DO YOU SUSPEND ILL
SERVICE OVER THE CHRISTMAS
HOLIDAYS? No suspension

ARE THERE ANY GROUPS OF LIBRARIES
FOR WHICH YOU WAIVE FEES? IF
SO, PLEASE NAME THEM: No fees
charged

JERSEY CITY STATE COLLEGE

NUC CODE: NjJS

OCLC CODE: NJJ

ADDRESS: Interlibrary Loan
Forrest A. Irwin
Library
Jersey City State
College
2039 Kennedy Blvd.
Jersey City, NJ 07305

TELEPHONE: (201) 547-3033

LIST NAMES OF BRANCHES WITH
SEPARATE POLICIES: None

BOOKS:
Will Lend: Yes
Length of Loan: 4 weeks
Renewable: Yes
Charges: None
Average Turnaround Time:
2 days
If you have indicated that a
book is not to be lent, will
you on receipt of a letter
from the requesting library
search the index for given
entries? (Not answered)

PERIODICALS:
Bound: Will not lend
Unbound: Will not lend
Loan Period: N/A
Renewable: N/A
Will lend if article exceeds
_____ number of pages (Not
answered)

MICROFORMS:
Will Lend: Yes
Specific Types of Microforms:
Non-periodical titles

GOVERNMENT PUBLICATIONS:
Will Lend: Yes

DISSERTATIONS:
Will Lend: Yes

THESES:
Will Lend: Yes

AUDIO-VISUAL MATERIALS:
Records: Do not own
Cassettes: Do not own
Other (slides, filmstrips,
etc.): Do not own

COMPUTER SOFTWARE:
Will Lend: No

PHOTODUPLICATION SERVICE:
No charge up to 0 exposures
Charge Per Exposure: 10¢
Minimum/handling Fee: None
Average Turnaround Time:
2-3 days

MICROFILMING SERVICE:
Service Available: No
Charges: N/A

DO YOU CHARGE THE BORROWING
LIBRARY FOR POSTAGE? No

FOR HOW LONG DO YOU SUSPEND ILL
SERVICE OVER THE CHRISTMAS
HOLIDAYS? 1 week

ARE THERE ANY GROUPS OF LIBRARIES
FOR WHICH YOU WAIVE FEES? IF
SO, PLEASE NAME THEM: New
Jersey academic, institu-
tional, and business
libraries

KEAN COLLEGE OF NEW JERSEY

NUC CODE: (Not answered)

OCLC CODE: NJK

ADDRESS: Interlibrary Loan
Nancy Thompson Library
Kean College of New
Jersey
Box 411, Morris Avenue
Union, NJ 07083

TELEPHONE: (201) 527-2302

LIST NAMES OF BRANCHES WITH
SEPARATE POLICIES: None

BOOKS:
Will Lend: Yes
Length of Loan: 1 month
Renewable: No
Charges: None
Average Turnaround Time:
(Not answered)
If you have indicated that a
book is not to be lent, will
you on receipt of a letter
from the requesting library
search the index for given
entries? (Not answered)

PERIODICALS:
Bound: Will not lend
Unbound: Will not lend
Loan Period: N/A
Renewable: N/A
Will lend if article exceeds
_____ number of pages (Not
answered)

MICROFORMS:
Will Lend: No
Specific Types of Microforms:
N/A

GOVERNMENT PUBLICATIONS:
Will Lend: No

DISSERTATIONS:
Will Lend: No

THESES:
Will Lend: Will lend

AUDIO-VISUAL MATERIALS:
Records: Will not lend
Cassettes: Will not lend
Other (slides, filmstrips,
etc.): Will not lend

COMPUTER SOFTWARE:
Will Lend: No

PHOTODUPLICATION SERVICE:
No charge up to 20 exposures
Charge Per Exposure: Will
not fill requests for over
20 pages
Minimum/handling Fee: None
Average Turnaround Time:
(Not answered)

MICROFILMING SERVICE:
Service Available: No
Charges: N/A

DO YOU CHARGE THE BORROWING
LIBRARY FOR POSTAGE? No

FOR HOW LONG DO YOU SUSPEND ILL
SERVICE OVER THE CHRISTMAS
HOLIDAYS? No suspension

ARE THERE ANY GROUPS OF LIBRARIES
FOR WHICH YOU WAIVE FEES? IF
SO, PLEASE NAME THEM: No fees
charged

MONMOUTH COUNTY LIBRARY

NUC CODE: None

OCLC CODE: None

ADDRESS: Interlibrary Loan
Monmouth County Library
25 Broad St.
Freehold, NJ 07728

TELEPHONE: (201) 431-7230

LIST NAMES OF BRANCHES WITH
SEPARATE POLICIES: None

BOOKS:
Will Lend: Yes
Length of Loan: 4 weeks
Renewable: Yes
Charges: None
Average Turnaround Time:
2 weeks
If you have indicated that a
book is not to be lent, will
you on receipt of a letter
from the requesting library
search the index for given
entries? Yes

PERIODICALS:
Bound: Will not lend
Unbound: Will not lend
Loan Period: N/A
Renewable: N/A
Will lend if article exceeds
_____ number of pages (Not
answered)

MICROFORMS:
Will Lend: No
Specific Types of Microforms:
N/A

GOVERNMENT PUBLICATIONS:
Will Lend: Yes

DISSERTATIONS:
Will Lend: No

THESES:
Will Lend: No

AUDIO-VISUAL MATERIALS:
Records: Will lend
Cassettes: Will lend
Other (slides, filmstrips,
etc.): Will not lend

COMPUTER SOFTWARE:
Will Lend: No

PHOTODUPLICATION SERVICE:
No charge up to 0 exposures
Charge Per Exposure: 10¢
Minimum/handling Fee: $1.00
minimum
Average Turnaround Time:
2 weeks

MICROFILMING SERVICE:
Service Available: No
Charges: N/A

DO YOU CHARGE THE BORROWING
LIBRARY FOR POSTAGE? No

FOR HOW LONG DO YOU SUSPEND ILL
SERVICE OVER THE CHRISTMAS
HOLIDAYS? No suspension

ARE THERE ANY GROUPS OF LIBRARIES
FOR WHICH YOU WAIVE FEES? IF
SO, PLEASE NAME THEM: Non-
profit libraries in New
Jersey

MONTCLAIR PUBLIC LIBRARY

NUC CODE: None

OCLC CODE: None

ADDRESS: Interlibrary Loan
           Montclair Public
           Library
           50 So. Fullerton
           Ave.
           Montclair, NJ 07042

TELEPHONE: (201) 744-0500

LIST NAMES OF BRANCHES WITH
  SEPARATE POLICIES: None

BOOKS:
  Will Lend: Yes
  Length of Loan: 1 month
  Renewable: Yes
  Charges: (Not answered)
  Average Turnaround Time:
    1 week
  If you have indicated that a
  book is not to be lent, will
  you on receipt of a letter
  from the requesting library
  search the index for given
  entries? Yes

PERIODICALS:
  Bound: Will not lend
  Unbound: Will not lend
  Loan Period: N/A
  Renewable: N/A
  Will lend if article exceeds
  _____ number of pages (Will
    not lend, regardless of
    length of article)

MICROFORMS:
  Will Lend: No
  Specific Types of Microforms:
  N/A

GOVERNMENT PUBLICATIONS:
  Will Lend: Yes

DISSERTATIONS:
  Will Lend: No

THESES:
  Will Lend: No

AUDIO-VISUAL MATERIALS:
  Records: Will not lend
  Cassettes: Will not lend
  Other (slides, filmstrips,
    etc.): Will not lend

COMPUTER SOFTWARE:
  Will Lend: No

PHOTODUPLICATION SERVICE:
  No charge up to 20 exposures
    for non-profit New Jersey
    organizations
  Charge Per Exposure: 10¢ per
    page plus postage and 50¢
    handling fee
  Minimum/handling Fee: 50¢
  Average Turnaround Time:
    1 week

MICROFILMING SERVICE:
  Service Available: Yes
  Charges: (Not answered)

DO YOU CHARGE THE BORROWING
  LIBRARY FOR POSTAGE? Yes

FOR HOW LONG DO YOU SUSPEND ILL
  SERVICE OVER THE CHRISTMAS
  HOLIDAYS? No suspension

ARE THERE ANY GROUPS OF LIBRARIES
  FOR WHICH YOU WAIVE FEES? IF
  SO, PLEASE NAME THEM: Non-
    profit N.J. organizations
    and N.J. libraries

MONTCLAIR STATE COLLEGE

NUC CODE: NjUpM

OCLC CODE: NJM

ADDRESS: Interlibrary Loan
           Harry A. Sprague
           Library
           Montclair State College
           Upper Montclair, NJ
           07043

TELEPHONE: (201) 893-4291

LIST NAMES OF BRANCHES WITH
  SEPARATE POLICIES: None

BOOKS:
  Will Lend: Yes
  Length of Loan: 31 days
  Renewable: No
  Charges: None
  Average Turnaround Time:
    3 days
  If you have indicated that a
  book is not to be lent, will
  you on receipt of a letter
  from the requesting library
  search the index for given
  entries? (Not answered)

PERIODICALS:
  Bound: Will not lend
  Unbound: Will not lend
  Loan Period: N/A
  Renewable: N/A
  Will lend if article exceeds
  _____ number of pages (Will
    not lend, regardless of
    length of article)

MICROFORMS:
  Will Lend: Yes
  Specific Types of Microforms:
  Will lend microfilm of mono-
    graphic material; will
    duplicate microfiche.

GOVERNMENT PUBLICATIONS:
  Will Lend: No

DISSERTATIONS:
  Will Lend: No

THESES:
  Will Lend: No

AUDIO-VISUAL MATERIALS:
  Records: Will not lend
  Cassettes: Will lend
  Other (slides, filmstrips,
    etc.): Will not lend

COMPUTER SOFTWARE:
  Will Lend: No

PHOTODUPLICATION SERVICE:
  No charge up to 10 exposures
  Charge Per Exposure: 10¢
  Minimum/handling Fee: None
  Average Turnaround Time:
    5 days

MICROFILMING SERVICE:
  Service Available: No
  Charges: N/A

DO YOU CHARGE THE BORROWING
  LIBRARY FOR POSTAGE? No

FOR HOW LONG DO YOU SUSPEND ILL
  SERVICE OVER THE CHRISTMAS
  HOLIDAYS? Dec.15-Jan.1

ARE THERE ANY GROUPS OF LIBRARIES
  FOR WHICH YOU WAIVE FEES? IF
  SO, PLEASE NAME THEM: New
    Jersey state colleges

MORRIS COUNTY FREE LIBRARY

NUC CODE: NjWhiM

OCLC CODE: NWM

ADDRESS: Interlibrary Loan
Morris County Free
Library
30 East Hanover Ave.
Whippany, NJ 07981

TELEPHONE: (201) 285-6101

LIST NAMES OF BRANCHES WITH
SEPARATE POLICIES: None

BOOKS:
Will Lend: Yes
Length of Loan: 28 days
Renewable: No
Charges: None
Average Turnaround Time:
1 week
If you have indicated that a
book is not to be lent, will
you on receipt of a letter
from the requesting library
search the index for given
entries? Yes

PERIODICALS:
Bound: Will not lend
Unbound: Will not lend
Loan Period: N/A
Renewable: N/A
Will lend if article exceeds
_____ number of pages (Will
not lend, regardless of
length of article)

MICROFORMS:
Will Lend: No
Specific Types of Microforms:
N/A

GOVERNMENT PUBLICATIONS:
Will Lend: Yes

DISSERTATIONS:
Will Lend: Do not own

THESES:
Will Lend: Do not own

AUDIO-VISUAL MATERIALS:
Records: Will not lend
Cassettes: Will not lend
Other (slides, filmstrips,
etc.): Will not lend

COMPUTER SOFTWARE:
Will Lend: Do not own

PHOTODUPLICATION SERVICE:
No charge up to 20 exposures
Charge Per Exposure: 10¢
Minimum/handling Fee: None
Average Turnaround Time:
1 day

MICROFILMING SERVICE:
Service Available: No
Charges: N/A

DO YOU CHARGE THE BORROWING
LIBRARY FOR POSTAGE? No

FOR HOW LONG DO YOU SUSPEND ILL
SERVICE OVER THE CHRISTMAS
HOLIDAYS? No suspension

ARE THERE ANY GROUPS OF LIBRARIES
FOR WHICH YOU WAIVE FEES? IF
SO, PLEASE NAME THEM: None

NEW JERSEY INSTITUTE OF TECHNOLOGY

NUC CODE: NjNC

OCLC CODE: NJI

ADDRESS: Interlibrary Loan
Robert W. Van Houten
Library
New Jersey Institute of
Technology
323 High St.
Newark, NJ 07102

TELEPHONE: (201) 645-5310

LIST NAMES OF BRANCHES WITH
SEPARATE POLICIES: None

BOOKS:
Will Lend: Yes
Length of Loan: 4 weeks
Renewable: Yes
Charges: (Not answered)
Average Turnaround Time:
3 weeks
If you have indicated that a
book is not to be lent, will
you on receipt of a letter
from the requesting library
search the index for given
entries? Yes, unless pages
to be copied exceed 75.

PERIODICALS:
Bound: Will not lend
Unbound: Will not lend
Loan Period: N/A
Renewable: N/A
Will lend if article exceeds
75 pages

MICROFORMS:
Will Lend: No
Specific Types of Microforms:
N/A

GOVERNMENT PUBLICATIONS:
Will Lend: Yes

DISSERTATIONS:
Will Lend: No

THESES:
Will Lend: No

AUDIO-VISUAL MATERIALS:
Records: Will not lend
Cassettes: Will not lend
Other (slides, filmstrips,
etc.): (Not answered)

COMPUTER SOFTWARE:
Will Lend: Do not own

PHOTODUPLICATION SERVICE:
No charge up to 0 exposures
Charge Per Exposure: 10¢
Minimum/handling Fee: (Not
answered)
Average Turnaround Time:
3 weeks

MICROFILMING SERVICE:
Service Available: No
Charges: N/A

DO YOU CHARGE THE BORROWING
LIBRARY FOR POSTAGE? No

FOR HOW LONG DO YOU SUSPEND ILL
SERVICE OVER THE CHRISTMAS
HOLIDAYS? 4 weeks

ARE THERE ANY GROUPS OF LIBRARIES
FOR WHICH YOU WAIVE FEES? IF
SO, PLEASE NAME THEM: None

NEW JERSEY STATE LIBRARY

NUC CODE: Nj

OCLC CODE: NJL

ADDRESS: Interlibrary Loan
New Jersey State
Library
CN 520
Trenton, NJ 08625

TELEPHONE: (609) 292-6248

LIST NAMES OF BRANCHES WITH
SEPARATE POLICIES: None

BOOKS:
Will Lend: Yes
Length of Loan: 28 days
Renewable: Yes
Charges: None
Average Turnaround Time:
2 days
If you have indicated that a
book is not to be lent, will
you on receipt of a letter
from the requesting library
search the index for given
entries? Yes

PERIODICALS:
Bound: Will not lend
Unbound: Will not lend
Loan Period: N/A
Renewable: N/A
Will lend if article exceeds
_____ number of pages (Not
answered)

MICROFORMS:
Will Lend: Yes
Specific Types of Microforms:
(Not answered)

GOVERNMENT PUBLICATIONS:
Will Lend: Yes

DISSERTATIONS:
Will Lend: Do not own

THESES:
Will Lend: Do not own

AUDIO-VISUAL MATERIALS:
Records: Do not own
Cassettes: Do not own
Other (slides, filmstrips,
etc.): Do not own

COMPUTER SOFTWARE:
Will Lend: No

PHOTODUPLICATION SERVICE:
No charge up to 10 exposures
Charge Per Exposure: 10¢
Minimum/handling Fee: $1.00/
none
Average Turnaround Time:
3-4 days

MICROFILMING SERVICE:
Service Available: No
Charges: N/A

DO YOU CHARGE THE BORROWING
LIBRARY FOR POSTAGE? No

FOR HOW LONG DO YOU SUSPEND ILL
SERVICE OVER THE CHRISTMAS
HOLIDAYS? No suspension

ARE THERE ANY GROUPS OF LIBRARIES
FOR WHICH YOU WAIVE FEES? IF
SO, PLEASE NAME THEM: None

NEWARK PUBLIC LIBRARY

NUC CODE: NjN

OCLC CODE: NPL

ADDRESS: Interlibrary Loan
Newark Public Library
5 Washington St.
P. O. Box 630
Newark, NJ 07101-0630

TELEPHONE: (201) 733-7800

LIST NAMES OF BRANCHES WITH
SEPARATE POLICIES: None

BOOKS:
Will Lend: Yes
Length of Loan: 30 days
Renewable: Yes, if no
reserves
Charges: None
Average Turnaround Time:
4 days
If you have indicated that a
book is not to be lent, will
you on receipt of a letter
from the requesting library
search the index for given
entries? (Not answered)

PERIODICALS:
Bound: Will not lend
Unbound: Will not lend
Loan Period: N/A
Renewable: N/A
Will lend if article exceeds
_____ number of pages (Will
not lend, regardless of
length of article)

MICROFORMS:
Will Lend: Yes
Specific Types of Microforms;
Some government documents

GOVERNMENT PUBLICATIONS:
Will Lend: Yes, except for
hearings

DISSERTATIONS:
Will Lend: Do not own

THESES:
Will Lend: Do not own

AUDIO-VISUAL MATERIALS:
Records: Will lend
Cassettes: Will lend
Other (slides, filmstrips,
etc.): Will not lend

COMPUTER SOFTWARE:
Will Lend: Do not own

PHOTODUPLICATION SERVICE:
No charge up to 20 exposures
for non-profit libraries
Charge Per Exposure: 10¢ for
non-profit groups; 25¢ for
profit-making groups
Minimum/handling Fee: $3.00
for profit-making groups
Average Turnaround Time:
2-3 days

MICROFILMING SERVICE:
Service Available: No
Charges: N/A

DO YOU CHARGE THE BORROWING
LIBRARY FOR POSTAGE? No

FOR HOW LONG DO YOU SUSPEND ILL
SERVICE OVER THE CHRISTMAS
HOLIDAYS? No suspension

ARE THERE ANY GROUPS OF LIBRARIES
FOR WHICH YOU WAIVE FEES? IF
SO, PLEASE NAME THEM: None

PATERSON FREE PUBLIC LIBRARY

NUC CODE: NjPat

OCLC CODE: (Not answered)

ADDRESS: Interlibrary Loan
Paterson Free Public
Library
250 Broadway
Paterson, NJ 07501

TELEPHONE: (201) 881-6782

LIST NAMES OF BRANCHES WITH
SEPARATE POLICIES: None

BOOKS:
Will Lend: Yes
Length of Loan: 1 month
Renewable: Yes
Charges: None
Average Turnaround Time:
2 weeks
If you have indicated that a
book is not to be lent, will
you on receipt of a letter
from the requesting library
search the index for given
entries? (Not answered)

PERIODICALS:
Bound: Will not lend
Unbound: Will lend
Loan Period: 1 month
Renewable: Yes
Will lend if article exceeds
10 pages

MICROFORMS:
Will Lend: No
Specific Types of Microfiche:
N/A

GOVERNMENT PUBLICATIONS:
Will Lend: No

DISSERTATIONS:
Will Lend: No

THESES:
Will Lend: No

AUDIO-VISUAL MATERIALS:
Records: Will lend
Cassettes: Will not lend
Other (slides, filmstrips,
etc.): Will lend

COMPUTER SOFTWARE:
Will Lend: No

PHOTODUPLICATION SERVICE:
No charge up to 20 exposures
Charge Per Exposure: 10¢
Minimum/handling Fee: None
Average Turnaround Time:
1 week

MICROFILMING SERVICE:
Service Available: No
Charges: N/A

DO YOU CHARGE THE BORROWING
LIBRARY FOR POSTAGE? No

FOR HOW LONG DO YOU SUSPEND ILL
SERVICE OVER THE CHRISTMAS
HOLIDAYS? No suspension

ARE THERE ANY GROUPS OF LIBRARIES
FOR WHICH YOU WAIVE FEES? IF
SO, PLEASE NAME THEM: None

PRINCETON UNIVERSITY

NUC CODE: NjP

OCLC CODE: PUL

ADDRESS: Interlibrary Loan
Princeton University
Library
Princeton, NJ 08544

TELEPHONE: (609) 452-3272

LIST NAMES OF BRANCHES WITH
SEPARATE POLICIES: None

BOOKS:
Will Lend: Yes
Length of Loan: 4 weeks
Renewable: Yes
Charges: $10.00 ($5.00 loan
plus $5.00 search fee)
Average Turnaround Time:
7 days
If you have indicated that a
book is not to be lent, will
you on receipt of a letter
from the requesting library
search the index for given
entries? Yes

PERIODICALS:
Bound: Will not lend
Unbound: Will not lend
Loan Period: N/A
Renewable: N/A
Will lend if article exceeds
_____ number of pages (Not
answered)

MICROFORMS:
Will Lend: Yes
Specific Types of Microforms:
Microfilm, microfiche,
microopaque

GOVERNMENT PUBLICATIONS:
Will Lend: Yes

DISSERTATIONS:
Will Lend: Yes, if not
available from University
Microfilms; 1955 to
present available from
University Microfilms

THESES:
Will Lend: No

AUDIO-VISUAL MATERIALS:
Records: (Not answered)
Cassettes: (Not answered)
Other (slides, filmstrips,
etc.): (Not answered)

COMPUTER SOFTWARE:
Will Lend: (Not answered)

PHOTODUPLICATION SERVICE:
No charge up to 0 exposures
Charge Per Exposure: 15¢
Minimum/handling Fee: $10.00
($5.00 minimum plus $5.00
search fee)
Average Turnaround Time:
10 days

MICROFILMING SERVICE:
Service Available: Yes
Charges: $35.00 per volume

DO YOU CHARGE THE BORROWING
LIBRARY FOR POSTAGE? No

FOR HOW LONG DO YOU SUSPEND ILL
SERVICE OVER THE CHRISTMAS
HOLIDAYS? No suspension

ARE THERE ANY GROUPS OF LIBRARIES
FOR WHICH YOU WAIVE FEES? IF
SO, PLEASE NAME THEM: RLG
members; New Jersey non-
profit institutions

RAMAPO COLLEGE OF NEW JERSEY

NUC CODE: NjMahR

OCLC CODE: RNJ

ADDRESS: Interlibrary Loan
Ramapo College of New
Jersey
505 Ramapo Valley Rd.
Mahwah, NJ 07430

TELEPHONE: (201) 825-2800

LIST NAMES OF BRANCHES WITH
SEPARATE POLICIES: None

BOOKS:
Will Lend: Yes
Length of Loan: 4 weeks
Renewable: Yes
Charges: None
Average Turnaround Time:
1 week
If you have indicated that a
book is not to be lent, will
you on receipt of a letter
from the requesting library
search the index for given
entries? (Not answered)

PERIODICALS:
Bound: Will not lend
Unbound: Will not lend
Loan Period: N/A
Renewable: N/A
Will lend if article exceeds
_____ number of pages (Not
answered)

MICROFORMS:
Will Lend: No
Specific Types of Microforms:
N/A

GOVERNMENT PUBLICATIONS:
Will Lend: Yes

DISSERTATIONS:
Will Lend: No

THESES:
Will Lend: No

AUDIO-VISUAL MATERIALS:
Records: Will not lend
Cassettes: Will not lend
Other (slides, filmstrips,
etc.): Will not lend

COMPUTER SOFTWARE:
Will Lend: No

PHOTODUPLICATION SERVICE:
No charge up to 0 exposures
Charge Per Exposure: At our
discretion
Minimum/handling Fee: At our
discretion
Average Turnaround Time:
2 weeks

MICROFILMING SERVICE:
Service Available: Yes
Charges: At our discretion

DO YOU CHARGE THE BORROWING
LIBRARY FOR POSTAGE? Not at
this time

FOR HOW LONG DO YOU SUSPEND ILL
SERVICE OVER THE CHRISTMAS
HOLIDAYS? 1 week

ARE THERE ANY GROUPS OF LIBRARIES
FOR WHICH YOU WAIVE FEES? IF
SO, PLEASE NAME THEM: New
Jersey state colleges and
other libraries

RUTGERS UNIVERSITY

NUC CODE: NjR

OCLC CODE: NJR

ADDRESS: Interlibrary Loan
Document Delivery
Services
Rutgers University
Alexander Library
P. O. Box 212
New Brunswick, NJ 08903

TELEPHONE: (201) 932-8345

LIST NAMES OF BRANCHES WITH
SEPARATE POLICIES: None

BOOKS:
Will Lend: Yes
Length of Loan: 1 month
Renewable: Yes
Charges: $5.00
Average Turnaround Time:
14 days
If you have indicated that a
book is not to be lent, will
you on receipt of a letter
from the requesting library
search the index for given
entries? (Not answered)

PERIODICALS:
Bound: Will not lend
Unbound: Will not lend
Loan Period: N/A
Renewable: N/A
Will lend if article exceeds
_____ number of pages (Not
answered)

MICROFORMS:
Will Lend: Yes
Specific Types of Microforms:
(Not answered)

GOVERNMENT PUBLICATIONS:
Will Lend: Yes

DISSERTATIONS:
Will Lend: No

THESES:
Will Lend: No

AUDIO-VISUAL MATERIALS:
Records: Will not lend
Cassettes: Will not lend
Other (slides, filmstrips,
etc.): Will not lend

COMPUTER SOFTWARE:
Will Lend: No

PHOTODUPLICATION SERVICE:
No charge up to 0 exposures
Charges: $7.00 for 1-20
exposures; 10¢ each
additional exposure
Average Turnaround Time:
10 days

MICROFILMING SERVICE:
Service Available: No
Charges: N/A

DO YOU CHARGE THE BORROWING
LIBRARY FOR POSTAGE? No

FOR HOW LONG DO YOU SUSPEND ILL
SERVICE OVER THE CHRISTMAS
HOLIDAYS? No suspension

ARE THERE ANY GROUPS OF LIBRARIES
FOR WHICH YOU WAIVE FEES? IF
SO, PLEASE NAME THEM: RLG
(Research Libraries Group)

SETON HALL UNIVERSITY

NUC CODE: (Not answered)

OCLC CODE: (Not answered)

ADDRESS: Interlibrary Loan
Seton Hall University
Library
400 So. Orange Ave.
So. Orange, NJ 07074

TELEPHONE: (201) 761-9443

LIST NAMES OF BRANCHES WITH
SEPARATE POLICIES: None

BOOKS:
Will Lend: Yes
Length of Loan: 3 weeks
Renewable: No
Charges: $5.00
Average Turnaround Time:
(Not answered)
If you have indicated that a
book is not to be lent, will
you on receipt of a letter
from the requesting library
search the index for given
entries? (Not answered)

PERIODICALS:
Bound: Will not lend
Unbound: Will not lend
Loan Period: N/A
Renewable: N/A
Will lend if article exceeds
_____ number of pages (Will
not lend, regardless of
length of article)

MICROFORMS:
Will Lend: No
Specific Types of Microforms:
N/A

GOVERNMENT PUBLICATIONS:
Will Lend: Yes

DISSERTATIONS:
Will Lend: No

THESES:
Will Lend: No

AUDIO-VISUAL MATERIALS:
Records; Will not lend
Cassettes: Will not lend
Other (slides, filmstrips,
etc.): Will not lend

COMPUTER SOFTWARE:
Will Lend: No

PHOTODUPLICATION SERVICE:
No charge up to 0 exposures
Charge Per Exposure: 10¢
Minimum/handling Fee: (Not
answered)
Average Turnaround Time:
(Not answered)

MICROFILMING SERVICE:
Service Available: No
Charges: N/A

DO YOU CHARGE THE BORROWING
LIBRARY FOR POSTAGE? (Not
answered)

FOR HOW LONG DO YOU SUSPEND ILL
SERVICE OVER THE CHRISTMAS
HOLIDAYS? Dec.25-Jan.2

ARE THERE ANY GROUPS OF LIBRARIES
FOR WHICH YOU WAIVE FEES? IF
SO, PLEASE NAME THEM: Rutgers;
Newark Public; Princeton;
Stockton State; University of
Rochester

SOMERSET COUNTY LIBRARY

NUC CODE: NjSoCo

OCLC CODE: SOM

ADDRESS: Interlibrary Loan
Somerset County Library
P. O. Box 6700
Bridgewater, NJ 08807

TELEPHONE: (201) 526-4016

LIST NAMES OF BRANCHES WITH
SEPARATE POLICIES: None

BOOKS:
Will Lend: Yes
Length of Loan: 2-4 weeks
Renewable: Yes
Charges: None
Average Turnaround Time:
2 weeks
If you have indicated that a
book is not to be lent, will
you on receipt of a letter
from the requesting library
search the index for given
entries? (Not answered)

PERIODICALS:
Bound: Will not lend
Unbound: Will not lend
Loan Period: N/A
Renewable: N/A
Will lend if article exceeds
_____ number of pages (Will
not lend, regardless of
length of article)

MICROFORMS:
Will Lend: No
Specific Types of Microforms:
N/A

GOVERNMENT PUBLICATIONS:
Will Lend: Yes

DISSERTATIONS:
Will Lend: Do not own

THESES:
Will Lend: Do not own

AUDIO-VISUAL MATERIALS:
Records: Will lend
Cassettes: Will lend
Other (slides, filmstrips,
etc.): Will lend

COMPUTER SOFTWARE:
Will Lend: Yes

PHOTODUPLICATION SERVICE:
No charge up to 20 exposures
Charge Per Exposure: 10¢
Minimum/handling Fee: None
Average Turnaround Time:
1 day

MICROFILMING SERVICE:
Service Available: No
Charges: N/A

DO YOU CHARGE THE BORROWING
LIBRARY FOR POSTAGE? No

FOR HOW LONG DO YOU SUSPEND ILL
SERVICE OVER THE CHRISTMAS
HOLIDAYS? No suspension

ARE THERE ANY GROUPS OF LIBRARIES
FOR WHICH YOU WAIVE FEES? IF
SO, PLEASE NAME THEM: None

STOCKTON STATE COLLEGE

NUC CODE: None

OCLC CODE: NJS

ADDRESS: Interlibrary Loan
          Stockton State College
          Library
          Pomona, NJ 08240

TELEPHONE: (609) 652-1776, X350

LIST NAMES OF BRANCHES WITH
  SEPARATE POLICIES: None

BOOKS:
  Will Lend: Yes
  Length of Loan: 1 month
  Renewable: Yes
  Charges: None
  Average Turnaround Time:
    24 hours
  If you have indicated that a
    book is not to be lent, will
    you on receipt of a letter
    from the requesting library
    search the index for given
    entries? Yes

PERIODICALS:
  Bound: Will not lend
  Unbound: Will not lend
  Loan Period: N/A
  Renewable: N/A
  Will lend if article exceeds
    _____ number of pages (Not
    answered)

MICROFORMS:
  Will Lend: No
  Specific Types of Microforms:
    N/A

GOVERNMENT PUBLICATIONS:
  Will Lend: Yes

DISSERTATIONS:
  Will Lend: No

THESES:
  Will Lend: No

AUDIO-VISUAL MATERIALS:
  Records: Will not lend
  Cassettes: Will not lend
  Other (slides, filmstrips,
    etc.): Will not lend

COMPUTER SOFTWARE:
  Will Lend: No

PHOTODUPLICATION SERVICE:
  No charge up to 20 exposures
  Charge Per Exposure: None at
    this time
  Minimum/handling Fee: None
    at this time
  Average Turnaround Time:
    24 hours

MICROFILMING SERVICE:
  Service Available: No
  Charges: N/A

DO YOU CHARGE THE BORROWING
  LIBRARY FOR POSTAGE? No

FOR HOW LONG DO YOU SUSPEND ILL
  SERVICE OVER THE CHRISTMAS
  HOLIDAYS? No suspension

ARE THERE ANY GROUPS OF LIBRARIES
  FOR WHICH YOU WAIVE FEES? IF
  SO, PLEASE NAME THEM: No fees
  charged at this time

TRENTON STATE COLLEGE

NUC CODE: NjTS

OCLC CODE: NJT

ADDRESS: Interlibrary Loan
          Trenton State College
          Roscoe L. West Library
          CN 550, Hillwood Lakes
          Trenton, NJ 08625

TELEPHONE: (609) 771-2464

LIST NAMES OF BRANCHES WITH
  SEPARATE POLICIES: None

BOOKS:
  Will Lend: Yes
  Length of Loan: 1 month
  Renewable: Yes
  Charges: Usually none
  Average Turnaround Time:
    1 day
  If you have indicated that a
    book is not to be lent, will
    you on receipt of a letter
    from the requesting library
    search the index for given
    entries? Yes

PERIODICALS:
  Bound: Will not lend
  Unbound: Will not lend
  Loan Period: N/A
  Renewable: N/A
  Will lend if article exceeds
    _____ number of pages (Not
    answered)

MICROFORMS:
  Will Lend: Only under special
    circumstances
  Specific Types of Microforms:
    Microfilm, microfiche,
    microcards, ultrafiche

GOVERNMENT PUBLICATIONS:
  Will Lend: Yes

DISSERTATIONS:
  Will Lend: Yes

THESES:
  Will Lend: Yes

AUDIO-VISUAL MATERIALS:
  Records: Will not lend
  Cassettes: Will not lend
  Other (slides, filmstrips,
    etc.): Will not lend

COMPUTER SOFTWARE:
  Will Lend: No

PHOTODUPLICATION SERVICE:
  No charge up to 20 exposures
  Charge Per Exposure: 5¢
  Minimum/handling Fee: None
  Average Turnaround Time:
    1 day

MICROFILMING SERVICE:
  Service Available: No
  Charges: N/A

DO YOU CHARGE THE BORROWING
  LIBRARY FOR POSTAGE? Not
  usually

FOR HOW LONG DO YOU SUSPEND ILL
  SERVICE OVER THE CHRISTMAS
  HOLIDAYS? Dec.15-Jan.15

ARE THERE ANY GROUPS OF LIBRARIES
  FOR WHICH YOU WAIVE FEES? IF
  SO, PLEASE NAME THEM: No fees
  charged

UNIVERSITY OF MEDICINE AND DENTISTRY OF NEW JERSEY

NUC CODE: (Not answered)

OCLC CODE: NJN

ADDRESS: Interlibrary Loan
University of Medicine
and Dentistry of New
Jersey
George F. Smith Library
100 Bergen St.
Newark, NJ   07103

TELEPHONE: (201) 456-5319

LIST NAMES OF BRANCHES WITH
SEPARATE POLICIES: None

BOOKS:
Will Lend: Yes
Length of Loan: 1 month
Renewable: Yes
Charges: $5.00 per request
Average Turnaround Time:
3-4 days
If you have indicated that a
book is not to be lent, will
you on receipt of a letter
from the requesting library
search the index for given
entries?   (Not answered)

PERIODICALS:
Bound: Will not lend
Unbound: Will not lend
Loan Period: N/A
Renewable: N/A
Will lend if article exceeds
_____ number of pages (Not
answered)

MICROFORMS:
Will Lend: No
Specific Types of Microforms:
N/A

GOVERNMENT PUBLICATIONS:
Will Lend: Yes

DISSERTATIONS:
Will Lend: Yes

THESES:
Will Lend: Yes

AUDIO-VISUAL MATERIALS:
Records: (Not answered)
Cassettes: Will lend
Other (slides, filmstrips,
etc.):   Will lend

COMPUTER SOFTWARE:
Will Lend: Yes

PHOTODUPLICATION SERVICE:
No charge up to 0 exposures
Charge Per Request: $5.00
Average Turnaround Time:
3-4 days

MICROFILMING SERVICE:
Service Available: No
Charges: N/A

DO YOU CHARGE THE BORROWING
LIBRARY FOR POSTAGE?   No

FOR HOW LONG DO YOU SUSPEND ILL
SERVICE OVER THE CHRISTMAS
HOLIDAYS?   No suspension

ARE THERE ANY GROUPS OF LIBRARIES
FOR WHICH YOU WAIVE FEES?   IF
SO, PLEASE NAME THEM: None

NOTE: "$5.00 fee acceptable"
must be typed on all ILL
requests

WILLIAM PATERSON COLLEGE

NUC CODE: NJPatSC

OCLC CODE: NJP

ADDRESS: Interlibrary Loan
William Paterson College
300 Pompton Rd.
Wayne, NJ   07470

TELEPHONE: (201) 595-2542

LIST NAMES OF BRANCHES WITH
SEPARATE POLICIES: None

BOOKS:
Will Lend: Yes
Length of Loan: 4 weeks
Renewable: Yes
Charges: No
Average Turnaround Time:
(Not answered)
If you have indicated that a
book is not to be lent, will
you on receipt of a letter
from the requesting library
search the index for given
entries?   (Not answered)

PERIODICALS:
Bound: Will not lend
Unbound: Will not lend
Loan Period: N/A
Renewable: N/A
Will lend if article exceeds
_____ number of pages (Not
answered)

MICROFORMS:
Many items in our collection,
including non-circulating
periodicals, indexes such as
CIS, and Abstracts, are in
microformat.   Loans of microforms are done only on items
that normally circulate to our
patrons.

GOVERNMENT PUBLICATIONS:
Will Lend: Yes

DISSERTATIONS:
Will Lend: No

THESES:
Will Lend: No

AUDIO-VISUAL MATERIALS:
We loan only those items
that normally circulate.

COMPUTER SOFTWARE:
Will Lend: No

PHOTODUPLICATION SERVICE:
No charge up to any exposures
Charge Per Exposure: None
Minimum/handling Fee: None
Average Turnaround Time:
(Not answered)

MICROFILMING SERVICE:
Service Available: No
Charges: N/A

DO YOU CHARGE THE BORROWING
LIBRARY FOR POSTAGE?   No

FOR HOW LONG DO YOU SUSPEND ILL
SERVICE OVER THE CHRISTMAS
HOLIDAYS?   No suspension

ARE THERE ANY GROUPS OF LIBRARIES
FOR WHICH YOU WAIVE FEES?   IF
SO, PLEASE NAME THEM: None

ALBUQUERQUE PUBLIC LIBRARY

NUC CODE: (Not answered)

OCLC CODE: QUE

ADDRESS: Interlibrary Loan
Albuquerque Public
Library
501 Copper N.W.
Albuquerque, NM 87102

TELEPHONE: (505) 766-7720

LIST NAMES OF BRANCHES WITH
SEPARATE POLICIES: None

BOOKS:
Will Lend: Yes
Length of Loan: 1 month
Renewable: Yes
Charges: None
Average Turnaround Time:
2 days
If you have indicated that a
book is not to be lent, will
you on receipt of a letter
from the requesting library
search the index for given
entries? (Not answered)

PERIODICALS:
Bound: Will not lend
Unbound: Will not lend
Loan Period: N/A
Renewable: N/A
Will lend if article exceeds
_____ number of pages (N/A)

MICROFORMS:
Will Lend: No
Specific Types of Microforms:
N/A

GOVERNMENT PUBLICATIONS:
Will Lend: Do not own

DISSERTATIONS:
Will Lend: Do not own

THESES:
Will Lend: Do not own

AUDIO-VISUAL MATERIALS:
Records: Will not lend
Cassettes: Will not lend
Other (slides, filmstrips,
etc.): Will not lend

COMPUTER SOFTWARE:
Will Lend: No

PHOTODUPLICATION SERVICE:
No charge up to 10 exposures
Charge Per Exposure: 10¢
Minimum/handling Fee: None
Average Turnaround Time:
2 days

MICROFILMING SERVICE:
Service Available: Yes
Charges: If under 5 pages,
there is no charge.
Otherwise, the charge is
25¢ per page.

DO YOU CHARGE THE BORROWING LIBRARY
FOR POSTAGE? No

FOR HOW LONG DO YOU SUSPEND ILL
SERVICE OVER THE CHRISTMAS
HOLIDAYS? Christmas day only

ARE THERE ANY GROUPS OF LIBRARIES
FOR WHICH YOU WAIVE FEES? IF
SO, PLEASE NAME THEM: None

CLARK COUNTY LIBRARY

NUC CODE: NvLC

OCLC CODE: NVC

ADDRESS: Interlibrary Loan
Clark County Library
1401 E. Flamingo Road
Las Vega, NM 89109

TELEPHONE: (702) 733-7810

LIST NAMES OF BRANCHES WITH
SEPARATE POLICIES: None

BOOKS:
Will Lend: Yes
Length of Loan: 4 weeks
Renewable: Yes
Charges: None
Average Turnaround Time:
5 days
If you have indicated that a
book is not to be lent, will
you on receipt of a letter
from the requesting library
search the index for given
entries? Yes

PERIODICALS:
Bound: Will not lend
Unbound: Will lend
Loan Period: 4 weeks
Renewable: Yes
Will lend if article exceeds
_____ number of pages (Not
answered)

MICROFORMS:
Will Lend: Yes
Specific Types of Microforms:
Newspapers on microfilm

GOVERNMENT PUBLICATIONS:
Will Lend: Yes

DISSERTATIONS:
Will Lend: Do not own

THESES:
Will Lend: Do not own

AUDIO-VISUAL MATERIALS:
Records: Will not lend
Cassettes: Will not lend
Other (slides, filmstrips,
etc.): Will not lend

COMPUTER SOFTWARE:
Will Lend: No

PHOTODUPLICATION SERVICE:
No charge up to ___ exposures
Charge Per Exposure: No charge
Minimum/handling Fee: None
Average Turnaround Time:
5 days

MICROFILMING SERVICE:
Service Available: No
Charges: N/A

DO YOU CHARGE THE BORROWING LIBRARY
FOR POSTAGE? No

FOR HOW LONG DO YOU SUSPEND ILL
SERVICE OVER THE CHRISTMAS
HOLIDAYS? No suspension

ARE THERE ANY GROUPS OF LIBRARIES
FOR WHICH YOU WAIVE FEES? IF
SO, PLEASE NAME THEM: No groups

EASTERN NEW MEXICO UNIVERSITY

NUC CODE: Nm PE

OCLC CODE: IPU

ADDRESS: Interlibrary Loan
          Golden Library
          Eastern New Mexico
          University
          Portales, NM 88130

TELEPHONE: (505) 562-2624

LIST NAMES OF BRANCHES WITH
  SEPARATE POLICIES:
      Eastern New Mexico University
        at Clovis
      Eastern New Mexico University
        at Roswell

BOOKS:
  Will Lend: Yes
  Length of Loan: 2 weeks
  Renewable: (Not answered)
  Charges: None
  Average Turnaround Time:
    24 hours
  If you have indicated that a
    book is not to be lent, will
    you on receipt of a letter
    from the requesting library
    search the index for given
    entries? Yes

PERIODICALS:
  Bound: Will not lend
  Unbound: (Not answered)
  Loan Period: N/A, but
    will supply photocopies
  Renewable: N/A
  Will lend if article exceeds
    _____ number of pages
    (Will not lend)

MICROFORMS:
  Will Lend: Yes
  Specific Types of Microforms:
    Microfiche, microcards,
    microfilms

GOVERNMENT PUBLICATIONS:
  Will Lend: Yes

DISSERTATIONS:
  Will Lend: Yes

THESES:
  Will Lend: Yes

AUDIO-VISUAL MATERIALS:
  Records: Will not lend
  Cassettes: Will not lend
  Other (slides, filmstrips,
    etc.): Will not lend

COMPUTER SOFTWARE:
  Will Lend: No

PHOTODUPLICATION SERVICE:
  No charge up to (none) exposures
  Charge Per Exposure: 20¢
  Minimum/handling Fee: $2.00
  Average Turnaround Time:
    24 hours

MICROFILMING SERVICE:
  Service Available: No
  Charges: N/A

DO YOU CHARGE THE BORROWING LIBRARY
FOR POSTAGE? No

FOR HOW LONG DO YOU SUSPEND ILL
SERVICE OVER THE CHRISTMAS
HOLIDAYS? 2 weeks

ARE THERE ANY GROUPS OF LIBRARIES
FOR WHICH YOU WAIVE FEES? IF
SO, PLEASE NAME THEM: AMIGOS
  and New Mexico

NEW MEXICO HIGHLANDS LIBRARY

NUC CODE: (Not answered)

OCLC CODE: (Not answered)

ADDRESS: Interlibrary Loan
          New Mexico Highlands
          University
          Donnelly Library
          Las Vegas, NM 87701

TELEPHONE: (505) 425-7511, X508

LIST NAMES OF BRANCHES WITH
  SEPARATE POLICIES: None

BOOKS:
  Will Lend: Yes
  Length of Loan: 1 month
  Renewable: Conditional
  Charges: None
  Average Turnaround Time:
    (Not answered)
  If you have indicated that a
    book is not to be lent, will
    you on receipt of a letter
    from the requesting library
    search the index for given
    entries? (Not answered)

PERIODICALS:
  Bound: Will not lend
  Unbound: Will not lend
  Loan Period: N/A
  Renewable: N/A
  Will lend if article exceeds
    50 pages

MICROFORMS:
  Will Lend: Yes
  Specific Types of Microforms:
    N/A

GOVERNMENT PUBLICATIONS:
  Will Lend: Yes

DISSERTATIONS:
  Will Lend: Yes

THESES:
  Will Lend: Yes

AUDIO-VISUAL MATERIALS:
  Records: (Not answered)
  Cassettes: (Not answered)
  Other (slides, filmstrips,
    etc.): (Not answered)

COMPUTER SOFTWARE:
  Will Lend: Yes

PHOTODUPLICATION SERVICE:
  No charge
  Charge Per Exposure: None
  Minimum/handling Fee: None
  Average Turnaround Time:
    (Not answered)

MICROFILMING SERVICE:
  Service Available: No
  Charges: N/A

DO YOU CHARGE THE BORROWING LIBRARY
FOR POSTAGE? No

FOR HOW LONG DO YOU SUSPEND ILL
SERVICE OVER THE CHRISTMAS
HOLIDAYS? Dec.25-Jan.2

ARE THERE ANY GROUPS OF LIBRARIES
FOR WHICH YOU WAIVE FEES? IF
SO, PLEASE NAME THEM: (None
  listed)

NEW MEXICO INSTITUTE OF MINING AND TECHNOLOGY

NUC CODE: NMSOI

OCLC CODE: NMT

ADDRESS: Interlibrary Loan
New Mexico Institute
of Mining and
Technology
Martin Spear Library
Socorro, NM 87801

TELEPHONE: (505) 835-5173

LIST NAMES OF BRANCHES WITH
SEPARATE POLICIES: None

BOOKS:
Will Lend: Yes
Length of Loan: 3 weeks
Renewable: Yes, but each
case is considered
separately
Charges: (Not answered)
Average Turnaround Time:
1-2 days
If you have indicated that a
book is not to be lent, will
you on receipt of a letter
from the requesting library
search the index for given
entries? Yes

PERIODICALS:
Bound: Will not lend
Unbound: Will not lend
Loan Period: N/A
Renewable: N/A
Will lend if article exceeds
_____ number of pages (Will
lend sometimes)

MICROFORMS:
Will Lend: Yes
Specific Types of Microforms:
(Not answered)

GOVERNMENT PUBLICATIONS:
Will Lend: Yes

DISSERTATIONS:
Will Lend: Yes, fiche copy
only

THESES:
Will Lend: Yes, fiche copy
only

AUDIO-VISUAL MATERIALS:
Records: Will not lend
Cassettes: Will not lend
Other (slides, filmstrips,
etc.): Will not lend

COMPUTER SOFTWARE:
Will Lend: Do not own

PHOTODUPLICATION SERVICE:
No charge up to _____
exposures (Not answered)
Charge Per Exposure:
(Not answered)
Minimum/handling Fee: (Not
answered)
Average Turnaround Time:
24 hours

MICROFILMING SERVICE:
Service Available: (Not
answered)
Charges: (Not answered)

DO YOU CHARGE THE BORROWING
LIBRARY FOR POSTAGE? Not
at this time

FOR HOW LONG DO YOU SUSPEND ILL
SERVICE OVER THE CHRISTMAS
HOLIDAYS? 2 weeks

ARE THERE ANY GROUPS OF LIBRARIES
FOR WHICH YOU WAIVE FEES? IF
SO, PLEASE NAME THEM: AMIGOS

NEW MEXICO STATE LIBRARY

NUC CODE: NM

OCLC CODE: NMS

ADDRESS: Interlibrary Loan
New Mexico State Library
325 Don Gaspar
Santa Fe, NM 87503

TELEPHONE: (505) 827-2033

LIST NAMES OF BRANCHES WITH
SEPARATE POLICIES: None

BOOKS:
Will Lend: Yes
Length of Loan: 30 days
Renewable: Yes
Charges: None
Average Turnaround Time:
(Not answered)
If you have indicated that a
book is not to be lent, will
you on receipt of a letter
from the requesting library
search the index for given
entries? Yes

PERIODICALS:
Bound: Will not lend
Unbound: Will not lend
Loan Period: N/A
Renewable: N/A
Will lend if article exceeds
_____ number of pages (Will
not lend)

MICROFORMS:
Will Lend: Yes
Specific Types of Microforms:
Microfilm only

GOVERNMENT PUBLICATIONS:
Will Lend: Yes

DISSERTATIONS:
Will Lend: Do not own

THESES:
Will Lend: Do not own

AUDIO-VISUAL MATERIALS:
Records: Will not lend
Cassettes: Will not lend
Other (slides, filmstrips,
etc.): Will not lend

COMPUTER SOFTWARE:
Will Lend: Do not own

PHOTODUPLICATION SERVICE:
No charge up to 20 exposures
Charge Per Exposure:
20 maximum
Minimum/handling Fee: None
Average Turnaround Time:
(Not answered)

MICROFILMING SERVICE:
Service Available: No
Charges: N/A

DO YOU CHARGE THE BORRWOING LIBRAR
FOR POSTAGE? No

FOR HOW LONG DO YOU SUSPEND ILL
SERVICE OVER THE CHRISTMAS
HOLIDAYS? Dec.18-Jan.7

ARE THERE ANY GROUPS OF LIBRARIES
FOR WHICH YOU WAIVE FEES? IF
SO, PLEASE NAME THEM: No fees

NEW MEXICO STATE UNIVERSITY

NUC CODE: NmLcU

OCLC CODE: IRU

ADDRESS: Interlibrary Loan
New Mexico State
University Library
P. O. Box 3475
Las Cruces, NM 88003

TELEPHONE: (505) 646-4737

LIST NAMES OF BRANCHES WITH
SEPARATE POLICIES: None

BOOKS:
Will Lend: Yes
Length of Loan: 3 weeks
Renewable: Yes
Charges: (Not answered)
Average Turnaround Time:
(Not answered)
If you have indicated that a
book is not to be lent, will
you on receipt of a letter
from the requesting library
search the index for given
entries? (Not answered)

PERIODICALS:
Bound: Will not lend
Unbound: Will not lend
Loan Period: N/A
Renewable: N/A
Will lend if article exceeds
_____ number of pages (Not
answered)

MICROFORMS:
Will Lend: Yes
Specific Types of Microforms:
All types

GOVERNMENT PUBLICATIONS:
Will Lend: Yes

DISSERTATIONS:
Will Lend: Yes, if 2nd copy
available; 1960 to present
available from University
Microfilms

THESES:
Will Lend: Yes, if 2nd copy
available

AUDIO-VISUAL MATERIALS:
Records: (Not answered)
Cassettes: (Not answered)
Other (slides, filmstrips,
etc.): (Not answered)

COMPUTER SOFTWARE:
Will Lend: (Not answered)

PHOTODUPLICATION SERVICE:
No charge up to 0 exposures
Charges: $2.00 for 1-13
exposures; 15¢ each
additional exposure
Average Turnaround Time:
(Not answered)

MICROFILMING SERVICE:
Service Available: No
Charges: N/A

DO YOU CHARGE THE BORROWING
LIBRARY FOR POSTAGE? (Not
answered)

FOR HOW LONG DO YOU SUSPEND ILL
SERVICE OVER THE CHRISTMAS
HOLIDAYS? (Not answered)

ARE THERE ANY GROUPS OF LIBRARIES
FOR WHICH YOU WAIVE FEES? IF
SO, PLEASE NAME THEM: (Not
answered)

UNIVERSITY OF NEW MEXICO

NUC CODE: NmU

OCLC CODE: IQU

ADDRESS: Interlibrary Loan
General Library
University of New
Mexico
Albuquerque, NM 87131

TELEPHONE: (505) 277-5617

LIST NAMES OF BRANCHES WITH
SEPARATE POLICIES:
Fine Arts Library

BOOKS:
Will Lend: Yes
Length of Loan: 2 weeks use
Renewable: Not usually
Charges: None
Average Turnaround Time:
24 hours
If you have indicated that a
book is not to be lent, will
you on receipt of a letter
from the requesting library
search the index for given
entries? Sometimes

PERIODICALS:
Bound: Will lend, except for
last 3 years
Unbound: Will lend sometimes
Loan Period: 1 week
Renewable: No
Will lend if article exceeds
50 pages

MICROFORMS:
Will Lend: Yes
Specific Types of Microforms:
Film only

GOVERNMENT PUBLICATIONS:
Will Lend: Yes

DISSERTATIONS:
Will Lend: Yes; 1954 to
present available from
University Microfilms

THESES:
Will Lend: Yes

AUDIO-VISUAL MATERIALS:
Records: Will not lend
Cassettes: Will lend
Other (slides, filmstrips,
etc.): Will not lend

COMPUTER SOFTWARE:
Will Lend: No

PHOTODUPLICATION SERVICE:
No charge up to 0 exposures
Charges: $2.50 for 1-5
exposures
Average Turnaround Time:
12 hours

MICROFILMING SERVICE:
Service Available: Yes
Charges: Negative is $2.50
minimum for 1-10 exposures;
positive is $18.50 per reel

DO YOU CHARGE THE BORROWING
LIBRARY FOR POSTAGE? No

FOR HOW LONG DO YOU SUSPEND ILL
SERVICE OVER THE CHRISTMAS
HOLIDAYS? No suspension

ARE THERE ANY GROUPS OF LIBRARIES
FOR WHICH YOU WAIVE FEES? IF
SO, PLEASE NAME THEM: CARLA
Consortium and AMIGOS
Consortium

UNIVERSITY OF NEW MEXICO MEDICAL CENTER

NUC CODE: NMUM-Albq

OCLC CODE: MQM

ADDRESS: Interlibrary Loan
         Medical Center Library
         University of New
          Mexico
         Albuquerque, NM 87131

TELEPHONE: (505) 277-2311

LIST NAMES OF BRANCHES WITH
  SEPARATE POLICIES: None

BOOKS:
  Will Lend: Yes
  Length of Loan: 2 weeks
  Renewable: Yes
  Charges: $4.00 (TALON coupon
    or payment must accompany
    order)
  Average Turnaround Time:
    24 hours
  If you have indicated that a
    book is not to be lent, will
    you on receipt of a letter
    from the requesting library
    search the index for given
    entries? (Not answered)

PERIODICALS:
  Bound: Will lend those prior
    to 1978
  Unbound: Will not lend
  Loan Period: 1 week
  Renewable: Yes
  Will lend if article exceeds
    50 pages

MICROFORMS:
  Will Lend: No
  Specific Types of Microforms:
    N/A

GOVERNMENT PUBLICATIONS:
  Will Lend: Yes

DISSERTATIONS:
  Will Lend: No

THESES:
  Will Lend: No

AUDIO-VISUAL MATERIALS:
  Records: (Not answered)
  Cassettes: Will lend
  Other (slides, filmstrips,
    etc.): Will not lend

COMPUTER SOFTWARE:
  Will Lend: No

PHOTODUPLICATION SERVICE:
  No charge up to 25 exposures
  Charge Per Exposure: 5¢ over
    25 exposures
  Minimum/handling Fee: $4.00
    (Payment must accompany
    order)
  Average Turnaround Time:
    24 hours

MICROFILMING SERVICE:
  Service Available: No
  Charges: N/A

DO YOU CHARGE THE BORROWING LIBRARY
  FOR POSTAGE? No

FOR HOW LONG DO YOU SUSPEND ILL
  SERVICE OVER THE CHRISTMAS
  HOLIDAYS? 2 weeks

ARE THERE ANY GROUPS OF LIBRARIES
  FOR WHICH YOU WAIVE FEES? IF
  SO, PLEASE NAME THEM: (None
  listed)

ADELPHI UNIVERSITY

NUC CODE: NGCA

OCLC CODE: VJA

ADDRESS: Interlibrary Loan
Adelphi University
Library
Garden City, NY 11530

TELEPHONE: (516) 663-1036

LIST NAMES OF BRANCHES WITH
SEPARATE POLICIES:
Social Work Library--
will not lend books, but
will xerox articles.

BOOKS:
Will Lend: Yes
Length of Loan: 4 weeks
Renewable: Yes, for 2 weeks
Charges: None
Average Turnaround Time:
(Not answered)
If you have indicated that a
book is not to be lent, will
you on receipt of a letter
from the requesting library
search the index for given
entries? (Not answered)

PERIODICALS:
Bound: Will not lend
Unbound: Will not lend
Loan Period: N/A
Renewable: N/A
Will lend if article exceeds
_____ number of pages (Will
not lend, regardless of
length of article)

MICROFORMS:
Will Lend: No
Specific Types of Microforms:
N/A

GOVERNMENT PUBLICATIONS:
Will Lend: Yes

DISSERTATIONS:
Will Lend: Yes

THESES:
Will Lend: Yes

AUDIO-VISUAL MATERIALS:
Records: (Not answered)
Cassettes: Will lend
Other (slides, filmstrips,
etc.): Will not lend

COMPUTER SOFTWARE:
Will Lend: No

PHOTODUPLICATION SERVICE:
No charge up to any exposures
Charge Per Exposure: None
Minimum/handling Fee: None
Average Turnaround Time:
(Not answered)

MICROFILMING SERVICE:
Service Available: Yes
Charges: None

DO YOU CHARGE THE BORROWING
LIBRARY FOR POSTAGE? No

FOR HOW LONG DO YOU SUSPEND ILL
SERVICE OVER THE CHRISTMAS
HOLIDAYS? No suspension

ARE THERE ANY GROUPS OF LIBRARIES
FOR WHICH YOU WAIVE FEES? IF
SO, PLEASE NAME THEM: None

ALBANY MEDICAL COLLEGE

NUC CODE: NALA

OCLC CODE: VXL

ADDRESS: Interlibrary Loan
Schaffer Library of
Health Sciences
Albany Medical College
47 New Scotland Ave.
Albany, NY 12208

TELEPHONE: (518) 445-5538

LIST NAMES OF BRANCHES WITH
SEPARATE POLICIES: None

BOOKS:
Will Lend: Yes
Length of Loan: 2 weeks
Renewable: Yes
Charges: $5.00 (National
RMLP ceiling applies)
Average Turnaround Time:
24 hours
If you have indicated that a
book is not to be lent, will
you on receipt of a letter
from the requesting library
search the index for given
entries? (Not answered)

PERIODICALS:
Bound: Will not lend
Unbound: Will not lend
Loan Period: N/A
Renewable: N/A
Will lend if article exceeds
_____ number of pages (Not
answered)

MICROFORMS:
Will Lend: Do not own
Specific Types Of Microforms:
N/A

GOVERNMENT PUBLICATIONS:
Will Lend: Yes, if cataloged
as books

DISSERTATIONS:
Will Lend: No

THESES:
Will lend: No

AUDIO-VISUAL MATERIALS:
Records: (Not answered)
Cassettes: Will lend
Other (slides, filmstrips,
etc.): Will lend, but
must sent $10.00 prepaid
fee.

COMPUTER SOFTWARE:
Will Lend: Do not own

PHOTODUPLICATION SERVICE:
No charge up to 0 exposures
Charge Per Exposure: (Not
answered)
Minimum/handling Fee: $5.00
per transaction per RMLP
policies.
Average Turnaround Time:
24 hours

MICROFILMING SERVICE:
Service Available: No
Charges: N/A

DO YOU CHARGE THE BORROWING
LIBRARY FOR POSTAGE?
Postage is included in
flat fee.

FOR HOW LONG DO YOU SUSPEND ILL
SERVICE OVER THE CHRISTMAS
HOLIDAYS? No suspension

ARE THERE ANY GROUPS OF LIBRARIES
FOR WHICH YOU WAIVE FEES? IF
SO, PLEASE NAME THEM: Member
libraries of the Capital
District Library Council.

AMERICAN MUSEUM OF NATURAL HISTORY

NUC CODE: NNM

OCLC CODE: YAM

ADDRESS: Interlibrary Loan
American Museum of
Natural History
Library
Central Park West at
79th St.
New York, NY 10024

TELEPHONE: (212) 873-1300, X494

LIST NAMES OF BRANCHES WITH
SEPARATE POLICIES: None

BOOKS:
Will Lend: Yes
Length of Loan: 2 weeks use
Renewable: Yes, usually
Charges: None
Average Turnaround Time:
2-4 weeks
If you have indicated that a
book is not to be lent, will
you on receipt of a letter
from the requesting library
search the index for given
entries? (Not answered)

PERIODICALS:
Bound: Will not lend
Unbound: Will lend
Loan Period: 2 weeks use
Renewable: Yes, sometimes
Will lend if article exceeds
_____ number of pages (Not
answered)

MICROFORMS:
Will Lend: Yes
Specific Types of Microforms:
Microfilm

GOVERNMENT PUBLICATIONS:
Will Lend: Do not own

DISSERTATIONS:
Will Lend: Do not own

THESES:
Will Lend: Do not own

AUDIO-VISUAL MATERIALS:
Records: Do not own
Cassettes: Do not own
Other (slides, filmstrips,
etc.): Do not own

COMPUTER SOFTWARE:
Will Lend: Do not own

PHOTODUPLICATION SERVICE:
No charge up to 0 exposures
Charge Per Exposure: 35¢
Minimum/handling Fee: $2.50
(includes 5 exposures)
Average Turnaround Time:
2-4 weeks

MICROFILMING SERVICE:
Service Available: No
Charges: N/A

DO YOU CHARGE THE BORROWING
LIBRARY FOR POSTAGE? No

FOR HOW LONG DO YOU SUSPEND ILL
SERVICE OVER THE CHRISTMAS
HOLIDAYS? 10 days

ARE THERE ANY GROUPS OF LIBRARIES
FOR WHICH YOU WAIVE FEES? IF
SO, PLEASE NAME THEM: Medical
Library Center of New York
City

BROOKHAVEN NATIONAL LABORATORY

NUC CODE: NUpB

OCLC CODE: ZBN

ADDRESS: Interlibrary Loan
Research Library
Brookhaven National
Laboratory
Upton, NY 11973

TELEPHONE: (516) 282-3138

LIST NAMES OF BRANCHES WITH
SEPARATE POLICIES: None

BOOKS:
Will Lend: Yes
Length of Loan: 2 weeks
Renewable: Yes
Charges: None
Average Turnaround Time:
2-3 days
If you have indicated that a
book is not to be lent, will
you on receipt of a letter
from the requesting library
search the index for given
entries? Yes

PERIODICALS:
Bound: Will not lend
Unbound: Will not lend
Loan Period: N/A
Renewable: N/A
Will lend if article exceeds
_____ number of pages (Not
answered)

MICROFORMS:
Will Lend: Do not own

GOVERNMENT PUBLICATIONS:
Will Lend: Yes

DISSERTATIONS:
Will Lend: Do not own

THESES:
Will Lend: Do not own

AUDIO-VISUAL MATERIALS:
Records: Do not own
Cassettes: Do not own
Other (slides, filmstrips,
etc.): Do not own

COMPUTER SOFTWARE:
Will Lend: Do not own

PHOTODUPLICATION SERVICE:
No charge up to 35 exposures
Charge Per Exposure: None
Minimum/handling Fee: None
Average Turnaround Time:
3-5 days

MICROFILMING SERVICE:
Service Available: No
Charges: N/A

DO YOU CHARGE THE BORROWING
LIBRARY FOR POSTAGE? No

FOR HOW LONG DO YOU SUSPEND ILL
SERVICE OVER THE CHRISTMAS
HOLIDAYS? No suspension

ARE THERE ANY GROUPS OF LIBRARIES
FOR WHICH YOU WAIVE FEES? IF
SO, PLEASE NAME THEM: None

BROOKLYN COLLEGE

NUC CODE: NBC

OCLC CODE: VDB

ADDRESS: Interlibrary Loan
Brooklyn College
Library
Bedford Avenue and
Avenue H
Brooklyn, NY 11210

TELEPHONE: (212) 780-5628

LIST NAMES OF BRANCHES WITH
SEPARATE POLICIES: None

BOOKS:
Will Lend: Yes
Length of Loan: 1 month
Renewable: Yes
Charges: None
Average Turnaround Time:
1 week from receipt of
request
If you have indicated that a
book is not to be lent, will
you on receipt of a letter
from the requesting library
search the index for given
entries? (Not answered)

PERIODICALS:
Bound: Will not lend
Unbound: Will not lend
Loan Period: N/A
Renewable: N/A
Will lend if article exceeds
_____ number of pages (Not
answered)

MICROFORMS:
Will Lend: No
Specific Types of Microforms:
N/A

GOVERNMENT PUBLICATIONS:
Will Lend: No

DISSERTATIONS:
Will Lend: No

THESES:
Will Lend: No

AUDIO-VISUAL MATERIALS:
Records: Will not lend
Cassettes: Will not lend
Other (slides, filmstrips,
etc.): Will not lend

COMPUTER SOFTWARE:
Will Lend: No

PHOTODUPLICATION SERVICE:
No charge up to 24 exposures
Charge Per Exposure: 10¢
Minimum/handling Fee: None
Average Turnaround Time:
1 week

MICROFILMING SERVICE:
Service Available: No
Charges: N/A

DO YOU CHARGE THE BORROWING
LIBRARY FOR POSTAGE? No

FOR HOW LONG DO YOU SUSPEND ILL
SERVICE OVER THE CHRISTMAS
HOLIDAYS? 12 days

ARE THERE ANY GROUPS OF LIBRARIES
FOR WHICH YOU WAIVE FEES? IF
SO, PLEASE NAME THEM: CUNY
and SUNY

BROOKLYN LAW SCHOOL

NUC CODE: NBL

OCLC CODE: ZBL

ADDRESS: Interlibrary Loan
Brooklyn Law School
Henry L. Ughetta Law
Library
250 Joralemon St.
Brooklyn, NY 11201

TELEPHONE: (212) 780-7974

LIST NAMES OF BRANCHES WITH
SEPARATE POLICIES: None

BOOKS:
Will Lend: Yes
Length of Loan: 2 weeks
Renewable: Yes
Charges: None
Average Turnaround Time:
1 day
If you have indicated that a
book is not to be lent, will
you on receipt of a letter
from the requesting library
search the index for given
entries? (Not answered)

PERIODICALS:
Bound: Will not lend
Unbound: Will not lend
Loan Period: N/A
Renewable: N/A
Will lend if article exceeds
_____ number of pages (Not
answered)

MICROFORMS:
Will Lend: No
Specific Types of Microforms:
N/A

GOVERNMENT PUBLICATIONS:
Will Lend: Yes

DISSERTATIONS:
Will Lend: Do not own

THESES:
Will Lend: Do not own

AUDIO-VISUAL MATERIALS:
Records: Will not lend
Cassettes: Will not lend
Other (slides, filmstrips,
etc.): Will not lend

COMPUTER SOFTWARE:
Will Lend: No

PHOTODUPLICATION SERVICE:
No charge up to any exposures
Charge Per Exposure: None
Minimum/handling Fee: None
Average Turnaround Time:
2 days

MICROFILMING SERVICE:
Service Available: No
Charges: N/A

DO YOU CHARGE THE BORROWING
LIBRARY FOR POSTAGE? No

FOR HOW LONG DO YOU SUSPEND ILL
SERVICE OVER THE CHRISTMAS
HOLIDAYS? No suspension

ARE THERE ANY GROUPS OF LIBRARIES
FOR WHICH YOU WAIVE FEES? IF
SO, PLEASE NAME THEM: No fees
charged

BROOKLYN PUBLIC LIBRARY

NUC CODE: NB

OCLC CODE: None

ADDRESS: Interlibrary Loan
Central Reserves
Brooklyn Public Library
Grand Army Plaza
Brooklyn, NY 11201

TELEPHONE: (212) 780-7787

LIST NAMES OF BRANCHES WITH
SEPARATE POLICIES: None

BOOKS:
Will Lend: Yes
Length of Loan: 3 weeks use
Renewable: Yes
Charges: Postage and
insurance
Average Turnaround Time:
3 days
If you have indicated that a
book is not to be lent, will
you on receipt of a letter
from the requesting library
search the index for given
entries? Yes

PERIODICALS:
Bound: Will not lend
Unbound: Will not lend
Loan Period: N/A
Renewable: N/A
Will lend if article exceeds
_____ number of pages (Not
answered)

MICROFORMS:
Will Lend: No
Specific Types of Microforms:
N/A

GOVERNMENT PUBLICATIONS:
Will Lend: Yes, if cataloged
as singles

DISSERTATIONS:
Will Lend: Yes

THESES:
Will Lend: Yes

AUDIO-VISUAL MATERIALS:
Records: Will not lend
Cassettes: Will not lend
Other (slides, filmstrips,
etc.): Will not lend

COMPUTER SOFTWARE:
Will Lend: No

PHOTODUPLICATION SERVICE:
No charge up to 20 exposures
Charge Per Exposure: 15¢
Minimum/handling Fee: None
Average Turnaround Time:
3 days

MICROFILMING SERVICE:
Service Available: No
Charges: N/A

DO YOU CHARGE THE BORROWING
LIBRARY FOR POSTAGE? Yes

FOR HOW LONG DO YOU SUSPEND ILL
SERVICE OVER THE CHRISTMAS
HOLIDAYS? 1 week

ARE THERE ANY GROUPS OF LIBRARIES
FOR WHICH YOU WAIVE FEES? IF
SO, PLEASE NAME THEM: None

BUFFALO AND ERIE COUNTY PUBLIC LIBRARY

NUC CODE: NBU

OCLC CODE: VHB

ADDRESS: Interlibrary Loan
Buffalo and Erie County
Public Library
Lafayette Square
Buffalo, NY 14203

TELEPHONE: (716) 856-8525, X232

LIST NAMES OF BRANCHES WITH
SEPARATE POLICIES: None

BOOKS:
Will Lend: Yes
Length of Loan: 1-4 weeks
Renewable: No
Charges: None
Average Turnaround Time:
2 days
If you have indicated that a
book is not to be lent, will
you on receipt of a letter
from the requesting library
search the index for given
entries? (Not answered)

PERIODICALS:
Bound: Will not lend
Unbound: Will not lend
Loan Period: N/A
Renewable: N/A
Will not lend regardless
of length of article

MICROFORMS:
Will Lend: Yes
Specific Types of Microforms:
Only from duplicate set of
microfilm

GOVERNMENT PUBLICATIONS:
Will Lend: Yes

DISSERTATIONS:
Will Lend: No

THESES:
Will Lend: No

AUDIO-VISUAL MATERIALS:
Records: Will not lend
Cassettes: Will not lend
Other (slides, filmstrips,
etc.): Will not lend

COMPUTER SOFTWARE:
Will Lend: No

PHOTODUPLICATION SERVICE:
No charge up to 0 exposures
Charge Per Exposure: 20¢
Minimum/handling Fee: $1.00
Average Turnaround Time:
3 days

MICROFILMING SERVICE:
Service Available: No
Charges: N/A

DO YOU CHARGE THE BORROWING
LIBRARY FOR POSTAGE? Only
for photocopy requests

FOR HOW LONG DO YOU SUSPEND ILL
SERVICE OVER THE CHRISTMAS
HOLIDAYS? 10-14 days

ARE THERE ANY GROUPS OF LIBRARIES
FOR WHICH YOU WAIVE FEES? IF
SO, PLEASE NAME THEM: None

C. W. POST CENTER OF LONG ISLAND UNIVERSITY

NUC CODE: (Not answered)

OCLC CODE: (Not answered)

ADDRESS: Interlibrary Loan
B. Davis Schwartz
Memorial Library
C. W. Post Center
Long Island University
Greenvale, NY 11548

TELEPHONE: (516) 299-2898

LIST NAMES OF BRANCHES WITH
SEPARATE POLICIES: None

BOOKS:
Will Lend: Yes
Length of Loan: 28 days
Renewable: Yes if not
requested by a C. W. Post
patron
Charges: None
Average Turnaround Time:
2 days
If you have indicated that a
book is not to be lent, will
you on receipt of a letter
from the requesting library
search the index for given
entries? (Not answered)

PERIODICALS:
Bound: Will not lend
Unbound: Will not lend
Loan Period: N/A
Renewable: N/A
Will lend if article exceeds
_____ number of pages (Will
not lend, regardless of
length of article)

MICROFORMS:
Will Lend: No
Specific Types of Microforms:
N/A

GOVERNMENT PUBLICATIONS:
Will Lend: No

DISSERTATIONS:
Will Lend: No

THESES:
Will Lend: No

AUDIO-VISUAL MATERIALS:
Records: Will not lend
Cassettes: Will not lend
Other (slides, filmstrips,
etc.): Will not lend

COMPUTER SOFTWARE:
Will Lend: No

PHOTODUPLICATION SERVICE:
No charge up to 10 exposures
Charge Per Exposure: 10¢
Minimum/handling Fee: None
Average Turnaround Time:
2 days

MICROFILMING SERVICE:
Service Available: No
Charges: N/A

DO YOU CHARGE THE BORROWING
LIBRARY FOR POSTAGE? No

FOR HOW LONG DO YOU SUSPEND ILL
SERVICE OVER THE CHRISTMAS
HOLIDAYS? 2 weeks

ARE THERE ANY GROUPS OF LIBRARIES
FOR WHICH YOU WAIVE FEES? IF
SO, PLEASE NAME THEM: Local
network libraries; Long
Island Library Resources
Council

CITY COLLEGE OF THE CITY UNIVERSITY OF NEW YORK

NUC CODE: NNCoCi

OCLC CODE: ZXC

ADDRESS: Interlibrary Loan
City College Library
135th St. & Convent
Ave.
New York, NY 10031

TELEPHONE: (212) 960-4155

LIST NAMES OF BRANCHES WITH
SEPARATE POLICIES: (Not
answered)

BOOKS:
Will Lend: Yes
Length of Loan: 4 weeks
Renewable: No
Charges: (Not answered)
Average Turnaround Time:
(Not answered)
If you have indicated that a
book is not to be lent, will
you on receipt of a letter
from the requesting library
search the index for given
entries? (Not answered)

PERIODICALS:
Bound: Will not lend
Unbound: Will not lend
Loan Period: N/A
Renewable: N/A
Will lend if article exceeds
_____ number of pages (Not
answered)

MICROFORMS:
Will Lend: (Not answered)
Specific Types of Microforms:
(Not answered)

GOVERNMENT PUBLICATIONS:
Will Lend: Yes

DISSERTATIONS:
Will Lend: Yes; write to City
University of New York,
Graduate School Library,
33 W. 42nd St., New York,
NY 10036

THESES:
Will Lend: Yes

AUDIO-VISUAL MATERIALS:
Records: Will not lend
Cassettes: Will not lend
Other (slides, filmstrips,
etc.): Will not lend

COMPUTER SOFTWARE:
Will Lend: (Not answered)

PHOTODUPLICATION SERVICE:
No charge up to any exposures
Charge Per Exposure: None
Minimum/handling Fee: None
Average Turnaround Time:
(Not answered)

MICROFILMING SERVICE:
Service Available: No
Charges: N/A

DO YOU CHARGE THE BORROWING
LIBRARY FOR POSTAGE? (Not
answered)

FOR HOW LONG DO YOU SUSPEND ILL
SERVICE OVER THE CHRISTMAS
HOLIDAYS? Dec.15-Jan.5

ARE THERE ANY GROUPS OF LIBRARIES
FOR WHICH YOU WAIVE FEES? IF
SO, PLEASE NAME THEM: (Not
answered)

CITY UNIVERSITY OF NEW YORK--GRADUATE SCHOOL

NUC CODE: NNCU-G

OCLC CODE: ZGM

ADDRESS: Interlibrary Loan
          Graduate School Library
          City University of New
            York
          33 W. 42nd St.
          New York, NY 10036

TELEPHONE: (212) 790-4528 or
                  790-4541

LIST NAMES OF BRANCHES WITH
  SEPARATE POLICIES: None

BOOKS:
  Will Lend: Yes
  Length of Loan: 1 month
  Renewable: Yes
  Charges: None
  Average Turnaround Time:
    (Not answered)
  If you have indicated that a
    book is not to be lent, will
    you on receipt of a letter
    from the requesting library
    search the index for given
    entries? (Not answered)

PERIODICALS:
  Bound: Will not lend
  Unbound: Will not lend
  Loan Period: N/A
  Renewable: N/A
  Will lend if article exceeds
    _____ number of pages (Not
    answered)

MICROFORMS:
  Will Lend: Yes
  Specific Types of Microforms:
    CUNY Ph.D. dissertations
    only

GOVERNMENT PUBLICATIONS:
  Will Lend: No

DISSERTATIONS:
  Will Lend: Yes

THESES:
  Will Lend: Yes

AUDIO-VISUAL MATERIALS:
  Records: Will not lend
  Cassettes: Will not lend
  Other (slides, filmstrips,
    etc.): Will not lend

COMPUTER SOFTWARE:
  Will Lend: No

PHOTODUPLICATION SERVICE:
  No charge up to 0 exposures
  Charge Per Exposure: 10¢
  Minimum/handling Fee: None
  Average Turnaround Time:
    (Not answered)

MICROFILMING SERVICE:
  Service Available: No
  Charges: N/A

DO YOU CHARGE THE BORROWING
  LIBRARY FOR POSTAGE? No

FOR HOW LONG DO YOU SUSPEND ILL
  SERVICE OVER THE CHRISTMAS
  HOLIDAYS? No suspension

ARE THERE ANY GROUPS OF LIBRARIES
  FOR WHICH YOU WAIVE FEES? IF
  SO, PLEASE NAME THEM: No
    photocopying charges to
    other CUNY libraries

CLARKSON COLLEGE OF TECHNOLOGY

NUC CODE: NPotC

OCLC CODE: VYT

ADDRESS: Interlibrary Loan
          Harriet Call Burnap
            Memorial Library
          Clarkson College of
            Technology
          Potsdam, NY 13676

TELEPHONE: (315) 268-2292

LIST NAMES OF BRANCHES WITH
  SEPARATE POLICIES: None

BOOKS:
  Will Lend: Yes
  Length of Loan: 4 weeks
  Renewable: Yes
  Charges: None
  Average Turnaround Time:
    3 days
  If you have indicated that a
    book is not to be lent, will
    you on receipt of a letter
    from the requesting library
    search the index for given
    entries? (Not answered)

PERIODICALS:
  Bound: Will not lend
  Unbound: Will not lend
  Loan Period: N/A
  Renewable: N/A
  Will lend if article exceeds
    _____ number of pages (Not
    answered)

MICROFORMS:
  Will Lend: No
  Specific Types of Microforms:
    N/A

GOVERNMENT PUBLICATIONS:
  Will Lend: Yes

DISSERTATIONS:
  Will Lend: Yes

THESES:
  Will Lend: Yes

AUDIO-VISUAL MATERIALS:
  Records: Will not lend
  Cassettes: Will not lend
  Other (slides, filmstrips,
    etc.): Will not lend

COMPUTER SOFTWARE:
  Will Lend: No

PHOTODUPLICATION SERVICE:
  No charge up to 10 exposures
  Charge Per Exposure: 10¢
  Minimum/handling Fee: $1.00
  Average Turnaround Time:
    3 days

MICROFILMING SERVICE:
  Service Available: No
  Charges: N/A

DO YOU CHARGE THE BORROWING
  LIBRARY FOR POSTAGE? No

FOR HOW LONG DO YOU SUSPEND ILL
  SERVICE OVER THE CHRISTMAS
  HOLIDAYS? No suspension

ARE THERE ANY GROUPS OF LIBRARIES
  FOR WHICH YOU WAIVE FEES? IF
  SO, PLEASE NAME THEM: If we
    have arranged for reciprocal
    borrowing privileges.

COLGATE UNIVERSITY

NUC CODE: NHC

OCLC CODE: VVC

ADDRESS: Interlibrary Loan
Colgate University
Everett N. Case Library
Hamilton, NY 13346

TELEPHONE: (315) 824-1000, X304

LIST NAMES OF BRANCHES WITH
SEPARATE POLICIES: None

BOOKS:
Will Lend: Yes
Length of Loan: 1 month
Renewable: Yes
Charges: None
Average Turnaround Time:
5 days
If you have indicated that a
book is not to be lent, will
you on receipt of a letter
from the requesting library
search the index for given
entries? (Not answered)

PERIODICALS:
Bound: Will not lend
Unbound: Will not lend
Loan Period: N/A
Renewable: N/A
Will lend if article exceeds
_____ number of pages (Not
answered)

MICROFORMS:
Will Lend: Yes
Specific Types of Microforms:
Cards, fiche

GOVERNMENT PUBLICATIONS:
Will Lend: Yes, but
restricted to library use

DISSERTATIONS:
Will Lend: No

THESES:
Will Lend: No

AUDIO-VISUAL MATERIALS:
Records: Will not lend
Cassettes: Will not lend
Other (slides, filmstrips,
etc.): Will not lend

COMPUTER SOFTWARE:
Will Lend: Do not own

PHOTODUPLICATION SERVICE:
No charge up to any exposures
Charge Per Exposure: None
Minimum/handling Fee: None
Average Turnaround Time:
5 days

MICROFILMING SERVICE:
Service Available: No
Charges: N/A

DO YOU CHARGE THE BORROWING
LIBRARY FOR POSTAGE? No

FOR HOW LONG DO YOU SUSPEND ILL
SERVICE OVER THE CHRISTMAS
HOLIDAYS? 3½-4 weeks

ARE THERE ANY GROUPS OF LIBRARIES
FOR WHICH YOU WAIVE FEES? IF
SO, PLEASE NAME THEM: None

COLUMBIA UNIVERSITY

NUC CODE: NNC

OCLC CODE: None

ADDRESS: Interlibrary Loan
Columbia University
Libraries
535 W. 114th St.
New York, NY 10027

TELEPHONE: (212) 280-3542

LIST NAMES OF BRANCHES WITH
SEPARATE POLICIES:
Columbia Health Sciences
Library (NNC-M)
Teachers College (NNUT)

BOOKS:
Will Lend: Yes
Length of Loan: 4 weeks from
date of receipt
Renewable: Yes
Charges: $10.00 prepayment
Average Turnaround Time:
Approximately 1 week
If you have indicated that a
book is not to be lent, will
you on receipt of a letter
from the requesting library
search the index for given
entries? (Not answered)

PERIODICALS:
Bound: Will lend in some
cases
Unbound: Will not lend
Loan Period: 2 weeks
Renewable: No
Will lend if article exceeds
_____ number of pages (Not
answered)

MICROFORMS:
Will Lend: Yes, in many cases
Specific Types of Microforms:
Microfilms, microfiche,
microcard

GOVERNMENT PUBLICATIONS:
Will Lend: Yes

DISSERTATIONS:
Will Lend: Only if not
available from University
Microfilms

THESES:
Will Lend: Yes

AUDIO-VISUAL MATERIALS:
Records: Will not lend
Cassettes: Will lend
Other (slides, filmstrips,
etc.): Will lend

COMPUTER SOFTWARE:
Will Lend: Not at this time

PHOTODUPLICATION SERVICE:
No charge up to 0 exposures
Charge Per Exposure: 10¢
Minimum Fee: $10.00
Handling Fee: $8.00
Average Turnaround Time:
7-10 days

MICROFILMING SERVICE:
Service Available: Yes
Charges: Please contact our
Preservation Records
Office, 110 Butler Library

DO YOU CHARGE THE BORROWING
LIBRARY FOR POSTAGE? No

FOR HOW LONG DO YOU SUSPEND ILL
SERVICE OVER THE CHRISTMAS
HOLIDAYS? Approximately
Dec.5-28

ARE THERE ANY GROUPS OF LIBRARIES
FOR WHICH YOU WAIVE FEES? IF
SO, PLEASE NAME THEM:
Library of Congress; Bronx
Botanical Garden; British
Lending Library; NYSU and
RLG member libraries

CORNELL UNIVERSITY

NUC CODE: NIC

OCLC CODE: COO

ADDRESS: Interlibrary Loan
          Cornell University
          Libraries
          Olin Library
          Ithaca, NY 14853

TELEPHONE: (607) 256-5293

LIST NAMES OF BRANCHES WITH
  SEPARATE POLICIES: None

BOOKS:
  Will Lend: Yes
  Length of Loan: 4 weeks
  Renewable: No
  Charges: $8.00 for non-
    profit, $15.00 for profit
  Average Turnaround Time:
    (Not answered)
  If you have indicated that a
    book is not to be lent, will
    you on receipt of a letter
    from the requesting library
    search the index for given
    entries? Possibly

PERIODICALS:
  Bound: May lend those over
    10 years old
  Unbound: Will not lend
  Loan Period: 4 weeks use
  Renewable: No
  May lend if article exceeds
    100 pages

MICROFORMS:
  Will Lend: Yes
  Specific Types of Microforms:
    Microfilm

GOVERNMENT PUBLICATIONS:
  Will Lend: Possibly

DISSERTATIONS:
  Will Lend: Yes, if pre-June,
    1954

THESES:
  Will Lend: Yes

AUDIO-VISUAL MATERIALS:
  Records: Will not lend
  Cassettes: Will not lend
  Other (slides, filmstrips,
    etc.): Will not lend

COMPUTER SOFTWARE:
  Will Lend: No

PHOTODUPLICATION SERVICE:
  No charge up to 0 exposures
  Charge Per Exposure: 20¢
  Minimum/handling Fee: $3.50
    for non-profit groups;
    $5.50 for profit groups
  Average Turnaround Time:
    (Not answered)

MICROFILMING SERVICE:
  Service Available: Yes
  Charges: Furnished upon
    request

DO YOU CHARGE THE BORROWING
  LIBRARY FOR POSTAGE? Routine
  loans and photocopying
  loans in U. S. postage
  charges are included in
  handling fee

FOR HOW LONG DO YOU SUSPEND ILL
  SERVICE OVER THE CHRISTMAS
  HOLIDAYS? 15-20 days

ARE THERE ANY GROUPS OF LIBRARIES
  FOR WHICH YOU WAIVE FEES? IF
  SO, PLEASE NAME THEM: RLG
  members; New York state
  libraries approaching us
  via NYSILL

CORNELL UNIVERSITY MEDICAL COLLEGE

NUC CODE: (Not answered)

OCLC CODE: (Not answered)

ADDRESS: Interlibrary Loan
          Cornell University
          Medical College
          Library
          1300 York Ave.
          New York, NY 10021

TELEPHONE: (212) 472-5300

LIST NAMES OF BRANCHES WITH
  SEPARATE POLICIES: None

BOOKS:
  Will Lend: Yes
  Length of Loan: 2 weeks
  Renewable: Yes
  Charges: None
  Average Turnaround Time:
    4-5 days
  If you have indicated that a
    book is not to be lent, will
    you on receipt of a letter
    from the requesting library
    search the index for given
    entries? Yes. If material
    is unique to Cornell
    University Medical College
    or The New York Hospital,
    we would fill ILL
    requests. We lend to
    member libraries of the
    Medical Library Center of
    New York and RLG.

PERIODICALS:
  Bound: Will lend 1976 to
    present
  Unbound: Will lend if 2d
    copy available
  Loan Period: 2 days
  Renewable: No
  Will lend if article exceeds
    50 pages. Will photocopy
    articles.

MICROFORMS:
  Will Lend: No
  Specific Types of Microforms:
    N/A

GOVERNMENT PUBLICATIONS:
  Will Lend: Yes, if cataloged
    as a book

DISSERTATIONS:
  Will Lend: No

THESES:
  Will Lend: No

AUDIO-VISUAL MATERIALS:
  Records: Will not lend
  Cassettes: (Not answered)
  Other (slides, filmstrips,
    etc.): (Not answered)

COMPUTER SOFTWARE:
  Will Lend: No

PHOTODUPLICATION SERVICE:
  No charge up to _____
    exposures (Not answered)
  Charge Per Exposure: (Not
    answered)
  Minimum/handling Fee: (Not
    answered)
  Average Turnaround Time:
    (Not answered)

MICROFILMING SERVICE:
  Service Available: No
  Charges: N/A

DO YOU CHARGE THE BORROWING
  LIBRARY FOR POSTAGE? No

FOR HOW LONG DO YOU SUSPEND ILL
  SERVICE OVER THE CHRISTMAS
  HOLIDAYS? (Not answered)

ARE THERE ANY GROUPS OF LIBRARIES
  FOR WHICH YOU WAIVE FEES? IF
  SO, PLEASE NAME THEM: Members
  of the Medical Library
  Center of New York.

FORDHAM UNIVERSITY

NUC CODE: NNF

OCLC CODE: VYF

ADDRESS: Interlibrary Loan
Fordham University
Library
Bronx, NY 10458

TELEPHONE: (212) 579-2414

LIST NAMES OF BRANCHES WITH
SEPARATE POLICIES:
Fordham University Library
at Lincoln Center
Fordham University School
of Law Library

BOOKS:
Will Lend: Yes, but only
those not in print
Length of Loan: 1 month
Renewable: No
Charges: Postage
Average Turnaround Time:
1 week
If you have indicated that a
book is not to be lent, will
you on receipt of a letter
from the requesting library
search the index for given
entries? No

PERIODICALS:
Bound: Will not lend
Unbound: Will not lend
Loan Period: N/A
Renewable: N/A
Will lend if article exceeds
_____ number of pages (Will
not lend, regardless of
length of article)

MICROFORMS:
Will Lend: No
Specific Types of Microforms:
N/A

GOVERNMENT PUBLICATIONS:
Will Lend: Yes, if circulating copy available

DISSERTATIONS:
Will Lend: Yes, but only
those from 1933-1961.
1962- available from
University Microfilms.

THESES:
Will Lend: Yes, but only
those from 1933-1961.

AUDIO-VISUAL MATERIALS:
Records: Will not lend
Cassettes: Will not lend
Other (slides, filmstrips,
etc.): Will not lend

COMPUTER SOFTWARE:
Will Lend: No

PHOTODUPLICATION SERVICE:
No charge up to 0 exposures
Charge Per Exposure: 10¢
Minimum/handling Fee: $5.00
Average Turnaround Time:
1 week

MICROFILMING SERVICE:
Service Available: No
Charges: N/A

DO YOU CHARGE THE BORROWING
LIBRARY FOR POSTAGE? Yes

FOR HOW LONG DO YOU SUSPEND ILL
SERVICE OVER THE CHRISTMAS
HOLIDAYS? Dec.15-Jan.5

ARE THERE ANY GROUPS OF LIBRARIES
FOR WHICH YOU WAIVE FEES? IF
SO, PLEASE NAME THEM: None

FOUR COUNTY LIBRARY SYSTEM

NUC CODE: NBiF

OCLC CODE: YXF

ADDRESS: Interlibrary Loan
Four County Library
System
Clubhouse Road
Binghamton, NY 13903

TELEPHONE: (607) 723-8236

LIST NAMES OF BRANCHES WITH
SEPARATE POLICIES: None

BOOKS:
Will Lend: Yes
Length of Loan: 4 weeks
Renewable: Yes
Charges: $5.00 for out-of-
state
Average Turnaround Time:
1 week
If you have indicated that a
book is not to be lent, will
you on receipt of a letter
from the requesting library
search the index for given
entries? Yes, if in Four
County core collection

PERIODICALS:
Bound: Will not lend
Unbound: Will not lend
Loan Period: N/A
Renewable: N/A

MICROFORMS:
Will Lend: No
Specific Types of Microforms:
N/A

GOVERNMENT PUBLICATIONS:
Will Lend: No

DISSERTATIONS:
Will Lend: Do not own

THESES:
Will Lend: Do not own

AUDIO-VISUAL MATERIALS:
Records: Will not lend
Cassettes: Will not lend
Other (slides, filmstrips,
etc.): Will not lend

COMPUTER SOFTWARE:
Will Lend: No

PHOTODUPLICATION SERVICE:
Do not photocopy

MICROFILMING SERVICE:
Service Available: No
Charges: N/A

DO YOU CHARGE THE BORROWING
LIBRARY FOR POSTAGE? No

FOR HOW LONG DO YOU SUSPEND ILL
SERVICE OVER THE CHRISTMAS
HOLIDAYS? No suspension

ARE THERE ANY GROUPS OF LIBRARIES
FOR WHICH YOU WAIVE FEES? IF
SO, PLEASE NAME THEM: Those
in New York state

GREAT NECK LIBRARY

NUC CODE: NGRN

OCLC CODE: (Not answered)

ADDRESS: Interlibrary Loan
Great Neck Library
Bayview Avenue at
Gristmill Lane
Great Neck, NY 11024

TELEPHONE: (516) 466-8055

LIST NAMES OF BRANCHES WITH
SEPARATE POLICIES: None

BOOKS:
Will Lend: Yes
Length of Loan: 28 days
Renewable: No
Charges: None
Average Turnaround Time:
1 week
If you have indicated that a
book is not to be lent, will
you on receipt of a letter
from the requesting library
search the index for given
entries? No

PERIODICALS:
Bound: Will not lend
Unbound: Will not lend
Loan Period: N/A
Renewable: N/A
Will lend if article exceeds
_____ number of pages (Will
not lend, regardless of
length of article)

MICROFORMS:
Will Lend: No
Specific Types of Microforms:
N/A

GOVERNMENT PUBLICATIONS:
Will Lend: No

DISSERTATIONS:
Will Lend: No

THESES:
Will Lend: No

AUDIO-VISUAL MATERIALS:
Records: Will not lend
Cassettes: Will not lend
Other (slides, filmstrips,
etc.): (Not answered)

COMPUTER SOFTWARE:
Will Lend: Do not own

PHOTODUPLICATION SERVICE:
No charge up to 25 exposures
Charge Per Exposure: 10¢
Minimum/handling Fee: None
Average Turnaround Time:
1 week

MICROFILMING SERVICE:
Service Available: No
Charges: N/A

DO YOU CHARGE THE BORROWING
LIBRARY FOR POSTAGE? No

FOR HOW LONG DO YOU SUSPEND ILL
SERVICE OVER THE CHRISTMAS
HOLIDAYS? No suspension

ARE THERE ANY GROUPS OF LIBRARIES
FOR WHICH YOU WAIVE FEES? IF
SO, PLEASE NAME THEM: None

HALF HOLLOW HILLS COMMUNITY LIBRARY

NUC CODE: (Not answered)

OCLC CODE: (Not answered)

ADDRESS: Interlibrary Loan
Half Hollow Hills
Community Library
55 Vanderbilt Pkwy.
Dix Hills, NY 11746

TELEPHONE: (516) 421-4530

LIST NAMES OF BRANCHES WITH
SEPARATE POLICIES: None

BOOKS:
Will Lend: Yes
Length of Loan: 3 weeks
Renewable: Yes, if not
reserved
Charges: 5¢ per day per item
after 3 weeks
Average Turnaround Time:
1 day
If you have indicated that a
book is not to be lent, will
you on receipt of a letter
from the requesting library
search the index for given
entries? Yes

PERIODICALS:
Bound: Will not lend
Unbound: Will not lend
Loan Period: N/A
Renewable: N/A
Will lend if article exceeds
_____ number of pages (Will
not lend, regardless of
length of article)

MICROFORMS:
Will Lend: No
Specific Types of Microforms:
N/A

GOVERNMENT PUBLICATIONS:
Will Lend: No

DISSERTATIONS:
Will Lend: No

THESES:
Will Lend: No

AUDIO-VISUAL MATERIALS:
Records: Will not lend
Cassettes: Will not lend
Other (slides, filmstrips,
etc.): Will not lend

COMPUTER SOFTWARE:
Will Lend: No

PHOTODUPLICATION SERVICE:
No charge up to 20 exposures
Charge Per Exposure: 10¢ each
after 1st 20
Minimum/handling Fee: None
Average Turnaround Time:
1 day

MICROFILMING SERVICE:
Service Available: No
Charges: N/A

DO YOU CHARGE THE BORROWING
LIBRARY FOR POSTAGE? No

FOR HOW LONG DO YOU SUSPEND ILL
SERVICE OVER THE CHRISTMAS
HOLIDAYS? No suspension

ARE THERE ANY GROUPS OF LIBRARIES
FOR WHICH YOU WAIVE FEES? IF
SO, PLEASE NAME THEM: None

HERBERT H. LEHMAN COLLEGE

NUC CODE: NNL

OCLC CODE: VYL

ADDRESS: Interlibrary Loan
           Herbert H. Lehman
              College Library
           Bedford Park Blvd.
           West
           Bronx, NY 10468

TELEPHONE: (212) 960-8580

LIST NAMES OF BRANCHES WITH
  SEPARATE POLICIES: None

BOOKS:
  Will Lend: Yes
  Length of Loan: 4 weeks
  Renewable: Yes
  Charges: None
  Average Turnaround Time:
    3 days
  If you have indicated that a
    book is not to be lent, will
    you on receipt of a letter
    from the requesting library
    search the index for given
    entries? (Not answered)

PERIODICALS:
  Bound: Will not lend
  Unbound: Will not lend
  Loan Period: N/A
  Renewable: N/A
  Will lend if article exceeds
    _____ number of pages (Will
    not lend, regardless of
    length of article)

MICROFORMS:
  Will Lend: No
  Specific Types of Microforms:
    N/A

GOVERNMENT PUBLICATIONS:
  Will Lend: Yes

DISSERTATIONS:
  Will Lend: No

THESES:
  Will Lend: No

AUDIO-VISUAL MATERIALS:
  Records: Will not lend
  Cassettes: Will not lend
  Other (slides, filmstrips,
    etc.): Will not lend

COMPUTER SOFTWARE:
  Will Lend: No

PHOTODUPLICATION SERVICE:
  No charge up to 20 exposures
  Charge Per Exposure: None
  Minimum/handling Fee: None
  Average Turnaround Time:
    3 days

MICROFILMING SERVICE:
  Service Available: No
  Charges: N/A

DO YOU CHARGE THE BORROWING
  LIBRARY FOR POSTAGE? No

FOR HOW LONG DO YOU SUSPEND ILL
  SERVICE OVER THE CHRISTMAS
  HOLIDAYS? No suspension

ARE THERE ANY GROUPS OF LIBRARIES
  FOR WHICH YOU WAIVE FEES? IF
  SO, PLEASE NAME THEM: None

HOFSTRA UNIVERSITY

NUC CODE: NHEMH

OCLC CODE: ZIH

ADDRESS: Interlibrary Loan
           Hofstra University
             Library
           Hempstead, NY 11550

TELEPHONE: (516) 560-5946

LIST NAMES OF BRANCHES WITH
  SEPARATE POLICIES: None

BOOKS:
  Will Lend: Yes
  Length of Loan: 4 weeks
  Renewable: No
  Charges: None
  Average Turnaround Time:
    1 week
  If you have indicated that a
    book is not to be lent, will
    you on receipt of a letter
    from the requesting library
    search the index for given
    entries? (Not answered)

PERIODICALS:
  Bound: Will not lend
  Unbound: Will not lend
  Loan Period: N/A
  Renewable: N/A
  Will lend if article exceeds
    _____ number of pages (Will
    not lend, regardless of
    length of article)

MICROFORMS:
  Will Lend: No
  Specific Types of Microforms:
    N/A

GOVERNMENT PUBLICATIONS:
  Will Lend: Will not lend
    out of state

DISSERTATIONS:
  Will Lend: Yes, if 2nd copy
    available

THESES:
  Will Lend: Yes, if 2nd copy
    available

AUDIO-VISUAL MATERIALS:
  Records: Will not lend
  Cassettes: Will not lend
  Other (slides, filmstrips,
    etc.): Will not lend

COMPUTER SOFTWARE:
  Will Lend: No

PHOTODUPLICATION SERVICE:
  We will copy short articles
    only
  No charge up to any exposures
  Charge Per Exposure: None
  Minimum/handling Fee: None
  Average Turnaround Time:
    1 week

MICROFILMING SERVICE:
  Service Available: No
  Charges: N/A

DO YOU CHARGE THE BORROWING
  LIBRARY FOR POSTAGE? No

FOR HOW LONG DO YOU SUSPEND ILL
  SERVICE OVER THE CHRISTMAS
  HOLIDAYS? No suspension

ARE THERE ANY GROUPS OF LIBRARIES
  FOR WHICH YOU WAIVE FEES? IF
  SO, PLEASE NAME THEM: None

HUNTER COLLEGE

NUC CODE: (Not answered)

OCLC CODE: ZHM

ADDRESS: Interlibrary Loan
          Hunter College Library
          695 Park Ave.
          New York, NY 10021

TELEPHONE: (212) 570-5521

LIST NAMES OF BRANCHES WITH
   SEPARATE POLICIES: None

BOOKS:
   Will Lend: Yes
   Length of Loan: 4 weeks
   Renewable: Yes
   Charges: None
   Average Turnaround Time:
      3-4 days
   If you have indicated that a
      book is not to be lent, will
      you on receipt of a letter
      from the requesting library
      search the index for given
      entries? (Not answered)

PERIODICALS:
   Bound: Will not lend
   Unbound: (Not answered)
   Loan Period: N/A
   Renewable: N/A
   Will lend if article exceeds
      _____ number of pages (Not
      answered)

MICROFORMS:
   Will Lend: No
   Specific Types of Microforms:
      N/A

GOVERNMENT PUBLICATIONS:
   Will Lend: Yes

DISSERTATIONS:
   Will Lend: Yes

THESES:
   Will Lend: Yes

AUDIO-VISUAL MATERIALS:
   Records: Will not lend
   Cassettes: Will not lend
   Other (slides, filmstrips,
      etc.): Will not lend

COMPUTER SOFTWARE:
   Will Lend: No

PHOTODUPLICATION SERVICE:
   No charge up to any exposures
   Charge Per Exposure: None
   Minimum/handling Fee: None
   Average Turnaround Time:
      3-4 days

MICROFILMING SERVICE:
   Service Available: No
   Charges: N/A

DO YOU CHARGE THE BORROWING
   LIBRARY FOR POSTAGE? No
      (service is reciprocal)

FOR HOW LONG DO YOU SUSPEND ILL
   SERVICE OVER THE CHRISTMAS
   HOLIDAYS? 10 days

ARE THERE ANY GROUPS OF LIBRARIES
   FOR WHICH YOU WAIVE FEES? IF
   SO, PLEASE NAME THEM: No fees
   charged

HUNTINGTON PUBLIC LIBRARY

NUC CODE: (Not answered)

OCLC CODE: (Not answered)

ADDRESS: Interlibrary Loan
          Huntington Public
          Library
          338 Main St.
          Huntington, NY 11743

TELEPHONE: (516) 427-5165

LIST NAMES OF BRANCHES WITH
   SEPARATE POLICIES: None

BOOKS:
   Will Lend: Yes
   Length of Loan: 3 weeks
   Renewable: Yes
   Charges: None
   Average Turnaround Time:
      2 days
   If you have indicated that a
      book is not to be lent, will
      you on receipt of a letter
      from the requesting library
      search the index for given
      entries? (Not answered)

PERIODICALS:
   Bound: Will not lend
   Unbound: Yes, but to library
      staff only
   Loan Period: 3 weeks
   Renewable: Yes
   Will lend if article exceeds
      an excessive number of pages

MICROFORMS:
   Will Lend: No
   Specific Types of Microforms:
      N/A

GOVERNMENT PUBLICATIONS:
   Will Lend: No

DISSERTATIONS:
   Will Lend: No

THESES:
   Will Lend: No

AUDIO-VISUAL MATERIALS:
   Records: Will not lend
   Cassettes: Will not lend
   Other (slides, filmstrips,
      etc.): Will not lend

COMPUTER SOFTWARE:
   Will Lend: No

PHOTODUPLICATION SERVICE:
   No charge up to 20 exposures
   Charge Per Exposure: None
   Minimum/handling Fee: None
   Average Turnaround Time:
      2 days

MICROFILMING SERVICE:
   Service Available: Yes
   Charges: None

DO YOU CHARGE THE BORROWING
   LIBRARY FOR POSTAGE? No

FOR HOW LONG DO YOU SUSPEND ILL
   SERVICE OVER THE CHRISTMAS
   HOLIDAYS? No suspension

ARE THERE ANY GROUPS OF LIBRARIES
   FOR WHICH YOU WAIVE FEES? IF
   SO, PLEASE NAME THEM: No fees
   charged

IONA COLLEGE

NUC CODE: NNerI

OCLC CODE: VXI

ADDRESS: Interlibrary Loan
Iona College
Library
715 North Ave.
New Rochelle, NY 10801

TELEPHONE: (914) 636-2100, X343

LIST NAMES OF BRANCHES WITH
SEPARATE POLICIES: None

BOOKS:
Will Lend: Yes
Length of Loan: 28 days
Renewable: Yes
Charges: None
Average Turnaround Time:
1 week
If you have indicated that a
book is not to be lent, will
you on receipt of a letter
from the requesting library
search the index for given
entries? (Not answered)

PERIODICALS:
Bound: Will not lend
Unbound: Will not lend
Loan Period: N/A
Renewable: N/A
Will lend if article exceeds
_____ number of pages (Not
answered)

MICROFORMS:
Will Lend: No
Specific Types of Microforms:
N/A

GOVERNMENT PUBLICATIONS:
Will Lend: Yes

DISSERTATIONS:
Will Lend: Yes

THESES:
Will Lend: Yes

AUDIO-VISUAL MATERIALS:
Records: Will not lend
Cassettes: Will not lend
Other (slides, filmstrips,
etc.): Will not lend

COMPUTER SOFTWARE:
Will Lend: No

PHOTODUPLICATION SERVICE:
No charge up to 25 exposures
Charge Per Exposure: 10¢
Minimum/handling Fee: None
Average Turnaround Time:
1 week

MICROFILMING SERVICE:
Service Available: No
Charges: N/A

DO YOU CHARGE THE BORROWING
LIBRARY FOR POSTAGE? No

FOR HOW LONG DO YOU SUSPEND ILL
SERVICE OVER THE CHRISTMAS
HOLIDAYS? (Not answered)

ARE THERE ANY GROUPS OF LIBRARIES
FOR WHICH YOU WAIVE FEES? IF
SO, PLEASE NAME THEM: New
York Metro Free Photocopy
participants; Westchester
County college libraries

ITHACA COLLEGE

NUC CODE: NII

OCLC CODE: XIM

ADDRESS: Interlibrary Loan
Ithaca College
Library
Ithaca, NY 14850

TELEPHONE: (607) 274-3891

LIST NAMES OF BRANCHES WITH
SEPARATE POLICIES: None

BOOKS:
Will Lend: Yes
Length of Loan: 4 weeks
Renewable: Yes
Charges: (Not answered)
Average Turnaround Time:
(Not answered)
If you have indicated that a
book is not to be lent, will
you on receipt of a letter
from the requesting library
search the index for given
entries? (Not answered)

PERIODICALS:
Bound: Will not lend
Unbound: Will not lend
Loan Period: N/A
Renewable: N/A
Will lend if article exceeds
_____ number of pages (Not
answered)

MICROFORMS:
Will Lend: Yes
Specific Types of Microforms:
Fiche only

GOVERNMENT PUBLICATIONS:
Will Lend: (Not answered)

DISSERTATIONS:
Will Lend: Yes

THESES:
Will Lend: Yes

AUDIO-VISUAL MATERIALS:
Records: Will not lend
Cassettes: Will not lend
Other (slides, filmstrips,
etc.): (Not answered)

COMPUTER SOFTWARE:
Will Lend: (Not answered)

PHOTODUPLICATION SERVICE:
No charge up to a reasonable
number of exposures
Charge Per Exposure: (Not
answered)
Minimum/handling Fee: None
Average Turnaround Time:
(Not answered)

MICROFILMING SERVICE:
Service Available: No
Charges: N/A

DO YOU CHARGE THE BORROWING
LIBRARY FOR POSTAGE? No

FOR HOW LONG DO YOU SUSPEND ILL
SERVICE OVER THE CHRISTMAS
HOLIDAYS? No suspension, but
limited service

ARE THERE ANY GROUPS OF LIBRARIES
FOR WHICH YOU WAIVE FEES? IF
SO, PLEASE NAME THEM: (Not
answered)

MANHATTAN COLLEGE

NUC CODE: NNMan

OCLC CODE: ZMC

ADDRESS: Interlibrary Loan
          Cardinal Hayes Library
          Manhattan College
          Bronx, NY 10471

TELEPHONE: (212) 920-0166

LIST NAMES OF BRANCHES WITH
  SEPARATE POLICIES: None

BOOKS:
  Will Lend: Yes
  Length of Loan: 3 weeks
  Renewable: Yes
  Charges: (Not answered)
  Average Turnaround Time:
    (Not answered)
  If you have indicated that a
  book is not to be lent, will
  you on receipt of a letter
  from the requesting library
  search the index for given
  entries? Yes

PERIODICALS:
  Bound: Will not lend
  Unbound: Will not lend
  Loan Period: N/A
  Renewable: N/A
  Will lend if article exceeds
  _____ number of pages (Not
    answered)

MICROFORMS:
  Will Lend: No
  Specific Types of Microforms:
    N/A

GOVERNMENT PUBLICATIONS:
  Will Lend: Yes, if
    circulating copy

DISSERTATIONS:
  Will Lend: No

THESES:
  Will Lend: No

AUDIO-VISUAL MATERIALS:
  Records: Will not lend
  Cassettes: Will not lend
  Other (slides, filmstrips,
    etc.): Will not lend

COMPUTER SOFTWARE:
  Will Lend: No

PHOTODUPLICATION SERVICE:
  No charge up to 10 exposures
  Charge Per Exposure: 5¢
  Minimum/handling Fee: None
  Average Turnaround Time:
    (Not answered)

MICROFILMING SERVICE:
  Service Available: No
  Charges: N/A

DO YOU CHARGE THE BORROWING
  LIBRARY FOR POSTAGE? No

FOR HOW LONG DO YOU SUSPEND ILL
  SERVICE OVER THE CHRISTMAS
  HOLIDAYS? No suspension

ARE THERE ANY GROUPS OF LIBRARIES
  FOR WHICH YOU WAIVE FEES? IF
  SO, PLEASE NAME THEM: Metro
    Free Interchange of Photo-
    copies System

MERCY COLLEGE

NUC CODE: (Not answered)

OCLC CODE: VZE

ADDRESS: Interlibrary Loan
          Mercy College
          Library
          555 Broadway
          Dobbs Ferry, NY 10522

TELEPHONE: (914) 693-4500, X257

LIST NAMES OF BRANCHES WITH
  SEPARATE POLICIES: None

BOOKS:
  Will Lend: Yes
  Length of Loan: 4 weeks
  Renewable: No
  Charges: None
  Average Turnaround Time:
    10 days
  If you have indicated that a
  book is not to be lent, will
  you on receipt of a letter
  from the requesting library
  search the index for given
  entries? (Not answered)

PERIODICALS:
  Bound: Will not lend
  Unbound: Will not lend
  Loan Period: N/A
  Renewable: N/A
  Will lend if article exceeds
  _____ number of pages (Will
    not lend, regardless of
    length of article)

MICROFORMS:
  Will Lend: No
  Specific Types of Microforms:
    N/A

GOVERNMENT PUBLICATIONS:
  Will Lend: No

DISSERTATIONS:
  Will Lend: No

THESES:
  Will Lend: No

AUDIO-VISUAL MATERIALS:
  Records: Will not lend
  Cassettes: Will not lend
  Other (slides, filmstrips,
    etc.): Will not lend

COMPUTER SOFTWARE:
  Will Lend: No

PHOTODUPLICATION SERVICE:
  No charge up to 0 exposures
  Charge Per Exposure: 10¢
  Minimum/handling Fee: None
  Average Turnaround Time:
    10 days

MICROFILMING SERVICE:
  Service Available: No
  Charges: N/A

DO YOU CHARGE THE BORROWING
  LIBRARY FOR POSTAGE? No

FOR HOW LONG DO YOU SUSPEND ILL
  SERVICE OVER THE CHRISTMAS
  HOLIDAYS? No suspension

ARE THERE ANY GROUPS OF LIBRARIES
  FOR WHICH YOU WAIVE FEES? IF
  SO, PLEASE NAME THEM:
    Westchester Library System
    members; New York Metro-
    politan Reference and
    Research Library Agency
    (METRO)

MID-YORK LIBRARY SYSTEM

NUC CODE: NUTMY

OCLC CODE: ZTM

ADDRESS: Interlibrary Loan
Mid-York Library
System
1600 Lincoln Ave.
Utica, NY 13502

TELEPHONE: (315) 891-3262

LIST NAMES OF BRANCHES WITH
SEPARATE POLICIES:
Utica Public Library

BOOKS:
Will Lend: Yes
Length of Loan: 1 month
Renewable: Yes, usually
Charges: Postage
Average Turnaround Time:
(Not answered)
If you have indicated that a
book is not to be lent, will
you on receipt of a letter
from the requesting library
search the index for given
entries? Yes

PERIODICALS:
Bound: Will not lend
Unbound: Will not lend
Loan Period: N/A
Renewable: N/A
Will lend if article exceeds
_____ number of pages (Not
answered)

MICROFORMS:
Will Lend: No
Specific Types of Microforms:
N/A

GOVERNMENT PUBLICATIONS:
Will Lend: No

DISSERTATIONS:
Will Lend: No

THESES:
Will Lend: No

AUDIO-VISUAL MATERIALS:
Records: Will not lend
Cassettes: Will not lend
Other (slides, filmstrips,
etc.): Will not lend

COMPUTER SOFTWARE:
Will Lend: No

PHOTODUPLICATION SERVICE:
No charge up to 0 exposures
Charge Per Exposure: (Not
answered)
Minimum/handling Fee: $5.00
Average Turnaround Time:
(Not answered)

MICROFILMING SERVICE:
Service Available: No
Charges: N/A

DO YOU CHARGE THE BORROWING
LIBRARY FOR POSTAGE? Yes

FOR HOW LONG DO YOU SUSPEND ILL
SERVICE OVER THE CHRISTMAS
HOLIDAYS? No suspension

ARE THERE ANY GROUPS OF LIBRARIES
FOR WHICH YOU WAIVE FEES? IF
SO, PLEASE NAME THEM: New
York State

MIDDLE COUNTRY PUBLIC LIBRARY

NUC CODE: (Not answered)

OCLC CODE: (Not answered)

ADDRESS: Interlibrary Loan
Middle Country Public
Library
101 Eastwood Blvd.
Centereach, NY 11720

TELEPHONE: (516) 585-9393

LIST NAMES OF BRANCHES WITH
SEPARATE POLICIES: None

BOOKS:
Will Lend: Yes
Length of Loan: 3 weeks
Renewable: Yes
Charges: None
Average Turnaround Time:
(Not answered)
If you have indicated that a
book is not to be lent, will
you on receipt of a letter
from the requesting library
search the index for given
entries? (Not answered)

PERIODICALS:
Bound: Will not lend
Unbound: Will not lend
Loan Period: N/A
Renewable: N/A
Will lend if article exceeds
_____ number of pages (Will
not lend, regardless of
length of article)

MICROFORMS:
Will Lend: (Not answered)
Specific Types of Microforms:
Film, fiche

GOVERNMENT PUBLICATIONS:
Will Lend: Yes

DISSERTATIONS:
Will Lend: No

THESES:
Will Lend: No

AUDIO-VISUAL MATERIALS:
Records: Will not lend
Cassettes: Will not lend
Other (slides, filmstrips,
etc.): Will not lend

COMPUTER SOFTWARE:
Will Lend: No

PHOTODUPLICATION SERVICE:
No charge for any exposures
Charge Per Exposure: None
Minimum/handling Fee: None
Average Turnaround Time:
(Not answered)

MICROFILMING SERVICE:
Service Available: Yes
Charges: (Not answered)

DO YOU CHARGE THE BORROWING
LIBRARY FOR POSTAGE? No

FOR HOW LONG DO YOU SUSPEND ILL
SERVICE OVER THE CHRISTMAS
HOLIDAYS? No suspension

ARE THERE ANY GROUPS OF LIBRARIES
FOR WHICH YOU WAIVE FEES? IF
SO, PLEASE NAME THEM: None

MOUNT SINAI SCHOOL OF MEDICINE

NUC CODE: None

OCLC CODE: VVL

ADDRESS: Interlibrary Loan
Levy Library
Mount Sinai School of
Medicine
One Gustave L. Levy
Plaza
New York, NY 10029

TELEPHONE: (212) 650-7795

LIST NAMES OF BRANCHES WITH
SEPARATE POLICIES: None

BOOKS:
Will Lend: Yes
Length of Loan: 2 weeks
Renewable: Yes
Charges: $5.00
Average Turnaround Time:
3 days
If you have indicated that a
book is not to be lent, will
you on receipt of a letter
from the requesting library
search the index for given
entries? (Not answered)

PERIODICALS:
Bound: Will not lend
Unbound: Will not lend
Loan Period: N/A
Renewable: N/A
Will lend if article exceeds
_____ number of pages (Not
answered)

MICROFORMS:
Will Lend: No
Specific Types of Microforms:
N/A

GOVERNMENT PUBLICATIONS:
Will Lend: No

DISSERTATIONS:
Will Lend: No

THESES:
Will Lend: No

AUDIO-VISUAL MATERIALS:
Records: Will not lend
Cassettes: Will not lend
Other (slides, filmstrips,
etc.): Will not lend

COMPUTER SOFTWARE:
Will Lend: No

PHOTODUPLICATION SERVICE:
No charge up to 0 exposures
Charge Per Transaction:
$5.00 up to 20 pages
Average Turnaround Time:
3 days

MICROFILMING SERVICE:
Service Available: No
Charges: N/A

DO YOU CHARGE THE BORROWING
LIBRARY FOR POSTAGE? No

FOR HOW LONG DO YOU SUSPEND ILL
SERVICE OVER THE CHRISTMAS
HOLIDAYS? Dec.15-Jan.1

ARE THERE ANY GROUPS OF LIBRARIES
FOR WHICH YOU WAIVE FEES? IF
SO, PLEASE NAME THEM: City
University of New York

NEW YORK ACADEMY OF MEDICINE

NUC CODE: NNNAM

OCLC CODE: VVK

ADDRESS: Interlibrary Loan
The New York Academy of
Medicine Library
2 East 103rd St.
New York, NY 10029

TELEPHONE: (212) 876-8200, X277

LIST NAMES OF BRANCHES WITH
SEPARATE POLICIES: None

BOOKS:
Will Lend: Yes
Length of Loan: 4 weeks
Renewable: Yes
Charges: $5.00-$10.00,
depending on requestor
Average Turnaround Time:
48 hours
If you have indicated that a
book is not to be lent, will
you on receipt of a letter
from the requesting library
search the index for given
entries? (Not answered)

PERIODICALS:
Bound: Will not lend
Unbound: Will not lend
Loan Period: N/A
Renewable: N/A
Will lend if article exceeds
_____ number of pages (Not
answered)

MICROFORMS:
Will Lend: No
Specific Types of Microforms:
N/A

GOVERNMENT PUBLICATIONS:
Will Lend: Depends on how
they are cataloged

DISSERTATIONS:
Will Lend: No

THESES:
Will Lend: No

AUDIO-VISUAL MATERIALS:
Records: Do not own
Cassettes: Do not own
Other (slides, filmstrips,
etc.): Do not own

COMPUTER SOFTWARE:
Will Lend: Do not own

PHOTODUPLICATION SERVICE:
No charge up to 0 exposures
Charge Per Exposure: 25¢ to
50¢
Minimum/handling Fee: $7.50
to $10.00 per item
Average Turnaround Time:
48 hours

MICROFILMING SERVICE:
Service Available: Yes
Charges: 20¢ per exposure
(2 pages) plus handling
charge of $7.50-$10.00 per
item

DO YOU CHARGE THE BORROWING
LIBRARY FOR POSTAGE? No

FOR HOW LONG DO YOU SUSPEND ILL
SERVICE OVER THE CHRISTMAS
HOLIDAYS? Dec.1-Jan.1

ARE THERE ANY GROUPS OF LIBRARIES
FOR WHICH YOU WAIVE FEES? IF
SO, PLEASE NAME THEM: Members,
Medical Library Center of
New York

NEW YORK HISTORICAL SOCIETY

NUC CODE: NHi

OCLC CODE: (Not answered)

ADDRESS: Interlibrary Loan
New York Historical
Society
170 Central Park West
New York, NY 10024

TELEPHONE: (212) 873-3400

WE DO NOT PARTICIPATE IN
INTERLIBRARY LOAN, BUT
WILL PROVIDE SOME PHOTOCOPY
SERVICES.

BOOKS:
Will Lend: No
Length of Loan: N/A
Renewable: N/A
Charges: N/A
Average Turnaround Time: N/A
If you have indicated that a
book is not to be lent, will
you on receipt of a letter
from the requesting library
search the index for given
entries? Yes. A $5.00
reference fee is charged
for substantial research.

PERIODICALS:
Bound: Will not lend
Unbound: Will not lend
Loan Period: N/A
Renewable: N/A
Will lend if article exceeds
_____ number of pages (Not
answered)

MICROFORMS:
Will Lend: No
Specific Types of Microforms:
N/A

GOVERNMENT PUBLICATIONS:
Will Lend: No

DISSERTATIONS:
Will Lend: No

THESES:
Will Lend: No

AUDIO-VISUAL MATERIALS:
Records: Do not own
Records: Do not own
Other (slides, filmstrips,
etc.): Will not lend

COMPUTER SOFTWARE:
Will Lend: (Not answered)

PHOTODUPLICATION SERVICE:
No charge up to 1 exposure
Charge Per Exposure: 35¢
Minimum/handling Fee: $5.00
handling
Average Turnaround Time:
1-2 weeks

MICROFILMING SERVICE:
Service Available: Yes
Charges: 25¢ per frame,
$5.00 minimum, $5.00
handling, $35.00 to
reproduce a reel

DO YOU CHARGE THE BORROWING
LIBRARY FOR POSTAGE? Yes

FOR HOW LONG DO YOU SUSPEND ILL
SERVICE OVER THE CHRISTMAS
HOLIDAYS? (Not answered)

ARE THERE ANY GROUPS OF LIBRARIES
FOR WHICH YOU WAIVE FEES? IF
SO, PLEASE NAME THEM: None

NEW YORK MEDICAL COLLEGE

NUC CODE: NMU-M

OCLC CODE: VVO

ADDRESS: Interlibrary Loan
New York Medical
College
Basic Sciences Bldg.
Valhalla, NY 10595

TELEPHONE: (914) 347-5237

LIST NAMES OF BRANCHES WITH
SEPARATE POLICIES: None

BOOKS:
Will Lend: Yes, but must
pick up in person
Length of Loan: 2 weeks
Renewable: Yes
Charges: $5.00
Average Turnaround Time:
(Not answered)
If you have indicated that a
book is not to be lent, will
you on receipt of a letter
from the requesting library
search the index for given
entries? (Not answered)

PERIODICALS:
Bound: Will lend
Unbound: Will lend
Charges: $5.00
Loan Period: 1 week
Renewable: Yes
Will lend if article exceeds
_____ number of pages (Will
lend, but must pick up in
person)

MICROFORMS:
Will Lend: (Not answered)
Specific Types of Microforms:
N/A

GOVERNMENT PUBLICATIONS:
Will Lend: (Not answered)

DISSERTATIONS:
Will Lend: (Not answered)

THESES:
Will Lend: (Not answered)

AUDIO-VISUAL MATERIALS:
Records: (Not answered)
Cassettes: (Not answered)
Other (slides, filmstrips,
etc.): (Not answered)

COMPUTER SOFTWARE:
Will Lend: (Not answered)

PHOTODUPLICATION SERVICE:
No charge up to 0 exposures
Charge Per Exposure: (Not
answered)
Minimum/handling Fee: $5.00
for up to 25 pages
Average Turnaround Time:
(Not answered)

MICROFILMING SERVICE:
Service Available: (Not
answered)
Charges: N/A

DO YOU CHARGE THE BORROWING
LIBRARY FOR POSTAGE? (Not
answered)

FOR HOW LONG DO YOU SUSPEND ILL
SERVICE OVER THE CHRISTMAS
HOLIDAYS? (Not answered)

ARE THERE ANY GROUPS OF LIBRARIES
FOR WHICH YOU WAIVE FEES? IF
SO, PLEASE NAME THEM: None

NEW YORK PUBLIC LIBRARY

NUC CODE: NN

ADDRESS: Interlibrary Loan
           Cooperative Services
             Division
           The New York Public
             Library
           5th Avenue and 42nd St.
           New York, NY 10018

TELEPHONE: (212) 930-0878

The regulations of the Board of Trustees prohibit the lending of materials from the collections of The Research Libraries. Loans are made only under very limited conditions to the United Nations and to other members of The Research Libraries Group, Inc. The Research Libraries serve as a subject referral library for the New York State Interlibrary Loan Program (NYSILL). Photocopies are furnished in response to NYSILL requests referred to the New York Public Library by the New York State Library. The Library's Photographic Services is able to supply all forms of photo duplication, subject to copyright and other restrictions. Inquiries concerning costs should be addressed to Photographic Services, Room 316, The New York Public Library, 5th Avenue and 42nd Street, New York, NY 10018.

PHOTODUPLICATION SERVICE:
   No charge up to 0 exposures
   Charge Per Exposure: 30¢
   Minimum/handling Fee: $3.75
   Average Turnaround Time:
     5 days

MICROFILMING SERVICE:
   Service Available: Yes
   Charges: 12¢ per negative
     frame; 18¢ per positive
     foot

NEW YORK STATE LIBRARY

NUC CODE: N

OCLC CODE: NYG

ADDRESS: Interlibrary Loan
           New York State Library
           Cultural Education Ctr.
           Empire State Plaza
           Albany, NY 12230

TELEPHONE: (518) 474-5383

LIST NAMES OF BRANCHES WITH
   SEPARATE POLICIES: None

BOOKS:
   Will Lend: Yes
   Length of Loan: 4 weeks
   Renewable: No
   Charges: (Not answered)
   Average Turnaround Time:
     (Not answered)
   If you have indicated that a
     book is not to be lent, will
     you on receipt of a letter
     from the requesting library
     search the index for given
     entries? (Not answered)

PERIODICALS:
   Bound: Will not lend
   Unbound: Will not lend
   Loan Period: N/A
   Renewable: N/A
   Will lend if article exceeds
     _____ number of pages (Not
     answered)

MICROFORMS:
   Will Lend: Yes
   Specific Types of Microforms:
     Cards, film

GOVERNMENT PUBLICATIONS:
   Will Lend: Yes

DISSERTATIONS:
   Will Lend: (Not answered)

THESES:
   Will Lend: (Not answered)

AUDIO-VISUAL MATERIALS:
   Records: (Not answered)
   Cassettes: (Not answered)
   Other (slides, filmstrips,
     etc.): (Not answered)

COMPUTER SOFTWARE:
   Will Lend: (Not answered)

PHOTODUPLICATION SERVICE:
   No charge up to 0 exposures
   Charge Per Exposure: 15¢
   Minimum Fee: $1.00
   Average Turnaround Time:
     (Not answered)

MICROFILMING SERVICE:
   Service Available: Yes
   Charges: Estimate sent on
     request

DO YOU CHARGE THE BORROWING
   LIBRARY FOR POSTAGE? No

FOR HOW LONG DO YOU SUSPEND ILL
   SERVICE OVER THE CHRISTMAS
   HOLIDAYS? (Not answered)

ARE THERE ANY GROUPS OF LIBRARIES
   FOR WHICH YOU WAIVE FEES? IF
   SO, PLEASE NAME THEM: (Not
   answered)

NEW YORK UNIVERSITY

NUC CODE: NNU

OCLC CODE: ZYU

ADDRESS: Interlibrary Loan
Bobst Library
New York University
70 Washington Sq. So.
New York, NY 10012

TELEPHONE: (212) 598-3678

LIST NAMES OF BRANCHES WITH
SEPARATE POLICIES:
Graduate School of Business
Library
Courant Institute of
Mathematical Sciences
Library
Institute of Fine Arts
Library
Law School Library
Medical Center Library

BOOKS:
Will Lend: Yes
Length of Loan: 4 weeks
Renewable: Yes, sometimes
Charges: Reciprocal fees only
Average Turnaround Time:
2-3 weeks
If you have indicated that a
book is not to be lent, will
you on receipt of a letter
from the requesting library
search the index for given
entries? Yes

PERIODICALS:
Bound: Will not lend
Unbound: Will not lend
Loan Period: N/A
Renewable: N/A
Will lend if article exceeds
_____ number of pages (Not
answered)

MICROFORMS:
Will Lend: Some of them
Specific Types of Microforms:
Film, fiche

GOVERNMENT PUBLICATIONS:
Will Lend: No

DISSERTATIONS:
Will Lend: Yes, but
reciprocal lending only;
1952 to present available
from University
Microfilms

THESES:
Will Lend: Do not own

AUDIO-VISUAL MATERIALS:
Records: Will not lend
Cassettes: Will not lend
Other (slides, filmstrips,
etc.): Will not lend

COMPUTER SOFTWARE:
Will Lend: No

PHOTODUPLICATION SERVICE:
No charge up to 2 exposures
Charges: $2.50 for 1-5
exposures; 20¢ each
additional exposure
Average Turnaround Time:
2-3 weeks

MICROFILMING SERVICE:
Service Available: No
Charges: N/A

DO YOU CHARGE THE BORROWING
LIBRARY FOR POSTAGE?
Reciprocal charges only

FOR HOW LONG DO YOU SUSPEND ILL
SERVICE OVER THE CHRISTMAS
HOLIDAYS? 2 weeks

ARE THERE ANY GROUPS OF LIBRARIES
FOR WHICH YOU WAIVE FEES? IF
SO, PLEASE NAME THEM:
NYSILL, RLG, and others
who have agreed

NORTHPORT PUBLIC LIBRARY

NUC CODE: (Not answered)

OCLC CODE: (Not answered)

ADDRESS: Interlibrary Loan
Northport Public
Library
151 Laurel Ave.
Northport, NY 11768

TELEPHONE: (516) 261-6930

LIST NAMES OF BRANCHES WITH
SEPARATE POLICIES: None

BOOKS:
Will Lend: Yes
Length of Loan: 28 days
Renewable: Yes, if no
reserves
Charges: None
Average Turnaround Time:
3 days
If you have indicated that a
book is not to be lent, will
you on receipt of a letter
from the requesting library
search the index for given
entries? (Not answered)

PERIODICALS:
Bound: Will not lend
Unbound: Will lend
Loan Period: 7 days
Renewable: Yes, if no
reserves
Will lend if article exceeds
_____ number of pages (Not
answered)

MICROFORMS:
Will Lend: No
Specific Types of Microforms:
N/A

GOVERNMENT PUBLICATIONS:
Will Lend: Do not own

DISSERTATIONS:
Will Lend: Do not own

THESES:
Will Lend: Do not own

AUDIO-VISUAL MATERIALS:
Records: Will not lend
Cassettes: Will not lend
Other (slides, filmstrips,
etc.): Will not lend

COMPUTER SOFTWARE:
Will Lend: No

PHOTODUPLICATION SERVICE:
No charge up to a reasonable
number of exposures
Charge Per Exposure: None
Minimum/handling Fee: None
Average Turnaround Time:
1 day

MICROFILMING SERVICE:
Service Available: No
Charges: N/A

DO YOU CHARGE THE BORROWING
LIBRARY FOR POSTAGE? No

FOR HOW LONG DO YOU SUSPEND ILL
SERVICE OVER THE CHRISTMAS
HOLIDAYS? No suspension

ARE THERE ANY GROUPS OF LIBRARIES
FOR WHICH YOU WAIVE FEES? IF
SO, PLEASE NAME THEM: None

PACE UNIVERSITY

NUC CODE: NNPC

OCLC CODE: VZP

ADDRESS: Interlibrary Loan
           Pace University
           One Pace Plaza
           New York, NY 10038

TELEPHONE: (212) 285-3662

LIST NAMES OF BRANCHES WITH
  SEPARATE POLICIES:
    Pace University at White
      Plains, NY
    Pace University at
      Briarcliff, NY
    Pace University at
      Pleasantville, NY
    Pace University Law School
      at White Plains, NY

BOOKS:
  Will Lend: Yes
  Length of Loan: 1 month
  Renewable: No
  Charges: None
  Average Turnaround Time:
    3 weeks
  If you have indicated that a
    book is not to be lent, will
    you on receipt of a letter
    from the requesting library
    search the index for given
    entries? (Not answered)

PERIODICALS:
  Bound: Will not lend
  Unbound: Will not lend
  Loan Period: N/A
  Renewable: N/A
  Will lend if article exceeds
    _____ number of pages (Will
    not lend, regardless of
    length of article. Will
    photocopy article.)

MICROFORMS:
  Will Lend: No
  Specific Types of Microforms:
    N/A

GOVERNMENT PUBLICATIONS:
  Will Lend: Yes

DISSERTATIONS:
  Will Lend: No

THESES:
  Will Lend: No

AUDIO-VISUAL MATERIALS:
  Records: Will not lend
  Cassettes: Will not lend
  Other (slides, filmstrips,
    etc.): Will not lend

COMPUTER SOFTWARE:
  Will Lend: No

PHOTODUPLICATION SERVICE:
  No charge up to 0 exposures
  Charge Per Exposure: 10¢
    Xerox and 20¢ microfilm copy
  Minimum/handling Fee: $1.50
  Average Turnaround Time:
    1 day

MICROFILMING SERVICE:
  Service Available: Yes
  Charges: 15¢ per page and
    $1.50 postage and handling
    charge

DO YOU CHARGE THE BORROWING
  LIBRARY FOR POSTAGE? Only
  for periodical articles

FOR HOW LONG DO YOU SUSPEND ILL
  SERVICE OVER THE CHRISTMAS
  HOLIDAYS? No suspension

ARE THERE ANY GROUPS OF LIBRARIES
  FOR WHICH YOU WAIVE FEES? IF
  SO, PLEASE NAME THEM:
    INTERSHARE, an ILL system of
    selected libraries in the New
    York City area.

PATCHOGUE-MEDFORD LIBRARY

NUC CODE: NPAT

OCLC CODE: None

ADDRESS: Interlibrary Loan
           Patchogue-Medford
           Library
           54-60 E. Main St.
           Patchogue, NY 11772

TELEPHONE: (516) 654-4700

LIST NAMES OF BRANCHES WITH
  SEPARATE POLICIES: None

BOOKS:
  Will Lend: Yes, if
    circulating
  Length of Loan: 3 weeks
  Renewable: Yes
  Charges: None
  Average Turnaround Time:
    1 day
  If you have indicated that a
    book is not to be lent, will
    you on receipt of a letter
    from the requesting library
    search the index for given
    entries? Yes, for reference
    and special collections
    material.

PERIODICALS:
  Bound: Will not lend
  Unbound: Will not lend
  Loan Period: N/A
  Renewable: N/A
  Will lend if article exceeds
    _____ number of pages (Will
    not lend, regardless of
    length of article)

MICROFORMS:
  Will Lend: No
  Specific Types of Microforms:
    N/A

GOVERNMENT PUBLICATIONS:
  Will Lend: Yes

DISSERTATIONS:
  Will Lend: Do not own

THESES:
  Will Lend: Do not own

AUDIO-VISUAL MATERIALS:
  Records: Will not lend
  Cassettes: Will not lend
  Other (slides, filmstrips,
    etc.): Will not lend

COMPUTER SOFTWARE:
  Will Lend: No

PHOTODUPLICATION SERVICE:
  No charge for exposures
  Minimum/handling Fee: None
  Average Turnaround Time:
    1 day

MICROFILMING SERVICE:
  Service Available: Yes
  Charges: None

DO YOU CHARGE THE BORROWING
  LIBRARY FOR POSTAGE? No

FOR HOW LONG DO YOU SUSPEND ILL
  SERVICE OVER THE CHRISTMAS
  HOLIDAYS? No suspension

ARE THERE ANY GROUPS OF LIBRARIES
  FOR WHICH YOU WAIVE FEES? IF
  SO, PLEASE NAME THEM: None

PLAINVIEW–OLD BETHPAGE PUBLIC LIBRARY

NUC CODE: (Not answered)

OCLC CODE: (Not answered)

ADDRESS: Interlibrary Loan
Plainview-Old Bethpage
Public Library
999 Old Country Rd.
Plainview, NY 11803

TELEPHONE: (516) 938-0077

LIST NAMES OF BRANCHES WITH
SEPARATE POLICIES: None

BOOKS:
Will Lend: Yes
Length of Loan: 4 weeks
Renewable: Yes
Charges: Only overdues
Average Turnaround Time:
(Not answered)
If you have indicated that a
book is not to be lent, will
you on receipt of a letter
from the requesting library
search the index for given
entries? (Not answered)

PERIODICALS:
Bound: Will not lend
Unbound: Will not lend
Loan Period: N/A
Renewable: N/A
Will lend if article exceeds
_____ number of pages (Not
answered)

MICROFORMS:
Will Lend: No
Specific Types of Microforms:
N/A

GOVERNMENT PUBLICATIONS:
Will Lend: Yes, if
circulating book

DISSERTATIONS:
Will Lend: No

THESES:
Will Lend: No

AUDIO-VISUAL MATERIALS:
Records: Will not lend
Cassettes: Will not lend
Other (slides, filmstrips,
etc.): Will not lend

COMPUTER SOFTWARE:
Will Lend: No

PHOTODUPLICATION SERVICE:
No charge up to any exposures
Charge Per Exposure: None
Minimum/handling Fee: None
Average Turnaround Time:
(Not answered)

MICROFILMING SERVICE:
Service Available: No
Charges: N/A

DO YOU CHARGE THE BORROWING
LIBRARY FOR POSTAGE? No

FOR HOW LONG DO YOU SUSPEND ILL
SERVICE OVER THE CHRISTMAS
HOLIDAYS? No suspension

ARE THERE ANY GROUPS OF LIBRARIES
FOR WHICH YOU WAIVE FEES? IF
SO, PLEASE NAME THEM: No
fees charged

POLYTECHNIC INSTITUTE OF NEW YORK AT BROOKLYN

NUC CODE: (Not answered)

OCLC CODE: (Not answered)

ADDRESS: Interlibrary Loan
Polytechnic Institute
of New York
333 Jay St.
Brooklyn, NY 11201

TELEPHONE: (212) 643-8690

LIST NAMES OF BRANCHES WITH
SEPARATE POLICIES: (Not
answered)

BOOKS:
Will Lend: Yes
Length of Loan: (Not
answered)
Renewable: (Not answered)
Charges: (Not answered)
Average Turnaround Time:
(Not answered)
If you have indicated that a
book is not to be lent, will
you on receipt of a letter
from the requesting library
search the index for given
entries? (Not answered)

PERIODICALS:
Bound: Will not lend
Unbound: Will not lend
Loan Period: N/A
Renewable: N/A
Will lend if article exceeds
_____ number of pages (Not
answered)

MICROFORMS:
Will Lend: No
Specific Types of Microforms:
N/A

GOVERNMENT PUBLICATIONS:
Will Lend: Yes

DISSERTATIONS:
Will Lend: No; 1960 to
present available from
University Microfilms

THESES:
Will Lend: No; 1968 to
present available from
University Microfilms

AUDIO-VISUAL MATERIALS:
Records: (Not answered)
Cassettes: (Not answered)
Other (slides, filmstrips,
etc.): (Not answered)

COMPUTER SOFTWARE:
Will Lend: (Not answered)

PHOTODUPLICATION SERVICE:
No charge up to 0 exposures
Charge Per Exposure: 50¢
Handling Fee: $10.00
Average Turnaround Time:
(Not answered)

MICROFILMING SERVICE:
Service Available: No
Charges: N/A

DO YOU CHARGE THE BORROWING
LIBRARY FOR POSTAGE? (Not
answered)

FOR HOW LONG DO YOU SUSPEND ILL
SERVICE OVER THE CHRISTMAS
HOLIDAYS? (Not answered)

ARE THERE ANY GROUPS OF LIBRARIES
FOR WHICH YOU WAIVE FEES? IF
SO, PLEASE NAME THEM: None

QUEENS COLLEGE

NUC CODE: NFQC

OCLC CODE: XQM

ADDRESS: Interlibrary Loan
           Paul Klapper Library
           Queens College
           Flushing, NY 11367

TELEPHONE: (212) 520-7300

LIST NAMES OF BRANCHES WITH
  SEPARATE POLICIES: None

BOOKS:
  Will Lend: Yes
  Length of Loan: 4 weeks use
  Renewable: Yes
  Charges: None
  Average Turnaround Time:
    (Not answered)
  If you have indicated that a
    book is not to be lent, will
    you on receipt of a letter
    from the requesting library
    search the index for given
    entries? No

PERIODICALS:
  Bound: Will not lend
  Unbound: Will not lend
  Loan Period: N/A
  Renewable: N/A
  Will lend if article exceeds
    _____ number of pages (Not
    answered)

MICROFORMS:
  Will Lend: Yes
  Specific Types of Microforms:
    (Not answered)

GOVERNMENT PUBLICATIONS:
  Will Lend: Yes

DISSERTATIONS:
  Will Lend: No

THESES:
  Will Lend: Yes

AUDIO-VISUAL MATERIALS:
  Records: Do not own
  Cassettes: Do not own
  Other (slides, filmstrips,
    etc.): Do not own

COMPUTER SOFTWARE:
  Will Lend: Do not own

PHOTODUPLICATION SERVICE:
  No charge up to 0 exposures
  Charge Per Exposure: 10¢
    for each additional page
    after the 1st 20 pages
  Minimum/handling Fee: $5.00
    for 1st 20 pages
  Average Turnaround Time:
    (Not answered)

MICROFILMING SERVICE:
  Service Available: No
  Charges: N/A

DO YOU CHARGE THE BORROWING
  LIBRARY FOR POSTAGE? No

FOR HOW LONG DO YOU SUSPEND ILL
  SERVICE OVER THE CHRISTMAS
  HOLIDAYS? No suspension

ARE THERE ANY GROUPS OF LIBRARIES
  FOR WHICH YOU WAIVE FEES? IF
  SO, PLEASE NAME THEM: Those
  with which we have
  reciprocal agreements.

RENSSELAER POLYTECHNIC INSTITUTE

NUC CODE: NTR

OCLC CODE: YRM

ADDRESS: Interlibrary Loan
           Folsom Library
           Rensselaer Polytechnic
             Institute
           Troy, NY 12181

TELEPHONE: (518) 270-6672

LIST NAMES OF BRANCHES WITH
  SEPARATE POLICIES: None

BOOKS:
  Will Lend: Yes
  Length of Loan: 3 weeks
  Renewable: Yes
  Charges: (Not answered)
  Average Turnaround Time:
    1 week
  If you have indicated that a
    book is not to be lent, will
    you on receipt of a letter
    from the requesting library
    search the index for given
    entries? (Not answered)

PERIODICALS:
  Bound: Will not lend
  Unbound: Will not lend
  Loan Period: N/A
  Renewable: N/A
  Will lend if article exceeds
    _____ number of pages (Will
    not lend, regardless of
    length of article)

MICROFORMS:
  Will Lend: No
  Specific Types of Microforms:
    Fiche to fiche, $1.00
    service plus 10¢ per fiche

GOVERNMENT PUBLICATIONS:
  Will Lend: No

DISSERTATIONS:
  Will Lend: No

THESES:
  Will Lend: No

AUDIO-VISUAL MATERIALS:
  Records: Will not lend
  Cassettes: Will not lend
  Other (slides, filmstrips,
    etc.): Will not lend

COMPUTER SOFTWARE:
  Will Lend: No

PHOTODUPLICATION SERVICE:
  No charge up to 0 exposures
  Charge Per Exposure: 15¢
  Minimum/handling Fee: $1.00
  Average Turnaround Time:
    1 week

MICROFILMING SERVICE:
  Service Available: No
  Charges: N/A

DO YOU CHARGE THE BORROWING
  LIBRARY FOR POSTAGE? Only
  if excessive.

FOR HOW LONG DO YOU SUSPEND ILL
  SERVICE OVER THE CHRISTMAS
  HOLIDAYS? Dec.20-Jan.1

ARE THERE ANY GROUPS OF LIBRARIES
  FOR WHICH YOU WAIVE FEES? IF
  SO, PLEASE NAME THEM: None

ROCHESTER PUBLIC LIBRARY

NUC CODE: NR

OCLC CODE: YQR

ADDRESS: Interlibrary Loan
Rochester Public
Library
115 South Ave.
Rochester, NY 14604

TELEPHONE: (716) 428-7363

LIST NAMES OF BRANCHES WITH
SEPARATE POLICIES: None

BOOKS:
Will Lend: Yes
Length of Loan: 2-4 weeks
Renewable: No
Charges: $5.00 per loan
Average Turnaround Time:
2 days
If you have indicated that a
book is not to be lent, will
you on receipt of a letter
from the requesting library
search the index for given
entries? Yes

PERIODICALS:
Bound: Will not lend
Unbound: Will not lend
Loan Period: N/A
Renewable: N/A
Will lend if article exceeds
_____ number of pages (Not
answered)

MICROFORMS:
Will Lend: No
Specific Types of Microforms:
N/A

GOVERNMENT PUBLICATIONS:
Will Lend: Yes

DISSERTATIONS:
Will Lend: Do not own

THESES:
Will Lend: Do not own

AUDIO-VISUAL MATERIALS:
Records: Will lend
Cassettes: Will lend
Other (slides, filmstrips,
etc.): Will lend

COMPUTER SOFTWARE:
Will Lend: Do not own

PHOTODUPLICATION SERVICE:
No charge up to 0 exposures
Charge Per Exposure: (Not
answered)
Minimum/handling Fee: $5.00
for up to 12 pages;
maximum 24 pages
Average Turnaround Time:
2 days

MICROFILMING SERVICE:
Service Available: No
Charges: N/A

DO YOU CHARGE THE BORROWING
LIBRARY FOR POSTAGE? Is
included in $5.00 charge

FOR HOW LONG DO YOU SUSPEND ILL
SERVICE OVER THE CHRISTMAS
HOLIDAYS? No suspension

ARE THERE ANY GROUPS OF LIBRARIES
FOR WHICH YOU WAIVE FEES? IF
SO, PLEASE NAME THEM: New
York state libraries who
request via NYSILL

ROCKEFELLER UNIVERSITY

NUC CODE: NNRU

OCLC CODE: (Not answered)

ADDRESS: Interlibrary Loan
The Rockefeller
University
Library
1230 York Ave.
New York, NY 10021

TELEPHONE: (212) 570-8915

LIST NAMES OF BRANCHES WITH
SEPARATE POLICIES: None

BOOKS:
Will Lend: Yes
Length of Loan: 2 weeks
Renewable: Yes
Charges: (Not answered)
Average Turnaround Time:
(Not answered)
If you have indicated that a
book is not to be lent, will
you on receipt of a letter
from the requesting library
search the index for given
entries? (Not answered)

PERIODICALS:
Bound: Will not lend
Unbound: Will not lend
Loan Period: N/A
Renewable: N/A
Will lend if article exceeds
_____ number of pages (Not
answered)

MICROFORMS:
Will Lend: No
Specific Types of Microforms:
N/A

GOVERNMENT PUBLICATIONS:
Will Lend: No

DISSERTATIONS:
Will Lend: No

THESES:
Will Lend: No

AUDIO-VISUAL MATERIALS:
Records: Will not lend
Cassettes: Will not lend
Other (slides, filmstrips,
etc.): Will not lend

COMPUTER SOFTWARE:
Will Lend: (Not answered)

PHOTODUPLICATION SERVICE:
No charge up to 0 exposures
Charge Per Exposures: (Not
answered)
Minimum/handling Fee: $5.00
Average Turnaround Time:
(Not answered)

MICROFILMING SERVICE:
Service Available: No
Charges: N/A

DO YOU CHARGE THE BORROWING
LIBRARY FOR POSTAGE? (Not
answered)

FOR HOW LONG DO YOU SUSPEND ILL
SERVICE OVER THE CHRISTMAS
HOLIDAYS? 8 days

ARE THERE ANY GROUPS OF LIBRARIES
FOR WHICH YOU WAIVE FEES? IF
SO, PLEASE NAME THEM: None

RUSSELL SAGE COLLEGE

NUC CODE: NTRS

OCLC CODE: ZRS

ADDRESS: Interlibrary Loan
            Russell Sage College
            46 Ferry St.
            Troy, NY 12180

TELEPHONE: (518) 270-2320

LIST NAMES OF BRANCHES WITH
    SEPARATE POLICIES: None

BOOKS:
    Will Lend: Yes
    Length of Loan: 3-4 weeks
    Renewable: No
    Charges: None, via ALA forms
    Average Turnaround Time:
        3 days
    If you have indicated that a
        book is not to be lent, will
        you on receipt of a letter
        from the requesting library
        search the index for given
        entries? Probably

PERIODICALS:
    Bound: Will not lend
    Unbound: Will not lend
    Loan Period: N/A
    Renewable: N/A
    Will lend if article exceeds
        _____ number of pages (Will
        not lend, regardless of
        length of article)

MICROFORMS:
    Will Lend: No
    Specific Types of Microforms:
        N/A

GOVERNMENT PUBLICATIONS:
    Will Lend: Do not own

DISSERTATIONS:
    Will Lend: Do not own

THESES:
    Will Lend: Do not own

AUDIO-VISUAL MATERIALS:
    Records: Will not lend
    Cassettes: Will not lend
    Other (slides, filmstrips,
        etc.): Will not lend

COMPUTER SOFTWARE:
    Will Lend: No

PHOTODUPLICATION SERVICE:
    No charge up to any exposures
    Charge Per Exposure: None
    Minimum/handling Fee: None
    Average Turnaround Time:
        2-3 days

MICROFILMING SERVICE:
    Service Available: No
    Charges: N/A

DO YOU CHARGE THE BORROWING
    LIBRARY FOR POSTAGE? No

FOR HOW LONG DO YOU SUSPEND ILL
    SERVICE OVER THE CHRISTMAS
    HOLIDAYS? Dec.22-Jan.5

ARE THERE ANY GROUPS OF LIBRARIES
    FOR WHICH YOU WAIVE FEES? IF
    SO, PLEASE NAME THEM: None

ST. JOHN'S UNIVERSITY

NUC CODE: NNStJ

OCLC CODE: ZSJ

ADDRESS: Interlibrary Loan
            St. John's University
            Library
            Jamaica, NY 11439

TELEPHONE: (212) 990-6161, X6727

LIST NAMES OF BRANCHES WITH
    SEPARATE POLICIES:
        Law Library

BOOKS:
    Will Lend: Yes
    Length of Loan: 2-4 weeks
    Renewable: Yes
    Charges: (Not answered)
    Average Turnaround Time:
        2-3 days
    If you have indicated that a
        book is not to be lent, will
        you on receipt of a letter
        from the requesting library
        search the index for given
        entries? Yes (moderate
        searching)

PERIODICALS:
    Bound: Will not lend
    Unbound: Will not lend
    Loan Period: N/A
    Renewable: N/A
    Will lend if article exceeds
        _____ number of pages (Not
        answered)

MICROFORMS:
    Will Lend: Yes, occasionally
    Specific Types of Microforms:
        (Not answered)

GOVERNMENT PUBLICATIONS:
    Will Lend: No

DISSERTATIONS:
    Will Lend: Yes

THESES:
    Will Lend: Yes

AUDIO-VISUAL MATERIALS:
    Records: Will not lend
    Cassettes: Will not lend
    Other (slides, filmstrips,
        etc.): Will not lend

COMPUTER SOFTWARE:
    Will Lend: No

PHOTODUPLICATION SERVICE:
    No charge up to 12 exposures
    Charge Per Exposure: 10¢
    Minimum/handling Fee: $2.00
    Average Turnaround Time:
        2-3 days

MICROFILMING SERVICE:
    Service Available: No
    Charges: N/A

DO YOU CHARGE THE BORROWING
    LIBRARY FOR POSTAGE? No
    (nominal charges absorbed)

FOR HOW LONG DO YOU SUSPEND ILL
    SERVICE OVER THE CHRISTMAS
    HOLIDAYS? Dec.15-Jan.1

ARE THERE ANY GROUPS OF LIBRARIES
    FOR WHICH YOU WAIVE FEES? IF
    SO, PLEASE NAME THEM: None

ST. LAWRENCE UNIVERSITY

NUC CODE: NCaS

OCLC CODE: XLM

ADDRESS: Interlibrary Loan
Owen D. Young Library
St. Lawrence University
Canton, NY 13617

TELEPHONE: (315) 379-5451

LIST NAMES OF BRANCHES WITH
SEPARATE POLICIES: None

BOOKS:
Will Lend: Yes
Length of Loan: 4 weeks
Renewable: Yes
Average Turnaround Time:
2 days
If you have indicated that a
book is not to be lent, will
you on receipt of a letter
from the requesting library
search the index for given
entries? Yes

PERIODICALS:
Bound: Will not lend
Unbound: Will not lend
Loan Period: N/A
Renewable: N/A
Will sometimes, but rarely,
lend if article exceeds
excessive number of pages

MICROFORMS:
Will Lend: Yes
Specific Types of Microforms:
Microfilm, fiche, cards

GOVERNMENT PUBLICATIONS:
Will Lend: Yes

DISSERTATIONS:
Will Lend: No

THESES:
Will Lend: No

AUDIO-VISUAL MATERIALS:
Records: Will not lend
Cassettes: Will not lend
Other (slides, filmstrips,
etc.): Will not lend

COMPUTER SOFTWARE:
Will Lend: Do not own

PHOTODUPLICATION SERVICE:
No charge up to 25 exposures
Charge Per Exposure: 5¢ after
1st 25
Minimum/handling Fee: None
Average Turnaround Time:
2 days

MICROFILMING SERVICE:
Service Available: No
Charges: N/A

DO YOU CHARGE THE BORROWING
LIBRARY FOR POSTAGE? No

FOR HOW LONG DO YOU SUSPEND ILL
SERVICE OVER THE CHRISTMAS
HOLIDAYS? No suspension

ARE THERE ANY GROUPS OF LIBRARIES
FOR WHICH YOU WAIVE FEES? IF
SO, PLEASE NAME THEM: Area
college libraries

SARAH LAWRENCE COLLEGE

NUC CODE: NBronSL

OCLC CODE: VVS

ADDRESS: Interlibrary Loan
Sarah Lawrence College
Library
Bronxville, NY 10708

TELEPHONE: (914) 337-0700, X479

LIST NAMES OF BRANCHES WITH
SEPARATE POLICIES: None

BOOKS:
Will Lend: Yes
Length of Loan: 4 weeks from
date received
Renewable: Yes
Charges: None
Average Turnaround Time:
3 days
If you have indicated that a
book is not to be lent, will
you on receipt of a letter
from the requesting library
search the index for given
entries? (Not answered)

PERIODICALS:
Bound: Will not lend
Unbound: Will not lend
Loan Period: N/A
Renewable: N/A
Will lend if article exceeds
_____ number of pages (Not
answered)

MICROFORMS:
Will Lend: Yes
Specific Types of Microforms:
Cards, film, fiche

GOVERNMENT PUBLICATIONS:
Will Lend: Yes

DISSERTATIONS:
Will Lend: Do not have

THESES:
Will Lend: Do not have

AUDIO-VISUAL MATERIALS:
Records: Will not lend
Cassettes: Will lend
Other (slides, filmstrips,
etc.): (Not answered)

COMPUTER SOFTWARE:
Will Lend: No

PHOTODUPLICATION SERVICE:
No charge up to 0 exposures
Charge Per Exposure: 10¢
Minimum/handling Fee: $2.00
Average Turnaround Time:
1 week

MICROFILMING SERVICE:
Service Available: No
Charges: N/A

DO YOU CHARGE THE BORROWING
LIBRARY FOR POSTAGE? No

FOR HOW LONG DO YOU SUSPEND ILL
SERVICE OVER THE CHRISTMAS
HOLIDAYS? 2 weeks

ARE THERE ANY GROUPS OF LIBRARIES
FOR WHICH YOU WAIVE FEES? IF
SO, PLEASE NAME THEM: None

SIENA COLLEGE

NUC CODE: (Not answered)

OCLC CODE: VKM

ADDRESS: Interlibrary Loan
Siena College
Library
Loudonville, NY 12211

TELEPHONE: (518) 783-2518

LIST NAMES OF BRANCHES WITH
SEPARATE POLICIES: None

BOOKS:
Will Lend: Yes
Length of Loan: 1 month
Renewable: Yes, if no
reserves
Charges: None
Average Turnaround Time:
Several hours
If you have indicated that a
book is not to be lent, will
you on receipt of a letter
from the requesting library
search the index for given
entries? (Not answered)

PERIODICALS:
Bound: Will lend
Unbound: Will lend
Loan Period: 2 weeks
Renewable: No
Will lend if article exceeds
_____ number of pages (Not
answered)

MICROFORMS:
Will Lend: Yes, except for
microfilm
Specific Types of Microforms:
LAC fiche cards

GOVERNMENT PUBLICATIONS:
Will Lend: Yes

DISSERTATIONS:
Will Lend: Yes

THESES:
Will Lend: Yes

AUDIO-VISUAL MATERIALS:
Records: Will lend
Cassettes: (Not answered)
Other (slides, filmstrips,
etc.): (Not answered)

COMPUTER SOFTWARE:
Will Lend: (Not answered)

PHOTODUPLICATION SERVICE:
No charge up to any exposures
Charge Per Exposure: None
Minimum/handling Fee: None
Average Turnaround Time:
Several hours

MICROFILMING SERVICE:
Service Available: No
Charges: N/A

DO YOU CHARGE THE BORROWING
LIBRARY FOR POSTAGE? No

FOR HOW LONG DO YOU SUSPEND ILL
SERVICE OVER THE CHRISTMAS
HOLIDAYS? No suspension

ARE THERE ANY GROUPS OF LIBRARIES
FOR WHICH YOU WAIVE FEES? IF
SO, PLEASE NAME THEM: None

SKIDMORE COLLEGE

NUC CODE: NSsS

OCLC CODE: VZS

ADDRESS: Interlibrary Loan
Lucy Scribner Library
Skidmore College
Saratoga Springs, NY
12866

TELEPHONE: (518) 584-5000, X642

LIST NAMES OF BRANCHES WITH
SEPARATE POLICIES: None

BOOKS:
Will Lend: Yes
Length of Loan: 1 month
Renewable: Yes
Charges: (Not answered)
Average Turnaround Time:
1 day
If you have indicated that a
book is not to be lent, will
you on receipt of a letter
from the requesting library
search the index for given
entries? (Not answered)

PERIODICALS:
Bound: Will not lend
Unbound: Will not lend
Loan Period: N/A
Renewable: N/A
Will lend if article exceeds
_____ number of pages (Not
answered)

MICROFORMS:
Will Lend: No
Specific Types of Microforms:
N/A

GOVERNMENT PUBLICATIONS:
Will Lend: Yes

DISSERTATIONS:
Will Lend: (Not answered)

THESES:
Will Lend: (Not answered)

AUDIO-VISUAL MATERIALS:
Records: Will not lend
Cassettes: Will not lend
Other (slides, filmstrips,
etc.): Will not lend

COMPUTER SOFTWARE:
Will Lend: (Not answered)

PHOTODUPLICATION SERVICE:
No charge up to 25 exposures
Charge Per Exposure: None
Minimum/handling Fee: None
Average Turnaround Time:
1 day

MICROFILMING SERVICE:
Service Available: No
Charges: N/A

DO YOU CHARGE THE BORROWING
LIBRARY FOR POSTAGE? No

FOR HOW LONG DO YOU SUSPEND ILL
SERVICE OVER THE CHRISTMAS
HOLIDAYS? App. Dec.18-Jan.2

ARE THERE ANY GROUPS OF LIBRARIES
FOR WHICH YOU WAIVE FEES? IF
SO, PLEASE NAME THEM: None

SOUTHERN ADIRONDACK LIBRARY SYSTEM

NUC CODE: NSsSA

OCLC CODE: VVA

ADDRESS: Interlibrary Loan
            Southern Adirondack
            Library System
            22 Whitney Place
            Saratoga Springs, NY
            12866

TELEPHONE: (518) 584-7300

LIST NAMES OF BRANCHES WITH
    SEPARATE POLICIES: None

BOOKS:
    Will Lend: Yes
    Length of Loan: 4 weeks
    Renewable: Yes
    Charges: None
    Average Turnaround Time:
        2-3 days
    If you have indicated that a
        book is not to be lent, will
        you on receipt of a letter
        from the requesting library
        search the index for given
        entries? Yes

PERIODICALS:
    Bound: Will not lend
    Unbound: Will not lend
    Loan Period: N/A
    Renewable: N/A
    Will lend if article exceeds
        _____ number of pages (Not
        answered)

MICROFORMS:
    Will Lend: No
    Specific Types of Microforms:
        N/A

GOVERNMENT PUBLICATIONS:
    Will Lend: Do not own

DISSERTATIONS:
    Will Lend: Do not own

THESES:
    Will Lend: Do not own

AUDIO-VISUAL MATERIALS:
    Records: Will not lend
    Cassettes: Will not lend
    Other (slides, filmstrips,
        etc.): Will not lend

COMPUTER SOFTWARE:
    Will Lend: Do not own

PHOTODUPLICATION SERVICE:
    No charge up to 10 exposures
    Charge Per Exposure: 10¢
        after 1st 10 pages
    Minimum/handling Fee: None
    Average Turnaround Time:
        2-3 days

MICROFILMING SERVICE:
    Service Available: No
    Charges: N/A

DO YOU CHARGE THE BORROWING
    LIBRARY FOR POSTAGE? No

FOR HOW LONG DO YOU SUSPEND ILL
    SERVICE OVER THE CHRISTMAS
    HOLIDAYS? No suspension

ARE THERE ANY GROUPS OF LIBRARIES
    FOR WHICH YOU WAIVE FEES? IF
    SO, PLEASE NAME THEM: None

STATE UNIVERSITY OF NEW YORK AGRICULTURAL AND TECHNICAL COLLEGE AT CANTON

NUC CODE: (Not answered)

OCLC CODE: ZCM

ADDRESS: Interlibrary Loan
            Southworth Library
            SUNY Agricultural and
                Technical College
            Canton, NY 13617

TELEPHONE: (315) 386-7228

LIST NAMES OF BRANCHES WITH
    SEPARATE POLICIES: None

BOOKS:
    Will Lend: Yes
    Length of Loan: 4 weeks
    Renewable: Yes
    Charges: None
    Average Turnaround Time:
        (Not answered)
    If you have indicated that a
        book is not to be lent, will
        you on receipt of a letter
        from the requesting library
        search the index for given
        entries? (Not answered)

PERIODICALS:
    Bound: Will not lend
    Unbound: Will not lend
    Loan Period: N/A
    Renewable: N/A
    Will lend if article exceeds
        40 pages

MICROFORMS:
    Will Lend: Yes
    Specific Types of Microforms:
        Microfilm

GOVERNMENT PUBLICATIONS:
    Will Lend: No

DISSERTATIONS:
    Will Lend: No

THESES:
    Will Lend: No

AUDIO-VISUAL MATERIALS:
    Records: Will not lend
    Cassettes: Will not lend
    Other (slides, filmstrips,
        etc.): Will not lend

COMPUTER SOFTWARE:
    Will Lend: Do not own

PHOTODUPLICATION SERVICE:
    No charge up to 25 exposures
    Charge Per Exposure: 10¢
        after 1st 25
    Minimum/handling Fee: None
    Average Turnaround Time:
        (Not answered)

MICROFILMING SERVICE:
    Service Available: No
    Charges: N/A

DO YOU CHARGE THE BORROWING
    LIBRARY FOR POSTAGE? No

FOR HOW LONG DO YOU SUSPEND ILL
    SERVICE OVER THE CHRISTMAS
    HOLIDAYS? No suspension

ARE THERE ANY GROUPS OF LIBRARIES
    FOR WHICH YOU WAIVE FEES? IF
    SO, PLEASE NAME THEM: None

STATE UNIVERSITY OF NEW YORK AT ALBANY

NUC CODE: NA1U

OCLC CODE: NAM

ADDRESS: Interlibrary Loan
Room 110
University Libraries
State University of New
York at Albany
1400 Washington Ave.
Albany, NY 12222

TELEPHONE: (518) 457-8536

LIST NAMES OF BRANCHES WITH
SEPARATE POLICIES: None

BOOKS:
Will Lend: Yes
Length of Loan: 1 month
Renewable: Yes
Charges: None
Average Turnaround Time:
2 days
If you have indicated that a
book is not to be lent, will
you on receipt of a letter
from the requesting library
search the index for given
entries? (Not answered)

PERIODICALS:
Bound: Will not lend
Unbound: Will not lend
Loan Period: N/A
Renewable: N/A
Will lend if article exceeds
_____ number of pages
(Occasional exceptions;
decisions are on a case-
by-case basis)

MICROFORMS:
Will Lend: Yes
Specific Types of Microforms:
Microfilms, microfiche

GOVERNMENT PUBLICATIONS:
Will Lend: Yes

DISSERTATIONS:
Will Lend: Yes

THESES:
Will Lend: Yes

AUDIO-VISUAL MATERIALS:
Records: Will lend
Cassettes: Will lend
Other (slides, filmstrips,
etc.): Will lend

COMPUTER SOFTWARE:
Will Lend: No

PHOTODUPLICATION SERVICE:
No charge up to 50 exposures
Charge Per Exposure: None
Minimum/handling Fee: None
Average Turnaround Time:
2 days

MICROFILMING SERVICE:
Service Available: No
Charges: N/A

DO YOU CHARGE THE BORROWING
LIBRARY FOR POSTAGE? No

FOR HOW LONG DO YOU SUSPEND ILL
SERVICE OVER THE CHRISTMAS
HOLIDAYS? No suspension

ARE THERE ANY GROUPS OF LIBRARIES
FOR WHICH YOU WAIVE FEES? IF
SO, PLEASE NAME THEM: No fees
charged

STATE UNIVERSITY OF NEW YORK AT BUFFALO

NUC CODE: NBuU

OCLC CODE: BUF

ADDRESS: Interlibrary Loan
State University of New
York at Buffalo
234 Lockwood Library
Buffalo, NY 14260

TELEPHONE: (716) 636-2812

LIST NAMES OF BRANCHES WITH
SEPARATE POLICIES: None

BOOKS:
Will Lend: Yes
Length of Loan: 4 weeks
Renewable: Yes
Charges: (Not answered)
Average Turnaround Time:
(Not answered)
If you have indicated that a
book is not to be lent, will
you on receipt of a letter
from the requesting library
search the index for given
entries? (Not answered)

PERIODICALS:
Bound: Will not lend
Unbound: Will not lend
Loan Period: N/A
Renewable: N/A
Will lend if article exceeds
_____ number of pages (Not
answered)

MICROFORMS:
Will Lend: Yes
Specific Types of Microforms:
All

GOVERNMENT PUBLICATIONS:
Will Lend: (Not answered)

DISSERTATIONS:
Will Lend: Yes

THESES:
Will Lend: Yes

AUDIO-VISUAL MATERIALS:
Records: (Not answered)
Cassettes: (Not answered)
Other (slides, filmstrips,
etc.): (Not answered)

COMPUTER SOFTWARE:
Will Lend: (Not answered)

PHOTODUPLICATION SERVICE:
No charge up to 0 exposures
Charge Per Exposure: 25¢
Minimum/handling Fee: None
Average Turnaround Time:
(Not answered)

MICROFILMING SERVICE:
Service Available: (Not
answered)
Charges: N/A

DO YOU CHARGE THE BORROWING
LIBRARY FOR POSTAGE? No

FOR HOW LONG DO YOU SUSPEND ILL
SERVICE OVER THE CHRISTMAS
HOLIDAYS? (Not answered)

ARE THERE ANY GROUPS OF LIBRARIES
FOR WHICH YOU WAIVE FEES? IF
SO, PLEASE NAME THEM: (Not
answered)

STATE UNIVERSITY OF NEW YORK AT BUFFALO--HEALTH SCIENCES LIBRARY

NUC CODE: (Not answered)

OCLC CODE: SBH

ADDRESS: Information Dissemina-
          tion Service
          Health Sciences Library
          Stockton Kimball Tower
          SUNY at Buffalo
          Buffalo, NY 14214

TELEPHONE: (716) 831-3351

LIST NAMES OF BRANCHES WITH
  SEPARATE POLICIES: None

BOOKS:
  Will Lend: Yes
  Length of Loan: 1 month
  Renewable: Yes
  Charges: $5.00
  Average Turnaround Time:
    1 day
  If you have indicated that a
    book is not to be lent, will
    you on receipt of a letter
    from the requesting library
    search the index for given
    entries? (Not answered)

PERIODICALS:
  Bound: Will not lend, unless
    circulating journal
  Unbound: Will not lend,
    unless circulating journal
  Loan Period: 1 week
  Renewable: N/A
  Will lend if article exceeds
    30 pages and is a circulat-
    ing journal

MICROFORMS:
  Will Lend: No
  Specific Types of Microforms:
    N/A

GOVERNMENT PUBLICATIONS:
  Will Lend: Yes

DISSERTATIONS:
  Will Lend: Yes

THESES:
  Will Lend: Yes

AUDIO-VISUAL MATERIALS:
  Records: Will not lend
  Cassettes: Will lend
  Other (slides, filmstrips,
    etc.): Will lend
  Charges: $10.00 and
    insurance to return

COMPUTER SOFTWARE:
  Will Lend: No

PHOTODUPLICATION SERVICE:
  No charge up to 30 exposures
  Charge Per Exposure: None
  Minimum/handling Fee: $5.00
    and 30 page limit
  Average Turnaround Time:
    1 day

MICROFILMING SERVICE:
  Service Available: No
  Charges: N/A

DO YOU CHARGE THE BORROWING
  LIBRARY FOR POSTAGE? No

FOR HOW LONG DO YOU SUSPEND ILL
  SERVICE OVER THE CHRISTMAS
  HOLIDAYS? 3 weeks to 1 month

ARE THERE ANY GROUPS OF LIBRARIES
  FOR WHICH YOU WAIVE FEES? IF
  SO, PLEASE NAME THEM: SUNY
  libraries

STATE UNIVERSITY OF NEW YORK AT STONY BROOK

NUC CODE: NSbSU

OCLC CODE: YSM

ADDRESS: Interlibrary Loan
          Section
          Library
          SUNY at Stony Brook
          Stony Brook, NY 11794

TELEPHONE: (516) 246-5977

LIST NAMES OF BRANCHES WITH
  SEPARATE POLICIES: None

BOOKS:
  Will Lend: Yes
  Length of Loan: 1 month
  Renewable: Yes
  Charges: None
  Average Turnaround Time:
    (Not answered)
  If you have indicated that a
    book is not to be lent, will
    you on receipt of a letter
    from the requesting library
    search the index for given
    entries? (Not answered)

PERIODICALS:
  Bound: Will not lend
  Unbound: Will not lend
  Loan Period: N/A
  Renewable: N/A
  Will lend if article exceeds
    _____ number of pages (Not
    answered)

MICROFORMS:
  Will Lend: Yes
  Specific Types of Microforms:
    (Not answered)

GOVERNMENT PUBLICATIONS:
  Will Lend: Yes

DISSERTATIONS:
  Will Lend: Yes; 1962 to
    present available from
    University Microfilms

THESES:
  Will Lend: Yes

AUDIO-VISUAL MATERIALS:
  Records: Will not lend
  Cassettes: Will not lend
  Other (slides, filmstrips,
    etc.): Will not lend

COMPUTER SOFTWARE:
  Will Lend: No

PHOTODUPLICATION SERVICE:
  No charge up to 0 exposures
  Charge Per Exposure: 10¢
  Minimum/handling Fee: $2.00
  Average Turnaround Time:
    (Not answered)

MICROFILMING SERVICE:
  Service Available: No
  Charges: N/A

DO YOU CHARGE THE BORROWING
  LIBRARY FOR POSTAGE? No

FOR HOW LONG DO YOU SUSPEND ILL
  SERVICE OVER THE CHRISTMAS
  HOLIDAYS? No suspension

ARE THERE ANY GROUPS OF LIBRARIES
  FOR WHICH YOU WAIVE FEES? IF
  SO, PLEASE NAME THEM: SUNY
  libraries; LILRC members

STATE UNIVERSITY OF NEW YORK AT STONY BROOK--HEALTH SCIENCES CENTER

NUC CODE: (Not answered)

OCLC CODE: VZB

ADDRESS: Interlibrary Loan
Health Sciences
Library
SUNY at Stony Brook
P. O. Box 66
East Setauket, NY 11733

TELEPHONE: (516) 246-2530

LIST NAMES OF BRANCHES WITH
SEPARATE POLICIES: None

BOOKS:
Will Lend: Yes
Length of Loan: 5 weeks
Renewable: Yes
Charges: $5.00
Average Turnaround Time:
2 weeks
If you have indicated that a
book is not to be lent, will
you on receipt of a letter
from the requesting library
search the index for given
entries? (Not answered)

PERIODICALS:
Bound: Will not lend
Unbound: Will not lend
Loan Period: N/A
Renewable: N/A
Will lend if article exceeds
_____ number of pages (Not
answered)

MICROFORMS:
Will Lend: No
Specific Types of Microforms:
N/A

GOVERNMENT PUBLICATIONS:
Will Lend: No

DISSERTATIONS:
Will Lend: No

THESES:
Will Lend: No

AUDIO-VISUAL MATERIALS:
Records: (Not answered)
Cassettes: (Not answered)
Other (slides, filmstrips,
etc.): (Not answered)

COMPUTER SOFTWARE:
Will Lend: No

PHOTODUPLICATION SERVICE:
No charge up to 0 exposures
Charge Per Exposure: (Not
answered)
Minimum/handling Fee: $5.00
Average Turnaround Time:
5 days

MICROFILMING SERVICE:
Service Available: No
Charges: N/A

DO YOU CHARGE THE BORROWING
LIBRARY FOR POSTAGE? No

FOR HOW LONG DO YOU SUSPEND ILL
SERVICE OVER THE CHRISTMAS
HOLIDAYS? 1 month

ARE THERE ANY GROUPS OF LIBRARIES
FOR WHICH YOU WAIVE FEES? IF
SO, PLEASE NAME THEM: State
Universities of New York;
health area libraries in
our region

STATE UNIVERSITY OF NEW YORK COLLEGE AT BROCKPORT

NUC CODE: (Not answered)

OCLC CODE: (Not answered)

ADDRESS: Interlibrary Loan
Drake Library
SUNY College at
Brockport
Brockport, NY 14420

TELEPHONE: (716) 395-2668

LIST NAMES OF BRANCHES WITH
SEPARATE POLICIES: None

BOOKS:
Will Lend: Yes
Length of Loan: 4 weeks
Renewable: Yes
Charges: (Not answered)
Average Turnaround Time:
(Not answered)
If you have indicated that a
book is not to be lent, will
you on receipt of a letter
from the requesting library
search the index for given
entries? (Not answered)

PERIODICALS:
Bound: Will not lend
Unbound: Will not lend
Loan Period: N/A
Renewable: N/A
Will lend if article exceeds
_____ number of pages (Not
answered)

MICROFORMS:
Will Lend: Yes
Specific Types of Microforms:
All

GOVERNMENT PUBLICATIONS:
Will Lend: Yes

DISSERTATIONS:
Will Lend: No

THESES:
Will Lend: Yes

AUDIO-VISUAL MATERIALS:
Records: (Not answered)
Cassettes: (Not answered)
Other (slides, filmstrips,
etc.): (Not answered)

COMPUTER SOFTWARE:
Will Lend: (Not answered)

PHOTODUPLICATION SERVICE:
No charge up to 0 exposures
Charge Per Exposure: 10¢
Minimum/handling Fee: (Not
answered)
Average Turnaround Time:
(Not answered)

MICROFILMING SERVICE:
Service Available: No
Charges: N/A

DO YOU CHARGE THE BORROWING
LIBRARY FOR POSTAGE? No

FOR HOW LONG DO YOU SUSPEND ILL
SERVICE OVER THE CHRISTMAS
HOLIDAYS? (Not answered)

ARE THERE ANY GROUPS OF LIBRARIES
FOR WHICH YOU WAIVE FEES? IF
SO, PLEASE NAME THEM: (Not
answered)

STATE UNIVERSITY OF NEW YORK COLLEGE AT BUFFALO

NUC CODE: (Not answered)

OCLC CODE: YBM

ADDRESS: Interlibrary Loan
E. H. Butler Library
SUNY College at
Buffalo
1300 Elmwood Ave.
Buffalo, NY 14222

TELEPHONE: (716) 878-6310 or
878-6313

LIST NAMES OF BRANCHES WITH
SEPARATE POLICIES: None

BOOKS:
Will Lend: Yes
Length of Loan: 4 weeks
Renewable: Yes
Charges: None
Average Turnaround Time:
(Not answered)
If you have indicated that a
book is not to be lent, will
you on receipt of a letter
from the requesting library
search the index for given
entries? Perhaps,
depending upon how busy
we are

PERIODICALS:
Bound: Will not lend
Unbound: Will not lend
Loan Period: N/A
Renewable: N/A
Will lend if article exceeds
_____ number of pages (Will
not lend, regardless of
length of article)

MICROFORMS:
Will Lend: Yes
Specific Types of Microforms:
Creative Studies
dissertations

GOVERNMENT PUBLICATIONS:
Will Lend: Yes

DISSERTATIONS:
Will Lend: No

THESES:
Will Lend: No

AUDIO-VISUAL MATERIALS:
Records: Will not lend
Cassettes: Will not lend
Other (slides, filmstrips,
etc.): Will not lend

COMPUTER SOFTWARE:
Will Lend: No

PHOTODUPLICATION SERVICE:
No charge up to 25 exposures
Charge Per Exposure: (Not
answered)
Minimum/handling Fee: None
Average Turnaround Time:
(Not answered)

MICROFILMING SERVICE:
Service Available: No
Charges: N/A

DO YOU CHARGE THE BORROWING
LIBRARY FOR POSTAGE? No

FOR HOW LONG DO YOU SUSPEND ILL
SERVICE OVER THE CHRISTMAS
HOLIDAYS? No suspension

ARE THERE ANY GROUPS OF LIBRARIES
FOR WHICH YOU WAIVE FEES? IF
SO, PLEASE NAME THEM: None

STATE UNIVERSITY OF NEW YORK COLLEGE AT CORTLAND

NUC CODE: None

OCLC CODE: YCM

ADDRESS: Interlibrary Loan
Memorial Library
P. O. Box 2000
State University
College at
Cortland
Cortland, NY 13045

TELEPHONE: (607) 753-2525

LIST NAMES OF BRANCHES WITH
SEPARATE POLICIES: None

BOOKS:
Will Lend: Yes
Length of Loan: 4 weeks
Renewable: Yes
Charges: None
Average Turnaround Time:
1-2 days
If you have indicated that a
book is not to be lent, will
you on receipt of a letter
from the requesting library
search the index for given
entries? (Not answered)

PERIODICALS:
Bound: Will not lend
Unbound: Will not lend
Loan Period: N/A
Renewable: N/A
Will lend if article exceeds
_____ number of pages (Not
answered)

MICROFORMS:
Will Lend: Yes
Specific Types of Microforms:
All

GOVERNMENT PUBLICATIONS:
Will Lend: Yes

DISSERTATIONS:
Will Lend: Yes

THESES:
Will Lend: Yes

AUDIO-VISUAL MATERIALS:
Records: Will not lend
Cassettes: Will lend
Other (slides, filmstrips,
etc.): Will not lend

COMPUTER SOFTWARE:
Will Lend: No

PHOTODUPLICATION SERVICE:
No charge up to any exposures
Charge Per Exposure: None
Minimum/handling Fee: None
Average Turnaround Time:
2-3 days
(Charges may possibly change
in future)

MICROFILMING SERVICE:
Service Available: No
Charges: N/A

DO YOU CHARGE THE BORROWING
LIBRARY FOR POSTAGE? No

FOR HOW LONG DO YOU SUSPEND ILL
SERVICE OVER THE CHRISTMAS
HOLIDAYS? No suspension

ARE THERE ANY GROUPS OF LIBRARIES
FOR WHICH YOU WAIVE FEES? IF
SO, PLEASE NAME THEM: None

STATE UNIVERSITY OF NEW YORK COLLEGE AT FREDONIA

NUC CODE: NFredU

OCLC CODE: XFM

ADDRESS: Interlibrary Loan
Daniel A. Reed Library
State University College
Fredonia, NY 14063

TELEPHONE: (716) 673-3184

LIST NAMES OF BRANCHES WITH
SEPARATE POLICIES: None

BOOKS:
Will Lend: Yes
Length of Loan: 1 month use
Renewable: Yes, if no
reserves
Charges: Postage to out-of-
state plus reciprocal
charges
Average Turnaround Time:
1 day
If you have indicated that a
book is not to be lent, will
you on receipt of a letter
from the requesting library
search the index for given
entries? Yes

PERIODICALS:
Bound: Will not lend
Unbound: Will not lend
Loan Period: N/A
Renewable: N/A
Will lend if article exceeds
_____ number of pages (We
will loan if plates or
other material cannot be
adequately copied)

MICROFORMS:
Will Lend: Yes
Specific Types of Microforms:
Microfilm, microfiche,
microcards, microprint

GOVERNMENT PUBLICATIONS:
Will Lend: Yes, in microprint

DISSERTATIONS:
Will Lend: No

THESES:
Will Lend: Yes, but with
restrictions on copying

AUDIO-VISUAL MATERIALS:
Records: Will not lend
Cassettes: Will not lend
Other (slides, filmstrips,
etc.): Will not lend
(Can duplicate cassettes if
requested)

COMPUTER SOFTWARE:
Will Lend: Do not own

PHOTODUPLICATION SERVICE:
No charge up to 0 exposures
Charge Per Exposure: 10¢
Handling Fee: $1.00 for out-
of-state
Minimum Fee: $1.10
Average Turnaround Time:
2 days

MICROFILMING SERVICE:
Service Available: Yes, for
16 mm only
Charges: 15¢ per frame

DO YOU CHARGE THE BORROWING
LIBRARY FOR POSTAGE? Out-
of-state only

FOR HOW LONG DO YOU SUSPEND ILL
SERVICE OVER THE CHRISTMAS
HOLIDAYS? App. Dec.5-Jan.2

ARE THERE ANY GROUPS OF LIBRARIES
FOR WHICH YOU WAIVE FEES? IF
SO, PLEASE NAME THEM: All
Western New York Library
Resource Council Members and
all SUNY libraries

STATE UNIVERSITY OF NEW YORK COLLEGE AT GENESEO

NUC CODE: (Not answered)

OCLC CODE: YGM

ADDRESS: Interlibrary Loan
Milne Library
State University
College
Geneseo, NY 14454

TELEPHONE: (716) 245-5591

LIST NAMES OF BRANCHES WITH
SEPARATE POLICIES: None

BOOKS:
Will Lend: Yes
Length of Loan: 3 weeks
Renewable: Yes
Charges: None
Average Turnaround Time:
(Not answered)
If you have indicated that a
book is not to be lent, will
you on receipt of a letter
from the requesting library
search the index for given
entries? (Not answered)

PERIODICALS:
Bound: Will not lend
Unbound: Will not lend
Loan Period: N/A
Renewable: N/A
Will lend if article exceeds
_____ number of pages (Not
answered)

MICROFORMS:
Will Lend: Yes
Specific Types of Microforms:
Cards, books, ERIC

GOVERNMENT PUBLICATIONS:
Will Lend: No

DISSERTATIONS:
Will Lend: (Not answered)

THESES:
Will Lend: (Not answered)

AUDIO-VISUAL MATERIALS:
Records: Will lend
Cassettes: (Not answered)
Other (slides, filmstrips,
etc.): (Not answered)

COMPUTER SOFTWARE:
Will Lend: (Not answered)

PHOTODUPLICATION SERVICE:
No charge up to 24 exposures
Charge Per Exposure: 5¢
Minimum/handling Fee: None
Average Turnaround Time:
(Not answered)

MICROFILMING SERVICE:
Service Available: No
Charges: N/A

DO YOU CHARGE THE BORROWING
LIBRARY FOR POSTAGE? No

FOR HOW LONG DO YOU SUSPEND ILL
SERVICE OVER THE CHRISTMAS
HOLIDAYS? No suspension

ARE THERE ANY GROUPS OF LIBRARIES
FOR WHICH YOU WAIVE FEES? IF
SO, PLEASE NAME THEM: None

STATE UNIVERSITY OF NEW YORK COLLEGE AT NEW PALTZ

NUC CODE: NNepaSu

OCLC CODE: ZLM

ADDRESS: Interlibrary Loan
           Sojourner Truth Library
           SUNY College at New
              Paltz
           New Paltz, NY 12561

TELEPHONE: (914) 257-2209

LIST NAMES OF BRANCHES WITH
   SEPARATE POLICIES: None

BOOKS:
   Will Lend: Yes
   Length of Loan: 4 weeks use
   Renewable: Yes, for 3 weeks
   Charges: (Not answered)
   Average Turnaround Time:
      2 days
   If you have indicated that a
      book is not to be lent, will
      you on receipt of a letter
      from the requesting library
      search the index for given
      entries? (Not answered)

PERIODICALS:
   Bound: Will not lend
   Unbound: Will not lend
   Loan Period: N/A
   Renewable: N/A
   Will lend if article exceeds
      _____ number of pages (Not
      answered)

MICROFORMS:
   Will Lend: Yes, but depends
      upon title
   Specific Types of Microforms:
      (Not answered)

GOVERNMENT PUBLICATIONS:
   Will Lend: Yes

DISSERTATIONS:
   Will Lend: No

THESES:
   Will Lend: No

AUDIO-VISUAL MATERIALS:
   Records: Do not own
   Cassettes: Do not own
   Other (slides, filmstrips,
      et.c): Do not own

COMPUTER SOFTWARE:
   Will Lend: Do not own

PHOTODUPLICATION SERVICE:
   No charge up to 5 exposures
   Charge Per Exposure: 10¢
   Minimum/handling Fee: None
   Average Turnaround Time:
      2 days

MICROFILMING SERVICE:
   Service Available: No
   Charges: N/A

DO YOU CHARGE THE BORROWING
   LIBRARY FOR POSTAGE? No

FOR HOW LONG DO YOU SUSPEND ILL
   SERVICE OVER THE CHRISTMAS
   HOLIDAYS? (Not answered)

ARE THERE ANY GROUPS OF LIBRARIES
   FOR WHICH YOU WAIVE FEES? IF
   SO, PLEASE NAME THEM: SUNY
   and SENYRC libraries

STATE UNIVERSITY OF NEW YORK COLLEGE AT OLD WESTBURY

NUC CODE: NOWU

OCLC CODE: ZOW

ADDRESS: Interlibrary Loan
           SUNY College at Old
              Westbury Library
           P. O. Box 229
           Old Westbury, NY 11568

TELEPHONE: (516) 876-3151 or
                 876-3152

LIST NAMES OF BRANCHES WITH
   SEPARATE POLICIES: None

BOOKS:
   Will Lend: Yes
   Length of Loan: App. 30 days
   Renewable: Yes
   Charges: None
   Average Turnaround Time:
      2 days
   If you have indicated that a
      book is not to be lent, will
      you on receipt of a letter
      from the requesting library
      search the index for given
      entries? (Not answered)

PERIODICALS:
   Bound: Will not lend
   Unbound: Will not lend
   Loan Period: N/A
   Renewable: N/A
   Will lend if article exceeds
      _____ number of pages (Will
      not lend, regardless of
      length of article)

MICROFORMS:
   Will Lend: No
   Specific Types of Microforms:
      N/A

GOVERNMENT PUBLICATIONS:
   Will Lend: Yes, if cataloged.
      Library not a depository.

DISSERTATIONS:
   Will Lend: Do not own

THESES:
   Will Lend: Do not own

AUDIO-VISUAL MATERIALS:
   Records: Will not lend
   Cassettes: Will not lend
   Other (slides, filmstrips,
      etc.): Will not lend

COMPUTER SOFTWARE:
   Will Lend: Do not own

PHOTODUPLICATION SERVICE:
   No charge up to 30 exposures
   Charge Per Exposure: None,
      but no item over 30
      exposures will be copied
   Minimum/handling Fee: None
   Average Turnaround Time:
      2 days

MICROFILMING SERVICE
   Service Available: No
   Charges: N/A

DO YOU CHARGE THE BORROWING
   LIBRARY FOR POSTAGE? No

FOR HOW LONG DO YOU SUSPEND ILL
   SERVICE OVER THE CHRISTMAS
   HOLIDAYS? No suspension

ARE THERE ANY GROUPS OF LIBRARIES
   FOR WHICH YOU WAIVE FEES? IF
   SO, PLEASE NAME THEM: No fees
   charged, but we may waive
   lending regulations to other
   SUNY libraries.

STATE UNIVERSITY OF NEW YORK COLLEGE AT ONEONTA

NUC CODE: NOneoU

OCLC CODE: ZBM

ADDRESS: Interlibrary Loan
James M. Milne Library
State University
College
Oneonta, NY 13820

TELEPHONE: (607) 431-2453

LIST NAMES OF BRANCHES WITH
SEPARATE POLICIES: None

BOOKS:
Will Lend: Yes
Length of Loan: 4 weeks use
Renewable: Yes
Charges: (Not answered)
Average Turnaround Time:
2 days
If you have indicated that a
book is not to be lent, will
you on receipt of a letter
from the requesting library
search the index for given
entries? (Not answered)

PERIODICALS:
Bound: Will not lend
Unbound: Will not lend
Loan Period: N/A
Renewable: N/A
Will lend if article exceeds
_____ number of pages (Not
answered)

MICROFORMS:
Will Lend: Yes, but only
non-periodical microforms

GOVERNMENT PUBLICATIONS:
Will Lend: Yes

DISSERTATIONS:
Will Lend: Yes

THESES:
Will Lend: Yes

AUDIO-VISUAL MATERIALS:
Records: Will not lend
Cassettes: Will not lend
Other (slides, filmstrips,
etc.): Will not lend

COMPUTER SOFTWARE:
Will Lend: No

PHOTODUPLICATION SERVICE:
No charge up to 0 exposures
Charge Per Exposure: 15¢
Minimum/handling Fee: $3.00
Average Turnaround Time:
2 days

MICROFILMING SERVICE:
Service Available: No
Charges: N/A

DO YOU CHARGE THE BORROWING
LIBRARY FOR POSTAGE? No

FOR HOW LONG DO YOU SUSPEND ILL
SERVICE OVER THE CHRISTMAS
HOLIDAYS? Last 3 weeks in
December

ARE THERE ANY GROUPS OF LIBRARIES
FOR WHICH YOU WAIVE FEES? IF
SO, PLEASE NAME THEM: SUNY
libraries; SCRLC libraries

STATE UNIVERSITY OF NEW YORK COLLEGE AT OSWEGO

NUC CODE: NOsU

OCLC CODE: YOM

ADDRESS: Interlibrary Loan
Penfield Library
State University
College
Oswego, NY 13126

TELEPHONE: (315) 341-3210

LIST NAMES OF BRANCHES WITH
SEPARATE POLICIES: None

BOOKS:
Will Lend: Yes
Length of Loan: 30 days
Renewable: Yes
Charges: (Not answered)
Average Turnaround Time:
1 day
If you have indicated that a
book is not to be lent, will
you on receipt of a letter
from the requesting library
search the index for given
entries? Yes

PERIODICALS:
Bound: Will not lend
Unbound: Will not lend
Loan Period: N/A
Renewable: N/A
Will lend if article exceeds
_____ number of pages (Will
decide on individual basis
loan of whole periodical)

MICROFORMS:
Will Lend: Yes
Specific Types of Microforms:
(Not answered)

GOVERNMENT PUBLICATIONS:
Will Lend: Yes

DISSERTATIONS:
Will Lend: Yes, if 2d copy
available

THESES:
Will Lend: Yes, if 2d copy
available

AUDIO-VISUAL MATERIALS:
Records: Will not lend
Cassettes: Will not lend
Other (slides, filmstrips,
etc.): Will not lend

COMPUTER SOFTWARE:
Will Lend: No

PHOTODUPLICATION SERVICE:
No charge up to 24 exposures
Charge Per Exposure: 10¢
Minimum/handling Fee: $1.50
Average Turnaround Time:
1 day

MICROFILMING SERVICE:
Service Available: (Not
answered)
Charges: N/A

DO YOU CHARGE THE BORROWING
LIBRARY FOR POSTAGE? No

FOR HOW LONG DO YOU SUSPEND ILL
SERVICE OVER THE CHRISTMAS
HOLIDAYS? Dec.24-Jan.1

ARE THERE ANY GROUPS OF LIBRARIES
FOR WHICH YOU WAIVE FEES? IF
SO, PLEASE NAME THEM: SUNY
and New York state libraries.
Also, any library wishing
reciprocal agreement.

STATE UNIVERSITY OF NEW YORK COLLEGE AT PLATTSBURGH

NUC CODE: NP1uU

OCLC CODE: YPM

ADDRESS: Interlibrary Loan
Benjamin F. Feinberg
Library
SUNY College at
Plattsburgh
Plattsburgh, NY 12901

TELEPHONE: (518) 564-3183

LIST NAMES OF BRANCHES WITH
SEPARATE POLICIES: None

BOOKS:
Will Lend: Yes
Length of Loan: 4 weeks from
date sent
Renewable: Yes
Charges: None
Average Turnaround Time:
2-3 days
If you have indicated that a
book is not to be lent, will
you on receipt of a letter
from the requesting library
search the index for given
entries? Yes

PERIODICALS:
Bound: Will not lend
Unbound: Will not lend
Loan Period: N/A
Renewable: N/A
Will lend if article exceeds
_____ number of pages (Will
not lend, regardless of
length of article)

MICROFORMS:
Will Lend: Yes
Specific Types of Microforms:
Certain microfiche only

GOVERNMENT PUBLICATIONS:
Will Lend: Yes

DISSERTATIONS:
Will Lend: Yes, if 2nd copy
available

THESES:
Will Lend: Yes, if 2nd copy
available

AUDIO-VISUAL MATERIALS:
Records: Will lend
Cassettes: Will not lend
Other (slides, filmstrips,
etc.): Will not lend

COMPUTER SOFTWARE:
Will Lend: Do not own

PHOTODUPLICATION SERVICE:
No charge up to 24 exposures
Charge Per Exposure: 10¢
over 24
Minimum/handling Fee: None
Average Turnaround Time:
2-3 days

MICROFILMING SERVICE:
Service Available: No
Charges: N/A

DO YOU CHARGE THE BORROWING
LIBRARY FOR POSTAGE? No

FOR HOW LONG DO YOU SUSPEND ILL
SERVICE OVER THE CHRISTMAS
HOLIDAYS? No suspension

ARE THERE ANY GROUPS OF LIBRARIES
FOR WHICH YOU WAIVE FEES? IF
SO, PLEASE NAME THEM: SUNY
libraries

STATE UNIVERSITY OF NEW YORK COLLEGE AT POTSDAM

NUC CODE: NPOTU

OCLC CODE: ZQM

ADDRESS: Interlibrary Loan
F. W. Crumb Library
State University
College
Potsdam, NY 13676

TELEPHONE: (315) 267-2489

LIST NAMES OF BRANCHES WITH
SEPARATE POLICIES:
Julia Crane Music Library--
scores not loaned, ILL
processed by Main Library

BOOKS:
Will Lend: Yes
Length of Loan: 4 weeks
Renewable: Yes
Charges: None
Average Turnaround Time:
1-2 days
If you have indicated that a
book is not to be lent, will
you on receipt of a letter
from the requesting library
search the index for given
entries? (Not answered)

PERIODICALS:
Bound: Will not lend
Unbound: Will not lend
Loan Period: N/A
Renewable: N/A
Will occasionally lend if
article exceeds 40 pages

MICROFORMS:
Will Lend: Yes
Specific Types of Microforms:
(Not answered)

GOVERNMENT PUBLICATIONS:
Will Lend: Yes

DISSERTATIONS:
Will Lend: No

THESES:
Will Lend: No

AUDIO-VISUAL MATERIALS:
Records: Will not lend
Cassettes: Will not lend
Other (slides, filmstrips,
etc.): Will lend

COMPUTER SOFTWARE:
Will Lend: No

PHOTODUPLICATION SERVICE:
No charge up to any exposures
Charge Per Exposure: None
Minimum/handling Fee: None
Average Turnaround Time:
1-2 days

MICROFILMING SERVICE:
Service Available: No
Charges: N/A

DO YOU CHARGE THE BORROWING
LIBRARY FOR POSTAGE? No

FOR HOW LONG DO YOU SUSPEND ILL
SERVICE OVER THE CHRISTMAS
HOLIDAYS? (Not answered)

ARE THERE ANY GROUPS OF LIBRARIES
FOR WHICH YOU WAIVE FEES? IF
SO, PLEASE NAME THEM: None

STATE UNIVERSITY OF NEW YORK COLLEGE AT PURCHASE

NUC CODE: NPurU

OCLC CODE: ZPM

ADDRESS: Interlibrary Loan
SUNY College at
Purchase
The Library
Purchase, NY 10577

TELEPHONE: (914) 253-5096 or
253-5099

LIST NAMES OF BRANCHES WITH
SEPARATE POLICIES: None

BOOKS:
Will Lend: Yes
Length of Loan: 4 weeks from
date sent
Renewable: Yes
Charges: None, except for
libraries that charge us
Average Turnaround Time:
2 days
If you have indicated that a
book is not to be lent, will
you on receipt of a letter
from the requesting library
search the index for given
entries? Yes

PERIODICALS:
Bound: Will not lend
Unbound: Will not lend
Loan Period: N/A
Renewable: N/A
Will lend if article exceeds
_____ number of pages (Not
answered)

MICROFORMS:
Will Lend: Yes
Specific Types of Microforms:
Will not lend periodicals

GOVERNMENT PUBLICATIONS:
Will Lend: Yes

DISSERTATIONS:
Will Lend: N/A

THESES:
Will Lend: N/A

AUDIO-VISUAL MATERIALS:
Records: Will not lend
Cassettes: Will not lend
Other (slides, filmstrips,
etc.): Will not lend

COMPUTER SOFTWARE:
Will Lend: No

PHOTODUPLICATION SERVICE:
No charge up to 0 exposures
Charge Per Exposure: 10¢
(on reciprocal basis only)
Minimum/handling Fee: (Not
answered)
Average Turnaround Time:
2 days

MICROFILMING SERVICE:
Service Available: No
Charges: N/A

DO YOU CHARGE THE BORROWING
LIBRARY FOR POSTAGE? No

FOR HOW LONG DO YOU SUSPEND ILL
SERVICE OVER THE CHRISTMAS
HOLIDAYS? Dec.20-Jan.2

ARE THERE ANY GROUPS OF LIBRARIES
FOR WHICH YOU WAIVE FEES? IF
SO, PLEASE NAME THEM: Fees
are charged only to those
libraries who charge us.

STATE UNIVERSITY OF NEW YORK--COLLEGE OF ENVIRONMENTAL SCIENCE AND FORESTRY

NUC CODE: NSySU-F

OCLC CODE: VXF

ADDRESS: Interlibrary Loan
Moon Library
College of Environmen-
tal Science and
Forestry
State University of
New York
Syracuse, NY 13210

TELEPHONE: (315) 470-6722

LIST NAMES OF BRANCHES WITH
SEPARATE POLICIES: (Not
answered)

BOOKS:
Will Lend: Yes
Length of Loan: 4 weeks
Renewable: Yes
Charges: (Not answered)
Average Turnaround Time:
(Not answered)
If you have indicated that a
book is not to be lent, will
you on receipt of a letter
from the requesting library
search the index for given
entries? (Not answered)

PERIODICALS:
Bound: Will not lend
Unbound: Will not lend
Loan Period: N/A
Renewable: N/A
Will lend if article exceeds
_____ number of pages (Not
answered)

MICROFORMS:
Will Lend: Yes
Specific Types of Microforms:
Films, fiche

GOVERNMENT PUBLICATIONS:
Will Lend: (Not answered)

DISSERTATIONS:
Will Lend: Yes; 1963 to
present available from
University Microfilms

THESES:
Will Lend: Yes

AUDIO-VISUAL MATERIALS:
Records: (Not answered)
Cassettes: (Not answered)
Other (slides, filmstrips,
etc.): (Not answered)

COMPUTER SOFTWARE:
Will Lend: (Not answered)

PHOTODUPLICATION SERVICE:
No charge up to 30 exposures
Charge Per Exposure: (Not
answered)
Minimum/handling Fee: None
Average Turnaround Time:
(Not answered)

MICROFILMING SERVICE:
Service Available: No
Charges: N/A

DO YOU CHARGE THE BORROWING
LIBRARY FOR POSTAGE? (Not
answered)

FOR HOW LONG DO YOU SUSPEND ILL
SERVICE OVER THE CHRISTMAS
HOLIDAYS? Dec.15-Jan.2

ARE THERE ANY GROUPS OF LIBRARIES
FOR WHICH YOU WAIVE FEES? IF
SO, PLEASE NAME THEM: (Not
answered)

SYRACUSE UNIVERSITY

NUC CODE: NSyU

OCLC CODE: SYB

ADDRESS: Interlibrary Loan
116 E. S. Byrd Library
Syracuse University
Syracuse, NY 13210

TELEPHONE: (315) 423-3725

LIST NAMES OF BRANCHES WITH
SEPARATE POLICIES: None

BOOKS:
Will Lend: Yes
Length of Loan: 2 weeks
Renewable: Yes
Charges: None
Average Turnaround Time:
(Not answered)
If you have indicated that a
book is not to be lent, will
you on receipt of a letter
from the requesting library
search the index for given
entries? (Not answered)

PERIODICALS:
Bound: Will not lend
Unbound: Will not lend
Loan Period: N/A
Renewable: N/A
Will lend if article exceeds
_____ number of pages (Will
not lend, regardless of
length of article)

MICROFORMS:
Will Lend: Yes
Specific Types of Microforms:
Microfilm

GOVERNMENT PUBLICATIONS:
Will Lend: No

DISSERTATIONS:
Will Lend: Yes, if pre-1954

THESES:
Will Lend: Yes

AUDIO-VISUAL MATERIALS:
Records: Will not lend
Cassettes: Will not lend
Other (slides, filmstrips,
etc.): Will not lend

COMPUTER SOFTWARE:
Will Lend: No

PHOTODUPLICATION SERVICE:
No charge up to 0 exposures
Charge Per Exposure: 10¢ per
exposure after 1st 15,
which are included in
minimum fee
Minimum/handling Fee: $3.00
(includes 15 exposures)
Average Turnaround Time:
1 week

MICROFILMING SERVICE:
Service Available: Yes, but
outside library
Charges: 25¢ per exposure,
$12.50 minimum

DO YOU CHARGE THE BORROWING
LIBRARY FOR POSTAGE? No

FOR HOW LONG DO YOU SUSPEND ILL
SERVICE OVER THE CHRISTMAS
HOLIDAYS? 2 weeks

ARE THERE ANY GROUPS OF LIBRARIES
FOR WHICH YOU WAIVE FEES? IF
SO, PLEASE NAME THEM: FAUL,
Central N. Y. Library
Resources Council

TEACHERS COLLEGE--COLUMBIA UNIVERSITY

NUC CODE: NNNC-T

OCLC CODE: VVT

ADDRESS: Interlibrary Loan
Teachers College
Library
Columbia University
525 West 120th St.
New York, NY 10027

TELEPHONE: (212) 678-3495

LIST NAMES OF BRANCHES WITH
SEPARATE POLICIES: None

BOOKS:
Will Lend: Yes
Length of Loan: 4 weeks
Renewable: Yes
Charges: $10.00
Average Turnaround Time:
3-4 days
If you have indicated that a
book is not to be lent, will
you on receipt of a letter
from the requesting library
search the index for given
entries? (Not answered)

PERIODICALS:
Bound: Will not lend
Unbound: Will not lend
Loan Period: N/A
Renewable: N/A
Will lend if article exceeds
_____ number of pages (Not
answered)

MICROFORMS:
Will Lend: No
Specific Types of Microforms:
N/A

GOVERNMENT PUBLICATIONS:
Will Lend: Yes

DISSERTATIONS:
Will Lend: Yes, pre-1963 for
Ed.D.; pre-1950 for Ph.D.
only

THESES:
Will Lend: Yes, pre-1963 for
Ed.D.; pre-1950 for Ph.D.
only

AUDIO-VISUAL MATERIALS:
Records: Will not lend
Cassettes: Will not lend
Other (slides, filmstrips,
etc.): Will not lend

COMPUTER SOFTWARE:
Will Lend: No

PHOTODUPLICATION SERVICE:
No charge up to 0 exposures
Charge Per Exposure: 10¢
Minimum/handling Fee: $10.00
Average Turnaround Time:
3-4 days

MICROFILMING SERVICE:
Service Available: No
Charges: N/A

DO YOU CHARGE THE BORROWING
LIBRARY FOR POSTAGE? Is
included in $10.00 service
charge

FOR HOW LONG DO YOU SUSPEND ILL
SERVICE OVER THE CHRISTMAS
HOLIDAYS? No suspension

ARE THERE ANY GROUPS OF LIBRARIES
FOR WHICH YOU WAIVE FEES? IF
SO, PLEASE NAME THEM: RLIN
members and requests made
through NYSILL system

TROCAIRE COLLEGE

NUC CODE: (Not answered)

OCLC CODE: (Not answered)

ADDRESS: Interlibrary Loan
Trocaire College
Library
110 Red Jacket Pkwy.
Buffalo, NY 14220

TELEPHONE: (716) 826-1200

LIST NAMES OF BRANCHES WITH
SEPARATE POLICIES: None

BOOKS:
Will Lend: Yes
Length of Loan: 4 weeks
Renewable: Yes
Charges: (Not answered)
Average Turnaround Time:
(Not answered)
If you have indicated that a
book is not to be lent, will
you on receipt of a letter
from the requesting library
search the index for given
entries? (Not answered)

PERIODICALS:
Bound: Will not lend
Unbound: Will not lend
Loan Period: N/A
Renewable: N/A
Will lend if article exceeds
_____ number of pages (Not
answered)

MICROFORMS:
Will Lend: No
Specific Types of Microforms:
N/A

GOVERNMENT PUBLICATIONS:
Will Lend: No

DISSERTATIONS:
Will Lend: No

THESES:
Will Lend: No

AUDIO-VISUAL MATERIALS:
Records: Will not lend
Cassettes: Will not lend
Other (slides, filmstrips,
etc.): Will not lend

COMPUTER SOFTWARE:
Will Lend: No

PHOTODUPLICATION SERVICE:
No charge up to any exposures
Charge Per Exposure: None
Minimum/handling Fee: None
Average Turnaround Time:
(Not answered)

MICROFILMING SERVICE:
Service Available: No
Charges: N/A

DO YOU CHARGE THE BORROWING
LIBRARY FOR POSTAGE? No

FOR HOW LONG DO YOU SUSPEND ILL
SERVICE OVER THE CHRISTMAS
HOLIDAYS? 4 weeks

ARE THERE ANY GROUPS OF LIBRARIES
FOR WHICH YOU WAIVE FEES? IF
SO, PLEASE NAME THEM: Western
New York Library Resources
Council

UNION THEOLOGICAL SEMINARY

NUC CODE: NNUT

OCLC CODE: VYN

ADDRESS: Interlibrary Loan
Union Theological
Seminary
Library
3041 Broadway at
Reinhold Niebuhr
Place
New York, NY 10027

TELEPHONE: (212) 662-7100, X273

LIST NAMES OF BRANCHES WITH
SEPARATE POLICIES: None

BOOKS:
Will Lend: Yes, but 1900 to
present only
Length of Loan: 1 month use
Renewable: Yes
Charges: $10.00 per title
(up to 3 volumes)
Average Turnaround Time:
(Not answered)
If you have indicated that a
book is not to be lent, will
you on receipt of a letter
from the requesting library
search the index for given
entries? Possibly; send
inquiry

PERIODICALS:
Bound: Will not lend
Unbound: Will not lend
Loan Period: N/A
Renewable: N/A
Will lend if article exceeds
_____ number of pages (Not
answered)

MICROFORMS:
Will Lend: Yes
Specific Types of Microforms:
Microfilm, microfiche

GOVERNMENT PUBLICATIONS:
Will Lend: Do not own

DISSERTATIONS:
Will Lend: Yes, if 2d copy
available

THESES:
Will Lend: Yes, if 2d copy
available

AUDIO-VISUAL MATERIALS:
Records: Do not own
Cassettes: Do not own
Other (slides, filmstrips,
etc.): Do not own

COMPUTER SOFTWARE:
Will Lend: Do not own

PHOTODUPLICATION SERVICE:
No charge up to 0 exposures
Charge Per Exposure: 1-12
exposures, $6.00; 13-24
exposures, $10.00
Minimum/handling Fee: $6.00
Average Turnaround Time:
(Not answered)

MICROFILMING SERVICE:
Service Available: Yes
Charges: Send inquiry

DO YOU CHARGE THE BORROWING
LIBRARY FOR POSTAGE? No

FOR HOW LONG DO YOU SUSPEND ILL
SERVICE OVER THE CHRISTMAS
HOLIDAYS? No suspension

ARE THERE ANY GROUPS OF LIBRARIES
FOR WHICH YOU WAIVE FEES? IF
SO, PLEASE NAME THEM: Member
libraries of the Research
Libraries Group and NYSILL

UNITED NATIONS

NUC CODE: NNUN

OCLC CODE: None

ADDRESS: Interlibrary Loan
Dag Hammarskjold
Library
United Nations
New York, NY 10017

TELEPHONE: (212) 754-7392

LIST NAMES OF BRANCHES WITH
SEPARATE POLICIES: None

BOOKS:
Will Lend: Yes
Length of Loan: 2 weeks
Renewable: Yes
Charges: None
Average Turnaround Time:
(Not answered)
If you have indicated that a
book is not to be lent, will
you on receipt of a letter
from the requesting library
search the index for given
entries? (Not answered)

PERIODICALS:
Bound: Will not lend
Unbound: Will not lend
Loan Period: N/A
Renewable: N/A
Will lend if article exceeds
_____ number of pages (Not
answered)

MICROFORMS:
Will Lend: No
Specific Types of Microforms:
N/A

GOVERNMENT PUBLICATIONS:
Will Lend: No (have U. N.
documents only)

DISSERTATIONS:
Will Lend: No

THESES:
Will Lend: No

AUDIO-VISUAL MATERIALS:
Records: Will not lend
Cassettes: Will not lend
Other (slides, filmstrips,
etc.): Will not lend

COMPUTER SOFTWARE:
Will Lend: No

PHOTODUPLICATION SERVICE:
No charge up to 0 exposures
Charge Per Exposure: 15¢
Minimum/handling Fee: None
Average Turnaround Time:
(Not answered)

MICROFILMING SERVICE:
Service Available: No
Charges: N/A

DO YOU CHARGE THE BORROWING
LIBRARY FOR POSTAGE? No

FOR HOW LONG DO YOU SUSPEND ILL
SERVICE OVER THE CHRISTMAS
HOLIDAYS? No suspension

ARE THERE ANY GROUPS OF LIBRARIES
FOR WHICH YOU WAIVE FEES? IF
SO, PLEASE NAME THEM: None

UNIVERSITY OF ROCHESTER

NUC CODE: NRU

OCLC CODE: RRR

ADDRESS: Interlibrary Loan
University of
Rochester
Library
Rochester, NY 14627

TELEPHONE: (716) 275-4454

LIST NAMES OF BRANCHES WITH
SEPARATE POLICIES:
Sibley Music Library
E. G. Miner Medical Library

BOOKS:
Will Lend: Yes
Length of Loan: 2 weeks
Renewable: Yes
Charges: None
Average Turnaround Time:
(Not answered)
If you have indicated that a
book is not to be lent, will
you on receipt of a letter
from the requesting library
search the index for given
entries? (Not answered)

PERIODICALS:
Bound: Will lend selectively
from main collection
Unbound: Will not lend
Loan Period: 1 week
Renewable: Yes
Will lend if article exceeds
_____ number of pages (Not
answered)

MICROFORMS:
Will Lend: Yes, selectively
Specific Types of Microforms:
Cards, films, fiche, print

GOVERNMENT PUBLICATIONS:
Will Lend: Yes

DISSERTATIONS:
Will Lend: Yes, those
before June 1962

THESES:
Will Lend: Yes

AUDIO-VISUAL MATERIALS:
Records: Do not own
Cassettes: Do not own
Other (slides, filmstrips,
etc.): Do not own

COMPUTER SOFTWARE:
Will Lend: Do not own

PHOTODUPLICATION SERVICE:
No charge up to 0 exposures
Charge Per Exposure: 15¢ for
nonprofit groups; 25¢ for
profit groups
Minimum/handling Fee: $1.00
plus postage
Average Turnaround Time:
(Not answered)

MICROFILMING SERVICE:
Service Available: No
Charges: N/A

DO YOU CHARGE THE BORROWING
LIBRARY FOR POSTAGE? No

FOR HOW LONG DO YOU SUSPEND ILL
SERVICE OVER THE CHRISTMAS
HOLIDAYS? (Not answered)

ARE THERE ANY GROUPS OF LIBRARIES
FOR WHICH YOU WAIVE FEES? IF
SO, PLEASE NAME THEM: None

UTICA COLLEGE

NUC CODE: NUtC

OCLC CODE: VVV

ADDRESS: Interlibrary Loan
Utica College
Library
Burrstone Rd.
Utica, NY 13502-9973

TELEPHONE: (315) 792-3044

LIST NAMES OF BRANCHES WITH
SEPARATE POLICIES: None

BOOKS:
Will Lend: Yes
Length of Loan: 4 weeks
usually
Renewable: Yes, if no
reserves
Charges: None
Average Turnaround Time:
1-2 days
If you have indicated that a
book is not to be lent, will
you on receipt of a letter
from the requesting library
search the index for given
entries? Yes

PERIODICALS:
Bound: Will not lend
Unbound: Will not lend
Loan Period: N/A
Renewable: N/A
Will possibly lend if
article exceeds 24 pages

MICROFORMS:
Will Lend: Not usually;
possibly during semester
breaks
Specific Types of Microforms:
(Not answered)

GOVERNMENT PUBLICATIONS:
Will Lend: Yes, if in
circulating collection

DISSERTATIONS:
Will Lend: No

THESES:
Will Lend: No

AUDIO-VISUAL MATERIALS:
Records: Will lend, but for
a shorter loan period
Cassettes: Will not lend
Other (slides, filmstrips,
etc.): Will not lend

COMPUTER SOFTWARE:
Will Lend: No

PHOTODUPLICATION SERVICE:
No charge up to 24 exposures
(may lend item if more, or
else not fill the request
at all)
Charge Per Exposure: None
Minimum/handling Fee: None
Average Turnaround Time:
1-2 days

MICROFILMING SERVICE:
Service Available: Yes, for
articles not exceeding 24
pages.
Charges: None

DO YOU CHARGE THE BORROWING
LIBRARY FOR POSTAGE? No

FOR HOW LONG DO YOU SUSPEND ILL
SERVICE OVER THE CHRISTMAS
HOLIDAYS? No suspension

ARE THERE ANY GROUPS OF LIBRARIES
FOR WHICH YOU WAIVE FEES? IF
SO, PLEASE NAME THEM: No fees
charged.

VASSAR COLLEGE

NUC CODE: NPV

OCLC CODE: VXW

ADDRESS: Interlibrary Loan
Vassar College Library
Raymond Ave.
Poughkeepsie, NY 12601

TELEPHONE: (914) 452-7000, X2124

LIST NAMES OF BRANCHES WITH
SEPARATE POLICIES: None;
all branch libraries dealt
with through general library

BOOKS:
Will Lend: Yes
Length of Loan: 1 month
Renewable: Yes, if not
on reserve
Charges: None
Average Turnaround Time:
3 days
If you have indicated that a
book is not to be lent, will
you on receipt of a letter
from the requesting library
search the index for given
entries? Yes

PERIODICALS:
Bound: Will not lend
Unbound: Will not lend
Loan Period: N/A
Renewable: N/A
Will lend if article exceeds
_____ number of pages (Not
answered)

MICROFORMS:
Will Lend: No
Specific Types of Microforms:
N/A

GOVERNMENT PUBLICATIONS:
Will Lend: No

DISSERTATIONS:
Will Lend: Do not own

THESES:
Will Lend: Do not own

AUDIO-VISUAL MATERIALS:
Records: Will not lend
Cassettes: Will not lend
Other (slides, filmstrips,
etc.): Will not lend

COMPUTER SOFTWARE:
Will Lend: No

PHOTODUPLICATION SERVICE:
No charge up to 0 exposures
Charge Per Exposure: 10¢
Minimum/handling Fee: $1.00
Average Turnaround Time:
3 days

MICROFILMING SERVICE:
Service Available: No
Charges: N/A

DO YOU CHARGE THE BORROWING
LIBRARY FOR POSTAGE? Only
for first-class rush
requests

FOR HOW LONG DO YOU SUSPEND ILL
SERVICE OVER THE CHRISTMAS
HOLIDAYS? Dec.15-Jan.15

ARE THERE ANY GROUPS OF LIBRARIES
FOR WHICH YOU WAIVE FEES? IF
SO, PLEASE NAME THEM: None

WESTCHESTER LIBRARY SYSTEM

NUC CODE: None

OCLC CODE: VVW

ADDRESS: Interlibrary Loan
         Westchester Library
           System
         8 Westchester Plaza
         Elmsford, NY 10523

TELEPHONE: (914) 592-8214

    Westchester Library System is a cooperative library system. Each of its 38 member libraries participates in liberal, in-county interlibrary loan. Interlibrary loan requests received at the central address above are referred to the participating libraries which own the materials. Each library has its own policy with regard to out-of-county interlibrary loan.

WHITE PLAINS PUBLIC LIBRARY

NUC CODE: (Not answered)

OCLC CODE: (Not answered)

ADDRESS: Interlibrary Loan
         White Plains Public
           Library
         100 Martine Ave.
         White Plains, NY 10801

TELEPHONE: (914) 682-4400

LIST NAMES OF BRANCHES WITH
  SEPARATE POLICIES: None

BOOKS:
  Will Lend: Yes
  Length of Loan: 3 weeks
  Renewable: Yes
  Charges: None
  Average Turnaround Time:
    1 week
  If you have indicated that a
    book is not to be lent, will
    you on receipt of a letter
    from the requesting library
    search the index for given
    entries? (Not answered)

PERIODICALS:
  Bound: Will not lend
  Unbound: Will not lend
  Loan Period: N/A
  Renewable: N/A
  Will lend if article exceeds
    _____ number of pages (Not
    answered)

MICROFORMS:
  Will Lend: No
  Specific Types of Microforms:
    N/A

GOVERNMENT PUBLICATIONS:
  Will Lend: No

DISSERTATIONS:
  Will Lend: Do not own

THESES:
  Will Lend: Do not own

AUDIO-VISUAL MATERIALS:
  Records: Will not lend
  Cassettes: Will not lend
  Other (slides, filmstrips,
    etc.): Will not lend

COMPUTER SOFTWARE:
  Will Lend: Do not own

PHOTODUPLICATION SERVICE:
  No charge up to 0 exposures
  Charge Per Exposure: 10¢
  Minimum/handling Fee: None
  Average Turnaround Time:
    1 week

MICROFILMING SERVICE:
  Service Available: No
  Charges: N/A

DO YOU CHARGE THE BORROWING
  LIBRARY FOR POSTAGE? Yes

FOR HOW LONG DO YOU SUSPEND ILL
  SERVICE OVER THE CHRISTMAS
  HOLIDAYS? No suspension

ARE THERE ANY GROUPS OF LIBRARIES
  FOR WHICH YOU WAIVE FEES? IF
  SO, PLEASE NAME THEM: Public
  libraries in Westchester
  County, NY.

YESHIVA UNIVERSITY

NUC CODE: NNYU

OCLC CODE: YYP

ADDRESS: Interlibrary Loan
Pollack Library
Yeshiva University
500 W. 185th St.
New York, NY 10033

TELEPHONE: (212) 960-5380

LIST NAMES OF BRANCHES WITH
SEPARATE POLICIES:
Mendel Gottesman Library of
Hebraica and Judaica
Stern College Library
Cardozo School of Law
Library
Albert Einstein College of
Medicine Library

BOOKS:
Will Lend: Yes
Length of Loan: 1 month
Renewable: Yes
Charges: Usually none
Average Turnaround Time:
All requests handled
promptly
If you have indicated that a
book is not to be lent, will
you on receipt of a letter
from the requesting library
search the index for given
entries? (Not answered)

PERIODICALS:
Bound: Will not lend
Unbound: Will not lend
Loan Period: N/A
Renewable: N/A
Will lend if article exceeds
_____ number of pages (Not
answered)

MICROFORMS:
Will Lend: Yes
Specific Types of Microforms:
(Not answered)

GOVERNMENT PUBLICATIONS:
Will Lend: No

DISSERTATIONS:
Will Lend: Yes

THESES:
Will Lend: Yes

AUDIO-VISUAL MATERIALS:
Records: Will not lend
Cassettes: Will not lend
Other (slides, filmstrips,
etc.): Will not lend

COMPUTER SOFTWARE:
Will Lend: No

PHOTODUPLICATION SERVICE:
No charge up to 0 exposures
Charge Per Exposure: 10¢
Minimum/handling Fee: $3.00
Average Turnaround Time:
All requests handled
promptly

MICROFILMING SERVICE:
Service Available: No
Charges: N/A

DO YOU CHARGE THE BORROWING
LIBRARY FOR POSTAGE? Only if
excessive

FOR HOW LONG DO YOU SUSPEND ILL
SERVICE OVER THE CHRISTMAS
HOLIDAYS? (Not answered)

ARE THERE ANY GROUPS OF LIBRARIES
FOR WHICH YOU WAIVE FEES? IF
SO, PLEASE NAME THEM: New York
Metropolitan Reference and
Research Library Agency
(METRO): free exchange of
photocopies

YESHIVA UNIVERSITY--MENDEL GOTTESMAN LIBRARY OF HEBRAICA-JUDAICA

NUC CODE: NNYU

OCLC CODE: YYP

ADDRESS: Interlibrary Loan
Mendel Gottesman
Library
Yeshiva University
500 W. 185th St.
New York, NY 10033

TELEPHONE: (212) 960-5382

LIST NAMES OF BRANCHES WITH
SEPARATE POLICIES:
Pollack Library

BOOKS:
Will Lend: Yes
Length of Loan: 4 weeks
Renewable: Yes
Charges: None
Average Turnaround Time:
(Not answered)
If you have indicated that a
book is not to be lent, will
you on receipt of a letter
from the requesting library
search the index for given
entries? (Not answered)

PERIODICALS:
Bound: Will not lend
Unbound: Will not lend
Loan Period: N/A
Renewable: N/A
Will lend if article exceeds
_____ number of pages (Not
answered)

MICROFORMS:
Will Lend: No
Specific Types of Microforms:
N/A

GOVERNMENT PUBLICATIONS:
Will Lend: Do not own

DISSERTATIONS:
Will Lend: No

THESES:
Will Lend: No

AUDIO-VISUAL MATERIALS:
Records: Do not own
Cassettes: Do not own
Other (slides, filmstrips,
etc.): Do not own

COMPUTER SOFTWARE:
Will Lend: Do not own

PHOTODUPLICATION SERVICE:
No charge up to 0 exposures
Charge Per Exposure: 10¢
Minimum/handling Fee: $2.50
Average Turnaround Time:
(Not answered)

MICROFILMING SERVICE:
Service Available: No
Charges: N/A

DO YOU CHARGE THE BORROWING
LIBRARY FOR POSTAGE? No

FOR HOW LONG DO YOU SUSPEND ILL
SERVICE OVER THE CHRISTMAS
HOLIDAYS?   No suspension

ARE THERE ANY GROUPS OF LIBRARIES
FOR WHICH YOU WAIVE FEES? IF
SO, PLEASE NAME THEM: Metro
members

YESHIVA UNIVERSITY SCHOOL OF LAW

NUC CODE: NNYU

OCLC CODE: YYP

ADDRESS: Interlibrary Loan
          Chutick Law Library
          Benjamin N. Cardozo
            School of Law
          Yeshiva University
          55 Fifth Ave.
          New York, NY 10003

TELEPHONE: (212) 790-0467

LIST NAMES OF BRANCHES WITH
  SEPARATE POLICIES: None

BOOKS:
  Will Lend: Yes
  Length of Loan: Varies
  Renewable: Yes
  Charges: $2.50 per title
  Average Turnaround Time:
    2 days
  If you have indicated that a
    book is not to be lent, will
    you on receipt of a letter
    from the requesting library
    search the index for given
    entries? (Not answered)

PERIODICALS:
  Bound: Will not lend
  Unbound: Will not lend
  Loan Period: N/A
  Renewable: N/A
  Will lend if article exceeds
    _____ number of pages (Not
    answered)

MICROFORMS:
  Will Lend: No
  Specific Types of Microforms:
    N/A

GOVERNMENT PUBLICATIONS:
  Will Lend: No

DISSERTATIONS:
  Will Lend: No

THESES:
  Will Lend: No

AUDIO-VISUAL MATERIALS:
  Records: Will not lend
  Cassettes: Will not lend
  Other (slides, filmstrips,
    etc.): Will not lend

COMPUTER SOFTWARE:
  Will Lend: No

PHOTODUPLICATION SERVICE:
  No charge up to 0 exposures
  Charge Per Exposure: 10¢
  Minimum/handling Fee: $2.50
  Average Turnaround Time:
    2 days

MICROFILMING SERVICE:
  Service Available: No
  Charges: N/A

DO YOU CHARGE THE BORROWING
  LIBRARY FOR POSTAGE? No

FOR HOW LONG DO YOU SUSPEND ILL
  SERVICE OVER THE CHRISTMAS
  HOLIDAYS? No suspension

ARE THERE ANY GROUPS OF LIBRARIES
  FOR WHICH YOU WAIVE FEES? IF
  SO, PLEASE NAME THEM: Waiver
  of fees on reciprocal basis
  only.

APPALACHIAN STATE UNIVERSITY

NUC CODE: NcBoA

OCLC CODE: NJB

ADDRESS: Interlibrary Loan
Belk Library
Appalachian State
University
Boone, NC 28608

TELEPHONE: (704) 262-2186

LIST NAMES OF BRANCHES WITH
SEPARATE POLICIES: None

BOOKS:
Will Lend: Yes
Length of Loan: 1 month
Renewable: Yes
Charges: None
Average Turnaround Time:
2-3 days
If you have indicated that a
book is not to be lent, will
you on receipt of a letter
from the requesting library
search the index for given
entries? Yes

PERIODICALS:
Bound: Will not lend
Unbound: Will not lend
Loan Period: N/A
Renewable: N/A
Will lend if article exceeds
_____ number of pages (Not
answered)

MICROFORMS:
Will Lend: Yes
Specific Types of Microforms:
Film, fiche, cards

GOVERNMENT PUBLICATIONS:
Will Lend: Yes

DISSERTATIONS:
Will Lend: Yes

THESES:
Will Lend: Yes

AUDIO-VISUAL MATERIALS:
Records: Will lend
selectively
Cassettes: Will lend
selectively
Other (slides, filmstrips,
etc.): Will lend
selectively

COMPUTER SOFTWARE:
Will Lend: No

PHOTODUPLICATION SERVICE:
No charge up to 3 exposures
Charge Per Exposure: 10¢
Minimum/handling Fee: $1.00
in-state; $2.50 out-of-
state
Average Turnaround Time:
2-3 days

MICROFILMING SERVICE:
Service Available: No
Charges: N/A

DO YOU CHARGE THE BORROWING
LIBRARY FOR POSTAGE? Only
for books sent first-class

FOR HOW LONG DO YOU SUSPEND ILL
SERVICE OVER THE CHRISTMAS
HOLIDAYS? Mid-Dec.-early Jan.

ARE THERE ANY GROUPS OF LIBRARIES
FOR WHICH YOU WAIVE FEES? IF
SO, PLEASE NAME THEM: We will
establish a reciprocal low
charge or no charge photocopying policy with
agreeing libraries

CUMBERLAND COUNTY PUBLIC LIBRARY

NUC CODE: (Not answered)

OCLC CODE: (Not answered)

ADDRESS: Interlibrary Loan
Cumberland County
Public Library
P. O. Box 1720
Fayetteville, NC 28301

TELEPHONE: (919) 483-8600

LIST NAMES OF BRANCHES WITH
SEPARATE POLICIES: None

BOOKS:
Will Lend: Yes
Length of Loan: 1 month
Renewable: Yes, if no
reserves
Charges: (Not answered)
Average Turnaround Time:
(Not answered)
If you have indicated that a
book is not to be lent, will
you on receipt of a letter
from the requesting library
search the index for given
entries? (Not answered)

PERIODICALS:
Bound: Will not lend
Unbound: Will not lend
Loan Period: N/A
Renewable: N/A
Will lend if article exceeds
_____ number of pages (Not
answered)

MICROFORMS:
Will Lend: No
Specific Types of Microforms:
N/A

GOVERNMENT PUBLICATIONS:
Will Lend: No

DISSERTATIONS:
Will Lend: Do not own

THESES:
Will Lend: Do not own

AUDIO-VISUAL MATERIALS:
Records: Will not lend
Cassettes: Will not lend
Other (slides, filmstrips,
etc.): Will not lend

COMPUTER SOFTWARE:
Will Lend: Do not own

PHOTODUPLICATION SERVICE:
No charge up to 0 exposures
Charge Per Exposure: 15¢ for
Xerox copies; 10¢ for
microform copies
Minimum/handling Fee: None
Average Turnaround Time:
3-5 days

MICROFILMING SERVICE:
Service Available: No
Charges: N/A

DO YOU CHARGE THE BORROWING
LIBRARY FOR POSTAGE? No

FOR HOW LONG DO YOU SUSPEND ILL
SERVICE OVER THE CHRISTMAS
HOLIDAYS? No suspension

ARE THERE ANY GROUPS OF LIBRARIES
FOR WHICH YOU WAIVE FEES? IF
SO, PLEASE NAME THEM: None

DAVIDSON COLLEGE

NUC CODE: NcDaD

OCLC CODE: NNM

ADDRESS: Interlibrary Loan
          Library of Davidson
          College
          Davidson, NC 28036

TELEPHONE: (704) 892-2000

LIST NAMES OF BRANCHES WITH
  SEPARATE POLICIES: None

BOOKS:
  Will Lend: Yes
  Length of Loan: 4 weeks
  Renewable: Yes
  Charges: None
  Average Turnaround Time:
    2 days
  If you have indicated that a
    book is not to be lent, will
    you on receipt of a letter
    from the requesting library
    search the index for given
    entries? (Not answered)

PERIODICALS:
  Bound: Will not lend
  Unbound: Will not lend
  Loan Period: N/A
  Renewable: N/A
  Will lend if article exceeds
    _____ number of pages (Not
    answered)

MICROFORMS:
  Will Lend: Yes
  Specific Types of Microforms:
    Microfilm

GOVERNMENT PUBLICATIONS:
  Will Lend: Yes

DISSERTATIONS:
  Will Lend: Yes

THESES:
  Will Lend: Yes

AUDIO-VISUAL MATERIALS:
  Records: Do not own
  Cassettes: Will not lend
  Other (slides, filmstrips,
    etc.): Will not lend

COMPUTER SOFTWARE:
  Will Lend: No

PHOTODUPLICATION SERVICE:
  No charge up to 0 exposures
  Charge Per Exposure: 10¢
  Minimum/handling Fee: None
  Average Turnaround Time:
    2 days

MICROFILMING SERVICE:
  Service Available: No
  Charges: N/A

DO YOU CHARGE THE BORROWING
  LIBRARY FOR POSTAGE? No

FOR HOW LONG DO YOU SUSPEND ILL
  SERVICE OVER THE CHRISTMAS
  HOLIDAYS? 2 weeks

ARE THERE ANY GROUPS OF LIBRARIES
  FOR WHICH YOU WAIVE FEES? IF
  SO, PLEASE NAME THEM:
    Libraries within 50-mile
    radius; do not charge for
    requests under 10 pages

EAST CAROLINA UNIVERSITY

NUC CODE: NcGrE

OCLC CODE: ERE

ADDRESS: Interlibrary Loan
          Joyner Library
          East Carolina
            University
          Greenville, NC 27834

TELEPHONE: (919) 757-6518

LIST NAMES OF BRANCHES WITH
  SEPARATE POLICIES: East
  Carolina University Health
  Sciences Library

BOOKS:
  Will Lend: Yes
  Length of Loan: 1 month
  Renewable: Yes
  Charges: None
  Average Turnaround Time:
    2-3 days
  If you have indicated that a
    book is not to be lent, will
    you on receipt of a letter
    from the requesting library
    search the index for given
    entries? Yes

PERIODICALS:
  Bound: Will not lend
  Unbound: Will not lend
  Loan Period: N/A
  Renewable: N/A
  Will lend if article exceeds
    _____ number of pages (Will
    not usually lend, regard-
    less of length of article)

MICROFORMS:
  Will Lend: Yes
  Specific Types of Microforms:
    Film, fiche, and cards

GOVERNMENT PUBLICATIONS:
  Will Lend: Yes

DISSERTATIONS:
  Will Lend: No

THESES:
  Will Lend: Yes

AUDIO-VISUAL MATERIALS:
  Records: Will not lend
  Cassettes: Will not lend
  Other (slides, filmstrips,
    etc.): Will not lend

COMPUTER SOFTWARE:
  Will Lend: No

PHOTODUPLICATION SERVICE:
  No charge up to 0 exposures
  Charge Per Exposure: 10¢
  Minimum/handling Fee: $1.00
  Average Turnaround Time:
    2-3 days

MICROFILMING SERVICE:
  Service Available: No
  Charges: N/A

DO YOU CHARGE THE BORROWING
  LIBRARY FOR POSTAGE? No

FOR HOW LONG DO YOU SUSPEND ILL
  SERVICE OVER THE CHRISTMAS
  HOLIDAYS? Dec.15-Jan.3

ARE THERE ANY GROUPS OF LIBRARIES
  FOR WHICH YOU WAIVE FEES? IF
  SO, PLEASE NAME THEM: None

FORSYTH COUNTY PUBLIC LIBRARY

NUC CODE: NcWs

OCLC CODE: (Not answered)

ADDRESS: Interlibrary Loan
            Forsyth County Public
            Library
            660 W. Fifth St.
            Winston-Salem, NC 27101

TELEPHONE: (919) 727-2208

LIST NAMES OF BRANCHES WITH
    SEPARATE POLICIES: East
        Winston Branch; Kerners-
        ville Branch; Rural Hall
        Branch; Reynolda Manor
        Branch; Southside Branch;
        Thruway Branch

BOOKS:
    Will Lend: Yes
    Length of Loan: 1 month
    Renewable: Yes
    Charges: None
    Average Turnaround Time:
        1 week
    If you have indicated that a
        book is not to be lent, will
        you on receipt of a letter
        from the requesting library
        search the index for given
        entries? Yes

PERIODICALS:
    Bound: Will not lend
    Unbound: Will not lend
    Loan Period: N/A
    Renewable: N/A
    Will lend if article exceeds
        _____ number of pages (Not
        answered)

MICROFORMS:
    Will Lend: No
    Specific Types of Microforms:
        Will supply hard copy
        articles from microfilm for
        15¢ per exposure

GOVERNMENT PUBLICATIONS:
    Will Lend: Yes

DISSERTATIONS:
    Will Lend: Do not own

THESES:
    Will Lend: Do not own

AUDIO-VISUAL MATERIALS:
    Records: Will not lend
    Cassettes: Do not own
    Other (slides, filmstrips,
        etc.): Will not lend

COMPUTER SOFTWARE:
    Will Lend: No

PHOTODUPLICATION SERVICE:
    No charge up to 10 exposures
    Charge Per Exposure: 10¢
    Minimum/handling Fee: None
    Average Turnaround Time:
        1 week

MICROFILMING SERVICE:
    Service Available: No
    Charges: N/A

DO YOU CHARGE THE BORROWING
LIBRARY FOR POSTAGE? No

FOR HOW LONG DO YOU SUSPEND ILL
SERVICE OVER THE CHRISTMAS
HOLIDAYS? 3-4 days

ARE THERE ANY GROUPS OF LIBRARIES
FOR WHICH YOU WAIVE FEES? IF
SO, PLEASE NAME THEM: None

GASTON COUNTY PUBLIC LIBRARY

NUC CODE: Ga

OCLC CODE: (Not answered)

ADDRESS: Interlibrary Loan
            Gaston County Public
            Library
            1555 E. Garrison Blvd.
            Gastonia, NC 28052

TELEPHONE: (704) 866-3762

LIST NAMES OF BRANCHES WITH
    SEPARATE POLICIES: This
        library provides ILL
        services for 7 branches
        except Lincolntown Public
        Library.

BOOKS:
    Will Lend: Yes
    Length of Loan: 3 weeks
    Renewable: Yes
    Charges: None
    Average Turnaround Time:
        7 days
    If you have indicated that a
        book is not to be lent, will
        you on receipt of a letter
        from the requesting library
        search the index for given
        entries? Yes

PERIODICALS:
    Bound: Will not lend
    Unbound: Will not lend
    Loan Period: N/A
    Renewable: N/A
    Will lend if article exceeds
        _____ number of pages (Not
        answered)

MICROFORMS:
    Will Lend: No
    Specific Types of Microforms:
        N/A

GOVERNMENT PUBLICATIONS:
    Will Lend: Yes, if in
        circulating collection

DISSERTATIONS:
    Will Lend: No

THESES:
    Will Lend: No

AUDIO-VISUAL MATERIALS:
    Records: Will not lend
    Cassettes: Will not lend
    Other (slides, filmstrips,
        etc.): Will not lend

COMPUTER SOFTWARE:
    Will Lend: No

PHOTODUPLICATION SERVICE:
    No charge up to 0 exposures
    Charge Per Exposure: 15¢
    Minimum/handling Fee: $1.00
    Average Turnaround Time:
        7 days

MICROFILMING SERVICE:
    Service Available: No
    Charges: N/A

DO YOU CHARGE THE BORROWING
LIBRARY FOR POSTAGE? No

FOR HOW LONG DO YOU SUSPEND ILL
SERVICE OVER THE CHRISTMAS
HOLIDAYS? No suspension

ARE THERE ANY GROUPS OF LIBRARIES
FOR WHICH YOU WAIVE FEES? IF
SO, PLEASE NAME THEM: None

GREENSBORO PUBLIC LIBRARY

NUC CODE: G

OCLC CODE: NGP

ADDRESS: Interlibrary Loan
Greensboro Public
Library
201 N. Greene St.
Drawer X-4
Greensboro, NC 27402

TELEPHONE: (919) 373-2159

LIST NAMES OF BRANCHES WITH
SEPARATE POLICIES: None

BOOKS:
Will Lend: Yes
Length of Loan: 1 month
Renewable: Yes
Charges: None
Average Turnaround Time:
1 day
If you have indicated that a
book is not to be lent, will
you on receipt of a letter
from the requesting library
search the index for given
entries? (Not answered)

PERIODICALS:
Bound: Will not lend
Unbound: Will not lend
Loan Period: N/A
Renewable: N/A
Will lend if article exceeds
_____ number of pages (Not
answered)

MICROFORMS:
Will Lend: No
Specific Types of Microforms:
N/A

GOVERNMENT PUBLICATIONS:
Will Lend: No

DISSERTATIONS:
Will Lend: No

THESES:
Will Lend: No

AUDIO-VISUAL MATERIALS:
Records: Will not lend
Cassettes: Will not lend
Other (slides, filmstrips,
etc.): Will not lend

COMPUTER SOFTWARE:
Will Lend: No

PHOTODUPLICATION SERVICE:
No charge up to 50 exposures
Charge Per Exposure: 10¢
Minimum/handling Fee: None
Average Turnaround Time:
(Not answered)

MICROFILMING SERVICE:
Service Available: Yes
Charges: (Not answered)

DO YOU CHARGE THE BORROWING
LIBRARY FOR POSTAGE? No

FOR HOW LONG DO YOU SUSPEND ILL
SERVICE OVER THE CHRISTMAS
HOLIDAYS? No suspension

ARE THERE ANY GROUPS OF LIBRARIES
FOR WHICH YOU WAIVE FEES? IF
SO, PLEASE NAME THEM: None

HENDERSON COUNTY PUBLIC LIBRARY

NUC CODE: NCHV

OCLC CODE: (Not answered)

ADDRESS: Interlibrary Loan
Henderson County Public
Library
301 N. Washington St.
Hendersonville, NC
28739

TELEPHONE: (704) 693-8427

LIST NAMES OF BRANCHES WITH
SEPARATE POLICIES: None

BOOKS:
Will Lend: Yes
Length of Loan: 3-4 weeks
Renewable: Not usually
Charges: Postage
Average Turnaround Time:
1 week
If you have indicated that a
book is not to be lent, will
you on receipt of a letter
from the requesting library
search the index for given
entries? Yes; if photo-
copying, necessary charges
will be made

PERIODICALS:
Bound: Will not lend
Unbound: Will not lend
Loan Period: N/A
Renewable: N/A
Will lend if article exceeds
_____ number of pages (Not
answered)

MICROFORMS:
Will Lend: No
Specific Types of Microforms:
N/A

GOVERNMENT PUBLICATIONS:
Will Lend: No

DISSERTATIONS:
Will Lend: No

THESES:
Will Lend: No

AUDIO-VISUAL MATERIALS:
Records: Will not lend
Cassettes: Will not lend
Other (slides, filmstrips,
etc.): Will not lend

COMPUTER SOFTWARE:
Will Lend: No

PHOTODUPLICATION SERVICE:
No charge up to 0 exposures
Charge Per Exposure: 10¢
Minimum/handling Fee: (Not
answered)
Average Turnaround Time:
1 week

MICROFILMING SERVICE:
Service Available: No
Charges: N/A

DO YOU CHARGE THE BORROWING
LIBRARY FOR POSTAGE? Yes

FOR HOW LONG DO YOU SUSPEND ILL
SERVICE OVER THE CHRISTMAS
HOLIDAYS? No suspension

ARE THERE ANY GROUPS OF LIBRARIES
FOR WHICH YOU WAIVE FEES? IF
SO, PLEASE NAME THEM: None

NORTH CAROLINA CENTRAL UNIVERSITY

NUC CODE: NcDurC

OCLC CODE: NCX

ADDRESS: Interlibrary Loan
James E. Shepard
Memorial Library
North Carolina Central
University
Durham, NC 27707

TELEPHONE: (919) 683-6473

LIST NAMES OF BRANCHES WITH
SEPARATE POLICIES: None

BOOKS:
Will Lend: Yes
Length of Loan: 1 month
Renewable: Yes
Charges: (Not answered)
Average Turnaround Time:
1 day
If you have indicated that a
book is not to be lent, will
you on receipt of a letter
from the requesting library
search the index for given
entries? (Not answered)

PERIODICALS:
Bound: Will not lend
Unbound: Will not lend
Loan Period: N/A
Renewable: N/A
Will lend if article exceeds
_____ number of pages (Not
answered)

MICROFORMS:
Will Lend: No
Specific Types of Microforms:
N/A

GOVERNMENT PUBLICATIONS:
Will Lend: No

DISSERTATIONS:
Will Lend: Yes

THESES:
Will Lend: Yes

AUDIO-VISUAL MATERIALS:
Records: Will not lend
Cassettes: Will not lend
Other (slides, filmstrips,
etc.); Will not lend

COMPUTER SOFTWARE:
Will Lend: No

PHOTODUPLICATION SERVICE:
No charge up to 0 exposures
Charge Per Exposure: 10¢
Minimum/handling Fee: $1.00
Average Turnaround Time:
1 day

MICROFILMING SERVICE:
Service Available: No
Charges: N/A

DO YOU CHARGE THE BORROWING
LIBRARY FOR POSTAGE? No

FOR HOW LONG DO YOU SUSPEND ILL
SERVICE OVER THE CHRISTMAS
HOLIDAYS? 2 weeks

ARE THERE ANY GROUPS OF LIBRARIES
FOR WHICH YOU WAIVE FEES? IF
SO, PLEASE NAME THEM: None

NORTH CAROLINA STATE LIBRARY

NUC CODE: Nc

OCLC CODE: NCS

ADDRESS: Interlibrary Loan
North Carolina State
Library
109 E. Jones St.
Raleigh, NC 27611

TELEPHONE: (919) 733-3683

LIST NAMES OF BRANCHES WITH
SEPARATE POLICIES: None

BOOKS:
Will Lend: Yes, except for
genealogical materials
Length of Loan: 4 weeks,
including travel time
Renewable: Yes, for 4 weeks
Charges: None
Average Turnaround Time:
2-3 days
If you have indicated that a
book is not to be lent, will
you on receipt of a letter
from the requesting library
search the index for given
entries? (Not answered)

PERIODICALS:
Bound: Will not lend
Unbound: Will not lend
Loan Period: N/A
Renewable: N/A
Will lend if article exceeds
_____ number of pages (Not
answered)

MICROFORMS:
Will Lend: Yes
Specific Types of Microforms:
Film

GOVERNMENT PUBLICATIONS:
Will Lend: Yes, if
circulating copy available

DISSERTATIONS:
Will Lend: Do not own

THESES:
Will Lend: Do not own

AUDIO-VISUAL MATERIALS:
Records: Do not own
Cassettes: Do not own
Other (slides, filmstrips,
etc.): Do not own

COMPUTER SOFTWARE:
Will Lend: No

PHOTODUPLICATION SERVICE:
No charge up to 10 exposures
Charge Per Exposure: 10¢
Minimum/handling Fee: None
Average Turnaround Time:
2-3 days

MICROFILMING SERVICE:
Service Available: No
Charges: N/A

DO YOU CHARGE THE BORROWING
LIBRARY FOR POSTAGE? No

FOR HOW LONG DO YOU SUSPEND ILL
SERVICE OVER THE CHRISTMAS
HOLIDAYS? No suspension

ARE THERE ANY GROUPS OF LIBRARIES
FOR WHICH YOU WAIVE FEES? IF
SO, PLEASE NAME THEM:
Southeastern state library
agencies

NORTH CAROLINA STATE UNIVERSITY AT RALEIGH

NUC CODE: NcRS

OCLC CODE: NRC

ADDRESS: Interlibrary Loan
        Hill Library
        North Carolina State
          University at
          Raleigh
        2205 Hillsborough St.
        P. O. Box 5007
        Raleigh, NC 27607

TELEPHONE: (919) 737-2116

LIST NAMES OF BRANCHES WITH
  SEPARATE POLICIES: None

BOOKS:
  Will Lend: Yes
  Length of Loan: 4 weeks
  Renewable: Yes, if no
    reserves
  Charges: (Not answered)
  Average Turnaround Time:
    (Not answered)
  If you have indicated that a
    book is not to be lent, will
    you on receipt of a letter
    from the requesting library
    search the index for given
    entries? (Not answered)

PERIODICALS:
  Bound: Will not lend
  Unbound: Will not lend
  Loan Period: N/A
  Renewable: N/A
  Will lend if article exceeds
    _____ number of pages
    (Based on individual
    decision)

MICROFORMS:
  Will Lend: Yes
  Specific Types of Microforms:
    Will generally lend newspa-
    pers; will reproduce most
    microfiche

GOVERNMENT PUBLICATIONS:
  Will Lend: Yes, most of them

DISSERTATIONS:
  Will Lend: Yes

THESES:
  Will Lend: Yes

AUDIO-VISUAL MATERIALS:
  Records: Will not lend
  Cassettes: Will not lend
  Other (slides, filmstrips,
    etc.): Will not lend

COMPUTER SOFTWARE:
  Will Lend: (Not answered)

PHOTODUPLICATION SERVICE:
  No charge up to 0 exposures
  Charge Per Exposure: 15¢
  Handling Fee: $1.00
  Average Turnaround Time:
    (Not answered)

MICROFILMING SERVICE:
  Service Available: Yes
  Charges: (Not answered)

DO YOU CHARGE THE BORROWING
  LIBRARY FOR POSTAGE? No

FOR HOW LONG DO YOU SUSPEND ILL
  SERVICE OVER THE CHRISTMAS
  HOLIDAYS? App. 3 weeks

ARE THERE ANY GROUPS OF LIBRARIES
  FOR WHICH YOU WAIVE FEES? IF
  SO, PLEASE NAME THEM: None

PEMBROKE STATE UNIVERSITY

NUC CODE: None

OCLC CODE: None

ADDRESS: Interlibrary Loan
        Mary Livermore Library
        Pembroke State
          University
        Pembroke, NC 28358

TELEPHONE: (919) 521-4214

LIST NAMES OF BRANCHES WITH
  SEPARATE POLICIES: None

BOOKS:
  Will Lend: Yes
  Length of Loan: 1 month
  Renewable: Yes
  Charges: None
  Average Turnaround Time:
    2 days
  If you have indicated that a
    book is not to be lent, will
    you on receipt of a letter
    from the requesting library
    search the index for given
    entries? Yes

PERIODICALS:
  Bound: Will not lend
  Unbound: Will not lend
  Loan Period: N/A
  Renewable: N/A
  Will lend if article exceeds
    _____ number of pages (Not
    answered)

MICROFORMS:
  Will Lend: Yes
  Specific Types of Microforms:
    Microfiche, ultrafiche

GOVERNMENT PUBLICATIONS:
  Will Lend: Yes

DISSERTATIONS:
  Will Lend: No

THESES:
  Will Lend: No

AUDIO-VISUAL MATERIALS:
  Records: Will not lend
  Cassettes: Will not lend
  Other (slides, filmstrips,
    etc.): Will not lend

COMPUTER SOFTWARE:
  Will Lend: No

PHOTODUPLICATION SERVICE:
  No charge up to 0 exposures
  Charge Per Exposure: 10¢
  Minimum/handling Fee: (Not
    answered)
  Average Turnaround Time:
    2 days

MICROFILMING SERVICE:
  Service Available: No
  Charges: N/A

DO YOU CHARGE THE BORROWING
  LIBRARY FOR POSTAGE? No

FOR HOW LONG DO YOU SUSPEND ILL
  SERVICE OVER THE CHRISTMAS
  HOLIDAYS? No suspension

ARE THERE ANY GROUPS OF LIBRARIES
  FOR WHICH YOU WAIVE FEES? IF
  SO, PLEASE NAME THEM: None

UNIVERSITY OF NORTH CAROLINA AT CHAPEL HILL

NUC CODE: NcU

OCLC CODE: NOC

ADDRESS: Interlibrary Loan
           224 Walter Royal Davis
           Library
           University of North
           Carolina at Chapel
           Hill
           Chapel Hill, NC 27514

TELEPHONE: (919) 962-1326

LIST NAMES OF BRANCHES WITH
  SEPARATE POLICIES:
  Health Sciences Library
  Carolina Population Center
  Library

BOOKS:
  Will Lend: Yes
  Length of Loan: 1 month
  Renewable: Yes
  Charges: None
  Average Turnaround Time:
  5 working days
  If you have indicated that a
    book is not to be lent, will
    you on receipt of a letter
    from the requesting library
    search the index for given
    entries? Yes, within
    reason; address inquiry
    to Humanities Reference
    Department at UNC

PERIODICALS:
  Bound: Will not lend
  Unbound: Will not lend
  Loan Period: N/A
  Renewable: N/A
  Will consider lending if
    article exceeds 100 pages

MICROFORMS:
  Will Lend: Yes, except
    newspapers
  Specific Types of Microforms:
  Film, fiche, opaque

GOVERNMENT PUBLICATIONS:
  Will Lend: Yes

DISSERTATIONS:
  Will Lend: Yes, if post-1931;
    1958 to present available
    from University Microfilms

THESES:
  Will Lend: Yes, if post-1931

AUDIO-VISUAL MATERIALS:
  Records: Will not lend
  Cassettes: Will not lend
  Other (slides, filmstrips,
    etc.): Will not lend

COMPUTER SOFTWARE:
  Will Lend: No

PHOTODUPLICATION SERVICE:
  No charge up to 0 exposures
  Charge Per Exposure: 10¢
  Minimum/handling Fee: $3.00
  Average Turnaround Time:
    10 working days

MICROFILMING SERVICE:
  Service Available: Yes
  Charges: $5.00 minimum, 15¢
    per frame

DO YOU CHARGE THE BORROWING
  LIBRARY FOR POSTAGE? No,
  unless special postage
  requested by borrower

FOR HOW LONG DO YOU SUSPEND ILL
  SERVICE OVER THE CHRISTMAS
  HOLIDAYS? 3 weeks for loan
  of books; photocopy service
  continues

ARE THERE ANY GROUPS OF LIBRARIES
  FOR WHICH YOU WAIVE FEES? IF
  SO, PLEASE NAME THEM: None

UNIVERSITY OF NORTH CAROLINA AT CHARLOTTE

NUC CODE: NcCU

OCLC CODE: NKM

ADDRESS: Interlibrary Loan
           Atkins Library
           University of North
             Carolina at Charlotte
           UNCC Station
           Charlotte, NC 28223

TELEPHONE: (704) 597-2495

LIST NAMES OF BRANCHES WITH
  SEPARATE POLICIES: None

BOOKS:
  Will Lend: Yes
  Length of Loan: 1 month from
    date sent
  Renewable: Yes
  Charges: (Not answered)
  Average Turnaround Time:
    (Not answered)
  If you have indicated that a
    book is not to be lent, will
    you on receipt of a letter
    from the requesting library
    search the index for given
    entries? (Not answered)

PERIODICALS:
  Bound: Will not lend
  Unbound: Will not lend
  Loan Period: N/A
  Renewable: N/A
  Will lend if article exceeds
    _____ number of pages (Not
    answered)

MICROFORMS:
  Will Lend: Yes
  Specific Types of Microforms:
  Microfilm

GOVERNMENT PUBLICATIONS:
  Will Lend: Yes

DISSERTATIONS:
  Will Lend: Do not own

THESES:
  Will Lend: Yes

AUDIO-VISUAL MATERIALS:
  Records: Will not lend
  Cassettes: Will not lend
  Other (slides, filmstrips,
    etc.): Will not lend

COMPUTER SOFTWARE:
  Will Lend: (Not answered)

PHOTODUPLICATION SERVICE:
  No charge up to 10 exposures
  Charge Per Exposure: 10¢
  Minimum Fee: $1.00
  Average Turnaround Time:
    (Not answered)

MICROFILMING SERVICE:
  Service Available: No
  Charges: N/A

DO YOU CHARGE THE BORROWING
  LIBRARY FOR POSTAGE? No

FOR HOW LONG DO YOU SUSPEND ILL
  SERVICE OVER THE CHRISTMAS
  HOLIDAYS? (Not answered)

ARE THERE ANY GROUPS OF LIBRARIES
  FOR WHICH YOU WAIVE FEES? IF
  SO, PLEASE NAME THEM: (Not
  answered)

UNIVERSITY OF NORTH CAROLINA AT GREENSBORO

NUC CODE: NcGU

OCLC CODE: NGU

ADDRESS: Interlibrary Loan
Jackson Library
University of North
Carolina at
Greensboro
Greensboro, NC 27412

TELEPHONE: (919) 379-5849

LIST NAMES OF BRANCHES WITH
SEPARATE POLICIES: None

BOOKS:
Will Lend: Yes
Length of Loan: 2 weeks
Renewable: Yes
Charges: None
Average Turnaround Time:
(Not answered)
If you have indicated that a
book is not to be lent, will
you on receipt of a letter
from the requesting library
search the index for given
entries? (Not answered)

PERIODICALS:
Bound: Will not lend
Unbound: Will not lend
Loan Period: N/A
Renewable: N/A
Will lend if article exceeds
_____ number of pages (Not
answered)

MICROFORMS:
Will Lend: Yes
Specific Types of Microforms:
(Not answered)

GOVERNMENT PUBLICATIONS:
Will Lend: Yes

DISSERTATIONS:
Will Lend: Yes

THESES:
Will Lend: Yes

AUDIO-VISUAL MATERIALS:
Records: Will not lend
Cassettes: (Not answered)
Other (slides, filmstrips,
etc.): (Not answered)

COMPUTER SOFTWARE:
Will Lend: No

PHOTODUPLICATION SERVICE:
No charge up to 0 exposures
Charge Per Exposure: (Not
answered)
Minimum/handling Fee: $1.25
Average Turnaround Time:
(Not answered)

MICROFILMING SERVICE:
Service Available: No
Charges: N/A

DO YOU CHARGE THE BORROWING
LIBRARY FOR POSTAGE? No

FOR HOW LONG DO YOU SUSPEND ILL
SERVICE OVER THE CHRISTMAS
HOLIDAYS? 2 weeks

ARE THERE ANY GROUPS OF LIBRARIES
FOR WHICH YOU WAIVE FEES? IF
SO, PLEASE NAME THEM: None

UNIVERSITY OF NORTH CAROLINA AT WILMINGTON

NUC CODE: NcWU

OCLC CODE: NXW

ADDRESS: Interlibrary Loan
William Madison Randall
Library
University of North
Carolina at
Wilmington
Wilmington, NC 28406

TELEPHONE: (919) 791-4330, X2273

LIST NAMES OF BRANCHES WITH
SEPARATE POLICIES: None

BOOKS:
Will Lend: Yes
Length of Loan: 4 weeks
Renewable: Yes
Charges: None
Average Turnaround Time:
1 day
If you have indicated that a
book is not to be lent, will
you on receipt of a letter
from the requesting library
search the index for given
entries? Yes

PERIODICALS:
Bound: Will not lend
Unbound: Will not lend
Loan Period: N/A
Renewable: N/A
Will lend if article exceeds
_____ number of pages (Not
answered)

MICROFORMS:
Will Lend: Usually not
Specific Types of Microforms:
(Not answered)

GOVERNMENT PUBLICATIONS:
Will Lend: Yes

DISSERTATIONS:
Will Lend: Yes

THESES:
Will Lend: Yes

AUDIO-VISUAL MATERIALS:
Records: Will not lend
Cassettes: Will not lend
Other (slides, filmstrips,
etc.): Will not lend

COMPUTER SOFTWARE:
Will Lend: Do not own

PHOTODUPLICATION SERVICE:
No charge up to 0 exposures
Charge Per Exposure: 10¢
for Xerox copies; 25¢ for
microform copies
Minimum/handling Fee: $1.25
Average Turnaround Time:
1 day

MICROFILMING SERVICE:
Service Available: No
Charges: N/A

DO YOU CHARGE THE BORROWING
LIBRARY FOR POSTAGE? No

FOR HOW LONG DO YOU SUSPEND ILL
SERVICE OVER THE CHRISTMAS
HOLIDAYS? App. Dec.15-Jan.3

ARE THERE ANY GROUPS OF LIBRARIES
FOR WHICH YOU WAIVE FEES? IF
SO, PLEASE NAME THEM: UNC
system libraries: no
handling charge for photocopies, 5¢ Xerox and 10¢
microform copies

WAKE COUNTY PUBLIC LIBRARIES

NUC CODE: NcR

OCLC CODE: NXA

ADDRESS: Interlibrary Loan
Wake County Public
Libraries
104 Fayetteville St.
Raleigh, NC 27601

TELEPHONE: (919) 755-6077

LIST NAMES OF BRANCHES WITH
SEPARATE POLICIES: None

BOOKS:
Will Lend: Yes
Length of Loan: 1 month
Renewable: Yes
Charges: None
Average Turnaround Time:
(Not answered)
If you have indicated that a
book is not to be lent, will
you on receipt of a letter
from the requesting library
search the index for given
entries? (Not answered)

PERIODICALS:
Bound: Will not lend
Unbound: Will not lend
Loan Period: N/A
Renewable: N/A
Will lend if article exceeds
_____ number of pages (Not
answered)

MICROFORMS:
Will Lend: No
Specific Types of Microforms:
N/A

GOVERNMENT PUBLICATIONS:
Will Lend: No

DISSERTATIONS:
Will Lend: No

THESES:
Will Lend: No

AUDIO-VISUAL MATERIALS:
Records: Will not lend
Cassettes: Will not lend
Other (slides, filmstrips,
etc.): Will not lend

COMPUTER SOFTWARE:
Will Lend: No

PHOTODUPLICATION SERVICE:
No charge up to 10 exposures
Charge Per Exposure: 10¢
Minimum/handling Fee: None
Average Turnaround Time:
(Not answered)

MICROFILMING SERVICE:
Service Available: No
Charges: N/A

DO YOU CHARGE THE BORROWING
LIBRARY FOR POSTAGE? No

FOR HOW LONG DO YOU SUSPEND ILL
SERVICE OVER THE CHRISTMAS
HOLIDAYS? 5 days

ARE THERE ANY GROUPS OF LIBRARIES
FOR WHICH YOU WAIVE FEES? IF
SO, PLEASE NAME THEM: None

WAKE FOREST UNIVERSITY

NUC CODE: NcWsW

OCLC CODE: EWF

ADDRESS: Interlibrary Loan
Z. Smith Reynolds
Library
P. O. Box 7777
Reynolds Station
Wake Forest University
Winston-Salem, NC
27109

TELEPHONE: (919) 761-5475

LIST NAMES OF BRANCHES WITH
SEPARATE POLICIES:
Babcock Graduate School of
Management
Wake Forest Law School
Bowman Gray School of
Medicine

BOOKS:
Will Lend: Yes
Length of Loan: 1 month
Renewable: Yes
Charges: None
Average Turnaround Time:
1 week
If you have indicated that a
book is not to be lent, will
you on receipt of a letter
from the requesting library
search the index for given
entries? Yes

PERIODICALS:
Bound: Will not lend
Unbound: Will not lend
Loan Period: N/A
Renewable: N/A
Will lend if article exceeds
_____ number of pages (Not
answered)

MICROFORMS:
Will Lend: Yes, in some cases
Specific Types of Microforms:
Film, card, and fiche

GOVERNMENT PUBLICATIONS:
Will Lend: Yes

DISSERTATIONS:
Will Lend: Do not own

THESES:
Will Lend: Yes

AUDIO-VISUAL MATERIALS:
Records: Will not lend
Cassettes: Will not lend
Other (slides, filmstrips,
etc.): Will not lend

COMPUTER SOFTWARE:
Will Lend: No

PHOTODUPLICATION SERVICE:
No charge up to 0 exposures
Charges: $3.00 for 1-19
exposures; 10¢ each
additional exposure
Average Turnaround Time:
1 week

MICROFILMING SERVICE:
Service Available: No
Charges: N/A

DO YOU CHARGE THE BORROWING
LIBRARY FOR POSTAGE? No

FOR HOW LONG DO YOU SUSPEND ILL
SERVICE OVER THE CHRISTMAS
HOLIDAYS? 2 weeks (after
Dec. 15)

ARE THERE ANY GROUPS OF LIBRARIES
FOR WHICH YOU WAIVE FEES? IF
SO, PLEASE NAME THEM: None

<u>WESTERN CAROLINA UNIVERSITY</u>

NUC CODE: NcCuW

OCLC CODE: NMW

ADDRESS: Interlibrary Loan
          Hunter Library
          Western Carolina
           University
          Cullowhee, NC   28723

TELEPHONE: (704) 227-7274 or
                  227-7362

LIST NAMES OF BRANCHES WITH
  SEPARATE POLICIES: None

BOOKS:
  Will Lend: Yes
  Length of Loan: 1 month for
    general items; 2 weeks for
    reference material
  Renewable: Yes
  Charges: None
  Average Turnaround Time:
    1 week maximum
  If you have indicated that a
    book is not to be lent, will
    you on receipt of a letter
    from the requesting library
    search the index for given
    entries? (Not answered)

PERIODICALS:
  Bound: Will not lend
  Unbound: Will not lend
  Loan Period: N/A
  Renewable: N/A
  Will lend if article exceeds
    _____ number of pages (Not
    answered)

MICROFORMS:
  Will Lend: Yes, but micro-
    films and microfiche only

GOVERNMENT PUBLICATIONS:
  Will Lend: Yes

DISSERTATIONS:
  Will Lend: No

THESES:
  Will Lend: Yes

AUDIO-VISUAL MATERIALS:
  Records: (Not answered)
  Cassettes: (Not answered)
  Other (slides, filmstrips,
    etc.): (Not answered)

COMPUTER SOFTWARE:
  Will Lend: (Not answered)

PHOTODUPLICATION SERVICE:
  No charge up to 0 exposures
  Charge Per Exposure: 10¢
  Minimum/handling Fee: $1.00
  Average Turnaround Time:
    1 week maximum

MICROFILMING SERVICE:
  Service Available: Yes
  Charges: 10¢ per page plus
    $1.00 handling

DO YOU CHARGE THE BORROWING
  LIBRARY FOR POSTAGE? No

FOR HOW LONG DO YOU SUSPEND ILL
  SERVICE OVER THE CHRISTMAS
  HOLIDAYS? Dec.20-Jan.3

ARE THERE ANY GROUPS OF LIBRARIES
  FOR WHICH YOU WAIVE FEES? IF
  SO, PLEASE NAME THEM: None

MINOT STATE COLLEGE

NUC CODE: NdMinS

OCLC CODE: NMI

ADDRESS: Interlibrary Loan
Memorial Library
Minot State College
Minot, ND 58701

TELEPHONE: (701) 857-3201

LIST NAMES OF BRANCHES WITH
SEPARATE POLICIES: None

BOOKS:
Will Lend: Yes
Length of Loan: 4 weeks
Renewable: No
Charges: None
Average Turnaround Time:
48 hours
If you have indicated that a
book is not to be lent, will
you on receipt of a letter
from the requesting library
search the index for given
entries? Yes

PERIODICALS:
Bound: Will not lend
Unbound: Will not lend
Loan Period: N/A
Renewable: N/A
Will lend if article exceeds
10 pages

MICROFORMS:
Will Lend: Yes
Specific Types of Microforms:
Microfiche, microfilm

GOVERNMENT PUBLICATIONS:
Will Lend: Yes

DISSERTATIONS:
Will Lend: Yes

THESES:
Will Lend: Yes

AUDIO-VISUAL MATERIALS:
Records: Will not lend
Cassettes: Will lend
Other (slides, filmstrips,
etc.): Will lend

COMPUTER SOFTWARE:
Will Lend: Do not own

PHOTODUPLICATION SERVICE:
No charge up to _____
exposures (Not answered)
Charge Per Exposure: (Not
answered)
Minimum/handling Fee: (Not
answered)
Average Turnaround Time:
(Not answered)

MICROFILMING SERVICE:
Service Available: No
Charges: N/A

DO YOU CHARGE THE BORROWING
LIBRARY FOR POSTAGE? No

FOR HOW LONG DO YOU SUSPEND ILL
SERVICE OVER THE CHRISTMAS
HOLIDAYS? Approximately
2 weeks

ARE THERE ANY GROUPS OF LIBRARIES
FOR WHICH YOU WAIVE FEES? IF
SO, PLEASE NAME THEM: None

NORTH DAKOTA STATE LIBRARY

NUC CODE: NdLibC

OCLC CODE: NDS

ADDRESS: Interlibrary Loan
North Dakota State
Library
Capitol Grounds
Liberty Memorial Bldg.
Bismarck, ND 58505

TELEPHONE: (701) 224-2492

LIST NAMES OF BRANCHES WITH
SEPARATE POLICIES: None

BOOKS:
Will Lend: Yes
Length of Loan: 4 weeks
Renewable: No
Charges: None
Average Turnaround Time:
1 week
If you have indicated that a
book is not to be lent, will
you on receipt of a letter
from the requesting library
search the index for given
entries? (Not answered)

PERIODICALS:
Bound: Will not lend
Unbound: Will not lend
Loan Period: N/A
Renewable: N/A
Will lend if article exceeds
_____ number of pages (Not
answered)

MICROFORMS:
Will Lend: Yes
Specific Types of Microforms:
Newspaper and state
documents

GOVERNMENT PUBLICATIONS:
Will Lend: Yes

DISSERTATIONS:
Will Lend: Yes

THESES:
Will Lend: Yes

AUDIO-VISUAL MATERIALS:
Records: Will not lend
Cassettes: Will not lend
Other (slides, filmstrips,
etc.): Will not lend

COMPUTER SOFTWARE:
Will Lend: No

PHOTODUPLICATION SERVICE:
No charge up to 10 exposures
Charge Per Exposure: 10¢
Minimum/handling Fee: None
Average Turnaround Time:
1 week

MICROFILMING SERVICE:
Service Available: No
Charges: N/A

DO YOU CHARGE THE BORROWING
LIBRARY FOR POSTAGE? No

FOR HOW LONG DO YOU SUSPEND ILL
SERVICE OVER THE CHRISTMAS
HOLIDAYS? No suspension

ARE THERE ANY GROUPS OF LIBRARIES
FOR WHICH YOU WAIVE FEES? IF
SO, PLEASE NAME THEM: None

NORTH DAKOTA STATE UNIVERSITY

NUC CODE: NdFa

OCLC CODE: TRI

ADDRESS: Interlibrary Loan
Library
North Dakota State
University
Fargo, ND 58105

TELEPHONE: (701) 237-8885

LIST NAMES OF BRANCHES WITH
SEPARATE POLICIES: None

BOOKS:
Will Lend: Yes
Length of Loan: 4 weeks
Renewable: Yes
Charges: None
Average Turnaround Time:
1-2 weeks
If you have indicated that a
book is not to be lent, will
you on receipt of a letter
from the requesting library
search the index for given
entries? (Not answered)

PERIODICALS:
Bound: Will not lend
Unbound: Will not lend
Loan Period: N/A
Renewable: N/A
Will lend if article exceeds
_____ number of pages (Not
answered)

MICROFORMS:
Will Lend: Yes, with
exceptions
Specific Types of Microforms:
(Not answered)

GOVERNMENT PUBLICATIONS:
Will Lend: Yes

DISSERTATIONS:
Will Lend: Yes

THESES:
Will Lend: Yes

AUDIO-VISUAL MATERIALS:
Records: Will lend, with
exceptions
Cassettes: Will lend, with
exceptions
Other (slides, filmstrips,
etc.): Will lend, with
exceptions

COMPUTER SOFTWARE:
Will Lend: No

PHOTODUPLICATION SERVICE:
No charge up to 0 exposures
Charge Per Exposure: 10¢
Minimum/handling Fee: $1.25
including first 10 pages
Average Turnaround Time:
1-2 weeks

MICROFILMING SERVICE:
Service Available: No
Charges: N/A

DO YOU CHARGE THE BORROWING
LIBRARY FOR POSTAGE? No

FOR HOW LONG DO YOU SUSPEND ILL
SERVICE OVER THE CHRISTMAS
HOLIDAYS? No suspension

ARE THERE ANY GROUPS OF LIBRARIES
FOR WHICH YOU WAIVE FEES? IF
SO, PLEASE NAME THEM: None

UNIVERSITY OF NORTH DAKOTA

NUC CODE: NdU

OCLC CODE: UND

ADDRESS: Interlibrary Loan
Fritz Library
University of North
Dakota
Grand Forks, ND 58202

TELEPHONE: (701) 777-4631

LIST NAMES OF BRANCHES WITH
SEPARATE POLICIES: None

BOOKS:
Will Lend: Yes
Length of Loan: 30 days
Renewable: Yes
Charges: (Not answered)
Average Turnaround Time:
(Not answered)
If you have indicated that a
book is not to be lent, will
you on receipt of a letter
from the requesting library
search the index for given
entries? (Not answered)

PERIODICALS:
Bound: Will not lend
Unbound: Will not lend
Loan Period: N/A
Renewable: N/A
Will lend if article exceeds
_____ number of pages (Not
answered)

MICROFORMS:
Will Lend: Yes
Specific Types of Microforms:
(Not answered)

GOVERNMENT PUBLICATIONS:
Will Lend: Yes

DISSERTATIONS:
Will Lend: Yes; 1965 to
present available from
University Microfilms

THESES:
Will Lend: Yes

AUDIO-VISUAL MATERIALS:
Records: (Not answered)
Cassettes: (Not answered)
Other (slides, filmstrips,
etc.): (Not answered)

COMPUTER SOFTWARE:
Will Lend: (Not answered)

PHOTODUPLICATION SERVICE:
No charge up to 0 exposures
Charge Per Exposure: 10¢
Minimum Fee: $2.00
Average Turnaround Time:
(Not answered)

MICROFILMING SERVICE:
Service Available: No
Charges: N/A

DO YOU CHARGE THE BORROWING
LIBRARY FOR POSTAGE? (Not
answered)

FOR HOW LONG DO YOU SUSPEND ILL
SERVICE OVER THE CHRISTMAS
HOLIDAYS? No suspension

ARE THERE ANY GROUPS OF LIBRARIES
FOR WHICH YOU WAIVE FEES? IF
SO, PLEASE NAME THEM: (Not
answered)

ANTIOCH COLLEGE

NUC CODE: OYesA

OCLC CODE: ANC

ADDRESS: Interlibrary Loan
          Antioch College Library
          Yellow Springs, OH
          45387

TELEPHONE: (513) 767-7331, X417

LIST NAMES OF BRANCHES WITH
  SEPARATE POLICIES: None

BOOKS:
  Will Lend: Yes
  Length of Loan: 3 weeks
  Renewable: Yes
  Charges: Reciprocal
  Average Turnaround Time:
    1 day
  If you have indicated that a
    book is not to be lent, will
    you on receipt of a letter
    from the requesting library
    search the index for given
    entries? Yes

PERIODICALS:
  Bound: Will not lend
  Unbound: Will not lend
  Loan Period: N/A
  Renewable: N/A
  Will lend if article exceeds
    50 pages

MICROFORMS:
  Will Lend: Yes
  Specific Types of Microforms:
    (Not answered)

GOVERNMENT PUBLICATIONS:
  Will Lend: Do not own

DISSERTATIONS:
  Will Lend: Yes, if 2nd copy
    available

THESES:
  Will Lend: Yes, if 2nd copy
    available

AUDIO-VISUAL MATERIALS:
  Records: Will not lend
  Cassettes: Will not lend
  Other (slides, filmstrips,
    etc.): Will not lend

COMPUTER SOFTWARE:
  Will Lend: Do not own

PHOTODUPLICATION SERVICE:
  No charge up to 5 exposures
  Charge Per Exposure: 10¢
  Minimum/handling Fee: $2.00
  Average Turnaround Time:
    1 day

MICROFILMING SERVICE:
  Service Available: No
  Charges: N/A

DO YOU CHARGE THE BORROWING
  LIBRARY FOR POSTAGE? No

FOR HOW LONG DO YOU SUSPEND ILL
  SERVICE OVER THE CHRISTMAS
  HOLIDAYS? About 2 weeks

ARE THERE ANY GROUPS OF LIBRARIES
  FOR WHICH YOU WAIVE FEES? IF
  SO, PLEASE NAME THEM: Dayton
  Miami Valley Consortium

BATTELLE COLUMBUS LABORATORIES

NUC CODE: OCOB

OCLC CODE: BKM

ADDRESS: Interlibrary Loan
          Battelle Columbus
            Laboratories
          Main Library
          505 King Ave.
          Columbus, OH 43201

TELEPHONE: (614) 424-6302

LIST NAMES OF BRANCHES WITH
  SEPARATE POLICIES: None

BOOKS:
  Will Lend: Yes
  Length of Loan: 4 weeks
  Renewable: Yes
  Charges: (Not answered)
  Average Turnaround Time:
    2 days
  If you have indicated that a
    book is not to be lent, will
    you on receipt of a letter
    from the requesting library
    search the index for given
    entries? (Not answered)

PERIODICALS:
  Bound: Will not usually lend
  Unbound: Will not usually
    lend
  Loan Period: 1 week
  Renewable: No
  Will lend if article exceeds
    _____ number of pages (Not
    answered)

MICROFORMS:
  Will Lend: No
  Specific Types of Microforms:
    N/A

GOVERNMENT PUBLICATIONS:
  Will Lend: Yes

DISSERTATIONS:
  Will Lend: Yes

THESES:
  Will Lend: Yes

AUDIO-VISUAL MATERIALS:
  Records: Do not own
  Cassettes: Do not own
  Other (slides, filmstrips,
    etc.): Do not own

COMPUTER SOFTWARE:
  Will Lend: No

PHOTODUPLICATION SERVICE:
  No charge up to 0 exposures
  Charge Per Exposure: 10¢
  Minimum/handling Fee: $4.00
  Average Turnaround Time:
    2 days

MICROFILMING SERVICE:
  Service Available: No
  Charges: N/A

DO YOU CHARGE THE BORROWING
  LIBRARY FOR POSTAGE? No

FOR HOW LONG DO YOU SUSPEND ILL
  SERVICE OVER THE CHRISTMAS
  HOLIDAYS? No suspension

ARE THERE ANY GROUPS OF LIBRARIES
  FOR WHICH YOU WAIVE FEES? IF
  SO, PLEASE NAME THEM: None

BOWLING GREEN STATE UNIVERSITY

NUC CODE: OBgU

OCLC CODE: BGU

ADDRESS: Interlibrary Loan
Service
Bowling Green State
University Library
Bowling Green, OH
43403

TELEPHONE: (419) 372-2759

LIST NAMES OF BRANCHES WITH
SEPARATE POLICIES: None

BOOKS:
Will Lend: Yes
Length of Loan: 3 weeks use
Renewable: No
Charges: $4.50 for medical
and corporate libraries; we
charge borrowing libraries
the same amount if they
charge us
Average Turnaround Time:
1-2 weeks
If you have indicated that a
book is not to be lent, will
you on receipt of a letter
from the requesting library
search the index for given
entries? Each case
considered individually

PERIODICALS:
Bound: Will not lend
Unbound: Will not lend
Loan Period: N/A
Renewable: N/A
Will lend if article exceeds
_____ number of pages (Will
not lend, regardless of
length of article)

MICROFORMS:
Will Lend: Yes, most of them
Specific Types of Microforms:
Cards, film, fiche (will
not loan ERIC microfiche)

GOVERNMENT PUBLICATIONS:
Will Lend: Yes, if document
librarian agrees

DISSERTATIONS:
Will Lend: Yes; all are
available from University
Microfilms

THESES:
Will Lend: Yes

AUDIO-VISUAL MATERIALS:
Records: Will not lend
Cassettes: Will not lend
Other (slides, filmstrips,
etc.): Will not lend

COMPUTER SOFTWARE:
Will Lend: Do not own

PHOTODUPLICATION SERVICE:
No charge up to 0 exposures
Charge Per Exposure: 10¢
Minimum/handling Fee: $3.00
Average Turnaround Time:
1-2 weeks

MICROFILMING SERVICE:
Service Available: No
Charges: N/A

DO YOU CHARGE THE BORROWING
LIBRARY FOR POSTAGE? No

FOR HOW LONG DO YOU SUSPEND ILL
SERVICE OVER THE CHRISTMAS
HOLIDAYS? Limit lending
books for the last 2 weeks
of December

ARE THERE ANY GROUPS OF LIBRARIES
FOR WHICH YOU WAIVE FEES? IF
SO, PLEASE NAME THEM: Ohio
state-assisted universities;
Consortium of Northwest Ohio
Colleges

CINCINNATI PUBLIC LIBRARY

NUC CODE: OC

OCLC CODE: OCP

ADDRESS: Interlibrary Loan
Cincinnati Public
Library
800 Vine St.
Cincinnati, OH 45202

TELEPHONE: (513) 369-6916

LIST NAMES OF BRANCHES WITH
SEPARATE POLICIES: None

BOOKS:
Will Lend: Yes
Length of Loan: 3 weeks
Renewable: Yes
Charges: $5.00 outside Ohio
Average Turnaround Time:
2 weeks
If you have indicated that a
book is not to be lent, will
you on receipt of a letter
from the requesting library
search the index for given
entries? Yes

PERIODICALS:
Bound: Will not lend
Unbound: Will not lend
Loan Period: N/A
Renewable: N/A
Will lend if article exceeds
_____ number of pages (Not
answered)

MICROFORMS:
Will Lend: No
Specific Types of Microforms:
N/A

GOVERNMENT PUBLICATIONS:
Will Lend: No

DISSERTATIONS:
Will Lend: Do not own

THESES:
Will Lend: Do not own

AUDIO-VISUAL MATERIALS:
Records: Will not lend
Cassettes: Will not lend
Other (slides, filmstrips,
etc.): Will not lend

COMPUTER SOFTWARE:
Will Lend: No

PHOTODUPLICATION SERVICE:
No charge up to 0 exposures
Charge Per Exposure: 15¢
Minimum/handling Fee: $1.00
Average Turnaround Time:
2 weeks

MICROFILMING SERVICE:
Service Available: No
Charges: N/A

DO YOU CHARGE THE BORROWING
LIBRARY FOR POSTAGE? No

FOR HOW LONG DO YOU SUSPEND ILL
SERVICE OVER THE CHRISTMAS
HOLIDAYS? No suspension

ARE THERE ANY GROUPS OF LIBRARIES
FOR WHICH YOU WAIVE FEES? IF
SO, PLEASE NAME THEM: Ohio
libraries

CLEVELAND HEALTH SCIENCES LIBRARY

NUC CODE: Oclw-H

OCLC CODE: CHS

ADDRESS: Interlibrary Loan
           Cleveland Health
             Sciences Library
           11000 Euclid Ave.
           Cleveland, OH 44106

TELEPHONE: (216) 368-3644

LIST NAMES OF BRANCHES WITH
  SEPARATE POLICIES: None

BOOKS:
   Will Lend: Yes
   Length of Loan: 2 weeks
   Renewable: Yes
   Charges: $5.00
   Average Turnaround Time:
     2-4 days
   If you have indicated that a
     book is not to be lent, will
     you on receipt of a letter
     from the requesting library
     search the index for given
     entries? (Not answered)

PERIODICALS:
   Bound: Will lend
   Unbound: Will lend
   Loan Period: 7 days
   Renewable: No
   Will lend if article exceeds
     50 pages

MICROFORMS:
   Will Lend: Yes
   Specific Types of Microforms:
     Some government reports

GOVERNMENT PUBLICATIONS:
   Will Lend: Yes

DISSERTATIONS:
   Will Lend: Yes

THESES:
   Will Lend: Yes

AUDIO-VISUAL MATERIALS:
   Records: Will lend
   Cassettes: Will lend
   Other (slides, filmstrips,
     etc.): Will lend

COMPUTER SOFTWARE:
   Will Lend: Yes

PHOTODUPLICATION SERVICE:
   No charge up to 0 exposures
   Charge Per Exposure: (Not
     answered)
   Minimum/handling Fee: $5.00
   Average Turnaround Time:
     2-4 days

MICROFILMING SERVICE:
   Service Available: No
   Charges: N/A

DO YOU CHARGE THE BORROWING
   LIBRARY FOR POSTAGE? Yes,
     if out of U.S., or if not
     UPS

ARE THERE ANY GROUPS OF LIBRARIES
   FOR WHICH YOU WAIVE FEES? IF
   SO, PLEASE NAME THEM: NLM
   RML Region V, Cleveland
   Area Metropolitan Library
   System, Northeast Ohio
   major academic libraries

CLEVELAND PUBLIC LIBRARY

NUC CODE: OC1

OCLC CODE: CLE

ADDRESS: Interlibrary Loan
           Cleveland Public
             Library
           325 Superior Ave.
           Cleveland, OH
             44114-1271

TELEPHONE: (216) 623-2868

LIST NAMES OF BRANCHES WITH
  SEPARATE POLICIES: None

BOOKS:
   Will Lend: Yes, except for
     best sellers
   Length of Loan: 28 days
   Renewable: No
   Charges: $5.00 for out-of-
     state libraries
   Average Turnaround Time:
     24 hours
   If you have indicated that a
     book is not to be lent, will
     you on receipt of a letter
     from the requesting library
     search the index for given
     entries? We respond to
       inquiries by letter free
       if work can be done within
       10 minutes; if longer, see
       Facts-for-a-Fee brochure

PERIODICALS:
   Bound: Will not lend
   Unbound: Will not lend
   Loan Period: N/A
   Renewable: N/A
   Will lend if article exceeds
     _____ number of pages (Not
     answered)

MICROFORMS:
   Will Lend: No
   Specific Types of Microforms:
     N/A

GOVERNMENT PUBLICATIONS:
   Will Lend: Yes, if 2nd copy
     available

DISSERTATIONS:
   Will Lend: Do not own

THESES:
   Will Lend: Do not own

AUDIO-VISUAL MATERIALS:
   Records: Will not lend
   Cassettes: Will not lend
   Other (slides, filmstrips,
     etc.): Will not lend

COMPUTER SOFTWARE:
   Will Lend: No

PHOTODUPLICATION SERVICE:
   No charge up to 0 exposures
   Charge Per Exposure: 40¢ and
     up
   Minimum Fee: $1.00
   Average Turnaround Time: Rush
     service, 1-3 days; regular
     service, 3-6 days

MICROFILMING SERVICE:
   Service Available: No
   Charges: N/A

DO YOU CHARGE THE BORROWING
   LIBRARY FOR POSTAGE?
     Charged for photocopies
     only

FOR HOW LONG DO YOU SUSPEND ILL
   SERVICE OVER THE CHRISTMAS
   HOLIDAYS? Dec.14-Jan.4

ARE THERE ANY GROUPS OF LIBRARIES
   FOR WHICH YOU WAIVE FEES? IF
   SO, PLEASE NAME THEM: None

CLEVELAND STATE UNIVERSITY

NUC CODE: (Not answered)

OCLC CODE: (Not answered)

ADDRESS: Interlibrary Loan
Cleveland State
University Library
Euclid Ave. at E.24th
Street
Cleveland, OH   44115

TELEPHONE: (216) 687-2382

LIST NAMES OF BRANCHES WITH
SEPARATE POLICIES: None

BOOKS:
Will Lend: Yes
Length of Loan: 1 month
Renewable: Yes
Charges: (Not answered)
Average Turnaround Time:
(Not answered)
If you have indicated that a
book is not to be lent, will
you on receipt of a letter
from the requesting library
search the index for given
entries?   (Not answered)

PERIODICALS:
Bound: Will not lend
Unbound: Will not lend
Loan Period: N/A
Renewable: N/A
Will lend if article exceeds
_____ number of pages (Not
answered)

MICROFORMS:
Will Lend: Yes
Specific Types of Microforms:
(Not answered)

GOVERNMENT PUBLICATIONS:
Will Lend: Yes

DISSERTATIONS:
Will Lend: Yes

THESES:
Will Lend: Yes

AUDIO-VISUAL MATERIALS:
Records: (Not answered)
Cassettes: (Not answered)
Other (slides, filmstrips,
etc.):   (Not answered)

COMPUTER SOFTWARE:
Will Lend: (Not answered)

PHOTODUPLICATION SERVICE:
No charge up to 0 exposures
Charge Per Exposure: 15¢
Minimum Fee: $2.00
Average Turnaround Time:
(Not answered)

MICROFILMING SERVICE:
Service Available: No
Charges: N/A

DO YOU CHARGE THE BORROWING
LIBRARY FOR POSTAGE?   (Not
answered)

FOR HOW LONG DO YOU SUSPEND ILL
SERVICE OVER THE CHRISTMAS
HOLIDAYS?   (Not answered)

ARE THERE ANY GROUPS OF LIBRARIES
FOR WHICH YOU WAIVE FEES?   IF
SO, PLEASE NAME THEM: (Not
answered)

CUYAHOGA COUNTY PUBLIC LIBRARY

NUC CODE: OC1Co

OCLC CODE: CXP

ADDRESS: Interlibrary Loan
Cuyahoga County Public
Library
4510 Memphis Ave.
Cleveland, OH   44144

TELEPHONE: (216) 398-1800

LIST NAMES OF BRANCHES WITH
SEPARATE POLICIES: None

BOOKS:
Will Lend: Yes
Length of Loan: 3 weeks
Renewable: Yes
Charges: None
Average Turnaround Time:
2 days
If you have indicated that a
book is not to be lent, will
you on receipt of a letter
from the requesting library
search the index for given
entries?   (Not answered)

PERIODICALS:
Bound: Will not lend
Unbound: Will lend
Loan Period: 3 weeks
Renewable: Yes
Will lend if article exceeds
_____ number of pages (Not
answered)

MICROFORMS:
Will Lend: Yes
Specific Types of Microforms:
Film, fiche

GOVERNMENT PUBLICATIONS:
Will Lend: Yes, Ohio
documents

DISSERTATIONS:
Will Lend: Do not own

THESES:
Will Lend: Do not own

AUDIO-VISUAL MATERIALS:
Records: Will lend
Cassettes: Will lend
Other (slides, filmstrips,
etc.):   Will lend

COMPUTER SOFTWARE:
Will Lend: No

PHOTODUPLICATION SERVICE:
No charge up to 0 exposures
Charge Per Exposure: 20¢
Minimum/handling Fee: (Not
answered)
Average Turnaround Time:
2 days

MICROFILMING SERVICE:
Service Available: No
Charges: N/A

DO YOU CHARGE THE BORROWING
LIBRARY FOR POSTAGE?   No

FOR HOW LONG DO YOU SUSPEND ILL
SERVICE OVER THE CHRISTMAS
HOLIDAYS?   No suspension

ARE THERE ANY GROUPS OF LIBRARIES
FOR WHICH YOU WAIVE FEES?   IF
SO, PLEASE NAME THEM: None

DAYTON AND MONTGOMERY COUNTY PUBLIC LIBRARY

NUC CODE: ODA

OCLC CODE: DMM

ADDRESS: Interlibrary Loan
Dayton and Montgomery
County Public Library
215 E. Third St.
Dayton, OH 45402

TELEPHONE: (513) 224-1651, X215

LIST NAMES OF BRANCHES WITH
SEPARATE POLICIES: None

BOOKS:
Will Lend: Yes
Length of Loan: 28 days
Renewable: Yes, for 2 weeks
Charges: $5.00 per volume
for all out-of-state
libraries
Average Turnaround Time:
48 hours
If you have indicated that a
book is not to be lent, will
you on receipt of a letter
from the requesting library
search the index for given
entries? (Not answered)

PERIODICALS:
Bound: Will not lend
Unbound: Will not lend
Loan Period: N/A
Renewable: N/A
Will lend if article exceeds
_____ number of pages (Not
answered)

MICROFORMS:
Will Lend: No
Specific Types of Microforms:
N/A

GOVERNMENT PUBLICATIONS:
Will Lend: Yes, if
circulating

DISSERTATIONS:
Will Lend: No

THESES:
Will Lend: No

AUDIO-VISUAL MATERIALS:
Records: Will not lend
Cassettes: Will not lend
Other (slides, filmstrips,
etc.): Will not lend

COMPUTER SOFTWARE:
Will Lend: No

PHOTODUPLICATION SERVICE:
No charge up to 0 exposures
Charge Per Exposure: 10¢
plus handling fee
Handling Fee: $1.00
Average Turnaround Time:
48 hours

MICROFILMING SERVICE:
Service Available: No
Charges: N/A

DO YOU CHARGE THE BORROWING
LIBRARY FOR POSTAGE? No

FOR HOW LONG DO YOU SUSPEND ILL
SERVICE OVER THE CHRISTMAS
HOLIDAYS? No suspension

ARE THERE ANY GROUPS OF LIBRARIES
FOR WHICH YOU WAIVE FEES? IF
SO, PLEASE NAME THEM: No
charge for books lent to
Ohio libraries

GREENE COUNTY DISTRICT LIBRARY

NUC CODE: (Not answered)

OCLC CODE: GRC

ADDRESS: Interlibrary Loan
Greene County District
Library
76 E. Market St.
Xenia, OH 45385

TELEPHONE: (513) 376-2995

LIST NAMES OF BRANCHES WITH
SEPARATE POLICIES: None

BOOKS:
Will Lend: Yes
Length of Loan: 2 weeks
Renewable: Yes, if no
reserves
Charges: (Not answered)
Average Turnaround Time:
10 days
If you have indicated that a
book is not to be lent, will
you on receipt of a letter
from the requesting library
search the index for given
entries? Yes

PERIODICALS:
Bound: Will not lend
Unbound: Will not lend
Loan Period: N/A
Renewable: N/A
Will lend if article exceeds
_____ number of pages (Will
not lend, regardless of
length of article)

MICROFORMS:
Will Lend: No
Specific Types of Microforms:
N/A

GOVERNMENT PUBLICATIONS:
Will Lend: No

DISSERTATIONS:
Will Lend: No

THESES:
Will Lend: No

AUDIO-VISUAL MATERIALS:
Records: Will not lend
Cassettes: Will not lend
Other (slides, filmstrips,
etc.): Will not lend

COMPUTER SOFTWARE:
Will Lend: No

PHOTODUPLICATION SERVICE:
No charge up to 0 exposures
Charge Per Exposure: 10¢
Minimum/handling Fee: (Not
answered)
Average Turnaround Time:
1 week

MICROFILMING SERVICE:
Service Available: No
Charges: N/A

DO YOU CHARGE THE BORROWING
LIBRARY FOR POSTAGE? No

FOR HOW LONG DO YOU SUSPEND ILL
SERVICE OVER THE CHRISTMAS
HOLIDAYS? No suspension

ARE THERE ANY GROUPS OF LIBRARIES
FOR WHICH YOU WAIVE FEES? IF
SO, PLEASE NAME THEM: None

HEBREW UNION COLLEGE

NUC CODE: OCH

OCLC CODE: HUC

ADDRESS: Interlibrary Loan
          Hebrew Union College
          Library
          3101 Clifton Ave.
          Cincinnati, OH 45220

TELEPHONE: (513) 221-1881, X242

LIST NAMES OF BRANCHES WITH
    SEPARATE POLICIES: None

BOOKS:
    Will Lend: Yes
    Length of Loan: 1 month
    Renewable: Yes
    Charges: Only to libraries
        that charge us
    Average Turnaround Time:
        3-5 days
    If you have indicated that a
        book is not to be lent, will
        you on receipt of a letter
        from the requesting library
        search the index for given
        entries? Yes

PERIODICALS:
    Bound: Will lend
    Unbound: Will not lend
    Loan Period: 1 month
    Renewable: Yes
    Will lend if article exceeds
        _____ number of pages
        (Length of article is not
        important)

MICROFORMS:
    Will Lend: Yes
    Specific Types of Microforms:
        Positives and negatives

GOVERNMENT PUBLICATIONS:
    Will Lend: Yes

DISSERTATIONS:
    Will Lend: Yes

THESES:
    Will Lend: Yes

AUDIO-VISUAL MATERIALS:
    Records: Will not lend
    Cassettes: Will lend
    Other (slides, filmstrips,
        etc.): Will lend

COMPUTER SOFTWARE:
    Will Lend: No

PHOTODUPLICATION SERVICE:
    No charge up to 0 exposures
    Charge Per Exposure: 15¢
    Minimum/handling Fee: $3.50
    Average Turnaround Time:
        3 days

MICROFILMING SERVICE:
    Service Available: Yes
    Charges: Write for prices

DO YOU CHARGE THE BORROWING
    LIBRARY FOR POSTAGE? No

FOR HOW LONG DO YOU SUSPEND ILL
    SERVICE OVER THE CHRISTMAS
    HOLIDAYS? No suspension

ARE THERE ANY GROUPS OF LIBRARIES
    FOR WHICH YOU WAIVE FEES? IF
    SO, PLEASE NAME THEM: Our
        other branches

KETTERING MEDICAL CENTER

NUC CODE: None

OCLC CODE: None

ADDRESS: Interlibrary Loan
          Medical Library
          Kettering Medical
          Center
          3535 Southern Blvd.
          Kettering, OH 45429

TELEPHONE: (513) 298-4331, X5562

LIST NAMES OF BRANCHES WITH
    SEPARATE POLICIES: None

BOOKS:
    Will Lend: Yes
    Length of Loan: 2 weeks use
    Renewable: Yes
    Charges: $2.00 per book
    Average Turnaround Time:
        (Not answered)
    If you have indicated that a
        book is not to be lent, will
        you on receipt of a letter
        from the requesting library
        search the index for given
        entries? (Not answered)

PERIODICALS:
    Bound: Will not lend
    Unbound: Will not lend
    Loan Period: N/A
    Renewable: N/A
    Will lend if article exceeds
        _____ number of pages (Will
        not lend, regardless of
        length of article)

MICROFORMS:
    Will Lend: Do not own

GOVERNMENT PUBLICATIONS:
    Will Lend: Do not own

DISSERTATIONS:
    Will Lend: Do not own

THESES:
    Will Lend: Do not own

AUDIO-VISUAL MATERIALS:
    Records: Will not lend
    Cassettes: Will not lend
    Other (slides, filmstrips,
        etc.): Will not lend

COMPUTER SOFTWARE:
    Will Lend: Do not own

PHOTODUPLICATION SERVICE:
    No charge up to 0 exposures
    Charge Per Exposure: (Not
        answered)
    Minimum/handling Fee: $2.00
    Average Turnaround Time:
        (Not answered)

MICROFILMING SERVICE:
    Service Available: No
    Charges: N/A

DO YOU CHARGE THE BORROWING
    LIBRARY FOR POSTAGE? No

FOR HOW LONG DO YOU SUSPEND ILL
    SERVICE OVER THE CHRISTMAS
    HOLIDAYS? (Not answered)

ARE THERE ANY GROUPS OF LIBRARIES
    FOR WHICH YOU WAIVE FEES? IF
    SO, PLEASE NAME THEM:
        Government libraries

LAKEWOOD PUBLIC LIBRARY

NUC CODE: OLaK

OCLC CODE: LAP

ADDRESS: Interlibrary Loan
Lakewood Public
Library
15425 Detroit Ave.
Lakewood, OH 44107

TELEPHONE: (216) 226-8275, X57

LIST NAMES OF BRANCHES WITH
SEPARATE POLICIES: None

BOOKS:
Will Lend: Yes
Length of Loan: 7-28 days
Renewable: Yes
Charges: None
Average Turnaround Time:
1 day
If you have indicated that a
book is not to be lent, will
you on receipt of a letter
from the requesting library
search the index for given
entries? (Not answered)

PERIODICALS:
Bound: Will not usually lend
Unbound: Will not usually
lend
Loan Period: For exceptional
loans, 7 days
Renewable: No
Will lend if article exceeds
_____ number of pages (Not
answered)

MICROFORMS:
Will Lend: No
Specific Types of Microforms:
N/A

GOVERNMENT PUBLICATIONS:
Will Lend: No

DISSERTATIONS:
Will Lend: No

THESES:
Will Lend: No

AUDIO-VISUAL MATERIALS:
Records: Will not lend
Cassettes: Will not lend
Other (slides, filmstrips,
etc.): Will not lend

COMPUTER SOFTWARE:
Will Lend: No

PHOTODUPLICATION SERVICE:
No charge up to 0 exposures
Charge Per Exposure: 10¢
Minimum/handling Fee: None
Average Turnaround Time:
1 day

MICROFILMING SERVICE:
Service Available: No
Charges: N/A

DO YOU CHARGE THE BORROWING
LIBRARY FOR POSTAGE? No

FOR HOW LONG DO YOU SUSPEND ILL
SERVICE OVER THE CHRISTMAS
HOLIDAYS? No suspension

ARE THERE ANY GROUPS OF LIBRARIES
FOR WHICH YOU WAIVE FEES? IF
SO, PLEASE NAME THEM: None

LORAIN PUBLIC LIBRARY

NUC CODE: OLor

OCLC CODE: LXP

ADDRESS: Interlibrary Loan
Lorain Public Library
351 Sixth St.
Lorain, OH 44052

TELEPHONE: (216) 244-1192

LIST NAMES OF BRANCHES WITH
SEPARATE POLICIES: None

BOOKS:
Will Lend: Yes
Length of Loan: 3 weeks
Renewable: Yes, if no
reserves
Charges: None
Average Turnaround Time:
1 week
If you have indicated that a
book is not to be lent, will
you on receipt of a letter
from the requesting library
search the index for given
entries? (Not answered)

PERIODICALS:
Bound: Will not lend
Unbound: Will not lend
Loan Period: N/A
Renewable: N/A
Will lend if article exceeds
_____ number of pages (Not
answered)

MICROFORMS:
Will Lend: No
Specific Types of Microforms:
N/A

GOVERNMENT PUBLICATIONS:
Will Lend: No

DISSERTATIONS:
Will Lend: Do not own

THESES:
Will Lend: Do not own

AUDIO-VISUAL MATERIALS:
Records: Will not lend
Cassettes: Will not lend
Other (slides, filmstrips,
etc.): Will not lend

COMPUTER SOFTWARE:
Will Lend: No

PHOTODUPLICATION SERVICE:
Policies being formulated
at this time
Average Turnaround Time:
(Not answered)

MICROFILMING SERVICE:
Service Available:
(Not answered)
Charges: N/A

DO YOU CHARGE THE BORROWING
LIBRARY FOR POSTAGE? (Not
answered)

FOR HOW LONG DO YOU SUSPEND ILL
SERVICE OVER THE CHRISTMAS
HOLIDAYS? No suspension

ARE THERE ANY GROUPS OF LIBRARIES
FOR WHICH YOU WAIVE FEES? IF
SO, PLEASE NAME THEM: None

MEDICAL COLLEGE OF OHIO

NUC CODE: OTMC

OCLC CODE: MCL

ADDRESS: Interlibrary Loan
           Raymon H. Mulford
             Library
           Medical College of Ohio
           C.S. #10008
           Toledo, OH 43699

TELEPHONE: (419) 381-4218

LIST NAMES OF BRANCHES WITH
   SEPARATE POLICIES: None

BOOKS:
   Will Lend: Yes
   Length of Loan: 1 month
   Renewable: Yes, for 2 weeks
   Charges: $4.50 per request
   Average Turnaround Time:
     2 days
   If you have indicated that a
     book is not to be lent, will
     you on receipt of a letter
     from the requesting library
     search the index for given
     entries? If non-circulating
     we will search a table of
     contents for a chapter or
     section or author(s), but
     we will not search a
     subject index

PERIODICALS:
   Bound: Will not lend
   Unbound: Will not lend
   Loan Period: N/A
   Renewable: N/A
   Will lend if article exceeds
     _____ number of pages (Will
     not lend, regardless of
     length of article)

MICROFORMS:
   Will Lend: No
   Specific Types of Microforms:
     N/A

GOVERNMENT PUBLICATIONS:
   Will Lend: Yes

DISSERTATIONS:
   Will Lend: Yes

THESES:
   Will Lend: Yes

AUDIO-VISUAL MATERIALS:
   Records: Will not lend
   Cassettes: Will not lend
   Other (slides, filmstrips,
     etc.): Will lend

COMPUTER SOFTWARE:
   Will Lend: No

PHOTODUPLICATION SERVICE:
   No charge up to 0 exposures
   Charge Per Request: $4.50
   Average Turnaround Time:
     2-3 days

MICROFILMING SERVICE:
   Service Available: No
   Charges: N/A

DO YOU CHARGE THE BORROWING
   LIBRARY FOR POSTAGE? No

FOR HOW LONG DO YOU SUSPEND ILL
   SERVICE OVER THE CHRISTMAS
   HOLIDAYS? No suspension

ARE THERE ANY GROUPS OF LIBRARIES
   FOR WHICH YOU WAIVE FEES? IF
   SO, PLEASE NAME THEM: Other
   resource libraries in the
   Kentucky-Ohio-Michigan
   Regional Medical Library
   Network

OBERLIN COLLEGE

NUC CODE: OO

OCLC CODE: OBE

ADDRESS: Interlibrary Loan
           Oberlin College Library
           Oberlin, OH 44074

TELEPHONE: (216) 775-8285

LIST NAMES OF BRANCHES WITH
   SEPARATE POLICIES: None

BOOKS:
   Will Lend: Yes
   Length of Loan: 3 weeks
   Renewable: Yes
   Charges: Postage
   Average Turnaround Time:
     2 weeks
   If you have indicated that a
     book is not to be lent, will
     you on receipt of a letter
     from the requesting library
     search the index for given
     entries? (Not answered)

PERIODICALS:
   Bound: Will not lend
   Unbound: Will not lend
   Loan Period: N/A
   Renewable: N/A
   Will lend if article exceeds
     _____ number of pages (Not
     answered)

MICROFORMS:
   Will Lend: Yes
   Specific Types of Microforms:
     Microfilm, microfiche

GOVERNMENT PUBLICATIONS:
   Will Lend: Yes

DISSERTATIONS:
   Will Lend: No

THESES:
   Will Lend: Yes, if 2nd copy
     available

AUDIO-VISUAL MATERIALS:
   Records: Will not lend
   Cassettes: Will not lend
   Other (slides, filmstrips,
     etc.): Will not lend

COMPUTER SOFTWARE:
   Will Lend: No

PHOTODUPLICATION SERVICE:
   No charge up to 0 exposures
   Charge Per Exposure: 15¢
   Minimum/handling Fee: $2.00
   Average Turnaround Time:
     2 weeks

MICROFILMING SERVICE:
   Service Available: No
   Charges: N/A

DO YOU CHARGE THE BORROWING
   LIBRARY FOR POSTAGE? Yes

FOR HOW LONG DO YOU SUSPEND ILL
   SERVICE OVER THE CHRISTMAS
   HOLIDAYS? 3 weeks

ARE THERE ANY GROUPS OF LIBRARIES
   FOR WHICH YOU WAIVE FEES? IF
   SO, PLEASE NAME THEM: NEOMAL

OHIO HISTORICAL SOCIETY

NUC CODE: OHi

OCLC CODE: OHT

ADDRESS: Interlibrary Loan
Archives-Library Div.
Ohio Historical Society
I-71 & 17th Ave.
Columbus, OH 43211

TELEPHONE: (614) 466-1500

LIST NAMES OF BRANCHES WITH
SEPARATE POLICIES: None

BOOKS:
Will Lend: No
Length of Loan: N/A
Renewable: N/A
Charges: N/A
Average Turnaround Time: N/A
If you have indicated that a
book is not to be lent, will
you on receipt of a letter
from the requesting library
search the index for given
entries? (Not answered)

PERIODICALS:
Bound: Will not lend
Unbound: Will not lend
Loan Period: N/A
Renewable: N/A
Will lend if article exceeds
_____ number of pages (Not
answered)

MICROFORMS:
Will Lend: Yes
Specific Types of Microforms:
Microfilm (8-12 rolls max.)
$8.00 service charge per
order, prepayment required

GOVERNMENT PUBLICATIONS:
Will Lend: No

DISSERTATIONS:
Will Lend: No

THESES:
Will Lend: No

AUDIO-VISUAL MATERIALS:
Records: Will not lend
Cassettes: Will not lend
Other (slides, filmstrips,
etc.): Will not lend

COMPUTER SOFTWARE:
Will Lend: No

PHOTODUPLICATION SERVICE:
No charge up to 0 exposures
Charges: Hard copy = 15¢ per
exposure plus $4.00; micro-
copy = 25¢ per exposure plus
$4.00 service fee; prepay-
ment required
Average Turnaround Time:
2-3 weeks

MICROFILMING SERVICE:
Service Available: Yes
Charges: $59.23 minimum

DO YOU CHARGE THE BORROWING
LIBRARY FOR POSTAGE? No

FOR HOW LONG DO YOU SUSPEND ILL
SERVICE OVER THE CHRISTMAS
HOLIDAYS? No suspension

ARE THERE ANY GROUPS OF LIBRARIES
FOR WHICH YOU WAIVE FEES? IF
SO, PLEASE NAME THEM: None

OHIO STATE UNIVERSITY AT COLUMBUS

NUC CODE: OU

OCLC CODE: OSU

ADDRESS: Interlibrary Loan
Ohio State
University Library
1858 Neil Avenue Mall
Columbus, OH 43210

TELEPHONE: (614) 422-6211

LIST NAMES OF BRANCHES WITH
SEPARATE POLICIES: (Not
answered)

BOOKS:
Will Lend: Yes
Length of Loan: 2 weeks use
Renewable: (Not answered)
Charges: (Not answered)
Average Turnaround Time:
(Not answered)
If you have indicated that a
book is not to be lent, will
you on receipt of a letter
from the requesting library
search the index for given
entries? (Not answered)

PERIODICALS:
Bound: Will lend
Unbound: Will not lend
Loan Period: (Not answered)
Renewable: (Not answered)
Will lend if article exceeds
20 pages

MICROFORMS:
Will Lend: Yes
Specific Types of Microforms:
All types

GOVERNMENT PUBLICATIONS:
Will Lend: No

DISSERTATIONS:
Will Lend: Yes, subject to
reciprocal agreements; 1954
to present available from
University Microfilms

THESES:
Will Lend: Yes

AUDIO-VISUAL MATERIALS:
Records: Will not lend
Cassettes: Will not lend
Other (slides, filmstrips,
etc.): (Not answered)

COMPUTER SOFTWARE:
Will Lend: (Not answered)

PHOTODUPLICATION SERVICE:
No charge up to 0 exposures
Charge Per Exposure: 15¢
Minimum Fee: $3.00 per
article
Average Turnaround Time:
(Not answered)

MICROFILMING SERVICE:
Service Available: (Not
answered)
Charges: N/A

DO YOU CHARGE THE BORROWING
LIBRARY FOR POSTAGE? (Not
answered)

FOR HOW LONG DO YOU SUSPEND ILL
SERVICE OVER THE CHRISTMAS
HOLIDAYS? No suspension

ARE THERE ANY GROUPS OF LIBRARIES
FOR WHICH YOU WAIVE FEES? IF
SO, PLEASE NAME THEM: (Not
answered)

OHIO UNIVERSITY

NUC CODE: OAU

OCLC CODE: OUN

ADDRESS: Interlibrary Loan
Ohio University
Library
Athens, OH 45701

TELEPHONE: (614) 594-5353

LIST NAMES OF BRANCHES WITH
SEPARATE POLICIES: None

BOOKS:
Will Lend: Yes
Length of Loan: 3 weeks
Renewable: Yes
Charges: Postage for
libraries outside of Ohio
Average Turnaround Time:
5-10 days
If you have indicated that a
book is not to be lent, will
you on receipt of a letter
from the requesting library
search the index for given
entries? Yes

PERIODICALS:
Bound: Will not lend
Unbound: Will not lend
Loan Period: N/A
Renewable: N/A
Will lend if article exceeds
50 pages and journal is not
in heavy demand

MICROFORMS:
Will Lend: Yes
Specific Types of Microforms:
Films, fiche

GOVERNMENT PUBLICATIONS:
Will Lend: Yes

DISSERTATIONS:
Will Lend: Yes; 1965 to
present available from
University Microfilms

THESES:
Will Lend: Yes

AUDIO-VISUAL MATERIALS:
Records: Will not lend
Cassettes: Will lend
Other (slides, filmstrips,
etc.): Will lend

COMPUTER SOFTWARE:
Will Lend: No

PHOTODUPLICATION SERVICE:
No charge up to 0 exposures
Charge Per Exposure: 15¢
Minimum Fee: $4.00
Handling Fee: $1.00
Average Turnaround Time:
5-10 days

MICROFILMING SERVICE:
Service Available: Yes
Charges: 15¢ per exposure

DO YOU CHARGE THE BORROWING
LIBRARY FOR POSTAGE? Only
out-of-state libraries

FOR HOW LONG DO YOU SUSPEND ILL
SERVICE OVER THE CHRISTMAS
HOLIDAYS? No suspension

ARE THERE ANY GROUPS OF LIBRARIES
FOR WHICH YOU WAIVE FEES? IF
SO, PLEASE NAME THEM: Ohio
state-supported universities

OHIO WESLEYAN UNIVERSITY

NUC CODE: ODW

OCLC CODE: OWU

ADDRESS: Interlibrary Loan
L. A. Beeghly Library
Ohio Wesleyan
University
Delaware, OH 43015

TELEPHONE: (614) 369-4431, X315

LIST NAMES OF BRANCHES WITH
SEPARATE POLICIES: None

BOOKS:
Will Lend: Yes
Length of Loan: 3 weeks use
Renewable: Yes, usually
Charges: We follow the
charging system of the
borrowing library
Average Turnaround Time:
(Not answered)
If you have indicated that a
book is not to be lent, will
you on receipt of a letter
from the requesting library
search the index for given
entries? No

PERIODICALS:
Bound: Will not lend
Unbound: Will not lend
Loan Period: N/A
Renewable: N/A
Will lend if article exceeds
_____ number of pages (Not
answered)

MICROFORMS:
Will Lend: No
Specific Types of Microforms:
Sometimes we will lend
microfilm

GOVERNMENT PUBLICATIONS:
Will Lend: No

DISSERTATIONS:
Will Lend: No

THESES:
Will Lend: No

AUDIO-VISUAL MATERIALS:
Records: Will not lend
Cassettes: Will not lend
Other (slides, filmstrips,
etc.): Will not lend

COMPUTER SOFTWARE:
Will Lend: No

PHOTODUPLICATION SERVICE:
No charge up to 0 exposures
Charge Per Exposure: 15¢
Minimum/handling Fee: $1.00
to $1.50, depending on
postage and size of order
Average Turnaround Time:
(Not answered)

MICROFILMING SERVICE:
Service Available: No
Charges: N/A

DO YOU CHARGE THE BORROWING
LIBRARY FOR POSTAGE? No,
except for multi-volume
sets and large bills

FOR HOW LONG DO YOU SUSPEND ILL
SERVICE OVER THE CHRISTMAS
HOLIDAYS? Dec.15-Jan.1

ARE THERE ANY GROUPS OF LIBRARIES
FOR WHICH YOU WAIVE FEES? IF
SO, PLEASE NAME THEM: None

PUBLIC LIBRARY OF COLUMBUS AND FRANKLIN COUNTY

NUC CODE: OCo

OCLC CODE: OCO

ADDRESS: Interlibrary Loan
Public Library of
Columbus and Franklin
County
96 So. Grant Ave.
Columbus, OH 43215

TELEPHONE: (614) 222-7173

LIST NAMES OF BRANCHES WITH
SEPARATE POLICIES: None

BOOKS:
Will Lend: Yes
Length of Loan: 5 weeks
Renewable: No
Charges: $5.00 for out-of-
county loan
Average Turnaround Time:
(Not answered)
If you have indicated that a
book is not to be lent, will
you on receipt of a letter
from the requesting library
search the index for given
entries? (Not answered)

PERIODICALS:
Bound: Will not lend
Unbound: Will not lend
Loan Period: N/A
Renewable: N/A
Will lend if article exceeds
_____ number of pages (Will
not lend, regardless of
length of article)

MICROFORMS:
Will Lend: No
Specific Types of Microforms:
N/A

GOVERNMENT PUBLICATIONS:
Will Lend: (Not answered)

DISSERTATIONS:
Will Lend: No

THESES:
Will Lend: No

AUDIO-VISUAL MATERIALS:
Records: Will not lend
Cassettes: Will not lend
Other (slides, filmstrips,
etc.): Will not lend

COMPUTER SOFTWARE:
Will Lend: No

PHOTODUPLICATION SERVICE:
No charge up to 0 exposures
Charge Per Exposure: 20¢
Minimum/handling Fee: 50¢
Average Turnaround Time:
(Not answered)

MICROFILMING SERVICE:
Service Available: Yes
Charges: Same as
photoduplication

DO YOU CHARGE THE BORROWING
LIBRARY FOR POSTAGE? No

FOR HOW LONG DO YOU SUSPEND ILL
SERVICE OVER THE CHRISTMAS
HOLIDAYS? None

ARE THERE ANY GROUPS OF LIBRARIES
FOR WHICH YOU WAIVE FEES? IF
SO, PLEASE NAME THEM:
Libraries in Franklin
County, and those with whom
we have made reciprocal
agreements

STARK COUNTY DISTRICT LIBRARY

NUC CODE: (Not answered)

OCLC CODE: SDL

ADDRESS: Interlibrary Loan
Stark County District
Library
715 Market Avenue N.
Canton, OH 44702

TELEPHONE: (216) 452-0665

LIST NAMES OF BRANCHES WITH
SEPARATE POLICIES: None

BOOKS:
Will Lend: Yes
Length of Loan: 1-4 weeks
Renewable: Yes
Charges: None
Average Turnaround Time:
(Not answered)
If you have indicated that a
book is not to be lent, will
you on receipt of a letter
from the requesting library
search the index for given
entries? (Not answered)

PERIODICALS:
Bound: Will not lend
Unbound: Will not lend
Loan Period: N/A
Renewable: N/A
Will lend if article exceeds
_____ number of pages (Will
not lend, regardless of
length of article)

MICROFORMS:
Will Lend: No
Specific Types of Microforms:
N/A

GOVERNMENT PUBLICATIONS:
Will Lend: No

DISSERTATIONS:
Will Lend: No

THESES:
Will Lend: No

AUDIO-VISUAL MATERIALS:
Records: Will not lend
Cassettes: Will not lend
Other (slides, filmstrips,
etc.): Will not lend

COMPUTER SOFTWARE:
Will Lend: No

PHOTODUPLICATION SERVICE:
No charge up to 0 exposures
Charge Per Exposure: 25¢
Minimum/handling Fee:
Postage
Average Turnaround Time:
(Not answered)

MICROFILMING SERVICE:
Service Available: No
Charges: N/A

DO YOU CHARGE THE BORROWING
LIBRARY FOR POSTAGE? Only
for photocopies

FOR HOW LONG DO YOU SUSPEND ILL
SERVICE OVER THE CHRISTMAS
HOLIDAYS? No suspension

ARE THERE ANY GROUPS OF LIBRARIES
FOR WHICH YOU WAIVE FEES? IF
SO, PLEASE NAME THEM: None

STATE LIBRARY OF OHIO

NUC CODE: O

OCLC CODE: OHI

ADDRESS: Interlibrary Loan
State Library of Ohio
65 S. Front St.
Columbus, OH 43215

TELEPHONE: (614) 462-6958

LIST NAMES OF BRANCHES WITH
SEPARATE POLICIES: None

BOOKS:
Will Lend: Yes
Length of Loan: 3 weeks
Renewable: Yes
Charges: (Not answered)
Average Turnaround Time:
(Not answered)
If you have indicated that a
book is not to be lent, will
you on receipt of a letter
from the requesting library
search the index for given
entries? (Not answered)

PERIODICALS:
Bound: (Not answered)
Unbound: Will not lend
Loan Period: N/A
Renewable: N/A
Will lend if article exceeds
_____ number of pages (Not
answered)

MICROFORMS:
Will Lend: (Not answered)
Specific Types of Microforms:
N/A

GOVERNMENT PUBLICATIONS:
Will Lend: Yes

DISSERTATIONS:
Will Lend: (Not answered)

THESES:
Will Lend: (Not answered)

AUDIO-VISUAL MATERIALS:
Records: (Not answered)
Cassettes: (Not answered)
Other (slides, filmstrips,
etc.): (Not answered)

COMPUTER SOFTWARE:
Will Lend: (Not answered)

PHOTODUPLICATION SERVICE:
No charge up to 20 exposures
Charge Per Exposure: (Not
answered)
Minimum/handling Fee: None
Average Turnaround Time:
(Not answered)

MICROFILMING SERVICE:
Service Available: No
Charges: N/A

DO YOU CHARGE THE BORROWING
LIBRARY FOR POSTAGE? No

FOR HOW LONG DO YOU SUSPEND ILL
SERVICE OVER THE CHRISTMAS
HOLIDAYS? No suspension

ARE THERE ANY GROUPS OF LIBRARIES
FOR WHICH YOU WAIVE FEES? IF
SO, PLEASE NAME THEM: (Not
answered)

TOLEDO-LUCAS COUNTY PUBLIC LIBRARY

NUC CODE: (Not answered)

OCLC CODE: TLM

ADDRESS: Interlibrary Loan
Toledo-Lucas County
Public Library
325 Michigan
Toledo, OH 43624

TELEPHONE: (419) 255-3830

LIST NAMES OF BRANCHES WITH
SEPARATE POLICIES: None

BOOKS:
Will Lend: Yes
Length of Loan: 2-4 weeks
Renewable: No
Charges: $5.00 per loan for
out-of-state
Average Turnaround Time:
2-3 days
If you have indicated that a
book is not to be lent, will
you on receipt of a letter
from the requesting library
search the index for given
entries? (Not answered)

PERIODICALS:
Bound: Will not lend
Unbound: Will not lend
Loan Period: N/A
Renewable: N/A
Will lend if article exceeds
_____ number of pages (Not
answered)

MICROFORMS:
Will Lend: No
Specific Types of Microforms:
N/A

GOVERNMENT PUBLICATIONS:
Will Lend: No

DISSERTATIONS:
Will Lend: (Not answered)

THESES:
Will Lend: (Not answered)

AUDIO-VISUAL MATERIALS:
Records: Will lend
Cassettes: Will lend
Other (slides, filmstrips,
etc.): Will lend

COMPUTER SOFTWARE:
Will Lend: No

PHOTODUPLICATION SERVICE:
No charge up to 0 exposures
Charge Per Exposure: 15¢
Minimum/handling Fee: (Not
answered)
Average Turnaround Time:
2-3 days

MICROFILMING SERVICE:
Service Available: No
Charges: N/A

DO YOU CHARGE THE BORROWING
LIBRARY FOR POSTAGE? No

FOR HOW LONG DO YOU SUSPEND ILL
SERVICE OVER THE CHRISTMAS
HOLIDAYS? No suspension

ARE THERE ANY GROUPS OF LIBRARIES
FOR WHICH YOU WAIVE FEES? IF
SO, PLEASE NAME THEM: None

UNIVERSITY OF AKRON

NUC CODE: OakU

OCLC CODE: AKR

ADDRESS: Interlibrary Loan
Bierce Library
University of Akron
Akron, OH 44325

TELEPHONE: (216) 375-7234

LIST NAMES OF BRANCHES WITH
SEPARATE POLICIES:
University Law Library
(Akron)--AKL

BOOKS:
Will Lend: Yes
Length of Loan: 2 weeks
Renewable: No
Charges: $5.00
Average Turnaround Time:
Same day
If you have indicated that a
book is not to be lent, will
you on receipt of a letter
from the requesting library
search the index for given
entries? (Not answered)

PERIODICALS:
Bound: Will not lend
Unbound: Will not lend
Loan Period: N/A
Renewable: N/A
Will lend if article exceeds
_____ number of pages (Not
answered)

MICROFORMS:
Will Lend: Yes, selectively
Specific Types of Microforms:
Film, fiche

GOVERNMENT PUBLICATIONS:
Will Lend: No

DISSERTATIONS:
Will Lend: No

THESES:
Will Lend: Yes

AUDIO-VISUAL MATERIALS:
Records: Will not lend
Cassettes: Will not lend
Other (slides, filmstrips,
etc.): Will not lend

COMPUTER SOFTWARE:
Will Lend: No

PHOTODUPLICATION SERVICE:
No charge up to 0 exposures
Charge Per Citation: $10.00
Average Turnaround Time:
(Not answered)

MICROFILMING SERVICE:
Service Available: No
Charges: N/A

DO YOU CHARGE THE BORROWING
LIBRARY FOR POSTAGE? No

FOR HOW LONG DO YOU SUSPEND ILL
SERVICE OVER THE CHRISTMAS
HOLIDAYS? No suspension

ARE THERE ANY GROUPS OF LIBRARIES
FOR WHICH YOU WAIVE FEES? IF
SO, PLEASE NAME THEM: NEOMAL
(Northeastern Ohio Major
Academic Libraries); state
supported libraries inside
Ohio

UNIVERSITY OF CINCINNATI

NUC CODE: OCU

OCLC CODE: CIN

ADDRESS: Interlibrary Loan
University of
Cincinnati Library
Cincinnati, OH 45221

TELEPHONE: (513) 475-2433

LIST NAMES OF BRANCHES WITH
SEPARATE POLICIES: None

BOOKS:
Will Lend: Yes
Length of Loan: 3 weeks
Renewable: Yes
Charges: Postage (out-of-
state only)
Average Turnaround Time:
2 days
If you have indicated that a
book is not to be lent, will
you on receipt of a letter
from the requesting library
search the index for given
entries? Yes

PERIODICALS:
Bound: Will not lend
Unbound: Will not lend
Loan Period: N/A
Renewable: N/A
Will lend if article exceeds
_____ number of pages (Not
answered)

MICROFORMS:
Will Lend: Yes
Specific Types of Microforms:
Microfilm, microfiche

GOVERNMENT PUBLICATIONS:
Will Lend: Yes

DISSERTATIONS:
Will Lend: Yes; 1954 to
present available from
University Microfilms

THESES:
Will Lend: Yes

AUDIO-VISUAL MATERIALS:
Records: Will not lend
Cassettes: Will not lend
Other (slides, filmstrips,
etc.): Will not lend

COMPUTER SOFTWARE:
Will Lend: Do not own

PHOTODUPLICATION SERVICE:
No charge up to 0 exposures
Charge Per Exposure: 20¢
Minimum/handling Fee: $2.00
Average Turnaround Time:
2 days

MICROFILMING SERVICE:
Service Available: No
Charges: N/A

DO YOU CHARGE THE BORROWING
LIBRARY FOR POSTAGE? For
books only

FOR HOW LONG DO YOU SUSPEND ILL
SERVICE OVER THE CHRISTMAS
HOLIDAYS? Dec.15-Jan.2

ARE THERE ANY GROUPS OF LIBRARIES
FOR WHICH YOU WAIVE FEES? IF
SO, PLEASE NAME THEM: No
postage charged for Ohio
libraries; no charge for
photocopies to state-
affiliated universities

UNIVERSITY OF TOLEDO

NUC CODE: OTU

OCLC CODE: TOL

ADDRESS: Interlibrary Loan
University of Toledo
Libraries
Toledo, OH 43606

TELEPHONE: (419) 537-2808

LIST NAMES OF BRANCHES WITH
SEPARATE POLICIES: None

BOOKS:
Will Lend: Yes
Length of Loan: 2 weeks
Renewable: Yes
Charges: (Not answered)
Average Turnaround Time:
(Not answered)
If you have indicated that a
book is not to be lent, will
you on receipt of a letter
from the requesting library
search the index for given
entries? (Not answered)

PERIODICALS:
Bound: Will not lend
Unbound: Will not lend
Loan Period: N/A
Renewable: N/A
Will lend if article exceeds
_____ number of pages (Not
answered)

MICROFORMS:
Will Lend: Yes
Specific Types of Microforms:
(Not answered)

GOVERNMENT PUBLICATIONS:
Will Lend: No

DISSERTATIONS:
Will Lend: Yes

THESES:
Will Lend: Yes

AUDIO-VISUAL MATERIALS:
Records: Will not lend
Cassettes: Will not lend
Other (slides, filmstrips,
etc.): Will not lend

COMPUTER SOFTWARE:
Will Lend: No

PHOTODUPLICATION SERVICE:
No charge up to 0 exposures
Charge Per Exposure: 10¢
Minimum Fee: $2.50
Average Turnaround Time:
(Not answered)

MICROFILMING SERVICE:
Service Available: (Not
answered)
Charges: N/A

DO YOU CHARGE THE BORROWING
LIBRARY FOR POSTAGE? No

FOR HOW LONG DO YOU SUSPEND ILL
SERVICE OVER THE CHRISTMAS
HOLIDAYS? No suspension

ARE THERE ANY GROUPS OF LIBRARIES
FOR WHICH YOU WAIVE FEES? IF
SO, PLEASE NAME THEM: State
university libraries in
Ohio

NO LOANS OR PHOTOCOPIES TO PUBLIC
LIBRARIES OUTSIDE OF OHIO

UPPER ARLINGTON PUBLIC LIBRARY

NUC CODE: (Not answered)

OCLC CODE: UAP

ADDRESS: Interlibrary Loan
Upper Arlington Public
Library
2800 Tremont Rd.
Upper Arlington, OH
43221

TELEPHONE: (614) 486-9621

LIST NAMES OF BRANCHES WITH
SEPARATE POLICIES:
Lane Road Branch--No ILL
Miller Park Branch--No ILL

BOOKS:
Will Lend: Yes
Length of Loan: 28 days
Renewable: Yes
Charges: None
Average Turnaround Time:
3 days
If you have indicated that a
book is not to be lent, will
you on receipt of a letter
from the requesting library
search the index for given
entries? Yes

PERIODICALS:
Bound: Will not lend
Unbound: Will not lend
Loan Period: N/A
Renewable: N/A
Will lend if article exceeds
_____ number of pages (Will
not lend, regardless of
length of article)

MICROFORMS:
Will Lend: No
Specific Types of Microforms:
N/A

GOVERNMENT PUBLICATIONS:
Will Lend: No

DISSERTATIONS:
Will Lend: No

THESES:
Will Lend: No

AUDIO-VISUAL MATERIALS:
Records: Will not lend
Cassettes: Will not lend
Other (slides, filmstrips,
etc.): Will not lend

COMPUTER SOFTWARE:
Will Lend: No

PHOTODUPLICATION SERVICE:
No charge up to 0 exposures
Charge Per Exposure: 10¢
Minimum/handling Fee: None
Average Turnaround Time:
3 days

MICROFILMING SERVICE:
Service Available: No
Charges: N/A

DO YOU CHARGE THE BORROWING
LIBRARY FOR POSTAGE? No

FOR HOW LONG DO YOU SUSPEND ILL
SERVICE OVER THE CHRISTMAS
HOLIDAYS? No suspension

ARE THERE ANY GROUPS OF LIBRARIES
FOR WHICH YOU WAIVE FEES? IF
SO, PLEASE NAME THEM: None

WITTENBERG UNIVERSITY

NUC CODE: OSW

OCLC CODE: WIT

ADDRESS: Interlibrary Loan
Wittenberg University
P. O. Box 720
Springfield, OH 45501

TELEPHONE: (513) 327-7514

LIST NAMES OF BRANCHES WITH
SEPARATE POLICIES: None

BOOKS:
Will Lend: Yes
Length of Loan: 3 weeks
Renewable: Yes
Charges: None
Average Turnaround Time:
24 hours
If you have indicated that a
book is not to be lent, will
you on receipt of a letter
from the requesting library
search the index for given
entries? (Not answered)

PERIODICALS:
Bound: Will not lend
Unbound: Will not lend
Loan Period: N/A
Renewable: N/A
Will lend if article exceeds
_____ number of pages (Not
answered)

MICROFORMS:
Will Lend: Yes, except
periodicals
Specific Types of Microforms:
(Not answered)

GOVERNMENT PUBLICATIONS:
Will Lend: Yes

DISSERTATIONS:
Will Lend: Yes, if 2nd copy
available

THESES:
Will Lend: Yes, if 2nd copy
available

AUDIO-VISUAL MATERIALS:
Records: Will not lend
Cassettes: Will not lend
Other (slides, filmstrips,
etc.): Will not lend

COMPUTER SOFTWARE:
Will Lend: No

PHOTODUPLICATION SERVICE:
No charge up to 0 exposures
Charge Per Exposure: 10¢
Minimum/handling Fee: $2.00
Average Turnaround Time:
24 hours

MICROFILMING SERVICE:
Service Available: No
Charges: N/A

DO YOU CHARGE THE BORROWING
LIBRARY FOR POSTAGE? No

FOR HOW LONG DO YOU SUSPEND ILL
SERVICE OVER THE CHRISTMAS
HOLIDAYS? 2 weeks

ARE THERE ANY GROUPS OF LIBRARIES
FOR WHICH YOU WAIVE FEES? IF
SO, PLEASE NAME THEM:
Dayton-Miami Valley
Consortium; Ohio libraries

WRIGHT STATE UNIVERSITY

NUC CODE: ODaWU

OCLC CODE: WSU

ADDRESS: Interlibrary Loan
Wright State University
Library
Dayton, OH 45435

TELEPHONE: (513) 873-2289

LIST NAMES OF BRANCHES WITH
SEPARATE POLICIES: None

BOOKS:
Will Lend: Yes
Length of Loan: 4 weeks from
date sent
Renewable: Yes
Charges: None
Average Turnaround Time:
2 days
If you have indicated that a
book is not to be lent, will
you on receipt of a letter
from the requesting library
search the index for given
entries? (Not answered)

PERIODICALS:
Bound: Will not lend
Unbound: Will not lend
Loan Period: N/A
Renewable: N/A
Will lend if article exceeds
_____ number of pages (Will
not lend, regardless of
length of article)

MICROFORMS:
Will Lend: Yes, some of them
Specific Types of Microforms:
Microfilm and microfiche

GOVERNMENT PUBLICATIONS:
Will Lend: Yes

DISSERTATIONS:
Will Lend: Yes

THESES:
Will Lend: Yes

AUDIO-VISUAL MATERIALS:
Records: Will not lend
Cassettes: Will not lend
Other (slides, filmstrips,
etc.): Will not lend

COMPUTER SOFTWARE:
Will Lend: No

PHOTODUPLICATION SERVICE:
No charge up to 0 exposures
Charge Per Exposure: 10¢
Minimum/handling Fee: $3.00
Average Turnaround Time:
(Not answered)

MICROFILMING SERVICE:
Service Available: No
Charges: N/A

DO YOU CHARGE THE BORROWING
LIBRARY FOR POSTAGE? No

FOR HOW LONG DO YOU SUSPEND ILL
SERVICE OVER THE CHRISTMAS
HOLIDAYS? No suspension

ARE THERE ANY GROUPS OF LIBRARIES
FOR WHICH YOU WAIVE FEES? IF
SO, PLEASE NAME THEM: State
university libraries in
Ohio; hospital libraries in
the Dayton area; some government libraries in the area

YOUNGSTOWN PUBLIC LIBRARY

NUC CODE: OY

OCLC CODE: YMM

ADDRESS: Interlibrary Loan
           Youngstown Public
           Library
           305 Wick Ave.
           Youngstown, OH 44503

TELEPHONE: (216) 744-8636, X41

LIST NAMES OF BRANCHES WITH
   SEPARATE POLICIES: None

BOOKS:
   Will Lend: Yes
   Length of Loan: 1 month
   Renewable: No
   Charges: $5.00 out-of-state
      fee
   Average Turnaround Time:
      1 day
   If you have indicated that a
      book is not to be lent, will
      you on receipt of a letter
      from the requesting library
      search the index for given
      entries? (Not answered)

PERIODICALS:
   Bound: Will not lend
   Unbound: Will not lend
   Loan Period: N/A
   Renewable: N/A
   Will lend if article exceeds
      _____ number of pages (Not
      answered)

MICROFORMS:
   Will Lend: No
   Specific Types of Microforms:
      N/A

GOVERNMENT PUBLICATIONS:
   Will Lend: No

DISSERTATIONS:
   Will Lend: Do not own

THESES:
   Will Lend: Do not own

AUDIO-VISUAL MATERIALS:
   Records: Do not own
   Cassettes: Do not own
   Other (slides, filmstrips,
      etc.): Do not own

COMPUTER SOFTWARE:
   Will Lend: Do not own

PHOTODUPLICATION SERVICE:
   No charge up to 2 exposures
   Charge Per Exposure: 25¢
   Minimum/handling Fee: None
   Average Turnaround Time:
      1 day

MICROFILMING SERVICE:
   Service Available: No
   Charges: N/A

DO YOU CHARGE THE BORROWING
   LIBRARY FOR POSTAGE? No

FOR HOW LONG DO YOU SUSPEND ILL
   SERVICE OVER THE CHRISTMAS
   HOLIDAYS? No suspension

ARE THERE ANY GROUPS OF LIBRARIES
   FOR WHICH YOU WAIVE FEES? IF
   SO, PLEASE NAME THEM: None

YOUNGSTOWN STATE UNIVERSITY

NUC CODE: OYC

OCLC CODE: YNG

ADDRESS: Interlibrary Loan
           Youngstown State
              University
           William F. Maag Library
           Youngstown, OH 44555

TELEPHONE: (216) 742-3680

LIST NAMES OF BRANCHES WITH
   SEPARATE POLICIES: None

BOOKS:
   Will Lend: Yes
   Length of Loan: 28 days
   Renewable: Yes
   Charges: Reciprocal
   Average Turnaround Time:
      1 day
   If you have indicated that a
      book is not to be lent, will
      you on receipt of a letter
      from the requesting library
      search the index for given
      entries? (Not answered)

PERIODICALS:
   Bound: Will not lend
   Unbound: Will not lend
   Loan Period: N/A
   Renewable: N/A
   Will lend if article exceeds
      _____ number of pages (Not
      answered)

MICROFORMS:
   Will Lend: Yes
   Specific Types of Microforms:
      Film, fiche

GOVERNMENT PUBLICATIONS:
   Will Lend: Yes

DISSERTATIONS:
   Will Lend: Do not own

THESES:
   Will Lend: Yes

AUDIO-VISUAL MATERIALS:
   Records: Will not lend
   Cassettes: Will not lend
   Other (slides, filmstrips,
      etc.): Will not lend

COMPUTER SOFTWARE:
   Will Lend: No

PHOTODUPLICATION SERVICE:
   No charge up to 0 exposures
   Charge Per Exposure: 20¢
      for hardcopy; 40¢ from
      microform
   Minimum/handling Fee: (Not
      answered)
   Average Turnaround Time:
      1 day

MICROFILMING SERVICE:
   Service Available: No
   Charges: N/A

DO YOU CHARGE THE BORROWING
   LIBRARY FOR POSTAGE? 50¢
      in-state, $1.00 out-of-
      state, for library rate
      (first-class doubled)

FOR HOW LONG DO YOU SUSPEND ILL
   SERVICE OVER THE CHRISTMAS
   HOLIDAYS? No suspension

ARE THERE ANY GROUPS OF LIBRARIES
   FOR WHICH YOU WAIVE FEES? IF
   SO, PLEASE NAME THEM: None

METROPOLITAN LIBRARY SYSTEM

NUC CODE: OkOk

OCLC CODE: OKE

ADDRESS: Interlibrary Loan
           Metropolitan Library
             System
           131 Dean McGee Ave.
           Oklahoma City, OK
           73102

TELEPHONE: (405) 235-0571, X19

LIST NAMES OF BRANCHES WITH
  SEPARATE POLICIES: None

BOOKS:
  Will Lend: Yes
  Length of Loan: 30 days
  Renewable: Yes
  Charges: None
  Average Turnaround Time:
    Cannot estimate at this
    time
  If you have indicated that a
    book is not to be lent, will
    you on receipt of a letter
    from the requesting library
    search the index for given
    entries? (Not answered)

PERIODICALS:
  Bound: Will not lend
  Unbound: Will not lend
  Loan Period: N/A
  Renewable: N/A
  Will lend if article exceeds
    _____ number of pages (Not
    answered)

MICROFORMS:
  Will Lend: No
  Specific Types of Microforms:
    N/A

GOVERNMENT PUBLICATIONS:
  Will Lend: Yes, some of them

DISSERTATIONS:
  Will Lend: Yes

THESES:
  Will Lend: Yes

AUDIO-VISUAL MATERIALS:
  Records: Will not lend
  Cassettes: Will not lend
  Other (slides, filmstrips,
    etc.): (Not answered)

COMPUTER SOFTWARE:
  Will Lend: No

PHOTODUPLICATION SERVICE:
  No charge up to 50 exposures
    for AMIGOS members
  Charge Per Exposure: 15¢
  Minimum/handling Fee:
    (Not answered)
  Average Turnaround Time:
    Cannot estimate at this
    time

MICROFILMING SERVICE:
  Service Available: No
  Charges: N/A

DO YOU CHARGE THE BORROWING
  LIBRARY FOR POSTAGE? No

FOR HOW LONG DO YOU SUSPEND ILL
  SERVICE OVER THE CHRISTMAS
  HOLIDAYS? No suspension

ARE THERE ANY GROUPS OF LIBRARIES
  FOR WHICH YOU WAIVE FEES? IF
  SO, PLEASE NAME THEM: AMIGOS

OKLAHOMA DEPARTMENT OF LIBRARIES

NUC CODE: Ok

OCLC CODE: OKD

ADDRESS: Interlibrary Loan
           Oklahoma Department of
             Libraries
           200 N.E. 18th St.
           Oklahoma City, OK
           73105

TELEPHONE: (405) 521-2502

LIST NAMES OF BRANCHES WITH
  SEPARATE POLICIES: None

BOOKS:
  Will Lend: Yes
  Length of Loan: 1 month
  Renewable: Yes
  Charges: Insurance one-way
    for Oklahoma items and a
    few other items
  Average Turnaround Time:
    24-48 hours
  If you have indicated that a
    book is not to be lent, will
    you on receipt of a letter
    from the requesting library
    search the index for given
    entries? Yes

PERIODICALS:
  Bound: Will lend, except for
    law periodicals
  Unbound: Will lend, except
    for law periodicals
  Loan Period: 1 month
  Renewable: Yes
  Will lend if article exceeds
    50 pages

MICROFORMS:
  Will Lend: Yes
  Specific Types of Microforms:
    (Not answered)

GOVERNMENT PUBLICATIONS:
  Will Lend: Yes

DISSERTATIONS:
  Will Lend: Do not own

THESES:
  Will Lend: Do not own

AUDIO-VISUAL MATERIALS:
  Records: Will not lend
  Cassettes: Will not lend
  Other (slides, filmstrips,
    etc.): Will not lend

COMPUTER SOFTWARE:
  Will Lend: Do not own

PHOTODUPLICATION SERVICE:
  No charge up to 0 exposures
  Charge Per Exposure: 20¢
  Minimum/handling Fee: $2.00
  Average Turnaround Time:
    24-48 hours

MICROFILMING SERVICE:
  Service Available: Yes
  Charges: Available upon
    request

DO YOU CHARGE THE BORROWING
  LIBRARY FOR POSTAGE? No

FOR HOW LONG DO YOU SUSPEND ILL
  SERVICE OVER THE CHRISTMAS
  HOLIDAYS? No suspension

ARE THERE ANY GROUPS OF LIBRARIES
  FOR WHICH YOU WAIVE FEES? IF
  SO, PLEASE NAME THEM: AMIGOS;
  any library willing to
  participate in a reciprocal
  agreement

OKLAHOMA STATE UNIVERSITY

NUC CODE: OkS

OCLC CODE: OKS

ADDRESS: Interlibrary Loan
Oklahoma State
University Library
Stillwater, OK 74078

TELEPHONE: (405) 624-6313

LIST NAMES OF BRANCHES WITH
SEPARATE POLICIES: None

BOOKS:
Will Lend: Yes
Length of Loan: 1 month
Renewable: No
Charges: (Not answered)
Average Turnaround Time:
48 hours
If you have indicated that a
book is not to be lent, will
you on receipt of a letter
from the requesting library
search the index for given
entries? (Not answered)

PERIODICALS:
Bound: Will not lend
Unbound: Will not lend
Loan Period: N/A
Renewable: N/A
Will lend if article exceeds
_____ number of pages (Not
answered)

MICROFORMS:
Will Lend: Yes
Specific Types of Microforms:
All types

GOVERNMENT PUBLICATIONS:
Will Lend: (Not answered)

DISSERTATIONS:
Will Lend: Yes

THESES:
Will Lend: Yes

AUDIO-VISUAL MATERIALS:
Records: (Not answered)
Cassettes: (Not answered)
Other (slides, filmstrips,
etc.): (Not answered)

COMPUTER SOFTWARE:
Will Lend: (Not answered)

PHOTODUPLICATION SERVICE:
No charge up to 20 exposures
Charge Per Exposure: 15¢
Minimum Fee: $2.50
Average Turnaround Time:
48 hours

MICROFILMING SERVICE:
Service Available: No
Charges: N/A

DO YOU CHARGE THE BORROWING
LIBRARY FOR POSTAGE? No

FOR HOW LONG DO YOU SUSPEND ILL
SERVICE OVER THE CHRISTMAS
HOLIDAYS? No suspension

ARE THERE ANY GROUPS OF LIBRARIES
FOR WHICH YOU WAIVE FEES? IF
SO, PLEASE NAME THEM: (Not
answered)

PIONEER MULTI-COUNTY LIBRARY

NUC CODE: OKN

OCLC CODE: OKM

ADDRESS: Interlibrary Loan
Pioneer Multi-County
Library
225 N. Webster St.
Norman, OK 73069

TELEPHONE: (405) 321-1481

LIST NAMES OF BRANCHES WITH
SEPARATE POLICIES: None

BOOKS:
Will Lend: Yes
Length of Loan: 3-4 weeks
Renewable: Yes, generally
Charges: None
Average Turnaround Time:
(Not answered)
If you have indicated that a
book is not to be lent, will
you on receipt of a letter
from the requesting library
search the index for given
entries? Yes

PERIODICALS:
Bound: Will not lend
Unbound: Will not lend
Loan Period: N/A
Renewable: N/A
Will lend if article exceeds
_____ number of pages (Not
answered)

MICROFORMS:
Will Lend: Yes
Specific Types of Microforms:
Microfilm

GOVERNMENT PUBLICATIONS:
Will Lend: Do not own

DISSERTATIONS:
Will Lend: Do not own

THESES:
Will Lend: Do not own

AUDIO-VISUAL MATERIALS:
Records: Will not lend
Cassettes: Will not lend
Other (slides, filmstrips,
etc.): Will not lend

COMPUTER SOFTWARE:
Will Lend: No

PHOTODUPLICATION SERVICE:
No charge up to 0 exposures
Charge Per Exposure: 10¢
Minimum/handling Fee: $1.00
minimum
Average Turnaround Time:
1 week

MICROFILMING SERVICE:
Service Available: No
Charges: N/A

DO YOU CHARGE THE BORROWING
LIBRARY FOR POSTAGE? No

FOR HOW LONG DO YOU SUSPEND ILL
SERVICE OVER THE CHRISTMAS
HOLIDAYS? No suspension

ARE THERE ANY GROUPS OF LIBRARIES
FOR WHICH YOU WAIVE FEES? IF
SO, PLEASE NAME THEM:
Signers of AMIGOS ILL Code

TULSA CITY-COUNTY LIBRARY

NUC CODE: OkT

OCLC CODE: TUL

ADDRESS: Interlibrary Loan
Tulsa City-County
Library
400 Civil Center
Tulsa, OK 74103

TELEPHONE: (918) 581-5320

LIST NAMES OF BRANCHES WITH
SEPARATE POLICIES: None

BOOKS:
Will Lend: Yes
Length of Loan: 1 month
from shipping date
Renewable: No
Charges: None
Average Turnaround Time:
1 week
If you have indicated that a
book is not to be lent, will
you on receipt of a letter
from the requesting library
search the index for given
entries? Yes

PERIODICALS:
Bound: Will not lend
Unbound: Will not lend
Loan Period: N/A
Renewable: N/A
Will lend if article exceeds
_____ number of pages (Will
not lend, regardless of
length of article)

MICROFORMS:
Will Lend: No
Specific Types of Microforms:
Fiche, film

GOVERNMENT PUBLICATIONS:
Will Lend: Yes

DISSERTATIONS:
Will Lend: Do not own

THESES:
Will Lend: Do not own

AUDIO-VISUAL MATERIALS:
Records: Will lend
Cassettes: Will lend
Other (slides, filmstrips,
etc.): Will not lend

COMPUTER SOFTWARE:
Will Lend: No

PHOTODUPLICATION SERVICE:
No charge up to 0 exposures
Charge Per Exposure: 10¢
Minimum/handling Fee: $1.00
Average Turnaround Time:
1 week

MICROFILMING SERVICE:
Service Available: No
Charges: N/A

DO YOU CHARGE THE BORROWING
LIBRARY FOR POSTAGE? No

FOR HOW LONG DO YOU SUSPEND ILL
SERVICE OVER THE CHRISTMAS
HOLIDAYS? No suspension

ARE THERE ANY GROUPS OF LIBRARIES
FOR WHICH YOU WAIVE FEES? IF
SO, PLEASE NAME THEM: AMIGOS
libraries

UNIVERSITY OF OKLAHOMA

NUC CODE: OkU

OCLC CODE: OKU

ADDRESS: Interlibrary Loan
University of Oklahoma
Libraries
401 W. Brooks
Norman, OK 73019

TELEPHONE: (405) 325-6422

LIST NAMES OF BRANCHES WITH
SEPARATE POLICIES: None

BOOKS:
Will Lend: Yes
Length of Loan: 1 month
Renewable: No
Charges: None
Average Turnaround Time:
2 days
If you have indicated that a
book is not to be lent, will
you on receipt of a letter
from the requesting library
search the index for given
entries? (Not answered)

PERIODICALS:
Bound: Will lend
Unbound: Will lend
Loan Period: 2 weeks
Renewable: No
Will lend if article exceeds
50 pages

MICROFORMS:
Will Lend: Yes
Specific Types of Microforms:
(Not answered)

GOVERNMENT PUBLICATIONS:
Will Lend: Yes

DISSERTATIONS:
Will Lend: Yes; 1953 to
present available from
University Microfilms

THESES:
Will Lend: Yes

AUDIO-VISUAL MATERIALS:
Records: Will not lend
Cassettes: Will not lend
Other (slides, filmstrips,
etc.): Will not lend

COMPUTER SOFTWARE:
Will Lend: No

PHOTODUPLICATION SERVICE:
No charge up to 0 exposures
Charge Per Exposure: 10¢
Handling Fee: $3.00
Average Turnaround Time:
3 days

MICROFILMING SERVICE:
Service Available: No
Charges: N/A

DO YOU CHARGE THE BORROWING
LIBRARY FOR POSTAGE? No

FOR HOW LONG DO YOU SUSPEND ILL
SERVICE OVER THE CHRISTMAS
HOLIDAYS? 1 week

ARE THERE ANY GROUPS OF LIBRARIES
FOR WHICH YOU WAIVE FEES? IF
SO, PLEASE NAME THEM: RLG;
CARLA; MASUA; school, public
and academic libraries in
Oklahoma

UNIVERSITY OF OKLAHOMA AT OKLAHOMA CITY -- HEALTH SCIENCES CENTER

NUC CODE: OKU M

OCLC CODE: OKH

ADDRESS: Interlibrary Loan
University of Oklahoma
at Oklahoma City --
Health Sciences
Center Library
P. O. Box 26901
Oklahoma City, OK
73190

TELEPHONE: (405) 271-2343

LIST NAMES OF BRANCHES WITH
SEPARATE POLICIES: None

BOOKS:
Will Lend: Yes
Length of Loan: 3 weeks
Renewable: Yes
Charges: $4.00 except where
covered by special
contractual agreements
Average Turnaround Time:
24 hours
If you have indicated that a
book is not to be lent, will
you on receipt of a letter
from the requesting library
search the index for given
entries? Yes

PERIODICALS:
Bound: Will not lend
Unbound: Will not lend
Loan Period: N/A
Renewable: N/A
Will lend if article exceeds
_____ number of pages (Not
answered)

MICROFORMS:
Will Lend: Do not own
Specific Types of Microforms:
N/A

GOVERNMENT PUBLICATIONS:
Will Lend: Yes

DISSERTATIONS:
Will Lend: Yes, 1954 to
present

THESES:
Will Lend: Yes, 1954 to
present

AUDIO-VISUAL MATERIALS:
Records: (Not answered)
Cassettes: Will lend
Other (slides, filmstrips,
etc.): Will lend

COMPUTER SOFTWARE:
Will Lend: Do not own

PHOTODUPLICATION SERVICE:
No charge up to 0 exposures
Charge Per Exposure: (Not
answered)
Minimum/handling Fee: $4.00
Average Turnaround Time:
24 hours

MICROFILMING SERVICE:
Service Available: No
Charges: N/A

DO YOU CHARGE THE BORROWING
LIBRARY FOR POSTAGE? No

FOR HOW LONG DO YOU SUSPEND ILL
SERVICE OVER THE CHRISTMAS
HOLIDAYS? 2 weeks

ARE THERE ANY GROUPS OF LIBRARIES
FOR WHICH YOU WAIVE FEES? IF
SO, PLEASE NAME THEM: OU,
OSU, ODL, TALON Resource
libraries, OCLC OK public
libraries for monographs,
medical students on
preceptorship

UNIVERSITY OF TULSA

NUC CODE: OkTU

OCLC CODE: OKT

ADDRESS: Interlibrary Loan
McFarlin Library
University of Tulsa
Tulsa, OK 74104

TELEPHONE: (918) 592-6000, X2879

LIST NAMES OF BRANCHES WITH
SEPARATE POLICIES:
College of Law Library
For material cited in
Petroleum Abstracts,
please address requests
to: Sidney Born Technical
Library; University of
Tulsa; Tulsa, OK 74104

BOOKS:
Will Lend: Yes, except for
special collections, rare,
and reference books
Length of Loan: 4 weeks use
Renewable: Yes, sometimes
Charges: None
Average Turnaround Time:
24 hours
If you have indicated that a
book is not to be lent, will
you on receipt of a letter
from the requesting library
search the index for given
entries? Yes, as staff
workload permits

PERIODICALS:
Bound: Will not lend
Unbound: Will not lend
Loan Period: N/A
Renewable: N/A
Will lend if article exceeds
_____ number of pages (Not
answered)

MICROFORMS:
Will Lend: Yes
Specific Types of Microforms:
Film, fiche, print, card

GOVERNMENT PUBLICATIONS:
Will Lend: Yes

DISSERTATIONS:
Will Lend: Yes, pre-1968.
1968 to present available
from University Microfilms

THESES:
Will Lend: Yes, pre-1968.
1968 to present available
from University Microfilms

AUDIO-VISUAL MATERIALS:
Records: Will not lend
Cassettes: Will not lend
Other (slides, filmstrips,
etc.): Will lend

COMPUTER SOFTWARE:
Will Lend: Do not own

PHOTODUPLICATION SERVICE:
Photocopying is currently
free to not-for-profit
organizations only. For-
profit organizations are
charged 40¢ per page.
Average Turnaround Time:
24 hours

MICROFILMING SERVICE:
Service Available: No
Charges: N/A

DO YOU CHARGE THE BORROWING
LIBRARY FOR POSTAGE? No

FOR HOW LONG DO YOU SUSPEND ILL
SERVICE OVER THE CHRISTMAS
HOLIDAYS? Approximately
last week in Dec.-first
week in Jan.

ARE THERE ANY GROUPS OF LIBRARIES
FOR WHICH YOU WAIVE FEES? IF
SO, PLEASE NAME THEM: Non-
profit organizations

JACKSON COUNTY LIBRARY

NUC CODE: (Not answered)

OCLC CODE: JCL

ADDRESS: Interlibrary Loan
Jackson County Library
413 W. Main
Medford, OR   97501

TELEPHONE: (503) 776-7281

LIST NAMES OF BRANCHES WITH
SEPARATE POLICIES:
Ashland Branch

BOOKS:
Will Lend: Yes, most of them
Length of Loan: 4 weeks
Renewable: No
Charges: Postage
Average Turnaround Time:
Varies
If you have indicated that a
book is not to be lent, will
you on receipt of a letter
from the requesting library
search the index for given
entries?   Yes

PERIODICALS:
Bound: Will not lend
Unbound: Will lend
Loan Period: 2 weeks
Renewable: No
Will lend if article exceeds
_____ number of pages
(Depends on the situation)

MICROFORMS:
Will Lend: Yes
Specific Types of Microforms:
Newspapers

GOVERNMENT PUBLICATIONS:
Will Lend: Yes

DISSERTATIONS:
Will Lend: Do not own

THESES:
Will Lend: Do not own

AUDIO-VISUAL MATERIALS:
Records: Do not own
Cassettes: Do not own
Other (slides, filmstrips,
etc.):   Do not own

COMPUTER SOFTWARE:
Will Lend: Do not own

PHOTODUPLICATION SERVICE:
No charge up to 0 exposures
Charge Per Exposure: 10¢
Minimum/handling Fee: (Not
answered)
Average Turnaround Time:
Varies

MICROFILMING SERVICE:
Service Available: No
Charges: N/A

DO YOU CHARGE THE BORROWING
LIBRARY FOR POSTAGE?   Yes

FOR HOW LONG DO YOU SUSPEND ILL
SERVICE OVER THE CHRISTMAS
HOLIDAYS?   No suspension

ARE THERE ANY GROUPS OF LIBRARIES
FOR WHICH YOU WAIVE FEES?   IF
SO, PLEASE NAME THEM: SOLF
(Southern Oregon Library
Federation)

LIBRARY ASSOCIATION OF PORTLAND

NUC CODE: OrP

OCLC CODE: (Not answered)

ADDRESS: Interlibrary Loan
Library Association
of Portland
801 Southwest 10th Ave.
Portland, OR   97205

TELEPHONE: (503) 223-7201, X267

LIST NAMES OF BRANCHES WITH
SEPARATE POLICIES: None

BOOKS:
Will Lend: Yes
Length of Loan: 3 weeks use
Renewable: Yes
Charges: None
Average Turnaround Time:
2 weeks
If you have indicated that a
book is not to be lent, will
you on receipt of a letter
from the requesting library
search the index for given
entries?   (Not answered)

PERIODICALS:
Bound: Will not lend
Unbound: Will not lend
Loan Period: N/A
Renewable: N/A
Will lend if article exceeds
_____ number of pages (Not
answered)

MICROFORMS:
Will Lend: No
Specific Types of Microforms:
N/A

GOVERNMENT PUBLICATIONS:
Will Lend: Yes, but subject
to department head's
approval

DISSERTATIONS:
Will Lend: Do not own

THESES:
Will Lend: Do not own

AUDIO-VISUAL MATERIALS:
Records: Will not lend
Cassettes: Will not lend
Other (slides, filmstrips,
etc.):   Will not lend

COMPUTER SOFTWARE:
Will Lend: No

PHOTODUPLICATION SERVICE:
No charge up to 10 exposures
Charge Per Exposure: 10¢
Minimum/handling Fee: None
Average Turnaround Time:
2 weeks

MICROFILMING SERVICE:
Service Available: No
Charges: N/A

DO YOU CHARGE THE BORROWING
LIBRARY FOR POSTAGE?   Yes

FOR HOW LONG DO YOU SUSPEND ILL
SERVICE OVER THE CHRISTMAS
HOLIDAYS?   2 weeks out-of-
state

ARE THERE ANY GROUPS OF LIBRARIES
FOR WHICH YOU WAIVE FEES?   IF
SO, PLEASE NAME THEM: No
photocopying charges to
Oregon libraries.

OREGON HEALTH SCIENCES UNIVERSITY MEDICAL LIBRARY

NUC CODE: ORPHS (formerly ORU-M)

OCLC CODE: OHS

ADDRESS: Interlibrary Loan
Medical Library
Oregon Health Sciences
University
3181 SW Sam Jackson
Park Road (97201)
P. O. Box 573
(97207-0573)
Portland, OR (See
above for P.O. Box
or street address
zip)

TELEPHONE: (503) 225-8026, 8027,
or 8028

LIST NAMES OF BRANCHES WITH
SEPARATE POLICIES:
Dental Library
Oregon Health Sciences
University
611 SW Campus Dr.
Portland, OR 97201

BOOKS:
Will Lend: Yes
Length of Loan: 14 days use
Renewable: Yes
Charges: In-state, $5.00;
out-of-state, $6.00
Average Turnaround Time:
1 day
If you have indicated that a
book is not to be lent, will
you on receipt of a letter
from the requesting library
search the index for given
entries? This would apply
to Class Reserve
materials and Reference
items.

PERIODICALS:
Bound: Will lend those 6
years or older
Unbound: Will lend those 6
years or older
Loan Period: 3-7 days
Renewable: Yes
Will lend if article exceeds
_____ number of pages (Not
answered)

MICROFORMS:
Will Lend: (Not answered)
Specific Types of Microforms:
N/A

GOVERNMENT PUBLICATIONS:
Will Lend: Yes

DISSERTATIONS:
Will Lend: Yes

THESES:
Will Lend: Yes

AUDIO-VISUAL MATERIALS:
Records: Will lend
Cassettes: Will lend
Other (slides, filmstrips,
etc.): Will not lend

COMPUTER SOFTWARE:
Will Lend: No

PHOTODUPLICATION SERVICE:
No charge up to _____ exposures
(Not answered)
Charge Per Exposure: (Not
answered)
Minimum/handling Fee: Regular
loan fee
Average Turnaround Time:
1 day

MICROFILMING SERVICE:
Service Available: No
Charges: N/A

DO YOU CHARGE THE BORROWING
LIBRARY FOR POSTAGE? No

FOR HOW LONG DO YOU SUSPEND ILL
SERVICE OVER THE CHRISTMAS
HOLIDAYS? Dec.15-Jan.2

NUC CODE: Or

OCLC CODE: OSO

ADDRESS: Interlibrary Loan
Oregon State Library
Salem, OR 97310-0640

TELEPHONE: (503) 378-4498

LIST NAMES OF BRANCHES WITH
SEPARATE POLICIES: None

BOOKS:
Will Lend: Yes
Length of Loan: 4 weeks
Renewable: Yes
Charges: None
Average Turnaround Time:
2 days
If you have indicated that a
book is not to be lent, will
you on receipt of a letter
from the requesting library
search the index for given
entries? (Not answered)

PERIODICALS:
Bound: (Not answered)
Unbound: Will lend
Loan Period: 4 weeks
Renewable: Yes
Will lend if article exceeds
_____ number of pages (Not
answered)

MICROFORMS:
Will Lend: Yes
Specific Types of Microforms:
Microfilm and microfiche
(except newspapers). Will
not lend microcards.

ARE THERE ANY GROUPS OF LIBRARIES
FOR WHICH YOU WAIVE FEES? IF
SO, PLEASE NAME THEM: None

OREGON STATE LIBRARY

GOVERNMENT PUBLICATIONS:
Will Lend: Yes

DISSERTATIONS:
Will Lend: Do not own

THESES:
Will Lend: Do not own

AUDIO-VISUAL MATERIALS:
Records: Will not lend
Cassettes: Will not lend
Other (slides, filmstrips,
etc.): Do not own

COMPUTER SOFTWARE:
Will Lend: Do not own

PHOTODUPLICATION SERVICE:
No charge up to 0 exposures
Charge Per Exposure: 10¢
Minimum/handling Fee: (Not
answered)
Average Turnaround Time:
2-3 days

MICROFILMING SERVICE:
Service Available: No
Charges: N/A

DO YOU CHARGE THE BORROWING
LIBRARY FOR POSTAGE? No

FOR HOW LONG DO YOU SUSPEND ILL
SERVICE OVER THE CHRISTMAS
HOLIDAYS? No suspension

ARE THERE ANY GROUPS OF LIBRARIES
FOR WHICH YOU WAIVE FEES? IF
SO, PLEASE NAME THEM: None

OREGON STATE UNIVERSITY

NUC CODE: OrCS

OCLC CODE: ORE

ADDRESS: Interlibrary Loan
Oregon State University
Library
Corvallis, OR 97331

TELEPHONE: (503) 754-4488

LIST NAMES OF BRANCHES WITH
SEPARATE POLICIES:
Marine Science Library

BOOKS:
Will Lend: Yes
Length of Loan: 3 weeks
Renewable: No
Charges: Postage
Average Turnaround Time:
Varies
If you have indicated that a
book is not to be lent, will
you on receipt of a letter
from the requesting library
search the index for given
entries? (Not answered)

PERIODICALS:
Bound: Will not lend
Unbound: Will not lend
Loan Period: N/A
Renewable: N/A
Will lend if article exceeds
_____ number of pages (Not
answered)

MICROFORMS:
Will Lend: Yes, some of them
Specific Types of Microforms:
(Not answered)

GOVERNMENT PUBLICATIONS:
Will Lend: Yes, some of them

DISSERTATIONS:
Will Lend: No

THESES:
Will Lend: Yes

AUDIO-VISUAL MATERIALS:
Records: Will not lend
Cassettes: Will not lend
Other (slides, filmstrips,
etc.): Will not lend

COMPUTER SOFTWARE:
Will Lend: Do not own

PHOTODUPLICATION SERVICE:
No charge up to 0 exposures
Charge Per Exposure: 10¢
Minimum/handling Fee: $3.00;
$5.00 commercial
Average Turnaround Time:
Varies

MICROFILMING SERVICE:
Service Available: No
Charges: N/A

DO YOU CHARGE THE BORROWING
LIBRARY FOR POSTAGE? Yes,
other than Oregon libraries

FOR HOW LONG DO YOU SUSPEND ILL
SERVICE OVER THE CHRISTMAS
HOLIDAYS? No suspension

ARE THERE ANY GROUPS OF LIBRARIES
FOR WHICH YOU WAIVE FEES? IF
SO, PLEASE NAME THEM: Oregon
academic and public libraries

WARNER PACIFIC COLLEGE

NUC CODE: OrPWP

OCLC CODE: OWP

ADDRESS: Interlibrary Loan
Otto F. Linn Library
Warner Pacific College
2219 S.E. 68th Ave.
Portland, OR 97215

TELEPHONE: (503) 775-4366

LIST NAMES OF BRANCHES WITH
SEPARATE POLICIES: None

BOOKS:
Will Lend: Yes, except for
Reference materials
Length of Loan: 3 weeks
Renewable: Yes
Charges: None
Average Turnaround Time:
(Not answered)
If you have indicated that a
book is not to be lent, will
you on receipt of a letter
from the requesting library
search the index for given
entries? (Not answered)

PERIODICALS:
Bound: Will not lend
Unbound: Will not lend
Loan Period: N/A
Renewable: N/A
Will lend if article exceeds
_____ number of pages
(Will not lend periodical,
but will photocopy article
at 5¢ per page.)

MICROFORMS:
Will Lend: Do not own
Specific Types Of Microforms:
N/A

GOVERNMENT PUBLICATIONS:
Will Lend: Do not own

DISSERTATIONS:
Will Lend: Yes

THESES:
Will Lend: Yes

AUDIO-VISUAL MATERIALS:
Records: Will not lend
Cassettes: Will lend
Other (slides, filmstrips,
etc.): Will lend

COMPUTER SOFTWARE:
Will Lend: Do not own

PHOTODUPLICATION SERVICE:
No charge up to 0 exposures
Charge Per Exposure: 5¢
Minimum/handling Fee: None
Average Turnaround Time: (Not
answered)

MICROFILMING SERVICE:
Service Available: No
Charges: N/A

DO YOU CHARGE THE BORROWING
LIBRARY FOR POSTAGE? Not
usually

FOR HOW LONG DO YOU SUSPEND ILL
SERVICE OVER THE CHRISTMAS
HOLIDAYS? No suspension

ARE THERE ANY GROUPS OF LIBRARIES
FOR WHICH YOU WAIVE FEES? IF
SO, PLEASE NAME THEM:
Virtually all, provided the
request is legitimate.

AMERICAN PHILOSOPHICAL SOCIETY

NUC CODE: PPAmP

OCLC CODE: None

ADDRESS: Interlibrary Loan
American Philosophical
Society Library
105 S. Fifth St.
Philadelphia, PA 19106

TELEPHONE: (215) 627-0706

LIST NAMES OF BRANCHES WITH
SEPARATE POLICIES: None

BOOKS:
Will Lend: Yes, except for
pre-1930 imprints
Length of Loan: 4 weeks
Renewable: Yes
Charges: None
Average Turnaround Time:
1 week
If you have indicated that a
book is not to be lent, will
you on receipt of a letter
from the requesting library
search the index for given
entries? Yes

PERIODICALS:
Bound: Will not lend
Unbound: Will not lend
Loan Period: N/A
Renewable: N/A
Will lend if article exceeds
_____ number of pages (Will
not lend, regardless of
length of article)

MICROFORMS:
Will Lend: Yes, but only
microfilm

GOVERNMENT PUBLICATIONS:
Will Lend: No

DISSERTATIONS:
Will Lend: Do not own

THESES:
Will Lend: Do not own

AUDIO-VISUAL MATERIALS:
Records: Will not lend
Cassettes: Will not lend
Other (slides, filmstrips,
etc.): Will not lend

COMPUTER SOFTWARE:
Will Lend: Do not own

PHOTODUPLICATION SERVICE:
No charge up to 0 exposures
Charge Per Exposure: 10¢
Minimum/handling Fee: $1.00
Average Turnaround Time:
2 weeks

MICROFILMING SERVICE:
Service Available: Yes
Charges: 5¢ per frame

DO YOU CHARGE THE BORROWING
LIBRARY FOR POSTAGE? Yes

FOR HOW LONG DO YOU SUSPEND ILL
SERVICE OVER THE CHRISTMAS
HOLIDAYS? From the second
week in Dec. to Jan.3

ARE THERE ANY GROUPS OF LIBRARIES
FOR WHICH YOU WAIVE FEES? IF
SO, PLEASE NAME THEM: None

BLOOMSBURG STATE COLLEGE

NUC CODE: PBbS

OCLC CODE: PBB

ADDRESS: Interlibrary Loan
Andruss Library
Bloomsburg State
College
Bloomsburg, PA 17815

TELEPHONE: (717) 389-2900

LIST NAMES OF BRANCHES WITH
SEPARATE POLICIES: None

BOOKS:
Will Lend: Yes
Length of Loan: 4 weeks
Renewable: Yes, if no
reserves
Charges: None
Average Turnaround Time:
(Not answered)
If you have indicated that a
book is not to be lent, will
you on receipt of a letter
from the requesting library
search the index for given
entries? Yes

PERIODICALS:
Bound: Will not lend
Unbound: Will not lend
Loan Period: N/A
Renewable: N/A
Will lend if article exceeds
_____ number of pages (Not
answered)

MICROFORMS:
Will Lend: Yes
Specific Types of Microforms:
Microfilm only

GOVERNMENT PUBLICATIONS:
Will Lend: Yes

DISSERTATIONS:
Will Lend: Yes

THESES:
Will Lend: Yes

AUDIO-VISUAL MATERIALS:
Records: Will not lend
Cassettes: Will not lend
Other (slides, filmstrips,
etc.): Will not lend

COMPUTER SOFTWARE:
Will Lend: No

PHOTODUPLICATION SERVICE:
No charge up to 0 exposures
Charge Per Exposure: 20¢
plus $2.50 handling Fee
Handling Fee: $2.50
Average Turnaround Time:
(Not answered)

MICROFILMING SERVICE:
Service Available: No
Charges: N/A

DO YOU CHARGE THE BORROWING
LIBRARY FOR POSTAGE? No

FOR HOW LONG DO YOU SUSPEND ILL
SERVICE OVER THE CHRISTMAS
HOLIDAYS? Approximately
3 weeks

ARE THERE ANY GROUPS OF LIBRARIES
FOR WHICH YOU WAIVE FEES? IF
SO, PLEASE NAME THEM:
Pennsylvania State college
system; Area College Library
Cooperative System (ACLCP);
Susquehanna Library Cooper-
ative (SLC)

BUCKNELL UNIVERSITY

NUC CODE: PLeB

OCLC CODE: PBU

ADDRESS: Interlibrary Loan
          Ellen Clarke Bertrand
          Library
          Bucknell University
          Lewisburg, PA 17837

TELEPHONE: (717) 524-1463

LIST NAMES OF BRANCHES WITH
  SEPARATE POLICIES: None

BOOKS:
  Will Lend: Yes
  Length of Loan: 3 weeks use
  Renewable: Yes
  Charges: None
  Average Turnaround Time:
    2 days
  If you have indicated that a
    book is not to be lent, will
    you on receipt of a letter
    from the requesting library
    search the index for given
    entries? (Not answered)

PERIODICALS:
  Bound: Will not lend
  Unbound: Will not lend
  Loan Period: N/A
  Renewable: N/A
  Will lend if article exceeds
    _____ number of pages (Not
    answered)

MICROFORMS:
  Will Lend: Yes
  Specific Types of Microforms:
    (Not answered)

GOVERNMENT PUBLICATIONS:
  Will Lend: Yes

DISSERTATIONS:
  Will Lend: No

THESES:
  Will Lend: No

AUDIO-VISUAL MATERIALS:
  Records: Will lend
  Cassettes: Will lend
  Other (slides, filmstrips,
    etc.): Will lend

COMPUTER SOFTWARE:
  Will Lend: (Not answered)

PHOTODUPLICATION SERVICE:
  No charge up to 0 exposures
  Charge Per Exposure: 5¢ from
    hard copy; 10¢ from
    microfilm
  Handling Fee: $2.00
  Average Turnaround Time:
    2 days

MICROFILMING SERVICE:
  Service Available: No
  Charges: N/A

DO YOU CHARGE THE BORROWING
  LIBRARY FOR POSTAGE? No

FOR HOW LONG DO YOU SUSPEND ILL
  SERVICE OVER THE CHRISTMAS
  HOLIDAYS? Open

ARE THERE ANY GROUPS OF LIBRARIES
  FOR WHICH YOU WAIVE FEES: IF
  SO, PLEASE NAME THEM:
    Susquehanna Library Cooper-
    ative (SLC); Area College
    Library Cooperative Program
    (ACLCP)

CALIFORNIA STATE COLLEGE

NUC CODE: (Not answered)

OCLC CODE: CSC

ADDRESS: Interlibrary Loan
          Louis L. Manderino
          Library
          California State
          College
          California, PA 15419

TELEPHONE: (412) 938-4097

LIST NAMES OF BRANCHES WITH
  SEPARATE POLICIES: None

BOOKS:
  Will Lend: Yes
  Length of Loan: 3 weeks
  Renewable: No
  Charges: Postage
  Average Turnaround Time:
    (Not answered)
  If you have indicated that a
    book is not to be lent, will
    you on receipt of a letter
    from the requesting library
    search the index for given
    entries? No

PERIODICALS:
  Bound: Will not lend
  Unbound: Will not lend
  Loan Period: N/A
  Renewable: N/A
  Will lend if article exceeds
    _____ number of pages (Not
    answered)

MICROFORMS:
  Will Lend: Yes
  Specific Types of Microforms:
    (Not answered)

GOVERNMENT PUBLICATIONS:
  Will Lend: Yes

DISSERTATIONS:
  Will Lend: Yes

THESES:
  Will Lend: Yes

AUDIO-VISUAL MATERIALS:
  Records: Will lend
  Cassettes: Will lend
  Other (slides, filmstrips,
    etc.): Will lend

COMPUTER SOFTWARE:
  Will Lend: No

PHOTODUPLICATION SERVICE:
  No charge up to 0 exposures
  Charge Per Exposure: 10¢
  Minimum/handling Fee: None
  Average Turnaround Time:
    1 week

MICROFILMING SERVICE:
  Service Available: No
  Charges: N/A

DO YOU CHARGE THE BORROWING
  LIBRARY FOR POSTAGE? No

FOR HOW LONG DO YOU SUSPEND ILL
  SERVICE OVER THE CHRISTMAS
  HOLIDAYS? 5 weeks

ARE THERE ANY GROUPS OF LIBRARIES
  FOR WHICH YOU WAIVE FEES? IF
  SO, PLEASE NAME THEM: State
  colleges in Pennsylvania

CARNEGIE LIBRARY OF PITTSBURGH

NUC CODE: PPi

OCLC CODE: CPL

ADDRESS: Interlibrary Loan
           Carnegie Library of
             Pittsburgh
           4400 Forbes Ave.
           Pittsburgh, PA
           15213-4080

TELEPHONE: (412) 622-3160

LIST NAMES OF BRANCHES WITH
  SEPARATE POLICIES: None

BOOKS:
  Will Lend: Yes
  Length of Loan: 28 days
  Renewable: No
  Charges: (Not answered)
  Average Turnaround Time:
    (Not answered)
  If you have indicated that a
  book is not to be lent, will
  you on receipt of a letter
  from the requesting library
  search the index for given
  entries? (Not answered)

PERIODICALS:
  Bound: Will not lend
  Unbound: Will not lend
  Loan Period: N/A
  Renewable: N/A
  Will lend if article exceeds
    _____ number of pages (Not
    answered)

MICROFORMS:
  Will Lend: Yes
  Specific Types of Microforms:
    Microfiche

GOVERNMENT PUBLICATIONS:
  Will Lend: Yes, if
    cataloged

DISSERTATIONS:
  Will Lend: Do not own

THESES:
  Will Lend: Do not own

AUDIO-VISUAL MATERIALS:
  Records: Will not lend
  Cassettes: Will not lend
  Other (slides, filmstrips,
    etc.): Will not lend

COMPUTER SOFTWARE:
  Will Lend: Do not own

PHOTODUPLICATION SERVICE:
  No charge up to 0 exposures
  Charge Per Exposure: 50¢
  Minimum/handling Fee: $3.00
  Average Turnaround Time:
    1 day

MICROFILMING SERVICE:
  Service Available: No
  Charges: N/A

DO YOU CHARGE THE BORROWING
  LIBRARY FOR POSTAGE? No

FOR HOW LONG DO YOU SUSPEND ILL
  SERVICE OVER THE CHRISTMAS
  HOLIDAYS? No suspension

ARE THERE ANY GROUPS OF LIBRARIES
  FOR WHICH YOU WAIVE FEES? IF
  SO, PLEASE NAME THEM: Pittsburgh District public
  libraries and other
  Pennsylvania public library
  centers (10 pages free)

CARNEGIE-MELLON UNIVERSITY

NUC CODE: PPICI

OCLC CODE: PMC

ADDRESS: Interlibrary Loan
           Hunt Library
           Carnegie-Mellon
             University
           Pittsburgh, PA 15213

TELEPHONE: (412) 578-2442

LIST NAMES OF BRANCHES WITH
  SEPARATE POLICIES:
    Engineering and Science
    Library
    Mellon Institute Library

BOOKS:
  Will Lend: Yes
  Length of Loan: 2 weeks
  Renewable: Yes
  Charges: (Not answered)
  Average Turnaround Time:
    3 days
  If you have indicated that a
  book is not to be lent, will
  you on receipt of a letter
  from the requesting library
  search the index for given
  entries? (Not answered)

PERIODICALS:
  Bound: Will not lend
  Unbound: Will not lend
  Loan Period: N/A
  Renewable: N/A
  Will lend if article exceeds
    _____ number of pages (Not
    answered)

MICROFORMS:
  Will Lend: Yes
  Specific Types of Microforms:
    (Not answered)

GOVERNMENT PUBLICATIONS:
  Will Lend: Yes

DISSERTATIONS:
  Will Lend: Yes; 1968 to
    present available from
    University Microfilms

THESES:
  Will Lend: Yes

AUDIO-VISUAL MATERIALS:
  Records: Will not lend
  Cassettes: Will not lend
  Other (slides, filmstrips,
    etc.): Will not lend

COMPUTER SOFTWARE:
  Will Lend: No

PHOTODUPLICATION SERVICE:
  No charge up to 0 exposures
  Charge Per Exposure: 10¢
  Minimum Fee: $1.00
  Handling Fee: $1.50
  Average Turnaround Time:
    3 days

MICROFILMING SERVICE:
  Service Available: (Not
    answered)
  Charges: N/A

DO YOU CHARGE THE BORROWING
  LIBRARY FOR POSTAGE? Yes

FOR HOW LONG DO YOU SUSPEND ILL
  SERVICE OVER THE CHRISTMAS
  HOLIDAYS? 2 weeks

ARE THERE ANY GROUPS OF LIBRARIES
  FOR WHICH YOU WAIVE FEES? IF
  SO, PLEASE NAME THEM: None

CARNEGIE-MELLON UNIVERSITY--MELLON INSTITUTE

NUC CODE: PPiM

OCLC CODE: PMC

ADDRESS: Interlibrary Loan
           Mellon Institute
           Library
           Carnegie-Mellon
           University
           4400 5th Ave.
           Pittsburgh, PA 15213

TELEPHONE: (412) 578-3172

LIST NAMES OF BRANCHES WITH
  SEPARATE POLICIES: None

BOOKS:
  Will Lend: Yes
  Length of Loan: 2 weeks from
    receipt
  Renewable: No
  Charges: Postage
  Average Turnaround Time:
    48 hours
  If you have indicated that a
    book is not to be lent, will
    you on receipt of a letter
    from the requesting library
    search the index for given
    entries? (Not answered)

PERIODICALS:
  Bound: Will not lend
  Unbound: Will not lend
  Loan Period: N/A
  Renewable: N/A
  Will lend if article exceeds
    _____ number of pages (Not
    answered)

MICROFORMS:
  Will Lend: No
  Specific Types of Microforms:
    N/A

GOVERNMENT PUBLICATIONS:
  Will Lend: Yes

DISSERTATIONS:
  Will Lend: Do not own

THESES:
  Will Lend: Do not own

AUDIO-VISUAL MATERIALS:
  Records: Do not own
  Cassettes: Do not own
  Other (slides, filmstrips,
    etc.): Do not own

COMPUTER SOFTWARE:
  Will Lend: Do not own

PHOTODUPLICATION SERVICE:
  No charge up to 0 exposures
  Charge Per Exposure:
    Hardcopy is 10¢ for academic
    and public libraries, 20¢
    for all other libraries;
    microform copy is 50¢ per
    exposure
  Minimum Fee: $1.00 for aca-
    demic and public, $2.00 for
    other libraries
  Handling Fee: $1.50 for
    public and academic, $3.00
    for other libraries

MICROFILMING SERVICE:
  Service Available: No
  Charges: N/A

DO YOU CHARGE THE BORROWING
  LIBRARY FOR POSTAGE? Yes,
  for books

FOR HOW LONG DO YOU SUSPEND ILL
  SERVICE OVER THE CHRISTMAS
  HOLIDAYS? Dec.15-Jan.2

ARE THERE ANY GROUPS OF LIBRARIES
  FOR WHICH YOU WAIVE FEES? IF
  SO, PLEASE NAME THEM: None

CLARION STATE COLLEGE

NUC CODE: PC1S

OCLC CODE: REC

ADDRESS: Interlibrary Loan
           Carlson Library
           Clarion State College
           Clarion, PA 16214

TELEPHONE: (814) 226-2376

LIST NAMES OF BRANCHES WITH
  SEPARATE POLICIES: None

BOOKS:
  Will Lend: Yes
  Length of Loan: 1 month
  Renewable: Yes
  Charges: Reciprocal
  Average Turnaround Time:
    2 days
  If you have indicated that a
    book is not to be lent, will
    you on receipt of a letter
    from the requesting library
    search the index for given
    entries? (Not answered)

PERIODICALS:
  Bound: Will not lend
  Unbound: Will not lend
  Loan Period: N/A
  Renewable: N/A
  Will lend if article exceeds
    _____ number of pages (Not
    answered)

MICROFORMS:
  Will Lend: Yes
  Specific Types of Microforms:
    Microform reels and cards

GOVERNMENT PUBLICATIONS:
  Will Lend: Yes

DISSERTATIONS:
  Will Lend: Yes

THESES:
  Will Lend: Yes

AUDIO-VISUAL MATERIALS:
  Records: Will not lend
  Cassettes: Will not lend
  Other (slides, filmstrips,
    etc.): Will not lend

COMPUTER SOFTWARE:
  Will Lend: No

PHOTODUPLICATION SERVICE:
  Reciprocal charges
  Average Turnaround Time:
    2 days

MICROFILMING SERVICE:
  Service Available: No
  Charges: N/A

DO YOU CHARGE THE BORROWING
  LIBRARY FOR POSTAGE? No

FOR HOW LONG DO YOU SUSPEND ILL
  SERVICE OVER THE CHRISTMAS
  HOLIDAYS? Dec.15-Jan.3

ARE THERE ANY GROUPS OF LIBRARIES
  FOR WHICH YOU WAIVE FEES? IF
  SO, PLEASE NAME THEM:
    Pennsylvania state colleges

COLLEGE OF PHYSICIANS OF PHILADELPHIA

NUC CODE: PPC

OCLC CODE: PPC

ADDRESS: Interlibrary Loan
College of Physicians
of Philadelphia
19 South 22nd St.
Philadelphia, PA 19103

TELEPHONE: (215) 561-6050

LIST NAMES OF BRANCHES WITH
SEPARATE POLICIES: None

BOOKS:
Will Lend: Yes
Length of Loan: 2 weeks
Renewable: Yes
Charges: $5.00
Average Turnaround Time:
Same day
If you have indicated that a
book is not to be lent, will
you on receipt of a letter
from the requesting library
search the index for given
entries? Yes

PERIODICALS:
Bound: Will lend
Unbound: Will not lend
Loan Period: 2 weeks
Renewable: Yes
Will lend if article exceeds
_____ number of pages (Not
answered)

MICROFORMS:
Will Lend: Do not own

GOVERNMENT PUBLICATIONS:
Will Lend: Yes

DISSERTATIONS:
Will Lend: Yes

THESES:
Will Lend: Yes

AUDIO-VISUAL MATERIALS:
Records: Will not lend
Cassettes: Will not lend
Other (slides, filmstrips,
etc.): Will not lend

COMPUTER SOFTWARE:
Will Lend: No

PHOTODUPLICATION SERVICE:
No charge up to 0 exposures
Charges: $5.00 flat rate
per article which includes
postage and handling
Average Turnaround Time:
Same day

MICROFILMING SERVICE:
Service Available: No
Charges: N/A

DO YOU CHARGE THE BORROWING
LIBRARY FOR POSTAGE? Is
included in flat rate.

FOR HOW LONG DO YOU SUSPEND ILL
SERVICE OVER THE CHRISTMAS
HOLIDAYS? No suspension

ARE THERE ANY GROUPS OF LIBRARIES
FOR WHICH YOU WAIVE FEES? IF
SO, PLEASE NAME THEM: None

DAUPHIN COUNTY LIBRARY SYSTEM

NUC CODE: (Not answered)

OCLC CODE: HBP

ADDRESS: Interlibrary Loan
Dauphin County Library
System
202 Dauphin Bldg.
101 Walnut St.
Harrisburg, PA 17101

TELEPHONE: (717) 234-4961

LIST NAMES OF BRANCHES WITH
SEPARATE POLICIES: None

BOOKS:
Will Lend: Yes
Length of Loan: 4 weeks
Renewable: Yes, unless
recent publication
Charges: (Not answered)
Average Turnaround Time:
(Not answered)
If you have indicated that a
book is not to be lent, will
you on receipt of a letter
from the requesting library
search the index for given
entries? (Not answered)

PERIODICALS:
Bound: Will not lend
Unbound: Will not lend
Loan Period: N/A
Renewable: N/A
Will lend if article exceeds
_____ number of pages (Will
not lend, regardless of
length of article. Will
photocopy article.)

MICROFORMS:
Will Lend: Do not own

GOVERNMENT PUBLICATIONS:
Will Lend: Do not own

DISSERTATIONS:
Will Lend: Do not own

THESES:
Will Lend: Do not own

AUDIO-VISUAL MATERIALS:
Records: Will lend
Cassettes: Will lend
Other (slides, filmstrips,
etc.): Will lend

COMPUTER SOFTWARE:
Will Lend: (Not answered)

PHOTODUPLICATION SERVICE:
No charge up to 0 exposures
Charge Per Exposure: 25¢
Minimum/handling Fee: (Not
answered)
Average Turnaround Time:
(Not answered)

MICROFILMING SERVICE:
Service Available: No
Charges: N/A

DO YOU CHARGE THE BORROWING
LIBRARY FOR POSTAGE? No

FOR HOW LONG DO YOU SUSPEND ILL
SERVICE OVER THE CHRISTMAS
HOLIDAYS? No suspension

ARE THERE ANY GROUPS OF LIBRARIES
FOR WHICH YOU WAIVE FEES? IF
SO, PLEASE NAME THEM:
Pennsylvania public librar-
ies (except for extensive
photocopying)

DICKINSON COLLEGE

NUC CODE: PCar1D

OCLC CODE: DKC

ADDRESS: Interlibrary Loan
Dickinson College
Library
Carlisle, PA 17013

TELEPHONE: (717) 245-1604

LIST NAMES OF BRANCHES WITH
SEPARATE POLICIES: None

BOOKS:
Will Lend: Yes
Length of Loan: 4 weeks
Renewable: Yes
Charges: $5.00 to public and
corporate libraries and
others from whom we usually
do not borrow.
Average Turnaround Time:
1 day
If you have indicated that a
book is not to be lent, will
you on receipt of a letter
from the requesting library
search the index for given
entries? Yes

PERIODICALS:
Bound: Will not lend
Unbound: Will not lend
Loan Period: N/A
Renewable: N/A
Will lend if article exceeds
_____ number of pages (Not
answered)

MICROFORMS:
Will Lend: Yes
Specific Types of Microforms:
Film and fiche

GOVERNMENT PUBLICATIONS:
Will Lend: Yes

DISSERTATIONS:
Will Lend: Do not own

THESES:
Will Lend: Do not own

AUDIO-VISUAL MATERIALS:
Records: Will not lend
Cassettes: Will not lend
Other (slides, filmstrips,
etc.): (Not answered)

COMPUTER SOFTWARE:
Will Lend: Do not own

PHOTODUPLICATION SERVICE:
No charge up to 0 exposures
Charge Per Exposure: $2.50
for 1-20 exposures; $5.00
for 21-40 exposures
Minimum/handling Fee: $2.50
Average Turnaround Time:
1 day

MICROFILMING SERVICE:
Service Available: No
Charges: N/A

DO YOU CHARGE THE BORROWING
LIBRARY FOR POSTAGE? Only
for international lending

FOR HOW LONG DO YOU SUSPEND ILL
SERVICE OVER THE CHRISTMAS
HOLIDAYS? No suspension

ARE THERE ANY GROUPS OF LIBRARIES
FOR WHICH YOU WAIVE FEES? IF
SO, PLEASE NAME THEM: ACLCP
consortium; CPC consortium;
SLC consortium

DREXEL UNIVERSITY

NUC CODE: PPD

OCLC CODE: DXU

ADDRESS: Interlibrary Loan
Drexel University
Library
32nd and Chestnut Sts.
Philadelphia, PA 19104

TELEPHONE: (215) 895-2769

LIST NAMES OF BRANCHES WITH
SEPARATE POLICIES: None

BOOKS:
Will Lend: Yes
Length of Loan: 4 weeks
Renewable: Yes
Charges: $3.00 charge to
non-academic institutions
only
Average Turnaround Time:
5 days
If you have indicated that a
book is not to be lent, will
you on receipt of a letter
from the requesting library
search the index for given
entries? Yes

PERIODICALS:
Bound: Will not lend
Unbound: Will not lend
Loan Period: N/A
Renewable: N/A
Will lend if article exceeds
_____ number of pages (Will
not lend, regardless of
length of article)

MICROFORMS:
Will Lend: Yes, except for
periodicals
Specific Types of Microforms:
Cards, fiche, films

GOVERNMENT PUBLICATIONS:
Will Lend: Yes

DISSERTATIONS:
Will Lend: Yes

THESES:
Will Lend: Yes

AUDIO-VISUAL MATERIALS:
Records: Will not lend
Cassettes: Will not lend
Other (slides, filmstrips,
etc.): Will not lend

COMPUTER SOFTWARE:
Will Lend: No

PHOTODUPLICATION SERVICE:
No charge up to 0 exposures
Charge Per Exposure: 10¢ for
academic; 20¢ for non-
academic
Minimum/handling Fee: $2.10
for academic; $3.20 for
non-academic
Average Turnaround Time:
10 days

MICROFILMING SERVICE:
Service Available: No
Charges: N/A

DO YOU CHARGE THE BORROWING
LIBRARY FOR POSTAGE? No,
unless other than library
rate

FOR HOW LONG DO YOU SUSPEND ILL
SERVICE OVER THE CHRISTMAS
HOLIDAYS? Dec.15-Jan.2

ARE THERE ANY GROUPS OF LIBRARIES
FOR WHICH YOU WAIVE FEES? IF
SO, PLEASE NAME THEM: Penn-
sylvania State Library;
Philadelphia Free Library;
Pennsylvania State Univer-
sity-Temple; University of
Pennsylvania-Lehigh;
Swarthmore College

DUQUESNE UNIVERSITY

NUC CODE: PPiD

OCLC CODE: DUQ

ADDRESS: Interlibrary Loan
Duquesne University
Library
Pittsburgh, PA 15282

TELEPHONE: (412) 434-6133

LIST NAMES OF BRANCHES WITH
SEPARATE POLICIES: None

BOOKS:
Will Lend: Yes
Length of Loan: 4 weeks
Renewable: Yes
Charges: Postage
Average Turnaround Time:
2-3 days
If you have indicated that a
book is not to be lent, will
you on receipt of a letter
from the requesting library
search the index for given
entries? (Not answered)

PERIODICALS:
Bound: Will not lend
Unbound: Will not lend
Loan Period: N/A
Renewable: N/A
Will lend if article exceeds
_____ number of pages (Not
answered)

MICROFORMS:
Will Lend: Yes
Specific Types of Microforms:
N/A

GOVERNMENT PUBLICATIONS:
Will Lend: Yes

DISSERTATIONS:
Will Lend: Yes

THESES:
Will Lend: Yes

AUDIO-VISUAL MATERIALS:
Records: Will not lend
Cassettes: Will not lend
Other (slides, filmstrips,
etc.): Will not lend

COMPUTER SOFTWARE:
Will Lend: No

PHOTODUPLICATION SERVICE:
No charge up to 0 exposures
Charge Per Exposure: 10¢
Minimum/handling Fee: $2.00
Average Turnaround Time:
2-3 days

MICROFILMING SERVICE:
Service Available: No
Charges: N/A

DO YOU CHARGE THE BORROWING
LIBRARY FOR POSTAGE? Yes

FOR HOW LONG DO YOU SUSPEND ILL
SERVICE OVER THE CHRISTMAS
HOLIDAYS? 1 week

ARE THERE ANY GROUPS OF LIBRARIES
FOR WHICH YOU WAIVE FEES? IF
SO, PLEASE NAME THEM: None

EAST STROUDSBURG STATE COLLEGE

NUC CODE: PEeS

OCLC CODE: ETS

ADDRESS: Interlibrary Loan
Kemp Library
East Stroudsburg State
College
East Stroudsburg, PA
18301

TELEPHONE: (717) 424-3594

LIST NAMES OF BRANCHES WITH
SEPARATE POLICIES: None

BOOKS:
Will Lend: Yes
Length of Loan: 3 weeks use
Renewable: No
Charges: Insurance occasionally
Average Turnaround Time:
1 day
If you have indicated that a
book is not to be lent, will
you on receipt of a letter
from the requesting library
search the index for given
entries? (Not answered)

PERIODICALS:
Bound: Will not lend
Unbound: Will not lend
Loan Period: N/A
Renewable: N/A
Will lend if article exceeds
_____ number of pages (Not
answered)

MICROFORMS:
Will Lend: No
Specific Types of Microforms:
N/A

GOVERNMENT PUBLICATIONS:
Will Lend: Yes, selectively

DISSERTATIONS:
Will Lend: No

THESES:
Will Lend: No

AUDIO-VISUAL MATERIALS:
Records: Will not lend
Cassettes: Will not lend
Other (slides, filmstrips,
etc.): Will not lend

COMPUTER SOFTWARE:
Will Lend: No

PHOTODUPLICATION SERVICE:
No charge up to 0 exposures
Charge Per Exposure: 10¢
Minimum/handling Fee: None
Average Turnaround Time:
1 day

MICROFILMING SERVICE:
Service Available: No
Charges: N/A

DO YOU CHARGE THE BORROWING
LIBRARY FOR POSTAGE? No

FOR HOW LONG DO YOU SUSPEND ILL
SERVICE OVER THE CHRISTMAS
HOLIDAYS? 2 weeks

ARE THERE ANY GROUPS OF LIBRARIES
FOR WHICH YOU WAIVE FEES? IF
SO, PLEASE NAME THEM:
Pennsylvania sister state
colleges

FRANKLIN AND MARSHALL COLLEGE

NUC CODE: PLF

OCLC CODE: LFM

ADDRESS: Interlibrary Loan
           Franklin and Marshall
              College
           Library
           P. O. Box 3003
           Lancaster, PA 17604

TELEPHONE: (717) 291-4223

LIST NAMES OF BRANCHES WITH
   SEPARATE POLICIES: None

BOOKS:
   Will Lend: Yes
   Length of Loan: 1 month
   Renewable: Yes
   Charges: None
   Average Turnaround Time:
     (Not answered)
   If you have indicated that a
     book is not to be lent, will
     you on receipt of a letter
     from the requesting library
     search the index for given
     entries? (Not answered)

PERIODICALS:
   Bound: Will not lend
   Unbound: Will not lend
   Loan Period: N/A
   Renewable: N/A
   Will lend if article exceeds
     _____ number of pages (Not
     answered)

MICROFORMS:
   Will Lend: No
   Specific Types of Microforms:
     N/A

GOVERNMENT PUBLICATIONS:
   Will Lend: Yes

DISSERTATIONS:
   Will Lend: No

THESES:
   Will Lend: No

AUDIO-VISUAL MATERIALS:
   Records: Will not lend
   Cassettes: Will not lend
   Other (slides, filmstrips,
     etc.): Will not lend

COMPUTER SOFTWARE:
   Will Lend: (Not answered)

PHOTODUPLICATION SERVICE:
   Copy free for Pennsylvania
     libraries
   For others:
   No charge up to 0 exposures
   Charge Per Exposure: 10¢
     per exposure after the 1st
     20
   Minimum/handling Fee: $2.00
     for 20 pages
   Average Turnaround Time:
     (Not answered)

MICROFILMING SERVICE:
   Service Available: No
   Charges: N/A

DO YOU CHARGE THE BORROWING
   LIBRARY FOR POSTAGE? No

FOR HOW LONG DO YOU SUSPEND ILL
   SERVICE OVER THE CHRISTMAS
   HOLIDAYS? No suspension

ARE THERE ANY GROUPS OF LIBRARIES
   FOR WHICH YOU WAIVE FEES? IF
   SO, PLEASE NAME THEM: ACLCP-
   Associated College Libraries
   of Central Pennsylvania

FRANKLIN INSTITUTE

NUC CODE: PPF

OCLC CODE: PPF

ADDRESS: Library Services
           Franklin Institute
              Library
           20th and The Parkway
           Philadelphia, PA 19103

TELEPHONE: (215) 448-1321

LIST NAMES OF BRANCHES WITH
   SEPARATE POLICIES: None

BOOKS:
   Will Lend: No
   Length of Loan: N/A
   Renewable: N/A
   Charges: N/A
   Average Turnaround Time:
     N/A
   If you have indicated that a
     book is not to be lent, will
     you on receipt of a letter
     from the requesting library
     search the index for given
     entries? Yes

PERIODICALS:
   Bound: Will not lend
   Unbound: Will not lend
   Loan Period: N/A
   Renewable: N/A
   Will lend if article exceeds
     _____ number of pages (Not
     answered)

MICROFORMS:
   Will Lend: No
   Specific Types of Microforms:
     N/A

GOVERNMENT PUBLICATIONS:
   Will Lend: Do not own

DISSERTATIONS:
   Will Lend: Do not own

THESES:
   Will Lend: Do not own

AUDIO-VISUAL MATERIALS:
   Records: Do not own
   Cassettes: Do not own
   Other (slides, filmstrips,
     etc.): Do not own

COMPUTER SOFTWARE:
   Will Lend: Do not own

PHOTODUPLICATION SERVICE:
   No charge up to 0 exposures
   Charge Per Exposure: $7.00
     for up to 10 exposures;
     $3.00 for each 10 additional
     pages. Must be prepaid.
   Average Turnaround Time:
     (Not answered)

MICROFILMING SERVICE:
   Service Available: No
   Charges: N/A

DO YOU CHARGE THE BORROWING
   LIBRARY FOR POSTAGE? No

FOR HOW LONG DO YOU SUSPEND ILL
   SERVICE OVER THE CHRISTMAS
   HOLIDAYS? No suspension

ARE THERE ANY GROUPS OF LIBRARIES
   FOR WHICH YOU WAIVE FEES? IF
   SO, PLEASE NAME THEM: None

FREE LIBRARY OF PHILADELPHIA

NUC CODE: PP

OCLC CODE: PLF

ADDRESS: Interlibrary Loan
            Free Library of
                Philadelphia
            Logan Square
            Philadelphia, PA 19103

TELEPHONE: (215) 686-5366

LIST NAMES OF BRANCHES WITH
    SEPARATE POLICIES:
        Library for the Blind and
            Physically Handicapped
        Fleisher Collection of
            Orchestral Music
        Drinker Library of Choral
            Music

BOOKS:
    Will Lend: Yes
    Length of Loan: 4 weeks
    Renewable: No
    Charges: (Not answered)
    Average Turnaround Time:
        (Not answered)
    If you have indicated that a
        book is not to be lent, will
        you on receipt of a letter
        from the requesting library
        search the index for given
        entries? (Not answered)

PERIODICALS:
    Bound: Will not lend
    Unbound: Will not lend
    Loan Period: N/A
    Renewable: N/A
    Will lend if article exceeds
        _____ number of pages (Not
        answered)

MICROFORMS:
    Will Lend: (Not answered)
    Specific Types of Microforms:
        N/A

GOVERNMENT PUBLICATIONS:
    Will Lend: No

DISSERTATIONS:
    Will Lend: (Not answered)

THESES:
    Will Lend: (Not answered)

AUDIO-VISUAL MATERIALS:
    Records: (Not answered)
    Cassettes: (Not answered)
    Other (slides, filmstrips,
        etc.): (Not answered)

COMPUTER SOFTWARE:
    Will Lend: (Not answered)

PHOTODUPLICATION SERVICE:
    No charge up to 10 exposures
    Charge Per Exposure: 10¢
    Minimum/handling Fee: $2.00
        over 10 exposures
    Average Turnaround Time:
        (Not answered)

MICROFILMING SERVICE:
    Service Available: Yes
    Charges: 2½¢ per frame,
        $3.50 minimum

DO YOU CHARGE THE BORROWING
    LIBRARY FOR POSTAGE? No

FOR HOW LONG DO YOU SUSPEND ILL
    SERVICE OVER THE CHRISTMAS
    HOLIDAYS? (Not answered)

ARE THERE ANY GROUPS OF LIBRARIES
    FOR WHICH YOU WAIVE FEES? IF
    SO, PLEASE NAME THEM: (Not
    answered)

GETTYSBURG COLLEGE

NUC CODE: PGC

OCLC CODE: GDC

ADDRESS: Interlibrary Loan
            Gettysburg College
                Library
            Gettysburg, PA 17325

TELEPHONE: (717) 334-3131, X364

LIST NAMES OF BRANCHES WITH
    SEPARATE POLICIES: None

BOOKS:
    Will Lend: Yes
    Length of Loan: 1 month
    Renewable: Yes
    Charges: (Not answered)
    Average Turnaround Time:
        (Not answered)
    If you have indicated that a
        book is not to be lent, will
        you on receipt of a letter
        from the requesting library
        search the index for given
        entries? Yes

PERIODICALS:
    Bound: Will not lend
    Unbound: Will not lend
    Loan Period: N/A
    Renewable: N/A
    Will lend if article exceeds
        _____ number of pages (In
        most cases, will send
        photocopy only)

MICROFORMS:
    Will Lend: Yes
    Specific Types of Microforms:
        (Not answered)

GOVERNMENT PUBLICATIONS:
    Will Lend: Yes

DISSERTATIONS:
    Will Lend: Do not own

THESES:
    Will Lend: Do not own

AUDIO-VISUAL MATERIALS:
    Records: Yes, but only to
        IDS members in Pennsylvania
    Cassettes: Yes, but only to
        IDS members in Pennsylvania
    Other (slides, filmstrips,
        etc.): Yes, but only to IDS
        members in Pennsylvania

COMPUTER SOFTWARE:
    Will Lend: Do not own

PHOTODUPLICATION SERVICE:
    No charge up to 0 exposures
    Charge Per Exposure: 10¢
    Minimum/handling Fee: None
    Average Turnaround Time:
        (Not answered)

MICROFILMING SERVICE:
    Service Available: No
    Charges: N/A

DO YOU CHARGE THE BORROWING
    LIBRARY FOR POSTAGE? No

FOR HOW LONG DO YOU SUSPEND ILL
    SERVICE OVER THE CHRISTMAS
    HOLIDAYS? 2 weeks

ARE THERE ANY GROUPS OF LIBRARIES
    FOR WHICH YOU WAIVE FEES? IF
    SO, PLEASE NAME THEM: ACLCP

HAHNEMANN UNIVERSITY OF THE HEALTH SCIENCES

NUC CODE: PPHa

OCLC CODE: HHN

ADDRESS: Interlibrary Loan
            Hahnemann University of
               the Health Sciences
               Library
            245 N. 15th St.
            Philadelphia, PA 19102

TELEPHONE: (215) 448-7630

LIST NAMES OF BRANCHES WITH
    SEPARATE POLICIES: None

BOOKS:
    Will Lend: Yes
    Length of Loan: 3 weeks
    Renewable: No
    Charges: $5.00
    Average Turnaround Time:
       3 days
    If you have indicated that a
       book is not to be lent, will
       you on receipt of a letter
       from the requesting library
       search the index for given
       entries? (Not answered)

PERIODICALS:
    Bound: Will not lend
    Unbound: Will not lend
    Loan Period: N/A
    Renewable: N/A
    Will lend if article exceeds
       _____ number of pages (Will
       not lend, regardless of
       length of article)

MICROFORMS:
    Will Lend: No
    Specific Types of Microforms:
       N/A

GOVERNMENT PUBLICATIONS:
    Will Lend: Yes

DISSERTATIONS:
    Will Lend: Yes

THESES:
    Will Lend: Yes

AUDIO-VISUAL MATERIALS:
    Records: Will not lend
    Cassettes: Will not lend
    Other (slides, filmstrips,
       etc.): Will not lend

COMPUTER SOFTWARE:
    Will Lend: No

PHOTODUPLICATION SERVICE:
    No charge up to 0 exposures
    Charge Per Exposure: 50¢
    Minimum/handling Fee: $5.00
       up to 10 pages
    Average Turnaround Time:
       Varies

MICROFILMING SERVICE:
    Service Available: No
    Charges: N/A

DO YOU CHARGE THE BORROWING
    LIBRARY FOR POSTAGE? No

FOR HOW LONG DO YOU SUSPEND ILL
    SERVICE OVER THE CHRISTMAS
    HOLIDAYS? No suspension

ARE THERE ANY GROUPS OF LIBRARIES
    FOR WHICH YOU WAIVE FEES? IF
    SO, PLEASE NAME THEM: Tri-
    State College Library
    Cooperative; Philadelphia
    medical colleges who belong
    to Mid-Eastern Regional
    Medical Library Service.

HAVERFORD COLLEGE

NUC CODE: PHC

OCLC CODE: HVC

ADDRESS: Interlibrary Loan
            Haverford College
               Library
            Haverford, PA 19041

TELEPHONE: (215) 896-1171

LIST NAMES OF BRANCHES WITH
    SEPARATE POLICIES: None

BOOKS:
    Will Lend: Yes
    Length of Loan: 1 month
    Renewable: Yes
    Charges: (Not answered)
    Average Turnaround Time:
       (Not answered)
    If you have indicated that a
       book is not to be lent, will
       you on receipt of a letter
       from the requesting library
       search the index for given
       entries? (Not answered)

PERIODICALS:
    Bound: Will not lend
    Unbound: Will not lend
    Loan Period: N/A
    Renewable: N/A
    Will lend if article exceeds
       _____ number of pages (Not
       answered)

MICROFORMS:
    Will Lend: No
    Specific Types of Microforms:
       N/A

GOVERNMENT PUBLICATIONS:
    Will Lend: Yes

DISSERTATIONS:
    Will Lend: No

THESES:
    Will Lend: Yes

AUDIO-VISUAL MATERIALS:
    Records: (Not answered)
    Cassettes: (Not answered)
    Other (slides, filmstrips,
       etc.): (Not answered)

COMPUTER SOFTWARE:
    Will Lend: (Not answered)

PHOTODUPLICATION SERVICE:
    No charge up to 0 exposures
    Charge Per Exposure: 10¢
    Handling Fee: $3.00
    Average Turnaround Time:
       (Not answered)

MICROFILMING SERVICE:
    Service Available: No
    Charges: N/A

DO YOU CHARGE THE BORROWING
    LIBRARY FOR POSTAGE? No

FOR HOW LONG DO YOU SUSPEND ILL
    SERVICE OVER THE CHRISTMAS
    HOLIDAYS? No suspension

ARE THERE ANY GROUPS OF LIBRARIES
    FOR WHICH YOU WAIVE FEES? IF
    SO, PLEASE NAME THEM: None

INDIANA UNIVERSITY OF PENNSYLVANIA

NUC CODE: PiNU

OCLC CODE: PZI

ADDRESS: Interlibrary Loan
Stapleton Library
Room 112
Indiana University of
Pennsylvania
Indiana, PA 15705-1096

TELEPHONE: (412) 357-2340

LIST NAMES OF BRANCHES WITH
SEPARATE POLICIES: None

BOOKS:
Will Lend: Yes
Length of Loan: 30 days use;
some reference books for
2 weeks use
Renewable: Yes
Charges: None
Average Turnaround Time:
3 days
If you have indicated that a
book is not to be lent, will
you on receipt of a letter
from the requesting library
search the index for given
entries? (Not answered)

PERIODICALS:
Bound: Will not lend
Unbound: Will not lend
Loan Period: N/A
Renewable: N/A
Will lend if article exceeds
_____ number of pages (Will
not lend, regardless of
length of article)

MICROFORMS:
Will Lend: Yes, microfilm
only

GOVERNMENT PUBLICATIONS:
Will Lend: Yes

DISSERTATIONS:
Will Lend: No

THESES:
Will Lend: No

AUDIO-VISUAL MATERIALS:
Records: Will not lend
Cassettes: Will not lend
Other (slides, filmstrips,
etc.): Will not lend

COMPUTER SOFTWARE:
Will Lend: No

PHOTODUPLICATION SERVICE:
No charge up to 0 exposures
Charge Per Exposure: 10¢
Minimum/handling Fee: $2.00
Average Turnaround Time:
3 days

MICROFILMING SERVICE:
Service Available: No
Charges: N/A

DO YOU CHARGE THE BORROWING
LIBRARY FOR POSTAGE? No

FOR HOW LONG DO YOU SUSPEND ILL
SERVICE OVER THE CHRISTMAS
HOLIDAYS? Dec.20-Jan.15

ARE THERE ANY GROUPS OF LIBRARIES
FOR WHICH YOU WAIVE FEES? IF
SO, PLEASE NAME THEM: None

LA SALLE COLLEGE

NUC CODE: PPLas

OCLC CODE: LAS

ADDRESS: Interlibrary Loan
La Salle College
Library
20th St. & Olney Ave.
Philadelphia, PA
19141-1199

TELEPHONE: (215) 951-1287

LIST NAMES OF BRANCHES WITH
SEPARATE POLICIES: None

BOOKS:
Will Lend: Yes
Length of Loan: 1 month
Renewable: Yes
Charges: We charge commercial and industrial
libraries $3.00 per volume
Average Turnaround Time:
1 day
If you have indicated that a
book is not to be lent, will
you on receipt of a letter
from the requesting library
search the index for given
entries? (Not answered)

PERIODICALS:
Bound: Will not lend
Unbound: Will not lend
Loan Period: N/A
Renewable: N/A
Will lend if article exceeds
_____ number of pages (Will
not lend, regardless of
length of article)

MICROFORMS:
Will Lend: No
Specific Types Of Microforms:
N/A

GOVERNMENT PUBLICATIONS:
Will Lend: Yes

DISSERTATIONS:
Will Lend: Yes

THESES:
Will Lend: Yes

AUDIO-VISUAL MATERIALS:
Records: Will not lend
Cassettes: Will not lend
Other (slides, filmstrips,
etc.): Will not lend

COMPUTER SOFTWARE:
Will Lend: No

PHOTODUPLICATION SERVICE:
No charge up to 10 exposures
Charge Per Exposure: 10¢
Minimum/handling Fee: We
charge commercial and
industrial libraries for
photocopies
Average Turnaround Time:
1 day

MICROFILMING SERVICE:
Service Available: No
Charges: N/A

DO YOU CHARGE THE BORROWING
LIBRARY FOR POSTAGE? No

FOR HOW LONG DO YOU SUSPEND ILL
SERVICE OVER THE CHRISTMAS
HOLIDAYS? No suspension

ARE THERE ANY GROUPS OF LIBRARIES
FOR WHICH YOU WAIVE FEES? IF
SO, PLEASE NAME THEM: None

LAFAYETTE COLLEGE

NUC CODE: PEL

OCLC CODE: LAF

ADDRESS: Interlibrary Loan
           Skillman Library
           Lafayette College
           Easton, PA 18042

TELEPHONE: (215) 250-5154 or
            250-5156

LIST NAMES OF BRANCHES WITH
   SEPARATE POLICIES: None

BOOKS:
   Will Lend: Yes
   Length of Loan: 4 weeks
   Renewable: Yes
   Charges: None
   Average Turnaround Time:
   1 day
   If you have indicated that a
      book is not to be lent, will
      you on receipt of a letter
      from the requesting library
      search the index for given
      entries? Yes

PERIODICALS:
   Bound: Will not lend
   Unbound: Will not lend
   Loan Period: N/A
   Renewable: N/A
   Will lend if article exceeds
      25 pages

MICROFORMS:
   Will Lend: No
   Specific Types of Microforms:
   N/A

GOVERNMENT PUBLICATIONS:
   Will Lend: Yes

DISSERTATIONS:
   Will Lend: No

THESES:
   WILL Lend: No

AUDIO-VISUAL MATERIALS:
   Records: Will not lend
   Cassettes: Will not lend
   Other (slides, filmstrips,
      etc.): Will not lend

COMPUTER SOFTWARE:
   Will Lend: No

PHOTODUPLICATION SERVICE:
   No charge up to 0 exposures
   Charge Per Exposure: 10¢
   Minimum/handling Fee: None
   Average Turnaround Time:
   1 day

MICROFILMING SERVICE:
   Service Available: No
   Charges: N/A

DO YOU CHARGE THE BORROWING
   LIBRARY FOR POSTAGE? No

FOR HOW LONG DO YOU SUSPEND ILL
   SERVICE OVER THE CHRISTMAS
   HOLIDAYS? 1 week

ARE THERE ANY GROUPS OF LIBRARIES
   FOR WHICH YOU WAIVE FEES? IF
   SO, PLEASE NAME THEM: None

MEDICAL COLLEGE OF PENNSYLVANIA

NUC CODE: (Not answered)

OCLC CODE: (Not answered)

ADDRESS: Interlibrary Loan
           Florence A. Moore
           Library
           Medical College of
           Pennsylvania
           3300 Henry Ave.
           Philadelphia, PA 19129

TELEPHONE: (215) 842-6910 or
            842-6911

LIST NAMES OF BRANCHES WITH
   SEPARATE POLICIES: None

BOOKS:
   Will Lend: Yes
   Length of Loan: 2 weeks
   Renewable: Yes
   Charges: Postage
   Average Turnaround Time:
   2 days
   If you have indicated that a
      book is not to be lent, will
      you on receipt of a letter
      from the requesting library
      search the index for given
      entries? Yes

PERIODICALS:
   Bound: Will not lend
   Unbound: Will not lend
   Loan Period: N/A
   Renewable: N/A
   Will lend if article exceeds
      _____ number of pages (Not
      answered)

MICROFORMS:
   Will Lend: No
   Specific Types of Microforms:
   N/A

GOVERNMENT PUBLICATIONS:
   Will Lend: Yes

DISSERTATIONS:
   Will Lend: No

THESES:
   Will Lend: No

AUDIO-VISUAL MATERIALS:
   Records: (Not answered)
   Cassettes: Will lend
   Other (slides, filmstrips,
      etc.): (Not answered)

COMPUTER SOFTWARE:
   Will Lend: No

PHOTODUPLICATION SERVICE:
   No charge up to 0 pages
   Charge Per Exposure: $4.50
      up to 7 pages plus 20¢
      per each additional page
   Average Turnaround Time:
   2 days

MICROFILMING SERVICE:
   Service Available: No
   Charges: N/A

DO YOU CHARGE THE BORROWING
   LIBRARY FOR POSTAGE? Yes

FOR HOW LONG DO YOU SUSPEND ILL
   SERVICE OVER THE CHRISTMAS
   HOLIDAYS? No suspension

ARE THERE ANY GROUPS OF LIBRARIES
   FOR WHICH YOU WAIVE FEES? IF
   SO, PLEASE NAME THEM: The
      other four medical
      libraries in Philadelphia:
      Jefferson, Hahneman,
      Temple University Medical
      School, University of
      Pennsylvania Medical
      Library

MILLERSVILLE STATE COLLEGE

NUC CODE: PMilS

OCLC CODE: MVS

ADDRESS: Interlibrary Loan
Library
Millersville State
College
Millersville, PA 17551

TELEPHONE: (717) 872-3611

LIST NAMES OF BRANCHES WITH
SEPARATE POLICIES: None

BOOKS:
Will Lend: Yes
Length of Loan: 3 weeks use
Renewable: Sometimes
Charges: None
Average Turnaround Time:
3 days
If you have indicated that a
book is not to be lent, will
you on receipt of a letter
from the requesting library
search the index for given
entries? Yes, for rare
books

PERIODICALS:
Bound: Will not lend
Unbound: Will not lend
Loan Period: N/A
Renewable: N/A
Will lend if article exceeds
_____ number of pages (Not
answered)

MICROFORMS:
Will Lend: No
Specific Types of Microforms:
N/A

GOVERNMENT PUBLICATIONS:
Will Lend: Yes

DISSERTATIONS:
Will Lend: Do not own

THESES:
Will Lend: Do not own

AUDIO-VISUAL MATERIALS:
Records: Will not lend
Cassettes: Will not lend
Other (slides, filmstrips,
etc.): Will not lend

COMPUTER SOFTWARE:
Will Lend: Do not own

PHOTODUPLICATION SERVICE:
No charge up to 0 exposures
Charge Per Exposure: 10¢
Minimum/handling Fee: $1.00
Average Turnaround Time:
3 days

MICROFILMING SERVICE:
Service Available: No
Charges: N/A

DO YOU CHARGE THE BORROWING
LIBRARY FOR POSTAGE? No

FOR HOW LONG DO YOU SUSPEND ILL
SERVICE OVER THE CHRISTMAS
HOLIDAYS? 2 weeks

ARE THERE ANY GROUPS OF LIBRARIES
FOR WHICH YOU WAIVE FEES? IF
SO, PLEASE NAME THEM: None

MONTGOMERY COUNTY-NORRISTOWN PUBLIC LIBRARY

NUC CODE: (Not answered)

OCLC CODE: MNL

ADDRESS: Interlibrary Loan
Montgomery County-
Norristown Public
Library
Swede and Elm Sts.
Norristown, PA 19401

TELEPHONE: (215) 277-3355

LIST NAMES OF BRANCHES WITH
SEPARATE POLICIES: None

BOOKS:
Will Lend: Yes
Length of Loan: 4 weeks
Renewable: No
Charges: (Not answered)
Average Turnaround Time:
(Not answered)
If you have indicated that a
book is not to be lent, will
you on receipt of a letter
from the requesting library
search the index for given
entries? (Not answered)

PERIODICALS:
Bound: Do not own
Unbound: Will not lend
Loan Period: N/A
Renewable: N/A
Will lend if article exceeds
_____ number of pages (Not
answered)

MICROFORMS:
Will Lend: No
Specific Types of Microforms:
N/A

GOVERNMENT PUBLICATIONS:
Will Lend: Yes, but only
those in book form

DISSERTATIONS:
Will Lend: Do not own

THESES:
Will Lend: Do not own

AUDIO-VISUAL MATERIALS:
Records: Will not lend
Cassettes: Will not lend
Other (slides, filmstrips,
etc.): Will not lend

COMPUTER SOFTWARE:
Will Lend: Do not own

PHOTODUPLICATION SERVICE:
No charge up to 5 exposures
Charge Per Exposure: 10¢ per
exposure after 1st 5
Minimum/handling Fee: None
Average Turnaround Time:
(Not answered)

MICROFILMING SERVICE:
Service Available: No
Charges: N/A

DO YOU CHARGE THE BORROWING
LIBRARY FOR POSTAGE? No

FOR HOW LONG DO YOU SUSPEND ILL
SERVICE OVER THE CHRISTMAS
HOLIDAYS? No suspension

ARE THERE ANY GROUPS OF LIBRARIES
FOR WHICH YOU WAIVE FEES? IF
SO, PLEASE NAME THEM: None

MUHLENBERG AND CEDAR CREST COLLEGES

NUC CODE: PAtM

OCLC CODE: EVI

ADDRESS: Interlibrary Loan
Muhlenberg and Cedar
Crest Colleges
Library
Allentown, PA 18104

TELEPHONE: (215) 433-3191, X755

LIST NAMES OF BRANCHES WITH
SEPARATE POLICIES: None

BOOKS:
Will Lend: Yes
Length of Loan: 3-5 weeks
Renewable: Yes
Charges: None
Average Turnaround Time:
2-4 days
If you have indicated that a
book is not to be lent, will
you on receipt of a letter
from the requesting library
search the index for given
entries? (Not answered)

PERIODICALS:
Bound: Will not lend
Unbound: Will not lend
Loan Period: N/A
Renewable: N/A
Will lend if article exceeds
_____ number of pages (Not
answered)

MICROFORMS:
Will Lend: Yes
Specific Types of Microforms:
Microfilm, microfiche

GOVERNMENT PUBLICATIONS:
Will Lend: Yes

DISSERTATIONS:
Will Lend: Do not own

THESES:
Will Lend: Do not own

AUDIO-VISUAL MATERIALS:
Records: Will not lend
Cassettes: Will not lend
Other (slides, filmstrips,
etc.): Will not lend

COMPUTER SOFTWARE:
Will Lend: No

PHOTODUPLICATION SERVICE:
No charge up to 10 exposures
Charge Per Exposure: 10¢
Minimum/handling Fee: None
Average Turnaround Time:
2-4 days

MICROFILMING SERVICE:
Service Available: No
Charges: N/A

DO YOU CHARGE THE BORROWING
LIBRARY FOR POSTAGE? No

FOR HOW LONG DO YOU SUSPEND ILL
SERVICE OVER THE CHRISTMAS
HOLIDAYS? Dec.24-Jan.2

ARE THERE ANY GROUPS OF LIBRARIES
FOR WHICH YOU WAIVE FEES? IF
SO, PLEASE NAME THEM: None

PENNSYLVANIA STATE UNIVERSITY

NUC CODE: PSt

OCLC CODE: UPM

ADDRESS: Interlibrary Loan
Pattee Library
Pennsylvania State
University
University Park, PA
16802

TELEPHONE: (814) 865-3489 (do
not accept telephone requests)

LIST NAMES OF BRANCHES WITH
SEPARATE POLICIES: None

BOOKS:
Will Lend: Yes
Length of Loan: 2 weeks use
Renewable: Yes
Charges: None
Average Turnaround Time:
7 days
If you have indicated that a
book is not to be lent, will
you on receipt of a letter
from the requesting library
search the index for given
entries? Yes, or will
supply photocopy of the
index

PERIODICALS:
Bound: Will not lend
Unbound: Will not lend
Loan Period: N/A
Renewable: N/A
Will lend if article exceeds
_____ number of pages (Will
not lend, regardless of
length of article)

MICROFORMS:
Will Lend: Yes
Specific Types of Microforms:
Cards, fiche, film

GOVERNMENT PUBLICATIONS:
Will Lend: Yes

DISSERTATIONS:
Will Lend: Yes. Available
from University Microfilms
from 1939 to present

THESES:
Will Lend: Yes

AUDIO-VISUAL MATERIALS:
Records: Will not lend
Cassettes: Will not lend
Other (slides, filmstrips,
etc.): Will not lend

COMPUTER SOFTWARE:
Will Lend: No

PHOTODUPLICATION SERVICE:
No charge up to 0 exposures
Charge Per Exposure: 15¢
Minimum/handling Fee: $2.00
at this time
Average Turnaround Time:
7 days

MICROFILMING SERVICE:
Service Available: Yes,
negative
Charges: 10¢ per frame,
$2.00 handling, 10¢
insurance

DO YOU CHARGE THE BORROWING
LIBRARY FOR POSTAGE? No

FOR HOW LONG DO YOU SUSPEND ILL
SERVICE OVER THE CHRISTMAS
HOLIDAYS? Mail service is
suspended from mid-
December to early January

ARE THERE ANY GROUPS OF LIBRARIES
FOR WHICH YOU WAIVE FEES? IF
SO, PLEASE NAME THEM: None

PENNSYLVANIA STATE UNIVERSITY--MILTON S. HERSHEY MEDICAL CENTER

NUC CODE: PHeM

OCLC CODE: None

ADDRESS: Interlibrary Loan
The George T. Harrell
Library
The Milton S. Hershey
Medical Center
Pennsylvania State
University
Hershey, PA 17033

TELEPHONE: (717) 534-8633

LIST NAMES OF BRANCHES WITH
SEPARATE POLICIES: None

BOOKS:
Will Lend: Yes
Length of Loan: 3 weeks
Renewable: Yes
Charges: None
Average Turnaround Time:
1 day
If you have indicated that a
book is not to be lent, will
you on receipt of a letter
from the requesting library
search the index for given
entries? Yes

PERIODICALS:
Bound: Will lend if older
than 10 years
Unbound: Will not lend
Loan Period: (Not answered)
Renewable: No
Will lend if article exceeds
_____ number of pages
(Length of article not
a factor)

MICROFORMS:
Will Lend: Do not own

GOVERNMENT PUBLICATIONS:
Will Lend: Yes

DISSERTATIONS:
Will Lend: Yes

THESES:
Will Lend: Yes

AUDIO-VISUAL MATERIALS:
Records: Do not own
Cassettes: Will lend
Other (slides, filmstrips,
etc.): Will lend

COMPUTER SOFTWARE:
Will Lend: Do not own

PHOTODUPLICATION SERVICE:
No charge up to 0 exposures
Charge Per Exposure: 25¢
each page over 10 pages
Minimum/handling Fee: $3.50
(includes 10 pages)
Average Turnaround Time:
1 day

MICROFILMING SERVICE:
Service Available: No
Charges: N/A

DO YOU CHARGE THE BORROWING
LIBRARY FOR POSTAGE? No

FOR HOW LONG DO YOU SUSPEND ILL
SERVICE OVER THE CHRISTMAS
HOLIDAYS? 2 weeks

ARE THERE ANY GROUPS OF LIBRARIES
FOR WHICH YOU WAIVE FEES? IF
SO, PLEASE NAME THEM: Other
Pennsylvania state univer-
sity campuses

PHILADELPHIA COLLEGE OF OSTEOPATHIC MEDICINE

NUC CODE: (Not answered)

OCLC CODE: (Not answered)

ADDRESS: Interlibrary Loan
PCOM Medical Library
Osteopathic Medical
Center of Philadelphia
Philadelphia College of
Osteopathic Medicine
Evans Hall
4150 City Ave.
Philadelphia, PA 19131

TELEPHONE: (215) 581-6526

LIST NAMES OF BRANCHES WITH
SEPARATE POLICIES: None

BOOKS:
Will Lend: No
Length of Loan: N/A
Renewable: N/A
Charges: N/A
Average Turnaround Time: N/A
If you have indicated that a
book is not to be lent, will
you on receipt of a letter
from the requesting library
search the index for given
entries? Yes

PERIODICALS:
Bound: Will not lend
Unbound: Will not lend
Loan Period: N/A
Renewable: N/A
Will lend if article exceeds
_____ number of pages (Will
not lend, regardless of
length of article)

MICROFORMS:
Will Lend: No
Specific Types of Microforms:
N/A

GOVERNMENT PUBLICATIONS:
Will Lend: No

DISSERTATIONS:
Will Lend: No

THESES:
Will Lend: No

AUDIO-VISUAL MATERIALS:
Records: Will not lend
Cassettes: Will lend
Other (slides, filmstrips,
etc.): Will not lend

COMPUTER SOFTWARE:
Will Lend: No

PHOTODUPLICATION SERVICE:
No charge up to 0 exposures
Charges: $3.00 for 1-10
exposures; 10¢ each
additional exposure
Average Turnaround Time:
8-10 days

MICROFILMING SERVICE:
Service Available: Not in-
house
Charges: N/A

DO YOU CHARGE THE BORROWING
LIBRARY FOR POSTAGE? No

FOR HOW LONG DO YOU SUSPEND ILL
SERVICE OVER THE CHRISTMAS
HOLIDAYS? No suspension

ARE THERE ANY GROUPS OF LIBRARIES
FOR WHICH YOU WAIVE FEES? IF
SO, PLEASE NAME THEM: None

PHILADELPHIA COLLEGE OF PHARMACY AND SCIENCE

NUC CODE: PPPCPh

OCLC CODE: PCP

ADDRESS: Interlibrary Loans
            Philadelphia College
              of Pharmacy and
              Science
            Joseph W. England
              Library
            42nd & Woodland Ave.
            Philadelphia, PA 19104

TELEPHONE: (215) 596-8961

LIST NAMES OF BRANCHES WITH
  SEPARATE POLICIES: None

BOOKS:
  Will Lend: Yes
  Length of Loan: 4 weeks
  Renewable: (Not answered)
  Charges: (Not answered)
  Average Turnaround Time:
    3 days
  If you have indicated that a
    book is not to be lent, will
    you on receipt of a letter
    from the requesting library
    search the index for given
    entries? (Not answered)

PERIODICALS:
  Bound: Will not lend
  Unbound: (Not answered)
  Loan Period: N/A
  Renewable: N/A
  Will lend if article exceeds
    _____ number of pages (Not
    answered)

MICROFORMS:
  Will Lend: No
  Specific Types of Microforms:
    N/A

GOVERNMENT PUBLICATIONS:
  Will Lend: Do not own

DISSERTATIONS:
  Will Lend: Yes

THESES:
  Will Lend: No

AUDIO-VISUAL MATERIALS:
  Records: Will not lend
  Cassettes: Will not lend
  Other (slides, filmstrips,
    etc.): Will not lend

COMPUTER SOFTWARE:
  Will Lend: Do not own

PHOTODUPLICATION SERVICE:
  No charge up to 0 exposures
  Charge Per Exposure: 25¢
    per exposure over 1st 30
  Minimum/handling Fee: $4.00
    plus postage
  Average Turnaround Time:
    3 days

MICROFILMING SERVICE:
  Service Available: No
  Charges: N/A

DO YOU CHARGE THE BORROWING
  LIBRARY FOR POSTAGE? Yes

FOR HOW LONG DO YOU SUSPEND ILL
  SERVICE OVER THE CHRISTMAS
  HOLIDAYS? Dec.23-Jan.5

ARE THERE ANY GROUPS OF LIBRARIES
  FOR WHICH YOU WAIVE FEES? IF
  SO, PLEASE NAME THEM: None

SHIPPENSBURG STATE COLLEGE

NUC CODE: PShS

OCLC CODE: SQP

ADDRESS: Interlibrary Loan
            Ezra Lehman Memorial
              Library
            Shippensburg State
              College
            Shippensburg, PA 17257

TELEPHONE: (717) 532-1462

LIST NAMES OF BRANCHES WITH
  SEPARATE POLICIES: None

BOOKS:
  Will Lend: Yes
  Length of Loan: 30 days
  Renewable: Yes
  Charges: None
  Average Turnaround Time:
    2 days
  If you have indicated that a
    book is not to be lent, will
    you on receipt of a letter
    from the requesting library
    search the index for given
    entries? Yes

PERIODICALS:
  Bound: Will not lend
  Unbound: Will not lend
  Loan Period: N/A
  Renewable: N/A
  Will lend if article exceeds
    15 pages

MICROFORMS:
  Will Lend: Yes
  Specific Types of Microforms:
    (Not answered)

GOVERNMENT PUBLICATIONS:
  Will Lend: Yes

DISSERTATIONS:
  Will Lend: Yes

THESES:
  Will Lend: Yes

AUDIO-VISUAL MATERIALS:
  Records: Will lend
  Cassettes: Will lend
  Other (slides, filmstrips,
    etc.): Will lend

COMPUTER SOFTWARE:
  Will Lend: Do not own

PHOTODUPLICATION SERVICE:
  No charge up to 15 exposures
  Charge Per Exposure: Free
    photocopying to libraries
    who reciprocate
  Minimum/handling Fee: None
  Average Turnaround Time:
    2 days

MICROFILMING SERVICE:
  Service Available: No
  Charges: N/A

DO YOU CHARGE THE BORROWING
  LIBRARY FOR POSTAGE? No

FOR HOW LONG DO YOU SUSPEND ILL
  SERVICE OVER THE CHRISTMAS
  HOLIDAYS? 1 month

ARE THERE ANY GROUPS OF LIBRARIES
  FOR WHICH YOU WAIVE FEES? IF
  SO, PLEASE NAME THEM:
    Pennsylvania libraries

SLIPPERY ROCK STATE COLLEGE

NUC CODE: PSrS

OCLC CODE: SRS

ADDRESS: Interlibrary Loan
          Bailey Library
          Slippery Rock State
            College
          Slippery Rock, PA 16057

TELEPHONE: (412) 794-7242 or
                794-7243

LIST NAMES OF BRANCHES WITH
  SEPARATE POLICIES: None

BOOKS:
  Will Lend: Yes
  Length of Loan: 3 weeks
  Renewable: Yes
  Charges: None
  Average Turnaround Time:
    2 days
  If you have indicated that a
    book is not to be lent, will
    you on receipt of a letter
    from the requesting library
    search the index for given
    entries? (Not answered)

PERIODICALS:
  Bound: Will not lend
  Unbound: Will not lend
  Loan Period: N/A
  Renewable: N/A
  Will lend if article exceeds
    _____ number of pages (Not
    answered)

MICROFORMS:
  Will Lend: No
  Specific Types of Microforms:
    N/A

GOVERNMENT PUBLICATIONS:
  Will Lend: Yes

DISSERTATIONS:
  Will Lend: Yes

THESES:
  Will Lend: Yes

AUDIO-VISUAL MATERIALS:
  Records: Will not lend
  Cassettes: Will not lend
  Other (slides, filmstrips,
    etc.): Will not lend

COMPUTER SOFTWARE:
  Will Lend: (Not answered)

PHOTODUPLICATION SERVICE:
  No charge up to 0 exposures
  Charge Per Exposure: 10¢
  Minimum/handling Fee: (Not
    answered)
  Average Turnaround Time:
    2 days

MICROFILMING SERVICE:
  Service Available: No
  Charges: N/A

DO YOU CHARGE THE BORROWING
  LIBRARY FOR POSTAGE? No

FOR HOW LONG DO YOU SUSPEND ILL
  SERVICE OVER THE CHRISTMAS
  HOLIDAYS? 1 week

ARE THERE ANY GROUPS OF LIBRARIES
  FOR WHICH YOU WAIVE FEES? IF
  SO, PLEASE NAME THEM: Pennsyl-
    vania state college
    libraries; Pennsylvania
    state institution libraries;
    other libraries with
    reciprocal agreements

STATE LIBRARY OF PENNSYLVANIA

NUC CODE: P

OCLC CODE: PHA

ADDRESS: Interlibrary Loan
          State Library of
            Pennsylvania
          P. O. Box 1601
          Harrisburg, PA 17105

TELEPHONE: (717) 787-4130

LIST NAMES OF BRANCHES WITH
  SEPARATE POLICIES: None

BOOKS:
  Will Lend: Yes
  Length of Loan: 1 month
  Renewable: Yes
  Charges: (Not answered)
  Average Turnaround Time:
    (Not answered)
  If you have indicated that a
    book is not to be lent, will
    you on receipt of a letter
    from the requesting library
    search the index for given
    entries? (Not answered)

PERIODICALS:
  Bound: Will not lend
  Unbound: Will not lend
  Loan Period: N/A
  Renewable: N/A
  Will lend if article exceeds
    _____ number of pages (Not
    answered)

MICROFORMS:
  Will Lend: Yes
  Specific Types of Microforms:
    All

GOVERNMENT PUBLICATIONS:
  Will Lend: Yes

DISSERTATIONS:
  Will Lend: (Not answered)

THESES:
  Will Lend: (Not answered)

AUDIO-VISUAL MATERIALS:
  Records: Will not lend
  Cassettes: Will not lend
  Other (slides, filmstrips,
    etc.): (Not answered)

COMPUTER SOFTWARE:
  Will Lend: (Not answered)

PHOTODUPLICATION SERVICE:
  No charge up to 20 exposures
  Charge Per Exposure: (Not
    answered)
  Minimum/handling Fee: None
  Average Turnaround Time:
    (Not answered)

MICROFILMING SERVICE:
  Service Available: No
  Charges: N/A

DO YOU CHARGE THE BORROWING
  LIBRARY FOR POSTAGE? No

FOR HOW LONG DO YOU SUSPEND ILL
  SERVICE OVER THE CHRISTMAS
  HOLIDAYS? No suspension

ARE THERE ANY GROUPS OF LIBRARIES
  FOR WHICH YOU WAIVE FEES? IF
  SO, PLEASE NAME THEM: (Not
    answered)

SWARTHMORE COLLEGE

NUC CODE: PSC

OCLC CODE: PSC

ADDRESS: Interlibrary Loan
           Swarthmore College
           Library
           Swarthmore, PA 19081

TELEPHONE: (215) 447-7491

LIST NAMES OF BRANCHES WITH
   SEPARATE POLICIES:
      Friends Historical Library
      Swarthmore College Peace
      Collection

BOOKS:
   Will Lend: Yes
   Length of Loan: 1 month
      (except Biology, 2 weeks)
   Renewable: Yes, except
      Biology
   Charges: None to academic
      libraries; $3.50 to profit-
      making institutions
   Average Turnaround Time:
      2-4 days
   If you have indicated that a
      book is not to be lent, will
      you on receipt of a letter
      from the requesting library
      search the index for given
      entries? (Not answered)

PERIODICALS:
   Bound: Will not lend
   Unbound: Will not lend
   Loan Period: N/A
   Renewable: N/A
   Will lend if article exceeds
      _____ number of pages (Not
      answered)

MICROFORMS:
   Will Lend: Yes
   Specific Types of Microforms:
      Most microfilms, fiche, and
      cards

GOVERNMENT PUBLICATIONS:
   Will Lend: Yes

DISSERTATIONS:
   Will Lend: Do not own

THESES:
   Will Lend: Yes, bachelor's
      theses only

AUDIO-VISUAL MATERIALS:
   Records: (Not answered)
   Cassettes: (Not answered)
   Other (slides, filmstrips,
      etc.): (Not answered)

COMPUTER SOFTWARE:
   Will Lend: No

PHOTODUPLICATION SERVICE:
   No charge up to 0 exposures
   Charge Per Exposure: 10¢
   Minimum/handling Fee: $1.00
      for libraries; reciprocal
      charges for libraries with
      higher charges; $3.00 for
      profit-making institutions.
   Average Turnaround Time:
      2-4 days

MICROFILMING SERVICE:
   Service Available: No
   Charges: N/A

DO YOU CHARGE THE BORROWING
   LIBRARY FOR POSTAGE? Extra
   charges such as 1st class
   or receipt insurance only.

FOR HOW LONG DO YOU SUSPEND ILL
   SERVICE OVER THE CHRISTMAS
   HOLIDAYS? Dec.24-Jan.2

ARE THERE ANY GROUPS OF LIBRARIES
   FOR WHICH YOU WAIVE FEES? IF
   SO, PLEASE NAME THEM: None

UNIVERSITY OF PENNSYLVANIA

NUC CODE: PU

OCLC CODE: PAU

ADDRESS: Interlibrary Loan
           University of
             Pennsylvania
             Libraries
           3420 Walnut St. CH
           Philadelphia, PA 19104

TELEPHONE: (215) 898-7558

LIST NAMES OF BRANCHES WITH
   SEPARATE POLICIES:
      Medical; Dental; Law;
      Veterinary

BOOKS:
   Will Lend: Yes
   Length of Loan: 4 weeks
   Renewable: Yes
   Charges: $10.00 (4 volumes
      per title)
   Average Turnaround Time:
      (Not answered)
   If you have indicated that a
      book is not to be lent, will
      you on receipt of a letter
      from the requesting library
      search the index for given
      entries? Only in rare
      circumstances

PERIODICALS:
   Bound: Will not lend
   Unbound: Will not lend
   Loan Period: N/A
   Renewable: N/A
   Will lend if article exceeds
      _____ number of pages (Will
      not lend, regardless of
      length of article)

MICROFORMS:
   Will Lend: Yes
   Specific Types of Microforms:
      Film, fiche, print

GOVERNMENT PUBLICATIONS:
   Will Lend: Yes

DISSERTATIONS:
   Will Lend: Yes, if pre-1953

THESES:
   Will Lend: Yes, if pre-1953

AUDIO-VISUAL MATERIALS:
   Records: Do not own
   Cassettes: Do not own
   Other (slides, filmstrips,
      etc.): Do not own

COMPUTER SOFTWARE:
   Will Lend: Do not own

PHOTODUPLICATION SERVICE:
   No charge up to 0 exposures
   Charge Per Exposure: 10¢
   Minimum/handling Fee: $5.00
   Average Turnaround Time:
      (Not answered)

MICROFILMING SERVICE:
   Service Available: Yes
   Charges: Same as photographic

DO YOU CHARGE THE BORROWING
   LIBRARY FOR POSTAGE? No

FOR HOW LONG DO YOU SUSPEND ILL
   SERVICE OVER THE CHRISTMAS
   HOLIDAYS? Dec.8-Jan.5 app.

ARE THERE ANY GROUPS OF LIBRARIES
   FOR WHICH YOU WAIVE FEES? IF
   SO, PLEASE NAME THEM: RLG:
   several local libraries with
   which we have longstanding
   arrangements.

UNIVERSITY OF PITTSBURGH

NUC CODE: PPiU

OCLC CODE: PIT

ADDRESS: Interlibrary Loan
    Hillman Library
    University of
      Pittsburgh
    Pittsburgh, PA 15260

TELEPHONE: (412) 624-4439

LIST NAMES OF BRANCHES WITH
SEPARATE POLICIES: None

BOOKS:
    Will Lend: Yes
    Length of Loan: 2 weeks
    Renewable: Yes
    Charges: None
    Average Turnaround Time:
      2 days
    If you have indicated that a
    book is not to be lent, will
    you on receipt of a letter
    from the requesting library
    search the index for given
    entries? No

PERIODICALS:
    Bound: Will not lend
    Unbound: Will not lend
    Loan Period: N/A
    Renewable: N/A
    Will lend if article exceeds
      _____ number of pages (Not
      answered)

MICROFORMS:
    Will Lend: Yes
    Specific Types of Microforms:
    Do not lend current 5
    years of Pittsburgh
    newspapers.

GOVERNMENT PUBLICATIONS:
    Will Lend: No

DISSERTATIONS:
    Will Lend: Yes, pre-1954

THESES:
    Will Lend: Yes, pre-1954

AUDIO-VISUAL MATERIALS:
    Records: Will not lend
    Cassettes: Will not lend
    Other (slides, filmstrips,
    etc.): Will not lend

COMPUTER SOFTWARE:
    Will Lend: No

PHOTODUPLICATION SERVICE:
    No charge up to 0 exposures
    Charge Per Exposure: 10¢
    Minimum/handling Fee: $2.50
    Average Turnaround Time:
      3-5 days

MICROFILMING SERVICE:
    Service Available: Yes
    Charges: Minimum charge of
    $30.00

DO YOU CHARGE THE BORROWING
LIBRARY FOR POSTAGE? No

FOR HOW LONG DO YOU SUSPEND ILL
SERVICE OVER THE CHRISTMAS
HOLIDAYS? Dec.15-Jan.6

ARE THERE ANY GROUPS OF LIBRARIES
FOR WHICH YOU WAIVE FEES? IF
SO, PLEASE NAME THEM: None

VILLANOVA UNIVERSITY--AUGUSTINIAN HISTORICAL INSTITUTE

NUC CODE: (Not answered)

OCLC CODE: (Not answered)

ADDRESS: Interlibrary Loan
    Augustinian Historical
      Institute
    Old Falvey
    Villanova University
    Villanova, PA 19085

TELEPHONE: (215) 645-7590

LIST NAMES OF BRANCHES WITH
SEPARATE POLICIES: None

BOOKS:
    Will Lend: (Not answered)
    Length of Loan: (Not answered)
    Renewable: (Not answered)
    Charges: (Not answered)
    Average Turnaround Time:
      (Not answered)
    If you have indicated that a
    book is not to be lent, will
    you on receipt of a letter
    from the requesting library
    search the index for given
    entries? (Not answered)

PERIODICALS:
    Bound: Will not lend
    Unbound: Will not lend
    Loan Period: N/A
    Renewable: N/A
    Will lend if article exceeds
      _____ number of pages (Not
      answered)

MICROFORMS:
    Will Lend: No
    Specific Types of Microforms:
    N/A

GOVERNMENT PUBLICATIONS:
    Will Lend: Do not own

DISSERTATIONS:
    Will Lend: Only at discretion
    of the director

THESES:
    Will Lend: Only at discretion
    of the director

AUDIO-VISUAL MATERIALS:
    Records: Will not lend
    Cassettes: Will not lend
    Other (slides, filmstrips,
    etc.): Will not lend

COMPUTER SOFTWARE:
    Will Lend: (Not answered)

PHOTODUPLICATION SERVICE:
    No charge up to 0 exposures
    Charge Per Exposure: 25¢
    Minimum/handling Fee: $2.50
    Average Turnaround Time:
      3 days

MICROFILMING SERVICE:
    Service Available: Yes
    Charges: Sent out

DO YOU CHARGE THE BORROWING
LIBRARY FOR POSTAGE? Yes

FOR HOW LONG DO YOU SUSPEND ILL
SERVICE OVER THE CHRISTMAS
HOLIDAYS? 2 weeks

ARE THERE ANY GROUPS OF LIBRARIES
FOR WHICH YOU WAIVE FEES? IF
SO, PLEASE NAME THEM: None

WEST CHESTER STATE COLLEGE

NUC CODE: PWcS

OCLC CODE: QWC

ADDRESS: Interlibrary Loan
Francis Harvey Green
Library
West Chester State
College
West Chester, PA 19380

TELEPHONE: (215) 436-3454

LIST NAMES OF BRANCHES WITH
SEPARATE POLICIES: None

BOOKS:
Will Lend: Yes
Length of Loan: 35 days
Renewable: Yes, for
30 days
Charges: None
Average Turnaround Time:
2 days
If you have indicated that a
book is not to be lent, will
you on receipt of a letter
from the requesting library
search the index for given
entries? (Not answered)

PERIODICALS:
Bound: Will not lend
Unbound: Will not lend
Loan Period: N/A
Renewable: N/A
Will lend if article exceeds
_____ number of pages (Not
answered)

MICROFORMS:
Will Lend: Yes
Specific Types of Microforms:
Cards, films, fiche

GOVERNMENT PUBLICATIONS:
Will Lend: Yes

DISSERTATIONS:
Will Lend: No

THESES:
Will Lend: No

AUDIO-VISUAL MATERIALS:
Records: Will not lend
Cassettes: Will not lend
Other (slides, filmstrips,
etc.): Will not lend

COMPUTER SOFTWARE:
Will Lend: No

PHOTODUPLICATION SERVICE:
No charge up to 0 exposures
Charge Per Exposure: 10¢
Minimum/handling Fee: $2.00
basic charge applicable to
institutions who charge fee
in kind
Average Turnaround Time:
2 days

MICROFILMING SERVICE:
Service Available: Yes
Charges: $2.00 plus 10¢ per
page

DO YOU CHARGE THE BORROWING
LIBRARY FOR POSTAGE? No

FOR HOW LONG DO YOU SUSPEND ILL
SERVICE OVER THE CHRISTMAS
HOLIDAYS? Mid-Dec. to mid-
Jan.

ARE THERE ANY GROUPS OF LIBRARIES
FOR WHICH YOU WAIVE FEES? IF
SO, PLEASE NAME THEM: Pennsylvania state schools,
State Dept., state
hospitals, federal government

WILKES COLLEGE

NUC CODE: (Not answered)

OCLC CODE: WBC

ADDRESS: Interlibrary Loan
Eugene Shedden Farley
Library
Wilkes College
Wilkes-Barre, PA 18766

TELEPHONE: (717) 824-4651, X241

LIST NAMES OF BRANCHES WITH
SEPARATE POLICIES: None

BOOKS:
Will Lend: Yes
Length of Loan: Usually
1 month
Renewable: Yes
Charges: None
Average Turnaround Time:
3 days
If you have indicated that a
book is not to be lent, will
you on receipt of a letter
from the requesting library
search the index for given
entries? Yes

PERIODICALS:
Bound: Will not lend
Unbound: Will not lend
Loan Period: N/A
Renewable: N/A
Will lend if article exceeds
_____ number of pages (Not
answered)

MICROFORMS:
Will Lend: No (rare
exceptions made)
Specific Types of Microforms:
(Not answered)

GOVERNMENT PUBLICATIONS:
Will Lend: No

DISSERTATIONS:
Will Lend: No

THESES:
Will Lend: No

AUDIO-VISUAL MATERIALS:
Records: Will not lend
Cassettes: Will not lend
Other (slides, filmstrips,
etc.): Will not lend

COMPUTER SOFTWARE:
Will Lend: No

PHOTODUPLICATION SERVICE:
$2.00 for 1st 15 exposures
Charge Per Exposure: 15¢
per exposure after 1st 15
Minimum/handling Fee: $2.00
Average Turnaround Time:
(Not answered)

MICROFILMING SERVICE:
Service Available: No
Charges: N/A

DO YOU CHARGE THE BORROWING
LIBRARY FOR POSTAGE? No, but
subject to change

FOR HOW LONG DO YOU SUSPEND ILL
SERVICE OVER THE CHRISTMAS
HOLIDAYS? 2 weeks

ARE THERE ANY GROUPS OF LIBRARIES
FOR WHICH YOU WAIVE FEES? IF
SO, PLEASE NAME THEM: Health
Information Library Network
of Northeastern Pennsylvania
(HILNEP) and NEPBC (local
consortium)

BROWN UNIVERSITY

NUC CODE: RPB

OCLC CODE: RBN

ADDRESS: (For Humanities and
Social Sciences)
   Interlibrary Loan
   Brown University
   Library
   Box A
   Providence, RI 02912
   (401) 863-2169

   (For Physical and Bio-
Medical Sciences)
   Interlibrary Loan
   Sciences Library
   Brown University
   Box I
   Providence, RI 02912
   (401) 863-2750

BOOKS:
   Will Lend: Yes
   Length of Loan: 2-4 weeks
   Renewable: Yes, once
   Charges: None
   Average Turnaround Time:
      (Not answered)
   If you have indicated that a
   book is not to be lent, will
   you on receipt of a letter
   from the requesting library
   search the index for given
   entries? (Not answered)

PERIODICALS:
   Bound: Will not lend
   Unbound: Will not lend
   Loan Period: N/A
   Renewable: N/A
   Will lend if article exceeds
   _____ number of pages (Not
      answered)

MICROFORMS:
   Will Lend: Yes, depending on
      the situation for microforms
      other than film

GOVERNMENT PUBLICATIONS:
   Will Lend: Yes, usually

DISSERTATIONS:
   Will Lend: Yes, if post-1964.
   1952 to present available
   from University Microfilms.

THESES:
   Will Lend: Yes, microfilm
      only, with author's
      permission

AUDIO-VISUAL MATERIALS:
   Records: (Not answered)
   Cassettes: (Not answered)
   Other (slides, filmstrips,
      etc.): (Not answered)

COMPUTER SOFTWARE:
   Will Lend: (Not answered)

PHOTODUPLICATION SERVICE:
   No charge up to 0 exposures
   Charges: $5.00 for 1-20
      exposures; $6.00 for 21-30
      exposures; $7.00 for 31-40
      exposures; (i.e., $1.00
      increase per every 10 pages
      interval over 20 pages)
   Average Turnaround Time:
      (Not answered)

MICROFILMING SERVICE:
   Service Available: Yes
   Charges: (Not answered)

DO YOU CHARGE THE BORROWING
   LIBRARY FOR POSTAGE? Only
      for 1st class, special
      handling, air mail, etc.

FOR HOW LONG DO YOU SUSPEND ILL
   SERVICE OVER THE CHRISTMAS
   HOLIDAYS? (Not answered)

ARE THERE ANY GROUPS OF LIBRARIES
   FOR WHICH YOU WAIVE FEES? IF
   SO, PLEASE NAME THEM: None

RHODE ISLAND COLLEGE

NUC CODE: RPRC

OCLC CODE: RCM

ADDRESS: Interlibrary Loan
   James P. Adams Library
   Rhode Island College
   600 Mt. Pleasant Ave.
   Providence, RI 02908

TELEPHONE: (401) 456-8190

LIST NAMES OF BRANCHES WITH
   SEPARATE POLICIES: None

BOOKS:
   Will Lend: Yes
   Length of Loan: 3 weeks
   Renewable: Yes, usually
   Charges: None
   Average Turnaround Time:
      2 days
   If you have indicated that a
   book is not to be lent, will
   you on receipt of a letter
   from the requesting library
   search the index for given
   entries? Yes, under special
   circumstances

PERIODICALS:
   Bound: Will not lend
   Unbound: Will not lend
   Loan Period: N/A
   Renewable: N/A
   Will lend if article exceeds
   _____ number of pages (Will
      lend occasionally; depends
      upon the circumstances)

MICROFORMS:
   Will Lend: Not usually
   Specific Types of Microforms:
      (Not answered)

GOVERNMENT PUBLICATIONS:
   Will Lend: Yes

DISSERTATIONS:
   Will Lend: Yes, if 2d copy
      available

THESES:
   Will Lend: Yes, if 2d copy
      available

AUDIO-VISUAL MATERIALS:
   Records: Will not lend
   Cassettes: Will not lend
   Other (slides, filmstrips,
      etc.): Will not lend

COMPUTER SOFTWARE:
   Will Lend: No

PHOTODUPLICATION SERVICE:
   No charge up to 0 exposures
   Charge Per Exposure: 10¢
   Minimum/handling Fee: None
   Average Turnaround Time:
      2 days

MICROFILMING SERVICE:
   Service Available: No
   Charges: N/A

DO YOU CHARGE THE BORROWING
   LIBRARY FOR POSTAGE? No

FOR HOW LONG DO YOU SUSPEND ILL
   SERVICE OVER THE CHRISTMAS
   HOLIDAYS? Christmas week

ARE THERE ANY GROUPS OF LIBRARIES
   FOR WHICH YOU WAIVE FEES? IF
   SO, PLEASE NAME THEM: NELINET
   agreement participating
   libraries; CRIARL (R.I.):
   ARIHSL medical libraries in
   R.I.

UNIVERSITY OF RHODE ISLAND AT KINGSTON

NUC CODE: RKS

OCLC CODE: RIU

ADDRESS: Interlibrary Loan
           University Library
           University of Rhode
           Island
           Kingston, RI 02881

TELEPHONE: (401) 792-5935

LIST NAMES OF BRANCHES WITH
   SEPARATE POLICIES: None

BOOKS:
   Will Lend: Yes
   Length of Loan: 2 weeks
   Renewable: Yes
   Charges: None
   Average Turnaround Time:
      7-10 days
   If you have indicated that a
      book is not to be lent, will
      you on receipt of a letter
      from the requesting library
      search the index for given
      entries? (Not answered)

PERIODICALS:
   Bound: Will not lend
   Unbound: Will not lend
   Loan Period: N/A
   Renewable: N/A
   Will lend if article exceeds
      _____ number of pages (Not
      answered)

MICROFORMS:
   Will Lend: No
   Specific Types of Microforms:
      N/A

GOVERNMENT PUBLICATIONS:
   Will Lend: Yes

DISSERTATIONS:
   Will Lend: Yes, if 2nd copy
      available; 1960 to present
      available from University
      Microfilms

THESES:
   Will Lend: Yes

AUDIO-VISUAL MATERIALS:
   Records: Will not lend
   Cassettes: Will not lend
   Other (slides, filmstrips,
      etc.): Will not lend

COMPUTER SOFTWARE:
   Will Lend: No

PHOTODUPLICATION SERVICE:
   No charge up to 0 exposures
   Charge Per Exposure: 10¢
   Minimum/handling Fee: $1.00
   Average Turnaround Time:
      7-10 days

MICROFILMING SERVICE:
   Service Available: Yes
   Charges: $1.00 minimum,
      10¢ per page

DO YOU CHARGE THE BORROWING
   LIBRARY FOR POSTAGE?   No

FOR HOW LONG DO YOU SUSPEND ILL
   SERVICE OVER THE CHRISTMAS
   HOLIDAYS? Dec.15-Jan.3

ARE THERE ANY GROUPS OF LIBRARIES
   FOR WHICH YOU WAIVE FEES? IF
   SO, PLEASE NAME THEM: NELINET
   ILL reciprocal agreement;
   New England State
   Universities

BENEDICT COLLEGE

NUC CODE: (Not answered)

OCLC CODE: BDC

ADDRESS: Interlibrary Loan
Benedict College
Harden & Blanding Sts.
Learning Resources
Center
Columbia, SC 29204

TELEPHONE: (803) 256-4220, X2180

LIST NAMES OF BRANCHES WITH
SEPARATE POLICIES: None

BOOKS:
Will Lend: Yes
Length of Loan: 2 weeks
Renewable: Yes
Charges: None
Average Turnaround Time:
3 days
If you have indicated that a
book is not to be lent, will
you on receipt of a letter
from the requesting library
search the index for given
entries? (Not answered)

PERIODICALS:
Bound: Will not lend
Unbound: Will not lend
Loan Period: N/A
Renewable: N/A
Will lend if article exceeds
_____ number of pages (Will
not lend, regardless of
length of article)

MICROFORMS:
Will Lend: No
Specific Types of Microforms:
N/A

GOVERNMENT PUBLICATIONS:
Will Lend: Yes

DISSERTATIONS:
Will Lend: No

THESES:
Will Lend: No

AUDIO-VISUAL MATERIALS:
Records: Will not lend
Cassettes: Will not lend
Other (slides, filmstrips,
etc.): Will not lend

COMPUTER SOFTWARE:
Will Lend: No

PHOTODUPLICATION SERVICE:
No charge up to 0 exposures
Charge Per Exposure: 5¢
Minimum/handling Fee: None
Average Turnaround Time:
3 days

MICROFILMING SERVICE:
Service Available: No
Charges: N/A

DO YOU CHARGE THE BORROWING
LIBRARY FOR POSTAGE? No

FOR HOW LONG DO YOU SUSPEND ILL
SERVICE OVER THE CHRISTMAS
HOLIDAYS? 2 weeks

ARE THERE ANY GROUPS OF LIBRARIES
FOR WHICH YOU WAIVE FEES? IF
SO, PLEASE NAME THEM: None

CLEMSON UNIVERSITY

NUC CODE: ScCleU

OCLC CODE: SEA

ADDRESS: Interlibrary Loan
Cooper Library
Clemson University
Clemson, SC 29631

TELEPHONE: (803) 656-3024

LIST NAMES OF BRANCHES WITH
SEPARATE POLICIES: (Not
answered)

BOOKS:
Will Lend: Yes
Length of Loan: 2 weeks use
Renewable: Yes
Charges: (Not answered)
Average Turnaround Time:
(Not answered)
If you have indicated that a
book is not to be lent, will
you on receipt of a letter
from the requesting library
search the index for given
entries? (Not answered)

PERIODICALS:
Bound: Will lend
Unbound: Will lend
Loan Period: 1 week
Renewable: No
Will lend if article exceeds
_____ number of pages (Not
answered)

MICROFORMS:
Will Lend: Yes
Specific Types of Microforms:
All types

GOVERNMENT PUBLICATIONS:
Will Lend: Yes

DISSERTATIONS:
Will Lend: Yes; 1963 to
present available from
University Microfilms

THESES:
Will Lend: Yes

AUDIO-VISUAL MATERIALS:
Records: Will not lend
Cassettes: Will not lend
Other (slides, filmstrips,
etc.): Will not lend

COMPUTER SOFTWARE:
Will Lend: (Not answered)

PHOTODUPLICATION SERVICE:
No charge up to 0 exposures
Charge Per Exposure: 10¢
Minimum Fee: $1.50
Handling Fee: $1.00
Average Turnaround Time:
(Not answered)

MICROFILMING SERVICE:
Service Available: Yes
Charges: 15¢ per frame

DO YOU CHARGE THE BORROWING
LIBRARY FOR POSTAGE? No

FOR HOW LONG DO YOU SUSPEND ILL
SERVICE OVER THE CHRISTMAS
HOLIDAYS? Dec.12-Jan.5

ARE THERE ANY GROUPS OF LIBRARIES
FOR WHICH YOU WAIVE FEES? IF
SO, PLEASE NAME THEM: (Not
answered)

COLLEGE OF CHARLESTON

NUC CODE: SccC

OCLC CODE: SBM

ADDRESS: Interlibrary Loan
Robert Scott Small
Library
College of Charleston
Charleston, SC 29424

TELEPHONE: (803) 792-5530

LIST NAMES OF BRANCHES WITH
SEPARATE POLICIES: None

BOOKS:
Will Lend: Yes
Length of Loan: 4 weeks
Renewable: Yes, for 2 weeks
Charges: None
Average Turnaround Time:
2 days
If you have indicated that a
book is not to be lent, will
you on receipt of a letter
from the requesting library
search the index for given
entries? (Not answered)

PERIODICALS:
Bound: Will not lend
Unbound: Will not lend
Loan Period: N/A
Renewable: N/A
Will lend if article exceeds
_____ number of pages (Not
answered)

MICROFORMS:
Will Lend: No
Specific Types of Microforms:
N/A

GOVERNMENT PUBLICATIONS:
Will Lend: Yes

DISSERTATIONS:
Will Lend: Yes

THESES:
Will Lend: Yes

AUDIO-VISUAL MATERIALS:
Records: Do not own
Cassettes: Do not own
Other (slides, filmstrips,
etc.): Do not own

COMPUTER SOFTWARE:
Will Lend: Do not own

PHOTODUPLICATION SERVICE:
No charge up to 0 exposures
Charge Per Exposure: 10¢
for Xerox copies; 20¢ for
microform copies
Minimum/handling Fee: 50¢
Average Turnaround Time:
2 days

MICROFILMING SERVICE:
Service Available: No
Charges: N/A

DO YOU CHARGE THE BORROWING
LIBRARY FOR POSTAGE? No

FOR HOW LONG DO YOU SUSPEND ILL
SERVICE OVER THE CHRISTMAS
HOLIDAYS? Usually 3 weeks

ARE THERE ANY GROUPS OF LIBRARIES
FOR WHICH YOU WAIVE FEES? IF
SO, PLEASE NAME THEM: None

FRANCIS MARION COLLEGE

NUC CODE: ScFlM

OCLC CODE: SFM

ADDRESS: Interlibrary Loan
Rogers Library
Francis Marion College
Florence, SC 29501

TELEPHONE: (803) 669-4121, X310

LIST NAMES OF BRANCHES WITH
SEPARATE POLICIES: None

BOOKS:
Will Lend: Yes
Length of Loan: 1 month
Renewable: Yes
Charges: (Not answered)
Average Turnaround Time:
(Not answered)
If you have indicated that a
book is not to be lent, will
you on receipt of a letter
from the requesting library
search the index for given
entries? (Not answered)

PERIODICALS:
Bound: Will not lend
Unbound: Will not lend
Loan Period: N/A
Renewable: N/A
Will lend if article exceeds
_____ number of pages (Not
answered)

MICROFORMS:
Will Lend: Yes
Specific Types of Microforms:
Fiche only

GOVERNMENT PUBLICATIONS:
Will Lend: Yes

DISSERTATIONS:
Will Lend: (Not answered)

THESES:
Will Lend: (Not answered)

AUDIO-VISUAL MATERIALS:
Records: (Not answered)
Cassettes: (Not answered)
Other (slides, filmstrips,
etc.): (Not answered)

COMPUTER SOFTWARE:
Will Lend: (Not answered)

PHOTODUPLICATION SERVICE:
No charge up to 0 exposures
Charge Per Exposure: 10¢
Minimum/handling Fee:
(Not answered)
Average Turnaround Time:
2 days

MICROFILMING SERVICE:
Service Available: No
Charges: N/A

DO YOU CHARGE THE BORROWING
LIBRARY FOR POSTAGE? No

FOR HOW LONG DO YOU SUSPEND ILL
SERVICE OVER THE CHRISTMAS
HOLIDAYS? Dec.24-Jan.1

ARE THERE ANY GROUPS OF LIBRARIES
FOR WHICH YOU WAIVE FEES? IF
SO, PLEASE NAME THEM: (Not
answered)

FURMAN UNIVERSITY

NUC CODE: ScGF

OCLC CODE: SFU

ADDRESS: Interlibrary Loan
            Furman University
            Library
            Greenville, SC 29613

TELEPHONE: (803) 294-2192

LIST NAMES OF BRANCHES WITH
  SEPARATE POLICIES: None

BOOKS:
    Will Lend: Yes
    Length of Loan: 1 month
    Renewable: Yes
    Charges: (Not answered)
    Average Turnaround Time:
      (Not answered)
    If you have indicated that a
      book is not to be lent, will
      you on receipt of a letter
      from the requesting library
      search the index for given
      entries? No

PERIODICALS:
    Bound: Will not lend
    Unbound: Will not lend
    Loan Period: N/A
    Renewable: N/A
    Will lend if article exceeds
      _____ number of pages (Not
      answered)

MICROFORMS:
    Will Lend: Yes
    Specific Types of Microforms:
      (Not answered)

GOVERNMENT PUBLICATIONS:
    Will Lend: Yes

DISSERTATIONS:
    Will Lend: No

THESES:
    Will Lend: No

AUDIO-VISUAL MATERIALS:
    Records: Will not lend
    Cassettes: Will not lend
    Other (slides, filmstrips,
      etc.): Will not lend

COMPUTER SOFTWARE:
    Will Lend: No

PHOTODUPLICATION SERVICE:
    No charge up to 0 exposures
    Charge Per Exposure: 10¢
    Minimum/handling Fee: $1.00
    Average Turnaround Time:
      1 week

MICROFILMING SERVICE:
    Service Available: No
    Charges: N/A

DO YOU CHARGE THE BORROWING
  LIBRARY FOR POSTAGE? No

FOR HOW LONG DO YOU SUSPEND ILL
  SERVICE OVER THE CHRISTMAS
  HOLIDAYS? 3 weeks

ARE THERE ANY GROUPS OF LIBRARIES
  FOR WHICH YOU WAIVE FEES? IF
  SO, PLEASE NAME THEM: None

GREENVILLE COUNTY LIBRARY

NUC CODE: ScG

OCLC CODE: SGR

ADDRESS: Interlibrary Loan
            Greenville County
            Library
            300 College St.
            Greenville, SC 29601

TELEPHONE: (803) 242-5000

LIST NAMES OF BRANCHES WITH
  SEPARATE POLICIES: None

BOOKS:
    Will Lend: Yes
    Length of Loan: 28 days
    Renewable: No
    Charges: None
    Average Turnaround Time:
      7 days
    If you have indicated that a
      book is not to be lent, will
      you on receipt of a letter
      from the requesting library
      search the index for given
      entries? (Not answered)

PERIODICALS:
    Bound: Will not lend
    Unbound: Will not lend
    Loan Period: N/A
    Renewable: N/A
    Will lend if article exceeds
      _____ number of pages (Will
      not lend, regardless of
      length of article)

MICROFORMS:
    Will Lend: No
    Specific Types of Microforms:
      N/A

GOVERNMENT PUBLICATIONS:
    Will Lend: No

DISSERTATIONS:
    Will Lend: No

THESES:
    Will Lend: No

AUDIO-VISUAL MATERIALS:
    Records: Will not lend
    Cassettes: Will not lend
    Other (slides, filmstrips,
      etc.): Will not lend

COMPUTER SOFTWARE:
    Will Lend: No

PHOTODUPLICATION SERVICE:
    No charge up to 0 exposures
    Charge Per Exposure: 50¢
      for Xerox copies; 75¢ for
      microform copies
    Minimum/handling Fee: None
    Average Turnaround Time:
      7 days

MICROFILMING SERVICE:
    Service Available: No
    Charges: N/A

DO YOU CHARGE THE BORROWING
  LIBRARY FOR POSTAGE? No

FOR HOW LONG DO YOU SUSPEND ILL
  SERVICE OVER THE CHRISTMAS
  HOLIDAYS? No suspension

ARE THERE ANY GROUPS OF LIBRARIES
  FOR WHICH YOU WAIVE FEES? IF
  SO, PLEASE NAME THEM: None

MEDICAL UNIVERSITY OF SOUTH CAROLINA

NUC CODE: SCCM

OCLC CODE: SMC

ADDRESS: Interlibrary Loan
          Medical University of
            South Carolina
          Library
          171 Ashley Ave.
          Charleston, SC 29425

TELEPHONE: (803) 792-2379

LIST NAMES OF BRANCHES WITH
  SEPARATE POLICIES:
    Waring Historical Library
      (no loans)

BOOKS:
  Will Lend: Yes
  Length of Loan: 3 weeks
  Renewable: Yes
  Charges: $4.75
  Average Turnaround Time:
    Same day
  If you have indicated that a
    book is not to be lent, will
    you on receipt of a letter
    from the requesting library
    search the index for given
    entries? (Not answered)

PERIODICALS:
  Bound: Will not lend
  Unbound: Will not lend
  Loan Period: N/A
  Renewable: N/A
  Will lend if article exceeds
    _____ number of pages (Not
    answered)

MICROFORMS:
  Will Lend: No
  Specific Types of Microforms:
    N/A

GOVERNMENT PUBLICATIONS:
  Will Lend: Yes

DISSERTATIONS:
  Will Lend: Yes

THESES:
  Will Lend: Yes

AUDIO-VISUAL MATERIALS:
  Records: Will not lend
  Cassettes: Will not lend
  Other (slides, filmstrips,
    etc.): Will not lend

COMPUTER SOFTWARE:
  Will Lend: No

PHOTODUPLICATION SERVICE:
  No charge up to 0 exposures
  Charge Per Exposure: N/A
  Minimum/handling Fee: $4.75
    per article
  Average Turnaround Time:
    Same day

MICROFILMING SERVICE:
  Service Available: No
  Charges: N/A

DO YOU CHARGE THE BORROWING
  LIBRARY FOR POSTAGE? No;
  we request insuring
  returns, however

FOR HOW LONG DO YOU SUSPEND ILL
  SERVICE OVER THE CHRISTMAS
  HOLIDAYS? Dec.15-Jan.3

ARE THERE ANY GROUPS OF LIBRARIES
  FOR WHICH YOU WAIVE FEES? IF
  SO, PLEASE NAME THEM:
    Medical resources libraries
    within the region

SOUTH CAROLINA STATE LIBRARY

NUC CODE: SC

OCLC CODE: DSC

ADDRESS: Interlibrary Loan
          South Carolina State
            Library
          P. O. Box 11469
          Columbia, SC 29211

TELEPHONE: (803) 758-3138

LIST NAMES OF BRANCHES WITH
  SEPARATE POLICIES: None

BOOKS:
  Will Lend: Yes
  Length of Loan: 4 weeks
  Renewable: Yes
  Charges: None
  Average Turnaround Time:
    1-2 days
  If you have indicated that a
    book is not to be lent, will
    you on receipt of a letter
    from the requesting library
    search the index for given
    entries? Yes. We cannot
    perform extensive
    research, but we will fill
    any reasonable request.

PERIODICALS:
  Bound: Will not lend
  Unbound: Will lend selectively
  Loan Period: 2 weeks
  Renewable: No
  Will lend if article exceeds
    _____ number of pages
    (Length of article is not
    a factor)

MICROFORMS:
  Will Lend: No
  Specific Types of Microforms:
    N/A

GOVERNMENT PUBLICATIONS:
  Will Lend: Yes

DISSERTATIONS:
  Will Lend: Do not own

THESES:
  Will Lend: Do not own

AUDIO-VISUAL MATERIALS:
  Records: Will not lend
  Cassettes: Will not lend
  Other (slides, filmstrips,
    etc.): Will not lend

COMPUTER SOFTWARE:
  Will Lend: No

PHOTODUPLICATION SERVICE:
  No charge up to 0 exposures
  Charge Per Exposure: 10¢
  Minimum/handling Fee: $1.00
  Average Turnaround Time:
    1-2 days

MICROFILMING SERVICE:
  Service Available: No
  Charges: N/A

DO YOU CHARGE THE BORROWING
  LIBRARY FOR POSTAGE? Not
  at this time

FOR HOW LONG DO YOU SUSPEND ILL
  SERVICE OVER THE CHRISTMAS
  HOLIDAYS? No suspension

ARE THERE ANY GROUPS OF LIBRARIES
  FOR WHICH YOU WAIVE FEES? IF
  SO, PLEASE NAME THEM: No
  minimum photocopy fee for
  libraries in South
  Carolina

SPARTANBURG COUNTY PUBLIC LIBRARY

NUC CODE: (Not answered)

OCLC CODE: SPL

ADDRESS: Interlibrary Loan
           Spartanburg County
             Public Library
           P. O. Box 2409
           Spartanburg, SC 29304

TELEPHONE: (803) 596-3505

LIST NAMES OF BRANCHES WITH
  SEPARATE POLICIES: None

BOOKS:
  Will Lend: Yes
  Length of Loan: 28 days
  Renewable: Yes
  Charges: None
  Average Turnaround Time:
    2 days
  If you have indicated that a
  book is not to be lent, will
  you on receipt of a letter
  from the requesting library
  search the index for given
  entries? (Not answered)

PERIODICALS:
  Bound: Will not lend
  Unbound: Will not lend
  Loan Period: N/A
  Renewable: N/A
  Will lend if article exceeds
  _____ number of pages (Not
    answered)

MICROFORMS:
  Will Lend: No
  Specific Types of Microforms:
    N/A

GOVERNMENT PUBLICATIONS:
  Will Lend: Yes

DISSERTATIONS:
  Will Lend: Do not own

THESES:
  Will Lend: Do not own

AUDIO-VISUAL MATERIALS:
  Records: Will not lend
  Cassettes: Will not lend
  Other (slides, filmstrips,
    etc.): Will not lend

COMPUTER SOFTWARE:
  Will Lend: No

PHOTODUPLICATION SERVICE:
  No charge up to 0 exposures
  Charge Per Exposure: 25¢
  Minimum/handling Fee: None
  Average Turnaround Time:
    2 days

MICROFILMING SERVICE:
  Service Available: No
  Charges: N/A

DO YOU CHARGE THE BORROWING
  LIBRARY FOR POSTAGE? No

FOR HOW LONG DO YOU SUSPEND ILL
  SERVICE OVER THE CHRISTMAS
  HOLIDAYS? No suspension

ARE THERE ANY GROUPS OF LIBRARIES
  FOR WHICH YOU WAIVE FEES? IF
  SO, PLEASE NAME THEM: None

UNIVERSITY OF SOUTH CAROLINA AT COLUMBIA

NUC CODE: ScU

OCLC CODE: SUC

ADDRESS: Interlibrary Loan
           Thomas Cooper Library
           University of South
             Carolina
           Columbia, SC 29208

TELEPHONE: (803) 777-4866

LIST NAMES OF BRANCHES WITH
  SEPARATE POLICIES:
    Law School Library
    School of Medicine Library
    South Caroliniana Library

BOOKS:
  Will Lend: Yes
  Length of Loan: 2 weeks use
  Renewable: Yes, once
  Charges: None
  Average Turnaround Time:
    1-3 days
  If you have indicated that a
  book is not to be lent, will
  you on receipt of a letter
  from the requesting library
  search the index for given
  entries? (Not answered)

PERIODICALS:
  Bound: Will not lend
  Unbound: Will not lend
  Loan Period: N/A
  Renewable: N/A
  Will lend if article exceeds
  _____ number of pages (Will
    not lend, regardless of
    length of article)

MICROFORMS:
  Will Lend: Yes
  Specific Types of Microforms:
    Microfilm, microfiche,
    microcards

GOVERNMENT PUBLICATIONS:
  Will Lend: Yes

DISSERTATIONS:
  Will Lend: Yes, if 2nd copy
    available; 1953 to present
    available from University
    Microfilms

THESES:
  Will Lend: Yes, if 2nd copy
    available

AUDIO-VISUAL MATERIALS:
  Records: Will not lend
  Cassettes: Will not lend
  Other (slides, filmstrips,
    etc.): Will not lend

COMPUTER SOFTWARE:
  Will Lend: No

PHOTODUPLICATION SERVICE:
  No charge up to 0 exposures
  Charge Per Exposure: 10¢
  Minimum/handling Fee: $3.00
  Average Turnaround Time:
    1-4 days

MICROFILMING SERVICE:
  Service Available: Yes,
    limited
  Charges: (Not answered)

DO YOU CHARGE THE BORROWING
  LIBRARY FOR POSTAGE? No

FOR HOW LONG DO YOU SUSPEND ILL
  SERVICE OVER THE CHRISTMAS
  HOLIDAYS? Dec.10-Jan.3

ARE THERE ANY GROUPS OF LIBRARIES
  FOR WHICH YOU WAIVE FEES? IF
  SO, PLEASE NAME THEM:
    Minimum charge of $1.00 to
    reciprocating ASERL
    libraries; also to in-state

UNIVERSITY OF SOUTH CAROLINA AT SPARTANBURG

NUC CODE: (Not answered)

OCLC CODE: (Not answered)

ADDRESS: Interlibrary Loan
           Library
           University of South
             Carolina at
             Spartanburg
           Spartanburg, SC   29303

TELEPHONE: (803) 578-1800, X410
             or X411

LIST NAMES OF BRANCHES WITH
   SEPARATE POLICIES: None

BOOKS:
   Will Lend: Yes
   Length of Loan: 3 weeks
   Renewable: Yes
   Charges: (Not answered)
   Average Turnaround Time:
     1 day
   If you have indicated that a
   book is not to be lent, will
   you on receipt of a letter
   from the requesting library
   search the index for given
   entries?   Yes

PERIODICALS:
   Bound: Will not lend
   Unbound: Will not lend
   Loan Period: N/A
   Renewable: N/A
   Will lend if article exceeds
     _____ number of pages   (Not
       answered)

MICROFORMS:
   Will Lend: No
   Specific Types of Microforms:
     N/A

GOVERNMENT PUBLICATIONS:
   Will Lend: Yes

DISSERTATIONS:
   Will Lend: (Not answered)

THESES:
   Will Lend: (Not answered)

AUDIO-VISUAL MATERIALS:
   Records: Will not lend
   Cassettes: Will not lend
   Other (slides, filmstrips,
     etc.):   Will not lend

COMPUTER SOFTWARE:
   Will Lend: No

PHOTODUPLICATION SERVICE:
   No charge up to 0 exposures
   Charge Per Exposure: 10¢
   Minimum/handling Fee: None
   Average Turnaround Time:
     1 day

MICROFILMING SERVICE:
   Service Available: No
   Charges: N/A

DO YOU CHARGE THE BORROWING
   LIBRARY FOR POSTAGE?   No

FOR HOW LONG DO YOU SUSPEND ILL
   SERVICE OVER THE CHRISTMAS
   HOLIDAYS?   2 weeks

ARE THERE ANY GROUPS OF LIBRARIES
   FOR WHICH YOU WAIVE FEES?   IF
   SO, PLEASE NAME THEM: None

SOUTH DAKOTA STATE LIBRARY

NUC CODE: Sd

OCLC CODE: SDS

ADDRESS: Interlibrary Loan
South Dakota State
Library
800 N. Illinois
Pierre, SD 57501

TELEPHONE: (605) 773-3131

LIST NAMES OF BRANCHES WITH
SEPARATE POLICIES: None

BOOKS:
Will Lend: Yes
Length of Loan: 4 weeks
Renewable: No
Charges: None
Average Turnaround Time:
24 hours
If you have indicated that a
book is not to be lent, will
you on receipt of a letter
from the requesting library
search the index for given
entries? (Not answered)

PERIODICALS:
Bound: Do not bind
Unbound: Will not lend
Loan Period: N/A
Renewable: N/A
Will lend if article exceeds
_____ number of pages (Not
answered)

MICROFORMS:
Will Lend: No
Specific Types of Microforms:
N/A

GOVERNMENT PUBLICATIONS:
Will Lend: Yes

DISSERTATIONS:
Will Lend: Do not own

THESES:
Will Lend: Do not own

AUDIO-VISUAL MATERIALS:
Records: Will not lend
Cassettes: Will not lend
Other (slides, filmstrips,
etc.): Will not lend

COMPUTER SOFTWARE:
Will Lend: No

PHOTODUPLICATION SERVICE:
No charge up to 25 exposures
Charge Per Exposure: None
Minimum/handling Fee: None
Average Turnaround Time:
24 hours

MICROFILMING SERVICE:
Service Available: No
Charges: N/A

DO YOU CHARGE THE BORROWING
LIBRARY FOR POSTAGE? No

FOR HOW LONG DO YOU SUSPEND ILL
SERVICE OVER THE CHRISTMAS
HOLIDAYS? No suspension

ARE THERE ANY GROUPS OF LIBRARIES
FOR WHICH YOU WAIVE FEES? IF
SO, PLEASE NAME THEM: No fees
charged

SOUTH DAKOTA STATE UNIVERSITY

NUC CODE: SdB

OCLC CODE: SDB

ADDRESS: Interlibrary Loan
Briggs Library
P. O. Box 2115
South Dakota State
University
Brookings, SD
57007-1098

TELEPHONE: (605) 688-5106

LIST NAMES OF BRANCHES WITH
SEPARATE POLICIES: None

BOOKS:
Will Lend: Yes
Length of Loan: 3 weeks
Renewable: No
Charges: (Not answered)
Average Turnaround Time:
(Not answered)
If you have indicated that a
book is not to be lent, will
you on receipt of a letter
from the requesting library
search the index for given
entries? (Not answered)

PERIODICALS:
Bound: Will lend
Unbound: Will not lend
Loan Period: 1 week
Renewable: (Not answered)
Will lend if article exceeds
30 pages

MICROFORMS:
Will Lend: Yes
Specific Types of Microforms:
All types

GOVERNMENT PUBLICATIONS:
Will Lend: (Not answered)

DISSERTATIONS:
Will Lend: No; 1959 to
present available from
University Microfilms

THESES:
Will Lend: Yes, if 2nd copy
available

AUDIO-VISUAL MATERIALS:
Records: (Not answered)
Cassettes: (Not answered)
Other (slides, filmstrips,
etc.): (Not answered)

COMPUTER SOFTWARE:
Will Lend: (Not answered)

PHOTODUPLICATION SERVICE:
No charge up to 25 pages for
in-state libraries
Charge Per Exposure: 10¢
Minimum Fee: $1.50
Average Turnaround Time:
(Not answered)

MICROFILMING SERVICE:
Service Available: (Not
answered)
Charges: N/A

DO YOU CHARGE THE BORROWING
LIBRARY FOR POSTAGE? No

FOR HOW LONG DO YOU SUSPEND ILL
SERVICE OVER THE CHRISTMAS
HOLIDAYS? Dec.15-Jan.5

ARE THERE ANY GROUPS OF LIBRARIES
FOR WHICH YOU WAIVE FEES? IF
SO, PLEASE NAME THEM: (Not
answered)

UNIVERSITY OF SOUTH DAKOTA AT VERMILLION

NUC CODE: SdU

OCLC CODE: USD

ADDRESS: Interlibrary Loan
          I. D. Weeks Library
          University of South
            Dakota
          Vermillion, SD 57069

TELEPHONE: (605) 677-5371

LIST NAMES OF BRANCHES WITH
    SEPARATE POLICIES:
    Lommen Health Sciences
        Library
    Law Library

BOOKS:
    Will Lend: Yes
    Length of Loan: 2 weeks
    Renewable: Yes
    Charges: None
    Average Turnaround Time:
      3-4 days
    If you have indicated that a
      book is not to be lent, will
      you on receipt of a letter
      from the requesting library
      search the index for given
      entries? Yes

PERIODICALS:
    Bound: Will not lend
    Unbound: Will not lend
    Loan Period: N/A
    Renewable: N/A
    Will lend if article exceeds
      _____ number of pages (Not
      answered)

MICROFORMS:
    Will Lend: Yes
    Specific Types of Microforms:
      Cards, fiche, films

GOVERNMENT PUBLICATIONS:
    Will Lend: Yes

DISSERTATIONS:
    Will Lend: Yes

THESES:
    Will Lend: Yes

AUDIO-VISUAL MATERIALS:
    Records: Will lend
    Cassettes: Will lend
    Other (slides, filmstrips,
      etc.): Will lend

COMPUTER SOFTWARE:
    Will Lend: No

PHOTODUPLICATION SERVICE:
    No charge up to 25 exposures
    Charge Per Exposure: 10¢
    Minimum/handling Fee: $1.00
    Average Turnaround Time:
      3-4 days

MICROFILMING SERVICE:
    Service Available: No
    Charges: N/A

DO YOU CHARGE THE BORROWING
    LIBRARY FOR POSTAGE? No

FOR HOW LONG DO YOU SUSPEND ILL
    SERVICE OVER THE CHRISTMAS
    HOLIDAYS? Service reduced
      approximately Dec.15-Jan.5

ARE THERE ANY GROUPS OF LIBRARIES
    FOR WHICH YOU WAIVE FEES? IF
    SO, PLEASE NAME THEM: SD;
      Minitex; BCR

AUSTIN PEAY STATE UNIVERSITY

NUC CODE: TCIA

OCLC CODE: TPA

ADDRESS: Interlibrary Loan
       Woodward Library
       Austin Peay State
       University
       Clarksville, TN   37040

TELEPHONE: (615) 648-7346

LIST NAMES OF BRANCHES WITH
  SEPARATE POLICIES: None

BOOKS:
  Will Lend: Yes
  Length of Loan: 3 weeks
  Renewable: Yes
  Charges: None
  Average Turnaround Time:
   24 hours
  If you have indicated that a
   book is not to be lent, will
   you on receipt of a letter
   from the requesting library
   search the index for given
   entries? Yes

PERIODICALS:
  Bound: Will not lend
  Unbound: Will not lend
  Loan Period: N/A
  Renewable: N/A
  Will lend if article exceeds
   _____ number of pages (Not
   answered)

MICROFORMS:
  Will Lend: Yes
  Specific Types of Microforms:
   Cards, film, fiche, print

GOVERNMENT PUBLICATIONS:
  Will Lend: Yes

DISSERTATIONS:
  Will Lend: No

THESES:
  Will Lend: Yes

AUDIO-VISUAL MATERIALS:
  Records: Will not lend
  Cassettes: Will not lend
  Other (slides, filmstrips,
   etc.): Will not lend

COMPUTER SOFTWARE:
  Will Lend: No

PHOTODUPLICATION SERVICE:
  No charge up to 20 exposures
  Charge Per Exposure: 5¢
  Minimum/handling Fee: None
  Average Turnaround Time:
   24 hours

MICROFILMING SERVICE:
  Service Available: No
  Charges: N/A

DO YOU CHARGE THE BORROWING
  LIBRARY FOR POSTAGE? No

FOR HOW LONG DO YOU SUSPEND ILL
  SERVICE OVER THE CHRISTMAS
  HOLIDAYS? Dec.15-Jan.2

ARE THERE ANY GROUPS OF LIBRARIES
  FOR WHICH YOU WAIVE FEES? IF
  SO, PLEASE NAME THEM: None

CHATTANOOGA-HAMILTON COUNTY BICENTENNIAL LIBRARY

NUC CODE: (Not answered)

OCLC CODE: TCH

ADDRESS: Interlibrary Loan
       Chattanooga-Hamilton
        County Bicentennial
        Library
       1001 Broad St.
       Chattanooga, TN   37402

TELEPHONE: (615) 757-5408

LIST NAMES OF BRANCHES WITH
  SEPARATE POLICIES: None

BOOKS:
  Will Lend: Yes
  Length of Loan: 28 days
  Renewable: Yes
  Charges: None
  Average Turnaround Time:
   1 week
  If you have indicated that a
   book is not to be lent, will
   you on receipt of a letter
   from the requesting library
   search the index for given
   entries? Yes, for non-
   circulating genealogical
   material

PERIODICALS:
  Bound: Will not lend
  Unbound: Will lend
  Loan Period: 28 days
  Renewable: Yes
  Will lend if article exceeds
   _____ number of pages (Not
   answered)

MICROFORMS:
  Will Lend: No
  Specific Types of Microforms:
   N/A

GOVERNMENT PUBLICATIONS:
  Will Lend: Yes

DISSERTATIONS:
  Will Lend: Do not own

THESES:
  Will Lend: Do not own

AUDIO-VISUAL MATERIALS:
  Records: Will not lend
  Cassettes: Will not lend
  Other (slides, filmstrips,
   etc.): Will not lend

COMPUTER SOFTWARE:
  Will Lend: Do not own

PHOTODUPLICATION SERVICE:
  No charge up to 11 exposures
  Charge Per Exposure: 10¢
   per additional exposure,
   plus postage
  Minimum/handling Fee: None
  Average Turnaround Time:
   1 week

MICROFILMING SERVICE:
  Service Available: No
  Charges: N/A

DO YOU CHARGE THE BORROWING
  LIBRARY FOR POSTAGE? No

FOR HOW LONG DO YOU SUSPEND ILL
  SERVICE OVER THE CHRISTMAS
  HOLIDAYS? No suspension

ARE THERE ANY GROUPS OF LIBRARIES
  FOR WHICH YOU WAIVE FEES? IF
  SO, PLEASE NAME THEM: None

EAST TENNESSEE STATE UNIVERSITY AT JOHNSON CITY

NUC CODE: TJoS

OCLC CODE: TET

ADDRESS: Interlibrary Loan
           Sherrod Library
           East Tennessee State
           University
           Johnson City, TN 37614

TELEPHONE: (615) 929-4365

LIST NAMES OF BRANCHES WITH
  SEPARATE POLICIES: None

BOOKS:
  Will Lend: Yes
  Length of Loan: 2 weeks
  Renewable: Yes
  Charges: None
  Average Turnaround Time:
    2 days
  If you have indicated that a
    book is not to be lent, will
    you on receipt of a letter
    from the requesting library
    search the index for given
    entries? Yes

PERIODICALS:
  Bound: Will not lend
  Unbound: Will not lend
  Loan Period: N/A
  Renewable: N/A
  Will lend if article exceeds
    50 pages

MICROFORMS:
  Will Lend: Yes
  Specific Types of Microforms:
    Periodicals and newspapers

GOVERNMENT PUBLICATIONS:
  Will Lend: Yes

DISSERTATIONS:
  Will Lend: Yes; 1973 to
    present available from
    University Microfilms

THESES:
  Will Lend: Yes

AUDIO-VISUAL MATERIALS:
  Records: Will not lend
  Cassettes: Will not lend
  Other (slides, filmstrips,
    etc.): Will not lend

COMPUTER SOFTWARE:
  Will Lend: No

PHOTODUPLICATION SERVICE:
  No charge up to 10 exposures
  Charge Per Exposure: 10¢
  Minimum/handling Fee: None
  Average Turnaround Time:
    2 days

MICROFILMING SERVICE:
  Service Available: No
  Charges: N/A

DO YOU CHARGE THE BORROWING
  LIBRARY FOR POSTAGE? No

FOR HOW LONG DO YOU SUSPEND ILL
  SERVICE OVER THE CHRISTMAS
  HOLIDAYS? 2 weeks

ARE THERE ANY GROUPS OF LIBRARIES
  FOR WHICH YOU WAIVE FEES? IF
  SO, PLEASE NAME THEM: None

KNOXVILLE-KNOX COUNTY PUBLIC LIBRARY

NUC CODE: TKL

OCLC CODE: TKL

ADDRESS: Interlibrary Loan
           Knoxville-Knox County
           Public Library
           500 W. Church Ave.
           Knoxville, TN 37902

TELEPHONE: (615) 523-0781, X126

LIST NAMES OF BRANCHES WITH
  SEPARATE POLICIES: None

BOOKS:
  Will Lend: Yes
  Length of Loan: 3 weeks
  Renewable: Yes
  Charges: None
  Average Turnaround Time:
    6 days
  If you have indicated that a
    book is not to be lent, will
    you on receipt of a letter
    from the requesting library
    search the index for given
    entries? (Not answered)

PERIODICALS:
  Bound: Will not lend
  Unbound: Will not lend
  Loan Period: N/A
  Renewable: N/A
  Will lend if article exceeds
    _____ number of pages (Not
    answered)

MICROFORMS:
  Will Lend: No
  Specific Types of Microforms:
    N/A

GOVERNMENT PUBLICATIONS:
  Will Lend: Yes

DISSERTATIONS:
  Will Lend: Yes, but we have
    very few

THESES:
  Will Lend: Yes, but we have
    very few

AUDIO-VISUAL MATERIALS:
  Records: Will not lend
  Cassettes: Will not lend
  Other (slides, filmstrips,
    etc.): Will not lend

COMPUTER SOFTWARE:
  Will Lend: No

PHOTODUPLICATION SERVICE:
  No charge up to 0 exposures
  Charge Per Exposure: 15¢
  Minimum/handling Fee: (Not
    answered)
  Average Turnaround Time:
    6 days

MICROFILMING SERVICE:
  Service Available: No
  Charges: N/A

DO YOU CHARGE THE BORROWING
  LIBRARY FOR POSTAGE? No

FOR HOW LONG DO YOU SUSPEND ILL
  SERVICE OVER THE CHRISTMAS
  HOLIDAYS? No suspension

ARE THERE ANY GROUPS OF LIBRARIES
  FOR WHICH YOU WAIVE FEES? IF
  SO, PLEASE NAME THEM: None

MEMPHIS PUBLIC LIBRARY

NUC CODE: TM

OCLC CODE: TMN

ADDRESS: Interlibrary Loan
Memphis Public Library
1850 Peabody Ave.
Memphis, TN 38104

TELEPHONE: (901) 528-2956

LIST NAMES OF BRANCHES WITH
SEPARATE POLICIES: None

BOOKS:
Will Lend: Yes
Length of Loan: 28 days
Renewable: Yes
Charges: None
Average Turnaround Time:
3 days
If you have indicated that a
book is not to be lent, will
you on receipt of a letter
from the requesting library
search the index for given
entries? Yes

PERIODICALS:
Bound: Will not lend
Unbound: Will not lend
Loan Period: N/A
Renewable: N/A
Will lend if article exceeds
_____ number of pages (Will
not lend, regardless of
length of article)

MICROFORMS:
Will Lend: No
Specific Types of Microforms:
N/A

GOVERNMENT PUBLICATIONS:
Will Lend: Yes

DISSERTATIONS:
Will Lend: Do not own

THESES:
Will Lend: Do not own

AUDIO-VISUAL MATERIALS:
Records: Will not lend
Cassettes: Will lend
Other (slides, filmstrips,
etc.): Yes, when
applicable

COMPUTER SOFTWARE:
Will Lend: Do not own

PHOTODUPLICATION SERVICE:
No charge up to 0 exposures
Charge Per Exposure: 15¢
Minimum/handling Fee: $2.00
Average Turnaround Time:
2 days

MICROFILMING SERVICE:
Service Available: No
Charges: N/A

DO YOU CHARGE THE BORROWING
LIBRARY FOR POSTAGE? No

FOR HOW LONG DO YOU SUSPEND ILL
SERVICE OVER THE CHRISTMAS
HOLIDAYS? No suspension

ARE THERE ANY GROUPS OF LIBRARIES
FOR WHICH YOU WAIVE FEES? IF
SO, PLEASE NAME THEM: None

MEMPHIS STATE UNIVERSITY

NUC CODE: TMM

OCLC CODE: TMA

ADDRESS: Interlibrary Loan
John W. Brister
Library
Memphis State
University
Memphis, TN 38152

TELEPHONE: (901) 454-2262

LIST NAMES OF BRANCHES WITH
SEPARATE POLICIES: None

BOOKS:
Will Lend: Yes
Length of Loan: 2 weeks from
receipt
Renewable: Yes, in fall and
spring semesters
Charges: None
Average Turnaround Time:
2 days
If you have indicated that a
book is not to be lent, will
you on receipt of a letter
from the requesting library
search the index for given
entries? (Not answered)

PERIODICALS:
Bound: Will not lend
Unbound: Will not lend
Loan Period: N/A
Renewable: N/A
Will lend if article exceeds
_____ number of pages (Will
not lend, regardless of
length of article)

MICROFORMS:
Will Lend: Yes
Specific Types of Microforms:
Microfilm only (will not
lend journals on microfilm)

GOVERNMENT PUBLICATIONS:
Will Lend: Yes

DISSERTATIONS:
Will Lend: Yes; 1965 to
present available from
University Microfilms

THESES:
Will Lend: Yes

AUDIO-VISUAL MATERIALS:
Records: Will not lend
Cassettes: Will not lend
Other (slides, filmstrips,
etc.): Will not lend

COMPUTER SOFTWARE:
Will Lend: No

PHOTODUPLICATION SERVICE:
No charge up to 0 exposures
Charges: $1.00 for 1-10
exposures; 10¢ each
additional exposure from
hardcopy and 25¢ each
additional exposure from
microform copy
Average Turnaround Time:
2 days

MICROFILMING SERVICE:
Service Available: No
Charges: N/A

DO YOU CHARGE THE BORROWING
LIBRARY FOR POSTAGE? No,
unless unusual mailing
requested

FOR HOW LONG DO YOU SUSPEND ILL
SERVICE OVER THE CHRISTMAS
HOLIDAYS? Dec.15-Jan.2

ARE THERE ANY GROUPS OF LIBRARIES
FOR WHICH YOU WAIVE FEES? IF
SO, PLEASE NAME THEM: Memphis-
Shelby County Public Library;
University of Tennessee;
University of Tennessee at
Martin; University of
Mississippi; University of
Tennessee Medical

MIDDLE TENNESSEE STATE UNIVERSITY

NUC CODE: (Not answered)

OCLC CODE: TXM

ADDRESS: Interlibrary Loan
Middle Tennessee State
University
Todd Library
P. O. Box 13
Murfreesboro, TN 37132

TELEPHONE: (615) 898-2772

LIST NAMES OF BRANCHES WITH
SEPARATE POLICIES: None

BOOKS:
Will Lend: Yes
Length of Loan: 2 weeks use
Renewable: Sometimes
Charges: Postage and
insurance
Average Turnaround Time:
2-3 days
If you have indicated that a
book is not to be lent, will
you on receipt of a letter
from the requesting library
search the index for given
entries? (Not answered)

PERIODICALS:
Bound: Will not lend
Unbound: Will not lend
Loan Period: N/A
Renewable: N/A
Will lend if article exceeds
_____ number of pages (Not
answered)

MICROFORMS:
Will Lend: Yes
Specific Types of Microforms:
Tennessee newspapers

GOVERNMENT PUBLICATIONS:
Will Lend: Yes

DISSERTATIONS:
Will Lend: Yes

THESES:
Will Lend: Yes

AUDIO-VISUAL MATERIALS:
Records: Will not lend
Cassettes: Will not lend
Other (slides, filmstrips,
etc.): Will not lend

COMPUTER SOFTWARE:
Will Lend: Will not lend

PHOTODUPLICATION SERVICE:
No charge up to 0 exposures
Charge Per Exposure: 15¢
Minimum/handling Fee: $1.00
Average Turnaround Time:
2-3 days

MICROFILMING SERVICE:
Service Available: No
Charges: N/A

DO YOU CHARGE THE BORROWING
LIBRARY FOR POSTAGE? Yes

FOR HOW LONG DO YOU SUSPEND ILL
SERVICE OVER THE CHRISTMAS
HOLIDAYS? 2 weeks

ARE THERE ANY GROUPS OF LIBRARIES
FOR WHICH YOU WAIVE FEES? IF
SO, PLEASE NAME THEM: None

OAK RIDGE NATIONAL LABORATORY

NUC CODE: TONL

OCLC CODE: ORN

ADDRESS: Interlibrary Loan
Oak Ridge National
Laboratory
Bldg. 4500N
P. O. Box X
Oak Ridge, TN 37830

TELEPHONE: (615) 574-6729

LIST NAMES OF BRANCHES WITH
SEPARATE POLICIES:
Biology Library
Fusion Energy Library
Y-12 Technical Library

BOOKS:
Will Lend: Yes
Length of Loan: 2-4 weeks
Renewable: Yes
Charges: None
Average Turnaround Time:
1 week
If you have indicated that a
book is not to be lent, will
you on receipt of a letter
from the requesting library
search the index for given
entries? Yes

PERIODICALS:
Bound: Will lend with special
permission
Unbound: Will lend with
special permission
Loan Period: 1 week
Renewable: No
Will lend if article exceeds
_____ number of pages (Not
answered)

MICROFORMS:
Will Lend: Yes, some of them
Specific Types of Microforms:
Microfiche; will not lend
journals on microfilm

GOVERNMENT PUBLICATIONS:
Will Lend: Yes

DISSERTATIONS:
Will Lend: Do not own

THESES:
Will Lend: Do not own

AUDIO-VISUAL MATERIALS:
Records: Do not own
Cassettes: Do not own
Other (slides, filmstrips,
etc.): Do not own

COMPUTER SOFTWARE:
Will Lend: No

PHOTODUPLICATION SERVICE:
No charge up to any exposures
Charge Per Exposure: None
Minimum/handling Fee: None
Average Turnaround Time:
1 week

MICROFILMING SERVICE:
Service Available: Microfiche
duplication only
Charges: None

DO YOU CHARGE THE BORROWING
LIBRARY FOR POSTAGE? No

FOR HOW LONG DO YOU SUSPEND ILL
SERVICE OVER THE CHRISTMAS
HOLIDAYS? No suspension

ARE THERE ANY GROUPS OF LIBRARIES
FOR WHICH YOU WAIVE FEES? IF
SO, PLEASE NAME THEM: None

PUBLIC LIBRARY OF NASHVILLE AND DAVIDSON COUNTY

NUC CODE: TN

OCLC CODE: TNN

ADDRESS: Interlibrary Loan
Public Library of
Nashville & Davidson
County
222 8th Avenue North
Nashville, TN   37203

TELEPHONE: (615) 244-4700, X52

LIST NAMES OF BRANCHES WITH
SEPARATE POLICIES: None

BOOKS:
Will Lend: Yes
Length of Loan: 4 weeks
Renewable: Yes
Charges: Postage
Average Turnaround Time:
3 days
If you have indicated that a
book is not to be lent, will
you on receipt of a letter
from the requesting library
search the index for given
entries?   Yes

PERIODICALS:
Bound: Will not lend
Unbound: Will not lend
Loan Period: N/A
Renewable: N/A
Will lend if article exceeds
_____ number of pages (Not
answered)

MICROFORMS:
Will Lend: No
Specific Types of Microforms:
N/A

GOVERNMENT PUBLICATIONS:
Will Lend: No

DISSERTATIONS:
Will Lend: No

THESES:
Will Lend: No

AUDIO-VISUAL MATERIALS:
Records: Will not lend
Cassettes: Will not lend
Other (slides, filmstrips,
etc.):   Will not lend

COMPUTER SOFTWARE:
Will Lend: No

PHOTODUPLICATION SERVICE:
No charge up to 0 exposures
Charge Per Exposure: 10¢
Minimum/handling Fee: (Not
answered)
Average Turnaround Time:
4 days

MICROFILMING SERVICE:
Service Available: No
Charges: N/A

DO YOU CHARGE THE BORROWING
LIBRARY FOR POSTAGE?   Yes

FOR HOW LONG DO YOU SUSPEND ILL
SERVICE OVER THE CHRISTMAS
HOLIDAYS?   No suspension

ARE THERE ANY GROUPS OF LIBRARIES
FOR WHICH YOU WAIVE FEES?   IF
SO, PLEASE NAME THEM: None

TENNESSEE STATE LIBRARY AND ARCHIVES

NUC CODE: T

OCLC CODE: TNS

ADDRESS: Interlibrary Loan
Tennessee State Library
and Archives
403 7th Avenue North
Nashville, TN   37219

TELEPHONE: (615) 741-2764

LIST NAMES OF BRANCHES WITH
SEPARATE POLICIES: None

BOOKS:
Will Lend: Yes, if
circulating copy available
Length of Loan: 2 weeks
Renewable: Yes
Charges: Insurance and
postage
Average Turnaround Time:
3-4 weeks
If you have indicated that a
book is not to be lent, will
you on receipt of a letter
from the requesting library
search the index for given
entries?   Yes

PERIODICALS:
Bound: Will lend
Unbound: Will lend
Loan Period: 2 weeks plus
Renewable: Yes
Will lend if article exceeds
_____ number of pages (N/A)

MICROFORMS:
Will Lend: Yes
Specific Types of Microforms:
Microfilms of Tennessee
newspapers

GOVERNMENT PUBLICATIONS:
Will Lend: Yes, if
circulating copy available

DISSERTATIONS:
Will Lend: Do not own

THESES:
Will Lend: Do not own

AUDIO-VISUAL MATERIALS:
Records: Do not own
Cassettes: Do not own
Other (slides, filmstrips,
etc.):   Do not own

COMPUTER SOFTWARE:
Will Lend: Do not own

PHOTODUPLICATION SERVICE:
No charge up to 6 exposures
Charge Per Exposure: 15¢
Minimum/handling Fee: None
Average Turnaround Time:
(Not answered)

MICROFILMING SERVICE:
Service Available: Yes
Charges: Reels, $12.50

DO YOU CHARGE THE BORROWING
LIBRARY FOR POSTAGE?   Yes

FOR HOW LONG DO YOU SUSPEND ILL
SERVICE OVER THE CHRISTMAS
HOLIDAYS?   No suspension

ARE THERE ANY GROUPS OF LIBRARIES
FOR WHICH YOU WAIVE FEES?   IF
SO, PLEASE NAME THEM: None

TENNESSEE STATE UNIVERSITY

NUC CODE: None

OCLC CODE: TUN

ADDRESS: Interlibrary Loan
Downtown Campus Library
Tennessee State
University
10th and Charlotte
Nashville, TN 37203

TELEPHONE: (615) 251-1417

LIST NAMES OF BRANCHES WITH
SEPARATE POLICIES: None

BOOKS:
Will Lend: Yes
Length of Loan: 4 weeks from
date shipped
Renewable: Yes
Charges: None
Average Turnaround Time:
1 day
If you have indicated that a
book is not to be lent, will
you on receipt of a letter
from the requesting library
search the index for given
entries? (Not answered)

PERIODICALS:
Bound: Will not lend
Unbound: Will not lend
Loan Period: N/A
Renewable: N/A
Will lend if article exceeds
_____ number of pages (Not
answered)

MICROFORMS:
Will Lend: Yes
Specific Types of Microforms:
(Not answered)

GOVERNMENT PUBLICATIONS:
Will Lend: Yes, some of them

DISSERTATIONS:
Will Lend: Yes, some of them

THESES:
Will Lend: Yes, some of them

AUDIO-VISUAL MATERIALS:
Records: Do not own
Cassettes: Do not own
Other (slides, filmstrips,
etc.): (Not answered)

COMPUTER SOFTWARE:
Will Lend: Do not own

PHOTODUPLICATION SERVICE:
No charge up to 0 exposures
Charge Per Exposure: 10¢
Minimum/handling Fee: (Not
answered)
Average Turnaround Time:
2 days

MICROFILMING SERVICE:
Service Available: No
Charges: N/A

DO YOU CHARGE THE BORROWING
LIBRARY FOR POSTAGE? No

FOR HOW LONG DO YOU SUSPEND ILL
SERVICE OVER THE CHRISTMAS
HOLIDAYS? Dec.15-Jan.2

ARE THERE ANY GROUPS OF LIBRARIES
FOR WHICH YOU WAIVE FEES? IF
SO, PLEASE NAME THEM:
Tennessee State Board of
Regents Colleges and
Universities

TENNESSEE TECHNOLOGICAL UNIVERSITY

NUC CODE: TCooP

OCLC CODE: TTU

ADDRESS: Interlibrary Loan
Tennessee Technological
University Library
Box 5066 Tennessee
Technological Station
Cookeville, TN 38501

TELEPHONE: (615) 528-3710

LIST NAMES OF BRANCHES WITH
SEPARATE POLICIES: None

BOOKS:
Will Lend: Yes
Length of Loan: 2 weeks use
Renewable: Yes
Charges: None
Average Turnaround Time:
1 week
If you have indicated that a
book is not to be lent, will
you on receipt of a letter
from the requesting library
search the index for given
entries? (Not answered)

PERIODICALS:
Bound: Will not lend
Unbound: Will not lend
Loan Period: N/A
Renewable: N/A
Will lend if article exceeds
_____ number of pages (Not
answered)

MICROFORMS:
Will Lend: Yes
Specific Types of Microforms:
Newspapers, dissertations
on microfilm, etc.

GOVERNMENT PUBLICATIONS:
Will Lend: Yes, with some
exceptions

DISSERTATIONS:
Will Lend: Yes

THESES:
Will Lend: Yes

AUDIO-VISUAL MATERIALS:
Records: Will not lend
Cassettes: Will not lend
Other (slides, filmstrips,
etc.): Will not lend

COMPUTER SOFTWARE:
Will Lend: No

PHOTODUPLICATION SERVICE:
No charge up to 3 exposures
Charge Per Exposure: 10¢
Minimum/handling Fee: $1.00
Average Turnaround Time:
3-4 days

MICROFILMING SERVICE:
Service Available: No
Charges: N/A

DO YOU CHARGE THE BORROWING
LIBRARY FOR POSTAGE? No

FOR HOW LONG DO YOU SUSPEND ILL
SERVICE OVER THE CHRISTMAS
HOLIDAYS? Dec.15-Jan.2

ARE THERE ANY GROUPS OF LIBRARIES
FOR WHICH YOU WAIVE FEES? IF
SO, PLEASE NAME THEM: None

TENNESSEE VALLEY AUTHORITY

NUC CODE: (Not answered)

OCLC CODE: TVA

ADDRESS: Interlibrary Loan
Tennessee Valley
Authority
Technical Library
400 W. Summit Hill
Ave., E2 A3 C-K
Knoxville, TN 37902

TELEPHONE: (615) 632-3464

LIST NAMES OF BRANCHES WITH
SEPARATE POLICIES:
Chattanooga Technical
Library, TN
Muscle Shoals Technical
Library, AL
ONR Library, Norris, TN
Land Between the Lakes
Library, Golden Pond, KY

BOOKS:
Will Lend: Yes
Length of Loan: 1 month
Renewable: Yes
Charges: None
Average Turnaround Time:
4 days
If you have indicated that a
book is not to be lent, will
you on receipt of a letter
from the requesting library
search the index for given
entries? (Not answered)

PERIODICALS:
Bound: Will not lend
Unbound: Will not lend
Loan Period: N/A
Renewable: N/A
Will lend if article exceeds
25 pages

MICROFORMS:
Will Lend: No
Specific Types of Microforms:
N/A

GOVERNMENT PUBLICATIONS:
Will Lend: Yes

DISSERTATIONS:
Will Lend: Do not own

THESES:
Will Lend: Do not own

AUDIO-VISUAL MATERIALS:
Records: Will not lend
Cassettes: Will not lend
Other (slides, filmstrips,
etc.): Will not lend

COMPUTER SOFTWARE:
Will Lend: No

PHOTODUPLICATION SERVICE:
No charge up to 25 exposures
Charge Per Exposure: None
Minimum/handling Fee: None
Average Turnaround Time:
2 days

MICROFILMING SERVICE:
Service Available: No
Charges: N/A

DO YOU CHARGE THE BORROWING
LIBRARY FOR POSTAGE? No

FOR HOW LONG DO YOU SUSPEND ILL
SERVICE OVER THE CHRISTMAS
HOLIDAYS? Dec.15-Jan.4

ARE THERE ANY GROUPS OF LIBRARIES
FOR WHICH YOU WAIVE FEES? IF
SO, PLEASE NAME THEM: None

UNIVERSITY OF TENNESSEE

NUC CODE: TU

OCLC CODE: TKN

ADDRESS: Interlibrary Loan
University of Tennessee
Library
Knoxville, TN 37916

TELEPHONE: (615) 974-4240

LIST NAMES OF BRANCHES WITH
SEPARATE POLICIES:
Law Library

BOOKS:
Will Lend: Yes
Length of Loan: 2 weeks use
Renewable: Yes
Charges: None
Average Turnaround Time:
2-3 days
If you have indicated that a
book is not to be lent, will
you on receipt of a letter
from the requesting library
search the index for given
entries? (Not answered)

PERIODICALS:
Bound: Will not lend
Unbound: Will not lend
Loan Period: N/A
Renewable: N/A
Will lend if article exceeds
_____ number of pages (Not
answered)

MICROFORMS:
Will Lend: Yes
Specific Types of Microforms:
Microcards, microfilm,
microfiche

GOVERNMENT PUBLICATIONS:
Will Lend: Yes

DISSERTATIONS:
Will Lend: Yes; 1954 to
present available from
University Microfilms

THESES:
Will Lend: Yes

AUDIO-VISUAL MATERIALS:
Records: Will not lend
Cassettes: Will not lend
Other (slides, filmstrips,
etc.): Will not lend

COMPUTER SOFTWARE:
Will Lend: No

PHOTODUPLICATION SERVICE:
No charge up to 0 exposures
Charge Per Exposure: 15¢
Minimum/handling Fee: $1.50
Average Turnaround Time:
2-3 days

MICROFILMING SERVICE:
Service Available: No
Charges: N/A

DO YOU CHARGE THE BORROWING
LIBRARY FOR POSTAGE? Yes

FOR HOW LONG DO YOU SUSPEND ILL
SERVICE OVER THE CHRISTMAS
HOLIDAYS? Dec.13-Jan.4

ARE THERE ANY GROUPS OF LIBRARIES
FOR WHICH YOU WAIVE FEES? IF
SO, PLEASE NAME THEM: Those
with which we have
reciprocal agreements

UNIVERSITY OF TENNESSEE AT CHATTANOOGA

NUC CODE: TCU

OCLC CODE: TUC

ADDRESS: Interlibrary Loan
Library
University of Tennessee
at Chattanooga
Chattanooga, TN 37402

TELEPHONE: (615) 755-4470

LIST NAMES OF BRANCHES WITH
SEPARATE POLICIES: None

BOOKS:
Will Lend: Yes
Length of Loan: 2 weeks
Renewable: Yes
Charges: None
Average Turnaround Time:
4 days
If you have indicated that a
book is not to be lent, will
you on receipt of a letter
from the requesting library
search the index for given
entries? (Not answered)

PERIODICALS:
Bound: Will not lend
Unbound: Will not lend
Loan Period: N/A
Renewable: N/A
Will lend if article exceeds
_____ number of pages (Not
answered)

MICROFORMS:
Will Lend: No
Specific Types of Microforms:
N/A

GOVERNMENT PUBLICATIONS:
Will Lend: (Not answered)

DISSERTATIONS:
Will Lend: Do not own

THESES:
Will Lend: Yes, if 2nd copy
available

AUDIO-VISUAL MATERIALS:
Records: Will not lend
Cassettes: Will not lend
Other (slides, filmstrips,
etc.): Will not lend

COMPUTER SOFTWARE:
Will Lend: No

PHOTODUPLICATION SERVICE:
No charge up to 0 exposures
Charge Per Exposure: 10¢
Minimum/handling Fee: None
Average Turnaround Time:
4 days

MICROFILMING SERVICE:
Service Available: No
Charges: N/A

DO YOU CHARGE THE BORROWING
LIBRARY FOR POSTAGE? No

FOR HOW LONG DO YOU SUSPEND ILL
SERVICE OVER THE CHRISTMAS
HOLIDAYS? Dec.10-Jan.3

ARE THERE ANY GROUPS OF LIBRARIES
FOR WHICH YOU WAIVE FEES? IF
SO, PLEASE NAME THEM:
University of Tennessee
System; HELP (Health
Education Library Program)

UNIVERSITY OF TENNESSEE AT MARTIN

NUC CODE: TMaU

OCLC CODE: THM

ADDRESS: Interlibrary Loan
Paul Meek Library
University of Tennessee
at Martin
Martin, TN 38238

TELEPHONE: (901) 587-7067 or
587-7068

LIST NAMES OF BRANCHES WITH
SEPARATE POLICIES: None

BOOKS:
Will Lend: Yes, except
special collections
Length of Loan: 3 weeks use
Renewable: Yes, if no
reserves
Charges: None
Average Turnaround Time:
24 hours
If you have indicated that a
book is not to be lent, will
you on receipt of a letter
from the requesting library
search the index for given
entries? Yes

PERIODICALS:
Bound: Will not lend
Unbound: Will not lend
Loan Period: N/A
Renewable: N/A
Will lend if article exceeds
_____ number of pages (Not
answered)

MICROFORMS:
Will Lend: No
Specific Types of Microforms:
N/A

GOVERNMENT PUBLICATIONS:
Will Lend: Yes

DISSERTATIONS:
Will Lend: No

THESES:
Will Lend: Yes, if 2d copy
available

AUDIO-VISUAL MATERIALS:
Records: Will not lend
Cassettes: Will not lend, but
will duplicate 1 copy only
Other (slides, filmstrips,
etc.): Will lend

COMPUTER SOFTWARE:
Will Lend: Do not own

PHOTODUPLICATION SERVICE:
No charge up to 0 exposures
Charge Per Exposure: 10¢
from hard copy; 10¢ from
90x fiche; 15¢ from 24x
fiche; 20¢ from film
Minimum/handling Fee: None
Average Turnaround Time:
24 hours

MICROFILMING SERVICE:
Service Available: No
Charges: N/A

DO YOU CHARGE THE BORROWING
LIBRARY FOR POSTAGE? Yes

FOR HOW LONG DO YOU SUSPEND ILL
SERVICE OVER THE CHRISTMAS
HOLIDAYS? Dec.20-Jan.2

ARE THERE ANY GROUPS OF LIBRARIES
FOR WHICH YOU WAIVE FEES? IF
SO, PLEASE NAME THEM:
Libraries with whom we have
free photocopying and/or
postage reciprocity

UNIVERSITY OF TENNESSEE CENTER FOR THE HEALTH SCIENCES

NUC CODE: TU-M

OCLC CODE: TUM

ADDRESS: Interlibrary Loan
            University of Tennessee
            Center for the Health
            Sciences
            UTCHS Library
            800 Madison Ave.
            Memphis, TN 38163

TELEPHONE: (901) 528-5634

LIST NAMES OF BRANCHES WITH
  SEPARATE POLICIES: None

BOOKS:
  Will Lend: Yes
  Length of Loan: 4 weeks
  Renewable: Yes
  Charges: $4.75 at this time
  Average Turnaround Time:
    24 hours
  If you have indicated that a
    book is not to be lent, will
    you on receipt of a letter
    from the requesting library
    search the index for given
    entries? (Not answered)

PERIODICALS:
  Bound: Will lend
  Unbound: Will lend
  Loan Period: 1 week
  Renewable: Yes
  Will lend if article exceeds
    50 pages

MICROFORMS:
  Will Lend: No
  Specific Types of Microforms:
    N/A

GOVERNMENT PUBLICATIONS:
  Will Lend: Yes

DISSERTATIONS:
  Will Lend: No

THESES:
  Will Lend: No

AUDIO-VISUAL MATERIALS:
  Records: Will not lend
  Cassettes: Will not lend
  Other (slides, filmstrips,
    etc.): Will not lend

COMPUTER SOFTWARE:
  Will Lend: No

PHOTODUPLICATION SERVICE:
  No charge up to 0 exposures
  Charge Per Exposure: (Not
    answered)
  Minimum Fee: $4.75 at this
    time
  Average Turnaround Time:
    24 hours

MICROFILMING SERVICE:
  Service Available: No
  Charges: N/A

DO YOU CHARGE THE BORROWING
  LIBRARY FOR POSTAGE? No

FOR HOW LONG DO YOU SUSPEND ILL
  SERVICE OVER THE CHRISTMAS
  HOLIDAYS? No suspension

ARE THERE ANY GROUPS OF LIBRARIES
  FOR WHICH YOU WAIVE FEES? IF
  SO, PLEASE NAME THEM:
    Resource libraries in our
    Medical Library Region

VANDERBILT UNIVERSITY

NUC CODE: TNV

OCLC CODE: TJC

ADDRESS: Interlibrary Loan
            Vanderbilt University
            Library
            419 21st Avenue South
            Nashville, TN 37203

TELEPHONE: (615) 322-2408

LIST NAMES OF BRANCHES WITH
  SEPARATE POLICIES:
    Medical Library

BOOKS:
  Will Lend: Yes
  Length of Loan: 2 weeks
  Renewable: Yes
  Charges: None
  Average Turnaround Time:
    7 days
  If you have indicated that a
    book is not to be lent, will
    you on receipt of a letter
    from the requesting library
    search the index for given
    entries? Yes

PERIODICALS:
  Bound: Will not lend
  Unbound: Will not lend
  Loan Period: N/A
  Renewable: N/A
  May lend if a serial (depends
    upon our use or need)

MICROFORMS:
  Will Lend: Yes, most of them
  Specific Types of Microforms:
    Microfilm, microfiche

GOVERNMENT PUBLICATIONS:
  Will Lend: Yes

DISSERTATIONS:
  Will Lend: Yes

THESES:
  Will Lend: Yes

AUDIO-VISUAL MATERIALS:
  Records: Will not lend
  Cassettes: Will not lend
  Other (slides, filmstrips,
    etc.): Will not lend

COMPUTER SOFTWARE:
  Will Lend: (Not answered)

PHOTODUPLICATION SERVICE:
  No charge up to 0 exposures
  Charge Per Exposure: 10¢
  Minimum/handling Fee: $3.00
    unless we have special
    agreement
  Average Turnaround Time:
    10 days

MICROFILMING SERVICE:
  Service Available: No
  Charges: N/A

DO YOU CHARGE THE BORROWING
  LIBRARY FOR POSTAGE? No,
    unless special handling
    requested

FOR HOW LONG DO YOU SUSPEND ILL
  SERVICE OVER THE CHRISTMAS
  HOLIDAYS? Second week in
  Dec. until Jan. 2

ARE THERE ANY GROUPS OF LIBRARIES
  FOR WHICH YOU WAIVE FEES? IF
  SO, PLEASE NAME THEM:
    Tennessee libraries; Oak
    Ridge National Laboratory

AUSTIN PUBLIC LIBRARY

NUC CODE: TxAu

OCLC CODE: TXG

ADDRESS: Interlibrary Loan
Austin Public Library
P. O. Box 2287
Austin, TX 78768

TELEPHONE: (512) 472-0299

LIST NAMES OF BRANCHES WITH
SEPARATE POLICIES: None

BOOKS:
Will Lend: Yes
Length of Loan: 28 days
Renewable: Yes, for 2 weeks
Charges: None
Average Turnaround Time:
1 day
If you have indicated that a
book is not to be lent, will
you on receipt of a letter
from the requesting library
search the index for given
entries? Yes, provided that
no more than three entries
are requested.

PERIODICALS:
Bound: Will not lend
Unbound: Will not lend
Loan Period: N/A
Renewable: N/A
Will lend if article exceeds
_____ number of pages (Will
not lend, regardless of
length of article)

MICROFORMS:
Will Lend: No
Specific Types of Microforms:
N/A

GOVERNMENT PUBLICATIONS:
Will Lend: Yes

DISSERTATIONS:
Will Lend: No

THESES:
Will Lend: No

AUDIO-VISUAL MATERIALS:
Records: Will not lend
Cassettes: Will not lend
Other (slides, filmstrips,
etc.): Will not lend

COMPUTER SOFTWARE:
Will Lend: No

PHOTODUPLICATION SERVICE:
No charge up to 0 exposures
Charge Per Exposure: 10¢
Minimum/handling Fee: None
Average Turnaround Time:
1 day

MICROFILMING SERVICE:
Service Available: No
Charges: N/A

DO YOU CHARGE THE BORROWING
LIBRARY FOR POSTAGE? No

FOR HOW LONG DO YOU SUSPEND ILL
SERVICE OVER THE CHRISTMAS
HOLIDAYS? No suspension

ARE THERE ANY GROUPS OF LIBRARIES
FOR WHICH YOU WAIVE FEES? IF
SO, PLEASE NAME THEM: TSLCN,
AMIGOS

DALLAS PUBLIC LIBRARY

NUC CODE: TxDa

OCLC CODE: IGA

ADDRESS: Interlibrary Loan
Dallas Public Library
1515 Young St.
Dallas, TX 75201

TELEPHONE: (214) 749-4341

LIST NAMES OF BRANCHES WITH
SEPARATE POLICIES: None

BOOKS:
Will Lend: Yes
Length of Loan: 21 days
Renewable: Yes
Charges: None
Average Turnaround Time:
48 hours
If you have indicated that a
book is not to be lent, will
you on receipt of a letter
from the requesting library
search the index for given
entries? (Not answered)

PERIODICALS:
Bound: Will not lend
Unbound: Will not lend
Loan Period: N/A
Renewable: N/A
Will lend if article exceeds
_____ number of pages (Will
not lend, regardless of
length of article)

MICROFORMS:
Will Lend: Yes
Specific Types of Microforms:
Dallas newspapers

GOVERNMENT PUBLICATIONS:
Will Lend: Yes

DISSERTATIONS:
Will Lend: Yes

THESES:
Will Lend: Yes

AUDIO-VISUAL MATERIALS:
Records: Will not lend
Cassettes: Will lend to
area libraries only
Other (slides, filmstrips,
etc.): (Not answered)

COMPUTER SOFTWARE:
Will Lend: No

PHOTODUPLICATION SERVICE:
No charge up to 50 exposures
Charge Per Exposure: 50¢
after 1st 50
Minimum/handling Fee: None
Average Turnaround Time:
(Not answered)

MICROFILMING SERVICE:
Service Available: No
Charges: N/A

DO YOU CHARGE THE BORROWING
LIBRARY FOR POSTAGE? No

FOR HOW LONG DO YOU SUSPEND ILL
SERVICE OVER THE CHRISTMAS
HOLIDAYS? No suspension

ARE THERE ANY GROUPS OF LIBRARIES
FOR WHICH YOU WAIVE FEES? IF
SO, PLEASE NAME THEM: None

EAST TEXAS STATE UNIVERSITY

NUC CODE: TxComS

OCLC CODE: IEA

ADDRESS: Interlibrary Loan
Gee Library
East Texas State
University
Commerce, TX 75428

TELEPHONE: (214) 886-3974

LIST NAMES OF BRANCHES WITH
SEPARATE POLICIES: None

BOOKS:
Will Lend: Yes
Length of Loan: 3 weeks
Renewable: Yes
Charges: None
Average Turnaround Time:
1 day
If you have indicated that a
book is not to be lent, will
you on receipt of a letter
from the requesting library
search the index for given
entries? Yes

PERIODICALS:
Bound: Will not lend
Unbound: Will not lend
Loan Period: N/A
Renewable: N/A
Will lend if article exceeds
_____ number of pages (Not
answered)

MICROFORMS:
Will Lend: Yes
Specific Types of Microforms:
Film, fiche, cards
Fiche-to-fiche copying
available; charges not yet
determined

GOVERNMENT PUBLICATIONS:
Will Lend: Yes

DISSERTATIONS:
Will Lend: Yes

THESES:
Will Lend: Yes

AUDIO-VISUAL MATERIALS:
Records: Will not lend
Cassettes: Will not lend
Other (slides, filmstrips,
etc.): Will not lend

COMPUTER SOFTWARE:
Will Lend: No

PHOTODUPLICATION SERVICE:
No charge up to 0 exposures
Charges: $1.00 for 1-10
exposures; 10¢ each
additional exposure
Average Turnaround Time:
1 day

MICROFILMING SERVICE:
Service Available: No
Charges: N/A

DO YOU CHARGE THE BORROWING
LIBRARY FOR POSTAGE? No

FOR HOW LONG DO YOU SUSPEND ILL
SERVICE OVER THE CHRISTMAS
HOLIDAYS? Approximately
2 weeks

ARE THERE ANY GROUPS OF LIBRARIES
FOR WHICH YOU WAIVE FEES? IF
SO, PLEASE NAME THEM:
Association for Higher
Education libraries; AMIGOS
libraries

EL PASO PUBLIC LIBRARY

NUC CODE: TxE

OCLC CODE: TXP

ADDRESS: Interlibrary Loan
El Paso Public Library
501 N. Oregon
El Paso, TX 79901

TELEPHONE: (915) 533-3556

LIST NAMES OF BRANCHES WITH
SEPARATE POLICIES: None

BOOKS:
Will Lend: Yes
Length of Loan: 1 month
Renewable: Yes
Charges: None
Average Turnaround Time:
1-2 days
If you have indicated that a
book is not to be lent, will
you on receipt of a letter
from the requesting library
search the index for given
entries? Yes

PERIODICALS:
Bound: Will not lend
Unbound: Will not lend
Loan Period: N/A
Renewable: N/A
Will lend if article exceeds
_____ number of pages (Not
answered)

MICROFORMS:
Will Lend: Yes
Specific Types of Microforms:
Local El Paso paper only

GOVERNMENT PUBLICATIONS:
Will Lend: No

DISSERTATIONS:
Will Lend: No

THESES:
Will Lend: No

AUDIO-VISUAL MATERIALS:
Records: Will not lend
Cassettes: Will not lend
Other (slides, filmstrips,
etc.): Will not lend

COMPUTER SOFTWARE:
Will Lend: No

PHOTODUPLICATION SERVICE:
No charge up to any exposures
Minimum/handling Fee: None
Average Turnaround Time:
(Not answered)

MICROFILMING SERVICE:
Service Available: No
Charges: N/A

DO YOU CHARGE THE BORROWING
LIBRARY FOR POSTAGE? No

FOR HOW LONG DO YOU SUSPEND ILL
SERVICE OVER THE CHRISTMAS
HOLIDAYS? No suspension

ARE THERE ANY GROUPS OF LIBRARIES
FOR WHICH YOU WAIVE FEES? IF
SO, PLEASE NAME THEM: No
fees charged

FORT WORTH PUBLIC LIBRARY

NUC CODE: TXF

OCLC CODE: IFA

ADDRESS: Interlibrary Loan
           Fort Worth Public
             Library
           300 Taylor
           Fort Worth, TX 76102

TELEPHONE: (817) 870-7731

LIST NAMES OF BRANCHES WITH
  SEPARATE POLICIES: None

BOOKS:
  Will Lend: Yes
  Length of Loan: 28 days
  Renewable: Yes
  Charges: None
  Average Turnaround Time:
    24 hours
  If you have indicated that a
  book is not to be lent, will
  you on receipt of a letter
  from the requesting library
  search the index for given
  entries? (Not answered)

PERIODICALS:
  Bound: Will not lend
  Unbound: Will not lend
  Loan Period: N/A
  Renewable: N/A
  Will lend if article exceeds
    _____ number of pages (Will
    not lend, regardless of
    length of article)

MICROFORMS:
  Will Lend: No
  Specific Types of Microforms:
    N/A

GOVERNMENT PUBLICATIONS:
  Will Lend: Yes, sometimes

DISSERTATIONS:
  Will Lend: Do not own

THESES:
  Will Lend: Do not own

AUDIO-VISUAL MATERIALS:
  Records: Will not lend
  Cassettes: Will lend
  Other (slides, filmstrips,
    etc.): Will not lend

COMPUTER SOFTWARE:
  Will Lend: Do not own

PHOTODUPLICATION SERVICE:
  Limit of 50 pages for
    photocopying
  Charge Per Exposure: None
  Minimum/handling Fee: None
  Average Turnaround Time:
    24 hours

MICROFILMING SERVICE:
  Service Available: No
  Charges: N/A

DO YOU CHARGE THE BORROWING
  LIBRARY FOR POSTAGE? No

FOR HOW LONG DO YOU SUSPEND ILL
  SERVICE OVER THE CHRISTMAS
  HOLIDAYS? No suspension

ARE THERE ANY GROUPS OF LIBRARIES
  FOR WHICH YOU WAIVE FEES? IF
  SO, PLEASE NAME THEM: No fees
  charged

HARRIS COUNTY PUBLIC LIBRARY

ADDRESS: Harris County Public Library
           49 San Jacinto St.
           Suite 200
           Houston, TX 77004

TELEPHONE: (713) 221-5350

DOES NOT ACCEPT ILL REQUESTS

HOUSTON PUBLIC LIBRARY

NUC CODE: TxH

OCLC CODE: TXN

ADDRESS: Interlibrary Loan
Houston Public Library
500 McKinney Ave.
Houston, TX 77002

TELEPHONE: (713) 224-8575

LIST NAMES OF BRANCHES WITH
SEPARATE POLICIES:
Clayton Genealogy Library
5300 Caroline St.
Houston, TX 77004

BOOKS:
Will Lend: Yes
Length of Loan: 4 weeks
Renewable: Yes
Charges: None
Average Turnaround Time:
1 week
If you have indicated that a
book is not to be lent, will
you on receipt of a letter
from the requesting library
search the index for given
entries? (Not answered)

PERIODICALS:
Bound: Will not lend
Unbound: Will not lend
Loan Period: N/A
Renewable: N/A
Will lend if article exceeds
_____ number of pages (Not
answered)

MICROFORMS:
Will Lend: No
Specific Types of Microforms:
N/A

GOVERNMENT PUBLICATIONS:
Will Lend: Yes

DISSERTATIONS:
Will Lend: No

THESES:
Will Lend: No

AUDIO-VISUAL MATERIALS:
Records: Will not lend
Cassettes: Will not lend
Other (slides, filmstrips,
etc.): Will not lend

COMPUTER SOFTWARE:
Will Lend: No

PHOTODUPLICATION SERVICE:
No charge to academic or
public libraries
Charge Per Exposure: 25¢ to
for-profit libraries
Minimum/handling Fee: $1.00
to for-profit libraries
Average Turnaround Time:
1 week

MICROFILMING SERVICE:
Service Available: No
Charges: N/A

DO YOU CHARGE THE BORROWING
LIBRARY FOR POSTAGE? No

FOR HOW LONG DO YOU SUSPEND ILL
SERVICE OVER THE CHRISTMAS
HOLIDAYS? None

ARE THERE ANY GROUPS OF LIBRARIES
FOR WHICH YOU WAIVE FEES? IF
SO, PLEASE NAME THEM: AMIGOS
members

LAMAR UNIVERSITY

NUC CODE: TxBeaL

OCLC CODE: TXR

ADDRESS: Interlibrary Loan
Lamar University
Library
P. O. Box 10021
Lamar University
Station
Beaumont, TX 77710

TELEPHONE: (713) 838-8132

LIST NAMES OF BRANCHES WITH
SEPARATE POLICIES: None

BOOKS:
Will Lend: Yes
Length of Loan: 30 days
Renewable: Yes
Charges: None
Average Turnaround Time:
24 hours
If you have indicated that a
book is not to be lent, will
you on receipt of a letter
from the requesting library
search the index for given
entries? Yes

PERIODICALS:
Bound: Will lend
Unbound: Will not lend
Loan Period: 1 week in-
library use only
Renewable: No
Will lend if article exceeds
50 pages

MICROFORMS:
Will Lend: Yes
Specific Types of Microforms:
Microfilm, microfiche,
microcards

GOVERNMENT PUBLICATIONS:
Will Lend: Yes

DISSERTATIONS:
Will Lend: Yes

THESES:
Will Lend: Yes

AUDIO-VISUAL MATERIALS:
Records: Will lend
Cassettes: Will lend
Other (slides, filmstrips,
etc.): Will lend

COMPUTER SOFTWARE:
Will Lend: No

PHOTODUPLICATION SERVICE:
No charge up to 0 exposures
Charge Per Exposure: 10¢
from hard copy; 25¢ from
microfilm
Minimum/handling Fee: $2.00
handling
Average Turnaround Time:
24 hours

MICROFILMING SERVICE:
Service Available: No
Charges: N/A

DO YOU CHARGE THE BORROWING
LIBRARY FOR POSTAGE? No

FOR HOW LONG DO YOU SUSPEND ILL
SERVICE OVER THE CHRISTMAS
HOLIDAYS? From 3 days
before holiday begins

ARE THERE ANY GROUPS OF LIBRARIES
FOR WHICH YOU WAIVE FEES? IF
SO, PLEASE NAME THEM: AMIGOS
members if they are non-
profit institutions; others
on a reciprocal basis

LUBBOCK CITY-COUNTY LIBRARY

NUC CODE: TxL

OCLC CODE: TXL

ADDRESS: Interlibrary Loan
Lubbock City-County
Library
1306 9th St.
Lubbock, TX 79401

TELEPHONE: (806) 744-6710

LIST NAMES OF BRANCHES WITH
SEPARATE POLICIES: None

BOOKS:
Will Lend: Yes
Length of Loan: 30 days
Renewable: Yes, if no
reserves
Charges: None
Average Turnaround Time:
24 hours
If you have indicated that a
book is not to be lent, will
you on receipt of a letter
from the requesting library
search the index for given
entries? (Not answered)

PERIODICALS:
Bound: Will not lend
Unbound: Will not lend
Loan Period: N/A
Renewable: N/A
Will lend if article exceeds
_____ number of pages (Will
not lend, regardless of
length of article)

MICROFORMS:
Will Lend: No
Specific Types of Microforms:
N/A

GOVERNMENT PUBLICATIONS:
Will Lend: No

DISSERTATIONS:
Will Lend: No

THESES:
Will Lend: No

AUDIO-VISUAL MATERIALS:
Records: Will not lend
Cassettes: Will not lend
Other (slides, filmstrips,
etc.): Will not lend

COMPUTER SOFTWARE:
Will Lend: No

PHOTODUPLICATION SERVICE:
No charge up to 25 exposures
Charge Per Exposure: 10¢
from hard copy and 20¢ from
microfilm, after 1st 25
Minimum/handling Fee: None
Average Turnaround Time:
48 hours

MICROFILMING SERVICE:
Service Available: No
Charges: N/A

DO YOU CHARGE THE BORROWING
LIBRARY FOR POSTAGE? No

FOR HOW LONG DO YOU SUSPEND ILL
SERVICE OVER THE CHRISTMAS
HOLIDAYS? No suspension

ARE THERE ANY GROUPS OF LIBRARIES
FOR WHICH YOU WAIVE FEES? IF
SO, PLEASE NAME THEM: AMIGOS
members

MIDWESTERN STATE UNIVERSITY

NUC CODE: TxWich

OCLC CODE: TMI

ADDRESS: Interlibrary Loan
Moffett Library
Midwestern State
University
Wichita Falls, TX 76308

TELEPHONE: (817) 692-6611, X4174

LIST NAMES OF BRANCHES WITH
SEPARATE POLICIES: None

BOOKS:
Will Lend: Yes
Length of Loan: 3 weeks
Renewable: Yes
Charges: None
Average Turnaround Time:
24 hours
If you have indicated that a
book is not to be lent, will
you on receipt of a letter
from the requesting library
search the index for given
entries? Yes

PERIODICALS:
Bound: Will not lend
Unbound: Will not lend
Loan Period: N/A
Renewable: N/A
Will lend if article exceeds
_____ number of pages (Not
answered)

MICROFORMS:
Will Lend: Yes
Specific Types of Microforms:
Film only lent

GOVERNMENT PUBLICATIONS:
Will Lend: Yes

DISSERTATIONS:
Will Lend: No

THESES:
Will Lend: Yes

AUDIO-VISUAL MATERIALS:
Records: Will not lend
Cassettes: Will not lend
Other (slides, filmstrips,
etc.): Will not lend

COMPUTER SOFTWARE:
Will Lend: No

PHOTODUPLICATION SERVICE:
No charge up to 0 exposures
Charge Per Exposure: 10¢
Minimum/handling Fee: $1.00
Average Turnaround Time:
24 hours

MICROFILMING SERVICE:
Service Available: No
Charges: N/A

DO YOU CHARGE THE BORROWING
LIBRARY FOR POSTAGE? No

FOR HOW LONG DO YOU SUSPEND ILL
SERVICE OVER THE CHRISTMAS
HOLIDAYS? 1 week

ARE THERE ANY GROUPS OF LIBRARIES
FOR WHICH YOU WAIVE FEES? IF
SO, PLEASE NAME THEM: None

NORTH TEXAS STATE UNIVERSITY

NUC CODE: TxDN

OCLC CODE: INT

ADDRESS: Interlibrary Loan
North Texas State
University Libraries
Denton, TX 76203

TELEPHONE: (817) 788-2411, X214

LIST NAMES OF BRANCHES WITH
SEPARATE POLICIES:
Media Library

BOOKS:
Will Lend: Yes
Length of Loan: 2 weeks use
Renewable: Yes
Charges: None
Average Turnaround Time:
2-3 days
If you have indicated that a
book is not to be lent, will
you on receipt of a letter
from the requesting library
search the index for given
entries? (Not answered)

PERIODICALS:
Bound: Will not lend
Unbound: Will not lend
Loan Period: N/A
Renewable: N/A
Will lend if article exceeds
_____ number of pages (Will
not lend, regardless of
length of article)

MICROFORMS:
Will Lend: Yes
Specific Types of Microforms:
(Not answered)

GOVERNMENT PUBLICATIONS:
Will Lend: Yes

DISSERTATIONS:
Will Lend: Yes, if 2nd copy
available (microfilm);
1953 to present available
from University Microfilms

THESES:
Will Lend: Yes, 2nd copy
before 1973 and microfilm
copy after 1973

AUDIO-VISUAL MATERIALS:
Records: Referred to Media
Library for consideration
Cassettes: Referred to Media
Library for consideration
Other (slides, filmstrips,
etc.): Referred to Media
Library for consideration

COMPUTER SOFTWARE:
Will Lend: Do not own

PHOTODUPLICATION SERVICE:
No charge up to 50 exposures
Charge Per Exposure: None
Minimum/handling Fee: None
Average Turnaround Time:
2-3 days

MICROFILMING SERVICE:
Service Available: No
Charges: N/A

DO YOU CHARGE THE BORROWING
LIBRARY FOR POSTAGE? No

FOR HOW LONG DO YOU SUSPEND ILL
SERVICE OVER THE CHRISTMAS
HOLIDAYS? Approximately
2 weeks

ARE THERE ANY GROUPS OF LIBRARIES
FOR WHICH YOU WAIVE FEES? IF
SO, PLEASE NAME THEM: AHE,
AMIGOS

RICE UNIVERSITY

NUC CODE: TxHR

OCLC CODE: RCE

ADDRESS: Interlibrary Loan
Rice University Library
P. O. Box 1892
Houston, TX 77005

TELEPHONE: (713) 527-8101, X2284

LIST NAMES OF BRANCHES WITH
SEPARATE POLICIES: (Not
answered)

BOOKS:
Will Lend: Yes
Length of Loan: 28 days
Renewable: Yes
Charges: $5.00
Average Turnaround Time:
(Not answered)
If you have indicated that a
book is not to be lent, will
you on receipt of a letter
from the requesting library
search the index for given
entries? (Not answered)

PERIODICALS:
Bound: Will not lend
Unbound: Will not lend
Loan Period: N/A
Renewable: N/A
Will lend if article exceeds
75 pages

MICROFORMS:
Will Lend: Yes
Specific Types of Microforms:
(Not answered)

GOVERNMENT PUBLICATIONS:
Will Lend: Yes

DISSERTATIONS:
Will Lend: Yes; 1960 to
present available from
University Microfilms

THESES:
Will Lend: Yes

AUDIO-VISUAL MATERIALS:
Records: (Not answered)
Cassettes: (Not answered)
Other (slides, filmstrips,
etc.): (Not answered)

COMPUTER SOFTWARE:
Will Lend: (Not answered)

PHOTODUPLICATION SERVICE:
No charge up to 0 exposures
Charge Per Exposure: 15¢
Handling Fee: $2.00
Minimum Fee: $2.15
Average Turnaround Time:
(Not answered)

MICROFILMING SERVICE:
Service Available: No
Charges: N/A

DO YOU CHARGE THE BORROWING
LIBRARY FOR POSTAGE? (Not
answered)

FOR HOW LONG DO YOU SUSPEND ILL
SERVICE OVER THE CHRISTMAS
HOLIDAYS? Service is
suspended

ARE THERE ANY GROUPS OF LIBRARIES
FOR WHICH YOU WAIVE FEES? IF
SO, PLEASE NAME THEM: (Not
answered)

SAM HOUSTON STATE UNIVERSITY

NUC CODE: (Not answered)

OCLC CODE: SHH

ADDRESS: Interlibrary Loan
Sam Houston State
    University Library
Huntsville, TX 77341

TELEPHONE: (713) 294-1629

LIST NAMES OF BRANCHES WITH
    SEPARATE POLICIES: None

BOOKS:
    Will Lend: Yes
    Length of Loan: 2 weeks use
    Renewable: Yes
    Charges: (Not answered)
    Average Turnaround Time:
        2-3 days
    If you have indicated that a
        book is not to be lent, will
        you on receipt of a letter
        from the requesting library
        search the index for given
        entries? (Not answered)

PERIODICALS:
    Bound: Will not lend
    Unbound: Will not lend
    Loan Period: N/A
    Renewable: N/A
    Will lend if article exceeds
        _____ number of pages (Not
        answered)

MICROFORMS:
    Will Lend: Yes
    Specific Types of Microforms:
        Microfilm, microfiche,
        microcards

GOVERNMENT PUBLICATIONS:
    Will Lend: Yes

DISSERTATIONS:
    Will Lend: Yes

THESES:
    Will Lend: Yes

AUDIO-VISUAL MATERIALS:
    Records: Will not lend
    Cassettes: Will not lend
    Other (slides, filmstrips,
        etc,): Will not lend

COMPUTER SOFTWARE:
    Will Lend: No

PHOTODUPLICATION SERVICE:
    No charge up to 0 exposures
    Charge Per Exposure: 10¢
        (no charge on reciprocal
        basis)
    Minimum/handling Fee: None
    Average Turnaround Time:
        2-3 days

MICROFILMING SERVICE:
    Service Available: No
    Charges: N/A

DO YOU CHARGE THE BORROWING
    LIBRARY FOR POSTAGE? No

FOR HOW LONG DO YOU SUSPEND ILL
    SERVICE OVER THE CHRISTMAS
    HOLIDAYS? About 10 days

ARE THERE ANY GROUPS OF LIBRARIES
    FOR WHICH YOU WAIVE FEES? IF
    SO, PLEASE NAME THEM: AMIGOS
    members

SAN ANTONIO COLLEGE

NUC CODE: TxSaC

OCLC CODE: SNC

ADDRESS: Interlibrary Loan
San Antonio College
    Library
1001 Howard St.
San Antonio, TX 78284

TELEPHONE: (512) 733-2490

LIST NAMES OF BRANCHES WITH
    SEPARATE POLICIES: None

BOOKS:
    Will Lend: Yes
    Length of Loan: 2 weeks
    Renewable: Yes
    Charges: None
    Average Turnaround Time:
        1 day
    If you have indicated that a
        book is not to be lent, will
        you on receipt of a letter
        from the requesting library
        search the index for given
        entries? (Not answered)

PERIODICALS:
    Bound: Will not lend
    Unbound: Will not lend
    Loan Period: N/A
    Renewable: N/A
    Will lend if article exceeds
        _____ number of pages (Will
        not lend, regardless of
        length of article)

MICROFORMS:
    Will Lend: Yes
    Specific Types of Microforms:
        Microfilm

GOVERNMENT PUBLICATIONS:
    Will Lend: No

DISSERTATIONS:
    Will Lend: No

THESES:
    Will Lend: No

AUDIO-VISUAL MATERIALS:
    Records: Will not lend
    Cassettes: Will not lend
    Other (slides, filmstrips,
        etc.): Will not lend

COMPUTER SOFTWARE:
    Will Lend: No

PHOTODUPLICATION SERVICE:
    No charge up to 0 exposures
    Charge Per Exposure: 10¢
    Minimum/handling Fee: None
    Average Turnaround Time:
        1 day

MICROFILMING SERVICE:
    Service Available: No
    Charges: N/A

DO YOU CHARGE THE BORROWING
    LIBRARY FOR POSTAGE? No

FOR HOW LONG DO YOU SUSPEND ILL
    SERVICE OVER THE CHRISTMAS
    HOLIDAYS? Approximately
    Dec.22-Jan.5

ARE THERE ANY GROUPS OF LIBRARIES
    FOR WHICH YOU WAIVE FEES? IF
    SO, PLEASE NAME THEM: CORAL
    and AMIGOS members

SAN ANTONIO PUBLIC LIBRARY

NUC CODE: TxSa

OCLC CODE: SAP

ADDRESS: Interlibrary Loan
San Antonio Public
Library
203 S. St. Mary's St.
San Antonio, TX 78205

TELEPHONE: (512) 226-7036,
226-7038, or 299-7803

LIST NAMES OF BRANCHES WITH
SEPARATE POLICIES: None

BOOKS:
Will Lend: Yes
Length of Loan: 3 weeks
Renewable: Yes
Charges: None
Average Turnaround Time:
13.5 days
If you have indicated that a
book is not to be lent, will
you on receipt of a letter
from the requesting library
search the index for given
entries? Yes

PERIODICALS:
Bound: Will not lend
Unbound: Will not lend
Loan Period: N/A
Renewable: N/A
Will lend if article exceeds
_____ number of pages (Not
answered)

MICROFORMS:
Will Lend: Yes
Specific Types of Microforms:
San Antonio newspapers on
microfilm

GOVERNMENT PUBLICATIONS:
Will Lend: Yes

DISSERTATIONS:
Will Lend: Do not own

THESES:
Will Lend: Do not own

AUDIO-VISUAL MATERIALS:
Records: Will not lend
Cassettes: Will not lend
Other (slides, filmstrips,
etc.): Will lend

COMPUTER SOFTWARE:
Will Lend: Do not own

PHOTODUPLICATION SERVICE:
No charge up to 30 exposures.
This is the limit.
Minimum/handling Fee: None
Average Turnaround Time:
7 days

MICROFILMING SERVICE:
Service Available: No
Charges: N/A

DO YOU CHARGE THE BORROWING
LIBRARY FOR POSTAGE? No

FOR HOW LONG DO YOU SUSPEND ILL
SERVICE OVER THE CHRISTMAS
HOLIDAYS? No suspension

ARE THERE ANY GROUPS OF LIBRARIES
FOR WHICH YOU WAIVE FEES? IF
SO, PLEASE NAME THEM: No
charges for any libraries

SOUTHERN METHODIST UNIVERSITY

NUC CODE: TxDam

OCLC CODE: ISM

ADDRESS: Interlibrary Loans
Fondren Library
Southern Methodist
University
Dallas, TX 75275

TELEPHONE: (214) 692-2400

LIST NAMES OF BRANCHES WITH
SEPARATE POLICIES:
Bridwell Library
Science Engineering
Industrial Information
Services
Underwood Law

BOOKS:
Will Lend: Yes
Length of Loan: 3 weeks
Renewable: Yes
Charges: (Not answered)
Average Turnaround Time:
(Not answered)
If you have indicated that a
book is not to be lent, will
you on receipt of a letter
from the requesting library
search the index for given
entries? (Not answered)

PERIODICALS:
Bound: Will lend
Unbound: Will lend
Loan Period: 1 week
Renewable: No
Will lend if article exceeds
_____ number of pages (Not
answered)

MICROFORMS:
Will Lend: (Not answered)
Specific Types of Microforms:
N/A

GOVERNMENT PUBLICATIONS:
Will Lend: Yes

DISSERTATIONS:
Will Lend: Yes; 1967 to
present available from
University Microfilms

THESES:
Will Lend: Yes

AUDIO-VISUAL MATERIALS:
Records: Will not lend
Cassettes: Will not lend
Other (slides, filmstrips,
etc.): Will not lend

COMPUTER SOFTWARE:
Will Lend: (Not answered)

PHOTODUPLICATION SERVICE:
No charge up to 0 exposures
Charge Per Exposure: 20¢
Minimum/handling Fee: $2.00
Average Turnaround Time:
(Not answered)

MICROFILMING SERVICE:
Service Available: (Not
answered)
Charges: N/A

DO YOU CHARGE THE BORROWING
LIBRARY FOR POSTAGE? (Not
answered)

FOR HOW LONG DO YOU SUSPEND ILL
SERVICE OVER THE CHRISTMAS
HOLIDAYS? Dec.15-Jan.2

ARE THERE ANY GROUPS OF LIBRARIES
FOR WHICH YOU WAIVE FEES? IF
SO, PLEASE NAME THEM: (Not
answered)

SOUTHWEST TEXAS STATE UNIVERSITY

NUC CODE: TxSmS

OCLC CODE: TXI

ADDRESS: Interlibrary Loan
          Learning Resources
             Center
          Southwest Texas State
             University
          San Marcos, TX
          78666-4604

TELEPHONE: (512) 245-2685

LIST NAMES OF BRANCHES WITH
   SEPARATE POLICIES: None

BOOKS:
   Will Lend: Yes
   Length of Loan: 1 month
   Renewable: Yes, for 2 weeks
   Charges: None
   Average Turnaround Time:
      2 days
   If you have indicated that a
      book is not to be lent, will
      you on receipt of a letter
      from the requesting library
      search the index for given
      entries? Yes

PERIODICALS:
   Bound: Will not lend
   Unbound: Will not lend
   Loan Period: N/A
   Renewable: N/A
   Will lend if article exceeds
   _____ number of pages (Not
      answered)

MICROFORMS:
   Will Lend: Yes
   Specific Types of Microforms:
      Film, fiche, cards

GOVERNMENT PUBLICATIONS:
   Will Lend: Yes

DISSERTATIONS:
   Will Lend: No

THESES:
   Will Lend: Yes, if 2nd copy
      available

AUDIO-VISUAL MATERIALS:
   Records: Will not lend
   Cassettes: Will lend
   Other (slides, filmstrips,
      etc.): Will lend, except
      for 16mm films

COMPUTER SOFTWARE:
   Will Lend: No

PHOTODUPLICATION SERVICE:
   No charge up to 0 exposures
   Charge Per Exposure: 10¢
   Minimum/handling Fee: None
   Average Turnaround Time:
      2 days

MICROFILMING SERVICE:
   Service Available: No
   Charges: None

DO YOU CHARGE THE BORROWING
   LIBRARY FOR POSTAGE? No

FOR HOW LONG DO YOU SUSPEND ILL
   SERVICE OVER THE CHRISTMAS
   HOLIDAYS? Dec.23-Jan.2

ARE THERE ANY GROUPS OF LIBRARIES
   FOR WHICH YOU WAIVE FEES? IF
   SO, PLEASE NAME THEM: AMIGOS
   members

STEPHEN F. AUSTIN STATE UNIVERSITY

NUC CODE: TxNacS

OCLC CODE: TXK

ADDRESS: Interlibrary Loan
          Ralph W. Steen Library
          P. O. Box 13055
          Stephen F. Austin State
             University
          Nacogdoches, TX 75962

TELEPHONE: (713) 569-4106

LIST NAMES OF BRANCHES WITH
   SEPARATE POLICIES: None

BOOKS:
   Will Lend: Yes
   Length of Loan: 2 weeks use
   Renewable: Yes
   Charges: None
   Average Turnaround Time:
      2 days
   If you have indicated that a
      book is not to be lent, will
      you on receipt of a letter
      from the requesting library
      search the index for given
      entries? No

PERIODICALS:
   Bound: Will not lend
   Unbound: Will not lend
   Loan Period: N/A
   Renewable: N/A
   Will lend if article exceeds
      50 pages

MICROFORMS:
   Will Lend: Yes
   Specific Types of Microforms:
      Microfilm, microfiche,
      microcard

GOVERNMENT PUBLICATIONS:
   Will Lend: Yes

DISSERTATIONS:
   Will Lend: Yes

THESES:
   Will Lend: Yes

AUDIO-VISUAL MATERIALS:
   Records: Will not lend
   Cassettes: Will not lend
   Other (slides, filmstrips,
      etc.): Will not lend

COMPUTER SOFTWARE:
   Will Lend: No

PHOTODUPLICATION SERVICE:
   No charge up to 0 exposures
   Charge Per Exposure: 10¢
   Minimum/handling Fee: $2.00
   Average Turnaround Time:
      2 days

MICROFILMING SERVICE:
   Service Available: No
   Charges: N/A

DO YOU CHARGE THE BORROWING
   LIBRARY FOR POSTAGE? No

FOR HOW LONG DO YOU SUSPEND ILL
   SERVICE OVER THE CHRISTMAS
   HOLIDAYS? Dec.15-Jan.2

ARE THERE ANY GROUPS OF LIBRARIES
   FOR WHICH YOU WAIVE FEES? IF
   SO, PLEASE NAME THEM: AMIGOS

TARLETON STATE UNIVERSITY

NUC CODE: TxSvT

OCLC CODE: TTS

ADDRESS: Interlibrary Loan
Tarleton State
University
Dick Smith Library
Tarleton Station
Stephenville, TX 76402

TELEPHONE: (817) 968-9249

LIST NAMES OF BRANCHES WITH
SEPARATE POLICIES: None

BOOKS:
Will Lend: Yes
Length of Loan: 30 days
Renewable: Yes
Charges: Ordinarily none.
Depends on fee policies of
other libraries.
Average Turnaround Time:
1-2 days
If you have indicated that a
book is not to be lent, will
you on receipt of a letter
from the requesting library
search the index for given
entries? (Not answered)

PERIODICALS:
Bound: Will lend under spe-
cial circumstances
Unbound: Will lend under
special circumstances
Loan Period: 14 days
Renewable: No
Will lend if article exceeds
50 pages

MICROFORMS:
Will Lend: Yes
Specific Types of Microforms:
Microfilm, microfiche,
ultrafiche; 2 weeks in-
library use only

GOVERNMENT PUBLICATIONS:
Will Lend: Yes

DISSERTATIONS:
Will Lend: Yes

THESES:
Will Lend: Yes

AUDIO-VISUAL MATERIALS:
Records: Will not lend
Cassettes: Will lend
Other (slides, filmstrips,
etc.): Will not lend

COMPUTER SOFTWARE:
Will Lend: No

PHOTODUPLICATION SERVICE:
No charge up to 50 exposures
Charge Per Exposure: 5¢
each after 1st 50; fees
reciprocally based
Minimum/handling Fee: None
Average Turnaround Time:
1-2 days

MICROFILMING SERVICE:
Service Available: No
Charges: N/A

DO YOU CHARGE THE BORROWING
LIBRARY FOR POSTAGE? No

FOR HOW LONG DO YOU SUSPEND ILL
SERVICE OVER THE CHRISTMAS
HOLIDAYS? Christmas, app.
Dec.15-Jan.6. Spring
Break, app. Mar.10-Mar.25

ARE THERE ANY GROUPS OF LIBRARIES
FOR WHICH YOU WAIVE FEES? IF
SO, PLEASE NAME THEM: AMIGOS
members

TEXAS A & I UNIVERSITY

NUC CODE: TxKT

OCLC CODE: (Not answered)

ADDRESS: Interlibrary Loan
James C. Jernigan
Library
Texas A & I University
Kingsville, TX 78363

TELEPHONE: (512) 595-3319

LIST NAMES OF BRANCHES WITH
SEPARATE POLICIES: None

BOOKS:
Will Lend: Yes
Length of Loan: 2 weeks use
Renewable: Yes
Charges: None
Average Turnaround Time:
1 day
If you have indicated that a
book is not to be lent, will
you on receipt of a letter
from the requesting library
search the index for given
entries? (Not answered)

PERIODICALS:
Bound: Will not lend
Unbound: Will not lend
Loan Period: N/A
Renewable: N/A
Will lend if article exceeds
50 pages in some cases

MICROFORMS:
Will Lend: Yes
Specific Types of Microforms:
Microfilm (newspapers,
censuses)

GOVERNMENT PUBLICATIONS:
Will Lend: Yes

DISSERTATIONS:
Will Lend: Yes

THESES:
Will Lend: Yes

AUDIO-VISUAL MATERIALS:
Records: Will not lend
Cassettes: Will not lend
Other (slides, filmstrips,
etc.): Will not lend

COMPUTER SOFTWARE:
Will Lend: Do not own

PHOTODUPLICATION SERVICE:
No charge up to 0 exposures
Charge Per Exposure: 10¢
Minimum/handling Fee: None
Average Turnaround Time:
1 day

MICROFILMING SERVICE:
Service Available: No
Charges: N/A

DO YOU CHARGE THE BORROWING
LIBRARY FOR POSTAGE? No

FOR HOW LONG DO YOU SUSPEND ILL
SERVICE OVER THE CHRISTMAS
HOLIDAYS? Dec.15-Jan.2

ARE THERE ANY GROUPS OF LIBRARIES
FOR WHICH YOU WAIVE FEES? IF
SO, PLEASE NAME THEM: Corpus
and surrounding areas

TEXAS A&M UNIVERSITY

NUC CODE: TxCM

OCLC CODE: TXA

ADDRESS: Interlibrary Loan
Evans Library
Texas A&M University
College Station, TX
77843

TELEPHONE: (713) 845-5641

LIST NAMES OF BRANCHES WITH
SEPARATE POLICIES:
Medical Sciences Library

BOOKS:
Will Lend: Yes
Length of Loan: 1 month
Renewable: Yes
Charges: None
Average Turnaround Time:
2-3 weeks
If you have indicated that a
book is not to be lent, will
you on receipt of a letter
from the requesting library
search the index for given
entries? (Not answered)

PERIODICALS:
Bound: Will lend those that
are 10+ years old
Unbound: Will not lend
Loan Period: 2 weeks use
Renewable: No
Will lend if article exceeds
50 pages

MICROFORMS:
Will Lend: No
Specific Types of Microforms:
N/A

GOVERNMENT PUBLICATIONS:
Will Lend: Yes

DISSERTATIONS:
Will Lend: Yes; 1963 to
present available from
University Microfilms

THESES:
Will Lend: Yes

AUDIO-VISUAL MATERIALS:
Records: Will not lend
Cassettes: Will not lend
Other (slides, filmstrips,
etc.): Will not lend

COMPUTER SOFTWARE:
Will Lend: No

PHOTODUPLICATION SERVICE:
No charge up to 0 exposures
Charge Per Exposure: 10¢
Minimum Fee: $1.00
Average Turnaround Time:
2-3 weeks

MICROFILMING SERVICE:
Service Available: No
Charges: N/A

DO YOU CHARGE THE BORROWING
LIBRARY FOR POSTAGE? No

FOR HOW LONG DO YOU SUSPEND ILL
SERVICE OVER THE CHRISTMAS
HOLIDAYS? Varies--at
least 2 weeks

ARE THERE ANY GROUPS OF LIBRARIES
FOR WHICH YOU WAIVE FEES? IF
SO, PLEASE NAME THEM: AMIGOS;
CARLA

TEXAS CHRISTIAN UNIVERSITY

NUC CODE: TxFtc

OCLC CODE: ICU

ADDRESS: Interlibrary Loan
Texas Christian
University Library
P. O. Box 32904
Ft. Worth, TX 76129

TELEPHONE: (817) 921-7117, X6116

LIST NAMES OF BRANCHES WITH
SEPARATE POLICIES: None

BOOKS:
Will Lend: Yes
Length of Loan: 3 weeks
Renewable: Yes
Charges: $4.00
Average Turnaround Time:
3-5 days
If you have indicated that a
book is not to be lent, will
you on receipt of a letter
from the requesting library
search the index for given
entries? (Not answered)

PERIODICALS:
Bound: Will not lend
Unbound: Will not lend
Loan Period: N/A
Renewable: N/A
Will lend if article exceeds
_____ number of pages (Not
answered)

MICROFORMS:
Will Lend: Yes
Specific Types of Microforms:
(Not answered)

GOVERNMENT PUBLICATIONS:
Will Lend: Yes

DISSERTATIONS:
Will Lend: Yes

THESES:
Will Lend: Yes

AUDIO-VISUAL MATERIALS:
Records: (Not answered)
Cassettes: (Not answered)
Other (slides, filmstrips,
etc.): (Not answered)

COMPUTER SOFTWARE:
Will Lend: (Not answered)

PHOTODUPLICATION SERVICE:
No charge up to 0 exposures
Charge Per Exposure: !0¢
after 25
Handling Fee: $4.00
Minimum Fee: $4.00
Average Turnaround Time:
3-5 days

MICROFILMING SERVICE:
Service Available: No
Charges: N/A

DO YOU CHARGE THE BORROWING
LIBRARY FOR POSTAGE? (Not
answered)

FOR HOW LONG DO YOU SUSPEND ILL
SERVICE OVER THE CHRISTMAS
HOLIDAYS? (Not answered)

ARE THERE ANY GROUPS OF LIBRARIES
FOR WHICH YOU WAIVE FEES? IF
SO, PLEASE NAME THEM: AMIGOS,
AHE, HARLIC, public librar-
ies in Texas

TEXAS COLLEGE OF OSTEOPATHIC MEDICINE

NUC CODE: None

OCLC CODE: TOM

ADDRESS: Interlibrary Loan
Texas College of
Osteopathic Medicine
Library
Camp Bowie at
Montgomery
Fort Worth, TX 76107

TELEPHONE: (817) 735-2588

LIST NAMES OF BRANCHES WITH
SEPARATE POLICIES: None

BOOKS:
Will Lend: Yes
Length of Loan: 3 weeks
Renewable: Yes
Charges: None
Average Turnaround Time:
24-36 hours
If you have indicated that a
book is not to be lent, will
you on receipt of a letter
from the requesting library
search the index for given
entries? (Not answered)

PERIODICALS:
Bound: Will not lend
Unbound: Will not lend
Loan Period: N/A
Renewable: N/A
Will lend if article exceeds
_____ number of pages (Will
not lend, regardless of
length of article)

MICROFORMS:
Will Lend: Yes
Specific Types of Microforms:
Microfilm

GOVERNMENT PUBLICATIONS:
Will Lend: No

DISSERTATIONS:
Will Lend: No

THESES:
Will Lend: No

AUDIO-VISUAL MATERIALS:
Records: Will lend
Cassettes: Will lend
Other (slides, filmstrips,
etc.): Will lend

COMPUTER SOFTWARE:
Will Lend: No

PHOTODUPLICATION SERVICE:
No charges
Average Turnaround Time:
24-36 hours

MICROFILMING SERVICE:
Service Available: No
Charges: N/A

DO YOU CHARGE THE BORROWING
LIBRARY FOR POSTAGE? No

FOR HOW LONG DO YOU SUSPEND ILL
SERVICE OVER THE CHRISTMAS
HOLIDAYS? (Not answered)

ARE THERE ANY GROUPS OF LIBRARIES
FOR WHICH YOU WAIVE FEES? IF
SO, PLEASE NAME THEM: No fees
charged

TEXAS TECH UNIVERSITY

NUC CODE: TxLT

OCLC CODE: ILU

ADDRESS: Interlibrary Loan
Texas Tech University
Library
Lubbock, TX 79409

TELEPHONE: (806) 742-2239

LIST NAMES OF BRANCHES WITH
SEPARATE POLICIES: None

BOOKS:
Will Lend: Yes
Length of Loan: 2 weeks
Renewable: Yes
Charges: None
Average Turnaround Time:
(Not answered)
If you have indicated that a
book is not to be lent, will
you on receipt of a letter
from the requesting library
search the index for given
entries? (Not answered)

PERIODICALS:
Bound: Will not lend
Unbound: Will not lend
Loan Period: N/A
Renewable: N/A
Will lend if article exceeds
_____ number of pages (Not
answered)

MICROFORMS:
Will Lend: Yes
Specific Types of Microforms:
All

GOVERNMENT PUBLICATIONS:
Will Lend: Yes

DISSERTATIONS:
Will Lend: Yes, on a
reciprocal basis. Some
available since 1960 from
University Microfilms

THESES:
Will Lend: Yes

AUDIO-VISUAL MATERIALS:
Records: (Not answered)
Cassettes: (Not answered)
Other (slides, filmstrips,
etc.): (Not answered)

COMPUTER SOFTWARE:
Will Lend: (Not answered)

PHOTODUPLICATION SERVICE:
No charge up to 10 exposures
Charge Per Exposure: 10¢
Minimum/handling Fee: None
Average Turnaround Time:
(Not answered)

MICROFILMING SERVICE:
Service Available: Yes
Charges: 6¢ per frame,
$4.50 handling fee

DO YOU CHARGE THE BORROWING
LIBRARY FOR POSTAGE? Yes

FOR HOW LONG DO YOU SUSPEND ILL
SERVICE OVER THE CHRISTMAS
HOLIDAYS? Dec.5-Jan.2

ARE THERE ANY GROUPS OF LIBRARIES
FOR WHICH YOU WAIVE FEES? IF
SO, PLEASE NAME THEM: CARLA,
AMIGOS, ALC

TEXAS WOMAN'S UNIVERSITY

NUC CODE: TxDW

OCLC CODE: IWU

ADDRESS: Interlibrary Loan
Texas Woman's
University Library
P. O. Box 23715, TWU
Denton, TX 76204

TELEPHONE: (817) 566-6415

LIST NAMES OF BRANCHES WITH
SEPARATE POLICIES: None

BOOKS:
Will Lend: Yes
Length of Loan: 2 weeks
Renewable: Yes
Charges: None
Average Turnaround Time:
(Not answered)
If you have indicated that a
book is not to be lent, will
you on receipt of a letter
from the requesting library
search the index for given
entries? (Not answered)

PERIODICALS:
Bound: Will not lend
Unbound: Will not lend
Loan Period: N/A
Renewable: N/A
Will lend if article exceeds
_____ number of pages (Not
answered)

MICROFORMS:
Will Lend: Yes
Specific Types of Microforms:
Microfiche, microcards,
microfilms

GOVERNMENT PUBLICATIONS:
Will Lend: No

DISSERTATIONS:
Will Lend: Yes, if 2nd copy
available; 1973 to present
available from University
Microfilms

THESES:
Will Lend: Yes, if 2nd copy
available

AUDIO-VISUAL MATERIALS:
Records: Will not lend
Cassettes: Will not lend
Other (slides, filmstrips,
etc.): Will not lend

COMPUTER SOFTWARE:
Will Lend: (Not answered)

PHOTODUPLICATION SERVICE:
No charge up to _____
exposures (Not answered)
Charges: $5.00 minimum
charge for out-of-state,
except for AMIGOS members
Average Turnaround Time:
(Not answered)

MICROFILMING SERVICE:
Service Available: No
Charges: N/A

DO YOU CHARGE THE BORROWING
LIBRARY FOR POSTAGE? No

FOR HOW LONG DO YOU SUSPEND ILL
SERVICE OVER THE CHRISTMAS
HOLIDAYS? Dec.17-Jan.3

ARE THERE ANY GROUPS OF LIBRARIES
FOR WHICH YOU WAIVE FEES? IF
SO, PLEASE NAME THEM: AMIGOS,
AHE

TRINITY UNIVERSITY

NUC CODE: TxSaT

OCLC CODE: TNY

ADDRESS: Interlibrary Loan
Trinity University
Library
715 Stadium Dr.
San Antonio, TX 78284

TELEPHONE: (512) 736-7355

LIST NAMES OF BRANCHES WITH
SEPARATE POLICIES:
Instructional Media Services
Trinity University Library
715 Stadium Dr.
San Antonio, TX 78284

BOOKS:
Will Lend: Yes
Length of Loan: 21 days
Renewable: Yes
Charges: None
Average Turnaround Time:
3 days
If you have indicated that a
book is not to be lent, will
you on receipt of a letter
from the requesting library
search the index for given
entries? (Not answered)

PERIODICALS:
Bound: Will not lend
Unbound: Will not lend
Loan Period: N/A
Renewable: N/A
Will lend if article exceeds
_____ number of pages (Will
not lend, regardless of
length of article)

MICROFORMS:
Will Lend: Yes
Specific Types of Microforms:
Microfilm

GOVERNMENT PUBLICATIONS:
Will Lend: Yes

DISSERTATIONS:
Will Lend: No

THESES:
Will Lend: Yes, if 2nd copy
available

AUDIO-VISUAL MATERIALS:
Records: Do not own
Cassettes: Do not own
Other (slides, filmstrips,
etc.): Do not own

COMPUTER SOFTWARE:
Will Lend: Do not own

PHOTODUPLICATION SERVICE:
No charge up to 0 exposures
Charge Per Exposure: 10¢
plus handling fee
Handling Fee: $2.50
Average Turnaround Time:
3 days

MICROFILMING SERVICE:
Service Available: No
Charges: N/A

DO YOU CHARGE THE BORROWING
LIBRARY FOR POSTAGE? No

FOR HOW LONG DO YOU SUSPEND ILL
SERVICE OVER THE CHRISTMAS
HOLIDAYS? Approximately 3
weeks

ARE THERE ANY GROUPS OF LIBRARIES
FOR WHICH YOU WAIVE FEES? IF
SO, PLEASE NAME THEM: CORAL,
Texas libraries

UNIVERSITY OF DALLAS

NUC CODE: TxDaU

OCLC CODE: IVD

ADDRESS: Interlibrary Loan
University of Dallas
Library
University of Dallas
Station
Irving, TX 75061

TELEPHONE: (214) 721-5057

LIST NAMES OF BRANCHES WITH
SEPARATE POLICIES: None

BOOKS:
Will Lend: Yes
Length of Loan: 2 weeks
Renewable: Yes
Charges: (Not answered)
Average Turnaround Time:
1-3 days
If you have indicated that a
book is not to be lent, will
you on receipt of a letter
from the requesting library
search the index for given
entries? (Not answered)

PERIODICALS:
Bound: Will not lend
Unbound: Will not lend
Loan Period: N/A
Renewable: N/A
Will lend if article exceeds
_____ number of pages (Not
answered)

MICROFORMS:
Will Lend: Yes
Specific Types of Microforms:
Fiche

GOVERNMENT PUBLICATIONS:
Will Lend: Yes

DISSERTATIONS:
Will Lend: Yes

THESES:
Will Lend: Yes

AUDIO-VISUAL MATERIALS:
Records: Will not lend
Cassettes: Will not lend
Other (slides, filmstrips,
etc.): Will not lend

COMPUTER SOFTWARE:
Will Lend: No

PHOTODUPLICATION SERVICE:
No charge up to 0 exposures
Charge Per Exposure: 10¢
Minimum Fee: $1.00
Average Turnaround Time:
1-3 days

MICROFILMING SERVICE:
Service Available: No
Charges: N/A

DO YOU CHARGE THE BORROWING
LIBRARY FOR POSTAGE? Yes

FOR HOW LONG DO YOU SUSPEND ILL
SERVICE OVER THE CHRISTMAS
HOLIDAYS? A few days before
and after Christmas and
New Year's Day

ARE THERE ANY GROUPS OF LIBRARIES
FOR WHICH YOU WAIVE FEES? IF
SO, PLEASE NAME THEM: AMIGOS
libraries

UNIVERSITY OF HOUSTON

NUC CODE: TxHU

OCLC CODE: TXH

ADDRESS: Interlibrary Loan
University of Houston
Libraries
4800 Calhoun Blvd.
Houston, TX 77004

TELEPHONE: (713) 749-4246

LIST NAMES OF BRANCHES WITH
SEPARATE POLICIES:
Law Library

BOOKS:
Will Lend: Yes
Length of Loan: 3 weeks
Renewable: Yes
Charges: None
Average Turnaround Time:
1-2 days
If you have indicated that a
book is not to be lent, will
you on receipt of a letter
from the requesting library
search the index for given
entries? (Not answered)

PERIODICALS:
Bound: Will not lend
Unbound: Will not lend
Loan Period: N/A
Renewable: N/A
Will lend if article exceeds
_____ number of pages (Will
not lend, regardless of
length of article)

MICROFORMS:
Will Lend: Yes
Specific Types of Microforms:
Microfilm

GOVERNMENT PUBLICATIONS:
Will Lend: Yes

DISSERTATIONS:
Will Lend: Yes; 1954 to
present available from
University Microfilms

THESES:
Will Lend: Yes

AUDIO-VISUAL MATERIALS:
Records: Will not lend
Cassettes: Will not lend
Other (slides, filmstrips,
etc.): Will not lend

COMPUTER SOFTWARE:
Will Lend: No

PHOTODUPLICATION SERVICE:
No charge up to 0 exposures
Charges: $2.00 for 1-10
exposures; 10¢ each
additional exposure
Charges for company-
affiliated libraries is
$4.00 minimum fee and $1.00
handling fee
Average Turnaround Time:
2-3 days

MICROFILMING SERVICE:
Service Available: No
Charges: N/A

DO YOU CHARGE THE BORROWING
LIBRARY FOR POSTAGE? No

FOR HOW LONG DO YOU SUSPEND ILL
SERVICE OVER THE CHRISTMAS
HOLIDAYS? Dec.14-Jan.6

ARE THERE ANY GROUPS OF LIBRARIES
FOR WHICH YOU WAIVE FEES? IF
SO, PLEASE NAME THEM: AMIGOS;
CARLA

UNIVERSITY OF HOUSTON AT CLEAR LAKE CITY

NUC CODE: TxClcU

OCLC CODE: UHC

ADDRESS: Interlibrary Loan
           University of Houston
             at Clear Lake City
             Library
           2700 Bay Area Blvd.
           Houston, TX 77058

TELEPHONE: (713) 488-9295 or
               488-9296

LIST NAMES OF BRANCHES WITH
  SEPARATE POLICIES: None

BOOKS:
  Will Lend: Yes
  Length of Loan: 3 weeks
  Renewable: Yes
  Charges: None
  Average Turnaround Time:
    1 day
  If you have indicated that a
    book is not to be lent, will
    you on receipt of a letter
    from the requesting library
    search the index for given
    entries? (Not answered)

PERIODICALS:
  Bound: Will lend those
    prior to 1956
  Unbound: Will not lend
  Loan Period: 3 days
  Renewable: No
  Will lend if article exceeds
    75 pages

MICROFORMS:
  Will Lend: No
  Specific Types of Microforms:
    Will lend special collec-
    tions and newspaper micro-
    film prior to 1976

GOVERNMENT PUBLICATIONS:
  Will Lend: Yes, microfilm
    and periodicals

DISSERTATIONS:
  Will Lend: Yes

THESES:
  Will Lend: Yes

AUDIO-VISUAL MATERIALS:
  Records: Will not lend
  Cassettes: Will not lend
  Other (slides, filmstrips,
    etc.): Will not lend

COMPUTER SOFTWARE:
  Will Lend: No

PHOTODUPLICATION SERVICE:
  No charge up to 0 exposures
  Charge Per Exposure: 10¢
  Minimum/handling Fee: 40¢
  Average Turnaround Time:
    1 day

MICROFILMING SERVICE:
  Service Available: No
  Charges: N/A

DO YOU CHARGE THE BORROWING
  LIBRARY FOR POSTAGE? No

FOR HOW LONG DO YOU SUSPEND ILL
  SERVICE OVER THE CHRISTMAS
  HOLIDAYS? Dec.18-Jan.4

ARE THERE ANY GROUPS OF LIBRARIES
  FOR WHICH YOU WAIVE FEES? IF
  SO, PLEASE NAME THEM: AMIGOS
  members

UNIVERSITY OF TEXAS AT ARLINGTON

NUC CODE: TxArU

OCLC CODE: IUA

ADDRESS: Interlibrary Loan
           University of Texas at
             Arlington
           Library Box 19497
           Arlington, TX 76019

TELEPHONE: (817) 273-3391, X97

LIST NAMES OF BRANCHES WITH
  SEPARATE POLICIES: None

BOOKS:
  Will Lend: Yes
  Length of Loan: 3 weeks
  Renewable: No
  Charges: (Not answered)
  Average Turnaround Time:
    (Not answered)
  If you have indicated that a
    book is not to be lent, will
    you on receipt of a letter
    from the requesting library
    search the index for given
    entries? (Not answered)

PERIODICALS:
  Bound: Will lend
  Unbound: Will not lend
  Loan Period: 1 week
  Renewable: No
  Will lend if article exceeds
    _____ number of pages (Not
    answered)

MICROFORMS:
  Will Lend: Yes
  Specific Types of Microforms:
    (Not answered)

GOVERNMENT PUBLICATIONS:
  Will Lend: Yes

DISSERTATIONS:
  Will Lend: (Not answered)

THESES:
  Will Lend: (Not answered)

AUDIO-VISUAL MATERIALS:
  Records: (Not answered)
  Cassettes: (Not answered)
  Other (slides, filmstrips,
    etc.): (Not answered)

COMPUTER SOFTWARE:
  Will Lend: (Not answered)

PHOTODUPLICATION SERVICE:
  No charge up to 0 exposures
  Charge Per Exposure: 10¢
  Minimum Fee: $2.50 up to
    25 pages
  Average Turnaround Time:
    (Not answered)

MICROFILMING SERVICE:
  Service Available: (Not
    answered)
  Charges: N/A

DO YOU CHARGE THE BORROWING
  LIBRARY FOR POSTAGE? No

FOR HOW LONG DO YOU SUSPEND ILL
  SERVICE OVER THE CHRISTMAS
  HOLIDAYS? Dec.14-Jan.4

ARE THERE ANY GROUPS OF LIBRARIES
  FOR WHICH YOU WAIVE FEES? IF
  SO, PLEASE NAME THEM: None

UNIVERSITY OF TEXAS AT AUSTIN

NUC CODE: TxU

OCLC CODE: IXA

ADDRESS: Interlibrary Loan
General Libraries
University of Texas at
Austin
Austin, TX 78712

TELEPHONE: (512) 471-3976

LIST NAMES OF BRANCHES WITH
SEPARATE POLICIES: (Not
answered)

BOOKS:
Will Lend: Yes
Length of Loan: (Not
answered)
Renewable: (Not answered)
Charges: (Not answered)
Average Turnaround Time:
(Not answered)
If you have indicated that a
book is not to be lent, will
you on receipt of a letter
from the requesting library
search the index for given
entries? (Not answered)

PERIODICALS:
Bound: Will not lend
Unbound: Will not lend
Loan Period: N/A
Renewable: N/A
Will lend if article exceeds
_____ number of pages (Not
answered)

MICROFORMS:
Will Lend: Yes
Specific Types of Microforms:
Microfilm, microcard

GOVERNMENT PUBLICATIONS:
Will Lend: Yes

DISSERTATIONS:
Will Lend: Yes, if pre-1958;
1957 to present available
from University Microfilms

THESES:
Will Lend: Yes

AUDIO-VISUAL MATERIALS:
Records: Will not lend
Cassettes: Will not lend
Other (slides, filmstrips,
etc.): Will not lend

COMPUTER SOFTWARE:
Will Lend: (Not answered)

PHOTODUPLICATION SERVICE:
No charge up to 0 exposures
Charge Per Exposure: 10¢
Minimum/handling Fee: $3.50
Average Turnaround Time:
(Not answered)

MICROFILMING SERVICE:
Service Available: Yes
Charges: 7¢ per frame from
original; $15.00 per reel
from existing film

DO YOU CHARGE THE BORROWING
LIBRARY FOR POSTAGE? (Not
answered)

FOR HOW LONG DO YOU SUSPEND ILL
SERVICE OVER THE CHRISTMAS
HOLIDAYS? (Not answered)

ARE THERE ANY GROUPS OF LIBRARIES
FOR WHICH YOU WAIVE FEES? IF
SO, PLEASE NAME THEM: AMIGOS

UNIVERSITY OF TEXAS AT DALLAS

NUC CODE: TxU-Da

OCLC CODE: ITD

ADDRESS: Interlibrary Loan
University of Texas at
Dallas Library
P. O. Box 643
Richardson, TX 75080

TELEPHONE: (214) 690-2900

LIST NAMES OF BRANCHES WITH
SEPARATE POLICIES: None

BOOKS:
Will Lend: Yes
Length of Loan: 1 month
Renewable: Yes
Charges: Postage if other
than library rate
Average Turnaround Time:
24 hours
It you have indicated that a
book is not to be lent, will
you on receipt of a letter
from the requesting library
search the index for given
entries? (Not answered)

PERIODICALS:
Bound: Will not lend
Unbound: Will not lend
Loan Period: N/A
Renewable: N/A
Will lend if article exceeds
_____ number of pages (Not
answered)

MICROFORMS:
Will Lend: No, but will
reproduce microfiche and
bill as photocopy
Specific Types of Microforms:
N/A

GOVERNMENT PUBLICATIONS:
Will Lend: Yes

DISSERTATIONS:
Will Lend: Yes; 1974 to
present available from
University Microfilms

THESES:
Will Lend: Yes

AUDIO-VISUAL MATERIALS:
Records: Will not lend
Cassettes: Will not lend
Other (slides, filmstrips,
etc.): Will not lend

COMPUTER SOFTWARE:
Will Lend: No

PHOTODUPLICATION SERVICE:
No charge up to 0 exposures
Charge Per Exposure: 10¢
Minimum/handling Fee: $1.00
Average Turnaround Time:
2 days

MICROFILMING SERVICE:
Service Available: No
Charges: N/A

DO YOU CHARGE THE BORROWING
LIBRARY FOR POSTAGE? No

FOR HOW LONG DO YOU SUSPEND ILL
SERVICE OVER THE CHRISTMAS
HOLIDAYS? Dec.15-Jan.2
approximately

ARE THERE ANY GROUPS OF LIBRARIES
FOR WHICH YOU WAIVE FEES? IF
SO, PLEASE NAME THEM: AMIGOS;
members of Association of
Higher Education of North
Texas

UNIVERSITY OF TEXAS AT EL PASO

NUC CODE: TxEU

OCLC CODE: TXU

ADDRESS: Interlibrary Loan
University of Texas at
El Paso Library
El Paso, TX 79968

TELEPHONE: (915) 747-5678

LIST NAMES OF BRANCHES WITH
SEPARATE POLICIES: None

BOOKS:
Will Lend: Yes
Length of Loan: 3 weeks
Renewable: Yes, in special
circumstances
Charges: (Not answered)
Average Turnaround Time:
24 hours
If you have indicated that a
book is not to be lent, will
you on receipt of a letter
from the requesting library
search the index for given
entries? Yes

PERIODICALS:
Bound: Will not lend
Unbound: Will not lend
Loan Period: N/A
Renewable: N/A
Will lend if article exceeds
_____ number of pages (Not
answered)

MICROFORMS:
Will Lend: Yes
Specific Types of Microforms:
Will lend theses only

GOVERNMENT PUBLICATIONS:
Will Lend: Yes

DISSERTATIONS:
Will Lend: Yes, if
circulating copy available.
1979 to present available
from University Microfilms

THESES:
Will Lend: Yes, if
circulating copy available.
1979 to present available
from University Microfilms

AUDIO-VISUAL MATERIALS:
Records: Will not lend
Cassettes: Will not lend
Other (slides, filmstrips,
etc.): Will not lend

COMPUTER SOFTWARE:
Will Lend: Do not own

PHOTODUPLICATION SERVICE:
No charge up to 0 exposures
Charge Per Exposure: 10¢
Minimum/handling Fee: $1.00
Average Turnaround Time:
(Not answered)

MICROFILMING SERVICE:
Service Available: Yes
Charges: 20¢ per exposure

DO YOU CHARGE THE BORROWING
LIBRARY FOR POSTAGE? No

FOR HOW LONG DO YOU SUSPEND ILL
SERVICE OVER THE CHRISTMAS
HOLIDAYS? Approximately
from Dec.20-Jan.5

ARE THERE ANY GROUPS OF LIBRARIES
FOR WHICH YOU WAIVE FEES? IF
SO, PLEASE NAME THEM: Yes,
federal libraries who are
unable to pay us

UNIVERSITY OF TEXAS AT SAN ANTONIO

NUC CODE: TxSaU

OCLC CODE: TXJ

ADDRESS: Interlibrary Loan
University of Texas at
San Antonio
John Peace Library
San Antonio, TX 78285

TELEPHONE: (512) 691-4574, X23

LIST NAMES OF BRANCHES WITH
SEPARATE POLICIES: None

BOOKS:
Will Lend: Yes
Length of Loan: 1 month
Renewable: Yes
Charges: None
Average Turnaround Time:
2 days maximum
If you have indicated that a
book is not to be lent, will
you on receipt of a letter
from the requesting library
search the index for given
entries? (Not answered)

PERIODICALS:
Bound: Will not lend
Unbound: Will not lend
Loan Period: N/A
Renewable: N/A
Will lend if article exceeds
_____ number of pages (Will
not lend, regardless of
length of article)

MICROFORMS:
Will Lend: No
Specific Types of Microforms:
N/A
Fiche to Fiche Service: $1.50
for 1-3 exposures, 25¢ each
additional exposure

GOVERNMENT PUBLICATIONS:
Will Lend: Yes

DISSERTATIONS:
Will Lend: Yes

THESES:
Will Lend: Yes

AUDIO-VISUAL MATERIALS:
Records: Will not lend
Cassettes: Will not lend
Other (slides, filmstrips,
etc.): Will not lend

COMPUTER SOFTWARE:
Will Lend: No

PHOTODUPLICATION SERVICE:
No charge up to 0 exposures
Charge Per Exposure: 10¢
each after minimum fee
Minimum Fee: $1.50 for 1-5
exposures
Average Turnaround Time:
2 days maximum

MICROFILMING SERVICE:
Service Available: No
Charges: N/A

DO YOU CHARGE THE BORROWING
LIBRARY FOR POSTAGE? No

FOR HOW LONG DO YOU SUSPEND ILL
SERVICE OVER THE CHRISTMAS
HOLIDAYS? Dec.5-Jan.5

ARE THERE ANY GROUPS OF LIBRARIES
FOR WHICH YOU WAIVE FEES? IF
SO, PLEASE NAME THEM: AMIGOS
and CORAL members (receive
50 free exposures and 10¢
for each additional
exposure)

UNIVERSITY OF TEXAS HEALTH SCIENCE CENTER AT HOUSTON

NUC CODE: TxU-PH

OCLC CODE: TPH

ADDRESS: Interlibrary Loan
University of Texas
   Health Science Center
   at Houston
School of Public Health
   Library
P. O. Box 20186
Houston, TX 77225-
   0186

TELEPHONE: (713) 792-4350

LIST NAMES OF BRANCHES WITH
   SEPARATE POLICIES:
   University of Texas Dental
      Branch Library
   Jessie Jones Library
      (Houston Academy of
      Medicine)

BOOKS:
   Will Lend: Yes
   Length of Loan: 21 days
   Renewable: Yes
   Charges: None
   Average Turnaround Time:
      2 weeks
   If you have indicated that a
      book is not to be lent, will
      you on receipt of a letter
      from the requesting library
      search the index for given
      entries? (Not answered)

PERIODICALS:
   Bound: Will not lend
   Unbound: Will not lend
   Loan Period: N/A
   Renewable: N/A
   Will lend if article exceeds
      25-30 pages

MICROFORMS:
   Will Lend: No
   Specific Types of Microforms:
      N/A

GOVERNMENT PUBLICATIONS:
   Will Lend: Yes, sometimes

DISSERTATIONS:
   Will Lend: No, but we will
      supply microfiche copy

THESES:
   Will Lend: No, but we will
      supply microfiche copy

AUDIO-VISUAL MATERIALS:
   Records: Will not lend
   Cassettes: Will not lend
   Other (slides, filmstrips,
      etc.): Will not lend

COMPUTER SOFTWARE:
   Will Lend: No

PHOTODUPLICATION SERVICE:
   No charge up to any exposures
   Minimum/handling Fee: None
   Average Turnaround Time:
      2 weeks

MICROFILMING SERVICE:
   Service Available: No
   Charges: N/A

DO YOU CHARGE THE BORROWING
   LIBRARY FOR POSTAGE? No

FOR HOW LONG DO YOU SUSPEND ILL
   SERVICE OVER THE CHRISTMAS
   HOLIDAYS? No suspension

ARE THERE ANY GROUPS OF LIBRARIES
   FOR WHICH YOU WAIVE FEES? IF
   SO, PLEASE NAME THEM: No fees
   charged

UNIVERSITY OF TEXAS HEALTH SCIENCE CENTER AT SAN ANTONIO

NUC CODE: TXSAS

OCLC CODE: TSA

ADDRESS: Interlibrary Loan
University of Texas
   Health Science Center
   at San Antonio
Library
7703 Floyd Curl Dr.
San Antonio, TX 78284

TELEPHONE: (512) 691-6423

LIST NAMES OF BRANCHES WITH
   SEPARATE POLICIES: None

BOOKS:
   Will Lend: Yes
   Length of Loan: 2 weeks from
      receipt
   Renewable: No
   Charges: $4.00 per
      transaction
   Average Turnaround Time:
      1 day
   If you have indicated that a
      book is not to be lent, will
      you on receipt of a letter
      from the requesting library
      search the index for given
      entries? (Not answered)

PERIODICALS:
   Bound: Will not lend
   Unbound: Will not lend
   Loan Period: N/A
   Renewable: N/A
   Will lend if article exceeds
      _____ number of pages (Not
      answered)

MICROFORMS:
   Will Lend: Yes
   Specific Types of Microforms:
      (Not answered)

GOVERNMENT PUBLICATIONS:
   Will Lend: Do not own

DISSERTATIONS:
   Will Lend: Yes

THESES:
   Will Lend: Yes

AUDIO-VISUAL MATERIALS:
   Records: Do not own
   Cassettes: Will lend
   Other (slides, filmstrips,
      etc.): Will lend

COMPUTER SOFTWARE:
   Will Lend: No

PHOTODUPLICATION SERVICE:
   No charge up to 0 exposures
   Charge Per Transaction: $4.00
   Average Turnaround Time:
      1 day

MICROFILMING SERVICE:
   Service Available: No
   Charges: N/A

DO YOU CHARGE THE BORROWING
   LIBRARY FOR POSTAGE? (Not
   answered)

FOR HOW LONG DO YOU SUSPEND ILL
   SERVICE OVER THE CHRISTMAS
   HOLIDAYS? No suspension

ARE THERE ANY GROUPS OF LIBRARIES
   FOR WHICH YOU WAIVE FEES? IF
   SO, PLEASE NAME THEM: Non-
   military members of CORAL;
   resource libraries in TALON
   Regional Medical Library
   Program

UNIVERSITY OF TEXAS MEDICAL BRANCH

NUC CODE: TXU-M

OCLC CODE: TMB

ADDRESS: Interlibrary Loan
          University of Texas
            Medical Branch
          Library
          9th and Market Sts.
          Galveston, TX 77550

TELEPHONE: (713) 765-2386

LIST NAMES OF BRANCHES WITH
  SEPARATE POLICIES: None

BOOKS:
  Will Lend: Yes
  Length of Loan: 2 weeks
  Renewable: Yes
  Charges: $4.00 per loan
  Average Turnaround Time:
    24 hours
  If you have indicated that a
    book is not to be lent, will
    you on receipt of a letter
    from the requesting library
    search the index for given
    entries? (Not answered)

PERIODICALS:
  Bound: Will lend
  Unbound: Will not lend
  Loan Period: 3 days
  Renewable: Yes
  Will lend if article exceeds
    40 pages

MICROFORMS:
  Will Lend: No
  Specific Types of Microforms:
    N/A

GOVERNMENT PUBLICATIONS:
  Will Lend: No

DISSERTATIONS:
  Will Lend: No

THESES:
  Will Lend: No

AUDIO-VISUAL MATERIALS:
  Records: Will not lend
  Cassettes: Will lend
  Other (slides, filmstrips,
    etc.): Will lend

COMPUTER SOFTWARE:
  Will Lend: No

PHOTODUPLICATION SERVICE:
  No charge up to 0 exposures
  Charge Per Exposure: (Not
    answered)
  Minimum/handling Fee: $4.00
  Average Turnaround Time:
    24 hours

MICROFILMING SERVICE:
  Service Available: No
  Charges: N/A

DO YOU CHARGE THE BORROWING
  LIBRARY FOR POSTAGE? No

FOR HOW LONG DO YOU SUSPEND ILL
  SERVICE OVER THE CHRISTMAS
  HOLIDAYS? 2½ weeks before
            and 1 week after Christmas

ARE THERE ANY GROUPS OF LIBRARIES
  FOR WHICH YOU WAIVE FEES? IF
  SO, PLEASE NAME THEM: TALON
    and AMIGOS members

BRIGHAM YOUNG UNIVERSITY

NUC CODE: UPB

OCLC CODE: None

ADDRESS: Interlibrary Loan
Harold B. Lee Library
Brigham Young
University
Provo, UT 84602

TELEPHONE: (801) 378-6344

LIST NAMES OF BRANCHES WITH
SEPARATE POLICIES:
Brigham Young University
Law Library

BOOKS:
Will Lend: Yes
Length of Loan: 2 weeks use
Renewable: Yes
Charges: None
Average Turnaround Time:
3 days
If you have indicated that a
book is not to be lent, will
you on receipt of a letter
from the requesting library
search the index for given
entries? Yes

PERIODICALS:
Bound: Will lend on special
loan only
Unbound: Will not lend
Loan Period: 1 week use
Renewable: No
Will lend if article exceeds
40 pages

MICROFORMS:
Will Lend: Yes, some of them
Specific Types of Microforms:
Microfilm, microfiche,
microcards (except ERIC
documents)

GOVERNMENT PUBLICATIONS:
Will Lend: Yes

DISSERTATIONS:
Will Lend: Yes, if 2nd copy
available; 1961 to present
available from University
Microfilms

THESES:
Will Lend: Yes, if 2nd copy
available

AUDIO-VISUAL MATERIALS:
Records: Will not lend
Cassettes: Will not lend
Other (slides, filmstrips,
etc,): Will not lend

COMPUTER SOFTWARE:
Will Lend: No

PHOTODUPLICATION SERVICE:
No charge up to 3 exposures
Charge Per Exposure: 10¢
Minimum/handling Fee: $2.50
for 1-15 exposures
Average Turnaround Time:
3 days

MICROFILMING SERVICE:
Service Available: Yes
Charges: We will quote
charge per request

DO YOU CHARGE THE BORROWING
LIBRARY FOR POSTAGE? Only
if special handling
requested

FOR HOW LONG DO YOU SUSPEND ILL
SERVICE OVER THE CHRISTMAS
HOLIDAYS? 2 weeks

ARE THERE ANY GROUPS OF LIBRARIES
FOR WHICH YOU WAIVE FEES? IF
SO, PLEASE NAME THEM: RLG
libraries; Utah university
and college libraries

BRIGHAM YOUNG UNIVERSITY LAW LIBRARY

NUC CODE: UPB-L

OCLC CODE: (Not answered)

ADDRESS: Interlibrary Loan
Brigham Young University
Law Library
Provo, UT 84602

TELEPHONE: (801) 378-3596

LIST NAMES OF BRANCHES WITH
SEPARATE POLICIES: (Not
answered)

BOOKS:
Will Lend: Yes
Length of Loan: 2 weeks use
Renewable: Yes
Charges: No charge
Average Turnaround Time:
24 hours
If you have indicated that a
book is not to be lent, will
you on receipt of a letter
from the requesting library
search the index for given
entries? (Not answered)

PERIODICALS:
Bound: Will not lend
Unbound: Will not lend
Loan Period: N/A
Renewable: N/A
Will lend if article exceeds
_____ number of pages (N/A)
Will photocopy articles

MICROFORMS:
Will Lend: No
Specific Types of Microforms:
Have microfiche only. Will
provide fiche on paper copy
for a charge of $2.00
handling and .25 per copy.

GOVERNMENT PUBLICATIONS:
Will Lend: Yes

DISSERTATIONS:
Do not own

THESES:
Do not own

AUDIO-VISUAL MATERIALS:
Records: Will not lend
Cassettes: Will not lend
Other (slides, filmstrips,
etc.): Will not lend

COMPUTER SOFTWARE:
Will Lend: No

PHOTODUPLICATION SERVICE:
No charge up to 0 exposures
Charge Per Exposure:
10¢ per page
Minimum/handling Fee: $2.00
Average Turnaround Time:
24 hours

MICROFILMING SERVICE:
Service Available: No
Charges: N/A

DO YOU CHARGE THE BORROWING LIBRARY
FOR POSTAGE? No

FOR HOW LONG DO YOU SUSPEND ILL
SERVICE OVER THE CHRISTMAS
HOLIDAYS? No suspension

ARE THERE ANY GROUPS OF LIBRARIES
FOR WHICH YOU WAIVE FEES? IF
SO, PLEASE NAME THEM: RLG
libraries; University of Utah
Law Library

SALT LAKE COUNTY LIBRARY SYSTEM

NUC CODE: UM

OCLC CODE: UUC

ADDRESS: Interlibrary Loan
    Salt Lake County
      Library System
    2197 East 7000 South
    Salt Lake City, UT
    84070

TELEPHONE: (801) 943-4636

LIST NAMES OF BRANCHES WITH
    SEPARATE POLICIES: (Not
    answered)

BOOKS:
    Will Lend: Yes
    Length of Loan: 4 weeks
    Renewable: No
    Charges: None
    Average Turnaround Time:
      1 week
    If you have indicated that a
      book is not to be lent, will
      you on receipt of a letter
      from the requesting library
      search the index for given
      entries? (Not answered)

PERIODICALS:
    Bound: N/A
    Unbound: Will lend
    Loan Period: 2 weeks
    Renewable: No
    Will lend if article exceeds
      _____ number of pages (Not
    answered)

MICROFORMS:
    Will Lend: Yes
    Specific Types of Microforms:
    35mm and 16 mm newspapers

GOVERNMENT PUBLICATIONS:
    Will Lend: Yes

DISSERTATIONS:
    N/A

THESES:
    N/A

AUDIO-VISUAL MATERIALS:
    Records: Will lend
    Cassettes: Will lend
    Other (slides, filmstrips,
      etc.): Will lend

COMPUTER SOFTWARE:
    Will Lend: No

PHOTODUPLICATION SERVICE:
    No charge up to 5 exposures
    Charge Per Exposure: 5¢
    Minimum/handling Fee: None
    Average Turnaround Time:
      1 week

MICROFILMING SERVICE:
    Service Available: No
    Charges: N/A

DO YOU CHARGE THE BORRWOING LIBRARY
    FOR POSTAGE? No

FOR HOW LONG DO YOU SUSPEND ILL
    SERVICE OVER THE CHRISTMAS
    HOLIDAYS? Not suspended

ARE THERE ANY GROUPS OF LIBRARIES
    FOR WHICH YOU WAIVE FEES? IF
    SO, PLEASE NAME THEM: (Not
    answered)

UNIVERSITY OF UTAH

NUC CODE: UU

OCLC CODE: UUM

ADDRESS: Interlibrary Loan
    University of Utah
      Libraries
    Salt Lake City, UT
    84112

TELEPHONE: (801) 581-6010

LIST NAMES OF BRANCHES WITH
    SEPARATE POLICIES: (Not
    answered)

BOOKS:
    Will Lend: Yes
    Length of Loan: 4 weeks use
    Renewable: No
    Charges: (Not answered)
    Average Turnaround Time:
      (Not answered)
    If you have indicated that a
      book is not to be lent, will
      you on receipt of a letter
      from the requesting library
      search the index for given
      entries? (Not answered)

PERIODICALS:
    Bound: Will not lend
    Unbound: Will not lend
    Loan Period: 1 week use
    Renewable: (Not answered)
    Will lend if article exceeds
    30 pages

MICROFORMS:
    Will Lend: Yes
    Specific Types of Microforms:
    (Not answered)

GOVERNMENT PUBLICATIONS:
    Will Lend: Yes

DISSERTATIONS:
    Will Lend: Yes; 1956 to
      present available from
      University Microfilms

THESES:
    Will Lend: Yes

AUDIO-VISUAL MATERIALS:
    Records: (Not answered)
    Cassettes: (Not answered)
    Other (slides, filmstrips,
      etc.): (Not answered)

COMPUTER SOFTWARE:
    Will Lend: (Not answered)

PHOTODUPLICATION SERVICE:
    No charge up to 0 exposures
    Charge Per Exposure: 15¢
    Minimum Fee: $1.00
    Average Turnaround Time:
      (Not answered)

MICROFILMING SERVICE:
    Service Available: Yes
    Charges: 15¢ per exposure;
      $10.00 minimum

DO YOU CHARGE THE BORROWING
    LIBRARY FOR POSTAGE? No

FOR HOW LONG DO YOU SUSPEND ILL
    SERVICE OVER THE CHRISTMAS
    HOLIDAYS? No suspension

ARE THERE ANY GROUPS OF LIBRARIES
    FOR WHICH YOU WAIVE FEES? IF
    SO, PLEASE NAME THEM: (Not
    answered)

UTAH STATE LIBRARY

NUC CODE: U

OCLC CODE: ULC

ADDRESS: Interlibrary Loan
Utah State Library
2150 South 300 West
Suite 16
Salt Lake City, UT
84115

TELEPHONE: (801) 533-5875

LIST NAMES OF BRANCHES WITH
SEPARATE POLICIES: N/A

BOOKS:
Will Lend: Yes
Length of Loan: 6 weeks
Renewable: No
Charges: No charge
Average Turnaround Time:
24 hours
If you have indicated that a
book is not to be lent, will
you on receipt of a letter
from the requesting library
search the index for given
entries? Yes

PERIODICALS:
Bound: Will not lend
Unbound: Will not lend
Loan Period: N/A
Renewable: N/A
Will lend if article exceeds
_____ number of pages (N/A)

MICROFORMS:
Will Lend: Yes
Specific Types of Microforms:
Federal and state documents

GOVERNMENT PUBLICATIONS:
Will Lend: Yes

DISSERTATIONS:
Will Lend: No

THESES:
Will Lend: No

AUDIO-VISUAL MATERIALS:
Records: Will not lend
Cassettes: Will not lend
Other (slides, filmstrips,
etc.): Will not lend

COMPUTER SOFTWARE:
Will Lend: No

PHOTODUPLICATION SERVICE:
No charge up to 0 exposures
Charge Per Exposure: 5¢ exposure
Minimum/handling Fee: None
Average Turnaround Time:
24 hours

MICROFILMING SERVICE:
Service Available: Yes
Charges: 25¢ per exposure

DO YOU CHARGE THE BORROWING LIBRARY
FOR POSTAGE? No

FOR HOW LONG DO YOU SUSPEND ILL
SERVICE OVER THE CHRISTMAS
HOLIDAYS? No suspension

ARE THERE ANY GROUPS OF LIBRARIES
FOR WHICH YOU WAIVE FEES? IF
SO, PLEASE NAME THEM: Utah
public libraries

UTAH STATE UNIVERSITY

NUC CODE: ULA

OCLC CODE: UUS

ADDRESS: Interlibrary Loan
Utah State University
Merrill Library
Logan, UT 84322

TELEPHONE: (801) 750-2637

LIST NAMES OF BRANCHES WITH
SEPARATE POLICIES: None

BOOKS:
Will Lend: Yes
Length of Loan: 2 weeks
Renewable: Yes
Charges: (Not answered)
Average Turnaround Time:
(Not answered)
If you have indicated that a
book is not to be lent, will
you on receipt of a letter
from the requesting library
search the index for given
entries? (Not answered)

PERIODICALS:
Bound: Will not lend
Unbound: Will not lend
Loan Period: N/A
Renewable: N/A
Will lend if article exceeds
_____ number of pages (Not
answered)

MICROFORMS:
Will Lend: (Not answered)
Specific Types of Microforms:
N/A

GOVERNMENT PUBLICATIONS:
Will Lend: (Not answered)

DISSERTATIONS:
Will Lend: Yes; 1959 to
present available from
University Microfilms

THESES:
Will Lend: Yes

AUDIO-VISUAL MATERIALS:
Records: (Not answered)
Cassettes: (Not answered)
Other (slides, filmstrips,
etc.): (Not answered)

COMPUTER SOFTWARE:
Will Lend: (Not answered)

PHOTODUPLICATION SERVICE:
No charge up to 0 exposures
Charge Per Exposure: 15¢
after first 20
Minimum Fee: $3.00 for 1-20
exposures
Average Turnaround Time:
(Not answered)

MICROFILMING SERVICE:
Service Available: Yes
Charges: (Not answered)

DO YOU CHARGE THE BORROWING
LIBRARY FOR POSTAGE? (Not
answered)

FOR HOW LONG DO YOU SUSPEND ILL
SERVICE OVER THE CHRISTMAS
HOLIDAYS? Suspend book
interlibrary loans only

ARE THERE ANY GROUPS OF LIBRARIES
FOR WHICH YOU WAIVE FEES? IF
SO, PLEASE NAME THEM: (Not
answered)

CASTLETON STATE COLLEGE

NUC CODE: (Not answered)

OCLC CODE: (Not answered)

ADDRESS: Interlibrary Loan
           Coolidge Library
           Castleton State College
           Castleton, VT 05735

TELEPHONE: (802) 468-5611

LIST NAMES OF BRANCHES WITH
  SEPARATE POLICIES: None

BOOKS:
  Will Lend: Yes
  Length of Loan: 1 month
  Renewable: No
  Charges: None
  Average Turnaround Time:
    (Not answered)
  If you have indicated that a
    book is not to be lent, will
    you on receipt of a letter
    from the requesting library
    search the index for given
    entries? (Not answered)

PERIODICALS:
  Bound: Will not lend
  Unbound: Will not lend
  Loan Period: N/A
  Renewable: N/A
  Will lend if article exceeds
    _____ number of pages (Not
    answered)

MICROFORMS:
  Will Lend: Yes
  Specific Types of Microforms:
    (Not answered)

GOVERNMENT PUBLICATIONS:
  Will Lend: Yes

DISSERTATIONS:
  Will Lend: Yes

THESES:
  Will Lend: Yes

AUDIO-VISUAL MATERIALS:
  Records: Will not lend
  Cassettes: Will not lend
  Other (slides, filmstrips,
    etc.): Will not lend

COMPUTER SOFTWARE:
  Will Lend: (Not answered)

PHOTODUPLICATION SERVICE:
  No charge up to any exposures
  Charge Per Exposure: None
  Minimum/handling Fee: None
  Average Turnaround Time:
    (Not answered)

MICROFILMING SERVICE:
  Service Available: No
  Charges: N/A

DO YOU CHARGE THE BORROWING
  LIBRARY FOR POSTAGE? No

FOR HOW LONG DO YOU SUSPEND ILL
  SERVICE OVER THE CHRISTMAS
  HOLIDAYS? 2 weeks

ARE THERE ANY GROUPS OF LIBRARIES
  FOR WHICH YOU WAIVE FEES? IF
  SO, PLEASE NAME THEM: None

GODDARD COLLEGE

NUC CODE: (Not answered)

OCLC CODE: (Not answered)

ADDRESS: Interlibrary Loan
           Goddard College Library
           Plainfield, VT 05602

TELEPHONE: (802) 454-8311, X15

LIST NAMES OF BRANCHES WITH
  SEPARATE POLICIES: None

BOOKS:
  Will Lend: Yes
  Length of Loan: 3 weeks
  Renewable: Yes, sometimes
  Charges: None
  Average Turnaround Time:
    1 week
  If you have indicated that a
    book is not to be lent, will
    you on receipt of a letter
    from the requesting library
    search the index for given
    entries? (Not answered)

PERIODICALS:
  Bound: Will not lend
  Unbound: Will not lend
  Loan Period: N/A
  Renewable: N/A
  Will lend if article exceeds
    _____ number of pages (Will
    copy if only 2-3 pages at
    no cost; longer articles
    at 20¢ per page

MICROFORMS:
  Will Lend: No
  Specific Types of Microforms:
    N/A

GOVERNMENT PUBLICATIONS:
  Will Lend: No

DISSERTATIONS:
  Will Lend: No. Must have
    written permission from
    author for photocopy (30¢
    per page)

THESES:
  Will Lend: No. Must have
    written permission from
    author for photocopy (30¢
    per page)

AUDIO-VISUAL MATERIALS:
  Records: Will not lend
  Cassettes: Will not lend
  Other (slides, filmstrips,
    etc.): Will not lend

COMPUTER SOFTWARE:
  Will Lend: No

PHOTODUPLICATION SERVICE:
  No charge up to 0 exposures
  Charge Per Exposure: 20¢
  Minimum/handling Fee: None
  Average Turnaround Time:
    1 week

MICROFILMING SERVICE:
  Service Available: No
  Charges: N/A

DO YOU CHARGE THE BORROWING
  LIBRARY FOR POSTAGE? Not
    unless very expensive

FOR HOW LONG DO YOU SUSPEND ILL
  SERVICE OVER THE CHRISTMAS
  HOLIDAYS? 2 weeks

ARE THERE ANY GROUPS OF LIBRARIES
  FOR WHICH YOU WAIVE FEES? IF
  SO, PLEASE NAME THEM: None

JOHNSON STATE COLLEGE

NUC CODE: (Not answered)

OCLC CODE: (Not answered)

ADDRESS: Interlibrary Loan
John Dewey Library
Johnson State College
Johnson, VT 05656

TELEPHONE: (802) 635-2356, X247

LIST NAMES OF BRANCHES WITH
SEPARATE POLICIES: None

BOOKS:
Will Lend: Yes
Length of Loan: 3 weeks
Renewable: No
Charges: Postage
Average Turnaround Time:
(Not answered)
If you have indicated that a
book is not to be lent, will
you on receipt of a letter
from the requesting library
search the index for given
entries? (Not answered)

PERIODICALS:
Bound: Will not lend
Unbound: Will not lend
Loan Period: N/A
Renewable: N/A
Will lend if article exceeds
_____ number of pages (Not
answered)

MICROFORMS:
Will Lend: No, but will make
photocopies
Specific Types of Microforms:
N/A

GOVERNMENT PUBLICATIONS:
Will Lend: Yes

DISSERTATIONS:
Will Lend: No

THESES:
Will Lend: No

AUDIO-VISUAL MATERIALS:
Records: Will not lend
Cassettes: Will not lend
Other (slides, filmstrips,
etc.): Will not lend

COMPUTER SOFTWARE:
Will Lend: No

PHOTODUPLICATION SERVICE:
No charge up to 8 exposures
Charge Per Exposure: 10¢
Minimum/handling Fee: None
Average Turnaround Time:
(Not answered)

MICROFILMING SERVICE:
Service Available: No
Charges: N/A

DO YOU CHARGE THE BORROWING
LIBRARY FOR POSTAGE? Yes

FOR HOW LONG DO YOU SUSPEND ILL
SERVICE OVER THE CHRISTMAS
HOLIDAYS? 2 weeks

ARE THERE ANY GROUPS OF LIBRARIES
FOR WHICH YOU WAIVE FEES? IF
SO, PLEASE NAME THEM: Lyndon
State College; Vermont Tech-
nical; Castleton State; and
University of Vermont

MIDDLEBURY COLLEGE

NUC CODE: VtMiM

OCLC CODE: MDY

ADDRESS: Interlibrary Loan
Middlebury College
Library
Middlebury, VT 05753

TELEPHONE: (802) 388-3711,
X2498 or X2497

LIST NAMES OF BRANCHES WITH
SEPARATE POLICIES: None

BOOKS:
Will Lend: Yes
Length of Loan: 4 weeks
Renewable: Very rarely
Charges: None
Average Turnaround Time:
2 days
If you have indicated that a
book is not to be lent, will
you on receipt of a letter
from the requesting library
search the index for given
entries? (Not answered)

PERIODICALS:
Bound: Will lend only if
article over 40 pages or
is too tight to duplicate
Unbound: Will not lend
Loan Period: 2 weeks
Renewable: No

MICROFORMS:
Will Lend: Yes
Specific Types of Microforms:
Reels, 4-6 at one time

GOVERNMENT PUBLICATIONS:
Will Lend: Yes

DISSERTATIONS:
Will Lend: No

THESES:
Will Lend: No

AUDIO-VISUAL MATERIALS:
Records: Will not lend
Cassettes: Will not lend
Other (slides, filmstrips,
etc.): Will not lend

COMPUTER SOFTWARE:
Will Lend: No

PHOTODUPLICATION SERVICE:
No charge up to 9 exposures
Charge Per Exposure: 10¢
after 1st 9
Minimum/handling Fee: None
Average Turnaround Time:
3 days

MICROFILMING SERVICE:
Service Available: No
Charges: N/A

DO YOU CHARGE THE BORROWING
LIBRARY FOR POSTAGE? No

FOR HOW LONG DO YOU SUSPEND ILL
SERVICE OVER THE CHRISTMAS
HOLIDAYS? Dec.15-Jan.3

ARE THERE ANY GROUPS OF LIBRARIES
FOR WHICH YOU WAIVE FEES? IF
SO, PLEASE NAME THEM: None

NORWICH UNIVERSITY

NUC CODE: VtNN

OCLC CODE: (Not answered)

ADDRESS: Interlibrary Loan
Norwich University
Library
Northfield, VT 05663

TELEPHONE: (802) 485-5011, X248

LIST NAMES OF BRANCHES WITH
SEPARATE POLICIES: None

BOOKS:
Will Lend: Yes
Length of Loan: 4 weeks
Renewable: Yes
Charges: (Not answered)
Average Turnaround Time:
(Not answered)
If you have indicated that a
book is not to be lent, will
you on receipt of a letter
from the requesting library
search the index for given
entries? (Not answered)

PERIODICALS:
Bound: (Not answered)
Unbound: (Not answered)
Loan Period: 4 weeks
Renewable: (Not answered)
Will lend if article exceeds
50 pages

MICROFORMS:
Will Lend: Yes
Specific Types of Microforms:
Cards, film, fiche

GOVERNMENT PUBLICATIONS:
Will Lend: Yes

DISSERTATIONS:
Will Lend: Yes

THESES:
Will Lend: Yes

AUDIO-VISUAL MATERIALS:
Records: Will lend
Cassettes: Will lend
Other (slides, filmstrips,
etc.): (Not answered)

COMPUTER SOFTWARE:
Will Lend: (Not answered)

PHOTODUPLICATION SERVICE:
No charge up to 10 exposures
Charge Per Exposure: 10¢
Minimum/handling Fee: None
Average Turnaround Time:
(Not answered)

MICROFILMING SERVICE:
Service Available: No
Charges: N/A

DO YOU CHARGE THE BORROWING
LIBRARY FOR POSTAGE? No

FOR HOW LONG DO YOU SUSPEND ILL
SERVICE OVER THE CHRISTMAS
HOLIDAYS? No suspension

ARE THERE ANY GROUPS OF LIBRARIES
FOR WHICH YOU WAIVE FEES? IF
SO, PLEASE NAME THEM: None

ST. MICHAEL'S COLLEGE

NUC CODE: VtWinos

OCLC CODE: SMD

ADDRESS: Interlibrary Loan
St. Michael's College
Library
College Parkway
Winooski, VT 05401

TELEPHONE: (801) 655-2000, X2405

LIST NAMES OF BRANCHES WITH
SEPARATE POLICIES: None

BOOKS:
Will Lend: Yes
Length of Loan: 1 month
usually
Renewable: Yes
Charges: None at present
Average Turnaround Time:
A few days
If you have indicated that a
book is not to be lent, will
you on receipt of a letter
from the requesting library
search the index for given
entries? (Not answered)

PERIODICALS:
Bound: Will lend
Unbound: Will lend
Loan Period: Varies 1 week to
1 month, depending on
materials wanted
Renewable: Yes
Will lend if article exceeds
_____ number of pages (Not
answered)

MICROFORMS:
Will Lend: Yes
Specific Types of Microforms:
N/A

GOVERNMENT PUBLICATIONS:
Will Lend: Yes

DISSERTATIONS:
Will Lend: Yes

THESES:
Will Lend: Yes

AUDIO-VISUAL MATERIALS:
Records: Will lend
Cassettes: Will lend
Other (slides, filmstrips,
etc.): Will lend

COMPUTER SOFTWARE:
Will Lend: Do not own

PHOTODUPLICATION SERVICE:
No charge up to 0 exposures
Charge Per Exposure: 10¢
Minimum/handling Fee: $1.00
Average Turnaround Time:
A few days

MICROFILMING SERVICE:
Service Available: Yes
Charges: 10¢ to 25¢,
depending on size of order
and our costs

DO YOU CHARGE THE BORROWING
LIBRARY FOR POSTAGE? Not
usually

FOR HOW LONG DO YOU SUSPEND ILL
SERVICE OVER THE CHRISTMAS
HOLIDAYS? Week before
Thanksgiving through first
week of January

ARE THERE ANY GROUPS OF LIBRARIES
FOR WHICH YOU WAIVE FEES? IF
SO, PLEASE NAME THEM: None

UNIVERSITY OF VERMONT

NUC CODE: VtU

OCLC CODE: VTU

ADDRESS: Interlibrary Loan
Bailey/Howe Library
University of Vermont
Burlington, VT 05405

TELEPHONE: (802) 656-2020

LIST NAMES OF BRANCHES WITH
SEPARATE POLICIES:
Dana Medical Library

BOOKS:
Will Lend: Yes
Length of Loan: 2 weeks use
Renewable: Yes
Charges: Reciprocal
Average Turnaround Time:
1-2 days
If you have indicated that a
book is not to be lent, will
you on receipt of a letter
from the requesting library
search the index for given
entries? (Not answered)

PERIODICALS:
Bound: Will not lend
Unbound: Will not lend
Loan Period: N/A
Renewable: N/A
Will lend if article exceeds
_____ number of pages (Not
answered)

MICROFORMS:
Will Lend: Yes
Specific Types of Microforms:
Will lend all types

GOVERNMENT PUBLICATIONS:
Will Lend: Yes

DISSERTATIONS:
Will Lend: Yes

THESES:
Will Lend: Yes

AUDIO-VISUAL MATERIALS:
Records: Will not lend
Cassettes: Will not lend
Other (slides, filmstrips,
etc.): Will not lend

COMPUTER SOFTWARE:
Will Lend: No

PHOTODUPLICATION SERVICE:
No charge up to 0 exposures
Charge Per Exposure: 10¢
Minimum Fee: $1.25
Handling Fee: 25¢
Average Turnaround Time:
2-3 days

MICROFILMING SERVICE:
Service Available: No
Charges: N/A

DO YOU CHARGE THE BORROWING
LIBRARY FOR POSTAGE? Only if
special mailing required

FOR HOW LONG DO YOU SUSPEND ILL
SERVICE OVER THE CHRISTMAS
HOLIDAYS? Mid Dec.-Jan.2

ARE THERE ANY GROUPS OF LIBRARIES
FOR WHICH YOU WAIVE FEES? IF
SO, PLEASE NAME THEM: None

UNIVERSITY OF VERMONT -- HEALTH SCIENCE COMPLEX

NUC CODE: (Not answered)

OCLC CODE: VTM

ADDRESS: Interlibrary Loan
Dana Medical Library
Health Science Complex
University of Vermont
Burlington, VT 05405

TELEPHONE: (802) 656-2200

LIST NAMES OF BRANCHES WITH
SEPARATE POLICIES: None

BOOKS:
Will Lend: Yes
Length of Loan: 3 weeks
Renewable: No
Charges: $5.00
Average Turnaround Time:
Same day
If you have indicated that a
book is not to be lent, will
you on receipt of a letter
from the requesting library
search the index for given
entries? Yes

PERIODICALS:
Bound: Will not lend
Unbound: Will not lend
Loan Period: N/A
Renewable: N/A
Will lend if article exceeds
_____ number of pages (Not
answered)

MICROFORMS:
Will Lend: No
Specific Types of Microforms:
N/A

GOVERNMENT PUBLICATIONS:
Will Lend: Yes

DISSERTATIONS:
Will Lend: Available from
University Microfilms

THESES:
Will Lend: Yes. Request
directly from University
of Vermont Archives

AUDIO-VISUAL MATERIALS:
Records: (Not answered)
Cassettes: (Not answered)
Other (slides, filmstrips,
etc.): (Not answered)

COMPUTER SOFTWARE:
Will Lend: (Not answered)

PHOTODUPLICATION SERVICE:
No charge up to 0 exposures
Charge Per Exposure: (Not
answered)
Minimum/handling Fee: $5.00
Average Turnaround Time:
(Not answered)

DO YOU CHARGE THE BORROWING
LIBRARY FOR POSTAGE? (Not
answered)

MICROFILMING SERVICE:
Service Available: No
Charges: N/A

FOR HOW LONG DO YOU SUSPEND ILL
SERVICE OVER THE CHRISTMAS
HOLIDAYS? No suspension

ARE THERE ANY GROUPS OF LIBRARIES
FOR WHICH YOU WAIVE FEES? IF
SO, PLEASE NAME THEM: Only by
reciprocal agreement

ALEXANDRIA LIBRARY

NUC CODE: ViAL

OCLC CODE: VAX

ADDRESS: Interlibrary Loan
Alexandria Library
717 Queen St.
Alexandria, VA 22314

TELEPHONE: (703) 838-4556

LIST NAMES OF BRANCHES WITH
SEPARATE POLICIES: None

BOOKS:
Will Lend: Yes, if
circulating
Length of Loan: 21 days
Renewable: Yes
Charges: None
Average Turnaround Time:
10 days
If you have indicated that a
book is not to be lent, will
you on receipt of a letter
from the requesting library
search the index for given
entries? (Not answered)

PERIODICALS:
Bound: Will not lend
Unbound: Will not lend
Loan Period: N/A
Renewable: N/A
Will lend if article exceeds
_____ number of pages (Not
answered)

MICROFORMS:
Will Lend: No
Specific Types of Microforms:
N/A

GOVERNMENT PUBLICATIONS:
Will Lend: No

DISSERTATIONS:
Will Lend: Do not own

THESES:
Will Lend: Do not own

AUDIO-VISUAL MATERIALS:
Records: Will not lend
Cassettes: Will not lend
Other (slides, filmstrips,
etc.): Will not lend

COMPUTER SOFTWARE:
Will Lend: No

PHOTODUPLICATION SERVICE:
No charge up to 10 exposures
Charge Per Exposure: 10¢
Minimum/handling Fee: $1.00
Average Turnaround Time:
10 days

MICROFILMING SERVICE:
Service Available: No
Charges: N/A

DO YOU CHARGE THE BORROWING
LIBRARY FOR POSTAGE? No

FOR HOW LONG DO YOU SUSPEND ILL
SERVICE OVER THE CHRISTMAS
HOLIDAYS? 2 weeks

ARE THERE ANY GROUPS OF LIBRARIES
FOR WHICH YOU WAIVE FEES? IF
SO, PLEASE NAME THEM: None

ARLINGTON COUNTY PUBLIC LIBRARY

NUC CODE: (Not answered)

OCLC CODE: VIA

ADDRESS: Interlibrary Loan
Arlington County Public
Library
1015 N. Quincy St.
Arlington, VA 22201

TELEPHONE: (703) 527-4777, X58

LIST NAMES OF BRANCHES WITH
SEPARATE POLICIES: None

BOOKS:
Will Lend: Yes
Length of Loan: 3 weeks
Renewable: Yes
Charges: None
Average Turnaround Time:
1 week
If you have indicated that a
book is not to be lent, will
you on receipt of a letter
from the requesting library
search the index for given
entries? Yes, particularly
for books on our Virginia
collection

PERIODICALS:
Bound: Will not lend
Unbound: Will lend if owned
by a branch
Loan Period: 3 weeks
Renewable: Yes
Will lend if article exceeds
_____ number of pages (Not
answered)

MICROFORMS:
Will Lend: No
Specific Types of Microforms:
N/A

GOVERNMENT PUBLICATIONS:
Will Lend: Yes, if cataloged
and circulating

DISSERTATIONS:
Will Lend: Do not own

THESES:
Will Lend: Do not own

AUDIO-VISUAL MATERIALS:
Records: Will not lend
Cassettes: Will not lend
Other (slides, filmstrips,
etc.): Will not lend

COMPUTER SOFTWARE:
Will Lend: Do not own

PHOTODUPLICATION SERVICE:
No charge up to 0 exposures
Charge Per Exposure: 15¢ for
xerox; 15¢ for microfilm
Minimum/handling Fee: None
Average Turnaround Time:
1 week

MICROFILMING SERVICE:
Service Available: No
Charges: N/A

DO YOU CHARGE THE BORROWING
LIBRARY FOR POSTAGE? No

FOR HOW LONG DO YOU SUSPEND ILL
SERVICE OVER THE CHRISTMAS
HOLIDAYS? No suspension

ARE THERE ANY GROUPS OF LIBRARIES
FOR WHICH YOU WAIVE FEES? IF
SO, PLEASE NAME THEM: Local
area public libraries

COLLEGE OF WILLIAM AND MARY

NUC CODE: ViW

OCLC CODE: VWM

ADDRESS: Interlibrary Loan
Earl Gregg Swem
Library
College of William and
Mary
Williamsburg, VA 23185

TELEPHONE: (804) 253-4162

LIST NAMES OF BRANCHES WITH
SEPARATE POLICIES:
Virginia Institute of Marine
Science (VIMS)
Virginia Associated Research
Center (VARC)
Law Library, Marshall Wythe
School of Law

BOOKS:
Will Lend: Yes
Length of Loan: 3 weeks use
Renewable: Yes
Charges: None
Average Turnaround Time:
2 days
If you have indicated that a
book is not to be lent, will
you on receipt of a letter
from the requesting library
search the index for given
entries? (Not answered)

PERIODICALS:
Bound: Will not lend
Unbound: Will not lend
Loan Period: N/A
Renewable: N/A
Will lend if article exceeds
_____ number of pages (Not
answered)

MICROFORMS:
Will Lend: Yes, some of them
Specific Types of Microforms:
Any

GOVERNMENT PUBLICATIONS:
Will Lend: Yes

DISSERTATIONS:
Will Lend: Yes, if 2nd copy
available

THESES:
Will Lend: Yes, if 2nd copy
available

AUDIO-VISUAL MATERIALS:
Records: Will not lend
Cassettes: Will not lend
Other (slides, filmstrips,
etc.): Will not lend

COMPUTER SOFTWARE:
Will Lend: No

PHOTODUPLICATION SERVICE:
No charge up to 10 exposures
Charge Per Exposure: 15¢
Minimum/handling Fee: $2.00
after 10 exposures for over
30 exposures
Average Turnaround Time:
3 days

MICROFILMING SERVICE:
Service Available: No
Charges: N/A

DO YOU CHARGE THE BORROWING
LIBRARY FOR POSTAGE? No

FOR HOW LONG DO YOU SUSPEND ILL
SERVICE OVER THE CHRISTMAS
HOLIDAYS? About 2 weeks

ARE THERE ANY GROUPS OF LIBRARIES
FOR WHICH YOU WAIVE FEES? IF
SO, PLEASE NAME THEM:
Virginia libraries

COLLEGE OF WILLIAM AND MARY--SCHOOL OF LAW

NUC CODE: (Not answered)

OCLC CODE: VWL

ADDRESS: Interlibrary Loan
Marshall-Wythe Law
Library
College of William and
Mary
Williamsburg, VA
23185

TELEPHONE: (804) 253-4428

LIST NAMES OF BRANCHES WITH
SEPARATE POLICIES: None

BOOKS:
Will Lend: Yes
Length of Loan: 1 month
Renewable: Yes
Charges: None
Average Turnaround Time:
7-10 days
If you have indicated that a
book is not to be lent, will
you on receipt of a letter
from the requesting library
search the index for given
entries? Yes

PERIODICALS:
Bound: Will not lend
Unbound: Will not lend
Loan Period: N/A
Renewable: N/A
Will lend if article exceeds
_____ number of pages (Not
answered)

MICROFORMS:
Will Lend: Yes, at our
discretion
Specific Types of Microforms:
(Not answered)

GOVERNMENT PUBLICATIONS:
Will Lend: Yes

DISSERTATIONS:
Will Lend: Do not own

THESES:
Will Lend: Do not own

AUDIO-VISUAL MATERIALS:
Records: Will not lend
Cassettes: Will not lend
Other (slides, filmstrips,
etc.): Will not lend

COMPUTER SOFTWARE:
Will Lend: Do not own

PHOTODUPLICATION SERVICE:
No charge up to 0 exposures
Charge Per Exposure: 15¢
Minimum/handling Fee: $1.00/
$1.00
Average Turnaround Time:
3 days

MICROFILMING SERVICE:
Service Available: Yes
Charges: 20¢ per copy

DO YOU CHARGE THE BORROWING
LIBRARY FOR POSTAGE? No

FOR HOW LONG DO YOU SUSPEND ILL
SERVICE OVER THE CHRISTMAS
HOLIDAYS? App. 10 days

ARE THERE ANY GROUPS OF LIBRARIES
FOR WHICH YOU WAIVE FEES? IF
SO, PLEASE NAME THEM: None

FAIRFAX COUNTY PUBLIC LIBRARY

NUC CODE: (Not answered)

OCLC CODE: (Not answered)

ADDRESS: Interlibrary Loan
Fairfax County Public
Library
3915 Chain Bridge Rd.
Fairfax, VA   22030

TELEPHONE: (703) 691-2741

LIST NAMES OF BRANCHES WITH
SEPARATE POLICIES: None--
centralized ILL for
entire library system

BOOKS:
Will Lend: Yes
Length of Loan: 3 weeks
Renewable: Yes, by prior
permission
Charges: None
Average Turnaround Time:
(Not answered)
If you have indicated that a
book is not to be lent, will
you on receipt of a letter
from the requesting library
search the index for given
entries? Yes

PERIODICALS:
Bound: Will not lend
Unbound: Will lend
Loan Period: 3 weeks
Renewable: Yes, by prior
permission
Will lend if article exceeds
_____ number of pages (Not
answered)

MICROFORMS:
Will Lend: No
Specific Types of Microforms:
N/A

GOVERNMENT PUBLICATIONS:
Will Lend: Yes, but are not
extensive in FCPL collection

DISSERTATIONS:
Will Lend: Yes

THESES:
Will Lend: Yes

AUDIO-VISUAL MATERIALS:
Records: Will not lend
Cassettes: Will not lend
Other (slides, filmstrips,
etc.): Will not lend

COMPUTER SOFTWARE:
Will Lend: No

PHOTODUPLICATION SERVICE:
No charge up to 10 exposures
Charge Per Exposure: 10¢
Minimum/handling Fee: $1.00
Average Turnaround Time:
1 week

MICROFILMING SERVICE:
Service Available: No
Charges: N/A

DO YOU CHARGE THE BORROWING
LIBRARY FOR POSTAGE? No

FOR HOW LONG DO YOU SUSPEND ILL
SERVICE OVER THE CHRISTMAS
HOLIDAYS? No suspension

ARE THERE ANY GROUPS OF LIBRARIES
FOR WHICH YOU WAIVE FEES? IF
SO, PLEASE NAME THEM: Members
of Metropolitan Washington
Council of Governments

GEORGE MASON UNIVERSITY

NUC CODE: ViFGM

OCLC CODE: VGM

ADDRESS: Interlibrary Loan
George Mason University
Library
4400 University Dr.
Fairfax, VA   22030

TELEPHONE: (703) 323-2395

LIST NAMES OF BRANCHES WITH
SEPARATE POLICIES:
Law School Library

BOOKS:
Will Lend: Yes
Length of Loan: 4 weeks
from date sent
Renewable: Yes
Charges: None
Average Turnaround Time:
4 days
If you have indicated that a
book is not to be lent, will
you on receipt of a letter
from the requesting library
search the index for given
entries? (Not answered)

PERIODICALS:
Bound: Will not lend
Unbound: Will not lend
Loan Period: N/A
Renewable: N/A
Will lend if article exceeds
_____ number of pages (Will
not lend, regardless of
length of article)

MICROFORMS:
Will Lend: Yes, selectively
Specific Types of Microforms:
ERIC fiche

GOVERNMENT PUBLICATIONS:
Will Lend: Yes

DISSERTATIONS:
Will Lend: Yes

THESES:
Will Lend: Yes

AUDIO-VISUAL MATERIALS:
Records: Will not lend
Cassettes: Will lend
Other (slides, filmstrips,
etc.): Will not lend

COMPUTER SOFTWARE:
Will Lend: No

PHOTODUPLICATION SERVICE:
No charge up to 2 exposures
Charge Per Exposure: 10¢
Minimum/handling Fee: $1.50/
$1.00
Average Turnaround Time:
6 days

MICROFILMING SERVICE:
Service Available: Yes
Charges: Depends on document

DO YOU CHARGE THE BORROWING
LIBRARY FOR POSTAGE? Only
for special handling

FOR HOW LONG DO YOU SUSPEND ILL
SERVICE OVER THE CHRISTMAS
HOLIDAYS? Dec.15-Jan.2

ARE THERE ANY GROUPS OF LIBRARIES
FOR WHICH YOU WAIVE FEES? IF
SO, PLEASE NAME THEM: Local
hospital libraries and
members of the Consortium
for Continuing Higher
Education in Northern
Virginia.

INSTITUTE OF TEXTILE TECHNOLOGY

NUC CODE: (Not answered)

OCLC CODE: (Not answered)

ADDRESS: Interlibrary Loan
Roger Milliken Textile
Library
Institute of Textile
Technology
P. O. Box 391
Charlottesville, VA
22902

TELEPHONE: (804) 296-5511

LIST NAMES OF BRANCHES WITH
SEPARATE POLICIES: None

BOOKS:
Will Lend: Yes
Length of Loan: 2 weeks
Renewable: No
Charges: (Not answered)
Average Turnaround Time:
1 day
If you have indicated that a
book is not to be lent, will
you on receipt of a letter
from the requesting library
search the index for given
entries? (Not answered)

PERIODICALS:
Bound: Will not lend
Unbound: Will not lend
Loan Period: N/A
Renewable: N/A
Will lend if article exceeds
_____ number of pages (Not
answered)

MICROFORMS:
Will Lend: No
Specific Types of Microforms:
N/A

GOVERNMENT PUBLICATIONS:
Will Lend: No

DISSERTATIONS:
Will Lend: Yes

THESES:
Will Lend: Yes

AUDIO-VISUAL MATERIALS:
Records: (Not answered)
Cassettes: (Not answered)
Other (slides, filmstrips,
etc.): Will lend

COMPUTER SOFTWARE:
Will Lend: No

PHOTODUPLICATION SERVICE:
No charge up to 0 exposures
Charge Per Exposure: 60¢
Minimum/handling Fee: 50¢
Average Turnaround Time:
1 day

MICROFILMING SERVICE:
Service Available: No
Charges: N/A

DO YOU CHARGE THE BORROWING
LIBRARY FOR POSTAGE? Yes

FOR HOW LONG DO YOU SUSPEND ILL
SERVICE OVER THE CHRISTMAS
HOLIDAYS? No suspension

ARE THERE ANY GROUPS OF LIBRARIES
FOR WHICH YOU WAIVE FEES? IF
SO, PLEASE NAME THEM: None

JAMES MADISON UNIVERSITY

NUC CODE: ViHart

OCLC CODE: VMC

ADDRESS: Interlibrary Loan
Madison Memorial
Library
James Madison
University
Harrisonburg, VA   22807

TELEPHONE: (703) 433-6150

LIST NAMES OF BRANCHES WITH
SEPARATE POLICIES: None

BOOKS:
Will Lend: Yes
Length of Loan: 3 weeks
Renewable: Yes
Charges: None
Average Turnaround Time:
2 days
If you have indicated that a
book is not to be lent, will
you on receipt of a letter
from the requesting library
search the index for given
entries? (Not answered)

PERIODICALS:
Bound: Yes, selectively
Unbound: Will not lend
Loan Period: 1 week
Renewable: No
Will lend if article exceeds
_____ number of pages (Not
answered)

MICROFORMS:
Will Lend: Yes
Specific Types of Microforms:
Microcards, microfiche,
microfilm

GOVERNMENT PUBLICATIONS:
Will Lend: Yes

DISSERTATIONS:
Will Lend: No

THESES:
Will Lend: Yes

AUDIO-VISUAL MATERIALS:
Records: Will lend
Cassettes: Will lend
Other (slides, filmstrips,
etc.): Will lend

COMPUTER SOFTWARE:
Will Lend: No

PHOTODUPLICATION SERVICE:
No charge up to 34 exposures
Charge Per Exposure: 10¢
Minimum/handling Fee: None
Average Turnaround Time:
2 days

MICROFILMING SERVICE:
Service Available: No
Charges: N/A

DO YOU CHARGE THE BORROWING
LIBRARY FOR POSTAGE? No

FOR HOW LONG DO YOU SUSPEND ILL
SERVICE OVER THE CHRISTMAS
HOLIDAYS? 1 week before
Christmas-Jan.2

ARE THERE ANY GROUPS OF LIBRARIES
FOR WHICH YOU WAIVE FEES? IF
SO, PLEASE NAME THEM: None

JEFFERSON-MADISON REGIONAL LIBRARY

NUC CODE: (Not answered)

OCLC CODE: (Not answered)

ADDRESS: Interlibrary Loan
            Jefferson-Madison
              Regional Library
            201 E. Market St.
            Charlottesville, VA
              22901

TELEPHONE: (804) 979-7151

LIST NAMES OF BRANCHES WITH
  SEPARATE POLICIES: None

BOOKS:
  Will Lend: Yes
  Length of Loan: 3 weeks
  Renewable: Yes, for
    3 weeks
  Charges: Postage
  Average Turnaround Time:
    1 day
  If you have indicated that a
    book is not to be lent, will
    you on receipt of a letter
    from the requesting library
    search the index for given
    entries? Yes

PERIODICALS:
  Bound: Will not lend
  Unbound: Will not lend
  Loan Period: N/A
  Renewable: N/A
  Will lend if article exceeds
    _____ number of pages (Not
    answered)

MICROFORMS:
  Will Lend: No
  Specific Types of Microforms:
    N/A

GOVERNMENT PUBLICATIONS:
  Will Lend: No

DISSERTATIONS:
  Will Lend: No

THESES:
  Will Lend: No

AUDIO-VISUAL MATERIALS:
  Records: Will not lend
  Cassettes: Will not lend
  Other (slides, filmstrips,
    etc.): Will not lend

COMPUTER SOFTWARE:
  Will Lend: No

PHOTODUPLICATION SERVICE:
  No charge up to 0 exposures
  Charge Per Exposure: 25¢
  Minimum/handling Fee: None
  Average Turnaround Time:
    1 day

MICROFILMING SERVICE:
  Service Available: Yes
  Charges: 25¢ per page

DO YOU CHARGE THE BORROWING
  LIBRARY FOR POSTAGE? Yes

FOR HOW LONG DO YOU SUSPEND ILL
  SERVICE OVER THE CHRISTMAS
  HOLIDAYS? No suspension

ARE THERE ANY GROUPS OF LIBRARIES
  FOR WHICH YOU WAIVE FEES? IF
  SO, PLEASE NAME THEM: None

NEWPORT NEWS PUBLIC LIBRARY SYSTEM

NUC CODE: (Not answered)

OCLC CODE: (Not answered)

ADDRESS: Interlibrary Loan
            Newport News Public
              Library System
            Virgil I. Grissom
              Branch Library
            366 DeShazor Dr.
            Newport News, VA 23602

TELEPHONE: (804) 877-0111

LIST NAMES OF BRANCHES WITH
  SEPARATE POLICIES: None

BOOKS:
  Will Lend: Yes
  Length of Loan: 4 weeks
  Renewable: Yes
  Charges: (Not answered)
  Average Turnaround Time:
    1 day
  If you have indicated that a
    book is not to be lent, will
    you on receipt of a letter
    from the requesting library
    search the index for given
    entries? Yes, within
    reason

PERIODICALS:
  Bound: Will not lend
  Unbound: Will not lend
  Loan Period: N/A
  Renewable: N/A
  Will lend if article exceeds
    _____ number of pages (Not
    answered)

MICROFORMS:
  Will Lend: No
  Specific Types of Microforms:
    N/A

GOVERNMENT PUBLICATIONS:
  Will Lend: Yes, if cataloged

DISSERTATIONS:
  Will Lend: Do not own

THESES:
  Will Lend: Do not own

AUDIO-VISUAL MATERIALS:
  Records: Will not lend
  Cassettes: Will not lend
  Other (slides, filmstrips,
    etc.): Will not lend

COMPUTER SOFTWARE:
  Will Lend: Do not own

PHOTODUPLICATION SERVICE:
  No charge up to 0 exposures
  Charge Per Exposure: 15¢
  Minimum/handling Fee: $1.00
    plus copy charges
  Average Turnaround Time:
    2 days

MICROFILMING SERVICE:
  Service Available: No
  Charges: N/A

DO YOU CHARGE THE BORROWING
  LIBRARY FOR POSTAGE? Yes

FOR HOW LONG DO YOU SUSPEND ILL
  SERVICE OVER THE CHRISTMAS
  HOLIDAYS? No suspension

ARE THERE ANY GROUPS OF LIBRARIES
  FOR WHICH YOU WAIVE FEES? IF
  SO, PLEASE NAME THEM: Tide-
  water public libraries (12)

NORFOLK PUBLIC LIBRARY

NUC CODE: VIN

OCLC CODE: None

ADDRESS: Interlibrary Loan
Norfolk Public Library
301 E. City Hall Ave.
Norfolk, VA 23510

TELEPHONE: (804) 441-2173 or
441-2174

LIST NAMES OF BRANCHES WITH
SEPARATE POLICIES: None

BOOKS:
Will Lend: Yes
Length of Loan: 4 weeks
Renewable: Sometimes
Charges: No charges unless
insured
Average Turnaround Time:
3 days
If you have indicated that a
book is not to be lent, will
you on receipt of a letter
from the requesting library
search the index for given
entries? (Not answered)

PERIODICALS:
Bound: Will not lend
Unbound: Will not lend
Loan Period: N/A
Renewable: N/A
Will lend if article exceeds
_____ number of pages (Not
answered)

MICROFORMS:
Will Lend: No
Specific Types of Microforms:
N/A

GOVERNMENT PUBLICATIONS:
Will Lend: No

DISSERTATIONS:
Will Lend: No

THESES:
Will Lend: No

AUDIO-VISUAL MATERIALS:
Records: (Not answered)
Cassettes: (Not answered)
Other (slides, filmstrips,
etc.): Will sometimes lend
slides and filmstrips

COMPUTER SOFTWARE:
Will Lend: No

PHOTODUPLICATION SERVICE:
No charge up to 0 exposures
Charge Per Exposure: 15¢
Minimum/handling Fee: 25¢
Average Turnaround Time:
1 week

MICROFILMING SERVICE:
Service Available: No
Charges: N/A

DO YOU CHARGE THE BORROWING
LIBRARY FOR POSTAGE? Area
libraries only

FOR HOW LONG DO YOU SUSPEND ILL
SERVICE OVER THE CHRISTMAS
HOLIDAYS? No suspension

ARE THERE ANY GROUPS OF LIBRARIES
FOR WHICH YOU WAIVE FEES? IF
SO, PLEASE NAME THEM: None

NORFOLK STATE UNIVERSITY

NUC CODE: Not listed

OCLC CODE: VNS

ADDRESS: Interlibrary Loan
Norfolk State
University
Lyman Beecher Brooks
Library
Norfolk, VA 23504

TELEPHONE: (804) 623-8449

LIST NAMES OF BRANCHES WITH
SEPARATE POLICIES: None

BOOKS:
Will Lend: Yes
Length of Loan: 21 days
Renewable: Yes
Charges: None
Average Turnaround Time:
3 days maximum
If you have indicated that a
book is not to be lent, will
you on receipt of a letter
from the requesting library
search the index for given
entries? (Not answered)

PERIODICALS:
Bound: Will not lend
Unbound: Will not lend
Loan Period: N/A
Renewable: N/A
Will lend if article exceeds
_____ number of pages (Will
not lend, regardless of
length of article)

MICROFORMS:
Will Lend: No
Specific Types of Microforms:
N/A

GOVERNMENT PUBLICATIONS:
Will Lend: No

DISSERTATIONS:
Will Lend: No

THESES:
Will Lend: No

AUDIO-VISUAL MATERIALS:
Records: Do not own
Cassettes: Do not own
Other (slides, filmstrips,
etc.): Do not own

COMPUTER SOFTWARE:
Will Lend: Do not own

PHOTODUPLICATION SERVICE:
No charge up to 0 exposures
Charge Per Exposure: 10¢
Minimum/handling Fee: None
Average Turnaround Time:
3 days maximum

MICROFILMING SERVICE:
Service Available: No
Charges: N/A

DO YOU CHARGE THE BORROWING
LIBRARY FOR POSTAGE? No

FOR HOW LONG DO YOU SUSPEND ILL
SERVICE OVER THE CHRISTMAS
HOLIDAYS? 2 weeks

ARE THERE ANY GROUPS OF LIBRARIES
FOR WHICH YOU WAIVE FEES? IF
SO, PLEASE NAME THEM:
Members of the Virginia
Tidewater Consortium and
others who will reciprocate

OLD DOMINION UNIVERSITY

NUC CODE: ViNO

OCLC CODE: VOD

ADDRESS: Interlibrary Loan
University Library
Old Dominion University
Norfolk, VA 23508

TELEPHONE: (804) 440-4170

LIST NAMES OF BRANCHES WITH
SEPARATE POLICIES: None

BOOKS:
Will Lend: Yes
Length of Loan: 1 month,
including transit
Renewable: Yes, once
Charges: None
Average Turnaround Time:
3 days
If you have indicated that a
book is not to be lent, will
you on receipt of a letter
from the requesting library
search the index for given
entries? (Not answered)

PERIODICALS:
Bound: Will not lend
Unbound: Will not lend
Loan Period: N/A
Renewable: N/A
Will lend if article exceeds
_____ number of pages (Will
not lend, regardless of
length of article)

MICROFORMS:
Will Lend: Yes, microfilm
only
Fiche-to-fiche duplication for
$1.00 per fiche

GOVERNMENT PUBLICATIONS:
Will Lend: Yes

DISSERTATIONS:
Will Lend: Yes

THESES:
Will Lend: Yes

AUDIO-VISUAL MATERIALS:
Records: Will not lend
Cassettes: Will lend
Other (slides, filmstrips,
etc.): Will not lend

COMPUTER SOFTWARE:
Will Lend: No

PHOTODUPLICATION SERVICE:
No charge up to 1 exposure
Charge Per Exposure: 10¢
Minimum/handling Fee: $1.50
min./$1.00 handling
Average Turnaround Time:
3 days

MICROFILMING SERVICE:
Service Available: No
Charges: N/A

DO YOU CHARGE THE BORROWING
LIBRARY FOR POSTAGE? No

FOR HOW LONG DO YOU SUSPEND ILL
SERVICE OVER THE CHRISTMAS
HOLIDAYS? Dec.14-Jan.3

ARE THERE ANY GROUPS OF LIBRARIES
FOR WHICH YOU WAIVE FEES? IF
SO, PLEASE NAME THEM: None

PRINCE WILLIAM COUNTY PUBLIC LIBRARY

NUC CODE: (Not answered)

OCLC CODE: (Not answered)

ADDRESS: Interlibrary Loan
Prince William County
Public Library
8601 Mathis Ave.
Manassas, VA 22111

TELEPHONE: (703) 361-8212

LIST NAMES OF BRANCHES WITH
SEPARATE POLICIES: None

BOOKS:
Will Lend: Yes
Length of Loan: 4 weeks
Renewable: No
Charges: None
Average Turnaround Time:
(Not answered)
If you have indicated that a
book is not to be lent, will
you on receipt of a letter
from the requesting library
search the index for given
entries? No

PERIODICALS:
Bound: Will not lend
Unbound: Will lend single
issues
Loan Period: 2 weeks
Renewable: No
Will lend if article exceeds
_____ number of pages (Not
answered)

MICROFORMS:
Will Lend: No
Specific Types of Microforms:
N/A

GOVERNMENT PUBLICATIONS:
Will Lend: No

DISSERTATIONS:
Will Lend: No

THESES:
Will Lend: No

AUDIO-VISUAL MATERIALS:
Records: Will not lend
Cassettes: Will not lend
Other (slides, filmstrips,
etc.): Will not lend

COMPUTER SOFTWARE:
Will Lend: No

PHOTODUPLICATION SERVICE:
No charge up to 10 exposures
Charge Per Exposure: 10¢
Minimum/handling Fee: None
Average Turnaround Time:
(Not answered)

MICROFILMING SERVICE:
Service Available: No
Charges: N/A

DO YOU CHARGE THE BORROWING
LIBRARY FOR POSTAGE? Not
at this time

FOR HOW LONG DO YOU SUSPEND ILL
SERVICE OVER THE CHRISTMAS
HOLIDAYS? No suspension

ARE THERE ANY GROUPS OF LIBRARIES
FOR WHICH YOU WAIVE FEES? IF
SO, PLEASE NAME THEM: None

RADFORD UNIVERSITY

NUC CODE: (Not answered)

OCLC CODE: VRA

ADDRESS: Interlibrary Loan
Radford University
Library
Radford, VA   24142

TELEPHONE: (703) 731-5471

LIST NAMES OF BRANCHES WITH
SEPARATE POLICIES: None

BOOKS:
Will Lend: Yes
Length of Loan: 1 month
Renewable: Yes
Charges: None
Average Turnaround Time:
(Not answered)
If you have indicated that a
book is not to be lent, will
you on receipt of a letter
from the requesting library
search the index for given
entries? (Not answered)

PERIODICALS:
Bound: Will not lend
Unbound: Will not lend
Loan Period: N/A
Renewable: N/A
Will lend if article exceeds
_____ number of pages (Will
not lend, regardless of
length of article)

MICROFORMS:
Will Lend: Yes
Specific Types of Microforms:
Reels, fiche, cards

GOVERNMENT PUBLICATIONS:
Will Lend: Yes

DISSERTATIONS:
Will Lend: No

THESES:
Will Lend: Yes, if 2d copy
available

AUDIO-VISUAL MATERIALS:
Records: Will not lend
Cassettes: Will not lend
Other (slides, filmstrips,
etc.): Will not lend

COMPUTER SOFTWARE:
Will Lend: No

PHOTODUPLICATION SERVICE:
Ordinarily, no charge for
exposures. We will contact
personally if huge number
of exposures desired
Minimum/handling Fee: None
Average Turnaround Time:
(Not answered)

MICROFILMING SERVICE:
Service Available: No
Charges: N/A

DO YOU CHARGE THE BORROWING
LIBRARY FOR POSTAGE? No

FOR HOW LONG DO YOU SUSPEND ILL
SERVICE OVER THE CHRISTMAS
HOLIDAYS? 2 weeks

ARE THERE ANY GROUPS OF LIBRARIES
FOR WHICH YOU WAIVE FEES? IF
SO, PLEASE NAME THEM: None

RICHMOND PUBLIC LIBRARY

NUC CODE: (Not answered)

OCLC CODE: VRP

ADDRESS: Interlibrary Loan
Richmond Public Library
101 E. Franklin St.
Richmond, VA   23219

TELEPHONE: (804) 780-4672

LIST NAMES OF BRANCHES WITH
SEPARATE POLICIES: None

BOOKS:
Will Lend: Yes
Length of Loan: 1 month
Renewable: Yes
Charges: None
Average Turnaround Time:
2 days
If you have indicated that a
book is not to be lent, will
you on receipt of a letter
from the requesting library
search the index for given
entries? (Not answered)

PERIODICALS:
Bound: Will not lend
Unbound: Will not lend
Loan Period: N/A
Renewable: N/A
Will lend if article exceeds
_____ number of pages (Not
answered)

MICROFORMS:
Will Lend: No
Specific Types of Microforms:
N/A

GOVERNMENT PUBLICATIONS:
Will Lend: No

DISSERTATIONS:
Will Lend: Do not own

THESES:
Will Lend: Do not own

AUDIO-VISUAL MATERIALS:
Records: Will not lend
Cassettes: Will not lend
Other (slides, filmstrips,
etc.): Will not lend

COMPUTER SOFTWARE:
Will Lend: No

PHOTODUPLICATION SERVICE:
No charge up to 0 exposures
Charge Per Exposure: 10¢
Minimum/handling Fee: None
Average Turnaround Time:
2 days

MICROFILMING SERVICE:
Service Available: No
Charges: N/A

DO YOU CHARGE THE BORROWING
LIBRARY FOR POSTAGE? No

FOR HOW LONG DO YOU SUSPEND ILL
SERVICE OVER THE CHRISTMAS
HOLIDAYS? 4 days

ARE THERE ANY GROUPS OF LIBRARIES
FOR WHICH YOU WAIVE FEES? IF
SO, PLEASE NAME THEM: None

ROANOKE CITY PUBLIC LIBRARY SYSTEM

NUC CODE: None

OCLC CODE: None

ADDRESS: Interlibrary Loan
           Roanoke City Public
           Library System
           706 S. Jefferson St.
           Roanoke, VA 24011

TELEPHONE (703) 981-2478

LIST NAMES OF BRANCHES WITH
  SEPARATE POLICIES: None

BOOKS:
  Will Lend: Yes
  Length of Loan: 3 weeks
  Renewable: Yes
  Charges: None
  Average Turnaround Time:
    1 day
  If you have indicated that a
    book is not to be lent, will
    you on receipt of a letter
    from the requesting library
    search the index for given
    entries? Yes

PERIODICALS:
  Bound: Will not lend
  Unbound: Will not lend
  Loan Period: N/A
  Renewable: N/A
  Will lend if article exceeds
    _____ number of pages (Will
    not lend, regardless of
    length of article)

MICROFORMS:
  Will Lend: No
  Specific Types of Microforms:
    N/A

GOVERNMENT PUBLICATIONS:
  Will Lend: No

DISSERTATIONS:
  Will Lend: No

THESES:
  Will Lend: No

AUDIO-VISUAL MATERIALS:
  Records: Will not lend
  Cassettes: Will not lend
  Other (slides, filmstrips,
    etc.): Will not lend

COMPUTER SOFTWARE:
  Will Lend: No

PHOTODUPLICATION SERVICE:
  No charge up to 8 exposures
  Charge Per Exposure: 15¢
  Minimum/handling Fee: None
  Average Turnaround Time:
    2 days

MICROFILMING SERVICE:
  Service Available: No
  Charges: N/A

DO YOU CHARGE THE BORROWING
  LIBRARY FOR POSTAGE? No

FOR HOW LONG DO YOU SUSPEND ILL
  SERVICE OVER THE CHRISTMAS
  HOLIDAYS? No suspension

ARE THERE ANY GROUPS OF LIBRARIES
  FOR WHICH YOU WAIVE FEES? IF
  SO, PLEASE NAME THEM: None

ROANOKE COUNTY PUBLIC LIBRARY

NUC CODE: (Not answered)

OCLC CODE: (Not answered)

ADDRESS: Interlibrary Loan
           Roanoke County Public
           Library
           3131 Electric Rd. S.W.
           Roanoke, VA 24018

TELEPHONE: (703) 774-1681

LIST NAMES OF BRANCHES WITH
  SEPARATE POLICIES: Vinton
    Branch, Hollins Branch,
    Glenvar Branch. Book
    policy is the same;
    magazine policy might be
    different; branches cannot
    copy microfilm

BOOKS:
  Will Lend: Yes
  Length of Loan: 1 month
  Renewable: Yes
  Charges: None
  Average Turnaround Time:
    48 hours
  If you have indicated that a
    book is not to be lent, will
    you on receipt of a letter
    from the requesting library
    search the index for given
    entries? No

PERIODICALS:
  Bound: Will not lend
  Unbound: Will not lend
  Loan Period: N/A
  Renewable: N/A
  Will lend if article exceeds
    _____ number of pages (Will
    not lend, regardless of
    length of article)

MICROFORMS:
  Will Lend: No
  Specific Types of Microforms:
    N/A

GOVERNMENT PUBLICATIONS:
  Will Lend: Do not own

DISSERTATIONS:
  Will Lend: Do not own

THESES:
  Will Lend: Do not own

AUDIO-VISUAL MATERIALS:
  Records: Will not lend
  Cassettes: Will not lend
  Other (slides, filmstrips,
    etc.): Will not lend

COMPUTER SOFTWARE:
  Will Lend: No

PHOTODUPLICATION SERVICE:
  No charge up to 10 exposures
  Charge Per Exposure: 10¢
  Minimum/handling Fee: None
  Average Turnaround Time:
    48 hours

MICROFILMING SERVICE:
  Service Available: No
  Charges: N/A

DO YOU CHARGE THE BORROWING
  LIBRARY FOR POSTAGE? No

FOR HOW LONG DO YOU SUSPEND ILL
  SERVICE OVER THE CHRISTMAS
  HOLIDAYS? No suspension

ARE THERE ANY GROUPS OF LIBRARIES
  FOR WHICH YOU WAIVE FEES? IF
  SO, PLEASE NAME THEM: None

UNITED STATES GEOLOGICAL SURVEY

NUC CODE: DGS or DIGS

OCLC CODE: GIS

ADDRESS: Interlibrary Loan
           U. S. Geological Survey
           12201 Sunrise Valley
           Drive
           Library -- 950 National
           Center
           Reston, VA 22092

TELEPHONE: (703) 860-6671

LIST NAMES OF BRANCHES WITH
   SEPARATE POLICIES: None

BOOKS:
   Will Lend: Yes
   Length of Loan: 1 month
   Renewable: Yes
   Charges: None
   Average Turnaround Time:
      5 days
   If you have indicated that a
      book is not to be lent, will
      you on receipt of a letter
      from the requesting library
      search the index for given
      entries? (Not answered)

PERIODICALS:
   Bound: Will lend
   Unbound: Will lend
   Loan Period: 1 month
   Renewable: Yes
   Will lend if article exceeds
      20 pages

MICROFORMS:
   Will Lend: Yes
   Specific Types of Microforms:
      Fiche, film

GOVERNMENT PUBLICATIONS:
   Will Lend: Yes

DISSERTATIONS:
   Will Lend: Yes

THESES:
   Will Lend: Yes

AUDIO-VISUAL MATERIALS:
   Records: Do not own
   Cassettes: Do not own
   Other (slides, filmstrips,
      etc.): Do not own

COMPUTER SOFTWARE:
   Will Lend: Do not own

PHOTODUPLICATION SERVICE:
   No charge up to any exposures
   Charge Per Exposure: None
   Minimum/handling Fee: None
   Average Turnaround Time:
      5 days

MICROFILMING SERVICE:
   Service Available: No
   Charges: N/A

DO YOU CHARGE THE BORROWING
   LIBRARY FOR POSTAGE? No

FOR HOW LONG DO YOU SUSPEND ILL
   SERVICE OVER THE CHRISTMAS
   HOLIDAYS? 3 weeks

ARE THERE ANY GROUPS OF LIBRARIES
   FOR WHICH YOU WAIVE FEES? IF
   SO, PLEASE NAME THEM: No fees
   charged

UNIVERSITY OF RICHMOND

NUC CODE: ViRU

OCLC CODE: VRU

ADDRESS: Interlibrary Loan
           Boatwright Library
           University of Virginia
           Richmond, VA 23173

TELEPHONE: (804) 285-6215

LIST NAMES OF BRANCHES WITH
   SEPARATE POLICIES:
      Science Library
      Law Library

BOOKS:
   Will Lend: Yes
   Length of Loan: 1 month
   Renewable: Yes
   Charges: $4.00 per title for
      non-academic libraries (some
      exceptions)
   Average Turnaround Time:
      48 hours
   If you have indicated that a
      book is not to be lent, will
      you on receipt of a letter
      from the requesting library
      search the index for given
      entries? If time is
      available

PERIODICALS:
   Bound: Will not lend
   Unbound: Will not lend
   Loan Period: N/A
   Renewable: N/A
   Will lend if article exceeds
      _____ number of pages (Not
      answered)

MICROFORMS:
   Will Lend: Yes, with some
      exceptions
   Specific Types of Microforms:
      (Not answered)

GOVERNMENT PUBLICATIONS:
   Will Lend: Yes, with some
      exceptions

DISSERTATIONS:
   Will Lend: Yes, if 2nd copy
      available

THESES:
   Will Lend: Yes, if 2nd copy
      available

AUDIO-VISUAL MATERIALS:
   Records: Will lend, with some
      exceptions
   Cassettes: Will lend, with
      some exceptions
   Other (slides, filmstrips,
      etc.): Will lend, with
      some exceptions

COMPUTER SOFTWARE:
   Will Lend: No

PHOTODUPLICATION SERVICE:
   No charge up to 0 exposures
   Charge Per Exposure: 10¢
   Minimum/handling Fee: $1.00
   Average Turnaround Time:
      48 hours

MICROFILMING SERVICE:
   Service Available: Yes
   Charges: 15¢ per exposure plus
      $1.50 handling fee

DO YOU CHARGE THE BORROWING
   LIBRARY FOR POSTAGE? No

FOR HOW LONG DO YOU SUSPEND ILL
   SERVICE OVER THE CHRISTMAS
   HOLIDAYS? No suspension

ARE THERE ANY GROUPS OF LIBRARIES
   FOR WHICH YOU WAIVE FEES? IF
   SO, PLEASE NAME THEM:
      Academic libraries and
      Richmond area libraries

VIRGINIA BEACH PUBLIC LIBRARY

NUC CODE: (Not answered)

OCLC CODE: VPL

ADDRESS: Interlibrary Loan
          Virginia Beach Public
          Library
          936 Independence Blvd.
          Virginia Beach, VA
          23455

TELEPHONE: (804) 464-9485

LIST NAMES OF BRANCHES WITH
  SEPARATE POLICIES: None

BOOKS:
  Will Lend: Yes
  Length of Loan: 5 weeks
  Renewable: Yes, for
  1 week
  Charges: Postage
  Average Turnaround Time:
  5 days
  If you have indicated that a
  book is not to be lent, will
  you on receipt of a letter
  from the requesting library
  search the index for given
  entries? Yes

PERIODICALS:
  Bound: Will not lend
  Unbound: Will not lend
  Loan Period: N/A
  Renewable: N/A
  Will lend if article exceeds
  _____ number of pages (Not
    answered)

MICROFORMS:
  Will Lend: No
  Specific Types of Microforms:
  N/A

GOVERNMENT PUBLICATIONS:
  Will Lend: Do not own

DISSERTATIONS:
  Will Lend: Do not own

THESES:
  Will Lend: Do not own

AUDIO-VISUAL MATERIALS:
  Records: Do not own
  Cassettes: Do not own
  Other (slides, filmstrips,
    etc.): Do not own

COMPUTER SOFTWARE:
  Will Lend: Do not own

PHOTODUPLICATION SERVICE:
  No charge up to 10 exposures
  Charge Per Exposure: 10¢
  Minimum/handling Fee: None
  Average Turnaround Time:
  5 days

MICROFILMING SERVICE:
  Service Available: No
  Charges: N/A

DO YOU CHARGE THE BORROWING
  LIBRARY FOR POSTAGE? Yes

FOR HOW LONG DO YOU SUSPEND ILL
  SERVICE OVER THE CHRISTMAS
  HOLIDAYS? No suspension

ARE THERE ANY GROUPS OF LIBRARIES
  FOR WHICH YOU WAIVE FEES? IF
  SO, PLEASE NAME THEM: None

VIRGINIA COMMONWEALTH UNIVERSITY

NUC CODE: VIRCU

OCLC CODE: VRC

ADDRESS: Interlibrary Loan
          Cabell Library
          Virginia Commonwealth
          University
          901 Park Ave.
          Richmond, VA 23284

TELEPHONE: (804) 257-1105

LIST NAMES OF BRANCHES WITH
  SEPARATE POLICIES:
  Medical College Library

BOOKS:
  Will Lend: Yes
  Length of Loan: 4 weeks
  Renewable: Yes
  Charges: None
  Average Turnaround Time:
  1 week
  If you have indicated that a
  book is not to be lent, will
  you on receipt of a letter
  from the requesting library
  search the index for given
  entries? (Not answered)

PERIODICALS:
  Bound: Will not lend
  Unbound: Will not lend
  Loan Period: N/A
  Renewable: N/A
  Will lend if article exceeds
  _____ number of pages (Will
    not lend, regardless of
    length of article)

MICROFORMS:
  Will Lend: No
  Specific Types of Microforms:
  Film, fiche

GOVERNMENT PUBLICATIONS:
  Will Lend: Yes

DISSERTATIONS:
  Will Lend: Yes, if 2nd copy
    available

THESES:
  Will Lend: Yes, if 2nd copy
    available

AUDIO-VISUAL MATERIALS:
  Records: Will not lend
  Cassettes: Will not lend
  Other (slides, filmstrips,
    etc.): Will not lend

COMPUTER SOFTWARE:
  Will Lend: No

PHOTODUPLICATION SERVICE:
  No charge up to any exposures
  Charge Per Exposure: None
  Minimum/handling Fee: None
  Average Turnaround Time:
  1 week

MICROFILMING SERVICE:
  Service Available: No
  Charges: N/A

DO YOU CHARGE THE BORROWING
  LIBRARY FOR POSTAGE? No

FOR HOW LONG DO YOU SUSPEND ILL
  SERVICE OVER THE CHRISTMAS
  HOLIDAYS? 2 weeks

ARE THERE ANY GROUPS OF LIBRARIES
  FOR WHICH YOU WAIVE FEES? IF
  SO, PLEASE NAME THEM: No fees
  charged

VIRGINIA INSTITUTE OF MARINE SCIENCE

NUC CODE: None

OCLC CODE: VIM

ADDRESS: Interlibrary Loan
           College of William and
           Mary
           Virginia Institute of
           Marine Science
           Library
           Gloucester Point, VA
           23062

TELEPHONE: (804) 642-2111, X211

LIST NAMES OF BRANCHES WITH
    SEPARATE POLICIES: None

BOOKS:
    Will Lend: Yes
    Length of Loan: 3 weeks use
    Renewable: Yes
    Charges: None
    Average Turnaround Time:
        1-3 days
    If you have indicated that a
        book is not to be lent, will
        you on receipt of a letter
        from the requesting library
        search the index for given
        entries? (Not answered)

PERIODICALS:
    Bound: Will not lend
    Unbound: Will not lend
    Loan Period: N/A
    Renewable: N/A
    Will lend if article exceeds
        _____ number of pages
        (Decided on a case-by-
        case basis)

MICROFORMS:
    Will Lend: Yes
    Specific Types of Microforms:
        Microfiche only

GOVERNMENT PUBLICATIONS:
    Will Lend: Do not own

DISSERTATIONS:
    Will Lend: Yes, fiche only

THESES:
    Will Lend: Yes, fiche only

AUDIO-VISUAL MATERIALS:
    Records: Do not own
    Cassettes: Do not own
    Other (slides, filmstrips,
        etc.): Do not own

COMPUTER SOFTWARE:
    Will Lend: Do not own

PHOTODUPLICATION SERVICE:
    No charge up to 10 exposures
    Charge Per Exposure: 15¢
    Minimum/handling Fee:
        $1.00 per article
    Average Turnaround Time:
        1-3 days

MICROFILMING SERVICE:
    Service Available: No
    Charges: N/A

DO YOU CHARGE THE BORROWING
    LIBRARY FOR POSTAGE? No

FOR HOW LONG DO YOU SUSPEND ILL
    SERVICE OVER THE CHRISTMAS
    HOLIDAYS? Dec.15-Jan.15

ARE THERE ANY GROUPS OF LIBRARIES
    FOR WHICH YOU WAIVE FEES? IF
    SO, PLEASE NAME THEM: Those
        Virginia and marine science
        libraries that reciprocate

VIRGINIA POLYTECHNIC INSTITUTE AND STATE UNIVERSITY

NUC CODE: (Not answered)

OCLC CODE: VPI

ADDRESS: Interlibrary Loan
           Carol M. Newman
           Library
           Virginia Polytechnic
           Institute and State
           University
           Blacksburg, VA   24061

TELEPHONE: (703) 961-6344

LIST NAMES OF BRANCHES WITH
    SEPARATE POLICIES:
        A-V: Learning Resources
        Center

BOOKS:
    Will Lend: Yes
    Length of Loan: 3 weeks
    Renewable: Yes
    Charges: (Not answered)
    Average Turnaround Time:
        (Not answered)
    If you have indicated that a
        book is not to be lent, will
        you on receipt of a letter
        from the requesting library
        search the index for given
        entries? (Not answered)

PERIODICALS:
    Bound: Will not lend
    Unbound: Will not lend
    Loan Period: N/A
    Renewable: N/A
    Will lend if article exceeds
        _____ number of pages (Not
        answered)

MICROFORMS:
    Will Lend: Yes
    Specific Types of Microforms:
        (Not answered)

GOVERNMENT PUBLICATIONS:
    Will Lend: Yes

DISSERTATIONS:
    Will Lend: Yes; 1952 to
        present available from
        University Microfilms

THESES:
    Will Lend: Yes

AUDIO-VISUAL MATERIALS:
    Records: (Not answered)
    Cassettes: (Not answered)
    Other (slides, filmstrips,
        etc.): (Not answered)

COMPUTER SOFTWARE:
    Will Lend: (Not answered)

PHOTODUPLICATION SERVICE:
    No charge up to 0 exposures
    Charge Per Exposure: 10¢
    Minimum/handling Fee: $1.00
        in-state; $2.00 out-of-
        state
    Average Turnaround Time:
        (Not answered)

MICROFILMING SERVICE:
    Service Available: No
    Charges: N/A

DO YOU CHARGE THE BORROWING
    LIBRARY FOR POSTAGE? No

FOR HOW LONG DO YOU SUSPEND ILL
    SERVICE OVER THE CHRISTMAS
    HOLIDAYS? (Not answered)

ARE THERE ANY GROUPS OF LIBRARIES
    FOR WHICH YOU WAIVE FEES? IF
    SO, PLEASE NAME THEM: (Not
        answered)

VIRGINIA STATE LIBRARY

NUC CODE: Vi

OCLC CODE: VIC

ADDRESS: Interlibrary Loan
        Virginia State
         Library
        12th and Capitol Sts.
        Richmond, VA 23219

TELEPHONE: (804) 786-2304

LIST NAMES OF BRANCHES WITH
  SEPARATE POLICIES: None

BOOKS:
  Will Lend: Yes
  Length of Loan: 4 weeks
  Renewable: Yes
  Charges: None
  Average Turnaround Time:
   (Not answered)
  If you have indicated that a
  book is not to be lent, will
  you on receipt of a letter
  from the requesting library
  search the index for given
  entries? (Not answered)

PERIODICALS:
  Bound: Will lend
  Unbound: Will not lend
  Loan Period: 4 weeks
  Renewable: (Not answered)
  Will lend if article exceeds
   10 pages

MICROFORMS:
  Will Lend: Yes
  Specific Types of Microforms:
   Film only

GOVERNMENT PUBLICATIONS:
  Will Lend: Yes

DISSERTATIONS:
  Will Lend: (Not answered)

THESES:
  Will Lend: (Not answered)

AUDIO-VISUAL MATERIALS:
  Records: (Not answered)
  Cassettes: (Not answered)
  Other (slides, filmstrips,
   etc.): (Not answered)

COMPUTER SOFTWARE:
  Will Lend: (Not answered)

PHOTODUPLICATION SERVICE:
  No charge up to 10 exposures
  Charge Per Exposure: 25¢
  Minimum/handling Fee: $3.00
   minimum/$5.00 handling
  Average Turnaround Time:
   (Not answered)

MICROFILMING SERVICE:
  Service Available: Yes
  Charges: $1.00 per foot,
   $10.00 minimum, $4.00
   handling

DO YOU CHARGE THE BORROWING
  LIBRARY FOR POSTAGE? No

FOR HOW LONG DO YOU SUSPEND ILL
  SERVICE OVER THE CHRISTMAS
  HOLIDAYS? No suspension

ARE THERE ANY GROUPS OF LIBRARIES
  FOR WHICH YOU WAIVE FEES? IF
  SO, PLEASE NAME THEM: (Not
   answered)

BELLINGHAM PUBLIC LIBRARY

NUC CODE: WaBe

OCLC CODE: (Not answered)

ADDRESS: Interlibrary Loan
Bellingham Public
Library
P. O. Box 1197
Bellingham, WA 98227

TELEPHONE: (206) 676-6860

LIST NAMES OF BRANCHES WITH
SEPARATE POLICIES: None

BOOKS
Will Lend: Yes
Length of Loan: 4 weeks
Renewable: No
Charges: Usually none
Average Turnaround Time:
2-3 days
If you have indicated that a
book is not to be lent, will
you on receipt of a letter
from the requesting library
search the index for given
entries? Yes

PERIODICALS:
Bound: Will not lend
Unbound: Will not lend
Loan Period: N/A
Renewable: N/A
Will lend if article exceeds
_____ number of pages (Not
answered)

MICROFORMS:
Will Lend: No
Specific Types of Microforms:
N/A

GOVERNMENT PUBLICATIONS:
Will Lend: Yes

DISSERTATIONS:
Will Lend: Do not own

THESES:
Will Lend: Do not own

AUDIO-VISUAL MATERIALS:
Records: Will not lend
Cassettes: Will not lend
Other (slides, filmstrips,
etc.): Will not lend

COMPUTER SOFTWARE:
Will Lend: No

PHOTODUPLICATION SERVICE:
No charge up to 0 exposures
Charge Per Exposure: 10¢
Minimum/handling Fee: None
Average Turnaround Time:
2-3 days

MICROFILMING SERVICE:
Service Available: No
Charges: N/A

DO YOU CHARGE THE BORROWING
LIBRARY FOR POSTAGE? Not
usually

FOR HOW LONG DO YOU SUSPEND ILL
SERVICE OVER THE CHRISTMAS
HOLIDAYS? No suspension

ARE THERE ANY GROUPS OF LIBRARIES
FOR WHICH YOU WAIVE FEES? IF
SO, PLEASE NAME THEM: None

CENTRAL WASHINGTON UNIVERSITY

NUC CODE: WaE1C

OCLC CODE: (Not answered)

ADDRESS: Interlibrary Loan
Central Washington
University
Library
Ellensburg, WA 98926

TELEPHONE: (509) 963-1021

LIST NAMES OF BRANCHES WITH
SEPARATE POLICIES: None

BOOKS:
Will Lend: Yes
Length of Loan: 2 weeks use
Renewable: Yes, if not
requested by CWU patron
Charges: None
Average Turnaround Time:
2 days
If you have indicated that a
book is not to be lent, will
you on receipt of a letter
from the requesting library
search the index for given
entries? (Not answered)

PERIODICALS:
Bound: Will not lend
Unbound: Will not lend
Loan Period: N/A
Renewable: N/A
Will lend if article exceeds
_____ number of pages (Not
answered)

MICROFORMS:
Will Lend: No
Specific Types of Microforms:
N/A

GOVERNMENT PUBLICATIONS:
Will Lend: Yes

DISSERTATIONS:
Will Lend: Do not own

THESES:
Will Lend: Yes

AUDIO-VISUAL MATERIALS:
Records: Will not lend
Cassettes: Rental and
handling fees through
Instructional Media Center
Other (slides, filmstrips,
etc.): Rental and handling
fees through Instructional
Media Center

COMPUTER SOFTWARE:
Will Lend: Do not own

PHOTODUPLICATION SERVICE:
No charge up to 0 exposures
Charge Per Exposure: 10¢
Minimum/handling Fee: $1.00 on
25 pages or more
Average Turnaround Time:
2 days

MICROFILMING SERVICE:
Service Available: No
Charges: N/A

DO YOU CHARGE THE BORROWING
LIBRARY FOR POSTAGE? No

FOR HOW LONG DO YOU SUSPEND ILL
SERVICE OVER THE CHRISTMAS
HOLIDAYS? No suspension

ARE THERE ANY GROUPS OF LIBRARIES
FOR WHICH YOU WAIVE FEES? IF
SO, PLEASE NAME THEM: None

EASTERN WASHINGTON UNIVERSITY

NUC CODE: WaChenE

OCLC CODE: WEA

ADDRESS: Interlibrary Loan
          The Library
          Eastern Washington
          University
          Cheney, WA 99004

TELEPHONE: (509) 359-2492
            SCAN 353-2492

LIST NAMES OF BRANCHES WITH
  SEPARATE POLICIES: None

BOOKS:
  Will Lend: Yes, except rare,
    reference, archival
    materials
  Length of Loan: 1 month
  Renewable: Yes
  Charges: None
  Average Turnaround Time:
    10-14 days
  If you have indicated that a
    book is not to be lent, will
    you on receipt of a letter
    from the requesting library
    search the index for given
    entries? Yes

PERIODICALS:
  Bound: Will not lend
  Unbound: Will not lend
  Loan Period: N/A
  Renewable: N/A
  Will lend if article exceeds
    _____ number of pages (Not
    answered)

MICROFORMS:
  Will Lend: Yes
  Specific Types of Microforms:
    Cards, film, fiche, print

GOVERNMENT PUBLICATIONS:
  Will Lend: Yes, if circulating

DISSERTATIONS:
  Will Lend: Yes

THESES:
  Will Lend: Yes

AUDIO-VISUAL MATERIALS:
  Records: Will not lend
  Cassettes: Will not lend
  Other (slides, filmstrips,
    etc.): Will not lend

COMPUTER SOFTWARE:
  Will Lend: No

PHOTODUPLICATION SERVICE:
  No charge up to 20 exposures
  Charge Per Exposure: 10¢
  Minimum/handling Fee: None
  Average Turnaround Time:
    10-14 days

MICROFILMING SERVICE:
  Service Available: No
  Charges: N/A

DO YOU CHARGE THE BORROWING
  LIBRARY FOR POSTAGE? No

FOR HOW LONG DO YOU SUSPEND ILL
  SERVICE OVER THE CHRISTMAS
  HOLIDAYS? No suspension

ARE THERE ANY GROUPS OF LIBRARIES
  FOR WHICH YOU WAIVE FEES? IF
  SO, PLEASE NAME THEM: None

GONZAGA UNIVERSITY

NUC CODE: (Not answered)

OCLC CODE: (Not answered)

ADDRESS: Interlibrary Loan
          Crosby Library
          Gonzaga University
          Spokane, WA 99258

TELEPHONE: (509) 328-4220, X3134

LIST NAMES OF BRANCHES WITH
  SEPARATE POLICIES: None

BOOKS:
  Will Lend: Yes
  Length of Loan: 4 weeks
  Renewable: No
  Charges: (Not answered)
  Average Turnaround Time:
    (Not answered)
  If you have indicated that a
    book is not to be lent, will
    you on receipt of a letter
    from the requesting library
    search the index for given
    entries? (Not answered)

PERIODICALS:
  Bound: Will not lend
  Unbound: Will not lend
  Loan Period: N/A
  Renewable: N/A
  Will lend if article exceeds
    _____ number of pages (Not
    answered)

MICROFORMS:
  Will Lend: (Not answered)
  Specific Types of Microforms:
    N/A

GOVERNMENT PUBLICATIONS:
  Will Lend: Yes

DISSERTATIONS:
  Will Lend: No

THESES:
  Will Lend: No

AUDIO-VISUAL MATERIALS:
  Records: (Not answered)
  Cassettes: (Not answered)
  Other (slides, filmstrips,
    etc.): (Not answered)

COMPUTER SOFTWARE:
  Will Lend: (Not answered)

PHOTODUPLICATION SERVICE:
  No charge up to 0 exposures
  Charge Per Exposure: 10¢
  Minimum/handling Fee:
    (Not answered)
  Average Turnaround Time:
    (Not answered)

MICROFILMING SERVICE:
  Service Available: No
  Charges: N/A

DO YOU CHARGE THE BORROWING
  LIBRARY FOR POSTAGE? (Not
  answered)

FOR HOW LONG DO YOU SUSPEND ILL
  SERVICE OVER THE CHRISTMAS
  HOLIDAYS? (Not answered)

ARE THERE ANY GROUPS OF LIBRARIES
  FOR WHICH YOU WAIVE FEES? IF
  SO, PLEASE NAME THEM: (Not
  answered)

KING COUNTY LIBRARY SYSTEM

WLN CODE: WsSKC

NUC CODE: (Not answered)

OCLC CODE: None

ADDRESS: Interlibrary Loan
King County Library
    System
300 8th Avenue N
Seattle, WA 98109

TELEPHONE: (206) 344-2684

LIST NAMES OF BRANCHES WITH
SEPARATE POLICIES: None

BOOKS:
Will Lend: Yes
Length of Loan: 3-4 weeks
Renewable: Yes
Charges: (Not answered)
Average Turnaround Time:
    2-4 weeks
If you have indicated that a
    book is not to be lent, will
    you on receipt of a letter
    from the requesting library
    search the index for given
    entries? Yes, in the case
    of car repair manuals,
    northwest history, or
    extremely valuable
    materials.

PERIODICALS:
Bound: Will not lend
Unbound: Will not lend
Loan Period: N/A
Renewable: N/A
Will lend if article exceeds
    20 pages

MICROFORMS:
Will Lend: Yes
Specific Types of Microforms:
    Microfiche, microfilm
    (mostly periodicals)

GOVERNMENT PUBLICATIONS:
Will Lend: Yes

DISSERTATIONS:
Will Lend: Yes

THESES:
Will Lend: Yes

AUDIO-VISUAL MATERIALS:
Records: Will not lend
Cassettes: Will lend spoken
    cassettes
Other (slides, filmstrips,
    etc.): Will lend

COMPUTER SOFTWARE:
Will Lend: No

PHOTODUPLICATION SERVICE:
No charge up to 10 exposures
Charge Per Exposure: 10¢
Minimum/handling Fee: (Not
    answered)
Average Turnaround Time:
    2 weeks

MICROFILMING SERVICE:
Service Available: No
Charges: N/A

DO YOU CHARGE THE BORROWING
LIBRARY FOR POSTAGE? Yes

FOR HOW LONG DO YOU SUSPEND ILL
SERVICE OVER THE CHRISTMAS
HOLIDAYS? No suspension

ARE THERE ANY GROUPS OF LIBRARIES
FOR WHICH YOU WAIVE FEES? IF
SO, PLEASE NAME THEM: No
    postage for libraries in the
    Washington Library Network.

NORTH CENTRAL REGIONAL LIBRARY

NUC CODE: (Not answered)

OCLC CODE: (Not answered)

ADDRESS: Interlibrary Loan
North Central Regional
    Library
238 Olds Station Rd.
Wenatchee, WA 98801

TELEPHONE: (509) 663-1117

LIST NAMES OF BRANCHES WITH
SEPARATE POLICIES: None

BOOKS:
Will Lend: Yes
Length of Loan: 1 month
Renewable: No
Charges: None
Average Turnaround Time:
    (Not answered)
If you have indicated that a
    book is not to be lent, will
    you on receipt of a letter
    from the requesting library
    search the index for given
    entries? (Not answered)

PERIODICALS:
Bound: Will not lend
Unbound: Will not lend
Loan Period: (Not answered)
Renewable: (Not answered)
Will lend if article exceeds
    _____ number of pages (Not
    answered)

MICROFORMS:
Will Lend: Do not own
Specific Types of Microforms:
    N/A

GOVERNMENT PUBLICATIONS:
Will Lend: No

DISSERTATIONS:
Will Lend: No

THESES:
Will Lend: No

AUDIO-VISUAL MATERIALS:
Records: Will not lend
Cassettes: Will not lend
Other (slides, filmstrips,
    etc.): (Not answered)

COMPUTER SOFTWARE:
Will Lend: No

PHOTODUPLICATION SERVICE:
No charge up to _____
    exposures (Not answered)
Charge Per Exposure: (Not
    answered)
Minimum/handling Fee: (Not
    answered)
Average Turnaround Time:
    (Not answered)

MICROFILMING SERVICE:
Service Available: No
Charges: N/A

DO YOU CHARGE THE BORROWING
LIBRARY FOR POSTAGE? Yes

FOR HOW LONG DO YOU SUSPEND ILL
SERVICE OVER THE CHRISTMAS
HOLIDAYS? 1 month

ARE THERE ANY GROUPS OF LIBRARIES
FOR WHICH YOU WAIVE FEES? IF
SO, PLEASE NAME THEM: None

PIERCE COUNTY LIBRARY

NUC CODE: WaTPC

OCLC CODE: (Not answered)

ADDRESS: Interlibrary Loan
Pierce County Library
2356 Tacoma Avenue So.
Tacoma, WA 98402

TELEPHONE: (206) 572-6760

LIST NAMES OF BRANCHES WITH
SEPARATE POLICIES: None

BOOKS:
Will Lend: Yes
Length of Loan: 4 weeks
Renewable: Yes
Charges: None
Average Turnaround Time:
2-3 weeks
If you have indicated that a
book is not to be lent, will
you on receipt of a letter
from the requesting library
search the index for given
entries? (Not answered)

PERIODICALS:
Bound: Do not own
Unbound: Will lend
Loan Period: 2-3 weeks
Renewable: Yes
Will lend if article exceeds
_____ number of pages (Not
answered)

MICROFORMS:
Will Lend: Yes
Specific Types of Microforms:
Microfilm

GOVERNMENT PUBLICATIONS:
Will Lend: Do not own

DISSERTATIONS:
Will Lend: Do not own

THESES:
Will Lend: Do not own

AUDIO-VISUAL MATERIALS:
Records: (Not answered)
Cassettes: (Not answered)
Other (slides, filmstrips,
etc.): (Not answered)

COMPUTER SOFTWARE:
Will Lend: Do not own

PHOTODUPLICATION SERVICE:
No charge up to 10 exposures
Charge Per Exposure: 10¢ after
first 10
Minimum/handling Fee: None
Average Turnaround Time:
1 week

MICROFILMING SERVICE:
Service Available: Yes
Charges: (Not answered)

DO YOU CHARGE THE BORROWING
LIBRARY FOR POSTAGE? No

FOR HOW LONG DO YOU SUSPEND ILL
SERVICE OVER THE CHRISTMAS
HOLIDAYS? No suspension

ARE THERE ANY GROUPS OF LIBRARIES
FOR WHICH YOU WAIVE FEES? IF
SO, PLEASE NAME THEM: None

SEATTLE PUBLIC LIBRARY

NUC CODE: WaS

OCLC CODE: None

ADDRESS: Interlibrary Loan
Seattle Public Library
1000 Fourth Ave.
Seattle, WA 98104

TELEPHONE: (206) 625-4963

LIST NAMES OF BRANCHES WITH
SEPARATE POLICIES: None

BOOKS:
Will Lend: Yes
Length of Loan: 2-4 weeks
Renewable: Yes, with
permission
Charges: No lending charges;
postage charged to out-of-
state libraries
Average Turnaround Time:
Varies
If you have indicated that a
book is not to be lent, will
you on receipt of a letter
from the requesting library
search the index for given
entries? Yes

PERIODICALS:
Bound: Will lend with
special permission if
library has circulating
copy
Unbound: Will lend with
special permission if
library has circulating
copy
Loan Period: 2-4 weeks
Renewable: Yes, with
permission
Will lend if article exceeds
30 pages (rarely)

MICROFORMS:
Will Lend: Yes
Specific Types of Microforms:
Microcards, microfilms
(newspapers)

GOVERNMENT PUBLICATIONS:
Will Lend: Yes; lent with
exceptions for those in
demand

DISSERTATIONS:
Will Lend: Do not own

THESES:
Will Lend: Do not own

AUDIO-VISUAL MATERIALS:
Records: Will not lend
Cassettes: Will not lend
Other (slides, filmstrips,
etc.): Will not lend

COMPUTER SOFTWARE:
Will Lend: No

PHOTODUPLICATION SERVICE:
No charge up to 0 exposures
Charge Per Exposure: 25¢
Minimum/handling Fee: (Not
answered)
Average Turnaround Time:
Varies

MICROFILMING SERVICE:
Service Available: No
Charges: N/A

DO YOU CHARGE THE BORROWING
LIBRARY FOR POSTAGE? Yes, for
out-of-state

FOR HOW LONG DO YOU SUSPEND ILL
SERVICE OVER THE CHRISTMAS
HOLIDAYS? No suspension

ARE THERE ANY GROUPS OF LIBRARIES
FOR WHICH YOU WAIVE FEES? IF
SO, PLEASE NAME THEM: None

SEATTLE UNIVERSITY

NUC CODE: WaSU

OCLC CODE: (Not answered)

ADDRESS: Interlibrary Loan
Seattle University
Library
Seattle, WA 98122

TELEPHONE: (206) 626-6859

LIST NAMES OF BRANCHES WITH
SEPARATE POLICIES: None

BOOKS:
Will Lend: Yes
Length of Loan: 2 weeks use
Renewable: Yes
Charges: None
Average Turnaround Time:
2-3 days
If you have indicated that a
book is not to be lent, will
you on receipt of a letter
from the requesting library
search the index for given
entries? Would do this for
non-circulating books
such as reference or
special collection.

PERIODICALS:
Bound: Will not lend
Unbound: Will not lend
Loan Period: N/A
Renewable: N/A
Might lend if article
exceeds 50 pages

MICROFORMS:
Will Lend: No
Specific Types of Microforms:
(Might lend in specific
situations, such as requests
for technical reports.)

GOVERNMENT PUBLICATIONS:
Will Lend: Yes

DISSERTATIONS:
Will Lend: Yes

THESES:
Will Lend: Yes

AUDIO-VISUAL MATERIALS:
Records: Will not lend
Cassettes: Will not lend
Other (slides, filmstrips,
etc.): Will not lend

COMPUTER SOFTWARE:
Will Lend: No

PHOTODUPLICATION SERVICE:
No charge up to 20 exposures
Charge Per Exposure: 10¢ per
page after 20
Minimum/handling Fee: None
Average Turnaround Time:
2-3 days

MICROFILMING SERVICE:
Service Available: No
Charges: N/A

DO YOU CHARGE THE BORROWING
LIBRARY FOR POSTAGE? No

FOR HOW LONG DO YOU SUSPEND ILL
SERVICE OVER THE CHRISTMAS
HOLIDAYS? No suspension

ARE THERE ANY GROUPS OF LIBRARIES
FOR WHICH YOU WAIVE FEES? IF
SO, PLEASE NAME THEM:
Photocopying charges waived
for members of Northwest
Association of Private
Colleges and Universities
(NAPCU)

SKAGIT VALLEY COLLEGE

NUC CODE: (Not answered)

OCLC CODE: (Not answered)

ADDRESS: Interlibrary Loan
Skagit Valley College
Library Media Center
2405 College Way
Mount Vernon, WA 98273

TELEPHONE: (206) 428-1117

LIST NAMES OF BRANCHES WITH
SEPARATE POLICIES: None

BOOKS:
Will Lend: Yes
Length of Loan: 3 weeks
Renewable: Yes, usually
Charges: None
Average Turnaround Time:
2 days
If you have indicated that a
book is not to be lent, will
you on receipt of a letter
from the requesting library
search the index for given
entries? (Not answered)

PERIODICALS:
Bound: Will not lend
Unbound: Will not lend
Loan Period: N/A
Renewable: N/A
Will lend if article exceeds
_____ number of pages (Not
answered)

MICROFORMS:
Will Lend: No
Specific Types of Microforms:
N/A

GOVERNMENT PUBLICATIONS:
Will Lend: Yes

DISSERTATIONS:
Will Lend: (Not answered)

THESES:
Will Lend: (Not answered)

AUDIO-VISUAL MATERIALS:
Records: Will not lend
Cassettes: Will not lend
Other (slides, filmstrips,
etc.): Will not lend

COMPUTER SOFTWARE:
Will Lend: No

PHOTODUPLICATION SERVICE:
No charge up to 20 exposures
Charge Per Exposure: 10¢
Minimum/handling Fee: $5.00
Average Turnaround Time:
3 days

MICROFILMING SERVICE:
Service Available: No
Charges: N/A

DO YOU CHARGE THE BORROWING
LIBRARY FOR POSTAGE? No

FOR HOW LONG DO YOU SUSPEND ILL
SERVICE OVER THE CHRISTMAS
HOLIDAYS? 1 week only

ARE THERE ANY GROUPS OF LIBRARIES
FOR WHICH YOU WAIVE FEES? IF
SO, PLEASE NAME THEM: None

SNO-ISLE REGIONAL LIBRARY

NUC CODE: WaMaS

OCLC CODE: None; belong to WLN

ADDRESS: Interlibrary Loan
           Sno-Isle Regional
           Library
           P. O. Box 148
           Marysville, WA 98270

TELEPHONE: (206) 659-8447, or
             (206) 259-9151

LIST NAMES OF BRANCHES WITH
  SEPARATE POLICIES: None

BOOKS:
  Will Lend: Yes
  Length of Loan: 1 month
    from date sent
  Renewable: Yes
  Charges: Postage and
    insurance
  Average Turnaround Time:
    1-2 weeks
  If you have indicated that a
    book is not to be lent, will
    you on receipt of a letter
    from the requesting library
    search the index for given
    entries? Yes

PERIODICALS:
  Bound: Do not own
  Unbound: Will lend
  Loan Period: 1 month from
    date sent
  Renewable: No
  Will lend if article exceeds
    10 pages

MICROFORMS:
  Will Lend: No
  Specific Types of Microforms:
    N/A

GOVERNMENT PUBLICATIONS:
  Will Lend: No

DISSERTATIONS:
  Will Lend: Do not own

THESES:
  Will Lend: Do not own

AUDIO-VISUAL MATERIALS:
  Records: Will not lend
  Cassettes: Will not lend
  Other (slides, filmstrips,
    etc.): Will not lend

COMPUTER SOFTWARE:
  Will Lend: No

PHOTODUPLICATION SERVICE:
  No charge up to 10 exposures
  Charge Per Exposure: 10¢ per
    page
  Minimum/handling Fee: $1.00
  Average Turnaround Time:
    1-2 weeks

MICROFILMING SERVICE:
  Service Available: No
  Charges: N/A

DO YOU CHARGE THE BORROWING
  LIBRARY FOR POSTAGE? No

FOR HOW LONG DO YOU SUSPEND ILL
  SERVICE OVER THE CHRISTMAS
  HOLIDAYS? No suspension

ARE THERE ANY GROUPS OF LIBRARIES
  FOR WHICH YOU WAIVE FEES? IF
  SO, PLEASE NAME THEM:
    Participants of Washington
    Library Network.

SPOKANE COUNTY LIBRARY

NUC CODE: WaSpCo

OCLC CODE: WSN

ADDRESS: Interlibrary Loan
           Spokane County Library
           East 12004 Main
           Spokane, WA 99206

TELEPHONE: (509) 926-6283
             SCAN 545-4280

LIST NAMES OF BRANCHES WITH
  SEPARATE POLICIES: None

BOOKS:
  Will Lend: Yes
  Length of Loan: 28 days
  Renewable: No
  Charges: None
  Average Turnaround Time:
    3 days
  If you have indicated that a
    book is not to be lent, will
    you on receipt of a letter
    from the requesting library
    search the index for given
    entries? (Not answered)

PERIODICALS:
  Bound: Do not own
  Unbound: Will lend
  Loan Period: 14 days
  Renewable: No
  Will lend if article exceeds
    _____ number of pages (Not
  answered)

MICROFORMS:
  Will Lend: Do not own
  Specific Types of Microforms:
    N/A

GOVERNMENT PUBLICATIONS:
  Will Lend: Do not own

DISSERTATIONS:
  Will Lend: Do not own

THESES:
  Will Lend: Do not own

AUDIO-VISUAL MATERIALS:
  Records: Will not lend
  Cassettes: Will not lend
  Other (slides, filmstrips,
    etc.): Do not own

COMPUTER SOFTWARE:
  Will Lend: Do not own

PHOTODUPLICATION SERVICE:
  No charge up to 20 exposures
  Charge Per Exposure: 10¢ per
    exposure after the first 20
  Minimum/handling Fee: None
  Average Turnaround Time:
    3 days

MICROFILMING SERVICE:
  Service Available: No
  Charges: N/A

DO YOU CHARGE THE BORROWING
  LIBRARY FOR POSTAGE? (Not
  answered)

FOR HOW LONG DO YOU SUSPEND ILL
  SERVICE OVER THE CHRISTMAS
  HOLIDAYS? No suspension

ARE THERE ANY GROUPS OF LIBRARIES
  FOR WHICH YOU WAIVE FEES? IF
  SO, PLEASE NAME THEM: None

SPOKANE PUBLIC LIBRARY

NUC CODE: WaSp

OCLC CODE: (Not answered)

ADDRESS: Interlibrary Loan
Spokane Public Library
W. 906 Main Ave.
Spokane, WA 99201

TELEPHONE: (509) 838-4281

LIST NAMES OF BRANCHES WITH
SEPARATE POLICIES: None

BOOKS:
Will Lend: Yes
Length of Loan: 1 month
Renewable: Yes
Charges: None
Average Turnaround Time:
3 days
If you have indicated that a
book is not to be lent, will
you on receipt of a letter
from the requesting library
search the index for given
entries? Yes

PERIODICALS:
Bound: Will not lend
Unbound: Will lend last 5
years popular magazines
Loan Period: 1 week use
Renewable: Yes
Will lend if article exceeds
_____ number of pages

MICROFORMS:
Will Lend: Not usually
Specific Types of Microforms:
N/A

GOVERNMENT PUBLICATIONS:
Will Lend: Yes

DISSERTATIONS:
Will Lend: Do not own

THESES:
Will Lend: Do not own

AUDIO-VISUAL MATERIALS:
Records: Will not lend
Cassettes: Will not lend
Other (slides, filmstrips,
etc.): Will not lend

COMPUTER SOFTWARE:
Will Lend: Do not own

PHOTODUPLICATION SERVICE:
No charge up to 0 exposures
Charge Per Exposure: 20¢ for
regular photocopies; 25¢ for
copies from microfilm
Minimum/handling Fee: None
Average Turnaround Time:
2-3 days

MICROFILMING SERVICE:
Service Available: No
Charges: N/A

DO YOU CHARGE THE BORROWING
LIBRARY FOR POSTAGE? No

FOR HOW LONG DO YOU SUSPEND ILL
SERVICE OVER THE CHRISTMAS
HOLIDAYS? Dec. 15-Jan. 2

ARE THERE ANY GROUPS OF LIBRARIES
FOR WHICH YOU WAIVE FEES? IF
SO, PLEASE NAME THEM: None

TACOMA PUBLIC LIBRARY

NUC CODE: WaT

OCLC CODE: (Not answered)

ADDRESS: Interlibrary Loan
Tacoma Public Library
1102 Tacoma Avenue So.
Tacoma, WA 98402

TELEPHONE: (206) 591-5625
(206) 781-5625

LIST NAMES OF BRANCHES WITH
SEPARATE POLICIES: None

BOOKS:
Will Lend: Yes
Length of Loan: 28 days
Renewable: Yes
Charges: None
Average Turnaround Time:
(Not answered)
If you have indicated that a
book is not to be lent, will
you on receipt of a letter
from the requesting library
search the index for given
entries? Yes

PERIODICALS:
Bound: Will not lend
Unbound: Will not lend
Loan Period: N/A
Renewable: N/A
Will lend if article exceeds
_____ number of pages (Not
answered)

MICROFORMS:
Will Lend: Yes
Specific Types of Microforms:
Will lend our newspapers on
microfilm

GOVERNMENT PUBLICATIONS:
Will Lend: No

DISSERTATIONS:
Will Lend: Do not own

THESES:
Will Lend: Do not own

AUDIO-VISUAL MATERIALS:
Records: Will not lend
Cassettes: Will not lend
Other (slides, filmstrips,
etc.): Will not lend

COMPUTER SOFTWARE:
Will Lend: (Not answered)

PHOTODUPLICATION SERVICE:
No charge up to _____
exposures (No charge at all)
Charge Per Exposure: None
Minimum/handling Fee: None
Average Turnaround Time: (Not
answered)

MICROFILMING SERVICE:
Service Available: No
Charges: N/A

DO YOU CHARGE THE BORROWING
LIBRARY FOR POSTAGE? No

FOR HOW LONG DO YOU SUSPEND ILL
SERVICE OVER THE CHRISTMAS
HOLIDAYS? No suspension

ARE THERE ANY GROUPS OF LIBRARIES
FOR WHICH YOU WAIVE FEES? IF
SO, PLEASE NAME THEM: No
charge to anyone

UNIVERSITY OF PUGET SOUND

NUC CODE: WaTU

OCLC CODE: (Not answered)

ADDRESS: Interlibrary Loan
University of Puget
Sound
Collins Memorial
Library
Tacoma, WA 98416

TELEPHONE: (206) 756-3257

LIST NAMES OF BRANCHES WITH
SEPARATE POLICIES:
Museum of Natural History

BOOKS:
Will Lend: Yes
Length of Loan: 4 weeks
Renewable: Yes
Charges: None
Average Turnaround Time:
1 week
If you have indicated that a
book is not to be lent, will
you on receipt of a letter
from the requesting library
search the index for given
entries? Yes, if requested

PERIODICALS:
Bound: Will lend
Unbound: Will not lend
Loan Period: 1 week
Renewable: Yes
Will lend if article exceeds
50 pages

MICROFORMS:
Will Lend: Yes
Specific Types of Microforms:
Microfilms, microcards,
microfiche

GOVERNMENT PUBLICATIONS:
Will Lend: Yes

DISSERTATIONS:
Will Lend: No

THESES:
Will Lend: Yes

AUDIO-VISUAL MATERIALS:
Records: Will not lend
Cassettes: Will not lend
Other (slides, filmstrips,
etc.): Will not lend

COMPUTER SOFTWARE:
Will Lend: Do not own

PHOTODUPLICATION SERVICE:
No charge up to 0 exposures
Charge Per Exposure: 10¢
Minimum/handling Fee: $1.00
Average Turnaround Time:
1 week

MICROFILMING SERVICE:
Service Available: No
Charges: N/A

DO YOU CHARGE THE BORROWING
LIBRARY FOR POSTAGE? Yes

FOR HOW LONG DO YOU SUSPEND ILL
SERVICE OVER THE CHRISTMAS
HOLIDAYS? No suspension

ARE THERE ANY GROUPS OF LIBRARIES
FOR WHICH YOU WAIVE FEES? IF
SO, PLEASE NAME THEM: Northwest
Association of Private
Colleges and Universities

UNIVERSITY OF WASHINGTON HEALTH SCIENCES LIBRARY

NUC CODE: WaU-HS

OCLC CODE: No separate code

ADDRESS: Interlibrary Loan
Health Sciences Library
University of
Washington
Seattle, WA 98195

TELEPHONE: (206) 543-8262

LIST NAMES OF BRANCHES WITH
SEPARATE POLICIES:
Other campus libraries
(except Law Library) are
accessed through University
of Washington Loan Service
at Main Library (Suzzallo
Library)

BOOKS:
Will Lend: Yes
Length of Loan: 2 weeks use
Renewable: Yes
Charges: $6.00 (outside
Washington)
Average Turnaround Time:
4 days
If you have indicated that a
book is not to be lent, will
you on receipt of a letter
from the requesting library
search the index for given
entries? (Not answered)

PERIODICALS:
Bound: Will lend those 8
years or older
Unbound: Will not lend
Loan Period: 1 week use
Renewable: Yes
Will lend if article exceeds
_____ number of pages (No
set rule; will usually
copy)

MICROFORMS:
Will Lend: No
Specific Types of Microforms:
N/A

GOVERNMENT PUBLICATIONS:
Treated as books or
periodicals

DISSERTATIONS:
Will Lend: Yes

THESES:
Will Lend: Yes

AUDIO-VISUAL MATERIALS:
Records: Will not lend
Cassettes: Will not lend
Other (slides, filmstrips,
etc.): Will not lend

COMPUTER SOFTWARE:
Will Lend: No

PHOTODUPLICATION SERVICE:
Flat Rate: $6.00 per item
(outside Washington)
Average Turnaround Time:
4 days

MICROFILMING SERVICE:
Service Available: Yes
Charges: Write for charges

DO YOU CHARGE THE BORROWING
LIBRARY FOR POSTAGE? No

FOR HOW LONG DO YOU SUSPEND ILL
SERVICE OVER THE CHRISTMAS
HOLIDAYS? No suspension

ARE THERE ANY GROUPS OF LIBRARIES
FOR WHICH YOU WAIVE FEES? IF
SO, PLEASE NAME THEM: None

WASHINGTON STATE LIBRARY

NUC CODE: (Not answered)

OCLC CODE: None

ADDRESS: Interlibrary Loan
          Washington State
          Library
          Olympia, WA   98504

TELEPHONE: (206) 753-3087

LIST NAMES OF BRANCHES WITH
  SEPARATE POLICIES: None

BOOKS:
  Will Lend: Yes
  Length of Loan: (Not
    answered)
  Renewable: (Not answered)
  Charges: (Not answered)
  Average Turnaround Time:
    (Not answered)
  If you have indicated that a
    book is not to be lent, will
    you on receipt of a letter
    from the requesting library
    search the index for given
    entries? (Not answered)

PERIODICALS:
  Bound: Will lend
  Unbound: Will lend
  Loan Period: (Not answered)
  Renewable: (Not answered)
  Will lend if article exceeds
    _____ number of pages (Not
  answered)

MICROFORMS:
  Will Lend: Yes
  Specific Types of Microforms:
    (Not answered)

GOVERNMENT PUBLICATIONS:
  Will Lend: Yes

DISSERTATIONS:
  Will Lend: Yes

THESES:
  Will Lend: Yes

AUDIO-VISUAL MATERIALS:
  Records: (Not answered)
  Cassettes: (Not answered)
  Other (slides, filmstrips,
    etc.): (Not answered)

COMPUTER SOFTWARE:
  Will Lend: (Not answered)

PHOTODUPLICATION SERVICE:
  No charge up to reasonable
    exposures
  Charge Per Exposure: (Not
    answered)
  Minimum/handling Fee: None
  Average Turnaround Time:
    (Not answered)

MICROFILMING SERVICE:
  Service Available: No
  Charges: N/A

DO YOU CHARGE THE BORROWING
  LIBRARY FOR POSTAGE? (Not
  answered)

FOR HOW LONG DO YOU SUSPEND ILL
  SERVICE OVER THE CHRISTMAS
  HOLIDAYS? (Not answered)

ARE THERE ANY GROUPS OF LIBRARIES
  FOR WHICH YOU WAIVE FEES? IF
  SO, PLEASE NAME THEM: (Not
  answered)

WASHINGTON STATE UNIVERSITY

NUC CODE: WaPS

OCLC CODE: None

ADDRESS: Interlibrary Loan
          Washington State
          University Library
          Pullman, WA
          99164-5610

TELEPHONE: (509) 335-7846

LIST NAMES OF BRANCHES WITH
  SEPARATE POLICIES: None

BOOKS:
  Will Lend: Yes
  Length of Loan: 4 weeks
  Renewable: Yes
  Charges: None at this time
  Average Turnaround Time:
    1 week
  If you have indicated that a
    book is not to be lent, will
    you on receipt of a letter
    from the requesting library
    search the index for given
    entries? (Not answered)

PERIODICALS:
  Bound: Will not lend
  Unbound: Will not lend
  Loan Period: N/A
  Renewable: N/A
  Will lend if article exceeds
    _____ number of pages (Not
  answered)

MICROFORMS:
  Will Lend: Yes
  Specific Types of Microforms:
    Microfilm, microfiche,
    microcards

GOVERNMENT PUBLICATIONS:
  Will Lend: Yes

DISSERTATIONS:
  Will Lend: Yes; 1956 to
    present available from
    University Microfilms

THESES:
  Will Lend: Yes

AUDIO-VISUAL MATERIALS:
  Records: Do not own
  Cassettes: Do not own
  Other (slides, filmstrips,
    etc.): Do not own

COMPUTER SOFTWARE:
  Will Lend: Do not own

PHOTODUPLICATION SERVICE:
  No charge up to 0 exposures
  Charge Per Exposure: 10¢
  Minimum/handling Fee: $1.50
  Average Turnaround Time:
    1 week

MICROFILMING SERVICE:
  Service Available: No
  Charges: N/A

DO YOU CHARGE THE BORROWING
  LIBRARY FOR POSTAGE? Only
  if first-class postage
  requested

FOR HOW LONG DO YOU SUSPEND ILL
  SERVICE OVER THE CHRISTMAS
  HOLIDAYS? No suspension

ARE THERE ANY GROUPS OF LIBRARIES
  FOR WHICH YOU WAIVE FEES? IF
  SO, PLEASE NAME THEM: None

WESTERN WASHINGTON UNIVERSITY

NUC CODE: WaBeW

OCLC CODE: (Not answered)

ADDRESS: Interlibrary Loan
Wilson Library
Western Washington
University
Bellingham, WA 98225

TELEPHONE: (206) 676-3076

LIST NAMES OF BRANCHES WITH
SEPARATE POLICIES: None

BOOKS:
Will Lend: Yes
Length of Loan: 1 month
Renewable: Yes
Charges: None
Average Turnaround Time:
1 day or less
If you have indicated that a
book is not to be lent, will
you on receipt of a letter
from the requesting library
search the index for given
entries? Yes

PERIODICALS:
Bound: Will not lend
Unbound: Will not lend
Loan Period: N/A
Renewable: N/A
Will lend if article exceeds
100 pages (at discretion of
Periodicals Supervisor)

MICROFORMS:
Will Lend: Yes, but
restricted to library use
only
Specific Types of Microforms:
Microfilm, microfiche,
microcards

GOVERNMENT PUBLICATIONS:
Will Lend: Yes

DISSERTATIONS:
Will Lend: No

THESES:
Will Lend: Yes

AUDIO-VISUAL MATERIALS:
Records: Will lend, usually
Cassettes: Will lend, usually
Other (slides, filmstrips,
etc.): Will lend, usually

COMPUTER SOFTWARE:
Will Lend: N/A

PHOTODUPLICATION SERVICE:
No charge up to 30 exposures
Charge Per Exposure: 5¢
after first 30
Minimum/handling Fee: None
Average Turnaround Time:
1 day or less

MICROFILMING SERVICE:
Service Available: No
Charges: N/A

DO YOU CHARGE THE BORROWING
LIBRARY FOR POSTAGE? No

FOR HOW LONG DO YOU SUSPEND ILL
SERVICE OVER THE CHRISTMAS
HOLIDAYS? No suspension

ARE THERE ANY GROUPS OF LIBRARIES
FOR WHICH YOU WAIVE FEES? IF
SO, PLEASE NAME THEM: None

WHATCOM COUNTY LIBRARY SYSTEM

NUC CODE: WaBeCo

OCLC CODE: (Not answered)

ADDRESS: Interlibrary Loan
Whatcom County Library
System
5205 Northwest Rd.
Bellingham, WA 98226

TELEPHONE: (206) 384-3150
(206) 733-1250
SCAN 738-2175

LIST NAMES OF BRANCHES WITH
SEPARATE POLICIES: None

BOOKS:
Will Lend: Yes
Length of Loan: 4 weeks
Renewable: Yes
Charges: None
Average Turnaround Time:
1 week
If you have indicated that a
book is not to be lent, will
you on receipt of a letter
from the requesting library
search the index for given
entries? (Not answered)

PERIODICALS:
Bound: Do not own
Unbound: Will Lend
Loan Period: 2 weeks
Renewable: Yes
Will lend if article exceeds
_____ number of pages (Not
answered)

MICROFORMS:
Will Lend: No
Specific Types of Microforms:
N/A

GOVERNMENT PUBLICATIONS:
Will Lend: No

DISSERTATIONS:
Will Lend: Do not own

THESES:
Will Lend: Do not own

AUDIO-VISUAL MATERIALS:
Records: Will not lend
Cassettes: Will lend
Other (slides, filmstrips,
etc.): Will not lend

COMPUTER SOFTWARE:
Will Lend: Do not own

PHOTODUPLICATION SERVICE:
No charge up to 10 exposures
Charge Per Exposure: 10¢
Minimum/handling Fee: None
Average Turnaround Time:
1 week

MICROFILMING SERVICE:
Service Available: No
Charges: N/A

DO YOU CHARGE THE BORROWING
LIBRARY FOR POSTAGE? No

FOR HOW LONG DO YOU SUSPEND ILL
SERVICE OVER THE CHRISTMAS
HOLIDAYS? No suspension

ARE THERE ANY GROUPS OF LIBRARIES
FOR WHICH YOU WAIVE FEES? IF
SO, PLEASE NAME THEM: None

WHITMAN COLLEGE

NUC CODE: WaWW

OCLC CODE: (Not answered)

ADDRESS: Interlibrary Loan
Penrose Memorial
Library
Whitman College
Walla Walla, WA 99362

TELEPHONE: (509) 527-5191

LIST NAMES OF BRANCHES WITH
SEPARATE POLICIES:
For A-V materials contact
Instructional Media Services

BOOKS:
Will Lend: Yes
Length of Loan: 3 weeks
Renewable: Yes
Charges: None
Average Turnaround Time:
1 day
If you have indicated that a
book is not to be lent, will
you on receipt of a letter
from the requesting library
search the index for given
entries? Yes

PERIODICALS:
Bound: Will not lend
Unbound: Will not lend
Loan Period: N/A
Renewable: N/A
May lend if article exceeds
25 pages; decided on
individual request basis

MICROFORMS:
Will Lend: Yes
Specific Types of Microforms:
Cards, films fiche, print

GOVERNMENT PUBLICATIONS:
Will Lend: Sometimes; decided
on an individual basis

DISSERTATIONS:
Will Lend: Sometimes; decided
on an individual basis

THESES:
Will Lend: Sometimes; decided
on an individual basis

AUDIO-VISUAL MATERIALS:
Records: Will lend sometimes
Cassettes: Will lend sometimes
Other (slides, filmstrips,
etc.): Will lend sometimes

COMPUTER SOFTWARE:
Will Lend: Do not own

PHOTODUPLICATION SERVICE:
No charge up to 25 exposures
Charge Per Exposure: 5¢
Minimum/handling Fee: $5.00
over 25 exposures
Average Turnaround Time:
2 days

MICROFILMING SERVICE:
Service Available: No
Charges: N/A

DO YOU CHARGE THE BORROWING
LIBRARY FOR POSTAGE? No,
except for books sent first-
class or overseas

FOR HOW LONG DO YOU SUSPEND ILL
SERVICE OVER THE CHRISTMAS
HOLIDAYS? No suspension

ARE THERE ANY GROUPS OF LIBRARIES
FOR WHICH YOU WAIVE FEES? IF
SO, PLEASE NAME THEM: None

YAKIMA VALLEY REGIONAL LIBRARY

NUC CODE: Way

OCLC CODE: None

ADDRESS: Interlibrary Loan
Yakima Valley Regional
Library
102 N. Third St.
Yakima, WA 98901

TELEPHONE: (509) 452-8541, X46

LIST NAMES OF BRANCHES WITH
SEPARATE POLICIES: None

BOOKS:
Will Lend: Yes
Length of Loan: 4 weeks
Renewable: Yes
Charges: Postage
Average Turnaround Time:
1 week
If you have indicated that a
book is not to be lent, will
you on receipt of a letter
from the requesting library
search the index for given
entries? (Not answered)

PERIODICALS:
Bound: Will not lend
Unbound: Will not lend
Loan Period: N/A
Renewable: N/A
Will lend if article exceeds
_____ number of pages (Not
answered)

MICROFORMS:
Will Lend: No
Specific Types of Microforms:
Newspapers on microfilm

GOVERNMENT PUBLICATIONS:
Will Lend: No

DISSERTATIONS:
Will Lend: No

THESES:
Will Lend: No

AUDIO-VISUAL MATERIALS:
Records: Will not lend
Cassettes: Will not lend
Other (slides, filmstrips,
etc,): Will not lend

COMPUTER SOFTWARE:
Will Lend: No

PHOTODUPLICATION SERVICE:
No charge up to 0 exposures
Charge Per Exposure: 10¢
Minimum/handling Fee: $1.00
Average Turnaround Time:
3 days

MICROFILMING SERVICE:
Service Available: No
Charges: N/A

DO YOU CHARGE THE BORROWING
LIBRARY FOR POSTAGE? Yes

FOR HOW LONG DO YOU SUSPEND ILL
SERVICE OVER THE CHRISTMAS
HOLIDAYS? No suspension

ARE THERE ANY GROUPS OF LIBRARIES
FOR WHICH YOU WAIVE FEES? IF
SO, PLEASE NAME THEM: None

BLUEFIELD STATE COLLEGE

NUC CODE: (Not answered)

OCLC CODE: (Not answered)

ADDRESS: Interlibrary Loan
Hardway Library
Bluefield State College
Bluefield, WV   24701

TELEPHONE: (304) 325-7102, X230

LIST NAMES OF BRANCHES WITH
SEPARATE POLICIES:
Greenbrier Community College
Center
Library
Lewisburg, WV   24901

BOOKS:
Will Lend: Yes
Length of Loan: App. 4 weeks
Renewable: Yes
Charges: None
Average Turnaround Time:
5 days
If you have indicated that a
book is not to be lent, will
you on receipt of a letter
from the requesting library
search the index for given
entries? Yes

PERIODICALS:
Bound: Will not lend
Unbound: Will not lend
Loan Period: N/A
Renewable: N/A
Will lend if article exceeds
_____ number of pages (Not
answered)

MICROFORMS:
Will Lend: Yes
Specific Types of Microforms:
(Not answered)

GOVERNMENT PUBLICATIONS:
Will Lend: Yes

DISSERTATIONS:
Will Lend: Do not own

THESES:
Will Lend: Do not own

AUDIO-VISUAL MATERIALS:
Records: Will not lend
Cassettes: Will not lend
Other (slides, filmstrips,
etc.): Will not lend

COMPUTER SOFTWARE:
Will Lend: Not housed here

PHOTODUPLICATION SERVICE:
No charge up to 0 exposures
Charge Per Exposure: 10¢
Minimum/handling Fee: None
Average Turnaround Time:
5 days

MICROFILMING SERVICE:
Service Available: No
Charges: N/A

DO YOU CHARGE THE BORROWING
LIBRARY FOR POSTAGE? No

FOR HOW LONG DO YOU SUSPEND ILL
SERVICE OVER THE CHRISTMAS
HOLIDAYS? App. 3 weeks

ARE THERE ANY GROUPS OF LIBRARIES
FOR WHICH YOU WAIVE FEES? IF
SO, PLEASE NAME THEM: None

CABELL COUNTY PUBLIC LIBRARY

NUC CODE: None

OCLC CODE: None

ADDRESS: Interlibrary Loan
Cabell County Public
Library
455 9th St.
Huntington, WV   25701

TELEPHONE: (304) 523-9451

LIST NAMES OF BRANCHES WITH
SEPARATE POLICIES: None

BOOKS:
Will Lend: Yes
Length of Loan: 1 month
Renewable: Yes
Charges: None
Average Turnaround Time:
1 week
If you have indicated that a
book is not to be lent, will
you on receipt of a letter
from the requesting library
search the index for given
entries? Yes, within
reason

PERIODICALS:
Bound: Will not lend
Unbound: Will not lend
Loan Period: N/A
Renewable: N/A
Will lend if article exceeds
_____ number of pages (Not
answered)

MICROFORMS:
Will Lend: No
Specific Types of Microforms:
N/A
Will copy for 25¢ per
exposure

GOVERNMENT PUBLICATIONS:
Will Lend: No

DISSERTATIONS:
Will Lend: Do not own

THESES:
Will Lend: Do not own

AUDIO-VISUAL MATERIALS:
Records: Will not lend
Cassettes: Will not lend
Other (slides, filmstrips,
etc.): Will not lend

COMPUTER SOFTWARE:
Will Lend: No

PHOTODUPLICATION SERVICE:
No charge up to any exposures
Charge Per Exposure: None
Minimum/handling Fee: None
Average Turnaround Time:
(Not answered)

MICROFILMING SERVICE:
Service Available: No
Charges: N/A

DO YOU CHARGE THE BORROWING
LIBRARY FOR POSTAGE? No

FOR HOW LONG DO YOU SUSPEND ILL
SERVICE OVER THE CHRISTMAS
HOLIDAYS? No suspension

ARE THERE ANY GROUPS OF LIBRARIES
FOR WHICH YOU WAIVE FEES? IF
SO, PLEASE NAME THEM: Fees
seldom charged

CONCORD COLLEGE

NUC CODE: None

OCLC CODE: None

ADDRESS: Interlibrary Loan
Concord College
Library
Athens, WV 24712

TELEPHONE: (304) 384-3115, X204

LIST NAMES OF BRANCHES WITH
SEPARATE POLICIES: None

BOOKS:
Will Lend: Yes
Length of Loan: 4 weeks
Renewable: No
Charges: None
Average Turnaround Time:
3 days
If you have indicated that a
book is not to be lent, will
you on receipt of a letter
from the requesting library
search the index for given
entries? (Not answered)

PERIODICALS:
Bound: Will not lend
Unbound: Will not lend
Loan Period: N/A
Renewable: N/A
Will lend if article exceeds
20 pages (1 week loan)

MICROFORMS:
Will Lend: Yes
Specific Types of Microforms:
Microcards, film, and fiche

GOVERNMENT PUBLICATIONS:
Will Lend: Yes

DISSERTATIONS:
Will Lend: Do not own

THESES:
Will Lend: Do not own

AUDIO-VISUAL MATERIALS:
Records: Will not lend
Cassettes: Will not lend
Other (slides, filmstrips,
etc.): Will not lend

COMPUTER SOFTWARE:
Will Lend: Do not own

PHOTODUPLICATION SERVICE:
No charge up to 0 exposures
Charge Per Exposure: 10¢
for xerox copies; 15¢ for
microform copies
Minimum/handling Fee: None
Average Turnaround Time:
3 days

MICROFILMING SERVICE:
Service Available: No
Charges: N/A

DO YOU CHARGE THE BORROWING
LIBRARY FOR POSTAGE? No

FOR HOW LONG DO YOU SUSPEND ILL
SERVICE OVER THE CHRISTMAS
HOLIDAYS? Dec.24-Jan.1

ARE THERE ANY GROUPS OF LIBRARIES
FOR WHICH YOU WAIVE FEES? IF
SO, PLEASE NAME THEM: West
Virginia College of Graduate
Studies; Mercer County, WV
libraries

FAIRMONT STATE COLLEGE

NUC CODE: WvFS

OCLC CODE: WVF

ADDRESS: Interlibrary Loan
Fairmont State College
Library
Reference Dept.
Fairmont, WV 26554

TELEPHONE: (304) 367-4121

LIST NAMES OF BRANCHES WITH
SEPARATE POLICIES: None

BOOKS:
Will Lend: Yes
Length of Loan: 2-3 weeks
Renewable: Yes
Charges: $1.00 to non-
academic libraries in WV;
$2.00 to all out-of-state
libraries
Average Turnaround Time:
1 day
If you have indicated that a
book is not to be lent, will
you on receipt of a letter
from the requesting library
search the index for given
entries? Yes

PERIODICALS:
Bound: Will not lend
Unbound: Will not lend
Loan Period: N/A
Renewable: N/A
Will lend if article exceeds
_____ number of pages (Not
answered)

MICROFORMS:
Will Lend: No
Specific Types of Microforms:
N/A

GOVERNMENT PUBLICATIONS:
Will Lend: Yes, with
exceptions

DISSERTATIONS:
Will Lend: Do not own

THESES:
Will Lend: Do not own

AUDIO-VISUAL MATERIALS:
Records: Will lend
Cassettes: Will lend
Other (slides, filmstrips,
etc.): Will lend

COMPUTER SOFTWARE:
Will Lend: Do not own

PHOTODUPLICATION SERVICE:
No charge up to 0 exposures
Charge Per Exposure: 10¢
Minimum/handling Fee: None
Average Turnaround Time:
1 day

MICROFILMING SERVICE:
Service Available: No
Charges: N/A

DO YOU CHARGE THE BORROWING
LIBRARY FOR POSTAGE? No

FOR HOW LONG DO YOU SUSPEND ILL
SERVICE OVER THE CHRISTMAS
HOLIDAYS? No suspension

ARE THERE ANY GROUPS OF LIBRARIES
FOR WHICH YOU WAIVE FEES? IF
SO, PLEASE NAME THEM: Book
loan fee waived for WV
academic libraries

GLENVILLE STATE COLLEGE

NUC CODE: WVV

OCLC CODE: WVV

ADDRESS: Interlibrary Loan
Robert F. Kidd Library
Glenville State College
Glenville, WV 26351

TELEPHONE: (304) 462-7361, X312

LIST NAMES OF BRANCHES WITH
SEPARATE POLICIES: None

BOOKS:
Will Lend: Yes
Length of Loan: 4 weeks
Renewable: Yes, for 2 weeks
Charges: None, if returned
in time
Average Turnaround Time:
Good
If you have indicated that a
book is not to be lent, will
you on receipt of a letter
from the requesting library
search the index for given
entries? (Not answered)

PERIODICALS:
Bound: Will not lend
Unbound: Will not lend
Loan Period: N/A
Renewable: N/A
Will lend if article exceeds
_____ number of pages (Will
not lend, regardless of
length of article)

MICROFORMS:
Will Lend: Yes
Specific Types of Microforms:
Microfiche

GOVERNMENT PUBLICATIONS:
Will Lend: Yes

DISSERTATIONS:
Will Lend: No

THESES:
Will Lend: No

AUDIO-VISUAL MATERIALS:
Records: Will not lend
Cassettes: Will not lend
Other (slides, filmstrips,
etc.): Will not lend

COMPUTER SOFTWARE:
Will Lend: No

PHOTODUPLICATION SERVICE:
No charge up to 0 exposures
Charge Per Exposure: 25¢
Minimum/handling Fee: $2.00
Average Turnaround Time:
(Not answered)

MICROFILMING SERVICE:
Service Available: No
Charges: N/A

DO YOU CHARGE THE BORROWING
LIBRARY FOR POSTAGE? Is
included in $2.00 service
charge

FOR HOW LONG DO YOU SUSPEND ILL
SERVICE OVER THE CHRISTMAS
HOLIDAYS? 4 weeks usually

ARE THERE ANY GROUPS OF LIBRARIES
FOR WHICH YOU WAIVE FEES? IF
SO, PLEASE NAME THEM: None

KANAWHA COUNTY PUBLIC LIBRARY

NUC CODE: (Not answered)

OCLC CODE: WVK

ADDRESS: Interlibrary Loan
Kanawha County Public
Library
123 Capitol St.
Charleston, WV 25301

TELEPHONE: (304) 343-4646

LIST NAMES OF BRANCHES WITH
SEPARATE POLICIES: None

BOOKS:
Will Lend: Yes
Length of Loan: 28 days
Renewable: Yes
Charges: Postage and
insurance
Average Turnaround Time:
5 days
If you have indicated that a
book is not to be lent, will
you on receipt of a letter
from the requesting library
search the index for given
entries? (Not answered)

PERIODICALS:
Bound: Will not lend
Unbound: Will not lend
Loan Period: N/A
Renewable: N/A
Will lend if article exceeds
_____ number of pages (Not
answered)

MICROFORMS:
Will Lend: No
Specific Types of Microforms:
N/A

GOVERNMENT PUBLICATIONS:
Will Lend: Yes, in special
cases

DISSERTATIONS:
Will Lend: Do not own

THESES:
Will Lend: Do not own

AUDIO-VISUAL MATERIALS:
Records: Will not lend
Cassettes: (Not answered)
Other (slides, filmstrips,
etc.): (Not answered)

COMPUTER SOFTWARE:
Will Lend: (Not answered)

PHOTODUPLICATION SERVICE:
No charge up to 0 exposures
Charge Per Exposure: 10¢ for
Xerox copies; 20¢ for micro-
film copies
Minimum/handling Fee: $1.00
Average Turnaround Time:
5 days

MICROFILMING SERVICE:
Service Available: Yes
Charges: (Not answered)

DO YOU CHARGE THE BORROWING
LIBRARY FOR POSTAGE? Yes,
out-of-state libraries

FOR HOW LONG DO YOU SUSPEND ILL
SERVICE OVER THE CHRISTMAS
HOLIDAYS? No suspension

ARE THERE ANY GROUPS OF LIBRARIES
FOR WHICH YOU WAIVE FEES? IF
SO, PLEASE NAME THEM: West
Virginia libraries

WEST LIBERTY STATE COLLEGE

NUC CODE: None

OCLC CODE: None

ADDRESS: Interlibrary Loan
Paul Elbin Library
West Liberty State
College
West Liberty, WV 26074

TELEPHONE: (304) 336-8035 or
336-8036

LIST NAMES OF BRANCHES WITH
SEPARATE POLICIES: None

BOOKS:
Will Lend: Yes
Length of Loan: 2 weeks
Renewable: Yes
Charges: (Not answered)
Average Turnaround Time:
1 day
If you have indicated that a
book is not to be lent, will
you on receipt of a letter
from the requesting library
search the index for given
entries? Yes, for reference
books

PERIODICALS:
Bound: Will not lend
Unbound: Will not lend
Loan Period: N/A
Renewable: N/A
Will lend if article exceeds
50 pages under special
circumstances

MICROFORMS:
Will Lend: Yes
Specific Types of Microforms:
Microfilm and microfiche

GOVERNMENT PUBLICATIONS:
Will Lend: Yes

DISSERTATIONS:
Will Lend: Yes

THESES:
Will Lend: Yes

AUDIO-VISUAL MATERIALS:
Records: Will lend
Cassettes: Will lend
Other (slides, filmstrips,
etc.): Will not lend

COMPUTER SOFTWARE:
Will Lend: No

PHOTODUPLICATION SERVICE:
No charge up to 0 exposures
Charge Per Exposure: 10¢ for
Xerox; 25¢ for microfilm
copies
Minimum/handling Fee: None
Average Turnaround Time:
1 day

MICROFILMING SERVICE:
Service Available: No
Charges: N/A

DO YOU CHARGE THE BORROWING
LIBRARY FOR POSTAGE? Only
out-of-state libraries

FOR HOW LONG DO YOU SUSPEND ILL
SERVICE OVER THE CHRISTMAS
HOLIDAYS? 1 week

ARE THERE ANY GROUPS OF LIBRARIES
FOR WHICH YOU WAIVE FEES? IF
SO, PLEASE NAME THEM: None

WEST VIRGINIA INSTITUTE OF TECHNOLOGY

NUC CODE: (Not answered)

OCLC CODE: WVT

ADDRESS: Interlibrary Loan
Vining Library
West Virginia Institute
of Technology
Montgomery, WV 25136

TELEPHONE: (304) 442-3321

LIST NAMES OF BRANCHES WITH
SEPARATE POLICIES: None

BOOKS:
Will Lend: Yes
Length of Loan: 4 weeks
Renewable: No
Charges: $1.00
Average Turnaround Time:
1 week
If you have indicated that a
book is not to be lent, will
you on receipt of a letter
from the requesting library
search the index for given
entries? (Not answered)

PERIODICALS:
Bound: Will not lend
Unbound: Will not lend
Loan Period: N/A
Renewable: N/A
Will lend if article exceeds
_____ number of pages (Not
answered)

MICROFORMS:
Will Lend: No
Specific Types of Microforms:
N/A

GOVERNMENT PUBLICATIONS:
Will Lend: Yes

DISSERTATIONS:
Will Lend: No

THESES:
Will Lend: No

AUDIO-VISUAL MATERIALS:
Records: Will not lend
Cassettes: Will not lend
Other (slides, filmstrips,
etc.): (Not answered)

COMPUTER SOFTWARE:
Will Lend: No

PHOTODUPLICATION SERVICE:
No charge up to 0 exposures
Charge Per Exposure: 15¢
Minimum/handling Fee: $1.00
Average Turnaround Time:
1 week

MICROFILMING SERVICE:
Service Available: No
Charges: N/A

DO YOU CHARGE THE BORROWING
LIBRARY FOR POSTAGE? No

FOR HOW LONG DO YOU SUSPEND ILL
SERVICE OVER THE CHRISTMAS
HOLIDAYS? Dec.15-Jan.15

ARE THERE ANY GROUPS OF LIBRARIES
FOR WHICH YOU WAIVE FEES? IF
SO, PLEASE NAME THEM: Waive
minimum $1.00 fee on books
and photocopying for state
supported colleges

WEST VIRGINIA LIBRARY COMMISSION

NUC CODE: Wv

OCLC CODE: (Not answered)

ADDRESS: Interlibrary Loan
West Virginia Library
Commission
Cultural Center
Charleston, WV 25305

TELEPHONE: (304) 348-2041

LIST NAMES OF BRANCHES WITH
SEPARATE POLICIES: None

BOOKS:
Will Lend: Yes
Length of Loan: 4 weeks
Renewable: Yes
Charges: (Not answered)
Average Turnaround Time:
2 weeks
If you have indicated that a
book is not to be lent, will
you on receipt of a letter
from the requesting library
search the index for given
entries? (Not answered)

PERIODICALS:
Bound: Will not lend
Unbound: Will not lend
Loan Period: N/A
Renewable: N/A
Will lend if article exceeds
_____ number of pages (Not
answered)

MICROFORMS:
Will Lend: No
Specific Types of Microforms:
N/A

GOVERNMENT PUBLICATIONS:
Will Lend: Yes

DISSERTATIONS:
Will Lend: No

THESES:
Will Lend: No

AUDIO-VISUAL MATERIALS:
Records: Will not lend
Cassettes: Will not lend
Other (slides, filmstrips,
etc.): Will not lend

COMPUTER SOFTWARE:
Will Lend: No

PHOTODUPLICATION SERVICE:
No charge up to 25 exposures
Charge Per Exposure: 10¢
Minimum/handling Fee: None
Average Turnaround Time:
2 weeks

MICROFILMING SERVICE:
Service Available: No
Charges: N/A

DO YOU CHARGE THE BORROWING
LIBRARY FOR POSTAGE? No

FOR HOW LONG DO YOU SUSPEND ILL
SERVICE OVER THE CHRISTMAS
HOLIDAYS? No suspension

ARE THERE ANY GROUPS OF LIBRARIES
FOR WHICH YOU WAIVE FEES? IF
SO, PLEASE NAME THEM: None

WHEELING COLLEGE

NUC CODE: (Not answered)

OCLC CODE: WWV

ADDRESS: Interlibrary Loan
Wheeling College
Library
Wheeling, WV 26003

TELEPHONE: (304) 243-2226

LIST NAMES OF BRANCHES WITH
SEPARATE POLICIES: None

BOOKS:
Will Lend: Yes
Length of Loan: 2 weeks
Renewable: Yes, if no
reserves
Charges: None
Average Turnaround Time:
1 day
If you have indicated that a
book is not to be lent, will
you on receipt of a letter
from the requesting library
search the index for given
entries? (Not answered)

PERIODICALS:
Bound: Will not lend
Unbound: Will not lend
Loan Period: N/A
Renewable: N/A
Will lend if article exceeds
_____ number of pages (Will
not lend, regardless of
length of article)

MICROFORMS:
Will Lend: No
Specific Types of Microforms:
N/A

GOVERNMENT PUBLICATIONS:
Will Lend: Yes

DISSERTATIONS:
Will Lend: No

THESES:
Will Lend: No

AUDIO-VISUAL MATERIALS:
Records: Will not lend
Cassettes: Will not lend
Other (slides, filmstrips,
etc.): Will not lend

COMPUTER SOFTWARE:
Will Lend: No

PHOTODUPLICATION SERVICE:
No charge up to 0 exposures
Charge Per Exposure: 10¢ for
photocopies; 25¢ for photo-
prints
Minimum/handling Fee: None
Average Turnaround Time:
1 day

MICROFILMING SERVICE:
Service Available: No
Charges: N/A

DO YOU CHARGE THE BORROWING
LIBRARY FOR POSTAGE? Yes

FOR HOW LONG DO YOU SUSPEND ILL
SERVICE OVER THE CHRISTMAS
HOLIDAYS? No suspension

ARE THERE ANY GROUPS OF LIBRARIES
FOR WHICH YOU WAIVE FEES? IF
SO, PLEASE NAME THEM: None

BROWN COUNTY LIBRARY

NUC CODE: WGR

OCLC CODE: GZG

ADDRESS: Interlibrary Loan
Nicolet Federated
Library System
515 Pine St.
Green Bay, WI 54301
The Nicolet Federated Library
System operates the inter-
library loan service for the
Brown County Library (the
System resource library).

TELEPHONE: (414) 497-3457

LIST NAMES OF BRANCHES WITH
SEPARATE POLICIES: None

BOOKS:
Will Lend: Yes
Length of Loan: 28 days
including mailing time
Renewable: No
Charges: None
Average Turnaround Time:
2 days
If you have indicated that a
book is not to be lent, will
you on receipt of a letter
from the requesting library
search the index for given
entries? (Not answered)

PERIODICALS:
Bound: Will not lend
Unbound: Will not lend
Loan Period: N/A
Renewable: N/A
Will lend if article exceeds
_____ number of pages (Not
answered)

MICROFORMS:
Will Lend: Yes
Specific Types of Microforms:
Microfilm (limit 2 reels at
a time)

GOVERNMENT PUBLICATIONS:
Will Lend: Yes

DISSERTATIONS:
Will Lend: Do not own

THESES:
Will Lend: Do not own

AUDIO-VISUAL MATERIALS:
Records: Not answered
Cassettes: Not answered
Other (slides, filmstrips,
etc.): Not answered

COMPUTER SOFTWARE:
Will Lend: Do not own

PHOTODUPLICATION SERVICE:
No charge up to 5 exposures
Charges: 10¢ per exposure
plus $1.00 handling charge
for more than 5 exposures
Average Turnaround Time:
2 days

MICROFILMING SERVICE:
Service Available: No
Charges: N/A

DO YOU CHARGE THE BORROWING
LIBRARY FOR POSTAGE? No,
except for A-V materials

FOR HOW LONG DO YOU SUSPEND ILL
SERVICE OVER THE CHRISTMAS
HOLIDAYS? No suspension

ARE THERE ANY GROUPS OF LIBRARIES
FOR WHICH YOU WAIVE FEES? IF
SO, PLEASE NAME THEM: Members
of the Nicolet Federated
Library System; Fox Valley
ILL Network; NEWIL and Fox
Valley Library Councils;
requests from any library
received on referral from
the Wisconsin State Refer-
and Loan Library and
Wisconsin Interlibrary
Services

FOREST PRODUCTS LABORATORY

NUC CODE: (Not answered)

OCLC CODE: AGF

ADDRESS: Interlibrary Loan
Library
Forest Products
Laboratory
P. O. Box 5130
Madison, WI 53705

TELEPHONE: (608) 264-5713

LIST NAMES OF BRANCHES WITH
SEPARATE POLICIES: None

BOOKS:
Will Lend: Yes
Length of Loan: 1 month
Renewable: Yes
Charges: None
Average Turnaround Time:
(Not answered)

PERIODICALS:
Bound: Will not lend
Unbound: Will not lend
Loan Period: N/A
Renewable: N/A
Will lend if article exceeds
_____ number of pages (Not
answered)

MICROFORMS:
Will Lend: No
Specific Types of Microforms:
N/A

GOVERNMENT PUBLICATIONS:
Will Lend: Yes

DISSERTATIONS:
Will Lend: Yes

THESES:
Will Lend: Yes

AUDIO-VISUAL MATERIALS:
Records: Will not lend
Cassettes: Will not lend
Other (slides, filmstrips,
etc.): Will not lend

COMPUTER SOFTWARE:
Will Lend: (Not answered)

PHOTODUPLICATION SERVICE:
No charge up to 30 exposures
Charge Per Exposure: 10¢
Minimum/handling Fee: None
Average Turnaround Time:
(Not answered)

MICROFILMING SERVICE:
Service Available: (Not
answered)
Charges: N/A

DO YOU CHARGE THE BORROWING
LIBRARY FOR POSTAGE? No

FOR HOW LONG DO YOU SUSPEND ILL
SERVICE OVER THE CHRISTMAS
HOLIDAYS? (Not answered)

ARE THERE ANY GROUPS OF LIBRARIES
FOR WHICH YOU WAIVE FEES? IF
SO, PLEASE NAME THEM: (Not
answered)

LAWRENCE UNIVERSITY

NUC CODE: WAL

OCLC CODE: WIB

ADDRESS: Interlibrary Loan
Lawrence University
Library
Appleton, WI 54912

TELEPHONE: (414) 735-6752

LIST NAMES OF BRANCHES WITH
SEPARATE POLICIES: None

BOOKS:
Will Lend: Yes
Length of Loan: 4 weeks
Renewable: Yes
Charges: None
Average Turnaround Time:
1 week
If you have indicated that a
book is not to be lent, will
you on receipt of a letter
from the requesting library
search the index for given
entries? Yes

PERIODICALS:
Bound: Will not lend
Unbound: Will not lend
Loan Period: N/A
Renewable: N/A
Will lend if article exceeds
_____ number of pages (Not
answered)

MICROFORMS:
Will Lend: Yes
Specific Types of Microforms:
Microfilm, microfiche,
microprint

GOVERNMENT PUBLICATIONS:
Will Lend: Yes

DISSERTATIONS:
Will Lend: No

THESES:
Will Lend: No

AUDIO-VISUAL MATERIALS:
Records: Will not lend
Cassettes: Will not lend
Other (slides, filmstrips,
etc.): Will not lend

COMPUTER SOFTWARE:
Will Lend: No

PHOTODUPLICATION SERVICE:
No charge up to 80 exposures
Charge Per Exposure: 5¢
Minimum/handling Fee: None
Average Turnaround Time:
1 week

MICROFILMING SERVICE:
Service Available: No
Charges: N/A

DO YOU CHARGE THE BORROWING
LIBRARY FOR POSTAGE? No

FOR HOW LONG DO YOU SUSPEND ILL
SERVICE OVER THE CHRISTMAS
HOLIDAYS? No suspension

ARE THERE ANY GROUPS OF LIBRARIES
FOR WHICH YOU WAIVE FEES? IF
SO, PLEASE NAME THEM: None

MADISON PUBLIC LIBRARY

NUC CODE: WMa

OCLC CODE: WIM

ADDRESS: Interlibrary Loan
Madison Public Library
201 W. Mifflin St.
Madison, WI 53703

TELEPHONE: (608) 266-6362

LIST NAMES OF BRANCHES WITH
SEPARATE POLICIES: None

BOOKS:
Will Lend: Yes
Length of Loan: 2 weeks
Renewable: No
Charges: Postage
reimbursement
Average Turnaround Time:
(Not answered)
If you have indicated that a
book is not to be lent, will
you on receipt of a letter
from the requesting library
search the index for given
entries? Within reason

PERIODICALS:
Bound: Will not lend
Unbound: Will lend
Loan Period: 2 weeks
Renewable: No
Will lend if article exceeds
_____ number of pages N/A

MICROFORMS:
Will Lend: No
Specific Types of Microforms:
N/A

GOVERNMENT PUBLICATIONS:
Will Lend: Yes, some of them

DISSERTATIONS:
Will Lend: Do not own

THESES:
Will Lend: Do not own

AUDIO-VISUAL MATERIALS:
Records: Will not lend
Cassettes: Will not lend
Other (slides, filmstrips,
etc.): Will not lend

COMPUTER SOFTWARE:
Will Lend: Do not own

PHOTODUPLICATION SERVICE:
No charge up to 0 exposures
Charge Per Exposure: 10¢
Minimum/handling Fee: $2.00
Average Turnaround Time:
(Not answered)

MICROFILMING SERVICE:
Service Available: No
Charges: N/A

DO YOU CHARGE THE BORROWING
LIBRARY FOR POSTAGE? Yes

FOR HOW LONG DO YOU SUSPEND ILL
SERVICE OVER THE CHRISTMAS
HOLIDAYS? No suspension

ARE THERE ANY GROUPS OF LIBRARIES
FOR WHICH YOU WAIVE FEES? IF
SO, PLEASE NAME THEM: None

MARQUETTE UNIVERSITY

NUC CODE: WMM

OCLC CODE: GZQ

ADDRESS: Interlibrary Loan
Marquette University
Memorial Library
1415 W. Wisconsin Ave.
Milwaukee, WI 53233

TELEPHONE: (414) 224-7257

LIST NAMES OF BRANCHES WITH
SEPARATE POLICIES: None

BOOKS:
Will Lend: Yes
Length of Loan: 2 weeks from
date of receipt
Renewable: Yes
Charges: None
Average Turnaround Time:
2 days
If you have indicated that a
book is not to be lent, will
you on receipt of a letter
from the requesting library
search the index for given
entries? Yes

PERIODICALS:
Bound: Will not lend
Unbound: Will not lend
Loan Period: N/A
Renewable: N/A
Will lend if article exceeds
_____ number of pages (Will
not lend, regardless of
length of article)

MICROFORMS:
Will Lend: Yes
Specific Types of Microforms:
All, except most
periodicals

GOVERNMENT PUBLICATIONS:
Will Lend: Yes

DISSERTATIONS:
Will Lend: Yes. 1960-
available from University
Microfilms

THESES:
Will Lend: Yes

AUDIO-VISUAL MATERIALS:
Records: Will not lend
Cassettes: Will not lend
Other (slides, filmstrips,
etc.): Will not lend

COMPUTER SOFTWARE:
Will Lend: No

PHOTODUPLICATION SERVICE:
No charge up to 0 exposures
Charge Per Exposure: 10¢
Minimum/handling Fee: $2.00
Average Turnaround Time:
2 days

MICROFILMING SERVICE:
Service Available: No
Charges: N/A

DO YOU CHARGE THE BORROWING
LIBRARY FOR POSTAGE? No

FOR HOW LONG DO YOU SUSPEND ILL
SERVICE OVER THE CHRISTMAS
HOLIDAYS? No suspension

ARE THERE ANY GROUPS OF LIBRARIES
FOR WHICH YOU WAIVE FEES? IF
SO, PLEASE NAME THEM:
Wisconsin Interlibrary
Services members; South-
eastern Wisconsin Health
Science Library Consortium
members; selected members
of Library Council of
Metropolitan Milwaukee
(reciprocal plan)

MEDICAL COLLEGE OF WISCONSIN

NUC CODE: None

OCLC CODE: WIC

ADDRESS: Interlibrary Loan
Medical College of
Wisconsin
Todd Wehr Library
P. O. Box 26509
8701 Watertown Plank Rd.
Milwaukee, WI 53226

TELEPHONE: (414) 257-8365

LIST NAMES OF BRANCHES WITH
SEPARATE POLICIES: None

BOOKS:
Will Lend: Yes
Length of Loan: Usually
4 weeks
Renewable: Yes, if no
reserves
Charges: $4.00 handling
charge
Average Turnaround Time:
0-1 day
If you have indicated that a
book is not to be lent, will
you on receipt of a letter
from the requesting library
search the index for given
entries? (Not answered)

PERIODICALS:
Bound: Will lend
Unbound: Will lend
Loan Period: 2 weeks
Renewable: No
Decision on whether to photo-
copy or send periodical is
MCW's

GOVERNMENT PUBLICATIONS:
Will Lend: Yes

DISSERTATIONS:
Will Lend: Yes

THESES:
Will Lend: Yes

AUDIO-VISUAL MATERIALS:
Records: Will not lend
Cassettes: Will not lend
Other (slides, filmstrips,
etc.): Will not lend

COMPUTER SOFTWARE:
Will Lend: No

PHOTODUPLICATION SERVICE:
No charge up to 0 exposures
Charge Per Exposure: 25¢
Minimum/handling Fee: $4.00
minimum
Average Turnaround Time:
0-1 day

MICROFILMING SERVICE:
Service Available: No
Charges: N/A

DO YOU CHARGE THE BORROWING
LIBRARY FOR POSTAGE? Yes, if
sent other than library rate

FOR HOW LONG DO YOU SUSPEND ILL
SERVICE OVER THE CHRISTMAS
HOLIDAYS? No suspension

ARE THERE ANY GROUPS OF LIBRARIES
FOR WHICH YOU WAIVE FEES? IF
SO, PLEASE NAME THEM: Only
libraries with which we have
reciprocal agreements

MILWAUKEE PUBLIC LIBRARY

NUC CODE: (Not answered)

OCLC CODE: GZD

ADDRESS: Interlibrary Loan
Milwaukee Public
Library
814 W. Wisconsin Ave.
Milwaukee, WI 53233

TELEPHONE: (414) 278-3082

LIST NAMES OF BRANCHES WITH
SEPARATE POLICIES: None

BOOKS:
Will Lend: Yes
Length of Loan: 4 weeks
Renewable: Yes
Charges: None
Average Turnaround Time:
2-3 days
If you have indicated that a
book is not to be lent, will
you on receipt of a letter
from the requesting library
search the index for given
entries? Yes

PERIODICALS:
Bound: Will not lend
Unbound: Will not lend
Loan Period: N/A
Renewable: N/A
Will lend if article exceeds
_____ number of pages (Will
not lend, regardless of
length of article)

MICROFORMS:
Will Lend: Yes
Specific Types of Microforms:
Microfilm

GOVERNMENT PUBLICATIONS:
Will Lend: Yes, for 2 weeks

DISSERTATIONS:
Will Lend: Yes

THESES:
Will Lend: Yes

AUDIO-VISUAL MATERIALS:
Records: Will lend
Cassettes: Will not lend
Other (slides, filmstrips,
etc.): Will not lend

COMPUTER SOFTWARE:
Will Lend: No

PHOTODUPLICATION SERVICE:
No charge up to 0 exposures
Charge Per Exposure: 50¢
Minimum/handling Fee: $1.15
Average Turnaround Time:
2-3 days

MICROFILMING SERVICE:
Service Available: No
Charges: N/A

DO YOU CHARGE THE BORROWING
LIBRARY FOR POSTAGE? No

FOR HOW LONG DO YOU SUSPEND ILL
SERVICE OVER THE CHRISTMAS
HOLIDAYS? No suspension

ARE THERE ANY GROUPS OF LIBRARIES
FOR WHICH YOU WAIVE FEES? IF
SO, PLEASE NAME THEM: None

WE APPRECIATE SOME INDICATION
THAT YOUR AREA AND SECTION OF
THE COUNTRY HAVE BEEN CLEARED
BEFORE YOU COME TO US, BUT WE
ARE NOT INSISTENT UPON IT.
THESE POLICIES MAY CHANGE
WITHOUT NOTICE.

OSHKOSH PUBLIC LIBRARY

NUC CODE: (Not answered)

OCLC CODE: GZK

ADDRESS: Interlibrary Loan
Oshkosh Public Library
106 Washington Ave.
Oshkosh, WI 54901

TELEPHONE: (414) 424-0485

LIST NAMES OF BRANCHES WITH
SEPARATE POLICIES: None

BOOKS:
Will Lend: Yes
Length of Loan: 7-28 days
Renewable: No
Charges: None
Average Turnaround Time:
(Not answered)
If you have indicated that a
book is not to be lent, will
you on receipt of a letter
from the requesting library
search the index for given
entries? Yes

PERIODICALS:
Bound: Will not lend
Unbound: Will lend
Loan Period: 7 days
Renewable: No
Will lend if article exceeds
_____ number of pages (Not
answered)

MICROFORMS:
Will Lend: No
Specific Types of Microforms:
N/A

GOVERNMENT PUBLICATIONS:
Will Lend: Yes

DISSERTATIONS:
Will Lend: No

THESES:
Will Lend: No

AUDIO-VISUAL MATERIALS:
Records: Will not lend
Cassettes: Will not lend
Other (slides, filmstrips,
etc.): Will not lend

COMPUTER SOFTWARE:
Will Lend: No

PHOTODUPLICATION SERVICE:
No charge up to 10 exposures
Charge Per Exposure: 10¢
Minimum/handling Fee: None
Average Turnaround Time:
(Not answered)

MICROFILMING SERVICE:
Service Available: No
Charges: N/A

DO YOU CHARGE THE BORROWING
LIBRARY FOR POSTAGE? No

FOR HOW LONG DO YOU SUSPEND ILL
SERVICE OVER THE CHRISTMAS
HOLIDAYS? No suspension

ARE THERE ANY GROUPS OF LIBRARIES
FOR WHICH YOU WAIVE FEES? IF
SO, PLEASE NAME THEM: None

ST. NORBERT COLLEGE

NUC CODE: None

OCLC CODE: None

ADDRESS: Interlibrary Loan
    Todd Wehr Library
    St. Norbert College
    De Pere, WI 54115

TELEPHONE: (414) 337-3283

LIST NAMES OF BRANCHES WITH
  SEPARATE POLICIES: None

BOOKS:
  Will Lend: Yes
  Length of Loan: 2 weeks
  Renewable: No
  Charges: Postage
  Average Turnaround Time:
    3 weeks
  If you have indicated that a
    book is not to be lent, will
    you on receipt of a letter
    from the requesting library
    search the index for given
    entries? (Not answered)

PERIODICALS:
  Bound: Will not lend
  Unbound: Will not lend
  Loan Period: N/A
  Renewable: N/A
  Will lend if article exceeds
    _____ number of pages (Will
    not lend, regardless of
    length of article)

MICROFORMS:
  Will Lend: No
  Specific Types of Microforms:
    N/A

GOVERNMENT PUBLICATIONS:
  Will Lend: No

DISSERTATIONS:
  Will Lend: No

THESES:
  Will Lend: No

AUDIO-VISUAL MATERIALS
  Records: Will not lend
  Cassettes: Will not lend
  Other (slides, filmstrips,
    etc.): Will not lend

COMPUTER SOFTWARE:
  Will Lend: No

PHOTODUPLICATION SERVICE:
  No charge up to 0 exposures
  Charge Per Exposure: 10¢
  Minimum/handling Fee:
    Postage
  Average Turnaround Time:
    1 week

MICROFILMING SERVICE:
  Service Available: No
  Charges: N/A

DO YOU CHARGE THE BORROWING
  LIBRARY FOR POSTAGE? Yes

FOR HOW LONG DO YOU SUSPEND ILL
  SERVICE OVER THE CHRISTMAS
  HOLIDAYS? Four consecutive
  days

ARE THERE ANY GROUPS OF LIBRARIES
  FOR WHICH YOU WAIVE FEES? IF
  SO, PLEASE NAME THEM: NEWIL
  (Northeast Wisconsin Inter-
  type Libraries), WILS
  (Wisconsin Inter Library
  Services)

STATE HISTORICAL SOCIETY OF WISCONSIN

NUC CODE: Whi

OCLC CODE: WIH

ADDRESS: Interlibrary Loan
    State Historical Society
      of Wisconsin
    816 State St.
    Madison, WI 53706

TELEPHONE: (608) 262-3421

LIST NAMES OF BRANCHES WITH
  SEPARATE POLICIES: None

BOOKS:
  Will Lend: Yes
  Length of Loan: 2 weeks
  Renewable: Yes
  Charges: Postage for out-
    of-state
  Average Turnaround Time:
    2 weeks
  If you have indicated that a
    book is not to be lent, will
    you on receipt of a letter
    from the requesting library
    search the index for given
    entries? No

PERIODICALS:
  Bound: Will lend
  Unbound: Will not lend
  Loan Period: 2 weeks
  Renewable: Yes
  Will lend if article exceeds
    _____ number of pages N/A

MICROFORMS:
  Will Lend: Yes
  Specific Types of Microforms:
    Film, fiche, cards

GOVERNMENT PUBLICATIONS:
  Will Lend: Yes

DISSERTATIONS:
  Will Lend: Do not own

THESES:
  Will Lend: Do not own

AUDIO-VISUAL MATERIALS:
  Records: Do not own
  Cassettes: Do not own
  Other (slides, filmstrips,
    etc.): Do not own

COMPUTER SOFTWARE:
  Will Lend: Do not own

PHOTODUPLICATION SERVICE:
  No charge up to _____
    exposures (Not answered)
  Charge Per Exposure: (Not
    answered)
  Minimum/handling Fee: (Not
    answered)
  Average Turnaround Time:
    1 week

MICROFILMING SERVICE:
  Service Available: Yes
  Charges: (Not answered)

DO YOU CHARGE THE BORROWING
  LIBRARY FOR POSTAGE? Yes,
  out-of-state

FOR HOW LONG DO YOU SUSPEND ILL
  SERVICE OVER THE CHRISTMAS
  HOLIDAYS? Dec.15-Jan.3

ARE THERE ANY GROUPS OF LIBRARIES
  FOR WHICH YOU WAIVE FEES? IF
  SO, PLEASE NAME THEM: None

UNIVERSITY OF WISCONSIN

NUC CODE: WU

OCLC CODE: GZM

ADDRESS: Interlibrary Loan
231 Memorial Library
University of Wisconsin
728 State St.
Madison, WI 53706

TELEPHONE: (608) 262-1193

LIST NAMES OF BRANCHES WITH
SEPARATE POLICIES:
Engineering (Wendt) Library
Medical (Middleton) Library
Law Library

BOOKS:
Will Lend: Yes
Length of Loan: 2 weeks from
receipt
Renewable: Yes
Charges: None
Average Turnaround Time:
2 days
If you have indicated that a
book is not to be lent, will
you on receipt of a letter
from the requesting library
search the index for given
entries? Yes, if a reproduction is being
requested

PERIODICALS:
Bound: Will not lend
Unbound: Will not lend
Loan Period: N/A
Renewable: N/A
Will lend if article exceeds
_____ number of pages (Not
answered)

MICROFORMS:
Will Lend: Yes
Specific Types of Microforms:
Film, fiche, cards

GOVERNMENT PUBLICATIONS:
Will Lend: Yes

DISSERTATIONS:
Will Lend: Yes, those from
1932-July, 1955

THESES:
Will Lend: Yes

AUDIO-VISUAL MATERIALS:
Records: Will not lend
Cassettes: Will not lend
Other (slides, filmstrips,
etc.): Will not lend

COMPUTER SOFTWARE:
Will Lend: No

PHOTODUPLICATION SERVICE:
No charge up to 0 exposures
Charge Per Exposure: 15¢
Minimum/handling Fee: $4.00
Average Turnaround Time:
3 days

MICROFILMING SERVICE:
Service Available: Yes
Charges: $15/positive reel,
$10/negative

DO YOU CHARGE THE BORROWING
LIBRARY FOR POSTAGE? Yes

FOR HOW LONG DO YOU SUSPEND ILL
SERVICE OVER THE CHRISTMAS
HOLIDAYS? No suspension

ARE THERE ANY GROUPS OF LIBRARIES
FOR WHICH YOU WAIVE FEES? IF
SO, PLEASE NAME THEM: None

UNIVERSITY OF WISCONSIN AT EAU CLAIRE

NUC CODE: (Not answered)

OCLC CODE: GZE

ADDRESS: Interlibrary Loan
William D. McIntyre
Library
University of Wisconsin
at Eau Claire
Eau Claire, WI 54701

TELEPHONE: (715) 836-5377

LIST NAMES OF BRANCHES WITH
SEPARATE POLICIES: None

BOOKS:
Will Lend: Yes
Length of Loan: 1 month
from date sent
Renewable: Rarely
Charges: (Not answered)
Average Turnaround Time:
3 days
If you have indicated that a
book is not to be lent, will
you on receipt of a letter
from the requesting library
search the index for given
entries? (Not answered)

PERIODICALS:
Bound: Will not lend
Unbound: Will not lend
Loan Period: N/A
Renewable: N/A
Will lend if article exceeds
_____ number of pages (Not
answered)

MICROFORMS:
Will Lend: Yes
Specific Types of Microforms:
Film and fiche (except ERIC)

GOVERNMENT PUBLICATIONS:
Will Lend: Yes

DISSERTATIONS:
Will Lend: Yes

THESES:
Will Lend: Yes

AUDIO-VISUAL MATERIALS:
Records: Will not lend
Cassettes: Will not lend
Other (slides, filmstrips,
etc.): Will not lend

COMPUTER SOFTWARE:
Will Lend: No

PHOTODUPLICATION SERVICE:
No charge up to 50 exposures
Charge Per Exposure: (Not
answered)
Minimum/handling Fee: None
Average Turnaround Time:
(Not answered)

MICROFILMING SERVICE:
Service Available: No
Charges: N/A

DO YOU CHARGE THE BORROWING
LIBRARY FOR POSTAGE? No

FOR HOW LONG DO YOU SUSPEND ILL
SERVICE OVER THE CHRISTMAS
HOLIDAYS? 2 weeks

ARE THERE ANY GROUPS OF LIBRARIES
FOR WHICH YOU WAIVE FEES? IF
SO, PLEASE NAME THEM: We
charge no fees to anyone

UNIVERSITY OF WISCONSIN AT GREEN BAY

NUC CODE: WGrU

OCLC CODE: GZW

ADDRESS: Interlibrary Loan
Library
University of Wisconsin
at Green Bay
Green Bay, WI 54302

TELEPHONE: (414) 465-2385

LIST NAMES OF BRANCHES WITH
SEPARATE POLICIES: None

BOOKS:
Will Lend: Yes
Length of Loan: 4 weeks use
Renewable: Yes
Charges: (Not answered)
Average Turnaround Time:
(Not answered)
If you have indicated that a
book is not to be lent, will
you on receipt of a letter
from the requesting library
search the index for given
entries? (Not answered)

PERIODICALS:
Bound: Will not lend
Unbound: Will not lend
Loan Period: N/A
Renewable: N/A
Will lend if article exceeds
_____ number of pages (Not
answered)

MICROFORMS:
Will Lend: Yes
Specific Types of Microforms:
All types selectively

GOVERNMENT PUBLICATIONS:
Will Lend: Yes

DISSERTATIONS:
Will Lend: Yes

THESES:
Will Lend: Yes

AUDIO-VISUAL MATERIALS:
Records: Will not lend
Cassettes: Will not lend
Other (slides, filmstrips,
etc.): Will not lend

COMPUTER SOFTWARE:
Will Lend: (Not answered)

PHOTODUPLICATION SERVICE:
No charge up to 0 exposures
Charge Per Exposure: 10¢
Minimum/handling Fee: $2.00
Average Turnaround Time:
(Not answered)

MICROFILMING SERVICE:
Service Available: No
Charges: N/A

DO YOU CHARGE THE BORROWING
LIBRARY FOR POSTAGE? No

FOR HOW LONG DO YOU SUSPEND ILL
SERVICE OVER THE CHRISTMAS
HOLIDAYS? No suspension

ARE THERE ANY GROUPS OF LIBRARIES
FOR WHICH YOU WAIVE FEES? IF
SO, PLEASE NAME THEM: (Not
answered)

UNIVERSITY OF WISCONSIN AT LA CROSSE

NUC CODE: WLacU

OCLC CODE: GZU

ADDRESS: Interlibrary Loan
Murphy Library
University of Wisconsin
at La Crosse
1631 Pine St.
La Crosse, WI 54601

TELEPHONE: (608) 785-8636

LIST NAMES OF BRANCHES WITH
SEPARATE POLICIES: None

BOOKS:
Will Lend: Yes, if
circulating
Length of Loan: 3 weeks
Renewable: Yes
Charges: Postage
Average Turnaround Time:
1 week
If you have indicated that a
book is not to be lent, will
you on receipt of a letter
from the requesting library
search the index for given
entries? (Not answered)

PERIODICALS:
Bound: Will not lend
Unbound: Will not lend
Loan Period: N/A
Renewable: N/A
Will lend if article exceeds
50 pages, depending on the
periodical

MICROFORMS:
Will Lend: Yes
Specific Types of Microforms:
All fiche, film, and cards
except periodicals

GOVERNMENT PUBLICATIONS:
Will Lend: Yes

DISSERTATIONS:
Will Lend: Yes

THESES:
Will Lend: Yes

AUDIO-VISUAL MATERIALS:
Records: Will lend
Cassettes: Will lend
Other (slides, filmstrips,
etc.): (Not answered)

COMPUTER SOFTWARE:
Will Lend: No

PHOTODUPLICATION SERVICE:
No charge up to 19 exposures
Charge Per Exposure: (Not
answered)
Minimum/handling Fee:
Postage
Average Turnaround Time:
1 week

MICROFILMING SERVICE:
Service Available: No
Charges: N/A

DO YOU CHARGE THE BORROWING
LIBRARY FOR POSTAGE? Yes

FOR HOW LONG DO YOU SUSPEND ILL
SERVICE OVER THE CHRISTMAS
HOLIDAYS? No suspension

ARE THERE ANY GROUPS OF LIBRARIES
FOR WHICH YOU WAIVE FEES? IF
SO, PLEASE NAME THEM: Any in
state

UNIVERSITY OF WISCONSIN AT MILWAUKEE

NUC CODE: WMUW

OCLC CODE: GZN

ADDRESS: Interlibrary Loan
University of Wisconsin
at Milwaukee
P. O. Box 604
Milwaukee, WI 53201

TELEPHONE: (414) 963-4785

LIST NAMES OF BRANCHES WITH
SEPARATE POLICIES: None

BOOKS:
Will Lend: Yes
Length of Loan: 3 weeks
Renewable: Yes
Charges: None
Average Turnaround Time:
4 days
If you have indicated that a
book is not to be lent, will
you on receipt of a letter
from the requesting library
search the index for given
entries? Yes

PERIODICALS:
Bound: Will not lend
Unbound: Will not lend
Loan Period: N/A
Renewable: N/A
Will lend if article exceeds
_____ number of pages (Not
answered)

MICROFORMS:
Will Lend: Yes
Specific Types of Microforms:
Fiche, film

GOVERNMENT PUBLICATIONS:
Will Lend: Yes

DISSERTATIONS:
Will Lend: Yes. 1966-
available from University
Microfilms

THESES:
Will Lend: Yes

AUDIO-VISUAL MATERIALS:
Records: Will not lend
Cassettes: Will not lend
Other (slides, filmstrips,
etc.): Will not lend

COMPUTER SOFTWARE:
Will Lend: Do not own

PHOTODUPLICATION SERVICE:
No charge up to 0 exposures
Charge Per Exposure: 30¢
Minimum/handling Fee: $5.00
Average Turnaround Time:
5 days

MICROFILMING SERVICE:
Service Available: No
Charges: N/A

DO YOU CHARGE THE BORROWING
LIBRARY FOR POSTAGE? No

FOR HOW LONG DO YOU SUSPEND ILL
SERVICE OVER THE CHRISTMAS
HOLIDAYS? No suspension

ARE THERE ANY GROUPS OF LIBRARIES
FOR WHICH YOU WAIVE FEES? IF
SO, PLEASE NAME THEM: WILS,
Milwaukee Public, Medical
School of Wisconsin, Marquette
only

UNIVERSITY OF WISCONSIN AT OSHKOSH

NUC CODE: WOSHU

OCLC CODE: GZO

ADDRESS: Interlibrary Loan
Libraries and Learning
Resources
University of Wisconsin
at Oshkosh
Oshkosh, WI 54901

TELEPHONE: (414) 424-3348

LIST NAMES OF BRANCHES WITH
SEPARATE POLICIES: None

BOOKS:
Will Lend: Yes
Length of Loan: 21 days
Renewable: Yes, once
Charges: None
Average Turnaround Time:
2-5 days
If you have indicated that a
book is not to be lent, will
you on receipt of a letter
from the requesting library
search the index for given
entries? (Not answered)

PERIODICALS:
Bound: Will not lend
Unbound: Will not lend
Loan Period: N/A
Renewable: N/A
Will lend if article exceeds
_____ number of pages (Will
not lend, regardless of
length of article)

MICROFORMS:
Will Lend: Yes
Specific Types of Microforms:
Cards, fiche, film (8 reel
limit)

GOVERNMENT PUBLICATIONS:
Will Lend: Yes

DISSERTATIONS:
Will Lend: Yes

THESES:
Will Lend: Yes

AUDIO-VISUAL MATERIALS:
Records: Will not lend
Cassettes: Will not lend
Other (slides, filmstrips,
etc.): Will not lend

COMPUTER SOFTWARE:
Will Lend: No

PHOTODUPLICATION SERVICE:
No charge up to 0 exposures
Charge Per Exposure: 10¢
Minimum/handling Fee: $1.00/
$1.50
Average Turnaround Time:
3-6 days

MICROFILMING SERVICE:
Service Available: No
Charges: N/A

DO YOU CHARGE THE BORROWING
LIBRARY FOR POSTAGE? No

FOR HOW LONG DO YOU SUSPEND ILL
SERVICE OVER THE CHRISTMAS
HOLIDAYS? No suspension

ARE THERE ANY GROUPS OF LIBRARIES
FOR WHICH YOU WAIVE FEES? IF
SO, PLEASE NAME THEM: Fox
Valley Library Council,
Northeast Wisconsin Inter-
type Libraries, University
of Wisconsin libraries

UNIVERSITY OF WISCONSIN AT PARKSIDE

NUC CODE: (Not answered)

OCLC CODE: GZP

ADDRESS: Interlibrary Loan
University of Wisconsin
   at Parkside Library
P. O. Box 2000
Kenosha, WI 53141

TELEPHONE: (414) 553-2595

LIST NAMES OF BRANCHES WITH
SEPARATE POLICIES: None

BOOKS:
Will Lend: Yes
Length of Loan: 4 weeks
Renewable: Yes, if not in
   demand
Charges: Return postage only
Average Turnaround Time:
   48 hours
If you have indicated that a
   book is not to be lent, will
   you on receipt of a letter
   from the requesting library
   search the index for given
   entries? Yes

PERIODICALS:
Bound: Will not lend
Unbound: Will not lend
Loan Period: N/A
Renewable: N/A
Will lend if article exceeds
   _____ number of pages (Will
   not lend, regardless of
   length of article)

MICROFORMS:
Will Lend: Yes
Specific Types of Microforms:
   Fiche, film, cards

GOVERNMENT PUBLICATIONS:
Will Lend: Yes

DISSERTATIONS:
Will Lend: Do not own

THESES:
Will Lend: Yes

AUDIO-VISUAL MATERIALS:
Records: Will lend
Cassettes: Will lend
Other (slides, filmstrips,
   etc.): Will lend

COMPUTER SOFTWARE:
Will lend: No

PHOTODUPLICATION SERVICE:
No charge up to 0 exposures
Charge Per Exposure: 20¢
Minimum/handling Fee: $5.00
Average Turnaround Time:
   48 hours

MICROFILMING SERVICE:
Service Available: No
Charges: N/A

DO YOU CHARGE THE BORROWING
LIBRARY FOR POSTAGE?
   Return postage only

FOR HOW LONG DO YOU SUSPEND ILL
SERVICE OVER THE CHRISTMAS
HOLIDAYS? No suspension

ARE THERE ANY GROUPS OF LIBRARIES
FOR WHICH YOU WAIVE FEES? IF
SO, PLEASE NAME THEM:
   Members of the Wisconsin
   Interlibrary Loan Service

UNIVERSITY OF WISCONSIN AT STOUT

NUC CODE: WMenu

OCLC CODE: GZS

ADDRESS: Interlibrary Loan
Library Learning Center
University of Wisconsin
   at Stout
Menomonie, WI 54751

TELEPHONE: (715) 232-1112

LIST NAMES OF BRANCHES WITH
SEPARATE POLICIES: None

BOOKS:
Will Lend: Yes
Length of Loan: 2-4 weeks
   from mailing
Renewable: No
Charges: None
Average Turnaround Time:
   2 days
If you have indicated that a
   book is not to be lent, will
   you on receipt of a letter
   from the requesting library
   search the index for given
   entries? (Not answered)

PERIODICALS:
Bound: Will not lend
Unbound: Will not lend
Loan Period: N/A
Renewable: N/A
Will lend if article exceeds
   _____ number of pages (Not
   answered)

MICROFORMS:
Will Lend: Yes
Specific Types of Microforms:
   Lend if circulating

GOVERNMENT PUBLICATIONS:
Will Lend: Yes, if
   circulating

DISSERTATIONS:
Will Lend: Yes

THESES:
Will Lend: Yes

AUDIO-VISUAL MATERIALS:
Records: Yes, with some
   restrictions
Cassettes: Will lend
Other (slides, filmstrips,
   etc.): Will lend

COMPUTER SOFTWARE:
Will Lend: No

PHOTODUPLICATION SERVICE:
No charge up to 20 exposures
Charge Per Exposure: 10¢
Minimum/handling Fee: None
Average Turnaround Time:
   2 days

MICROFILMING SERVICE:
Service Available: Yes
Charges: Cost plus

DO YOU CHARGE THE BORROWING
LIBRARY FOR POSTAGE? No

FOR HOW LONG DO YOU SUSPEND ILL
SERVICE OVER THE CHRISTMAS
HOLIDAYS? Reduced

ARE THERE ANY GROUPS OF LIBRARIES
FOR WHICH YOU WAIVE FEES? IF
SO, PLEASE NAME THEM:
   Wisconsin Interloan Service

UNIVERSITY OF WISCONSIN AT WHITEWATER

NUC CODE: WWhiwU

OCLC CODE: GZT

ADDRESS: Interlibrary Loan
           Harold Andersen Library
           University of Wisconsin
             at Whitewater
           Whitewater, WI 53190

TELEPHONE: (414) 472-1032

LIST NAMES OF BRANCHES WITH
  SEPARATE POLICIES: None

BOOKS:
  Will Lend: Yes
  Length of Loan: 2 weeks use
  Renewable: Yes
  Charges: Reciprocal
  Average Turnaround Time:
    2-3 days
  If you have indicated that a
    book is not to be lent, will
    you on receipt of a letter
    from the requesting library
    search the index for given
    entries? (Not answered)

PERIODICALS:
  Bound: Will not lend
  Unbound: Will not lend
  Loan Period: N/A
  Renewable: N/A
  Will lend if article exceeds
    _____ number of pages (Not
    answered)

MICROFORMS:
  Will Lend: Yes
  Specific Types of Microforms:
    (Not answered)

GOVERNMENT PUBLICATIONS:
  Will Lend: Yes

DISSERTATIONS:
  Will Lend: Yes

THESES:
  Will Lend: Yes

AUDIO-VISUAL MATERIALS:
  Records: Will lend
  Cassettes: Will lend
  Other (slides, filmstrips,
    etc.): Will lend, except
    for 16mm films, video
    cassettes, unmailable kits

COMPUTER SOFTWARE:
  Will Lend: No

PHOTODUPLICATION SERVICE:
  No charge up to 3 exposures
  Charge Per Exposure: 10¢
    (16 exposures and up)
  Minimum/handling Fee: $2.00
    for 4-15 exposures
  Average Turnaround Time:
    2-3 days

MICROFILMING SERVICE:
  Service Available: No
  Charges: N/A

DO YOU CHARGE THE BORROWING
  LIBRARY FOR POSTAGE?
  Reciprocal

FOR HOW LONG DO YOU SUSPEND ILL
  SERVICE OVER THE CHRISTMAS
  HOLIDAYS? No suspension

ARE THERE ANY GROUPS OF LIBRARIES
  FOR WHICH YOU WAIVE FEES? IF
  SO, PLEASE NAME THEM: None

WISCONSIN DEPARTMENT OF PUBLIC INSTRUCTION

NUC CODE: WMaPI-RL

OCLC CODE: GZR

ADDRESS: Interlibrary Loan
           Wisconsin Department of
             Public Instruction
           2109 South Stoughton Rd
           Madison, WI 53716

TELEPHONE: (608) 266-1053

LIST NAMES OF BRANCHES WITH
  SEPARATE POLICIES: None

BOOKS:
  Lend only uniquely-held books
    not available from other
    in-state sources
  Length of Loan: 4 weeks
  Renewable: No
  Charges: Lost books, $25 or
    price of item
  Average Turnaround Time:
    1 week
  If you have indicated that a
    book is not to be lent, will
    you on receipt of a letter
    from the requesting library
    search the index for given
    entries? Yes, if local
    resources have been
    exhausted and book not
    available within the
    region

PERIODICALS:
  Bound: Will not lend
  Unbound: Will not lend
  Loan Period: N/A
  Renewable: N/A
  Will lend if article exceeds
    _____ number of pages (Will
    not lend, regardless of
    length of article)

MICROFORMS:
  Will Lend: No
  Specific Types of Microforms:
    N/A

GOVERNMENT PUBLICATIONS:
  Will loan Wisconsin govern-
    ment publications if not
    available elsewhere

DISSERTATIONS:
  Will Lend: Do not own

THESES:
  Will Lend: Do not own

AUDIO-VISUAL MATERIALS:
  Records: Yes, selectively
  Cassettes: Yes, selectively
  Other (slides, filmstrips,
    etc.): Will lend selectively

COMPUTER SOFTWARE:
  Will Lend: Do not own

PHOTODUPLICATION SERVICE:
  No charge up to 20 exposures
  Charge Per Exposure: Will
    not photocopy over 20
    exposures for out-of-state
    requests
  Minimum/handling Fee: None
  Average Turnaround Time:
    1 week

MICROFILMING SERVICE:
  Service Available: No
  Charges: N/A

DO YOU CHARGE THE BORROWING
  LIBRARY FOR POSTAGE? No

FOR HOW LONG DO YOU SUSPEND ILL
  SERVICE OVER THE CHRISTMAS
  HOLIDAYS? No suspension

ARE THERE ANY GROUPS OF LIBRARIES
  FOR WHICH YOU WAIVE FEES? IF
  SO, PLEASE NAME THEM: None

UNIVERSITY OF WYOMING

NUC CODE: WyU

OCLC CODE: WYU

ADDRESS: Interlibrary Loan
           University of Wyoming
           Library
           Laramie, WY 82071

TELEPHONE: (307) 766-5168

LIST NAMES OF BRANCHES WITH
    SEPARATE POLICIES:
    Health Science Information
    Network
    Law Library

BOOKS:
    Will Lend: Yes
    Length of Loan: 4 weeks use
      (geology-1 week)
    Renewable: Not generally
    Charges: (Not answered)
    Average Turnaround Time:
      3 days or less
    If you have indicated that a
      book is not to be lent, will
      you on receipt of a letter
      from the requesting library
      search the index for given
      entries? (Not answered)

PERIODICALS:
    Bound: Will lend
    Unbound: Will not lend
    Loan Period: 3 days to
      4 weeks use
    Renewable: No
    Will lend if article exceeds
      50 pages

MICROFORMS:
    Will Lend: Yes
    Specific Types of Microforms:
      (Not answered)

GOVERNMENT PUBLICATIONS:
    Will Lend: Yes

DISSERTATIONS:
    Will Lend: Yes; 1972 to
      present available from
      University Microfilms

THESES:
    Will Lend: Yes

AUDIO-VISUAL MATERIALS:
    Records: Will not lend
    Cassettes: Will lend
    Other (slides, filmstrips,
      etc.): Will lend

COMPUTER SOFTWARE:
    Will Lend: No

PHOTODUPLICATION SERVICE:
    No charge up to 0 exposures
    Charge Per Exposure: 10¢
      after first 50 exposures
    Minimum/handling Fee: $3.00
      for 1-50 exposures
    Average Turnaround Time:
      3 days or less

MICROFILMING SERVICE:
    Service Available: No
    Charges: N/A

DO YOU CHARGE THE BORROWING
    LIBRARY FOR POSTAGE? Only
      those who charge us

FOR HOW LONG DO YOU SUSPEND ILL
    SERVICE OVER THE CHRISTMAS
    HOLIDAYS? No suspension

ARE THERE ANY GROUPS OF LIBRARIES
    FOR WHICH YOU WAIVE FEES? IF
    SO, PLEASE NAME THEM: None

WYOMING STATE LIBRARY

NUC CODE: Wy

OCLC CODE: WYZ

ADDRESS: Interlibrary Loan
           Wyoming State Library
           Supreme Court Building
           Cheyenne, WY 82002

TELEPHONE: (307) 777-6333

LIST NAMES OF BRANCHES WITH
    SEPARATE POLICIES: There are
    23 county libraries with
    branches in Wyoming. All
    have similar policies.

BOOKS:
    Will Lend: Yes
    Length of Loan: 4 weeks
    Renewable: Yes
    Charges: None
    Average Turnaround Time:
      24 hours
    If you have indicated that a
      book is not to be lent, will
      you on receipt of a letter
      from the requesting library
      search the index for given
      entries? (Not answered)

PERIODICALS:
    Bound: Will lend
    Unbound: Will lend
    Loan Period: 4 weeks
    Renewable: Yes
    Will lend if article exceeds
      10 pages

MICROFORMS:
    Will Lend: Yes
    Specific Types of Microforms:
      Film and fiche

GOVERNMENT PUBLICATIONS:
    Will Lend: Yes

DISSERTATIONS:
    N/A

THESES:
    N/A

AUDIO-VISUAL MATERIALS:
    Records: Will lend
    Cassettes: Will lend
    Other (slides, filmstrips,
      etc.): N/A

COMPUTER SOFTWARE:
    Will Lend: N/A

PHOTODUPLICATION SERVICE:
    No charge up to 20 exposures
    Charge Per Exposure: 10¢
    Minimum/handling Fee: None
    Average Turnaround Time:
      24 hours

MICROFILMING SERVICE:
    Service Available: No
    Charges: N/A

DO YOU CHARGE THE BORROWING LIBRARY
    FOR POSTAGE? No

FOR HOW LONG DO YOU SUSPEND ILL
    SERVICE OVER THE CHRISTMAS
    HOLIDAYS? Do not suspend
    service

ARE THERE ANY GROUPS OF LIBRARIES
    FOR WHICH YOU WAIVE FEES? IF
    SO, PLEASE NAME THEM: (Not
    answered)

UNIVERSIDAD DE PUERTO RICO

NUC CODE: PrU

OCLC CODE: (Not answered)

ADDRESS: Interlibrary Loan
Biblioteca General
Universidad de Puerto
Rico
Rio Piedras, PR 00936

TELEPHONE:

LIST NAMES OF BRANCHES WITH
SEPARATE POLICIES: None

BOOKS:
Will Lend: Yes
Length of Loan: 2 weeks
Renewable: Yes
Charges: (Not answered)
Average Turnaround Time:
(Not answered)
If you have indicated that a
book is not to be lent, will
you on receipt of a letter
from the requesting library
search the index for given
entries? (Not answered)

PERIODICALS:
Bound: Will not lend
Unbound: Will not lend
Loan Period: N/A
Renewable: N/A
Will lend if article exceeds
_____ number of pages (Not
answered)

MICROFORMS:
Will Lend: (Not answered)
Specific Types of Microforms:
N/A

GOVERNMENT PUBLICATIONS:
Will Lend: No

DISSERTATIONS:
Will Lend: No

THESES:
Will Lend: No

AUDIO-VISUAL MATERIALS:
Records: (Not answered)
Cassettes: (Not answered)
Other (slides, filmstrips,
etc.): (Not answered)

COMPUTER SOFTWARE:
Will Lend: (Not answered)

PHOTODUPLICATION SERVICE:
No charge up to 0 exposures
Charge Per Exposure: 10¢
Minimum Fee: $2.50
Average Turnaround Time:
(Not answered)

MICROFILMING SERVICE:
Service Available: Yes
Charges: 45¢ per foot

DO YOU CHARGE THE BORROWING
LIBRARY FOR POSTAGE? No

FOR HOW LONG DO YOU SUSPEND ILL
SERVICE OVER THE CHRISTMAS
HOLIDAYS? No suspension

ARE THERE ANY GROUPS OF LIBRARIES
FOR WHICH YOU WAIVE FEES? IF
SO, PLEASE NAME THEM: (Not
answered)

Index

LSL
Ref
Z
713.5
U6
M67
1984

Morris

67067

*Important reading from the
American Library Association*

Educating the Public Library User
Compiled and edited by John Lubans

An anthology of original papers exploring approaches to instruction of patrons in the fruitful use of libraries. Among the contributors are Peggy Sullivan, John C. Shirk, and Lee White.
ISBN 0-8389-0382-7 viii, 145p. $15.00 paper LC 83-11762 1983

Interlibrary Loan Practices Handbook
Virginia Boucher

Reflects the impact on interlibrary lending of the growth of library networks and consortia, the decreases in collection development funds, and the evolution of interlibrary lending into a common library service.
ISBN 0-8389-3298-3 Approx. 304p. $20.00 paper LC 83-21359 1984

AMERICAN LIBRARY ASSOCIATION
Publishing Services
50 East Huron Street
Chicago, IL 60611
(312) 944-6780

LSL
REF
Z
713.5
W6
m67
1984
Morris

67067